Department
~ to
n Hall.

α.

CRC Handbook of tables for
Organic Compound Identification

CRC HANDBOOK

of tables for

ORGANIC COMPOUND IDENTIFICATION

Third Edition

Compiled by
ZVI RAPPOPORT, Ph.D.
Hebrew University of Jerusalem, Israel

CRC Press, Inc.
Boca Raton, Florida

Direct all inquiries to CRC Press, Inc., 2000 Corporate Blvd., N.W., Boca Raton, Florida, 33431.

© 1967 by CRC Press, Inc.
Formerly the Chemical Rubber Company
2nd Printing, April 1972
3rd Printing, May 1973
4th Printing, April 1975
5th Printing, January 1976
6th Printing, December 1976
7th Printing, September 1977
8th Printing, June 1979
9th Printing, September 1980
10th Printing, July 1981
11th Printing, March 1983
12th Printing, December 1983
13th Printing, November 1984

International Standard Book Number (ISBN) 0-8493-0303-6
Former International Standard Book Number (ISBN) 0-87819-303-0

Library of Congress Card No. 63-19660
Printed in the United States.

First Edition
Tables for Identification of Organic Compounds

Compiled by
Max Frankel, Ph.D.
Saul Patai, Ph.D.

Assisted by
Albert Zikha, Ph.D.
Robert Farkas—Kadmon

© 1960 by SCIENCE PRESS, LTD., JERUSALEM, ISRAEL

Second Edition
Tables for Identification of Organic Compounds

Compiled by
Max Frankel, Ph.D.
Saul Patai, Ph.D.

Assisted by
Albert Zilkha, Ph.D.
Zvi Rappoport, Ph.D.
Robert Farkas—Kadmon

© 1964 by THE CHEMICAL RUBBER CO.

Third Edition
Handbook of Tables for Organic Compound Identification

Compiled by
Zvi Rappoport, Ph.D.

CONTROLLED RELEASE PESTICIDES FORMULATIONS
By **Nate F. Cardarelli, M.S.,** University of Akron.

DIFFUSE REFLECTANCE SPECTROSCOPY IN ENVIRONMENTAL PROBLEM—SOLVING
By **R. W. Frei, Ph.D.,** Sandox, Ltd. (Switzerland), and **J. D. MacNeil, M.Sc., Ph.D.,** Canada Department of Agriculture.

DRUGS AS TERATOGENS
By **James L. Schardein, B.A., M.S.,** Parke, Davis and Company.

FUNDAMENTAL MEASURES AND CONSTANTS FOR SCIENCE AND TECHNOLOGY
By **Frederick D. Rossini, Ph.D.,** Rice University, Houston.

IMMUNOASSAYS FOR DRUGS SUBJECT TO ABUSE
Edited by **S. J. Mulé, Ph.D.,** New York State Narcotic Addiction Control Commission, et al.

MASS SPECTROSCOPY OF PESTICIDES AND POLLUTANTS
By **Stephen Safe, B.Sc., M.Sc., D.Phil.,** and **Otto Hutzinger, Ing.Chem., M.Sc., Ph.D.,** National Research Council of Canada.

MERCURY IN THE ENVIRONMENT
By **Lars T. Friberg, M.D.,** National Institute of Public Health (Stockholm), and **Jaroslav J. Vostal, M.D., Ph.D.,** University of Rochester.

ORGANOPHOSPHORUS PESTICIDES: ORGANIC AND BIOLOGICAL CHEMISTRY
By **Morifusa Eto, Ph.D.,** Kyushu University, Japan.

RECENT DEVELOPMENTS IN SEPARATION SCIENCE
Edited by **Norman N. Li, Sc.D.,** Exxon Research and Engineering Co.

TRACE ELEMENT MEASUREMENTS AT THE COAL-FIRED STEAM PLANT
By **W. S. Lyon, Jr. B.S., M.S.,** Oak Ridge National Laboratory.

CRC CRITICAL REVIEWS™ JOURNALS:

CRC CRITICAL REVIEWS™ IN ANALYTICAL CHEMISTRY
Edited by **Bruce H. Campbell, Ph.D.,** J. T. Baker Chemical Co.

CRC CRITICAL REVIEWS™ IN TOXICOLOGY
Edited by **Leon Golberg, M.D., B.Chir., D.Sc., D.Phil., F.R.C.Path.,** Chemical Industry Institute of Toxicology

Direct inquiries to CRC Press, Inc.

PREFACE

The present volume is a revised and enlarged third edition of the book formerly titled TABLES FOR IDENTIFICATION OF ORGANIC COMPOUNDS. Four new classes of compounds, i.e., sulfonyl chlorides, sulfonamides, thiols and thioethers were added, bringing the number of classes included in the book to twenty-six. The tables of alkanes, alkenes, alkynes, aromatic hydrocarbons, phenols, nitriles and sulfonic acids were all thoroughly revised and considerably enlarged. In all, the addition of 2400 compounds to the third edition, raised the total number of parent compounds in the book to over 8150.

Three tables containing the dissociation constants of more than 1050 phenols, organic acids and organic bases were added. Correlation charts for I.R., Far I.R. and N.M.R. were also included.

Explanatory sections entitled "Explanations and References" precede the tables. In these sections the formulas of the derivatives and the full reaction equations for their preparation by the most important methods, together with some essential details and references to their preparations, are given.

An index covering both the names and synonyms of the compounds was added at the end of the book. An index listing the names of all tables and major subjects was also added.

The main objective of this book is to assist chemists in the identification of organic compounds. The organization of the compounds in classes according to increasing boiling points should also assist in the search for standard vapor phase chromatography work.

For further information of techniques of organic analysis one or more of the following books should be consulted:

N. D. Cheronis, J. B. Entrikin and E. M. Hodnett, *Semimicro Qualitative Organic Analysis*, 3rd Ed., Interscience Publishers, New York, 1965.

L. Meites, *Handbook of Analytical Chemistry*, McGraw Hill Book Co., 1963.

F. Feigl, *Spot Tests in Organic Analysis*, 6th Ed., Elsevier Publishing Co., 1960.

A. I. Vogel, *A Textbook of Practical Organic Chemistry*, 3rd Ed., Longmans Green and Co., London, 1957.

R. L. Shriner, R. C. Fuson and D. Y. Curtin, *The Systematic Identification of Organic Compounds*, 4th Ed., John Wiley and Sons, New York, 1956.

F. Wild, *Characterization of Organic Compounds*, 2nd Ed., Cambridge University Press, 1958.

The publication of the third edition would not have been possible without the work of those involved in the preparation of the earlier editions. The editor is thankful for the part in the earlier work contributed by Professors M. Frankel, S. Patai and A. Zilkha, and the late Mr. R. Farkas-Kadmon. Thanks are due also to Mrs. E. Shohamy and Mr. A. Glazer for assisting in collection of new data, to Mrs. Y. Elmaleh for typing the index, and especially to Prof. S. Patai, who as consulting editor, read all the new material and gave many helpful suggestions. The cooperation of Dr. Robert C. Weast and Mrs. F. Thomas in the publication of the book is gratefully acknowledged.

Z. R.

Jerusalem
January 1967

Contents

Contents (Continued)

LIST OF ABBREVIATIONS USED

Abbrev.	Meaning	Abbrev.	Meaning	Abbrev.	Meaning
$[\alpha]^t_D$	specific rotation	fum.	fuming	pr.	prisms
a.	acid	glac.	glacial	purp.	purple
abs.	absolute	glit.	glittering	pyr.	pyridine
abt.	about	glyc.	glycerol	rac.	racemic (or: racemate)
ac. a.	acetic acid	gran.	granular		
ac. anh.	acetic anhydride	grn.	green	rect.	rectangular
acet.	acetone	h.	hot	recr.	recrystallization
add.	addition	htng.	heating	redsh.	reddish
al.	alcohol	hyd.	hydrate or hydrolyses	rhomb.	rhombic
alk.	alkali			r.	rapid
amor.	amorphous	hyg., hygr.	hygroscopic	r.h.	rapid heating
anh.	anhydrous	*i.*	inactive	s.	soluble
arom.	aromatic	i.	insoluble	sec.	secondary
aqu.	aqueous	ign.	ignites	scar.	scarcely
asym., *as.*	asymmetric	insol.	insoluble	s. h.	slow heating
bl.	blue	l., L.	levorotatory (or: L-configuration)	sh.	short
blk.	black			sl.	slightly
boil.	boiling			sld.	solid
b.p., B.P.	boiling point	leaf., lf.	leaflets	slend.	slender
br.	brown	lg.	large	sm.	small
bz.	benzene	lgr.	ligroin	soft.	softens
brt.	bright	liq.	liquid	sol., soln.	solution(s)
brnsh.	brownish	lng.	long	solv.	solvent(s)
c.	cold	lt.	light	st.	steel
ca.	about	lvs.	leaves	stab.	stable
caust.	caustic	*m-*	meta	subl.	sublimes
chl.	chloroform	me., meth.	methyl	*sym.*	symmetrical
cl.-bz.	chlorobenzene	micr.	microscopic	tab., tabl.	tablet(s), tables
col.	colorless	mixt.	mixture	*tert.*	tertiary
comp.	compound	ml.	milliliter	tetr.	tetragonal
conc.	concentrated	mod.	modification	tol.	toluene
cor.	corrected	monohyd.	monohydrate	trans.	transparent
cr., cryst.	crystals	monocl.	monoclinic	thk.	thick
d.	decomposes	m.p., M.P.	melting point	tricl.	triclinic
d., D.	dextrorotatory (or: D-configuration)	need., nd.	needles	trim.	trimeric
deriv.	derivative	*o-*	ortho	uns.	unsymmetrical
deliq.	deliquescent	ol.	olive	unst.	unstable
dil.	dilute	or.	orange	vac.	vacuum, in vacuo
dist.	distillate	ord.	ordinary	v.	very
dk.	dark	org.	organic	var.	variable
dl., d,l; D,L.	racemic	orth.	orthorhombic	*vic-*	vicinal
efflor.	efflorescent	oxid.	oxidation	visc.	viscous
et.	ethyl	*p-*	para	volat.	volatile or volatilizes
et. ac.	ethyl acetate	pa.	pale	vlt.	violet
eth.	ether	part.	partly	w.	water
exp.	explodes	pet.	petroleum	wh.	white
f.	from	pet. eth.	petroleum ether	yel.	yellow
fl.	flakes	ph.	phenyl	yelsh, ylsh.	yellowish
fluores.	fluorescent	ph. hydraz.	phenyl hydrazine	>	above, greater than
f.p.	freezing point	$PhNO_2$	nitrobenzene	<	below, smaller than
frz.	freezes	pl.	plates	∞	miscible
		powd.	powder	xyl.	xylene

EXPLANATIONS AND REFERENCES TO THE TABLES

The following section gives explanations and references for the preparation of the derivatives appearing in the Tables. Formulas of the derivatives as well as the main methods for their preparation are given. Usually, only the reagents and the solvents required for the preparation of a derivative are mentioned without specific details for the reaction conditions and the exact procedure. The aim of these notes is mainly to enable the worker to choose the method preferable in the conditions and the reagents available to him in his laboratory for the derivatization of his specific compound. However, THIS IS ONLY A REFERENCE SECTION AND NOT AN INSTRUCTION MANUAL AND THE QUOTED REFERENCES SHOULD BE CONSULTED FOR THE ACTUAL PREPARATION OF DERIVATIVES, ESPECIALLY REGARDING SAFETY HAZARDS INVOLVED IN THE WORK.

References are usually given for the preparation of all the derivatives having separate columns in the Tables, as well as for important ones listed in the "miscellaneous" section of the Tables. References to five different popular analytical textbooks are given, assuming that at least one of them, or another equivalent publication, would be available to the worker. These are:

N. D. Cheronis, J. B. Entrikin and E. M. Hodnett, *Semimicro Qualitative Organic Analysis*, 3rd edition, Interscience, New York, 1965, quoted in the text as "Cheronis."

R. P. Linstead and B. C. L. Weedon, *A Guide to Qualitative Organic Chemical Analysis*, Butterworth Scientific Publication, London, 1956, quoted in the text as "Linstead."

R. L. Shriner, R. C. Fuson and D. Y. Curtin, *The Systematic Identification of Organic Compounds*, 4th edition, John Wiley and Sons, New York, 1956, quoted in the text as "Shriner."

A. I. Vogel, *A Textbook of Practical Organic Chemistry*, 3rd edition, Longmans, Green and Co., London, 1957, quoted in the text as "Vogel."

F. Wild, *Characterization of Organic Compounds*, 2nd edition, Cambridge University Press, Cambridge, 1958, quoted in the text as "Wild."

In addition, leading references from the original literature are also given. Although the literature coverage is not complete (especially for the common derivatives) it was attempted to describe different methods, and to give as many references as possible to less common derivatives having limited scope. More references can be found in the textbooks mentioned above.

Derivatives appear either in a separate column or in the "miscellaneous" section in the Tables, where separate columns are usually given for derivatives which should be tried first, and for which enough data are available. Derivatives which should be tried as a second choice, or preferred derivatives for which not enough data are available appear in the "miscellaneous" section. The explanations and the references for the different derivatives are arranged usually in the same order as in the Tables. Occasionally, this order is changed in the explanatory notes in order to describe the derivatives in a logical order (e.g., in Table 17 the phenylurethane appears in a separate column, while the phenylhydantoin appears in the "miscellaneous" section; in the "explanations and references" section the phenylhydantoin appears directly after the phenylurethane).

Derivatives which are followed by an asterisk are those recommended for first trial. Other derivatives should be tried after these.

Although "Ar" usually stands for monovalent aromatic group, we used it a few times in the following sections as a polyvalent aromatic residue. This was done only for demonstration purposes.

EXPLANATIONS AND REFERENCES TO TABLE I

As a result of their inertness no general suitable derivative exists for alkanes and cycloalkanes. Characterization is based only on the physical constants given in the Table: melting and boiling points, index of refraction and density. Any laboratory text-book will give adequate directions for the determination of these constants.

WARNING: This is not an instruction manual. References should be consulted for the preparation of derivatives.

TABLE I. ALKANES AND CYCLOALKANES
a) Gases and Liquids (Listed in order of increasing b.p.*)**

No.	Name	Boiling point, °C	Melting point, °C	n_D^{20}	D_4^{20}
1	Methane.....................................	−161.49	−182.48[T]	....	....
2	Ethane......................................	−88.63	−183.27[T]	....	....
3	Propane.....................................	−42.07	−187.69[T]	....	0.5005[S]
4	Cyclopropane	−32.86	−127.42	....	0.720[−79]
5	2-Methylpropane (Isobutane)	−11.73	−159.6	....	0.5572[S]
6	n-Butane	−0.50	−138.35	1.3326[S]	0.5788[S]
7	2,2-Dimethylpropane (Neopentane)	9.503	−16.55	1.342[S]	0.5910[S]
8	Cyclobutane	13.08[741]; 12.5	−80.	1.37520[0]	0.7038[0]
9	1,1-Dimethylcyclopropane	20.63	−108.96	1.3668	0.6589
10	2-Methylbutane..............................	27.852	−159.9	1.35373	0.61967
11	trans-1,2-Dimethylcyclopropane	29	....	1.3713	0.6769
12	Ethylcyclopropane...........................	35.94	−149.41	1.3786	0.6839
13	n-Pentane...................................	36.074	−129.721	1.35748	0.62624
14	Methylcyclobutane	36.3	....	1.3830	0.6933
15	cis-1,2-Dimethylcyclopropane	37	−140.9	1.3822	0.6928
16	Spiropentane................................	38.977	−107.06	1.41200	0.755
17	Cyclopentane................................	49.262	−93.879	1.40645	0.74538
18	2,2-Dimethylbutane	49.741	−99.87	1.36876	0.64916
19	1,1,2-Trimethylcyclopropane.................	56–7[750]	....	1.3848[19.5]	0.6822[19.5]
20	2,3-Dimethylbutane	57.988	−128.538	1.37495	0.66164
21	2-Methylpentane.............................	60.271	−153.67	1.37145	0.65315
22	3-Methylpentane.............................	63.282	....	1.37652	0.66431
23	1,2,3-Trimethylcyclopropane	65–7[755]	....	1.3945[18]	0.6946[18]
24	n-Hexane....................................	68.74	−95.348	1.37486	0.65937
25	Ethylcyclobutane............................	70.64	−142.85	1.4020	0.7280
26	Methylcyclopentane	71.812	−142.455	1.4097	0.74864
27	2,2-Dimethylpentane.........................	79.197	−123.811	1.38215	0.67385
28	2,4-Dimethylpentane.........................	80.5	−119.242	1.38145	0.67270
29	Cyclohexane.................................	80.738	6.554	1.42623	0.77855
30	2,2,3-Trimethylbutane	80.882	−24.912	1.38944	0.69011
31	3,3-Dimethylpentane.........................	86.064	−134.46	1.39092	0.69327
32	1,1-Dimethylcyclopentane	87.846	−69.795	1.41356	0.75448
33	2,3-Dimethylpentane.........................	89.784	....	1.39196	0.69508
34	2-Methylhexane	90.052	−118.276	1.38485	0.67859
35	trans-1,3-Dimethylcyclopentane	90.773	−133.702	1.40894	0.74479
36	cis-1,3-Dimethylcyclopentane	91.725	−133.975	1.41074	0.74880
37	3-Methylhexane	91.850	....	1.38864	0.68713
38	trans-1,2-Dimethylcyclopentane	91.869	−117.58	1.41200	0.75144
39	3-Ethylpentane	93.475	−118.604	1.39339	0.69816
40	Quadricyclane (Quadricyclo [2,2,1,0[2.6],0[3.5]] heptane)..................................	98	....	1.4804	....
41	n-Heptane..................................	98.427	−90.61	1.38764	0.68376
42	2,2,4-Trimethylpentane	99.238	−107.38	1.39145	0.69192
43	cis-1,2-Dimethylcyclopentane	99.532	−53.892	1.42217	0.77262
44	Methylcyclohexane..........................	100.934	−126.593	1.42312	0.76939
45	Ethylcyclopentane...........................	103.466	−138.446	1.41981	0.76647
46	1,1,3-Trimethylcyclopentane	104.893	−142.44	1.41119	0.74825
47	2,2-Dimethylhexane.........................	106.84	−121.18	1.39349	0.69528
48	2,5-Dimethylhexane.........................	109.103	−91.20	1.39246	0.69354
49	1,trans-2,cis-4-Trimethylcyclopentane	109.29	−130.78	1.41060	0.74727
50	2,4-Dimethylhexane.........................	109.429	....	1.39534	0.70036
51	2,2,3-Trimethylpentane	109.841	−112.27	1.40295	0.71602
52	1,trans-2,cis-3-Trimethylcyclopentane	110.2	−112.705	1.4138	0.7535
53	3,3-Dimethylhexane	111.969	−126.1	1.40009	0.7100
54	2,3,4-Trimethylpentane	113.467	−109.21	1.40422	0.71906
55	1,1,2-Trimethylcyclopentane	113.729	−21.64	1.42298	0.77252
56	2,3,3-Trimethylpentane	114.76	−100.70	1.40750	0.72619
57	2,3-Dimethylhexane	115.607	....	1.40113	0.71214
58	3-Ethyl-2-methylpentane	115.65	−114.96	1.40401	0.71932

*Derivative data given in order: m.p., crystal color, solvent from which crystallized.

**T = triple point; S = at saturation pressure.

No.	Name	Boiling point, °C	Melting point, °C	n_D^{20}	D_4^{20}
59	1,*cis*-2,*trans*-4-Trimethylcyclopentane	116.731	−132.55	1.41855	0.76345
60	1,*cis*-2,*trans*-3-Trimethylcyclopentane	117.5	−112.	1.4218	0.7704
61	2-Methylheptane.............................	117.647	−109.04	1.39494	0.69792
62	4-Methylheptane.............................	117.709	−120.955	1.39792	0.70463
63	3,4-Dimethylhexane	117.725	....	1.40406	0.71923
64	1,*cis*-2,*cis*-4-Trimethylcyclopentane	118.	....	1.422	0.766
65	3-Ethyl-3-methylpentane	118.259	−90.87	1.40775	0.72742
66	3-Ethylhexane...............................	118.534	....	1.40162	0.71358
67	3-Methylheptane.............................	118.925	−120.5	1.39848	0.70582
68	Cycloheptane (Suberane)	118–20	−7.98	1.4449	0.8275⁰
69	*trans*-1,4-Dimethylcyclohexane	119.351	−36.962	1.42090	0.76255
70	1,1-Dimethylcyclohexane	119.543	−33.495	1.42900	0.78094
71	*cis*-1,3-Dimethylcyclohexane	120.088	−75.573	1.42294	0.76603
72	*trans*-1-Ethyl-3-methylcyclopentane	120.8	−108.	1.4186	0.7619
73	*trans*-1-Ethyl-2-methylcyclopentane	121.2	....	1.4219	0.7690
74	*cis*-1-Ethyl-3-methylcyclopentane	121.4	....	1.4203	0.7724
75	1-Ethyl-1-methylcyclopentane	121.522	−143.80	1.42718	0.78093
76	2,2,4,4-Tetramethylpentane	122.284	−66.54	1.40694	0.71947
77	1,*cis*-2,*cis*-3-Trimethylcyclopentane	123.0	−116.43	1.4262	0.7792
78	*trans*-1,2-Dimethylcyclohexane	123.419	−88.194	1.42695	0.77601
79	2,2,5-Trimethylhexane	124.084	−105.78	1.39972	0.70721
80	*cis*-1,4-Dimethylcyclohexane	124.321	−87.436	1.42966	0.78285
81	*trans*-1,3-Dimethylcyclohexane	124.45	−90.108	1.43085	0.78472
82	*n*-Octane	125.665	−56.795	1.39743	0.70252
83	Isopropylcyclopentane	126.419	−111.375	1.42582	0.77653
84	2,2,4-Trimethylhexane	126.54	−120.	1.4033	0.7156
85	*cis*-1-Ethyl-2-methylcyclopentane	128.050	−105.95	1.42933	0.78522
86	*cis*-1,2-Dimethylcyclohexane	129.728	−50.023	1.43596	0.79627
87	2,4,4-Trimethylhexane	130.38	−113.38	1.40745	0.72381
88	*n*-Propylcyclopentane	130.8	−118.7	1.4266	0.7761
89	2,3,5-Trimethylhexane	131.34	−127.8	1.4061	0.7219
90	Ethylcyclohexane	131.783	−111.323	1.43304	0.78792
91	2,2-Dimethylheptane.........................	132.69	−113.0	1.4016	0.7105
92	2,2,3,4-Tetramethylpentane	133.016	−121.09	1.41472	0.73895
93	2,4-Dimethylheptane.........................	133.5	....	1.4033	0.716
94	Methylcycloheptane	133–5	....	1.4410	0.8052
95	2,2,3-Trimethylhexane	133.6	....	1.4105	0.7292
96	4-Ethyl-2-methylhexane	133.8	....	1.4068	0.723
97	3-Ethyl-2,2-dimethylpentane	133.83	−99.2	1.4123	0.7348
98	4,4-Dimethylheptane.........................	135.2	....	1.4076	0.725
99	2,6-Dimethylheptane.........................	135.21	−102.9	1.4007	0.7089
100	2,5-Dimethylheptane.........................	136.0	....	1.4038	0.715
101	3,5-Dimethylheptane.........................	136.0	....	1.4067	0.723
102	Bicyclo[4.2.0]octane	136.0	....	1.4613	0.8573
103	*cis*-Bicyclo[3.3.0]octane	136–6.5	....	1.4595²⁵	0.8638²⁵
104	2,4-Dimethyl-3-ethylpentane	136.73	−122.2	1.4137	0.7379
105	1,1,3-Trimethylcyclohexane...................	137–8	....	1.4362	0.7868²⁵
106	3,3-Dimethylheptane.........................	137.3	....	1.4085	0.725
107	2,2,5,5-Tetramethylhexane	137.5	....	1.40550	0.71875
108	2,3,3-Trimethylhexane	137.68	−116.80	1.4141	0.738
109	3-Ethyl-2-methylhexane	138	....	1.4120	0.731
110	*trans*-1,3,5-Trimethylcyclohexane	138.5–9⁷⁵⁴	....	1.42740ₕ	0.7720
111	2,3,4-Trimethylhexane	139.0	....	1.4144	0.7392
112	*cis*-1,3,5-Trimethylcyclohexane	140–0.5⁷⁵²	....	1.43010ₕ	0.7773
113	*trans*-1,2,4-Trimethylcyclohexane	140–1	....	1.43121ₕₑ	0.7813
114	2,2,3,3-Tetramethylpentane	140.274	−9.9	1.42360	0.75666
115	4-Ethyl-3-methylhexane	140.4	....	1.416	0.742
116	3,3,4-Trimethylhexane	140.46	−101.2	1.4178	0.7454
117	2,3-Dimethylheptane.........................	140.5	....	1.4085	0.7260

*Derivative data given in order: m.p., crystal color, solvent from which crystallized.

No.	Name	Boiling point, °C	Melting point, °C	n_D^{20}	D_4^{20}
118	3,4-Dimethylheptane	140.6	....	1.4111	0.7314
1,19	3-Ethyl-3-methylhexane	140.6	....	1.4142	0.741
120	4-Ethylheptane	141.2	....	1.4096	0.730
121	2,3,3,4-Tetramethylpentane	141.551	−102.123	1.42222	0.75473
122	2,3-Dimethyl-3-ethylpentane	142.	....	1.419	0.754
123	trans-1,2,3-Trimethylcyclohexane	142–3.5[762]	....	1.43582[He]	0.7914
124	1-Isopropyl-3-methylcyclopentane (Pulegan)	142–4	....	1.4236	0.7730[22]
125	4-Methyloctane	142.48	−113.2	1.4061	0.7199
126	1-Isopropyl-2-methylcyclopentane	142.5[759]	....	1.4279	0.7792
127	3-Ethylheptane	143.0	....	1.4093	0.727
128	2-Methyloctane	143.26	−80.4	1.4031	0.7134
129	cis-1,2,3-Trimethylcyclohexane	144–6[753]	....	1.43682[He]	0.7930
130	3-Methyloctane	144.18	−107.6	1.4062	0.7207
131	2,4,6-Trimethylheptane	144.8	....	1.4071	0.7225
132	cis-1,2,4-Trimethylcyclohexane	146	....	1.43209	0.786
133	3,3-Diethylpentane	146.168	−33.11	1.42051	0.75359
134	2,2-Dimethyl-4-ethylhexane	147	....	1.4131	0.733
135	2,2,4-Trimethylheptane	147.7	....	1.4092	0.7275
136	2,2,4,5-Tetramethylhexane	147.8	....	1.41318	0.73546
137	2,2,5-Trimethylheptane	148	....	1.409	0.726
138	2,2,6-Trimethylheptane	148.2	....	1.4059	0.7195
139	2,2,3,5-Tetramethylhexane	148.4	....	1.4142	0.7378
140	Nopinane (7,7-Dimethylbicyclo[3.1.1]heptane)	149[747]	....	1.4641	0.86111[22/22]
141	trans-1-Ethyl-4-methylcyclohexane	149.05–.15	−80.8	1.4304	0.7798
142	Cyclooctane	150[750]	14 (4.3)	1.4586	0.8349
143	1-Ethyl-2-methylcyclohexane	150–2	....	1.432	0.784
144	n-Nonane	150.81	−53.519	1.40542	0.71763
145	1,3,3-Trimethylbicyclo[2.2.1]heptane (Fenchane)	151–2	....	1.44714	0.8345
146	trans-1-Ethyl-4-methylcyclohexane	151.69	....	1.4382	0.7972
147	cis-1,1,3,5-Tetramethylcyclohexane	152.4–.5	....	1.4319	0.7813
148	cis-1-Ethyl-4-methylcyclohexane	152.55–.60	....	1.4374	0.7969
149	2,5,5-Trimethylheptane	152.8	....	1.4136	0.7368
150	2,4,4-Trimethylheptane	153	....	1.412	0.733
151	2,3,3,5-Tetramethylhexane	153	....	1.4196	0.746
152	2,2,4,4-Tetramethylhexane	153.3	....	1.4208	0.7470
153	Isopropylcyclohexane	154.5	−89.8	1.44095	0.80232
154	1,1,3,3-Tetramethylcyclohexane	154.8–5.0	....	1.4374	0.7936
155	2,2,3,4-Tetramethylhexane	154.9	....	1.4226	0.7548
156	2,2-Dimethyloctane	155	....	1.4082	0.7245
157	3-Ethyl-2,2,4-trimethylpentane	155.3	....	1.4223	0.7571
158	3,3,5-Trimethylheptane	155.6	....	1.4170	0.7428
159	2,3,6-Trimethylheptane	155.7	....	1.4125	0.7345
160	2,4-Dimethyloctane	155.8–6.0	....	1.4090	0.7259[20/20]
161	d,l-cis-1-Ethyl-3-methylcyclohexane	155.97	....	1.4432	0.8094
162	d,l-2,5-Dimethyloctane	156–8	....	1.4160	0.7370
163	1,1,3,5-Tetramethylcyclohexane	156.4–.5	....	1.4370	0.7929
164	n-Butylcyclopentane	156.56	−107.985	1.4316	0.7846
165	n-Propylcyclohexane	156.724	−94.90	1.43705	0.79360
166	2,3,5-Trimethylheptane	157	....	1.416	0.741
167	2,5-Dimethyl-3-ethylhexane	157	....	1.416	0.741
168	2,4,5-Trimethylheptane	157	....	1.4160	0.741
169	2,4-Dimethyl-3-isopropylpentane	157	....	1.42463	0.75830
170	2,2,3-Trimethylheptane	158	....	1.417	0.7420
171	2,4-Dimethyl-4-ethylhexane	158	....	1.419	0.747
172	2,2-Dimethyl-3-ethylhexane	159	....	1.420	0.749
173	2,2,3,4,4-Pentamethylpentane	159.3	....	1.43069	0.76703
174	1,1,3,4-Tetramethylcyclohexane	159.5–6.1	....	1.4380	0.7976
175	5-Ethyl-2-methylheptane	159.7	....	1.4134	0.736
176	2,7-Dimethyloctane	159.9	....	1.4086	0.7242

*Derivative data given in order: m.p., crystal color, solvent from which crystallized.

No.	Name	Boiling point, °C	Melting point, °C	n_D^{20}	D_4^{20}
177	3,6-Dimethyloctane.........................	160	....	1.4145^{18}	0.7363
178	3,5-Dimethyloctane.........................	160	....	1.413	0.736
179	4-Isopropylheptane	160	....	1.417	0.741
180	2,3,3-Trimethylheptane	160	....	1.4202	0.7488
181	4-Ethyl-2-methylheptane	160	....	1.413	0.736
182	2,6-Dimethyloctane.........................	160–0.5	....	1.4113	0.7285
183	2,2,3,3-Tetramethylhexane	160.3	....	1.42818	0.76446
184	trans-1-Isopropyl-4-methylcyclohexane (p-Menthane).............................	161	....	1.4393	0.792
185	4,4-Dimethyloctane.........................	161	....	1.4144	0.7347
186	2,3,4,5-Tetramethylhexane	161	....	1.424	0.757
187	5-Ethyl-3-methylheptane	161	....	1.414	0.737
188	3,3-Dimethyloctane.........................	161.2	....	1.4165	0.7390
189	4,5-Dimethyloctane.........................	162	....	1.4173	0.7458
190	3,4-Diethylhexane..........................	162	....	1.420	0.754
191	4-Propylheptane	162	....	1.4150	0.7364
192	1,1,4-Trimethylcycloheptane (Eucarvane)	$162–3^{720}$	....	1.4420	0.8011
193	trans-1,2,3,5-Tetramethylcyclohexane	162–4	....	1.44657_{He}	0.8140
194	2,3,4,4-Tetramethylhexane	162.2	....	1.4270	0.7639
195	2,3,4-Trimethylheptane	163	....	1.421	0.751
196	3-Isopropyl-2-methylhexane.................	163	....	1.421	0.751
197	2,2,7-Trimethylbicyclo[2.2.1]heptane (α-Fenchane)	$163.5–4.5^{753}$	....	1.4590	0.8579
198	3-Ethyl-3-methylheptane	163.8	....	1.4208	0.7501
199	2,4-Dimethyl-3-ethylhexane.................	164	....	1.424	0.759
200	3,4,4-Trimethylheptane	164	....	1.424	0.757
201	3,3,4-Trimethylheptane	164	....	1.424	0.757
202	3,4,5-Trimethylheptane	164	....	1.424	0.759
203	2,3-Dimethyl-4-ethylhexane.................	164	....	1.424	0.759
204	1-Methyl-3-propylcyclohexane	164–5 (171–3)	....	1.4377	0.7895^{21}
205	2,3-Dimethyloctane.........................	$164.4–4.6^{764}$	....	1.4152	0.7377
206	d,l-Pinane	164.5–5.0	....	1.4609	0.8551
207	2,3,3,4-Tetramethylhexane	164.6	....	1.4297	0.7694
208	3,3-Dimethyl-4-ethylhexane.................	165	....	1.427	0.764
209	5-Methylnonane	165.1	−87.7	1.4122	0.7326
210	4-Methylnonane	165.7	−98.7	1.4123	0.7323
211	3-Ethyl-2-methylheptane	166	....	1.418	0.746
212	3,4-Dimethyloctane.........................	166	....	1.4182	0.746
213	d-α-Pinane................................	$166–6.5^{762}$	....	1.4630	0.8560
214	d,l-1-Isopropyl-3-methylcyclohexane (d,l-m-Menthane)............................	166–7	....	1.44^{24}	0.7965^{24}
215	2,2,3,3,4-Pentamethylpentane	166.1	....	1.43606	0.78009
216	trans-1,2,4,5-Tetramethylcyclohexane	166.2–8.0	....	1.44446_{He}	0.8100
217	3,3-Diethylhexane..........................	166.3	....	1.428	0.767
218	2-Methylnonane	166.8	−74.5	1.4099	0.7281
219	d-1-Isopropyl-3-methylcyclohexane (d-m-Menthane).............................	167	....	1.446^{23}	0.8116^{23}
220	3-Ethyl-4-methylheptane	167	....	1.422	0.753
221	4-Ethyl-3-methylheptane	167	....	1.422	0.753
222	4-Ethyl-4-methylheptane	167	....	1.421	0.752
223	l-β-Pinane	$167.5–8^{748}$	....	1.4605	0.8567
224	3-Methylnonane	167.8	−84.8	1.4125	0.7334
225	3-Ethyloctane	168	....	1.416	0.740
226	4-Ethyloctane	168	....	1.416	0.740
227	3-Ethyl-2,2,3-trimethylpentane	168	....	1.436	0.781
228	l-1-Isopropyl-3-methylcyclohexane (l-m-Menthane)	168	....	1.4358	0.7938
229	cis-1-Isopropyl-4-methylcyclohexane (cis-p-Menthane)...........................	168.5	....	1.4515	0.816
230	cis-1,2,3,5-Tetramethylcyclohexane	$168–70^{762}$	....	1.44847_{He}	0.8166
231	2,3-Dimethyl-3-ethylhexane.................	169	....	1.427	0.765

*Derivative data given in order: m.p., crystal color, solvent from which crystallized.

TABLE I. ALKANES AND CYCLOALKANES
a) Gases and Liquids (Listed in order of increasing b.p.*) (Continued)

No.	Name		Boiling point, °C	n_D^{20}	D_4^{20}
232	1-Isopropyl-4-methylcyclohexane (p-Menthane)	169–70	....	1.4375[21]	0.7929
233	3,4-Dimethyl-3-ethylhexane	170	....	1.431	0.7722
234	3,3,4,4-Tetramethylhexane	170	....	1.4368	0.7824
235	Cyclononane	170–2	9.7	1.4328[16]	0.8534[15.2]
236	1-Isopropyl-2-methylcyclohexane (o-Menthane)	171	....	1.447[21]	0.8135[21]
237	cis-1,2,4,5-Tetramethylcyclohexane	171[755]	....	1.44647[He]	0.8122
238	1-Methyl-1-propylcyclohexane	172	....	1.4440	0.8101
239	n-Decane	174.123	−29.661	1.41189	0.73005
240	1-Methyl-4-propylcyclohexane	174.3–7.1	....	1.4393	0.798
241	1-Methyl-2-propylcyclohexane	175.5–6.0[756]	....	1.4468[19]	0.8130[19]
242	n-Pentylcyclopentane	180; 60[10]	−83.	1.4358	0.7912
243	n-Butylcyclohexane	180.947	−74.725	1.44075	0.79918
244	trans-Decahydronaphthalene (trans-Decalin)	187.25	−30.40	1.4695	0.8699
245	Isoamylcyclohexane	193.	....	1.4423	0.8023
246	cis-Decahydronaphthalene (cis-Decalin)	195.69	−43.01	1.4810	0.8965
247	n-Undecane (n-Hendecane)	195.89	−25.594	1.41716	0.74017
248	Cyclodecane	201	9.6	1.4692	0.8577[20.4]
249	n-Pentylcyclohexane	202.8	−57.5	1.4437	0.8037
250	n-Hexylcyclopentane	203	....	1.4392	0.7965
251	9-Methyl-trans-decahydronaphthalene	205; 77[10]	....	1.4631	0.8620
252	1,10-Dimethyl-trans-decahydronaphthalene	213; 83[10]	....	1.4659	0.8633
253	9-Methyl-cis-decahydronaphthalene	215; 85[10]	....	1.4804	0.8910
254	n-Dodecane	216.278; 51.84[1]	−9.587 (−12)	1.42160	0.74869
255	1,10-Dimethyl-cis-decahydronaphthalene	220; 88.99[10]	....	1.4812	0.8896
256	n-Hexylcyclohexane	224.0; 92.0[10]	−43	1.4462	0.8076
257	n-Heptylcyclopentane	224	....	1.4421	0.8010
258	9-Ethyl-trans-decahydronaphthalene	225; 93.06[10]	....	1.466	0.8610
259	9-Ethyl-cis-decahydronaphthalene	233; 99[10]	....	1.480	0.8860
260	1-Methyl-trans-decahydronaphthalene	235; 101[10]	....	1.4270	....
261	n-Tridecane	235.44; 66.35[1]	−5.392	1.4256	0.7564
262	Bicyclohexyl	236.5–7.5; 100[10]	3.5–4.0	1.4795	0.8848
263	n-Octylcyclopentane	243	....	1.4446	0.8048
264	n-Heptylcyclohexane	244	....	1.4484	0.8109
265	n-Tetradecane	235.57; 80.13[1]	5.863	1.4289	0.7628
266	n-Nonylcyclopentane	262	....	1.4467	0.8081
267	n-Octylcyclohexane	264	....	1.4503	0.8138
268	n-Pentadecane	270.63; 93.26[1]	9.926	1.4319	0.7685
269	n-Decylcyclopentane	279.3	....	1.44862	0.81097
270	n-Nonylcyclohexane	282	....	1.4519	0.8163
271	n-Undecylcyclopentane (n-Hendecylcyclopentane)	296	....	1.4503	0.8135
272	n-Decylcyclohexane	299	....	1.45338	0.81858
273	2-Methylheptadecane	311; 178.5[15]	....	1.4394[14]	0.7838[15]
274	n-Dodecylcyclopentane	312	....	1.4518	0.8158
275	n-Undecylcyclohexane (n-Hendecylcyclohexane)	316	5.8	1.4547	0.8206
276	n-Tridecylcyclopentane	327	5	1.4531	0.8178
277	n-Dodecylcyclohexane	331	12.5	1.4559	0.8223
278	n-Tetradecylcyclopentane	341	9	1.4543	0.8196

*Derivative data given in order: m.p., crystal color, solvent from which crystallized.

TABLE I. ALKANES AND CYCLOALKANES
b) Solids (Listed in order of increasing m.p.*)**

No.	Name	Melting point, °C	Boiling point, °C	n_D	D_4
1	Pentadecylcyclopentane	17	355	1.4554^{20}	0.8213^{20}
2	n-Hexadecane (Cetane)	18.165	286.793; 105.20[1]	1.43453^{20}	0.7734^{20}
3	Tridecylcyclohexane	18.5	346	1.4570^{20}	0.8239^{20}
4	Hexadecylcyclopentane	21	....	1.4543^{25}	0.8194^{25}
5	n-Heptadecane	21.98	301.82; 117.26[1]	1.4348^{25}; 1.4369^{20}_U	0.7745^{25}; 0.7780^{20}_U
6	Tetradecylcyclohexane	24	....	1.4559^{25}	0.8221^{25}
7	Heptadecylcyclopentane	27	....	1.4532^{30}	0.8173^{30}
8	n-Octadecane	28.18	316.12; 128.28[1]	1.4191^{70}; 1.4390^{20}	0.7751^{30}; 0.7819^{20}_U
9	Pentadecylcyclohexane	29	....	1.4545^{30}	0.8201^{30}
10	Octadecylcyclopentane	30	....	1.4541^{30}	0.8186^{30}
11	n-Nonadecane	32.1	329.7; 138.8[1]	1.4211^{70}; 1.4409^{20}_U	0.7787^{30}; 0.7855^{20}_U
12	Hexadecylcyclohexane	33.6	....	1.4596^{20}_U	0.8279^{20}_U
13	Nonadecylcyclopentane	35	....	1.4588^{20}_U	0.8266^{20}_U
14	n-Eicosane	36.8	342.7; 148.9[1]	1.4230^{70}; 1.4426^{20}_U	0.7550^{70}; 0.7887^{20}_U
15	Heptadecylcyclohexane	37.8	....	1.4603^{20}_U	0.8290^{20}_U
16	Eicosylcyclopentane	38	....	1.4595^{20}_U	0.8276^{20}_U
17	n-Heneicosane	40.5	356.5; 152.94[1]	1.4247^{70}; 1.4441^{20}_U	0.7583^{70}; 0.7917^{20}_U
18	Octadecylcyclohexane	41.6	....	1.4610^{20}_U	0.8300^{20}_U
19	Heneicosylcyclopentane	42	....	1.4602^{20}_U	0.8286^{20}_U
20	n-Docosane	44.4 (47)	368.6; 161.88[1]	1.4260^{70}; 1.4455^{20}_U	0.7631^{70}
21	Docosylcyclopentane	45	....	1.4608^{20}_U	0.8295^{20}_U
22	Nonadecylcyclohexane	45.2	....	1.4616^{20}_U	0.8310^{20}_U
23	n-Tricosane	47.6	380.2; 170.48[1]	1.4276^{20}; 1.4468^{20}_U	0.7641^{70}; 0.7969^{20}_U
24	Eicosylcyclohexane	48.5	....	1.4622^{20}_U	0.8318^{20}_U
25	Tricosylcyclopentane	49	....	1.4614^{20}_U	0.8304^{20}_U
26	n-Tetracosane	50.9	391.3; 178.7[1]	1.4286^{70}; 1.4480^{20}_U	0.7657^{70}; 0.7991^{20}_U
27	Tetracosylcyclopentane	51	....	1.4619^{20}	0.8312^{20}_U
28	Heneicosylcyclohexane	51.5	....	1.4627^{20}	0.8326^{20}_U
29	n-Pentacosane	53.7	401.9; 186.55[1]	1.4302^{70}; 1.4491^{20}_U	0.7693^{70}; 0.8012^{20}_U
30	Pentacosylcyclopentane	54	....	1.4624^{20}_U	0.8319^{20}_U
31	Docosylcyclohexane	54.4	....	1.4632^{20}_U	0.8334^{20}_U
32	Hexacosylcyclopentane	56	....	1.4628^{20}_U	0.8326^{20}_U
33	Nortricyclene (Tricyclo[2.2.1.0$^{2.6}$]heptane)	56	106–7	....	....
34	n-Hexacosane	56.4	412.2; 194.18[1]	1.4310^{70}; 1.4501^{20}_U	0.7704^{70}; 0.8032^{20}_U
35	Cyclohexadecane	57	93–8$^{0.8}$	....	....
36	Tricosylcyclohexane	57	....	1.4637^{20}_U	0.8341^{20}_U
37	Heptacosylcyclopentane	59	....	1.4633^{20}_U	0.8333^{20}_U
38	n-Heptacosane	59.0	422.1; 201.54[1]	1.4321^{70}; 1.4511^{20}_U	0.7732^{70}; 0.8050^{20}_U
39	Tetracosylcyclohexane	59.5	....	1.4641^{20}_U	0.8347^{20}_U
40	Cyclopentadecane	60–1	....	$1.4592^{61.5}$	$0.8634^{61.5}$
41	Octacosylcyclopentane	61	....	1.4637^{20}_U	0.8339^{20}_U
42	n-Octacosane	61.4	431.6; 208.58[1]	1.4330^{70}; 1.4520^{20}_U	0.7750^{70}; 0.8067^{20}_U
43	Pentacosylcyclohexane	61.9	....	1.4645^{20}	0.8353^{20}_U
44	Nonacosylcyclopentane	63	....	1.4640^{20}	0.8345^{20}_U
45	n-Nonacosane	63.7	440.8; 172.36$^{0.1}$	0.7797^{65}; 1.4529^{20}_U	1.4361^{65}; 0.8083^{20}_U

*Derivative data given in order: m.p., crystal color, solvent from which crystallized.
**U = undercooled liquid.

TABLE I. ALKANES AND CYCLOALKANES
b) Solids (Listed in order of increasing m.p.*)** (Continued)

No.	Name	Melting point, °C	Boiling point, °C	n_D	D_4
46	**Hexacosylcyclohexane**	64	....	1.4649_U^{20}	0.8359_U^{20}
47	**Triacontylcyclopentane**	65	....	1.4644_U^{20}	0.8350_U^{20}
48	**d,l-Isobornane**	65–7	....	1.44186^{67}	0.82757^{67}
	(2,2,3-Trimethylbicyclo[2.2.1]heptane)				
49	**n-Triacontane**	65.8	449.7;	$1.4348^{70};$	$0.7797^{70};$
			222.00^1	1.4536_U^{20}	0.8097_U^{20}
50	**Heptacosylcyclohexane**	66.1	....	1.4653_U^{20}	0.8365_U^{20}
51	**Hentriacontylcyclopentane**.	67	....	1.4648_U^{20}	0.8356_U^{20}
52	**n-Hentriacontane**	67.9	458;	1.4543_U^{20}	0.8111_U^{20}
			$184.17^{0.1}$		
53	**Octacosylcyclohexane**	68	....	1.4656_U^{20}	0.8370_U^{20}
54	**Dotriacontylcyclopentane**.	69	....	1.4651_U^{20}	0.8360_U^{20}
55	**n-Dotriacontane (Bicetyl)**.	69.7	467;	1.4550_U^{20}	$0.7791^{75};$
			234.8^1		0.8124_U^{20}
56	**Nonacosylcyclohexane**	69.9	....	1.4659_U^{20}	0.8374_U^{20}
57	**Tritriacontylcyclopentane**	70	....	1.4654_U^{20}	0.8365_U^{20}
58	**Tritriacontane**.	71.4	....	1.4557_U^{20}	0.8136_U^{20}
59	**Triacontylcyclohexane**	71.6	....	1.4662_U^{20}	0.8379_U^{20}
60	**Tetratriacontylcyclopentane**	72	....	1.4657_U^{20}	0.8370_U^{20}
61	**Tetratriacontane**.	72.6;	285.4^3	$1.4296^{90};$	$0.7728^{90};$
		73.1		1.4563_U^{20}	0.8148_U^{20}
62	**28-Methylnonacosane**.	73–4	$222^{0.3}$	....	....
63	**Hentriacontylcyclohexane**	73.3	....	1.4665_U^{20}	0.8383^{20}
64	**Pentatriacontylcyclopentane**	74	....	1.4660_U^{20}	0.8374^{20}
65	**Pentatriacontane**.	74.7	331	1.4568_U^{20}	0.8157^{20}
66	**Dotriacontylcyclohexane**	74.8	....	1.4668_U^{20}	0.8388_U^{20}
67	**Hexatriacontylcyclopentane**	75	....	1.4662_U^{20}	0.8378^{20}
68	**Hexatriacontane**.	76.2	....	1.4573_U^{20}	0.8169^{20}
69	**Tritriacontylcyclohexane**	76.3	....	1.4670^{20}	0.8391^{20}
70	**Heptatriacontane**	77.7	....	1.4578^{20}	0.8179^{20}
71	**Tetratriacontylcyclohexane**	77.7	....	1.4673_U^{20}	0.8395^{20}
72	**Octatriacontane**	79	....	1.4583_U^{20}	0.8188^{20}
73	**Pentatriacontylcyclohexane**	79.1	....	1.4675_U^{20}	0.8399_U^{20}
74	**Nonatriacontane**.	80.3	....	1.4588_U^{20}	0.8197_U^{20}
75	**Hexatriacontylcyclohexane**	80.4	....	1.4678_U^{20}	0.8402^{20}
76	**Tetracontane**.	81.5	....	1.4593_U^{20}	0.8205_U^{20}
77	**Norbornane (Bicyclo[2.2.1]heptane)**	86–7, subl.	....	....	....
78	**2,2,3,3-Tetramethylbutane**.	100.69	106.47	1.4695^{20}	0.8242_{solid}^{23}
79	**Bornane (Camphane)**.	158–9, subl.	....	....	....
80	**Adamantane**	268 (252–3)	....	1.568	1.07_{solid}

*Derivative data given in order: m.p., crystal color, solvent from which crystallized.

**U = undercooled liquid.

EXPLANATIONS AND REFERENCES TO TABLE II

*Bromine addition compound.**

$$RCH{=}CHR' \;+\; Br_2 \;\rightarrow\; RCHBr{-}CHBrR'$$

Bromine addition
compound

From the alkene and bromine in carbon tetrachloride.
For directions and examples see: Cheronis, p. 576; Shriner, p. 106.
From the alkene and bromine in water.
See: Vogel, p. 241.
From the alkene and bromine in chloroform.
See: C. G. Schmitt and C. E. Boord, *J. Amer. Chem. Soc.*, **54**, 751 (1932).

*2,4-Dinitrobenzenesulfenyl chloride addition compound.**

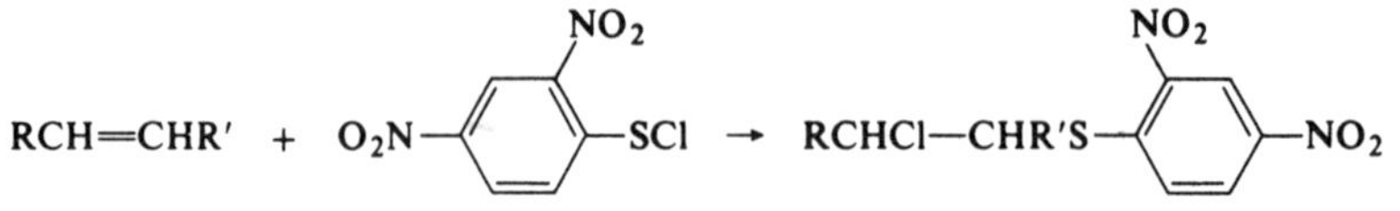

2,4-Dinitrobenzenesulfenyl
chloride adduct

From the alkene and 2,4-dinitrobenzenesulfenyl chloride in glacial acetic acid.
For directions and examples see: Cheronis, p. 577; N. Kharasch and C. M. Buess, *J. Amer. Chem. Soc.*, **71**, 2724 (1949); D. J. Cram, *J. Amer. Chem. Soc.*, **71**, 3883 (1949); N. Kharasch, C. M. Buess and S. I. Strashun, *J. Amer. Chem. Soc.*, **74**, 3422 (1952).
From the alkene and 2,4-dinitrobenzenesulfenyl chloride in benzene or in carbon tetrachloride.
See: N. Kharasch and C. M. Buess, *J. Amer. Chem. Soc.*, **71**, 2724 (1949).

*S-Alkylmercaptosuccinic acid.**

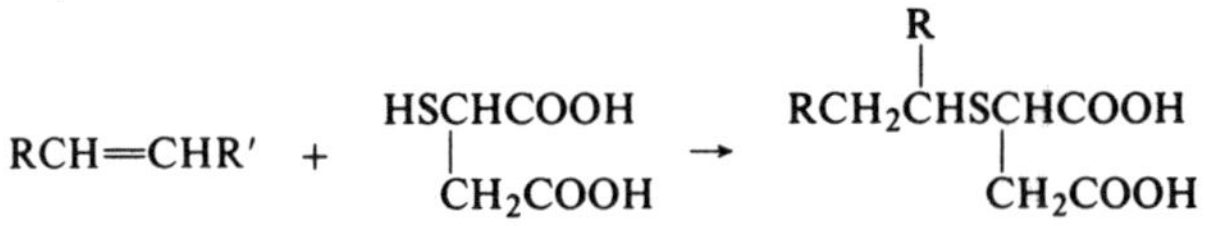

S-Alkylmercaptosuccinic
acid

From the alkene, mercaptosuccinic acid and benzoyl peroxide in methanol.
For directions and examples see: J. G. Hendrickson and L. F. Hatch, *J. Org. Chem.*, **25**, 1747 (1960).

Maleic anhydride adduct (from dienes).

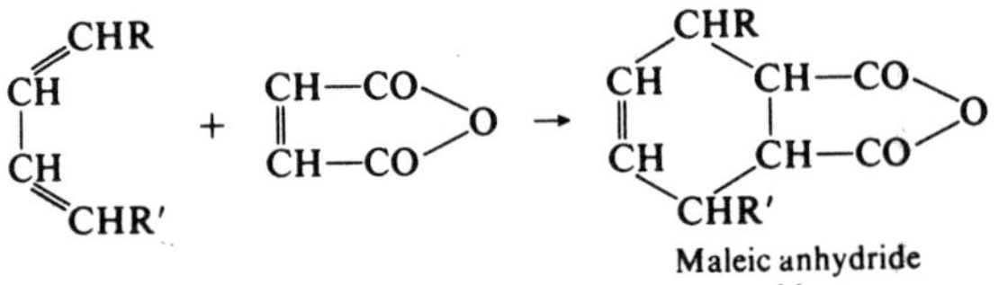

Maleic anhydride
adduct

From the diene and maleic anhydride in benzene.
For directions and examples see: Linstead, p. 51; Vogel, p. 943.
From the diene and maleic anhydride in xylene.
See: Linstead, p. 51.
For general references see: M. C. Kloetzel in *Organic Reactions*, Vol. 4 (Ed. R. Adams), John Wiley and Sons, New York, 1948, p. 1; H. L. Holmes in *Organic Reactions*, Vol. 4, (Ed. R. Adams), John Wiley and Sons, New York, 1948, p. 60; O. Diels and K. Alder, *Chem. Ber.*, **62**, 2081 (1929).

Nitrosochloride addition compound.

$$RCH{=}CHR' \;+\; NOCl \;\rightarrow\; RCH(NO)CHClR'$$

Nitrosochloride
adduct

---

*Derivatives recommended for first trial.
WARNING: This is not an instruction manual. References should be consulted for the preparation of derivatives.

From the alkene and nitrosyl chloride (prepared from sodium nitrite in concentrated hydrochloric acid) in ether-acetic acid mixture.

For directions and examples see: Linstead, p. 52; R. Perrot, *Compt. Rend.*, **203**, 329 (1936).

From the alkene and nitrosyl chloride (prepared from thionyl chloride and nitrogen trioxide) in ether.

See: M. Tuot, *Compt. Rend.*, **204**, 697 (1937).

---

*Derivatives recommended for first trial.

WARNING: This is not an instruction manual. References should be consulted for the preparation of derivatives.

TABLE II. ORGANIC DERIVATIVES OF ALKENES, CYCLOALKENES, DIENES AND POLYENES
a) Liquids 1) (Listed in order of increasing b.p.*)**

No.	Name	Boiling point, °C	Melting point, °C	n_D^{20}	D_4^{20}	Bromine addition product					Miscellaneous
						x-Bromo-	B.P., °C	M.P., °C	n_D^{20}	D_4^{20}	
1	**Ethene** (Ethylene)....	−103.71	−169.15[T]	....	0.384[0]	di-	131.36	9.85	1.53868	2.1792	....
2	**Propene** (Propylene)..	−47.70	−185.25[T]	....	0.5139	di-	141.99	−55.5	1.52004	1.93268	....
3	**Cyclopropene**	−36[744]	....	....	....	...	....	....	....	....	....
4	**Allene**	−34.5	−136	....	....	tetra-	......	10.7	1.6200	2.703	....
5	**2-Methylpropene**	−6.90	−140.35	1.3467	0.5942[S]	di-	149	....	1.5080	1.7595	2,4-Dinitrophenyl-sulfenyl chloride, 86-7
6	**1-Butene**	−6.26	−185.35	1.3465	0.5951	di-	166.3	....	1.5150	1.7951	2,4-Dinitrophenyl-sulfenyl chloride, 77.5-8.5
7	**1,3-Butadiene**	−4.41	−108.92	1.4292[.25]; 0.650[−6]	0.6255[−6.5]	tetra-	......	118, lgr.	....	.....	....
8	*trans*-**2-Butene**	0.88	−105.55	....	0.6042[S]	di-	161.0	....	1.5110	1.7852	....
9	**Cyclobutene**	2.4	....	....	0.733[0]	...	....	....	....	....	....
10	*cis*-**2-Butene**	3.72	−138.91	....	0.6306[1]	di-	161.0	....	1.5110	1.7852	....
11	**1,2-Butadiene** (Methylallene)	10.85	−136.19	1.4208[3]	0.652[S]	tetra-	97.5[7]	−2	1.6070	2.5085	....
12	**3-Methyl-1-butene** ...	20.06	−168.49	1.3643	0.6272	di-	61-2[12]	....	1.50932	1.6776	....
13	**1,4-Pentadiene**	25.97	−148.28	1.38876	0.66706	tetra-	......	85.5-6.0, eth.	....	.....	....
14	**1-Pentene**	29.97	−165.22	1.37148	0.64050	di-	68[12]	....	1.5012[12]	1.592[19]	Mercaptosuccinic acid adduct, 107.3-.6
15	**2-Methyl-1-butene** ...	31.16	−137.56	1.3778	0.6504	di-	47.4-48[9]	....	1.5088	1.6711	Mercaptosuccinic acid adduct, 122.3-.6
16	**3-Methylcyclobutene** .	32	....	1.4005	....	...	....	....	....	....	....
17	**2-Methyl-1,3-butadiene** (Isoprene).	34.07	−145.95	1.42194	0.68095	di- tetra-	90-6[12] 155-60[12]	....	....	.....	Maleic anh. adduct, 63-4, lgr.
18	*trans*-**2-Pentene**	36.35	−140.24	1.3793	0.6482	di-	91.0[50]	....	1.5096	1.6809	....
19	*cis*-**2-Pentene**	36.94	−151.39	1.3830	0.6556	di-	92.4[50]	....	1.5096	1.6817	....
20	**1-Methyl-1-cyclobutene**	37.1	....	1.4088	0.7244	...	....	....	....	....	....
21	**2-Methyl-2-butene** ...	38.57	−133.77	1.3874	0.6623	...	....	....	....	....	Nitrosochloride, 74; Mercaptosuccinic acid adduct, 153.7-4.0
22	**3-Methyl-1,2-butadiene** (1,1-Dimethylallene)	40	....	1.410	0.680	tetra-	150-2[17]	....	1.594[17]	2.305[17]	....
23	**Cyclopentadiene**	40.83[772]	−85	1.4398[19.5]	0.7983[19.5]	...	....	....	....	....	Dimer, 32; Maleic anh. adduct, 164-5; Benzoquinone adduct, 75-6
24	**1,3-Pentadiene** (Piperylene)	41.1	−88.9	1.4309	0.6803	tetra-	......	114.5, al.	....	.....	Maleic anh. adduct, 61, pet. eth.; Oxid. by KMnO4 → HCOOH + CH3COOH
25	**3,3-Dimethyl-1-butene**	41.24	−115.2	1.3760	0.6529	di-	95.3-5.6[10]	....	1.5109	1.5615	....
26	**1,** *trans*-**3-Pentadiene** .	42.03	−87.47	1.43008	0.67603	tetra-	131[3]	115, al.	....	.....	
27	**1,** *cis*-**3-Pentadiene** ...	44.07	−140.82	1.43634	0.69102	tetra-	131[3]	115, al.	....	.....	

*Derivative data given in order: m.p., crystal color, solvent from which crystallized.

**T = triple point; S = at saturation pressure.

TABLE II. ORGANIC DERIVATIVES OF ALKENES, CYCLOALKENES, DIENES AND POLYENES

a) Liquids 1) (Listed in order of increasing b.p.)* (Continued)

No.	Name	Boiling point, °C	Melting point, °C	n_D^{20}	D_4^{20}	x-Bromo-	B.P., °C	M.P., °C	n_D^{20}	D_4^{20}	Miscellaneous
							Bromine addition product				
28	Cyclopentene.......	44.24	−135.08	1.42246	0.77199	di-	71.5[12]	....	1.5510[19]	1.8713[19]	Mercaptosuccinic acid adduct, 142.8–3.1; Pseudo-nitrosite, 69–70; Perbenzoic acid oxid. → epoxy-cyclopentane, b.p., 102–3
29	1,2-Pentadiene (Ethylallene).......	44.86	−137.26	1.42091	0.69257	tetra-	94–6[0.1]	....	....	2.3469[18/18]	....
30	2,3-Pentadiene (1,3-Dimethylallene)	48.27	−125.26	1.42842	0.69502	....	....	....	....	....	....
31	4-Methyl-1-pentene ..	53.88	−153.63	1.3828	0.6642	di-	87[21]	....	1.4980	1.5689	Mercaptosuccinic acid adduct, 102.6–.9
32	3-Methyl-1-pentene ..	54.14	−153.0	1.3842	0.6675	di-	99[30]	....	1.5060	1.6016	....
33	3-Methyl-1,4-penta-diene	55	....	1.405	0.695	....	....	....	....	....	....
34	2,3-Dimethyl-1-butene	55.67	−157.27	1.3904	0.6779	di-	80[17]	....	1.5105	1.6033	....
35	2-Methyl-1,4-penta-diene	56	....	1.405	0.694	....	....	....	....	....	....
36	4-Methyl-cis-2-pentene	56.3	−134.43	1.3880	0.6690	di-	72–3[18]	....	1.5060	1.5983	....
37	4-Methyl-trans-2-pentene	58.55	−140.81	1.3889	0.6686	di-	78[22]	....	1.5070	1.5996	....
38	1,5-Hexadiene (Biallyl)..........	59.46	−140.8	1.4042	0.6923	tetra-	....	52	....	....	Dil. HNO_3 → succinic ac., 185
39	2-Methyl-1-pentene ..	60.7	−135.72	1.3920	0.6817	di-	87–8[20]	....	1.5015	1.5581	....
40	1-Hexene...........	63.49	−139.82	1.38788	0.67317	di-	89–90[18]	....	1.5024	1.5774	2,4-Dinitrophenyl-sulfenyl chloride, 61–2; Mercapto-succinic acid adduct, 94.5–5.7
41	2-Ethyl-1-butene.....	64–6	−131.53	1.3969	0.6894	di-	87[21]	....	1.5112	1.6045	....
42	trans-1,3-Hexadiene..	64.5–5.5	....	1.4060[19]	0.6925[19]	tetra-	....	19	....	....	....
43	3-Methylcyclopentene	65.0	....	1.4207	0.7622	....	....	....	....	....	....
44	cis-3-Hexene........	66.44	−137.82	1.3947	0.6796	di-	80–1[13]	....	1.5045	1.6027	....
45	3-Hexene (cis-trans mixture)	66.6–67	....	1.3942	0.6816	di-	80–1[13]	....	1.5045	1.6027	....
46	trans-3-Hexene......	67.08	−113.43	1.3943	0.6772	di-	80–1[13]	....	1.5045	1.6027	....
47	2-Methyl-2-pentene ..	67.29	−135.7	1.4004	0.6863	di-	71–2[18]	....	1.5063	1.5849	Mercaptosuccinic acid adduct, 152.1–.6
48	3-Methyl-trans-2-pentene	67.63	−134.84	1.4016	0.6942	di-	72–4[15]	....	1.5085	....	....
49	trans-2-Hexene......	67.87	−132.97	1.3935	0.6784	di-	90[16]	....	1.5025	1.5812	....
50	2-Hexene (cis-trans mixture)	67.9–8.1	....	1.3928	0.6813	di-	90[16]	....	1.5025	1.5812	....
51	2,3-Hexadiene.......	68	....	1.395	0.680	......	....	....	....	....	....
52	2,3-Dimethyl-1,3-butadiene.........	68.78	−76.01	1.4394	0.7267	di- tetra-	....	47, lgr. 138, bz.	....	....	Maleic anh. adduct, 78–9
53	cis-2-Hexene........	68.84	−141.14	1.3977	0.6869	di-	90[16]	....	1.5025	1.5812	....
54	4-Methyl-1,2-penta-diene (1-Isopropyl-allene)	70	....	1.424	0.708	......	....	....	....	....	....
55	3-Methyl-cis-2-pentene	70.45	−138.45	1.4045	0.6986	di-	72–4[15]	....	1.5085	....	....

*Derivative data given in order: m.p., crystal color, solvent from which crystallized.

No.	Name	Boiling point, °C	Melting point, °C	n_D^{20}	D_4^{20}	Bromine addition product					Miscellaneous
						x-Bromo-	B.P., °C	M.P., °C	n_D^{20}	D_4^{20}	
56	2-Methyl-2,3-penta-diene (Trimethyl allene)	72	....	1.425	0.711	....	....	....	....	....	....
57	1,4-Hexadiene	72.3–2.5	....	1.4402[19]	0.7057[19]	tetra- 2 forms	....	a) 63–4; b) f.p. <–50	....	....	
58	4,4-Dimethyl-1-pentene	72.49	–136.6	1.3918	0.6827	di-	77–8[9]	....	1.4970	1.5129	Mercaptosuccinic acid adduct, 119.0–.5
59	1, (cis and/or trans)-3-hexadiene	73		1.438	0.705	....	....	....	....	....	
60	2,3-Dimethyl-2-butene	73.21	–74.28	1.4122	0.7080	di-	....	173–4; 121			
61	2-Ethyl-1,3-butadiene	75	....	1.445	0.717	....	....	....			
62	4-Methylcyclopentene	75.2	....	1.4306	0.7796	....	....	....			
63	1-Methylcyclopentene	75.8	–127	1.4330	0.7802	....	....	....			
64	2-Methyl-1,(cis and/or trans)-3-pentadiene	76	....	1.446	0.719						
65	1,2-Hexadiene (n-Propylallene)	76		1.4282	0.7149	tetra-	130[3]		1.5850	2.1873	
66	2-Methyl-1,(cis and/or trans)-3-pentadiene	76	....	1.446	0.719						
67	4-Methyl-1,3-penta-diene	76.3	....	1.451	0.719						
68	4,4-Dimethyl-trans-2-pentene	76.75	–115.24	1.3982	0.6889	di-	92.8–93[14]		1.5080	1.5538	....
69	3,3-Dimethyl-1-pentene	77.54	–134.3	1.3984	0.6974	di-	95.3–6[10]	....	1.5109	1.5615	
70	2,3,3-Trimethyl-1-butene	77.87	–109.85	1.4029	0.7050	di-	98–9[14]	38–9	....	....	
71	3-Methyl-1,3-penta-diene	78.0–.3	....	1.4494	0.7499						
72	trans-1,3,5-Hexatriene	78.5; 77–8.5		1.4884[13.5]	0.74229[15/15]	hexa-	....	78			
73	cis-1,3,5-Hexatriene	78.5	....	1.4577	0.7179						
74	3-Methyl-1,2-penta-diene	79; 70	....	1.425	0.715						
75	2,4-Hexadiene	79.4–81.6[765]	–79	1.4493	0.7152	2,5-di-tetra-	85[11]	182	1.534[19]	1.622[19]	Maleic anh. adduct, 95–6, lgr.; SO₂ adduct, 43–3.5
76	3-Methyl-1,5-hexa-diene	80–1	....	1.4116	0.7103						
77	4,4-Dimethyl-1,2-pentadiene (tert-Butylallene)	80–3	....	....	0.7184						
78	1,3-Cyclohexadiene	80.31[757]	–104.8	1.4740	0.8413	di- tetra- 2 forms	....	68, iso-merizes → m. 108 1, trans-2,cis-3, trans-4, 92; 1,cis-2, trans-3, trans-4, 156	....	....	Maleic anh. adduct, 145–6, heptane; Benzoquinone adduct, 196–7, lgr.
79	4,4-Dimethyl-cis-2-pentene	80.42	–135.46	1.4024	0.6996	di-	92.8–3.0[14]	....	1.5080	1.5538	....

*Derivative data given in order: m.p., crystal color, solvent from which crystallized.

TABLE II. ORGANIC DERIVATIVES OF ALKENES, CYCLOALKENES, DIENES AND POLYENES

a) Liquids 1) (Listed in order of increasing b.p.)* (Continued)

No.	Name	Boiling point, °C	Melting point, °C	n_D^{20}	D_4^{20}	Bromine addition product					Miscellaneous
						x-Bromo-	B.P., °C	M.P., °C	n_D^{20}	D_4^{20}	
80	3,4-Dimethyl-1-pentene	81	....	1.3995	0.701	....	....	....	....	....	....
81	Cyclohexene	82.97	−103.51	1.44654	0.81096	di-	101–3[13]	....	1.5445[19]	1.7759[19]	Mercaptosuccinic acid adduct, 150.5–1.5; KMnO₄ oxid. → adipic ac., 154; 2,4-Dinitro-phenylsulfenyl chloride, 117–8; HBr → cyclo-hexyl bromide, b.p. 165
82	2,4-Dimethyl-2-pentene	83–4	−127.7	1.40165[22]	0.6958[22]	di-	88[17]	....	1.50920[22.5]	1.5431[22.5]	
83	3-Methyl-1-hexene	84.0	....	1.397	0.695	di-	84.0–.2[6]	....	1.5028	1.5248	
84	2,3-Dimethyl-1-pentene	84.26	−134.8	1.4033	0.7051	di-	72.5–3.0[3]		1.5028	1.5245	
85	3-Ethyl-1-pentene	85.13	−127.4	1.3980	0.6962	di-	93.5[15]		1.5006	1.5251	
86	5-Methyl-1-hexene	85.31	....	1.3966	0.6920	di-	142.6–3.6[101]		1.4970	1.5072	
87	5-Methyl-trans-2-hexene	86.0	....	1.400	0.700	di-	87–8[10]		1.4960	1.5027	
88	2-Methyl-3-hexene	86.0	....	1.399	0.694	di-	96[19]		1.5060	1.5310	
89	2,4-Dimethyl-2,3-pentadiene (Tetramethylallene)	86.5	....	1.40039	0.7006	....	....				
90	4-Methyl-1-hexene	86.73	−141.45	1.4000	0.6985	di-	94.7–5.7[11]	....	1.4980	1.5027	
91	3,4-Dimethyl-2-pentene	87.0	....	1.407	0.713	di-	65.5–6.0		1.5104	1.5400	
92	4-Methyl-cis-2-hexene	87.37	....	1.4024	0.6996	di-	91–2[11]		1.5045	1.5382	
93	4-Methyl-trans-2-hexene	87.6	−126.5	1.4023	0.6975	di-	91–2[11]		1.5045	1.5382	
94	3,3-Dimethylcyclopentene	88	....	1.423	0.771	....					
95	2-Ethyl-3-methyl-1-butene	89	....	1.410	0.715	di-	72.5–3.5[3]		1.5062	1.5261	
96	5-Methyl-cis-2-hexene	91		1.400	0.700	di-	89–90[11]		1.4990	1.5152	
97	5-Methyl-1,4-hexadiene	91–2.5		1.4390	0.7258	1,2-di-	101–4[18]		1.5233[16]	1.566[16]	
98	2-Methyl-1-hexene	92.0	−102.84	1.4034	0.7030	di-	100.5–1.5[23]	....	1.5000	1.5066	
99	1,3-Dimethylcyclopentene	92	....	1.428	0.766	....					
100	2-Methyl-1,5-hexadiene	92.5[769]	....	1.423/6[17.3]	0.7289[18.5]						Nitrosochloride, 75–6
101	2,4-Dimethyl-1,3-pentadiene	93	−114	1.4412	0.7368	....					
102	1,4-Dimethylcyclopentene	93.2	....	1.4283	0.779	....					
103	3-Methyl-trans-3-hexene	93.5	....	1.4107	0.7099	....					
104	1-Heptene	93.64	−119.03	1.39980	0.69698	di-	106.2[13]	....	1.4990	1.5208	Mercaptosuccinic acid adduct, 103.4–.9

*Derivative data given in order: m.p., crystal color, solvent from which crystallized.

a) Liquids 1) (Listed in order of increasing b.p.)* (Continued)

No.	Name	Boiling point, °C	Melting point, °C	n_D^{20}	D_4^{20}	Bromine addition product					Miscellaneous
						x-Bromo-	B.P., °C	M.P., °C	n_D^{20}	D_4^{20}	
105	3-Methyl-*trans*-2-hexene	94.0	....	1.410	0.7120	*di*-	65.0–5.1[2]	....	1.5040	1.5240	....
106	2-Ethyl-1-pentene	94	....	1.405	0.708	*di*-	77–8[4]		1.4990	1.4929	....
107	3-Methyl-*cis*-3-hexene	95.35	....	1.4123	0.7132	....	....	....	....	....	....
108	2-Methyl-2-hexene	95.41	−130.35	1.4106	0.7082	*di*-	73.0–.1[8]	....	1.4990	1.5116	....
109	*trans*-3-Heptene	95.67	−136.63	1.4043	0.6981	*di*-	105.5–6.5[23]	....	1.5010	1.5153	....
110	*cis*-3-Heptene	95.75	....	1.4059	0.7030	*di*-	105.5–6.5[23]	....	1.5010	1.5153	....
111	5-Methyl-1,2-hexadiene (Isobutylallene)	96	....	1.4282[19]	0.7225[19]	....	....	....	....	....	....
112	3-Ethyl-2-pentene	96.01	....	1.4148	0.7204	*di*-	76.0–.4[3]	....	1.5090	1.5426	....
113	2,3-Dimethyl-2-pentene	97.5	−118.3	1.4208	0.7277	*di*-	97–9[15]	....	1.517[22]	1.547[22]	....
114	*trans*-2-Heptene	97.95	−109.48	1.4045	0.7012	*di*-	96.2[12]	....	1.5000	1.5129	....
115	3-Ethylcyclopentene	98.1	....	1.4319	0.7830	....	....	....	....	....	....
116	*cis*-2-Heptene	98.5	....	1.406	0.708	*di*-	96.2[12]	....	1.5000	1.5129	....
117	5-Methyl-1,3-cyclohexadiene	100.5–1.5[762]	....	1.4662[22.5]	0.8252	....	....	....	....	....	....
118	2,2-Dimethyl-*trans*-3-hexene	100.9	....	1.4063	0.7039	*di*-	96.5–7.0[8]	....	1.5032	1.4856	....
119	1,4-Heptadiene	101	....	1.4202	0.7106	*di*-	....	....	1.5734	2.091	....
120	2,4,4-Trimethyl-1-pentene	101.44	−93.48	1.4086	0.7150	....	....	....	....	....	....
121	3,3-Dimethyl-1,5-hexadiene	101.6	....	1.4160	0.7249	....	....	....	....	....	....
122	3,4-Dimethyl-1,5-hexadiene	101.8	....	1.4211	0.7304	....	....	....	....	....	....
123	2,5-Dimethyl-3-hexene	102	....	1.406	0.710	*di*-	109[19]	....	1.5058	1.5034	....
124	5,5-Dimethyl-1-hexene	102.5	....	1.4049	0.709	....	....	....	....	....	....
125	4-Methylcyclohexene	102.74	−115.5	1.4414	0.7947	*di*-	130[40]	....	....	1.650[15/15]	....
126	3-Methylcyclohexene	104.0	....	1.4444	0.8010	....	....	....	....	....	....
127	2-Isopropyl-3-methyl-1-butene	104	....	1.4085	0.722	....	....	....	....	....	....
128	3,4,4-Trimethyl-1-pentene	104	....	1.412	0.719	....	....	....	....	....	....
129	3,5-Dimethyl-1-hexene	104	....	1.404	0.708	....	....	....	....	....	....
130	3,3-Dimethyl-1-hexene	104	....	1.4070	0.7140	....	....	....	....	....	....
131	5,5-Dimethyl-*trans*-2-hexene	104.1	....	1.4055	0.7066	....	....	....	....	....	....
132	2,4,4-Trimethyl-2-pentene	104.91	−106.33	1.4160	0.7218	....	....	....	....	....	....
133	3,3,4-Trimethyl-1-pentene	105	....	1.4144	0.729	....	....	....	....	....	....
134	2,2-Dimethyl-*cis*-3-hexene	105.4	−137.4	1.4099	0.7128	....	....	....	....	....	....
135	1,2-Heptadiene (*n*-Butylallene)	105.5–6.0	....	1.432[18]	0.7306[18]	2,3-*di*- tetra-	108–10[12]; 140[3]	....	1.5200[18] 1.5718	1.5595[18] 2.0675	....
136	1,2-Dimethylcyclopentene	105.8	−90.4	1.4448	0.7976	....	....	....	....	....	....
137	4-Ethylcyclopentene	106	....	1.440	0.798	....	....	....	....	....	....
138	4,4-Dimethyl-2-hexene	106	....	1.413	0.722	*di*-	92–3[4]	...٬....	1.5113	1.5148	....
139	1-Ethylcyclopentene	106.3	−118.4	1.4410	0.7982	....	....	....	....	....	....
140	5,5-Dimethyl-*cis*-2-hexene	106.9	....	1.4113	0.7169	....	....	....	....	....	....

*Derivative data given in order: m.p., crystal color, solvent from which crystallized.

No.	Name	Boiling point, °C	Melting point, °C	n_D^{20}	D_4^{20}	Bromine addition product					Miscellaneous
						x-Bromo-	B.P., °C	M.P., °C	n_D^{20}	D_4^{20}	
141	2-Methyl-2,4-hexadiene	107	....	1.4266[24.5]	0.7439	....	....	....	....	....	....
142	2-Methyl-1,3-cyclohexadiene	107–8	....	1.4662[18]	0.8272[18/18]	....	....	....	....	....	....
143	3-Methyl-2,4-hexadiene	107–8	....	1.46146[15]	0.7625[15]	....	....	....	....	....	....
144	4,4-Dimethyl-1-hexene	107.2	....	1.4102	0.7198	di-	224–5	....	1.5003	1.4689	....
145	3-Ethyl-4-methyl-1-pentene	107.5	....	1.4097	0.7200	....	....	....	....	....	....
146	2,4-Heptadiene	107.5–8.0	....	1.4578	0.7384	....	....	....	....	....	....
147	2,4-Dimethyl-trans-3-hexene	107.6	....	1.4126	0.7145	....	....	....	....	....	....
148	Quadricyclene (Quadricyclo [2,2,1,0[2.6], 0[3.5]]heptane).......	108[740] sl.d.	....	1.4804	....	....	....	....	....	....	....
149	2,3,4-Trimethyl-1-pentene	108	....	1.415	0.729	....	....	....	....	....	....
150	4-Methyl-1,3-hexadiene	108–10	....	1.4523	0.7558	....	....	....	....	....	....
151	2,3,3-Trimethyl-1-pentene	108.3	–69	1.4174	0.7352	....	....	....	....	....	....
152	4,5-Dimethyl-1-hexene	109	....	1.414	0.728	....	....	....	....	....	....
153	1,5,5-Trimethylcyclopentene (Isolaurolene)	109[754]	....	1.4324	0.7824	....	....	....	....	....	Reduces Tollen's reagent on warming
154	2,4-Dimethyl-cis-3-hexene	109	....	1.4140	0.7178	....	....	....	....	....	....
155	3,3-Dimethyl-2-ethyl-1-butene..........	110	....	1.4159	0.728	....	....	....	....	....	....
156	3-Ethyl-2-methyl-1-pentene	110	....	1.415	0.730	....	....	....	....	....	....
157	4,5-Dimethyl-2-hexene	110	....	1.413	0.725	....	....	....	....	....	....
158	1-Methylcyclohexene .	110.0	–121	1.4503	0.8102	di-	100–2[12]	....	....	....	2,4-Dinitrophenylsulfenyl chloride, 139–40
159	2-Ethyl-4-methyl-1-pentene	110.3	....	1.4105	0.7195	....	....	....	....	....	....
160	3-Ethyl-1-hexene	110.3	....	1.407	0.715	....	....	....	....	....	....
161	2,3-Dimethyl-1-hexene	110.5	....	1.4113	0.7214	....	....	....	....	....	....
162	2,4-Dimethyl-2-hexene	110.6	....	1.4118	0.7213	....	....	....	....	....	....
163	3-Methyl-1-heptene ..	111	....	1.406	0.711	....	....	....	....	....	....
164	2,4-Dimethyl-1-hexene	111.2	....	1.4110	0.720	....	....	....	....	....	....
165	2,5-Dimethyl-1-hexene	111.6	....	1.4105	0.7172	....	....	....	....	....	....
166	3-Ethyl-3-methyl-1-pentene	112	....	1.418	0.7305	....	....	....	....	....	....
167	3,4-Dimethyl-1-hexene	112	....	1.413	0.724	....	....	....	....	....	....
168	3,4,4-Trimethyl-2-pentene	112	....	1.4232	0.7395	....	....	....	....	....	....
169	3,5-Dimethyl-2-hexene	112	....	1.416	0.725	....	....	....	....	....	....
170	2-Methyl-3-heptene ..	112	....	1.402	0.706	....	....	....	....	....	....
171	5-Methyl-3-heptene ..	112	....	1.410	0.713	....	....	....	....	....	....
172	2,5-Dimethyl-2-hexene	112.2	....	1.4140	0.720	di-	88[13]	....	1.4740	1.3980	....
173	3-Methyl-1,5-heptadiene........	112.5	....	1.4230[22.5]	....	....	....	....	....	....	....
174	2-Ethyl-3-methyl-1-pentene	112.5	....	1.4142	0.729	....	....	....	....	....	....

*Derivative data given in order: m.p., crystal color, solvent from which crystallized.

TABLE II. ORGANIC DERIVATIVES OF ALKENES, CYCLOALKENES, DIENES AND POLYENES

a) Liquids 1) (Listed in order of increasing b.p.)* (Continued)

No.	Name	Boiling point, °C	Melting point, °C	n_D^{20}	D_4^{20}	x-Bromo-	B.P., °C	M.P., °C	n_D^{20}	D_4^{20}	Miscellaneous
							Bromine addition product				
175	4-Methyl-1-heptene ..	112.8	....	1.410	0.717	....	....	....	....	....	....
176	6-Methyl-3-heptene ..	113[734]	....	1.4114	0.7256	di-	....	97	....	....	....
177	4-Ethyl-1-hexene	113	....	1.412	0.726	....	....	....	....	....	....
178	4-Ethyl-2-hexene	113	....	1.412	0.725	....	....	....	....	....	....
179	2-Isopropyl-1-pentene.	113	....	1.414	0.725	....	....	....	....	....	....
180	5-Methyl-1-heptene ..	113.3	....	1.4094	0.7164	....	....	....	....	....	....
181	4-Methyl-2-heptene ..	113.5–4.1	....	1.4096	0.7154	....	....	....	....	....	....
182	2,3-Dimethyl-3-hexene	114	....	1.416	0.728	....	....	....	....	....	....
183	4-Methyl-2-octene ...	114	....	1.4100[25]	0.7188[25]	....	....	....	....	....	....
184	2,4-Dimethyl-2,4-hexadiene	114–5	....	1.45457[16.5]	0.7635[16.5]	....	....	....	....	....	....
185	6-Methyl-2,4-heptadiene	114–6	....	1.4397[25]	0.7041[25]	....	....	....	....	....	....
186	3-Ethyl-4-methyl-trans-2-pentene.....	114.3	....	1.4210	0.7350	....	....	....	....	....	....
187	Cycloheptene (Suberene)........	114.38	−56	1.4580	0.8254	di-	unstable	....	....	....	Nitrosochloride, 118; Oxid. → pimelic ac., 105
188	1-Methyl-1,4-cyclohexadiene	114.5–4.8	< −70	1.4703	0.848	tetra-	....	171	....	....	....
189	3-Ethyl-4-methyl-cis-2-pentene.........	115	....	1.424	0.739	....	....	....	....	....	....
191	1,3,5-Cycloheptatriene (Tropilidene)......	115.5	−79.49	1.5243	....	....	....	....	....	....	Maleic anh. adduct, 104.2–5.0, CCl₄
192	3,4-Dimethyl-2-hexene	116	....	1.418	0.737	....	....	....	....	....	....
193	3-Ethyl-3-hexene	116	....	1.418	0.729	....	....	....	....	....	....
194	6-Methyl-1,3-heptadiene........	116–8	....	....	0.741[22]	....	....	....	....	....	....
195	2,5-Dimethyl-1,3-hexadiene	116–8	> −80	1.45024	0.7412	....	....	....	....	....	....
196	2,3,4-Trimethyl-2-pentene	116.3	−113.3	1.4275	0.7434	....	....	....	....	....	....
197	4,4-Dimethylcyclohexene	116.98	−80.5	1.4420	0.7996	....	....	....	....	....	....
198	6-Methyl-2-heptene ..	117	....	1.412	0.718	....	....	....	....	....	....
199	2-n-Propyl-1-pentene .	117.7	....	1.4136	0.7240	....	....	....	....	....	....
200	5-Methyl-2-heptene ..	118	....	1.414	0.723	....	....	....	....	....	....
201	3,3-Dimethylcyclohexene	119	....	1.445	0.804	....	....	....	....	....	....
202	2-Methyl-1-heptene ..	119–22	−87.38	1.41195	0.72025	....	....	....	....	....	....
203	2,5-Dimethyl-1,5-hexadiene	119–23	solid at −80; liq. at −23	1.45054	0.7637	....	....	....	....	....	....
204	2-Ethyl-1-hexene	120	....	1.4157	0.7270	....	....	....	....	....	Mercaptosuccinic acid adduct, 101.9–2.7
205	d,l-1,2,3-Trimethyl-cyclopentene (Laurolene).......	120–1[752]	....	1.4421	0.7950	....	....	....	....	....	....
206	4-Methyl-3-heptene ..	120.4	....	1.41712[25]	0.7411[25]	....	....	....	....	....	....
207	3-Ethyl-2-hexene	121	....	1.424	0.737	....	....	....	....	....	....
208	3-Methyl-3-heptene ..	121	....	1.418	0.728	....	....	....	....	....	....
209	1-Octene	121.28	−101.76	1.40870	0.71492	di-	240–2; 118.5[15]	....	1.4970	1.4580	Mercaptosuccinic acid adduct, 96.1–.6

*Derivative data given in order: m.p., crystal color, solvent from which crystallized.

a) Liquids 1) (Listed in order of increasing b.p.)* (Continued)

No.	Name	Boiling point, °C	Melting point, °C	n_D^{20}	D_4^{20}	Bromine addition product					Miscellaneous
						x-Bromo-	B.P., °C	M.P., °C	n_D^{20}	D_4^{20}	
210	*trans*-4-Octene	121.4[739]	f.p. −94	1.41157	0.71467	*di-* (*meso*)	103[8]	....	1.4967[24]	1.4525	....
211	**1,3-Cycloheptadiene** (Hydrotropilidene)..	121.52	−110.42	....	0.8929[0]	....	....	....	....	....	$H_2 \rightarrow$ Cyclo-heptane, b.p. 118–20
212	**3-Methyl-2-heptene**	121.6	....	1.4183	0.7296	....	....	....	....	....	
213	*cis*-4-Octene	121.7[739]	f.p. −118	1.41361	0.72048	*di-* (*d,l*)	84.0–8.4[4.3]	....	1.4981	1.4569	....
214	**2,3-Dimethyl-2-hexene**	121.8	−115.1	1.4268	0.7408	....	....	....	....	....	
215	**3,4-Dimethyl-*trans*-3-hexene**	122	....	1.430	0.747	*di-*	85–7[5]	....	1.5060	1.387	....
216	**6-Methyl-1-heptene**	122–4; 113–5	....	1.4070	0.7125	....	....	....	....	....	
217	*cis*-3-Octene	122.3[741]	f.p. −126	1.41246	0.71888	....	....	....	....	....	
218	*trans*-3-Octene	122.4[741]	f.p. −110.4	1.41241	0.71630	....	....	....	....	....	
219	**2-Methyl-2-heptene**	123–5	....	1.4138	0.7241	....	....	....	....	....	
220	*trans*-2-Octene	125.0	−87.7	1.4132	0.7199	....	....	....	....	....	Mercaptosuccinic acid adduct, 142.9–3.5
221	*cis*-2-Octene	125.64	−100.2	1.4150	0.7243	....	....	....	....	....	
222	**2-Methyl-1,3-hepta-diene**	127–8[747]	....	1.4432	0.7432	....	....	....	....	....	
223	**1,4-Dimethylcyclo-hexene**	128	....	1.446	0.802	....	....	....	....	....	Nitrosochloride, 83–4
224	**1,5-Dimethylcyclo-hexene**	128	....	1.448	0.8051	....	....	....	....	....	Nitrosochloride, 118–9
225	**2,6-Dimethyl-2-heptene**	128.9	....	1.412	0.722[15 15]	....	....	....	....	....	
226	**4-Vinylcyclohexene**	129.5–30.5; 36[23]	....	1.4623	0.8320	α,β-*di-*	....	69.5–70, eth.	....	....	
227	**4-Methyl-2,4-hepta-diene**	131–2	....	1.4621	0.7551	....	....	....	....	....	
228	**3,4-Dimethyl-2,4-hexadiene**	132–4; 71–3[100]	....	1.4410	0.7832[19]	....	....	....	....	....	
229	**3-Methyl-2,4-hepta-diene**	132–5	....	1.4649[15]	0.7667[15]	....	....	....	....	....	$HBr \rightarrow$ Dihydro-bromide, b.p. 109–11[16]
230	**Bicyclo[4,2,0]oct-7-ene**	132.5	....	1.4761	....	*di-*	74[0.5]	....	....	....	
231	**4-Ethylcyclohexene**	133	....	1.449	0.810	....	....	....	....	....	
232	**1,6-Dimethylcyclo-hexene**	133	....	1.454	0.815	....	....	....	....	....	
233	**3,5-Dimethyl-2,4-heptadiene**	133–44[740]	....	1.4487	0.7728	....	....	....	....	....	
234	**2,4-Octadiene**	133.5–4.0	....	1.4542[25]	0.7427[25]	....	....	....	....	....	
235	**2,5-Dimethyl-2,4-hexadiene**	133.6; 28[10]	14.6–.8	1.4796[19.5]	0.7646[18]	*tetra-*	....	101	....	....	Oxid. in air → poly-meric peroxide, 59
236	**3-Ethylcyclohexene**	134	....	1.451	0.814	....	....	....	....	....	
237	**1,2,3,3-Tetramethyl-cyclopentene) (Campholene)**	134–5	....	1.44406	0.8035[15]	....	....	....	....	....	
238	**1-Ethylcyclohexene**	136	....	1.4575	0.823	....	....	....	....	....	
239	**1,2-Dimethylcyclo-hexene**	137	....	1.4588	0.8250	*di-*	....	142–3, acet.	....	....	Nitrosochloride, 58–60
240	**1,3-Dimethylcyclo-hexene**	137	....	1.445	0.802	....	....	....	....	....	
241	**Bicyclo[4,2,0]oct-2-ene**	137–9	....	1.4810[30]	0.8948	....	....	....	....	....	

*Derivative data given in order: m.p., crystal color, solvent from which crystallized.

TABLE II. ORGANIC DERIVATIVES OF ALKENES, CYCLOALKENES, DIENES AND POLYENES
a) Liquids 1) (Listed in order of increasing b.p.)* (Continued)

No.	Name	Boiling point, °C	Melting point, °C	n_D^{20}	D_4^{20}	Bromine addition product					Miscellaneous
						x-Bromo-	B.P., °C	M.P., °C	n_D^{20}	D_4^{20}	
243	1-Methylcycloheptene	137.5–8.5	....	1.4581	0.8243[22]	....	....	....	....	....	Nitrosochloride, 106; Nitrosate, 97–8
244	2-Methyl-4-octene ...	138[739]	....	1.4181	0.7392						
245	δ-Fenchene (1,5,5-Tri-methylbicyclo[2,2,1] hept-2-ene)	139–40	....	1.44862	0.8433						Nitrosochloride, 131
246	1,5,5-Trimethylcyclo-hexene (α-Cyclo-geraniolene)	139–41[759]	....	1.44612[21.5]	0.7981[23]						Nitrosochloride, 100–20, aq. me., al.; Nitrosate, 102–4
247	2,6-Dimethyl-2,4-heptadiene	139–43[752]	....	1.4587[44]	0.74820	....	....	....	....	....	....
248	1,4,4-Trimethylcyclo-hexene (Pulenene)...	139.5–40.5	....	1.444[23.2]	0.8032[18.8]	di-	120–0.5[10]	....	1.5247[19]	1.5324[19]	Nitrosochloride, 118–22, et. ac.
249	1,5,6-Trimethylcyclo-hexene	140	....	1.4572	0.831[25/25]	....	....	....	....	....	....
250	2,3-Dimethyl-2-nor-bornene (Santene; 2,3-Dimethylbicyclo [2,2,1]-hept-2-ene) ..	140–1; 35[15]	....	1.46699	0.8640						Dichloride, 88–9; Nitrosate, 216d.; Nitrosochloride, 109–10; Nitrosite, 3 forms: a) 122–4, bl.; b) 127–8, grn.; c) 104, col.
251	2,6-Dimethyl-1,3-heptadiene (Iso-geraniolene)	140–2; 31[7]	....	1.4606[22]	0.7923[22]						....
252	Cyclooctatetraene....	140.56; 142–3; 42–2.5[17]	−4.68; −7	1.5290	0.9206	....	....	....	....	....	Maleic anh. adduct, 167–8; Benzo-quinone adduct, 141, al.; Acrylic ac. adduct, 112–3, lgr.; AgNO₃ adduct, 173–4
253	7-Methyl-3-octene ...	141[746]	....	1.4168	0.7278	....	....	....	....	....	
254	2,6-Dimethyl-1,5-heptadiene (Geraniolene)	141–2; 165–70	−70	1.44361[22]	0.7626[22]	....	....	....	....	....	
255	1,8-Nonadiene.......	141–4	....	1.4302	0.7511						
256	1,3,5-Trimethylcyclo-hexene (Tetrahydro-mesitylene)	142.5–3.5	....	1.449[13.5]	0.8025[14.3]						Nitrosochloride, 134
257	3-Methyl-2-octene ...	143–5[734]	....	1.4247	0.7409[25]	....	....	....	....	....	
258	Cyclooctene........	143.8–4.5[773]	....	1.4693	....						Br₂ → Bromocyclo-octene, b.p. 7–8[23]; n_D^{20}: 1.5182; Di-chloride, b.p. 130.4–0.6[25]; m.p. −5; n_D^{20}: 1.5061, D_4^{20}: 1.1620
259	3,6-Dimethyl-2,4-heptadiene	144–6	....	1.46335[14]	0.7853[0]	....	....	....	....	....	....
260	4-Nonene...........	144–6; 44–6[12]	....	1.4212[18]	0.732[18]	di-	119–20[12]	....	1.4988[17]	1.410[17]	....
261	1,4,5-Trimethylcyclo-hexene	144–6	....	1.4482	0.805	....	....	....	....	....	

*Derivative data given in order: m.p., crystal color, solvent from which crystallized.

a) Liquids 1) (Listed in order of increasing b.p.)* (Continued)

No.	Name	Boiling point, °C	Melting point, °C	n_D^{20}	D_4^{20}	Bromine addition product					Miscellaneous
						x-Bromo-	B.P., °C	M.P., °C	n_D^{20}	D_4^{20}	
262	1-Vinylcyclohexene	145; 63–5[53]	....	1.4950[19]	....	....	....	....	....	....	50% $H_2SO_4 \rightarrow$ dimer, b.p. 118–9[5]
263	cis-1,4-Cyclooctadiene	145.1[758]	−53	....	0.8754	tetra-	....	139	....	....	....
264	1,3,5-Cyclooctatriene	145–6; 76[90]	....	1.5035[25]	0.8971[25]	....	....	....	....	....	Maleic anh. adduct, 144–5; AgNO₃ adduct, 125–6, al.
265	4,4-Dimethyl-1,7-octadiene	145–8	....	1.4330	0.7647						
266	ξ-Fenchene (2,7,7-Trimethylbicyclo[2,2,1]hept-2-ene)	146.2–6.8[752]	....	1.4865	0.8626	....	....	....	....	....	$[\alpha]_D^{20}$: −24.1
267	1,6,6-Trimethylcyclohexene	146.2–7.2[767]; 144–6	....	1.456[20.4]	0.8217[20.3]						Nitrosochloride, 133–4, et. ac.
268	1-Nonene	146.87	−81.37	1.41572	....	di-	141.5[20]	....	1.4942	1.3980	....
269	3-Nonene	147.4[750]		1.4173	0.7294						
270	1,5-Cyclooctadiene	148–9	....	1.4905	0.8818[24]						N-Bromosuccinimide → bromocyclooctadiene, b.p. 64[1.9], n_D^{25}: 1.5410, D_4^{25}: 1.3420
271	4-Methyl-3,5-octadiene	148–51	....	1.46285[25]	0.7640[25]						
272	7-Methyl-2,4-octadiene	149	....	1.4543[18]	0.7521[18]	tetra-	184[18]				
273	1-Ethyl-4-methylcyclohexene	149; 153–4	....	1.453[16]	0.8169[16]	....	....	....	....	....	Nitrosochloride, 2 forms: a) 103–4, pr., eth.; b) 98–9, cr., eth.
274	1-Ethyl-3-methylcyclohexene	149–51	....	1.454	0.8296	....	....	....	....	....	
275	2-Nonene	149.4–9.9		1.420[21]	0.738[21]						
276	1,2,3-Trimethylcyclohexene	149.6–150[749]		1.463[12]	0.8347[12]						
277	1-Ethyl-5-methylcyclohexene	150		1.4527[25]	0.812[25]						
278	β-Fenchene (2,2-Dimethyl-5-methylenebicyclo[2,2,1]heptane)	150.5–3.5		1.46511	0.8599	di-	....	81–2			$[\alpha]_D^{25}$: +62.5; Nitrosochloride, 120
279	2,6-Dimethyl-2,5-heptadiene	150.6–1.0	....	1.4490	....						
280	2,7-Nonadiene	150.6	−72.5	1.4358	0.7499						
281	Allylcyclohexane (3-Cyclohexylpropene)	151	....	1.4536[13]	0.8196[13]	di-	143–4[16]		1.537[0]		
282	1-Ethylidene-4-methylcyclohexane	152–3	....	1.4571[21]	0.81[21]						Nitrosochloride, 2 forms: a) 117–8, least soluble; b) 113–4, more soluble
283	4,5-Dimethyl-2,6-octadiene	152.9–3.8	....	1.4375[25]	0.7611[25]						
284	1-Ethylidene-3-methylcyclohexane	153	....	1.458[4]	0.8135[19/19]						Nitrosochloride, 114, acet.
285	3,6-Dimethyl-2,6-octadiene	153–5	....	1.44453	0.7767	....	....	....	....	....	....
286	2,6-Dimethyl-2,7-octadiene	155–6[720]	....	1.4385[18]	0.7605[18]						

*Derivative data given in order: m.p., crystal color, solvent from which crystallized.

a) Liquids 1) (Listed in order of increasing b.p.)* (Continued)

No.	Name	Boiling point, °C	Melting point, °C	n_D^{20}	D_4^{20}	Bromine addition product					Miscellaneous
						x-Bromo-	B.P., °C	M.P., °C	n_D^{20}	D_4^{20}	
287	α-Pinene	156.0–6.3	−50	1.4560	0.8600	di-	....	169–70, al.	....	....	Nitrosochloride, 109; Hydrobromide, 89; Nitrosobromide, 91–2d.; Acid KMnO₄ → pinonic ac., 103–5
288	1-Ethylidene-2-methylcyclohexane ..	158	....	1.47	0.823⁰	....	....	....	....	....	....
289	2,4-Dimethyl-2,4-octadiene	161–3⁷⁴⁶	....	1.4558⁹·⁸	0.7802⁹·⁸						
290	1,4,4-Trimethylcycloheptene (Eucarvene) .	161–5⁷²⁰	....	1.4561	0.8185	....	....				
291	β-Pinene (Nopinene; Pseudopinene)	163–4	....	1.4782	0.8694						[α]_D: −22
292	2,7-Dimethyl-2,6-octadiene	163.5–4.5	....	1.44814	0.7849	tetra-	....	124–7			
293	3,7-Dimethyl-2,4-octadiene	164–7; 58¹²	....	1.456	0.7933						....
294	l-4-Carene (3,7,7-Trimethylbicyclo[2,2,1]hept-2-ene)	165.5–7.0⁷⁰⁷		1.474³⁰	0.8552³⁰₃₀						[α]_D^{30}: +62.2
295	Myrcene (2-Methyl-6-methylene-2,7-octadiene)	166	....	1.4722	0.7982						Maleic anh. adduct, 33–4; 1,4-Naphthoquinone adduct, 81
296	2,6-Dimethyl-2,6-octadiene	168; 56¹⁴		1.45245¹⁵	0.775²¹						Methiodide, 130d.
297	l-3-Carene (3,7,7-Trimethylbicyclo[2,2,1]-hept-3-ene)	168–9⁷⁰⁵; 123–4²⁰⁰	....	1.469³⁰	0.8586³⁰₃₀						[α]_D^{30}: +7.69; Nitrosochloride, 100–1
298	3,8-o-Menthadiene (cis-3-Isopropenyl-4-methylcyclohexene)	169–70	....	1.4749	0.8507						....
299	5-Decene	170⁷⁵⁰	−112 to −111	1.4260	0.7474	di-	119⁹	....	1.4912	1.3484	....
300	p-8-Menthene (1-Isopropenyl-4-methylcyclohexane)	170	....	1.4523	0.8142						
301	d-m-8-Menthene (1-Isopropenyl-3-methylcyclohexane) .	170	....	1.4546	0.8179						[α]_D: +9.73
302	l-m-8-Menthene (1-Isopropenyl-3-methylcyclohexane) .	170–1	....	1.4574	0.8189						[α]_D: −8.06
303	6,8-o-Menthadiene (3-Isopropenyl-2-methylcyclohexene) .	170–1	....	1.4758	0.8481						
304	5,8-o-Menthadiene (4-Isopropenyl-3-methylcyclohexene) .	170–1	....	1.4778	0.8490¹⁷₁₇	....					
305	1-Decene	170.57	−66.31	1.42146	0.74081	di-	145–160¹⁸	....	1.4891²⁴	1.324²⁸	Mercaptosuccinic acid adduct, 93.5–.8
306	4-Decene	170.6	....	1.4243	0.7404	....	....	....	....	....	....

*Derivative data given in order: m.p., crystal color, solvent from which crystallized.

a) Liquids 1) (Listed in order of increasing b.p.)* (Continued)

No.	Name	Boiling point, °C	Melting point, °C	n_D^{20}	D_4^{20}	Bromine addition product					Miscellaneous
						x-Bromo-	B.P., °C	M.P., °C	n_D^{20}	D_4^{20}	
307	p-Menthene (1-Isopropylidene-4-methylcyclohexane) .	172–4	....	1.4568	0.819^{21}	....	....	....	....	....	Nitrosochloride, 101–3
308	1-Isopropenyl-1,4-cyclohexadiene	172–6	....	1.5216	0.9068	tetra-	....	113	....	....	....
309	o-Menthene (1-Isopropylidene-2-methylcyclohexane) .	173; 160–2	....	1.467	0.8345	....	....	....	....	....	....
310	m-Menthene (1-Isopropylidene-3-methylcyclohexane) .	173–5	....	1.4670	0.8214						
311	α-Terpinene (1-Isopropyl-4-methyl-1,3-cyclohexadiene) .	173.5–4.8^{755}	....	1.477	0.8375	....	....	....	....	....	Dihydrochloride, 53–4, me. al.; Dihydrobromide, 58–9, me. al.; Dihydroiodide, 76, me. al.; Nitrosite, 155; Maleic anh. adduct, 62; 66–7
312	2,4-p-Menthadiene(2-Isopropyl-5-methyl-1,3-cyclohexadiene) .	174–6	....	1.4845^{27}	0.8441^{27}_{27}	....	....	....	....	....	....
313	l-5-Isopropyl-2-methyl-1,3-cyclohexadiene	174–7	....	1.4732	0.8425	....	....	....	....	....	$[\alpha]_D^{20}$: −112.76; Nitrosite, α: 120–1; β: 105–6
314	1,5-p-Menthadiene (5-Isopropyl-2-methyl-1,3-cyclohexadiene)	175–6	....	1.4777	0.8463^{25}	....	....	....	....	....	$[\alpha]_D$: +49.1; Nitrosite, α: 113–4; β: 105. Maleic anh. adduct, 126–7, pet. eth.
315	d-Silvestrene	175–8	....	1.4760	0.8479	tetra-	....	135	....	....	Dihydrochloride, 72; Nitrosochloride, 106–7
316	d-Limonene	176–6.4	....	1.4743	0.8411	tetra-	....	104	....	....	Nitrosochloride, 100–4; 2,4-Dinitrophenylsulfenyl chloride, 195–6
317	Isocarvestrene (5-Isopropenyl-1-methylcyclohexene)	176–7^{765}	....	1.4804	0.8496	tetra-	....	137–8, me. al.-chl.	....	....	Dihydrochloride, 71.5, me. al.
318	l-3-Isopropenyl-1-methylcyclohexene .	176–8	....	1.4761^{18}	0.848^{19}	....	....	....	....	....	$[\alpha]_D^{18}$: −68.2; Dihydrochloride, 72
319	Dipentene (d,l-Limonene)	177.6–8.0	....	1.4727^{20}	0.8402^{20}	tetra-	....	125, eth.	....	....	Dihydrochloride, 50–1, al.
320	3,8-m-Menthadiene (1-Isopropenyl-5-methylcyclohexene) .	179^{730}	....	1.4972	....						$[\alpha]_D$: +17.5
321	Menogerene (5-Isopropylidene-2-methyl-1,3-cyclohexadiene)	180–1^{769}	....	1.5005	0.8672	di-	....	115	....	....	
322	γ-Terpinene (1-Isopropyl-4-methyl-1,4-cyclohexadiene)	183	....	$1.4765^{14.5}$	0.849	tetra-	....	129–30, pet. eth.	....	....	$[\alpha]_D^{25}$: +36; Nitrosochloride, 111; Nitrosate, 116d., ac. a.-me. al.
323	d,l-2,8-m-Menthadiene (1-Isopropenyl-3-methylcyclohexene) .	184–7	....	1.503	0.864^{20}_{20}	....	....	....	....	....	....

* Derivative data given in order: m.p., crystal color, solvent from which crystallized.

TABLE II. ORGANIC DERIVATIVES OF ALKENES, CYCLOALKENES, DIENES AND POLYENES

a) Liquids 1) (Listed in order of increasing b.p.)* (Continued)

No.	Name	Boiling point, °C	Melting point, °C	n_D^{20}	D_4^{20}	Bromine addition product x-Bromo-	B.P., °C	M.P., °C	n_D^{20}	D_4^{20}	Miscellaneous
324	**Menogene** (3-Iso-propylidene-6-methyl cyclohexene	184.6[764.5]	. . . .	1.5026	0.8624	. . . . . .	. . . .	. . . .	. . . . . .	. . . . . .	Nitrosite, 155, me. al. or chl.; Maleic anh. adduct, 205–8
325	**Terpinolene** (4-Iso-propylidene-1-methylcyclohexene) .	186	. . . .	1.4883	0.8633[15/15]	di-tetra-2 forms	. . . .	69–70 a) 119, ac. a.; b) 122	. . . . . .	. . . . . .	Maleic anh. adduct, 182
326	**2-Undecene** (2-Hendecene).	192–3; 78.5[14]	. . . .	1.43325	0.7735[15/15]	di-	145–6[9]	. . . .	. . . . . .	. . . . . .	. . . .
327	**5-Undecene** (5-Hendecene).	192.2	. . . .	1.4289	0.7511	. . . . . .	. . . .	. . . .	. . . . . .	. . . . . .	. . . .
328	**1-Undecene** (1-Undecene)	192.67	−49.19	1.42609	0.75032	di-	186[23]	. . . .	1.4916	1.3122	. . . .
329	*cis*-**Cyclodecene**	194–5[740]	. . . .	1.4854	0.8770	di-	. . . .	121	. . . . . .	. . . . . .	$O_3 \rightarrow$ Sebacic acid, 134.5
330	**1-Dodecene**	213.36; 88.7[10]	−35.23	1.43002	0.75836	di-	. . . .	−15	. . . . . .	. . . . . .	. . . .
331	**1-Tridecene**	232.78; 104.5[10]	−23.07	1.4336	0.7653	. . . . . .	. . . .	. . . .	. . . . . .	. . . . . .	. . . .
332	**1-Tetradecene**	251.1; 119.0[10]	−12.85	1.43631	0.7713	di-	. . . .	0	. . . . . .	. . . . . .	Mercaptosuccinic acid adduct, 104.0–.8
333	**Cedrene**	262–3; 124–6[12]	. . . .	1.5001[19]	0.9359[15/15]	. . . . . .	. . . .	. . . .	. . . . . .	. . . . . .	. . . .
334	**1-Pentadecene**	268.17; 133.7[10]	−3.73	1.4389	0.77641	di-	204–5[17]	. . . .	1.4897	1.2235	. . . .
335	**1-Hexadecene**	284.4; 103.9[1]	4.12	1.44120	0.78112	di-	225–7[15]	13.5, al.	. . . . . .	. . . . . .	1% Hot $KMnO_4 \rightarrow$ *n*-pentadecylic ac., 52.3; Mercapto-succinic acid ad-duct, 105.0–.8
336	**1-Heptadecene**	299.7; 116[1]	11.2	1.4432	0.7852	. . . . . .	. . . .	. . . .	. . . . . .	. . . . . .	. . . .
337	**2-Methyl-2-hepta-decene**	314; 277[100]	−2.5	. . . .	0.7953	di-	267–8[28]	. . . .	. . . . . .	. . . . . .	. . . .
338	**1-Octadecene**	314.2; 128[1]	17.6	1.4449	0.7888	di-	. . . .	24, al.	. . . . . .	. . . . . .	. . . .

* Derivative data given in order: m.p., crystal color, solvent from which crystallized.

TABLE II. ORGANIC DERIVATIVES OF ALKENES, CYCLOALKENES, DIENES AND POLYENES
a) Liquids 2) (B.p. at reduced pressure only. Listed alphabetically)

No.	Name	Boiling point, °C	Melting point, °C	n_D^{20}	D_4^{20}	Miscellaneous
1	Bicyclo[12,2,2]octadeca-14,16,18-triene	163.5–4.5[5.5]	....	1.5204[25]	....	Maleic anh. adduct, 143–4
2	Bicyclo[4,2,0]oct-3-ene	81[140]	....	1.4832		....
3	Butylcyclooctatetraene	98[20]	....	1.5083[25]	0.8876[25]	....
4	*trans*-Cyclodecene	68–70[10]	....	1.4822	0.8672	$O_3 \rightarrow$ Sebacic acid, 134.5
5	1,5,9,13-Cyclohexadecatetraene	93–8[0.8]	....	1.5472		....
6	*trans*-Cyclononene	73–4[30]	....	1.4799	0.8615	Phenylazide adduct, 97.8–8.2
7	1,3-Cyclooctadecadiene	115[3]	....	1.4899	0.8814	....
8	1,3-Cyclooctadiene	48[25]	−57 to −55	1.4940[25]	0.8699[25]	....
9	1,3,6-Cyclooctatriene	68[60]	−62 to −56	......	0.8940[25]	....
10	1,3-Cyclotetradecadiene	106–8[3]	....	1.4982	0.8723[25]	Nitrosochloride, 109–10; Nitrosate, 210d.
11	1,2-Dimethylcyclooctatetraene	107[96]	....	1.5219[25]	0.8950[25]	Maleic anh. adduct, 184.5–5.5, bz.-lgr.; $AgNO_3$ adduct, 142.5–4.5, al.
12	2,6-Dimethyl-2,5-octadiene	59.0–.5[12]	....	1.4500	0.733	....
13	Ethylcyclooctatetraene	81[37]	....	1.5187[25]	0.8996[25]	Maleic anh. adduct, 97–8.5, bz.-cyclohexane; $AgNO_3$ adduct, 124–5.5, al.
14	5-Methylcycloheptene	69–70[38]	....	1.42016[31]	0.76061[31]	....
15	Methylcyclooctatetraene	84.5[67]	....	1.5249[25]	0.8978[25]	....
16	7-Pentadecene	114[3.2]	....	1.4420	0.7765	....
17	Propylcyclooctatetraene	73[9]	....	1.5131[25]	0.8870[25]	....

*Derivative data given in order: m.p., crystal color, solvent from which crystallized.

TABLE II. ORGANIC DERIVATIVES OF ALKENES, CYCLOALKENES, DIENES AND POLYENES

b) Solids (Listed in order of increasing m.p.)*

No.	Name'	Melting point, °C	Boiling point, °C	n_D^{20}	D_4^{20}	Bromine addition product					Miscellaneous
						x-Bromo-	B.p., °C	M.p., °C	n_D^{20}	D_4^{20}	
1	1-Nonadecene	23.4	328.0; 138.8[1]	1.4445	0.7886	. . . . . .	. . . . .	. . . .	. . . . .	. . . . .	. . . .
2	Eicosene	28.6	341.2	1.4439^{30}	0.7882^{30}	. . . . . .	. . . . .	. . . .	. . . . .	. . . . .	. . . .
3	Bicyclo[4,7]pentadiene (endo-4,7-Methylene-4,7,8,9-tetrahydroindene) . .	32	170	1.5070^{25}	0.9766^{33}	. . . . . .	. . . . .	. . . .	. . . . .	. . . . .	Phenylazide adduct, 128
4	1-Heneicosene	33.3	355	1.4494^S	0.7977^S	. . . . . .	. . . . .	. . . .	. . . . .	. . . . .	. . . .
5	1-Docosene	37.8	. . . .	1.4505^S	0.8002^S	. . . . . .	. . . . .	. . . .	. . . . .	. . . . .	. . . .
6	1-Tricosene	41.6	379	1.4516^S	0.8023^S	. . . . . .	. . . . .	. . . .	. . . . .	. . . . .	. . . .
7	1-Tetracosene	45.3	390	1.4527^S	0.8045^S	. . . . . .	. . . . .	. . . .	. . . . .	. . . . .	. . . .
8	1-Pentacosene	48.7	401	1.4536^S	0.8063^S	. . . . . .	. . . . .	. . . .	. . . . .	. . . . .	. . . .
9	cis,cis,cis,1,4,7-Cyclononatriene	49.5–50	. . . .	. . . . . .	. . . . . .	. . . . . .	. . . . .	. . . .	. . . . .	. . . . .	AgNO₃ adduct, 243d.
10	d,l-Camphene (2,2-Dimethyl-3-methylenebicyclo[2,2,1]heptene)	50	159–60	. . . . . .	. . . . . .	di-	91–2	153.5^{15}	. . . . .	. . . . .	. . . .
11	l-Camphene	51.3	159–60	. . . . . .	. . . . . .	. . . . . .	. . . . .	. . . .	. . . . .	. . . . .	2,4-Dinitrophenyl-sulfenyl chloride, 121–2; Hydrochloride, 125–7
12	1-Heptacosene	54.7	421	1.4552^S	0.8097^S	. . . . . .	. . . . .	. . . .	. . . . .	. . . . .	. . . .
13	1-Triacontene	62.4	448	1.4573^S	0.8141^S	. . . . . .	. . . . .	. . . .	. . . . .	. . . . .	. . . .
14	1-Hentriacontene	64.6	457	1.4580^S	0.8153^S	. . . . . .	. . . . .	. . . .	. . . . .	. . . . .	. . . .
15	1-Dotriacontene	66.7	465	1.4585^S	0.8165^S	. . . . . .	. . . . .	. . . .	. . . . .	. . . . .	. . . .
16	1-Tritriacontene	68.7	473	1.4591^S	0.8176^S	. . . . . .	. . . . .	. . . .	. . . . .	. . . . .	. . . .
17	1-Tetratriacontene	70.5	481	1.4596^S	0.8186^S	. . . . . .	. . . . .	. . . .	. . . . .	. . . . .	. . . .
18	1-Pentatriacontene	72.3	489	1.4601^S	0.8196^S	. . . . . .	. . . . .	. . . .	. . . . .	. . . . .	. . . .
19	1-Hexatriacontene	73.9	496	1.4605^S	0.8205^S	. . . . . .	. . . . .	. . . .	. . . . .	. . . . .	. . . .
20	1-Heptatriacontene.	75.5	503	1.4610^S	0.8214^S	. . . . . .	. . . . .	. . . .	. . . . .	. . . . .	. . . .
21	1-Octatriacontene.	77	510	1.4614^S	0.8223^S	. . . . . .	. . . . .	. . . .	. . . . .	. . . . .	. . . .
22	1-Nonatriacontene	78.4	517	1.4618^S	0.8231^S	. . . . . .	. . . . .	. . . .	. . . . .	. . . . .	. . . .
23	1-Tetracontene	79.8	523	1.4622^S	0.8238^S	. . . . . .	. . . . .	. . . .	. . . . .	. . . . .	. . . .
24	Bicyclo(2,2,2)-oct-2-ene	111–2	128–34	. . . . . .	. . . . . .	2,3-trans-di-	. . . . .	55.0–5.5	. . . . .	. . . . .	. . . .

*Derivative data given in order: m.p., crystal color, solvent from which crystallized.

S = Supercooled liquid at 20°

EXPLANATIONS AND REFERENCES TO TABLE III

*Hg salt (Mercuric acetylide).**

$$2\,RC\equiv CH \;+\; K_2HgI_4 \;+\; 2\,KOH \;\rightarrow\; (RC\equiv C)_2Hg \;+\; 4\,KI \;+\; 2\,H_2O$$
Mercuric salt

From the terminal alkyne and K_2HgI_4 (prepared from mercuric chloride, potassium iodide and potassium hydroxide).

For directions and examples see: Linstead, p. 52; J. R. Johnson and W. L. McEwen, *J. Amer. Chem. Soc,* **48,** 469 (1926).

Hydration to form carbonyl compound.

Terminal acetylenes:
$$RC\equiv CH \;+\; H_2O \;\xrightarrow[\text{HgSO}_4]{\text{H}_2\text{SO}_4}\; RCOCH_3$$
Methyl ketone

Other acetylenes:
$$RC\equiv CR' \;+\; H_2O \;\xrightarrow[\text{HgSO}_4]{\text{H}_2\text{SO}_4}\; RCOCH_2R' \;+\; RCH_2COR'$$
Mixture of ketones

From the alkyne in methanol and a catalyst composed of boron trifluoride etherate, red mercuric oxide and trichloroacetic acid.

For directions and examples see: J. G. Sharefkin and E. M. Boghosian, *Anal. Chem.,* **33,** 640 (1961).

From the alkyne, mercuric sulfate and sulfuric acid in 70% methanol, in 70% acetone or in 60% acetic acid.

See: Cheronis, p. 576; H. Erdmann and F. Kother, *Z. Anorg. Chem.,* **18,** 48 (1898); R. J. Thomas, K. N. Campbell and G. F. Hennion, *J. Amer. Chem. Soc.,* **60,** 718 (1938).

From the alkyne, mercuric oxide and sulfuric acid in alcohol.

See: J. R. Johnson, A. M. Schwartz and T. L. Jacobs, *J. Amer. Chem. Soc.,* **60,** 1882 (1938).

NOTE: For directions and examples for the preparation of the semicarbazones and the 2,4-dinitrophenyl-hydrazones of the formed carbonyl compounds see explanations and references to Table IX and X, p. 141, 142, 143.

*Derivatives recommended for first trial.

WARNING: This is not an instruction manual. References should be consulted for the preparation of derivatives.

TABLE III. ORGANIC DERIVATIVES OF ALKYNES (ACETYLENES)
a) Liquids (Listed in order of increasing b.p.)*

No.	Name	Boiling point, °C	Melting point, °C	n_D^{20}	D_4^{20}	Hydration product (RC≡CR' → RCOCH$_2$R') and its derivatives				Hg salt	Miscellaneous
						Ketone	B.p., °C	2,4-Dinitrophenylhydrazone of ketone	Semicarbazone of ketone		
1	Ethyne (Acetylene)	−84.0 (sat. press.)	−80.8, subl.	....	0.6179^{-84}	(Acetaldehyde)	(20.2)	(168)	(162–3)	....	
2	Propyne (Methyl acetylene)	−23.22	−102.7	....	0.6174^{-23}	Acetone	56	128	190	204	....
3	1-Butyne (Ethyl acetylene)	8.09; 8.3	−125.72	1.3962	0.6682^8	2-Butanone	82	116–7	135–6	162–3, al.	....
4	1,3-Butadiyne (Diacetylene)	10.3	−35 to −36	1.4120	0.7249	....			....	161.5–2.0	KOBr → 1,4-Dibromo deriv., 49–50, bz.
5	3-Methyl-1-butyne (Isopropyl acetylene)	26.35; 28	−89.7	1.3723	0.666					....	Tetrabromo deriv., b.p. 275
6	2-Butyne (Dimethyl acetylene)	27.2–.6	−32.26	1.3921	0.6901	2-Butanone	82	116–7	135–6	....	Tetrabromo deriv., 243, eth.; 2,4-Dinitrophenylsulfenyl chloride, 65–6
7	3-Methyl-3-buten-1-yne (Isopropenyl acetylene)	33	....	1.4158	0.6801^{11}						3,4-Dibromo deriv., b.p. 50.0–1.5^{10}
8	3,3-Dimethyl-1-butyne (tert-Butyl acetylene)	38–9	−81.20	1.37725^{15}	0.6737^{15}					92.5–3.0	Cu salt, 140, red
9	1-Pentyne (Propyl acetylene)	40.18	−105.7	1.3852	0.6901	2-Pentanone	102.3	145	112; 106	118.4	Tetrabromo deriv., b.p. 275
10	1-Penten-4-yne (Allyl acetylene)	42–3		1.4125^{16}	0.738^{16}	Allyl methyl ketone	111–2	160	....	....	1,2-Dibromo deriv., b.p. 79.5–80.5^{10}; 4,4,5-Tetrabromo deriv., b.p. 132–6^{10}
11	cis-3-Penten-1-yne (cis-Propenyl acetylene)	44.6	....	1.4330	....					48	....
12	trans-3-penten-1-yne (trans-Propenyl acetylene)	52.2		1.4377	0.7270					155–7	1,2-Dibromo deriv., b.p., 60–2^{10}; 3,4-Dibromo deriv., 66–76^{10}
13	2-Pentyne (Ethyl methyl acetylene)	56.07	−109.3	1.4039	0.7107	2-Pentanone + 3-Pentanone	102.3 / 102	145 / 156	112; 106 / 138–9	....	KMnO$_4$ → formic ac. + propionic ac.
14	1-Penten-3-yne (Methyl vinyl acetylene)	59.2–60.1	....	1.4496	0.740J	....					
15	4-Methyl-1-pentyne (Isobutyl acetylene)	61.1–.2; 99	−105.1	1.3936^{15}_α	0.7092^{15}					100.0–.5	
16	3-Methyl-1-pentyne (sec-Butyl acetylene)	65–70^{770}; 57.7	....	1.3916	0.7037					74–5	
17	1-Hexyne (Butyl acetylene)	71.33	−131.9	1.3989	0.7155	2-Hexanone	128	106–7	125	96.2–.4	....
18	4-Methyl-2-pentyne (Isopropyl methyl acetylene)	72.0–.5	−110.37	1.4078^{19}	0.716^{19}						
19	4,4-Dimethyl-1-pentyne	73–5	....	1.4028	0.7154					125–6.5	
20	1,3-Pentadiyne	75.0–.5; 55–6	−45 to −35	1.4431^{21}	0.7375^{21}						
21	1,4-Hexadiyne	78–83	....	....	0.825^0_4						
22	3-Hexyne (Diethyl acetylene)	81.5^{744}	−51	1.4112^{25}	0.7263^{25}	3-Hexanone	125	130	112	....	2,4-Dinitrophenylsulfenyl chloride, 65–6

* Derivative data given in order: m.p., crystal color, solvent from which crystallized.

TABLE III. ORGANIC DERIVATIVES OF ALKYNES (ACETYLENES)

a) Liquids (Listed in order of increasing b.p.)* (Continued)

No.	Name	Boiling point, °C	Melting point, °C	n_D^{20}	D_4^{20}	Hydration product ($RC\equiv CR' \rightarrow RCOCH_2R'$) and its derivatives				Hg salt	Miscellaneous
						Ketone	B.p., °C	2,4-Dinitrophenylhydrazone of ketone	Semicarbazone of ketone		
23	**4,4-Dimethyl-2-pentyne** (*tert*-Butyl methyl acetylene)	82.9–3.0	....	1.4071	0.7176	....	......	......	......	....	....
24	**2-Hexyne** (Methyl propyl acetylene)	83.7–4.0	−92	1.4135	0.7317	2-Hexanone + 3-Hexanone	128 / 125	106–7 / 130	125 / 112	....	....
25	**1-Hexen-3-yne** (Ethyl vinyl acetylene)......	85[758]	....	1.4522·	0.7492	....	......	......	......	....	1,2-Dibromo deriv., b.p. 87.0–.5[10]; 3,3,4,4-Tetrabromo deriv., b.p. 140–50[10]
26	**1,5-Hexadien-3-yne** (Divinyl acetylene)....	85.0	−87.83	1.5045	0.7857						
27	**1-Hexen-4-yne**	87[753]	....	1.446[14]	0.767[14]						1,2-Dibromo deriv., b.p. 93.0–.5[10] 1,2,4,5-Tetrabromo deriv., b.p. 154.5–5.0[10]
28	**3-Ethyl-1-pentyne**	87.0–8.5	....	1.4102	0.7246						
29	**1,5-Hexadiyne** (Dipropargyl).............	87.5–8.5[758]; 20[46]	−4.266	1.4381[23]	0.79943						
30	**2-Hexen-4-yne**	88–9	....	1.4918	0.7710	Allyl ethyl ketone	74.5–6.5[90]	95–106	......		
31	**2-Methyl-3-hexyne**	95.2	−116.7	1.4114	0.7263	....					
32	**4-Methyl-2-hexyne**	95.94	f.p.: −107.63	1.4170	0.73855						
33	**3-Ethyl-3-penten-1-yne**..	96.5	....	1.4338[25]	0.7886[25]						
34	**5-Methyl-3-heptyne**	98–100[745]	....	1.4102	0.7360	....					
35	**1-Heptyne** (*n*-Pentyl acetylene)	99.74	−80.9	1.4087	0.7328	2-Heptanone	151.2	89	123; 127	61, me. al.	
36	**5-Methyl-2-hexyne**	102.46	−92.91	1.41762	0.73776	....					
37	**8-Methyl-4-nonyne**	104.5	....	1.4311	0.7681						
38	**3-Heptyne** (Ethyl propyl acetylene)	105–6	....	1.415	0.7337	4-Heptanone	144	75	132		
39	**2-Heptyne** (*n*-Butyl methyl acetylene)	111.5–2.5	....	1.4230	0.748	2-Heptanone + 3-Heptanone	151.2 / 148	89	123; 127 / 101		
40	**2,2,5,5-Tetramethyl-3-hexyne** (Di-*tert*-butyl acetylene)	111.9[746]	19.4	1.4055	0.7120	....					
41	**1,6-Heptadiyne**	112; 30[26]	−85	1.451[17]	0.8164[17]	....					
42	**1-Octyne** (*n*-Hexyl acetylene)	126.2	−79.3	1.4159	0.7461	2-Octanone	173	64–5; 58	124–5	80.4–.7, me. al.	
43	**4-Octyne** (Dipropyl acetylene)	130.4–.6[745]	....	1.4226	0.7484						
44	**3-Octyne** (Butyl ethyl acetylene)	131.0–.5	....	1.4261	0.748						
45	**2-Octyne** (Hexyl methyl acetylene)	138.0–.4	....	1.4285	0.761	2-Octanone + 3-Octanone	173 / 169–70[738]	64–5; 58 / 64–5	124–5 / 117.0–.5		
46	**4-Nonyne** (*n*-Butyl propyl acetylene)	150–4[752]	....	1.4296[25]	0.757[25]	4-Nonanone + 5-Nonanone	187–8 / 188.4	57–8	73–4 / 90	....	....

*Derivative data given in order: m.p., crystal color, solvent from which crystallized.

29

TABLE III. ORGANIC DERIVATIVES OF ALKYNES (ACETYLENES)
a) Liquids (Listed in order of increasing b.p.)* (Continued)

No.	Name	Boiling point, °C	Melting point, °C	n_D^{20}	D_4^{20}	Hydration product ($RC{\equiv}CR' \rightarrow RCOCH_2R'$) and its derivatives — Ketone	B.p., °C	2,4-Dinitrophenyl-hydrazone of ketone	Semicarbazone of ketone	Hg salt	Miscellaneous
47	1-Nonyne (Heptyl acetylene)	150.8	−50	1.4217	0.7568	2-Nonanone	195.3	55–6	118–20	67.8–8.5, me. al.	....
48	3-Nonyne (Methyl pentyl acetylene)	$153\text{–}5^{745}$; 92^{97}	....	1.4299	0.7616	3-Nonanone + 4-Nonanone	187^{751} / 187–8	55–6 / 57–8	111–2 / 73–4	....	....
49	Cyclooctyne	$157.5\text{–}8.0^{740}$	....	1.4850	0.868	....	....	....	....	....	....
50	2-Nonyne (Methyl hexyl acetylene)	161	....	1.4331	0.769	3-Nonanone + 2-Nonanone	187^{751} / 195.3	55–6 / 55–6	111–2 / 118–20	....	....
51	1,8-Nonadiyne	162; $55.0\text{–}.5^{13}$	−27.28	1.4490	0.8158	....	....	....	....	....	....
52	1-Decyne (n-Octyl acetylene)	174.0	−44	1.4265	0.7655	2-Decanone	215.5	124	63; 81	80.0–.7	....
53	3-Decyne (Ethyl hexyl acetylene)	175–6	....	1.433^{21}	0.7765^{21}	3-Decanone + 4-Decanone	211 / 206–7	....	100–1 / 51–2	....	....
54	5-Decyne (Dibutyl acetylene)	177; 100^{80}	−73	1.4332	0.7688	5-Decanone	....	60–1.5	57.5–8.0	....	NaNH₂ at 210° → 1-Decyne, b.p. 174
55	Cyclononyne	$177\text{–}8^{740}$	−36.4	1.4890	0.8972	Cyclononanone	m.p.: 34	146	184–5	....	....
56	2,7-Nonadiyne	180	4.30	1.4674	0.8332	....	....	....	....	....	....
57	1-Undecyne (1-Hendecyne; Nonyl acetylene)	195; 96.43^{30}	−25	1.4306	0.7728	2-Undecanone	228	63	122.0–.5	79	....
58	Cyclodecyne	$203\text{–}4^{740}$; 78.5^{12}	....	1.4950	0.8975	Cyclodecanone	$100\text{–}2^{12}$	....	203–5	....	Ozonolysis → sebacic acid, 134.5
59	6-Dodecyne (Dipentyl acetylene)	209^{745}; 90^{8}	....	1.4380^{25}	0.7816^{25}	....	....	....	....	....	NaNH₂ → 1-Dodecyne, b.p. 215
60	1-Dodecyne (Decyl acetylene)	215; 89.09^{10}	19	1.4340	0.7788	....	....	....	....	84.2–.8	....
61	1-Tridecyne (n-Undecyl acetylene)	234; 102.95^{10}	−5	1.4371	0.7842						
62	1-Tetradecyne (Dodecyl acetylene)	252; 118.31^{10}	0	1.4396	0.7888						
63	1-Pentadecyne (Tridecyl acetylene)	268; 129.79^{10}	10	1.4419	0.7928						
64	1-Hexadecyne (Tetradecyl acetylene)	284; 103.3^{1}	15	1.4440	0.7965						

*Derivative data given in order: m.p., crystal color, solvent from which crystallized.

30

TABLE III. ORGANIC DERIVATIVES OF ALKYNES (ACETYLENES)

b) Solids (Listed in order of increasing m.p.)*

No.	Name	Melting point, °C	Boiling point, °C	n_D^{20}	D_4^{20}	Miscellaneous
1	1-Heptadecyne	22	299	1.4437[25]	0.7961[25]	....
2	2,6-Octadiyne	27	62[19]	1.453[21]	0.828[30]	....
3	1-Octadecyne	27	313; 180[15]	1,4474	0.8025	....
4	2-Octadecyne	30	184[15]	....	0.8016	......
5	1-Nonadecyne	33	327; 144[1.5]	1.4488[S]	0.8050[S]	Hg salt, 96–7, n-BuOH
6	1-Eicosyne	35	340; 153[1.1]	1.4501[S]	0.8073[S]	....
7	2-Heneicosyne	35–6	180[2]	1.4499[40]	....	....
8	1-Heneicosyne	41	....	1.4513[S]	0.8094[S]	....
9	1-Docosyne	45	363	1.4524[S]	0.8114[S]	....
10	1-Tricosyne	49	374	1.4534[S]	0.8131[S]	....
11	1-Tetracosyne	52	385	1.4544[S]	0.8148[S]	....
12	1-Pentacosyne	55	395	1.4552[S]	0.8163[S]	....
13	1-Hexacosyne	57	405	1.456[S]	0.8177[S]	....
14	1-Heptacosyne	60	415	1.4568[S]	0.8190[S]	....
15	1-Octacosyne	62	426	1.4575[S]	0.8202[S]	....
16	1-Nonacosyne	65	432	1.4581[S]	0.8213[S]	....
17	1-Triacontyne	67	441	1.4587[S]	0.8224[S]	....
18	1-Hentriacontyne	69	449	1.4593[S]	0.8234[S]	....
19	1-Dotriacontyne	71	457	1.4598[S]	0.8243[S]	....
20	1-Tritriacontyne	73	464	1.4603[S]	0.825[S]	....
21	1-Tetratriacontyne	74	472	1.4608[S]	0.8260[S]	....
22	1-Pentatriacontyne	76	479	1.4612[S]	0.8268[S]	....
23	1-Hexatriacontyne	77	486	1.4617[S]	0.8275[S]	....
24	1-Heptatriacontyne	79	493	1.4621[S]	0.8282[S]	....
25	1-Octatriacontyne	80	499	1.4625[S]	0.8289[S]	....
26	1-Nonatriacontyne	82	505	1.4628[S]	0.8295[S]	....
27	1-Tetracontyne	83	512	1.4632[S]	0.8301[S]	....

Derivative data given in order: m.p., crystal color, solvent from which crystallized.

S = supercooled liquid at 20°

EXPLANATIONS AND REFERENCES TO TABLE IV

*Nitro derivative.**

$$ArH + HNO_3 \rightarrow ArNO_2 + H_2O$$
Nitro
derivative

From the aromatic hydrocarbon with concentrated nitric and sulfuric acids.
For directions and examples see: Cheronis, p. 578–80; Linstead, p. 48, 49; Shriner, p. 249; Vogel, p. 520; Wild, p. 24.
From the aromatic hydrocarbon with fuming and concentrated nitric acids.
See: Shriner, p. 249; Wild, p. 24.
From the aromatic hydrocarbon with fuming nitric acid in acetic acid.
See: Vogel, p. 520.
From the aromatic hydrocarbon with nitric and sulfuric acids in chloroform.
See: Vogel, p. 580.

*Acetamido and Benzamido derivatives.**

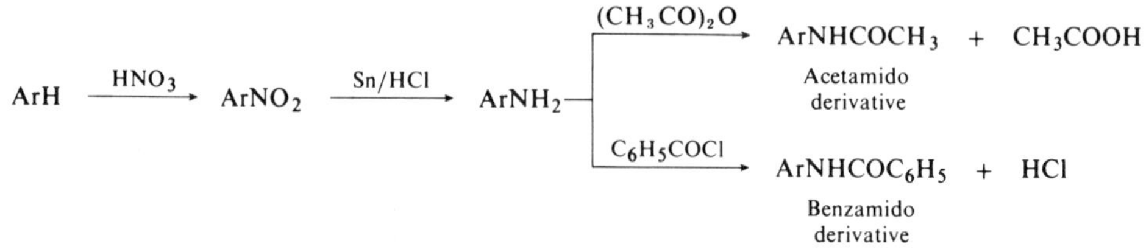

$$ArH \xrightarrow{HNO_3} ArNO_2 \xrightarrow{Sn/HCl} ArNH_2$$

$$\xrightarrow{(CH_3CO)_2O} ArNHCOCH_3 + CH_3COOH$$
Acetamido
derivative

$$\xrightarrow{C_6H_5COCl} ArNHCOC_6H_5 + HCl$$
Benzamido
derivative

Nitration of the aromatic hydrocarbon is followed by reduction with tin and hydrochloric acid. The resulting amine is acetylated with acetic anhydride or benzoylated with benzoyl chloride.
For directions and examples see: Cheronis, p. 581; V. L. Ipatieff and L. A. Schmerling, *J. Amer. Chem. Soc.*, **59**, 1056 (1937); **60**, 1476 (1938); **65**, 2470 (1943).

o-Aroylbenzoic acid (product with phthalic anhydride).

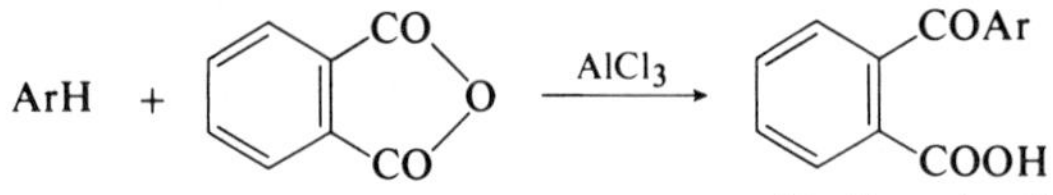

*o-*Aroylbenzoic acid

From the aromatic hydrocarbon, phthalic anhydride and aluminum chloride in carbon disulfide.
For directions and examples see: Cheronis, p. 548; Shriner, p. 250; Vogel, p. 519; Wild, p. 28; H. W. Underwood and W. L. Walsh, *J. Amer. Chem. Soc.*, **57**, 940 (1935).
From the aromatic hydrocarbon, phthalic anhydride and aluminum chloride without solvent.
See: G. F. Lewenz and K. T. Serijan, *J. Amer. Chem. Soc.*, **75**, 4087 (1953).

2,4-Dinitrobenzenesulfenyl chloride derivative (Aryl 2,4-dinitrophenyl sulfide).

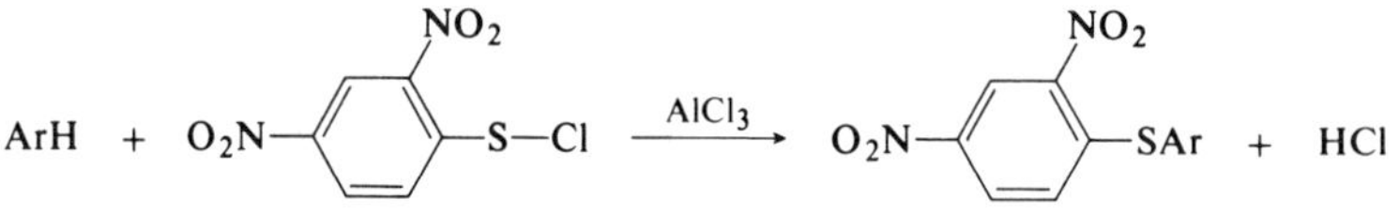

Aryl 2,4-dinitrophenyl
sulfide

From the aromatic hydrocarbon, 2,4-dinitrobenzenesulfenyl chloride and aluminum chloride in 1,2-dichloroethane.
For directions and explanations see: Cheronis, p. 585; C. M. Buess and N. Kharasch, *J. Amer. Chem. Soc.*, **72**, 3529 (1950).

Picrate.

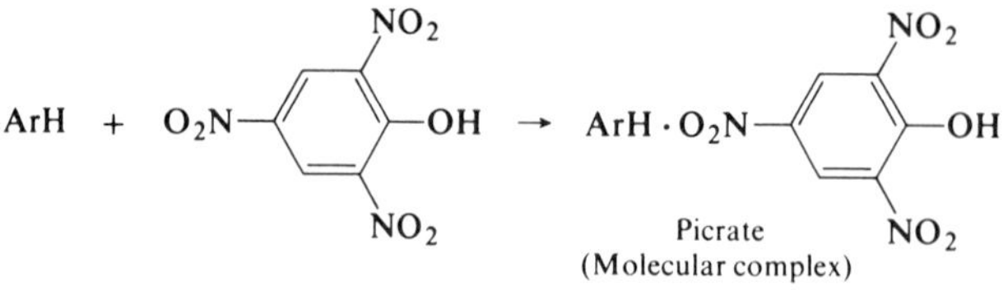

Picrate
(Molecular complex)

---

*Derivatives recommended for first trial.
WARNING: This is not an instruction manual. References should be consulted for the preparation of derivatives.

From the aromatic hydrocarbon and picric acid in alcohol.
For directions and examples see: Linstead, p. 50; Vogel, p. 518; Wild, pp. 29–30.
From excess of liquid aromatic hydrocarbon and picric acid without solvent.
See: Wild, pp. 28–9; Baril and Hauber, *J. Amer. Chem. Soc.*, **53**, 1087 (1931).
From the aromatic hydrocarbon in methanol or in dry benzene.
See: Cheronis, pp. 582–3.

Styphnate.

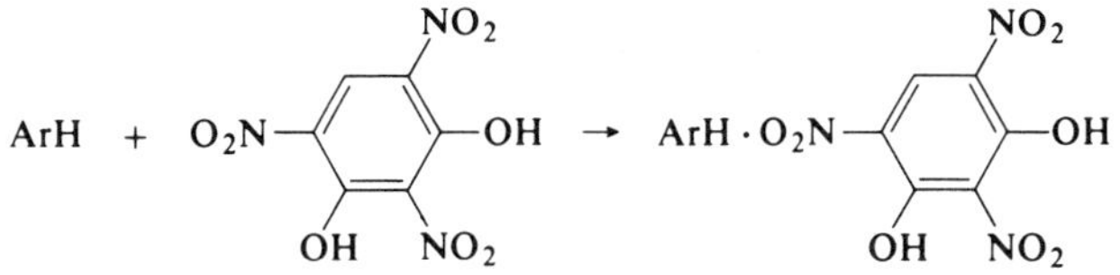

Styphnic acid

Styphnate (Molecular complex)

From the aromatic hydrocarbon and styphnic acid (2,4,6-trinitroresorcinol) in acetic acid.
For directions and examples see: Vogel, p. 519; W. J. Hickinbottom, *Reactions of Organic Compounds*, 2nd ed., Longmans, Green and Co., London, 1948, p. 76.

1,3,5-Trinitrobenzene derivative.

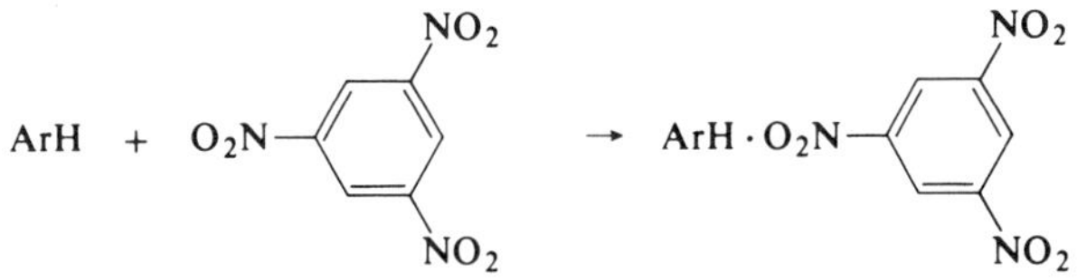

1,3,5-Trinitrobenzene molecular complex

From the aromatic hydrocarbon and 1,3,5-trinitrobenzene in alcohol, acetic acid, or benzene.
For directions and examples see: Vogel, p. 519.

*2,4,7-Trinitrofluorenone (TNF) derivative.**

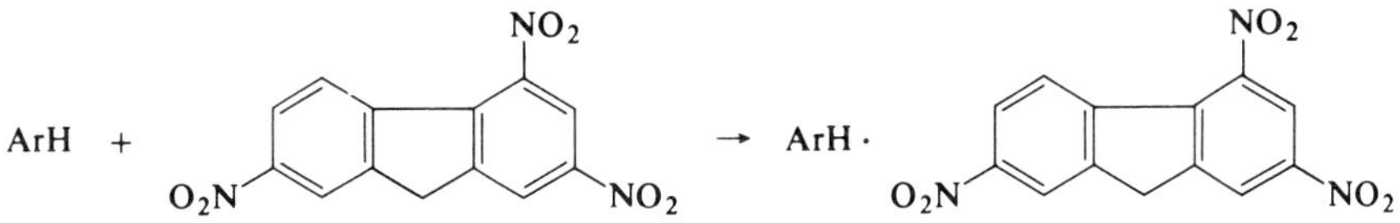

TNF

2,4,7-Trinitrofluorenone molecular complex

From the aromatic hydrocarbon and 2,4,7-trinitrofluorenone in methanol-benzene and ethanol-benzene mixtures.
For directions and examples see: Cheronis, pp. 582–3; M. Orchin, *J. Amer. Chem. Soc.*, **68**, 1727 (1946); M. Orchin, L. Reggel and E. O. Woolfolk, *J. Amer. Chem. Soc.*, **69**, 1225 (1947).
From the aromatic hydrocarbon and 2,4,7-trinitrofluorenone in glacial acetic acid.
See: M. C. Kloetzel and H. E. Mertel, *J. Amer. Chem. Soc.*, **72**, 4786 (1950); M. D. Soffer and R. A. Stewart, *J. Amer. Chem. Soc.*, **74**, 567 (1952).
From the aromatic hydrocarbon and 2,4,7-trinitrofluorenone without solvent.
See: D. E. Laskowski and W. C. McCrone, *Anal. Chem.*, **30**, 542 (1958).

Acids from side-chain oxidation.

$$ArR \xrightarrow[NaOH]{KMNO_4} ArCOONa \xrightarrow{H^+} ArCOOH$$

Aromatic acid

*Derivatives recommended for first trial.
WARNING: This is not an instruction manual. References should be consulted for the preparation of derivatives.

From the alkyl-substituted aromatic hydrocarbon with potassium permanganate in sodium hydroxide or sodium carbonate solution.

For directions and examples see: Cheronis, p. 585, 627; Linstead, p. 50; Shriner, p. 250; Vogel, p. 520; Wild, p. 26.

From the alkyl-substituted aromatic hydrocarbon with sodium bichromate and sulfuric acid.

See: Cheronis, p. 627; Shriner, p. 250; Wild, p. 26.

*Sulfonamide.**

$$ArH \ + \ ClSO_3H \ \rightarrow \ \underset{\substack{\text{Sulfonyl} \\ \text{chloride}}}{ArSO_2Cl} \ \xrightarrow{NH_3} \ \underset{\text{Sulfonamide}}{ArSO_2NH_2}$$

From the aromatic hydrocarbon and chlorosulfonic acid in chloroform, followed by aqueous ammonia.

For directions and examples see: Linstead, p. 49; Wild, p. 27; E. H. Huntress and F. H. Carten, *J. Amer. Chem. Soc.,* **62,** 511 (1940); E. H. Huntress and J. S. Autenrieth, *J. Amer. Chem. Soc.,* **63,** 3446 (1941).

From the aromatic hydrocarbon with chlorosulfonic acid without solvent, followed by ammonolysis with dry ammonium carbonate.

See: Wild, p. 27.

---

*Derivatives recommended for first trial.

WARNING: This is not an instruction manual. References should be consulted for the preparation of derivatives.

TABLE IV. ORGANIC DERIVATIVES OF AROMATIC HYDROCARBONS
a) Liquids. (Listed in order of increasing b.p.)*

No.	Name	Boiling point, °C	Melting point, °C	n_D^{20}	D_4^{20}	Picrate	1,3,5-Trinitrobenzene derivative	Nitro derivative	Acetamido derivative	Phthalic anhydride derivative	2,4-Dinitrophenyl sulfenyl chloride derivative	Miscellaneous
1	Benzene..................	80.1	5.5	1.5011	0.87901	84	......	1,3-*di*: 89; 1,3,5-*tri*: 122	....	127	120	Sulfonamide, 156
2	Toluene..................	110.6	−95	1.49613	0.86694	88.2, pa. yel.	......	2,4-*di*: 70	2,4-*di*: 221	137	102–3	Oxid. → benzoic acid, 121; Sulfonamide, 137
3	Ethylbenzene	136.2	−93.9	1.49594	0.86690	96.6, pa. yel.	......	2,4,6-*tri*: 37	2,4-*di*: 223	122; 128	97	Oxid. → benzoic acid, 121; Sulfonamide, 109
4	1,4-Xylene................	138.3	13.26	1.49581	0.86105	90	......	2,3,5-*tri*: 139	....	132; 148	134–5	Oxid. → terephthalic acid, >300, subl.; Sulfonamide, 147
5	1,3-Xylene................	139.1	−47.89	1.49722	0.86417	91	......	2,4,6-*tri*: 183		126; 142	......	Oxid. → isophthalic acid, 348, h.w.; Sulfonamide, 137
6	1,2-Xylene................	144.4	−25.18	1.50545	0.88020	88	......	4,5-*di*: 118	....	178	......	Oxid. → phthalic acid, 206–8; Sulfonamide, 144
7	Isopropylbenzene (Cumene) ..	152.4	−96.04	1.49146	0.86179	......	......	2,4,6-*tri*: 109	4-*mono*: 106; 2,4-*di*: 216	133	......	Oxid. → benzoic acid, 121; Sulfonamide, 106
8	*n*-Propylbenzene...........	159.2	−99.59	1.49202	0.86204	103	......	2,4-*di*: b.p. 150[1]	4-*mono*: 96; 2,4-*di*: 208	125	......	Oxid. → benzoic
9	1-Ethyl-3-methylbenzene (*m*-Ethyltoluene)	161.3	−96.55	1.49661	0.86455							Oxid. → isophthalic acid, 348, h.w.
10	1-Ethyl-4-methylbenzene (*p*-Ethyltoluene)	162.1	−62.35	1.49500	0.86118							Oxid. → terephthalic acid, >300, subl.
11	1,3,5-Trimethylbenzene (Mesitylene)..............	164.7	−44.72	1.49937	0.86518	97	......	2,4-*di*: 86; 2,4,6-*tri*: 235	....	212	......	Oxid. → trimesic acid, 380; Sulfonamide, 141
12	1-Ethyl-2-methylbenzene (*o*-Ethyltoluene)..........	165.2	−80.83	1.50456	0.88069							Oxid. → phthalic acid, 206–8
13	*tert*-Butylbenzene...........	169.1	−58.34	1.49266	0.86650	......	......	2,4-*di*: 62; 2,4,6-*tri*: 124	4-*mono*: 170; 2,4-*di*: 210	......	130–1	Oxid. → benzoic acid, 121
14	1,2,4-Trimethylbenzene (Pseudocumene)..........	169.4	−43.91	1.50484	0.87582	97	......	3,5,6-*tri*: 185				Oxid. → trimellitic acid, 225–35 d.
15	Isobutylbenzene	172.8	−51.53	1.48646	0.85321	......	......		4-*mono*: 127.0–7.5	......	99–100	Oxid. → benzoic acid, 121
16	*sec*-Butylbenzene	173.3	−75.57	1.49020	0.86207	......	......	2,4-*di*: b.p. 161–2[5]	4-*mono*: 126; 2,6-*di*: 192		88–9	Oxid. → benzoic
17	3-Isopropyl-1-methylbenzene (3-Isopropyltoluene; *m*-Cymene)................	175.1	−63.75	1.4930	0.8610	......	....	....	....	....	....	....

*Derivative data given in order: m.p., crystal color, solvent from which crystallized.

TABLE IV. ORGANIC DERIVATIVES OF AROMATIC HYDROCARBONS
a) Liquids. (Listed in order of increasing b.p.)* (Continued)

No.	Name	Boiling point, °C	Melting point, °C	n_D^{20}	D_4^{20}	Picrate	1,3,5-Trinitrobenzene derivative	Nitro derivative	Acetamido derivative	Phthalic anhydride derivative	2,4-Dinitrophenyl sulfenyl chloride derivative	Miscellaneous
18	1,2,3-Trimethylbenzene (Hemimellitene)..........	176.08	−25.41	1.51393	0.89438	90.5	......	......	......	......	......	Oxid. → hemimellitic acid, 190-7 d.
19	trans-Propenylbenzene.......	176.5-7.5	−27.1 to −25.9	1.5463²⁵	0.902	......						....
20	Indane...................	177	−51.4	1.5381	0.9645	......						....
21	4-Isopropyl-1-methylbenzene (4-Isopropyltoluene; 4-Cymene)...............	177.1	−67.94	1.4909	0.8537	......	......	2,6-di: 54; 2,3,6-tri: 118	....	123-4	......	Sulfonamide, 115
22	2-Isopropyl-1-methylbenzene (2-Isopropyltoluene; 2-Cymene)..............	178.35	−71.71	1.5006	0.8766	......	......	......	......	......	......	Br₂ → Tetrabromo, 59.5-60.5
23	1,3-Diethylbenzene..........	181.1	....	1.49552	0.86394	......	......	2,4,6-tri: 62	....	114	......	
24	1-Methyl-3-propylbenzene (m-Propyltoluene)........	181.8	....	1.4936	0.8610	......						....
25	Indene...................	182.4	−2	1.5764	0.9915	98, yel.	......		......		......	Acid → polymer
26	n-Butylbenzene.............	183.27	−88.15	1.48979	0.86013	......			4-mono: 105; 2,4-di: 214	97	72-3	....
27	1-Methyl-4-propylbenzene (p-Propyltoluene)........	183.3	....	1.4919	0.8584	......	......	......	......	......	......	....
28	1,2-Diethylbenzene..........	183.4	....	1.50346	0.87996	......						....
29	1,4-Diethylbenzene..........	183.8	....	1.49483	0.86196	......						....
30	1,3-Dimethyl-5-ethylbenzene..	183.8	−84.4	1.4981	0.8648	......	......	2,4,6-tri: 117.0-7.6	....			Br₂ → Tribromo, 89
31	1-Methyl-2-propylbenzene (o-Propyltoluene)..........	184.8	−60.2	1.4998	0.8744	......						....
32	2,2-Dimethyl-1-phenylpropane (Neopentylbenzene).......	186	....	1.4880	0.858							
33	1,4-Dimethyl-2-ethylbenzene..	186.9	....	1.5043	0.8772	......	......	3,5,6-tri: 127-8, al.	4-mono: 142; 2,4-di: 181	......	......	Sulfonamide, 107-8
34	2-Methylindane	187.0	....	1.5070	0.9034							
35	3-Methyl-2-phenylbutane	188	....	1.486	0.8701	......	......	......	4-mono: 147-8; 2,4-di: 193	......	......	4-Benzamido deriv., 141-2
36	1-Methylindane	188-90	....	1.5274	0.939	......						Heat with Pt. at 310-350 → Naphthalene, 80.3
37	1,3-Dimethyl-4-ethylbenzene..	188.4	−63.0	1.5038	0.8763	......	......	2,5,6-tri: 127.5-9.0	....			Br₂ → 2,5,6-Tribromo, 94-5; 81-2
38	3-tert-Butyl-1-methylbenzene (3-tert-Butyltoluene).......	189.3	−41.39	1.4944	0.8657	......	......	......	......	......	......	....
39	1,2-Dimethyl-4-ethylbenzene..	189.55	−67.1	1.5031	0.8745	......	......	......	......	......	......	Oxid. → trimellitic acid, 225-35 d.
40	1,3-Dimethyl-2-ethylbenzene..	190	....	1.5107	0.8904	......	......	......	......	......	......	Oxid. → hemimellitic acid, 190-7 d.

*Derivative data given in order: m.p., crystal color, solvent from which crystallized.

No.	Name	Boiling point, °C	Melting point, °C	n_D^{20}	D_4^{20}	Picrate	1,3,5-Trinitro-benzene derivative	Nitro derivative	Acetamido derivative	Phthalic anhydride derivative	2,4-Dinitrophenyl sulfenyl chloride derivative	Miscellaneous
41	3-Phenylpentane	191	. . . . . .	1.4877	0.8649	. . . . . .	. . . . . .	. . . .	4-*mono*: 145–6; 2,4-*di*: 199–200	. . . . . .	. . . . . .	4-Benzamido deriv., 154
42	1-Ethyl-3-isopropylbenzene . . .	192	. . . . . .	1.4955	0.859	. . . . . .	. . . . . .	. . . .				
43	2-Methyl-2-phenylbutane	192.38	. . . . . .	1.4934	0.8737				4-*mono*: 142; 2,4-*di*: 181		. . . . . .	4-Benzamido deriv., 112–3
44	4-*tert*-Butyl-1-methylbenzene (4-*tert*-Butyltoluene)	192.8	− 52.49	1.4918	0.8612	. . . . . .	. . . . . .	2,6-*di*: 96	. . . .			
45	1-Ethyl-2-isopropylbenzene . . .	193		1.5080	0.888							
46	2-Phenylpentane	193		1.4876	0.8576				4-*mono*: 107; 2,4-*di*: 181–2			4-Benzamido, 127–8
47	1,2-Dimethyl-3-ethylbenzene . .	193.9	− 49.5	1.5117	0.8921						. . . . . .	Oxid. → hemimellitic acid, 190–7 d.
48	3-*sec*-Butyl-1-methylbenzene (3-*sec*-Butyltoluene)	194	. . . . . .	1.490	0.858							
49	3-Isobutyl-1-methylbenzene (3-Isobutyltoluene)	194	. . . . . .	1.4888	0.8536							
50	*d*-2-Methyl-1-phenylbutane . . .	194	. . . . . .	1.4880	0.8617							
51	1,3-Dimethyl-5-isopropyl-benzene	194.5; 191	. . . . . .	1.4955	0.8591							Oxid. → trimesic acid, 380
52	2-Phenyl-*cis*-2-butene	194.5		1.5402²⁵	0.9191²⁵						81–2	
53	4-Isobutyl-1-methylbenzene (*p*-Isobutyltoluene)	196	. . . . . .	1.4874	0.8517							
54	2-*sec*-Butyl-1-methylbenzene (2-*sec*-Butyltoluene)	196	. . . . . .	1.497	0.873							
55	2-Isobutyl-1-methylbenzene (*o*-Isobutyltoluene)	196	. . . . . .	1.4935	0.8649							
56	1,4-Dimethyl-2-isopropyl-benzene	196.2		1.5010	0.8738							
57	1-Ethyl-4-isopropylbenzene . . .	196.6	. . . . . .	1.4923	0.8585							
58	*d,l*-2-Methyl-1-phenylbutane . .	197	. . . . . .	1.486	0.859				4-*mono*: 115–6; 2,4-*di*: 193–4		. . . . . .	4-Benzamido, 126
59	1,2,3,5-Tetramethylbenzene (Isodurene)	197.9		1.5125	0.8899			4,6-*di*: 181; 157	. . . .	213	. . . . . .	
60	3-Methyl-1-phenylbutane (Isopentylbenzene)	198.9; 196		1.4847	0.8558				4-*mono*: 114; 2,4-*di*: 215–6			
61	1,3-Dimethyl-2-isopropyl-benzene	199	. . . . . .	1.509	0.890	. . . . . .	. . . . . .	. . . .	. . . .	. . . . . .	. . . . . .	
62	1,3-Dimethyl-4-isopropyl-benzene	199.1; 195	. . . . . .	1.5018	0.869							
63	3-Methylindene	199.2–200; 198.5	. . . .	1.55907²⁷	0.9640	76–8, or.-yel., al.	. . . . . .	. . . .				
64	4-*sec*-Butyl-1-methylbenzene (*p*-*sec*-Butyltoluene)	200	. . . . . .	1.4932	0.8650	. . . . . .	. . . . . .	. . . .				

*Derivative data given in order: m.p., crystal color, solvent from which crystallized.

No.	Name	Boiling point, °C	Melting point, °C	n_D^{20}	D_4^{20}	Picrate	1,3,5-Trinitro-benzene derivative	Nitro derivative	Acetamido derivative	Phthalic anhydride derivative	2,4-Dinitrophenyl sulfenyl chloride derivative	Miscellaneous
65	2-tert-Butyl-1-methylbenzene (2-tert-Butyltoluene)	200.5	......	1.5076	0.8897	......	......	......	......	......	......	......
66	3,5-Diethyl-1-methylbenzene (3,5-Diethyltoluene)	200.7	−74.12	1.4969	0.8630	......	......	2,4,6-tri: 106–6.5	......	......	......	......
67	2-Butyl-1-methylbenzene (2-Butyltoluene)	201; 208	......	1.4958	0.8721	......	......	......	......	......	......	......
68	1-Ethyl-3-propylbenzene	201	......	1.4930	0.8607	......	......	......	......	......	......	......
69	1,2-Dimethyl-4-isopropyl-benzene	201.8	......	1.4993	0.8699	......	......	......	......	......	......	......
71	1,2-Dimethyl-3-isopropyl-benzene	202.6	......	1.508	0.888	......	......	......	......	......	......	......
72	1-Ethyl-2-propylbenzene	203	......	1.4992	0.8744	......	......	......	......	......	......	......
73	1,3-Di-isopropylbenzene	203.2	−63.1	1.4883	0.85593	......	......	4,6-di: 76.9–7.2, 2-ProH	......	......	......	......
74	1,2-Diethyl-4-methylbenzene	203.6	......	1.5039	0.8762	......	......	......	......	......	......	......
75	1,2-Di-isopropylbenzene	203.8	......	1.4960	0.8771	......	......	......	......	......	......	......
76	1,4-Dimethyl-2-propyl-benzene	204.3	......	1.4999	0.8717	......	......	......	......	......	......	......
77	1,2,3,4-Tetramethylbenzene (Prehnitene)	205.0	−6.3	1.5201	0.9053	92–5	......	5,6-di: 176	......	......	......	......
78	1-Ethyl-4-propylbenzene	205	......	1.4921	0.8594	......	......	......	......	......	......	......
79	3-Butyl-1-methylbenzene (m-Butyltoluene)	205	......	1.491	0.859	......	......	......	......	......	......	......
80	2,4-Diethyl-1-methylbenzene (2,4-Diethyltoluene)	205	......	1.5027	0.8748	......	......	......	......	......	......	......
81	n-Pentylbenzene	205.4	−75	1.4878	0.8585	......	......	4-mono: 101–2; 2,4-di: 202	......	......	......	4-Benzamido, 128–9
82	3-Methyl-3-phenylpentane	206	......	1.4958	0.8755	......	......	......	......	......	......	......
83	1,3-Dimethyl-5-tert-butyl-benzene	206–6.5	−21.5	1.4958	0.8645	......	......	2,4,6-tri: 107 (one form); 114 (another form)	......	......	......	......
84	1,3-Dimethyl-4-propylbenzene	206.6	......	1.4998	0.8723	......	......	......	......	......	......	......
85	1,2-Diethyl-3-methylbenzene	206.6	......	1.5105	0.8910	......	......	......	......	......	......	......
86	4-Butyl-1-methylbenzene (4-Butyltoluene)	207	......	1.490	0.857	......	......	......	......	......	......	......
87	2,5-Diethyl-1-methylbenzene (2,5-Diethyltoluene)	207.1	......	1.5034	0.8758	......	......	......	......	......	......	......
88	1,2,3,4-Tetrahydronaphthalene (Tetralin)	207.6	−35.79	1.54135	0.9702	......	......	5,7-di: 95	......	153–5	......	$Cl_2 \rightarrow$ 5,6,7,8-Tetrachloro, 172
89	1,3-Diethyl-2-propylbenzene	207.6	......	1.5063	0.8856	......	......	......	......	......	......	......
90	2,6-Diethyl-1-methylbenzene (2,6-Diethyltoluene)	208.8	......	1.5106	0.8907	......	......	......	......	......	......	......
91	1,2-Dimethyl-4-propylbenzene	208.9	......	1.5000	0.8715	......	......	......	......	......	......	......
92	1,3-Dimethyl-5-propylbenzene	209	......	1.4933	0.8610	......	......	......	......	......	......	......
93	2-Methyl-3-phenylpentane	209	......	1.4912	0.8678	......	......	......	......	......	......	......
94	4-tert-Butyl-1,3-dimethyl-benzene	210–4	......	1.5030^{37}	0.9372^{30}	......	......	2,5,6-tri: 112, al.	......	......	......	......
95	1,4-Di-isopropylbenzene	210.4	−17.1	1.48983	0.85676	......	......	......	......	......	......	......
96	1,2-Dimethyl-3-propylbenzene	210.7	......	1.5075	0.8864	......	......	......	......	......	......	......

*Derivative data given in order: m.p., crystal color, solvent from which crystallized.

TABLE IV. ORGANIC DERIVATIVES OF AROMATIC HYDROCARBONS
a) Liquids. (Listed in order of increasing b.p.)* (Continued)

No.	Name	Boiling point, °C	Melting point, °C	n_D^{20}	D_4^{20}	Picrate	1,3,5-Trinitro-benzene derivative	Nitro derivative	Acetamido derivative	Phthalic anhydride derivative	2,4-Dinitro-phenyl sulfenyl chloride derivative	Miscellaneous
97	1-*tert*-Butyl-4-ethylbenzene . . .	211	. . . .	1.4950	0.8635	. . . . . .	. . . . . .	2,6-*di*: 94–5, al.	. . . .	. . . . . .	. . . . . .	. . . . .
98	d,l-3-Phenylhexane	211; 208.3	. . . .	1.4867	0.8596	. . . . . .	. . . . . .	. . . .	2,4-*di*: 207–8	. . . . . .	. . . . . .	. . . . .
99	2-Ethyl-1,3,5-trimethyl-benzene	212.4	−12.2	1.5074	0.883	. . . . . .	. . . . . .	4,6-*di*: 111, al.	. . . .	. . . . . .	. . . . . .	. . . . .
100	3-Ethyl-4-isopropyl-1-methyl-benzene	213	. . . .	1.5006	0.8722	. . . . . .	. . . . . .	. . . .	. . . .	. . . . . .	. . . . . .	. . . . .
101	5-Ethyl-1,2,4-trimethylbenzene	213	−13.5	1.5075	0.833	. . . . . .	. . . . . .	3,6-*di*: 87–8, al.	. . . .	. . . . . .	. . . . . .	3,6-Dibromo, 60–1, acet.
102	6-Ethyl-1,2,4-trimethylbenzene	213	. . . .	1.5118	0.8897	. . . . . .	. . . . . .	. . . .	. . . .	. . . . . .	. . . . . .	. . . . .
103	2-Phenylhexane	214	. . . .	1.4882	0.8600	. . . . . .	. . . . . .	. . . .	2,4-*di*: 178	. . . . . .	. . . . . .	. . . . .
104	2-Methyl-1-phenylpentane	215	. . . .	1.4847	0.8624	. . . . . .	. . . . . .	. . . .	. . . .	. . . . . .	. . . . . .	. . . . .
105	4-Isopropyl-1-propylbenzene . .	215	. . . .	1.4972	0.8614	. . . . . .	. . . . . .	. . . .	. . . .	. . . . . .	. . . . . .	. . . . .
106	1,3-Dipropylbenzene	215–8	. . . .	1.5155[16]	0.9137[17]	. . . . . .	. . . . . .	. . . .	. . . .	. . . . . .	. . . . . .	. . . . .
107	5-Ethyl-1,2,3-trimethylbenzene	215.8	. . . .	1.5101	0.8863	. . . . . .	. . . . . .	. . . .	. . . .	. . . . . .	. . . . . .	. . . . .
108	3-Ethyl-1,2,4-trimethylbenzene	216.6	. . . .	1.5133	0.895	. . . . . .	. . . . . .	5,6-*di*: 79–80, al.	. . . .	. . . . . .	. . . . . .	. . . . .
109	1,2,4-Triethylbenzene	217.7	. . . .	1.4982	0.8791	. . . . . .	. . . . . .	. . . .	. . . .	. . . . . .	. . . . . .	. . . . .
110	1,3,5-Triethylbenzene	218; 211.2	. . . .	1.4965	0.8568[25]	. . . . . .	. . . . . .	2,4,6-*tri*: 112.4–2.6	. . . .	129	. . . . . .	2,4,6-Tribromo, 105
111	2-Methyl-1,2,3,4-tetrahydro-naphthalene (2-Methyl-tetralin)	218	. . . .	1.5311	0.952	. . . . . .	. . . . . .	. . . .	. . . .	. . . . . .	. . . . . .	. . . . .
112	1-Methyl-1,2,3,4-tetrahydro-naphthalene (1-Methyl-tetralin)	219	. . . .	1.5357	0.9580	. . . . . .	. . . . . .	. . . .	. . . .	. . . . . .	. . . . . .	. . . . .
113	4-Ethyl-1,2,3-trimethyl-benzene	220.4	. . . .	1.5180	0.9019	. . . . . .	. . . . . .	. . . .	. . . .	. . . . . .	. . . . . .	. . . . .
114	1,4-Dipropylbenzene	221	. . . .	1.4914	0.8564	. . . . . .	. . . . . .	. . . .	. . . .	. . . . . .	. . . . . .	. . . . .
115	3-Methyl-1-phenylpentane	221	. . . .	1.4876	0.8605	. . . . . .	. . . . . .	. . . .	. . . .	. . . . . .	. . . . . .	. . . . .
116	2-Propyl-1,3,5-trimethyl-benzene	221	. . . .	1.5033	0.8782	. . . . . .	. . . . . .	. . . .	. . . .	. . . . . .	. . . . . .	. . . . .
117	1,1-Dimethyl-1,2,3,4-tetra-hydronaphthalene (1,1-Dimethyltetralin)	221	. . . .	1.5292	0.950	. . . . . .	. . . . . .	Ar-x, x-*di*: 64.5	. . . .	. . . . . .	. . . . . .	. . . . .
118	3-*tert*-Butyl-1-isopropyl-benzene	222	. . . .	1.4832	0.8512	. . . . . .	. . . . . .	. . . .	. . . .	. . . . . .	. . . . . .	. . . . .
119	1-Methyl-3-pentylbenzene (3-Pentyltoluene)	223	. . . .	1.4911	0.8593	. . . . . .	. . . . . .	. . . .	. . . .	. . . . . .	. . . . . .	. . . . .
120	4-*tert*-Butyl-1-isopropyl-benzene	224	. . . .	1.4872	0.8665	. . . . . .	. . . . . .	. . . .	. . . .	. . . . . .	. . . . . .	. . . . .
121	2-Methyl-2-phenylhexane	225	. . . .	1.4943	0.8737	. . . . . .	. . . . . .	. . . .	. . . .	. . . . . .	. . . . . .	. . . . .
122	2,4-Di-isopropyl-1-methyl-benzene (2,4-Di-isopropyl-toluene)	225	. . . .	1.4990	0.8664	. . . . . .	. . . . . .	. . . .	. . . .	. . . . . .	. . . . . .	. . . .
123	3-Methyl-3-phenylhexane	226	. . . .	1.4980	0.8776	. . . . . .	. . . . . .	. . . .	. . . .	. . . . . .	. . . . . .	. . . . .
124	*n*-Hexylbenzene	226.1	−61.2	1.4864	0.8575	. . . . . .	. . . . . .	. . . .	2,4-*di*: 205–6	. . . . . .	. . . . . .	. . . . .
125	3-Phenylheptane	227	. . . .	1.4862	0.8607	. . . . . .	. . . . . .	. . . .	. . . .	. . . . . .	. . . . . .	. . . . .
126	2,6-Di-isopropyl-1-methyl-benzene (2,6-Di-isopropyl-toluene)	228	. . . .	1.5032	0.8768	. . . . . .	. . . . . .	. . . .	. . . .	. . . . . .	. . . . . .	. . . . .

*Derivative data given in order: m.p., crystal color, solvent from which crystallized.

TABLE IV. ORGANIC DERIVATIVES OF AROMATIC HYDROCARBONS
a) Liquids. (Listed in order of increasing b.p.)* (Continued)

No.	Name	Boiling point, °C	Melting point, °C	n_D^{20}	D_4^{20}	Picrate	1,3,5-Trinitrobenzene derivative	Nitro derivative	Acetamido derivative	Phthalic anhydride derivative	2,4-Dinitrophenyl sulfenyl chloride derivative	Miscellaneous
127	**5-Propyl-1,2,4-trimethyl-benzene**	228	. . . . . .	1.5095	0.887	. . . . . .	. . . . . .	. . . . . .	. . . . . .	. . . . . .	. . . . . .	. . . .
128	**6-Methyl-1,2,3,4-tetra-hydronaphthalene (6-Methyltetralin)**	229	. . . . . .	1.5357	0.9537	. . . . . .	. . . . . .	. . . . . .	. . . . . .	. . . . . .	. . . . . .	. . . .
129	**2,2-Dimethyl-1,2,3,4-tetra-hydronaphthalene (2,2-Dimethyltetralin)**	230	. . . . . .	1.5200	0.935	. . . . . .						
130	**2-Phenylheptane**	231		1.4863	0.8610	. . . . . .						
131	**5-Methyl-1,2,3,4-tetra-hydronaphthalene (5-Methyltetralin)**	234.4	. . . . . .	1.54395	0.9720							
132	**2-Ethyl-1,2,3,4-tetrahydro-naphthalene (2-Ethyltetralin)**	235	. . . . . .	1.523	0.938							
133	**Cyclohexylbenzene**	235–6	7–8	1.5329	0.9502							
134	**1-Ethyl-1,2,3,4-tetrahydro-naphthalene (1-Ethyltetralin)**	236	. . . . . .	1.5321	0.9535							
135	**2,5-Dimethyl-1,2,3,4-tetra-hydronaphthalene (2,5-Dimethyltetralin)**	236	. . . . . .	1.526	0.946							
136	**2,8-Dimethyl-1,2,3,4-tetra-hydronaphthalene (2,8-Dimethyltetralin)**	236	. . . . . .	1.526	0.941							
137	**2,7-Dimethyl-1,2,3,4-tetra-hydronaphthalene (2,7-Dimethyltetralin)**	237–8	. . . . . .	1.526	0.941							
138	**2,6-Dimethyl-1,2,3,4-tetra-hydronaphthalene (2,6-Dimethyltetralin)**	238	. . . . . .	1.526	0.941							Oxid. → trimellitic acid, 225–35 d.
139	**1,4-Di-*sec*-butylbenzene**	239	. . . . . .	1.4892	0.8590							. . . .
140	**1,5-Dimethyl-1,2,3,4-tetra-hydronaphthalene (1,5-Dimethyltetralin)**	239	. . . . . .	1.526	0.9410							. . . .
141	**3-Ethyl-3-phenylhexane**	239	. . . . . .	1.4943	0.875							
142	**6-Ethyl-1,2,3,4-tetrahydro-naphthalene (6-Ethyl-tetralin)**	241	. . . . . .	1.5331	0.9568							
143	**2-Methyl-1-phenyl-1-butene** . .	241–2	. . . . . .	1.528^{18}	. . . . . .							Nitrosit, 129–30
144	**5-Ethyl-1,2,3,4-tetrahydro-naphthalene (5-Ethyltetralin)**	242	. . . . . .	1.540	0.973							
145	*n*-**Heptylbenzene**	244	. . . . . .	1.4875	0.8595							
146	**1-Methylnaphthalene**	244.8	−30.57	1.6174	1.02025	142, or.-red, al.	153.5–4.5, al.	4-*mono*: 71; 4,5-*di*: 143	. . . .	68	. . . . .	Styphnate, 135, al.
147	**5,6-Dimethyl-1,2,3,4-tetra-hydronaphthalene (5,6-Dimethyltetralin)**	252	. . . . . .	1.552	0.975	. . . . . .	. . . . . .				. . . . . .	Oxid. → melophanic acid, 238–42
148	**6,7-Dimethyl-1,2,3,4-tetra-hydronaphthalene (6,7-Dimethyltetralin)**	252	10	1.5360	0.954	. . . . . .	. . . . . .	5,8-*di*: 203	. . . .			
149	**5,7-Dimethyl-1,2,3,4-tetra-hydronaphthalene (5,7-Dimethyltetralin)**	253.1	−6	1.5405	0.9583	. . . . . .	. . . . . .				. . . . .	Heating with S at 320° → 1,3-Dimethylnaphthalene, b.p. 263

*Derivative data given in order: m.p., crystal color, solvent from which crystallized.

TABLE IV. ORGANIC DERIVATIVES OF AROMATIC HYDROCARBONS
a) Liquids. (Listed in order of increasing b.p.)* (Continued)

No.	Name	Boiling point, °C	Melting point, °C	n_D^{20}	D_4^{20}	Picrate	1,3,5-Trinitro-benzene deriva-tive	Nitro derivative	Acetamido derivative	Phthalic anhy-dride deriva-tive	2,4-Di-nitro-phenyl sulfenyl chloride deriva-tive	Miscellaneous
150	5,8-Dimethyl-1,2,3,4-tetra-hydronaphthalene (5,8-Dimethyltetralin)..........	254	....	1.547	0.967	......	......	......	......	......	......	Heating with S at 230° → 1,4-Di-methylnaphtha-lene, b.p. 268
151	2-Ethylnaphthalene	257.9	−7.5	1.59761	0.9922	77.0- 7.5, al.	88–9, 2-PrOH	....	....	....	......	Styphnate, 88–90
152	1-Ethylnaphthalene	258.67	−13.88	1.6062	1.00816	98.5	111.5 12, al.	....	....	....	......	Styphnate, 111–3, al.
153	1,7-Dimethylnaphthalene.....	263	−13	1.60831	1.0115	121	137	....	....	....	......	Styphnate, 143
154	1,6-Dimethylnaphthalene.....	263	−14	1.6072	1.003	114–5, or., al.	139, yel.	....	....	....	......	Styphnate, 122
155	1,3-Dimethylnaphthalene.....	263	−4.0	1.6078	1.0063	118	135, yel., al.	....	....	....	......	Styphnate, 117–8, w.-me. al.; 2,4,7-Trinitrofluorenone deriv., 142–5, or.
156	n-Octylbenzene (1-Phenyl-octane).................	264.5	−36	1.4845	0.8562	......	......	2,4-di: 2	....	....	....	....
157	1-Allylnaphthalene..........	265–7	....	1.6140	1.0228	69	......					....
158	1-Isopropylnaphthalene......	267.9	−16	1.5950	0.99565	85–6	......					Dimer, 198.5–9.5; Tetrabromo, 141 −2
159	1,4-Dimethylnaphthalene.....	268; 262–4	7.66	1.6127	1.0166	144, or., me. al.	165–6, yel., me. al.	....	....	....	......	Styphnate, 126–7 or., me. al.
160	1,1-Diphenylethane	268–70	....	1.5761	1.0033	......	......	......	......	......	......	Oxid. → benzo-phenone, 49
161	2-Isopropylnaphthalene......	a) 268.2; b) 262	....	1.5772; 1.5861	0.9795	93–5; 91–3	......	....	....	....	......	....
162	2-Propylnaphthalene	273.5; 277–9	....	1.5872	0.9770	93–4, or., al.	99	....	....	....	......	....
163	1-Propylnaphthalene	277; 272.5	−10	1.5952	0.9918	91–2	86–7, al.	....	....	....	......	....
164	1,3,7-Trimethylnaphthalene ..	280	13.5	1.5759	1.007	144, or., al.	......	....	....	....	......	Styphnate, 151.5, or., me. al.
165	1-Isopropyl-7-methyl-naphthalene (Apocadalene)..	282	....	1.5884	0.9833	102, or., al.	......	....	....	....	......	Styphnate, 166 (163–4), yel., al.
166	n-Nonylbenzene (1-Phenyl-nonane).................	282	−24	1.4838	0.8558	......	......	....	....	....	......	4-Sulfonamide, 94.5–5.0; Maleic anhydride → 3-(4-Nonylbenzoyl) acrylic acid, 82–3
167	2-Butylnaphthalene	283–5; 292	−8.1	1.57774	0.9673	71–3, or.-yel., al.	......	....	....	....	......	....
168	2-tert-Butylnaphthalene......	285–90	−4	1.5768	0.9687	102–3	......					
169	1-tert-Butylnaphthalene......	287–9	....	1.5726	0.9629	96, yel.	......					
170	1-Butylnaphthalene	289.34	−19.76	1.5819	0.97673	104–5, or.-yel.	......					

*Derivative data given in order: m.p., crystal color, solvent from which crystallized.

TABLE IV. ORGANIC DERIVATIVES OF AROMATIC HYDROCARBONS
a) Liquids. (Listed in order of increasing b.p.)* (Continued)

No.	Name	Boiling point, °C	Melting point, °C	n_D^{20}	D_4^{20}	Picrate	1,3,5-Trinitro-benzene derivative	Nitro derivative	Acetamido derivative	Phthalic anhydride derivative	2,4-Di-nitro-phenyl sulfenyl chloride derivative	Miscellaneous
171	**4,5-Benzindane** (1,2-Cyclo-pentanonaphthalene)	294–5	......	1.6290	1.066	110	119–20	....	....	....	......	2,4,7-Trinitro-fluorenone deriv., 133
172	**n-Decylbenzene** (1-Phenyl-decane)	300	−14.38	1.48319	0.85553	......	......					....
173	**1-Pentylnaphthalene**	307	−22	1.5725	0.9656	......	75, yel.					
174	**2-Pentylnaphthalene**	310	−21	1.5694	0.9561	......	74, yel.					
175	**n-Undecylbenzene** (n-Hendecyl-benzene; 1-Phenylundecane)..	316	−5	1.4828	0.8553	......	......					4-Sulfonamide, 95.7–6.2
176	**1-Hexylnaphthalene**.........	322	−17.7	1.5647	0.9566	......	69–74					....
177	**2-Hexylnaphthalene**.........	324	−5.6	1.620	0.9479	......	67–8, yel.					
178	**n-Dodecylbenzene** (1-Phenyl-dodecane)...............	331	3	1.4824	0.8551	......						4-Sulfonamide, 97.5
179	**1-Heptylnaphthalene**	340	......	1.5582	0.9491	......						
180	**2-Heptylnaphthalene**	341	1	1.5556	0.9410	......						........•........
181	**Tridecylbenzene** (1-Phenyl-tridecane)	346	10	1.4821	0.8550	......						
182	**1-Octylnaphthalene**	356	−2.0	1.5532	0.9427	......						
183	**2-Octylnaphthalene**	357	2 forms: stable: −0.5; meta-stable: 13	1.5501	0.9356	......						
184	**1-Nonylnaphthalene**........	372	......	1.5477	0.9371	......						
185	**2-Nonylnaphthalene**........	372	12	1.5454	0.9298	......						
186	**1-Decylnaphthalene**	387	......	1.5435	0.9322	......						....

*Derivative data given in order: m.p., crystal color, solvent from which crystallized.

TABLE IV. ORGANIC DERIVATIVES OF AROMATIC HYDROCARBONS
b) Solids. (Listed in order of increasing m.p.)*

No.	Name	Melting point, °C	Boiling point, °C	Picrate	Styphnate	sym-Trinitrobenzene derivative	2,4,7-Trinitrofluorenone derivative	Nitro derivative	Phthalic anhydride derivative	2,4-Dinitrophenyl sulfenyl chloride derivative	Miscellaneous
1	**1,2,6-Trimethylnaphthalene....**	14	146[10]	122–3, al.	150–1, al.	....		....			n_D^{20}: 1.6010
2	**Diphenylmethane**	26–7	264.7; 261–2; 120[10]	....		....		2,4,2′,4′-tetra: 172			n_D^{20}: 1.5770; D_{25}^{25}: 1.0056; $CrO_3 \rightarrow$ Benzophenone, 49
3	**1,2,3-Trimethylnaphthalene....**	27–8, al.	125–30[12]	143, or., al.	143.5, yel.	154–6, al.	....	....			n_D^{25}: 1.5725
4	**1,6,7-Trimethylnaphthalene....**	28, me. al.	285; 138[12]	125–6, or., me. al.	148–9, or., me. al.	142–3, yel., me. al.					
5	**2-Isopropylazulene**	31, bl.-vlt.		....	....	di: 113–4					
6	**1,4-Dimethyl-7-isopropyl-azulene (δ-Guaiazulene)**	31.5, bl.-vlt., al.	167–8[12]	122–2.5, bl., al.	105–6, bl., me. al.	151–1.5					D_4^{19}: 0.9728 (super-cooled); 2,4,6-Tri-nitrotoluene deriv., 89
7	**2,6-Dimethylphenanthrene**	33–4, me. al.	....	135–6, yel., al.	148–50, yel., me. al.	....					
8	**1,2,5-Trimethylnaphthalene....**	33.5; 31–2, al.	147–8[11]	138–40, al.	131, al.	159–60, al.					n_D^{20}: 1.6110; D_{20}^{20}: 1.0103; 2,4,6-Tri-nitrotoluene deriv., 90–0.5
9	**1-Propylphenanthrene**	34–5, me. al.	....	100–1, yel., me. al.							
10	**5-Isopropylazulene**	34.5	....	....		134; 122–3					
11	**2-Propylphenanthrene**	35–6, al.	170[0.2]	91–2, al.							
12	**2-Methylnaphthalene**	37–8; 34.4	240–2; 110–2[16]	116, al.	....	123, yel.	125–6, al.	1-mono: 81			$CrO_3 \rightarrow \beta$-Naphthoic acid, 182
13	**1-Ethyl-5-methylnaphthalene...**	40, al.	133[10]	97, or., al.							
14	**9-Isopropylphenanthrene**	41–2		109–10							
15	**6-Isopropylazulene**	43	....	....		124					
16	**2-Ethyl-6-methylnaphthalene...**	44–5	145–50[11]	109, or.	119, yel.	116–7, yel.					2,4,6-Trinitrotoluene deriv., 62, yel.
17	**2-Isopropylphenanthrene**	44–5, al.		108, yel., me. al.							
18	**6-Isopropyl-1-methyl-phenanthrene**	45–6	....	143, or.							
19	**2-Ethylazulene**	45.5; 44–5, bl.	....	110–1	....	107					
20	**2,5-Dimethylphenanthrene**	46–7, al.	204–5[15]	127–9, yel., al.	132–3, or., al.						
21	**1,3,5-Trimethylnaphthalene....**	47, me. al.	139.5[10]	141–2, me. al.	138, yel.						
22	**3-Ethyl-6-methylphenanthrene** .	47–8	....	156–6.5, or.							
23	**2-Methylazulene**	47–8		130–1, bl., al.		140–1, dk. red, al.					
24	**1,3,8-Trimethylnaphthalene....**	48, me. al.		127.5, or., al.	140.5, al.						
25	**4-Methylphenanthrene**	49–50, 95% al.	....	140–1, al.	135, or., al.						

*Derivative data given in order: m.p., crystal color, solvent from which crystallized.

TABLE IV. ORGANIC DERIVATIVES OF AROMATIC HYDROCARBONS
b) Solids. (Listed in order of increasing m.p.)* (Continued)

No.	Name	Melting point, °C	Boiling point, °C	Picrate	Styphnate	sym-Tri-nitro-benzene derivative	2,4,7-Tri-nitrofluo-renone derivative	Nitro derivative	Phthalic anhy-dride deriva-tive	2,4-Di-nitro-phenyl sulfenyl chloride deriva-tive	Miscellaneous
26	1,4-Dimethylphenanthrene	50–1 (cor.), me. al.	....	143.5, or.-yel.	135.5–6.5, or.	....	....	....	....	......	....
27	Bibenzyl (1,2-Diphenylethane)	53	284	....	....	102	....	4,4'-di: 180; 2,2',4,4'-tetra: 169	......	132–3	D^{50}_{50}: 0.9782; $CrO_3 \rightarrow$ Benzoic acid, 121
28	Methylenefluorene (Biphenyleneethylene)	53	....	152–3	....	....					
29	3,5-Dimethylphenanthrene	53–4, me. al.	....	139, or., me. al.	124–5, or.-yel.	....					
30	1,3-Dimethylazulene	54	....	164–6	....	164–6, al.	....				
31	7-Methyl-3,4-benzphenanthrene	54.0–4.5, al.	....	134.0–4.5, red, al.	....	....	178.5–8.8	....			
32	Pentamethylbenzene	54.3; 51	231.8	131	....	121	......	6-mono: 154	....		
33	1,2,4-Trimethylnaphthalene	55–6; 50, me. al.	146^{12}	148–8.5, or., me. al.	123.5, yel., me. al.	165–6.5, me. al.					
34	3,3'-Dimethylstilbene (sym-Di-m-tolylethylene)	55–6	....	97							
35	1,4,5,7-Tetramethylnaphthalene	56	162–5^{11}	153	....	....	152.8–3.4				
36	1,2,4,8-Tetramethylnaphthalene	56–7	150^{10}	145.5	....	167, red, me. al.					2,4,6-Trinitrotoluene deriv., 88, yel.
37	2,9-Dimethylphenanthrene	56–7, al.	....	138, yel., al.	....						
38	1,5-Dimethylphenanthrene	57–8, me. al.	....	134–5, or., me. al.							
39	2-Benzylnaphthalene	58	350	93–4, yel., al.	....	....	124.3–5.4	....	....		D^0: 1.176
40	1-Benzylnaphthalene	58–9	350	103–4, yel.	....	....	....	....	....		D^{17}: 1.166
41	1,2-Dimethylazulene	58–9, bl., al.	....	129–30, blk., al.	....	166–7, br.-blk., al.					
42	9-Propylphenanthrene	59	265–70^{22}	99, yel., al.	....						
43	1,7-Dimethyl-4-isopropyl-naphthalene	60, al.-w.	....	92, or.-red, al.	120, yel.						
44	3-Methylphenanthrene	62–3	140–50^6	137–8, yel., al.							
45	3,4-Dimethylphenanthrene	62–3, me. al.	....	129–30, or.-red, al.	142–3, or.-red, al.	....					
46	1-Ethylphenanthrene	62.5, al.	....	108–9, or., al.	144, yel., al.	....					
47	sym-Diphenylacetylene (Tolane)	62.5, al.	....	111, yel.	....	96, yel.					
48	9-Ethylphenanthrene	62.5–3.0; 66, bz.-pet. eth.	198–200	123–4, or.-red, al.	....	....	....	....	....		D^{78}_4: 1.0603; n^{78}_D: 1.6582

* Derivative data given in order: m.p., crystal color, solvent from which crystallized.

No.	Name	Melting point, °C	Boiling point, °C	Picrate	Styphnate	*sym*-Trinitrobenzene derivative	2,4,7-Trinitrofluorenone derivative	Nitro derivative	Phthalic anhydride derivative	2,4-Dinitrophenyl sulfenyl chloride derivative	Miscellaneous
49	1,4,5-Trimethylnaphthalene....	63	145[12]	144–5, red, al.	129–30	....	....	......	......	......	
50	4-Methylfluorene	63, al.	....	....							In H$_2$SO$_4$ sol. → grn.
51	1,4,6,7-Tetramethylnaphthalene	63–4, al.	....	148–9	....	....	172.4–3.4				
52	1,2,3-Trimethylphenanthrene...	63.8–4.8		187–8, or.	....	200.7–1.5, yel., bz.-al.	....				
53	1,8-Dimethylnaphthalene......	65; 63	140[18]	156; 148	160	....	....				
54	8-Methyl-3,4-benzphenanthrene	65–6, al.	....	107–8, red, al.	....						
55	2-Ethylphenanthrene	67–8, me. al.; 64–5	....	95.5–6.0, yel., al.; 92–3	....	....	180.7–0.9				
56	3,4-Benzphenanthrene	68, al.	....	120.8–8.5, red, al.			170.8–1.1				
57	1,3,7-Trimethylphenanthrene ..	68–9, me. al.	....	163–4, al.	160–1	....	....				
58	4-Isopropyl-1-methyl-phenanthrene...............	68–8.5, me. al.		113.6–4, or., al.	....	....					
59	4,8-Dimethylazulene.........	69–70, bl., al.	....	157–8, blk., al.	....	179–80, red-br., al.					
60	Biphenyl	69.2; 71	254–5; 145[22]	....		....	....	4,4'-*di*: 237; 229; 2,2',4,4'-*tetra*: 150	225	142–3	n_4^{20}: 1.475; D_4^{20}: 0.866
61	2-Methyl-3,4-benzphenanthrene	70.4–1.0, al.	....	141.8–3.2, red, bz.-al.	....	145, bz.-pet. eth.	158–8.5, or.-red, aq. al.	....			....
62	3-Methylpyrene	71–2, al.		211–2, br.-red, bz.	....	....	....			......	Conc. H$_2$SO$_4$ sol. → yel. with grn. fluorescence; on heating → olive grn. with vlt. fluorescence
63	1,4,7-Trimethylphenanthrene...	72–3		141–2, me. al.	129–30	....	....	......			....
64	1,4-Dimethylanthracene.......	74, al.	....	140							
66	4,9-Dimethyl-1,2-benz-anthracene................	75, me. al.	....	116, br., me. al.	....	124–5, red, me. al.					
67	Benzalfluorene (ω-Phenyl-dibenzfulvene)	76, al.	....	115–6							Dibromide, 116 d.
68	1,3-Dimethylphenanthrene.....	76–7, ac. a.	....	153–5, or., al.	165–6	....	....				
69	1-Methyl-3,4-benzphenanthrene	77.8	210[0.4]	112–3, red, al.	....	....	171.8–2.2				
70	3-Isopropyl-1-methyl-phenanthrene..............	79	180[1.5]	150	155						

* Derivative data given in order: m.p., crystal color, solvent from which crystallized.

TABLE IV. ORGANIC DERIVATIVES OF AROMATIC HYDROCARBONS
b) Solids. (Listed in order of increasing m.p.)* (Continued)

No.	Name	Melting point, °C	Boiling point, °C	Picrate	Styphnate	sym-Trinitrobenzene derivative	2,4,7-Trinitrofluorenone derivative	Nitro derivative	Phthalic anhydride derivative	2,4-Dinitrophenyl sulfenyl chloride derivative	Miscellaneous
71	1,2'-Binaphthyl	79–80; 76	....	127.0–7.5 (cor.), or.	....	....	145.0–6.9	....	....	......	
72	2,3-Dimethylphenanthrene	79–80	....	146–7, or.-red, al.	147–8, or., al.	....	....	....	....	.....	
73	1,2,4,5-Tetramethylbenzene (Durene)	79.2; 80	196–8	....	....	....	....	3,6-di: 205	263		
74	1-Ethyl-2-methylphenanthrene	80, me. al.	....	134–5, me. al.	....	152.5–3.0	...				
75	1,5-Dimethylnaphthalene	80.0–0.5, 85% al.	....	140	....						
76	6-Methyl-3,4-benzphenanthrene	80–1, al.	206–8[2]	118.0–8.5, red, me. al.	....	....	144.2–4.5	....			
77	Naphthalene	80.3	218	149	....	153	153–4	1-mono: 61; 57	172	173–4	
78	1,3,6,8-Tetramethylnaphthalene	81	115–6[2]	151–2	....	175–6					
79	1-Ethyl-7-methylphenanthrene (Homopimanthrene)	81, al.	....	115–6, yel., me. al.	....						Quinoxaline deriv., 154, ac. a.
80	9-Methylanthracene	81.5	196–7[12]	137 d., red-br.	...						D_4^{99}: 1.065, n_D^{99}: 1.6959; Irradiation in acetone → dimer, 228.0–8.5; Photo-oxide, ca. 80, exp.
81	1-Isopropyl-7-methyl-phenanthrene	82–3	170[1]	119–20, or.	148–9, yel.	163–4, yel.					
82	6-Methylazulene	83, bl.-vlt.	....	137; 125	....	141					
83	1,3-Dimethylanthracene	83	....	136	....	....					bl. fluorescence
84	2,2'-Dimethylstilbene (sym-Di-o-tolylethylene)	83	176–80[10]	102	....						
85	1-Methylanthracene	85–6, me. al.	199–200	115.6–6.2, red, me. al.	176.4–7.0, red, me. al.	...	219.0–9.8, red, bz.				D_4^{99}: 1.0471; n_D^{99}: 1.6802; Irradiation → dimer, 246
86	1,7-Dimethylphenanthrene	86	....	132, me. al.	159, me. al.	....					
87	1,6-Diphenylnaphthalene	86–7	....	106–8	....						
88	1,6-Dimethylphenanthrene	87–8, me. al.	....	134, yel., al.	....						
89	1,9-Dimethylphenanthrene	88, al.	....	163.5, or.-yel., me. al.	181	....					
90	9-Methylphenanthrene	90–1, aq. al.	....	152–3, al.	....						
91	1,2,10-Trimethylanthracene	90.6–1.4, yel.	....	138.5–9.5, al.	...	169.6–170.2, al.					
92	7-Ethyl-1-methylphenanthrene	91.0–1.5; 84–5	....			141–2	135–6	....			
93	Triphenylmethane	92	358	....	...	....	....	4,4',4''-tri: 206	....	......	Br₂ → bromo deriv., 152
95	5-Isopropylnaphthanthrene	92, ac. a.	....	157	....	....					

*Derivative data given in order: m.p., crystal color, solvent from which crystallized.

TABLE IV. ORGANIC DERIVATIVES OF AROMATIC HYDROCARBONS

No.	Name	Melting point, °C	Boiling point, °C	Picrate	Styphnate	sym-Trinitro-benzene derivative	2,4,7-Tri-nitrofluo-renone derivative	Nitro derivative	Phthalic anhy-dride deriva-tive	2,4-Di-nitro-phenyl sulfenyl chloride deriva-tive	Miscellaneous
96	3,9-Dimethyl-1,2-benz-anthracene	93	....	137-8, red, al.	....	145, red, bz.-lgr.	....				....
97	5,6-Benzindane (2,3-Cyclo-pentenonaphthalene)	94	....	120-1	....						
98	12-Isopropylnaphthanthracene	94-5, ac. a.	....	157-8							
99	Acenaphthene	96.2, yel., al.	278	162, or.-red, al.	....	168, yel., al.	175-6	5-mono: 101	198	187-9 d.	n_D^{99}: 1.6066; D_4^{99}: 1.0242; 1,2-Di-bromide, 121-3
100	2,7-Dimethylnaphthalene	96-7, al.	262	136.0-6.5, yel., me. al.	158.0-9.5, yel., me. al.						
101	7-Isopropyl-1-methylfluorene	96.5-7.0, al.	....	....				di: ca. 245			
102	Azulene	98.5-99	270 d.; 115-35[10]	120 d.	....	167					Heat at 270° → Naphthalene, 80.3; 2,4,6-Trinitrotolu-ene deriv., 95.5-100
103	Retene (7-Isopropyl-1-methyl-phenanthrene)	100.5-101, al.	390; 158-6.5[0.2]	124-5	141-2	139	....			......	D: 1.035
104	Phenanthrene	101, al.; 96.3	340; 332	144; 132.8	....	158; 145	197			250-1	n_D: 1.5973; D: 1.182
105	2,7-Dimethylphenanthrene	101-2, me. al.	....	152-3, or., al.							
106	2,3,6-Trimethylnaphthalene	102; 92-3	286; 146-8[14]	130, yel., me. al.	165, yel., me. al.						
107	2-Phenylnaphthalene	102-3	....	....			169.5-70.5				
108	1,2,3,4-Tetrahydroanthracene	103-5	....				182.4				
109	2,3-Dimethylnaphthalene (Guaiene)	104.0-4.5 (subl.), al.	265-6	123-4							D_4^{20}: 1.008
110	Ethylidenefluorene	104, ac. a.	....	155-6							Dibromide, 93.5
111	1,7-Dimethylfluorene (Gibberene)	107.0-7.5	....	85-6, or.-red	....	98, yel., al.	....				In H_2SO_4 sol. → bl.
112	1,1'-Dinaphthylmethane	110, al.	>360; 270[14]	142	....	141.5	216				
113	Fluoranthrene	110	....	185-6			216				
114	2,6-Dimethylnaphthalene	111	261-2	143			156				
115	2,4-Dimethylphenanthrene	111, al.	....	138-9; 142, me. al.							
116	Fluorene	113.5; 116-7	293-5	87; 77	....	105	179	2-mono: 156; 2,7-di: 199	228	......	CrO_3 → Fluorenone, 84
117	4,10-Dimethyl-1,2-benzan-thracene	114, pa. yel., me. al.	....	162, blk.							
118	4H-Cyclopenta(def)phenan-threne (Phenanthrindene)	116, al.	353	166	....					......	Benzylidene deriv., 108
119	1,3,8-Trimethylphenanthrene	116	....	174-5	....	188	199				
120	11-Methylnaphthanthracene	117-8	....	159-60, dk. red	....	170, or.	238.2-8.6				

*Derivative data given in order: m.p., crystal color, solvent from which crystallized.

No.	Name	Melting point, °C	Boiling point, °C	Picrate	Styphnate	sym-Trinitrobenzene derivative	2,4,7-Trinitrofluorenone derivative	Nitro derivative	Phthalic anhydride derivative	2,4-Dinitrophenyl sulfenyl chloride derivative	Miscellaneous
121	5-Methylchrysene	117.2–7.8, bz.-al.	....	142.6–3.0, or.-red, al.	....	172.6–3.6, bz.-al.	....	......	......	......	......
122	1,2,5,6-Tetramethylnaphthalene	118	150–60¹⁰	156–7, red.	166, bz.	180.0–0.5, bz.					
123	Cyclohept(fg)acenaphthene (Acepleiadene)	118–20 (subl.), red, al.	....	150 d.	....					....	Maleic anh. add. comp., 248–50, bz.
124	1,2,7-Trimethylphenanthrene	120–1, al.	....	148–9	169–70						
125	1',10-Dimethyl-1,2-dibenzanthracene	122–3, al.	....	147–8, red, al.	....					.....	In H_2SO_4 sol. → red
126	9,10-Dimethyl-1,2-benzanthracene	122–3	....	112–3, blk., al. di: 102–6, red, al.							Highly carcinogenic
127	Benz(bc)aceanthrylene	122–3, al.	....	141.5–2.0, dk. red., al.	....	162.5–3.0, or., al.					
128	1-Methylphenanthrene	123, aq. al.	....	139, yel., al.	152–3, yel.						
129	1,6,7-Trimethylphenanthrene	123–4, al.	....	165–6, or.	111–2						
130	1,1'-Diacenaphthene	(a) 124, al.; (b) 169, pet. eth.	....	di: 270, red							
131	trans-Stilbene	124, al.	305⁷²⁰	94–5	....	115–20					
132	3,4-Benzfluorene	124–5, al.	....	130–1, red, al.	....		191.8				
133	9-Isopropylnaphthanthracene	125, al.	....	152							
134	6-Methylnaphthanthracene	126.2–7.2, al.	....	149–50, red-br., al.	....	....	221.4–1.8; 163–4, al.				
135	5,8-Dimethyl-1,2-benzanthracene	131, bz.-al.	....	175, red, al.	....	....					
136	8-Isopropylnaphthanthracene	132–3	....	118							
137	1,4,5,8-Tetramethylnaphthalene	132–3	....	154.6–5.4	143.4–4.2		158–9				
138	12-Methylnaphthanthracene	138, yel.	....	115–6, red	....	....	234.5–5.0; 209.5–9.7, red, al.				
139	2-Methyl-1',2'-benzpyrene	138–9, pa. yel., me. al.; after fusing, 140.0–0.2	....	184–5, br., bz.-lgr.	....	211.5–2.0, red, bz.-lgr.					
140	1,5-Dimethylanthracene	139–40, pa. yel.	....	166–7, scar., al.							
141	7-Methylnaphthanthracene	140	....	174, dk. red	....	....	236.1–6.5				

*Derivative data given in order: m.p., crystal color, solvent from which crystallized.

No.	Name	Melting point, °C	Boiling point, °C	Picrate	Styphnate	sym-Trinitrobenzene derivative	2,4,7-Trinitrofluorenone derivative	Nitro derivative	Phthalic anhydride derivative	2,4-Dinitrophenyl sulfenyl chloride derivative	Miscellaneous
142	3,6-Dimethylphenanthrene.....	141, al.	....	172–3, or.-yel., me. al.	....						....
143	5-Methyl-3,4-benzphenanthrene	141.4–1.9	....	....		....	130.6–1.4, red	....			....
144	1,4-Dimethylchrysene.........	142	....	141, red, al.							....
145	1,2-Dimethylphenanthrene.....	142–3, al.	....	148, or., al.	153, yel., al.						....
146	8,10-Dimethyl-1,2-benzanthracene..................	146, bz.-al.	....	166, red, al.	....						....
147	1,2,8-Trimethylphenanthrene...	146–7, al.	210–20[15]	164–5, or., al.	....	193.0–3.5, al.					....
148	3-Methyl-1',2'-benzpyrene.....	146.7–8.1, yel., al.-eth.	....	179.5–80.0, br.-red, bz.-lgr.			210.5–11.0, bz.-lgr.				....
149	9-Methyl-1',2'-benzpyrene.....	146.8–8.0, yel., hexane	....				218.5–9.5, red, bz.-lgr.				....
150	9-Phenylfluorene.............	147–8, al.	....	....		....		di: ca. 240; tetra: ca. 235 d.	....	....	Bromide, di: 181–2; tri: 167–71
151	2-Methylnaphthanthracene	149–50, al.	....	180			218.7–9.2	....			....
152	Pyrene....................	149–50, pa. yel.	385	222, red, al.; 220; 227			242–3	....			....
153	9-Methylnaphthanthracene	150.5–1.5, al.	....	157–8			225.1–5.4				....
154	4-Methylchrysene............	151.0–1.5, bz-al.	....	two forms: 135.0–5.5, red, bz.-lgr.; 137.5–8.0, or., bz.-lgr.	....						....
155	trans-trans-1,4-Diphenyl-1,3-butadiene (trans-trans-Distyryl).................	152.5	350	152–3	....					....	Maleic anh. add. comp., 198–200
156	Cinnamalfluorene............	155, pa. yel., ac. a.	....	di: 178–9							Tetrabromide, ca. 160 d.
157	5-Methylnaphthanthracene	155.9–6.9, bz.-pet. eth.	....	153			235.4–5.6	....			....
158	1,2-Benzanthracene	159–60	....	133	....		160	....			....
159	8-Methylnaphthanthracene	160.0–0.6	....	166			243.2–3.6				
160	1,1'-Binaphthyl.............	160.5	240–4[12]	145							
161	Di-1-naphthastilbene (sym.-Di-1-naphthylethylene)......	161, pa. yel., al.	....	tri: 210							

* Derivative data given in order: m.p., crystal color, solvent from which crystallized.

TABLE IV. ORGANIC DERIVATIVES OF AROMATIC HYDROCARBONS

b) Solids. (Listed in order of increasing m.p.)* (Continued)

No.	Name	Melting point, °C	Boiling point, °C	Picrate	Styphnate	sym-Trinitrobenzene derivative	2,4,7-Trinitrofluorenone derivative	Nitro derivative	Phthalic anhydride derivative	2,4-Dinitrophenyl sulfenyl chloride derivative	Miscellaneous
162	6-Methylchrysene	161.0–1.4, et. ac.-al.		170.0–0.6, or., bz.-al.		189.8–190.6, yel., bz.-al.					
163	3-Methylnaphthanthracene	163.0–3.9, al.		146.0–6.8			239.0–9.6				
164	2,6-Dimethyl-1,2-benzanthracene	164, ac. a.		199–200							
165	Cyclopentadienophenanthrene	164–5		146–7		172–3					In H_2SO_4 sol. → bl.
166	10,11-Benzfluoranthene	165; 166,		194–5		220.0–0.5					
167	Hexamethylbenzene	165	264	170		174					
168	3-Methylchrysene	170.0–0.5, bz.-pet-eth.		164.0–4.5, grn., al.							
169	Cholanthrene	170–1; 173 (subl.), pa. yel., bz.-al.		167–8, vlt.-blk., bz.			245–6				
170	6-Methyl-1′,2′-benzpyrene	171.0–1.5, yel., bz.-lgr.		181.5–2.5, br., bz.-lgr.	209–10, red, bz.-lgr.						
171	6,7-Dimethyl-1,2-benzanthracene	174, et. ac.		170							
172	1,2-Benzpyrene	176.5–7.5, pa. yel., bz.-me. al.	310–2[10]	197–8, vlt.-blk.							
173	5,10-Dimethyl-1,2-benzanthracene	177, bz.-al.		174, red-blk., bz.							
174	4,5-Benzpyrene	178–9, bz.		229–30, red, bz.							
175	9,10-Dimethylanthracene	180–1, al.		176–7 d.							
176	10-Methylnaphthanthracene	183.0–3.6, yel., al.		159.0–9.4							2,4,6-Trinitrotoluene deriv., 224.8–5.0
177	5,6-Dimethyl-1,2-benzanthracene	187–8, al.		191–3, red, al.							
178	2,2′-Binaphthyl	188; 181	452	184				171			Lt. bl. fluorescence; $KMnO_4$ → Phthalic acid, 206–8
179	1,2-Benzfluorene (Chrysofluorene)	189–90, ac. a.; 183–4	413; 398–400	di: 127.5; 124–6		144–5	213.5–5.5				
180	1,8-Dimethylphenanthrene	191–2, bz.		151–2, yel.			193–4				
181	8-Methyl-1′,2′-benzpyrene	192–3, yel., bz.		205, dk. br., bz.		233 d., red, bz.					
182	Bifluorenylidene (Diphenyleneethylene)	194–5 (cor.), red		177–8				two di-forms: 171, dk. red; 170, or. red			Dibromide, 312, red, bz.
183	1,2,7,8-Dibenzanthracene	196, bz.		212, brt. red							Bl.-grn. fluorescence in sol.

*Derivative data given in order: m.p., crystal color, solvent from which crystallized.

No.	Name	Melting point, °C	Boiling point, °C	Picrate	Styphnate	sym-Trinitrobenzene derivative	2,4,7-Trinitrofluorenone derivative	Nitro derivative	Phthalic anhydride derivative	2,4-Dinitrophenyl sulfenyl chloride derivative	Miscellaneous
184	4-Methylnaphthanthracene	197.4–8.0, al.	......	139–40, lt. red	......	......	228.2–8.8	......	......	......	......
185	1,2,3,4-Dibenzanthracene	200–2, pa. yel., ac. a.	......	207, red							In conc. H_2SO_4 sol. → pa. vlt.-red
186	Di-2-fluorenylmethane	201–2, al.	......	......	......	......	di: 256–7	......	......	......	$Na_2Cr_2O_7$ → Di-2-fluorenyl ketone, 297–8, yel., ac. a.
187	2,3-Benzfluorene	208–9					221.2–2.0				
188	5-Methyl-1′,2′-benzpyrene	215.7–6.2, yel., eth.-al.	......	207–8, vlt.-blk., bz.-lgr.	......	230–1, red, bz.-lgr.					
189	Anthracene	216.2	340 (cor.); 226.5[53]	138	......	164	194			......	D_4^{27}: 1.25; Dibromide, 122; CrO_3 → Anthraquinone, 273
190	11,12-Benzfluoranthene	217	480	170–1	......	182	236–7				
191	4-Methyl-1′,2′-benzpyrene	217.5–8.0, yel.	......	203–4, vlt.-br., bz.	......	......					
192	2,8-Dimethylchrysene	218, bz.	......	171–2, bz.	204, or., bz.	195, yel., bz.					
193	2-Methylchrysene	224.5–5.5, bz.-al.	......	143–6, yel., al.							
194	6,12-Dimethylchrysene	237	......	......	207 d., bz.	222					
195	1,2-Benzphenanthrene (Chrysene)	254, bz.	448	273	......	186	248–9	......	214	......	Dibromide, 275
196	Di-2-naphthastilbene (sym-Di-2-naphthylethylene)	254–5, bz.	......	215							
197	1-Methylchrysene	254–5 (cor.), (vacuum), bz.				174–6, yel., bz.					
198	2,3,6,7-Dibenzphenanthrene	257, grn.-yel.	......	184, or.-red							Bl. fluorescence in sol.; intense yel.-grn. in u.v.
199	2,3,5,6-Dibenzphenanthrene	261, grn.-yel., ac. a.	......	di: 213, or.-red							Bl. fluorescence in bz. sol.; grn. fluorescence in u.v.
200	1,2,5,6-Dibenzanthracene	262, met., ac. a.	......	di: 214, or.							......
201	Perylene	273–4	......	......			270–1				......
202	Picene (1,2,7,8-Dibenzphenanthrene)	365–6, xyl.	518–20	......			257–8				Dibromide, 295; 2,7-Dianthraquinone add. comp., 299–300
203	1,2,3,4,5,6,7,8-Tetrabenzanthracene	428–9	......	......			318–9, red				
204	Coronene (Hexabenzobenzene)	438–40 (cor.), yel., bz.	525	>250 d., red, bz.	......	>280 d., or., bz.					

*Derivative data given in order: m.p., crystal color, solvent from which crystallized.

EXPLANATIONS AND REFERENCES TO TABLE V

S-Alkylthiuronium picrate (S-Alkylisothiourea picrate)*

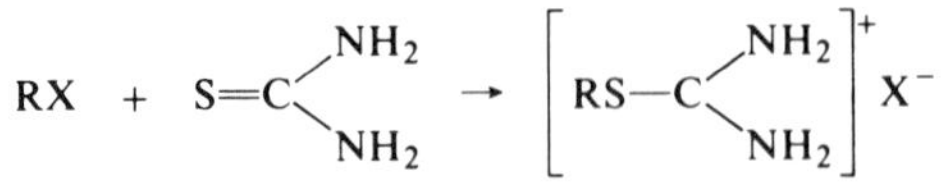

$$RX \ + \ S{=}C{\overset{NH_2}{\underset{NH_2}{<}}} \ \rightarrow \ \left[RS{-}C{\overset{NH_2}{\underset{NH_2}{<}}} \right]^{+} X^{-}$$

S-Alkylthiuronium salt

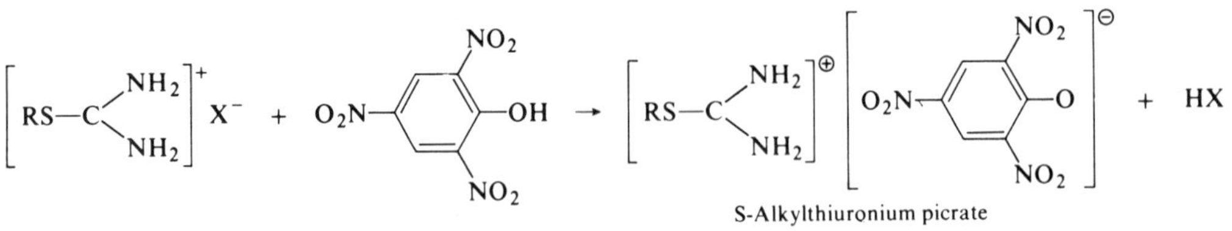

$$\left[RS{-}C{\overset{NH_2}{\underset{NH_2}{<}}} \right]^{+} X^{-} \ + \ O_2N{-}\underset{NO_2}{\overset{NO_2}{\bigcirc}}{-}OH \ \rightarrow \ \left[RS{-}C{\overset{NH_2}{\underset{NH_2}{<}}} \right]^{\oplus} \left[O_2N{-}\underset{NO_2}{\overset{NO_2}{\bigcirc}}{-}O \right]^{\ominus} \ + \ HX$$

S-Alkylthiuronium picrate

From the alkyl halide with thiourea in 95% ethanol, followed by addition of picric acid in ethanol.
For directions and examples see: Linstead, pp. 82–3; Shriner, p. 245; Vogel, pp. 291–2; Wild, p. 43; E. L. Brown and N. Campbell, *J. Chem. Soc.*, 1699 (1937); W. J. Levy and N. Campbell, *J. Chem. Soc.*, 1442 (1939).
From the alkyl halide with thiourea in ethylene glycol, followed by addition of picric acid in ethanol.
See: Cheronis, p. 550; H. M. Crosby and J. B. Entrikin, *J. Chem. Ed.*, **41**, 360 (1964).

1-Naphthylamide (α-Naphthalide).*

$$RX \ + \ Mg \ \rightarrow \ RMgX$$

$$RMgX \ + \ 1{-}C_{10}H_7N{=}C{=}O \ \rightarrow \ 1{-}C_{10}H_7N{=}\overset{R}{\overset{|}{C}}OMgX \ \xrightarrow{H_2O} \ 1{-}C_{10}H_7NHCOR \ + \ Mg(OH)X$$

1-Naphthylamide

From the Grignard reagent (prepared from the alkyl halide and magnesium in dry ether) with 1-naphthyl-isocyanate in ether.
For directions and examples see: Cheronis, pp. 551, 553; Linstead, p. 83; Shriner, p. 244; Vogel, pp. 290–1; Wild, pp. 35–37; H. Gilman and M. Furry, *J. Amer. Chem. Soc.*, **50**, 1214 (1928); H. W. Underwood and J. C. Gale, *J. Amer. Chem. Soc.*, **56**, 2117 (1934).

Anilide.*

$$RX \ + \ Mg \ \rightarrow \ RMgX$$

$$RMgX \ + \ C_6H_5N{=}C{=}O \ \rightarrow \ C_6H_5N{=}\overset{R}{\overset{|}{C}}OMgX \ \xrightarrow{H_2O} \ C_6H_5NHCOR \ + \ Mg(OH)X$$

Anilide

From the Grignard reagent (prepared from the alkyl halide and magnesium in dry ether) with phenyliso-cyanate in ether.
For directions and examples see: Cheronis, pp. 551, 554; Linstead, p. 83; Shriner, p. 244; Vogel, pp. 290–1; Wild, pp. 35–7; A. M. Schwartz and J. R. Johnson, *J. Amer. Chem. Soc.*, **53**, 1063 (1931); H. W. Underwood and J. C. Gale, *J. Amer. Chem. Soc.*, **56**, 2117 (1934).

Alkylmercuric halide.*

$$RX \ + \ Mg \ \rightarrow \ RMgX$$

$$RMgX \ + \ HgX_2 \ \rightarrow \ RHgX \ + \ MgX_2$$

Alkyl
mercuric
halide

From the Grignard reagent (prepared from the alkyl halide and magnesium in dry ether) with the mercuric salt of the same halogen in ether.
For directions and examples see: Cheronis, pp. 551, 554; Shriner, p. 244; Vogel, p. 291; Wild, p. 38; C. S. Marvel, C. Gauerke and E. L. Hill, *J. Amer. Chem. Soc.*, **47**, 3009 (1925); E. L. Hill, *J. Amer. Chem. Soc.*, **50**, 167 (1928); K. H. Slotta and K. R. Jacobi, *J. prakt. Chem.*, **120**, 249 (1929).

---

*Derivatives recommended for first trial.
WARNING: This is not an instruction manual. References should be consulted for the preparation of derivatives.

Picrate of alkyl 2-naphthyl ether (Molecular complex). *

$$RX + \text{(2-naphthol)-OH} \xrightarrow{NaOH} \text{(naphthyl)-OR} + NaBr + H_2O$$

Alkyl 2-naphthyl
ether

$$\text{(naphthyl)-OR} + O_2N\text{-(picric acid, }NO_2, NO_2)\text{-OH} \longrightarrow \text{(naphthyl)-OR} \cdot O_2N\text{-(}NO_2, NO_2)\text{-OH}$$

Picrate of alkyl 2-naphthyl ether
(Molecular complex)

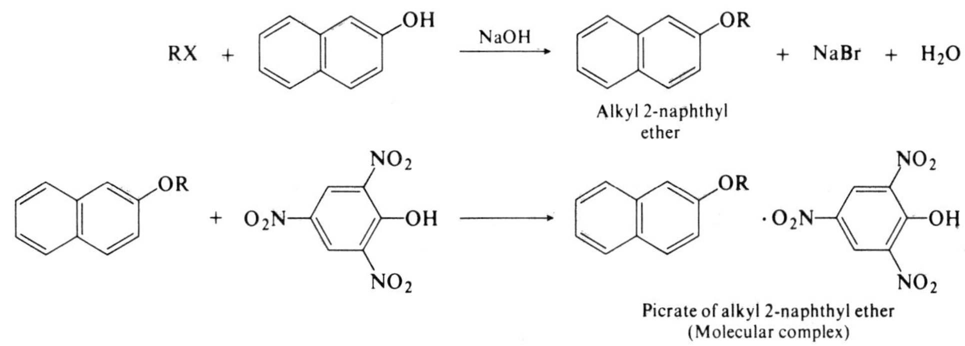

The alkyl 2-naphthyl ether is obtained from the alkyl halide with 2-naphthol in ethanolic sodium or potassium hydroxide.

For directions and examples see: Cheronis, p. 551; Linstead, p. 83; Shriner, p. 244; Vogel, p. 292; Wild, p. 44.

The picrate is obtained from the alkyl 2-naphthyl ether and picric acid in chloroform or ethanol.

See: Cheronis, p. 551; Linstead, p. 83; Vogel, p. 292; Wild, p. 44; O. L. Baril and G. A. Megrdichian, *J. Amer. Chem. Soc.*, **58**, 1415 (1936); V. H. Dermer and O. C. Dermer, *J. Org. Chem.*, **3**, 289 (1938).

Alkyl 2,4-dinitrophenyl thioether (Alkyl 2,4-dinitrophenyl sulfide).

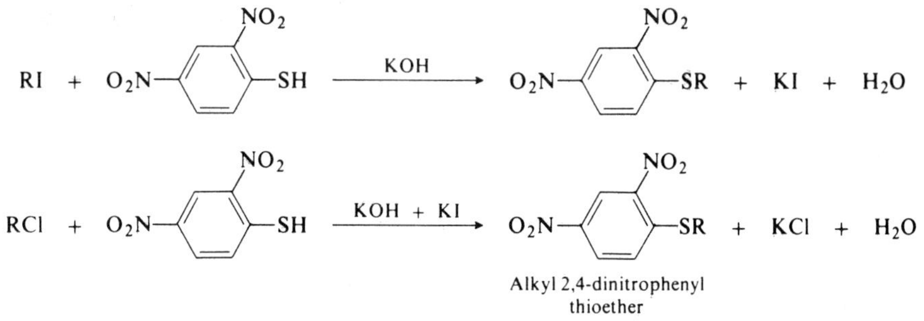

$$RI + O_2N\text{-(}NO_2\text{)-SH} \xrightarrow{KOH} O_2N\text{-(}NO_2\text{)-SR} + KI + H_2O$$

$$RCl + O_2N\text{-(}NO_2\text{)-SH} \xrightarrow{KOH + KI} O_2N\text{-(}NO_2\text{)-SR} + KCl + H_2O$$

Alkyl 2,4-dinitrophenyl
thioether

From the alkyl bromide or iodide with 2,4-dinitrothiophenol in butyl carbitol (2-(2-butoxyethoxy)ethanol) and aqueous potassium hydroxide.

For directions and examples see: Cheronis, p. 557; R. W. Bost, P. K. Starnes and E. L. Wood, *J. Amer. Chem. Soc.*, **73**, 1968 (1951).

From the alkyl chloride with 2,4-dinitrothiophenol in butyl carbitol (2-(2-butoxyethoxy)ethanol) with potassium iodide and aqueous potassium hydroxide.

See: Cheronis, p. 557; R. W. Bost, P. K. Starnes and E. L. Wood, *J. Amer. Chem. Soc.*, **73**, 1968 (1951).

Alkyl 2,4-dinitrophenyl sulfone.

$$O_2N\text{-(}NO_2\text{)-SR} \xrightarrow{KMnO_4} O_2N\text{-(}NO_2\text{)-SO_2R}$$

Alkyl 2,4-dinitrophenyl
sulfone

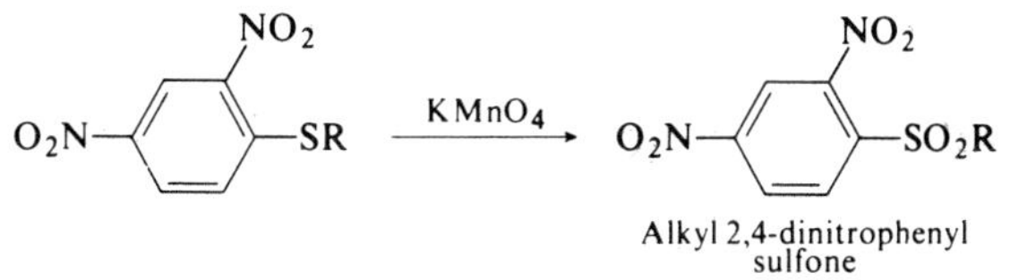

From the alkyl 2,4-dinitrophenyl thioether (prepared from the alkyl halide as above) in glacial acetic acid, with aqueous potassium permanganate.

For directions and examples see: R. W. Bost, J. O. Turner and R. D. Norton, *J. Amer. Chem. Soc.*, **54**, 1985 (1932).

---

*Derivatives recommended for first trial.
WARNING: This is not an instruction manual. References should be consulted for the preparation of derivatives.

6-Nitro-2-mercaptobenzothiazole derivative.

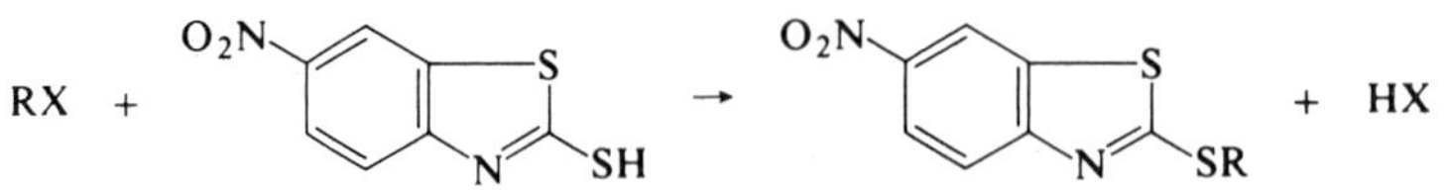

$$RX \; + \; \text{(6-nitro-2-mercaptobenzothiazole, } O_2N\ldots SH) \; \rightarrow \; \text{(Alkyl 6-nitrobenzothiazolyl sulfide, } O_2N\ldots SR) \; + \; HX$$

Alkyl 6-nitrobenzothiazolyl
sulfide

From the alkyl halide (especially a dihalide) and 6-nitro-2-mercaptobenzothiazole in butyl carbitol (2-(2-butoxyethoxy)ethanol) and aqueous sodium hydroxide.
For directions and examples see: Cheronis, p. 557; H. B. Cutter and H. R. Golden, *J. Amer. Chem. Soc.,* **69,** 831 (1947); H. B. Cutter and A. Kreuchunas, *Anal. Chem.,* **25,** 198 (1953).

Substituted N-alkylphthalimides.

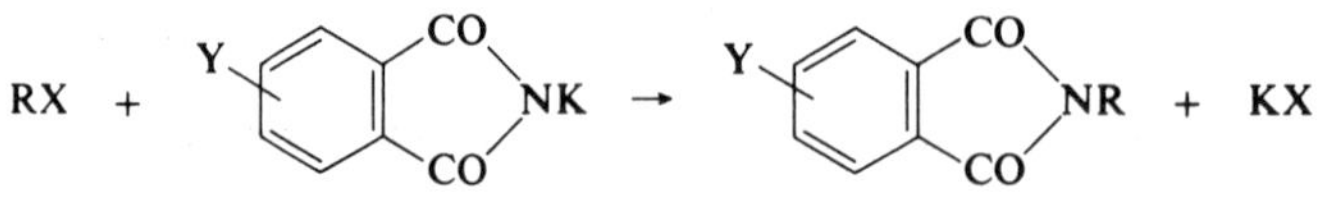

$$RX \; + \; \text{(Substituted potassium phthalimide, } Y\ldots NK) \; \rightarrow \; \text{(Substituted N-alkylphthalimide, } Y\ldots NR) \; + \; KX$$

Substituted potassium   Substituted
phthalimide   N-alkylphthalimide

From the alkyl halide with the potassium salt of the substituted phthalimide.
For directions and examples see: Wild, p. 41.
From the alkyl halide with the potassium salt of the substituted phthalimide or with the substituted phthalimide and potassium carbonate in dimethylformamide.
See: J. H. Billman and R. V. Cash, *J. Amer. Chem. Soc.,* **75,** 2499 (1953).
From the alkyl halide with the substituted phthalimide and potassium hydroxide in methanol-dioxane mixture.
See: C. H. Allen and R. V. V. Nicholls, *J. Amer. Chem. Soc.,* **56,** 1409 (1934).

Nitro derivative. *

$$ArX \; \xrightarrow{HNO_3} \; Ar(NO_2)X$$

Nitroaryl
halide

From the aromatic halide with fuming and concentrated nitric acids.
For directions and examples see: Wild, p. 450.
From the aromatic halide with 100% nitric acid.
See: Cheronis, pp. 559–561, 563.
From the aromatic halide with nitric and sulfuric acids.
See: Cheronis, pp. 560, 563; Vogel, p. 543.

Sulfonamide. *

$$ArX \; \xrightarrow{ClSO_3H} \; Ar(X)SO_2Cl$$

Sulfonyl
chloride

$$Ar(X)SO_2Cl \; \xrightarrow{NH_3} \; Ar(X)SO_2NH_2$$

Sulfonamide

The sulfonyl chloride is prepared from the aromatic halide and chlorosulfonic acid in chloroform or without solvent. The sulfonamide is obtained from the sulfonyl chloride with concentrated ammonia or dry ammonium carbonate.
For directions and examples see: Cheronis, pp. 564, 638, 639; E. H. Huntress and F. H. Carten, *J. Amer. Chem. Soc.,* **62,** 511 (1940).
NOTE: For additional information regarding directions and examples for the derivatization of aromatic halides (through the above reactions or additional ones, e.g., side-chain oxidation) see explanations and references to Table IV, pp. 32, 33, 34.

---

*Derivatives recommended for first trial.
WARNING: This is not an instruction manual. References should be consulted for the preparation of derivatives.

TABLE V. ORGANIC DERIVATIVES OF HALIDES
A) Alkyl and cycloalkyl halides 1. Chlorides
a) Liquids (Listed in order of increasing atmospheric b.p.)*

No.	Name	Boiling point, °C	n_D^{20}	D_4^{20}	S-Alkyl thiuronium picrate	1-Naphthyl amide	Anilide	Alkyl mercuric halide	Picrate of 2-naphthyl ether	2,4-Dinitrophenyl thioether	2,4-Dinitrophenyl sulfone	Miscellaneous
1	Methyl chloride	−24	. . . . . .	. . . . . .	224	160	114	167	. . . . . .	128	185; 189	Methyl-2-naphthyl ether, 70
2	Vinyl chloride	−14	. . . . . .	. . . . . .	104	. . . . . .	. . . . . .	. . . . . .	. . . . . .	. . . . . .	. . . . . .	Polymerizes to solid on irradiation
3	Ethyl chloride	13	. . . . . .	0.917_8^6	188	126	104	192	104	115	156; 160	. . . .
4	Isopropyl chloride	36.5	1.378	0.859	196;148	. . . . . .	103	. . . . . .	95	. . . . . .	. . . . . .	. . . .
5	1-Chloropropene.	37	. . . . . .	. . . . . .	. . . . . .	. . . . . .	114	. . . . . .	. . . . . .	. . . . . .	. . . . . .	. . . .
6	Allyl chloride	44.5	1.416	0.940	155	. . . . . .	114	. . . . . .	99	. . . . . .	. . . . . .	3-Nitrophthalimide deriv., 100–1
7	n-Propyl chloride	46.5	1.388	0.889	181; 176	121	92	147	8l	84	126	. . . .
8	tert-Butyl chloride	51	1.386	0.846	160–1	147	128	122–3	. . . . . .	. . . . . .	. . . . . .	. . . .
9	Chloroprene	59	1.458	0.9583	. . . .	. . . . . .	. . . . . .	. . . . . .	. . . . . .	. . . . . .	. . . . . .	Heating with maleic anh. and boiling the adduct in water → 4-chloro-1,2,3,6-tetrahydrophthalic acid, 173–5
10	sec-Butyl chloride.	68	1.397	0.874	190; 166	129	108	30.5	86	66	120	. . . .
11	Isobutyl chloride.	69	1.398	0.881	174	125	109	. . . . . .	85	76	105	. . . .
12	Methallyl chloride (3-Chloro-2-methyl-1-propene)	72	1.4340	0.9475	. . . .	. . . . . .	. . . . . .	. . . . . .	. . . . . .	. . . . . .	. . . . . .	Phthalimide deriv., 89–90
13	n-Butyl chloride	78	1.402	0.886	180; 177	112	63	128	67	66	92	. . . .
14	Neopentyl chloride	85	. . . . . .	0.879	. . . .	. . . . . .	130–1	117–8	. . . . . .	. . . . . .	. . . . . .	. . . .
15	tert-Amyl chloride	86	1.405	0.865	. . . .	138	92	. . . . . .	. . . . . .	. . . . . .	. . . . . .	. . . .
16	3-Chloro-1-pentene	93–4	1.4254	0.8978	. . . .	. . . . . .	. . . . . .	. . . . . .	. . . . . .	. . . . . .	. . . . . .	Phthalimide deriv., 78–9
17	DL-3-Chloro-2-methyl-1-butene	94	1.4304	0.9088	. . . .	. . . . . .	. . . . . .	. . . . . .	. . . . . .	. . . . . .	. . . . . .	Br₂ → dibromo deriv., 197–8
18	Trimethylvinyl chloride (3-Chloro-2-methyl-2-butene)	94	1.4320	0.925 (0.905)	. . . .	. . . . . .	. . . . . .	. . . . . .	. . . . . .	. . . . . .	. . . . . .	Br₂ in ether → dibromo deriv., 197
19	DL-2-Chloropentane	97	1.4079	0.8695	. . . .	102–3	94–6	. . . . . .	. . . . . .	. . . . . .	. . . . . .	. . . .
20	3-Pentyl chloride (3-Chloropentane)	97	1.4082	0.8723	. . . .	117–8	127; 122	. . . . . .	. . . . . .	. . . . . .	. . . . . .	. . . .
21	Isoamyl chloride.	100	1.409	0.872	179; 173	111	108	86	94	80	124	. . . .
22	n-Amyl chloride (n-Pentyl chloride)	106	1.412	0.882	154	112	96	110	67	80	83	. . . .
23	1-Chloro-2-pentene	109–10	1.435^{21}	$0.908_4^{21.5}$	. . . .	. . . . . .	. . . . . .	. . . . . .	. . . . . .	. . . . . .	. . . . . .	Phthalimide deriv., 69–70
24	2-Chloro-2-methylpentane	110–3	1.4126	0.863	. . . .	116–8	71–4	. . . . . .	. . . . . .	. . . . . .	. . . . . .	. . . .
25	3-Chloro-2,2-dimethylbutane (Pinacolyl chloride)	112	1.4181	0.8767	. . . .	. . . . . .	89–90	. . . . . .	. . . . . .	. . . . . .	. . . . . .	. . . .
26	Cyclopentyl chloride	114–5	1.4510	1.005	. . . .	. . . . . .	108	. . . . . .	. . . . . .	. . . . . .	. . . . . .	. . . .
27	4-Chloro-2,2-dimethylbutane	115	1.4160	0.8670	. . . .	138–9	133	. . . . . .	. . . . . .	. . . . . .	. . . . . .	. . . .
28	3-Chloro-3-methylpentane	115–7	1.421	0.89	. . . .	87–8	. . . . . .	. . . . . .	. . . . . .	. . . . . .	. . . . . .	. . . .
29	2-Chloro-2,3-dimethylbutane	117–9	. . . . . .	0.8769^{22}	. . . .	. . . . . .	. . . . . .	. . . . . .	. . . . . .	. . . . . .	. . . . . .	Carbonation of Grignard and conversion of acid to amide, 125–7; Br₂ → 2,3-dibromo deriv., 166–8 (173–4)
30	3-Hexyl chloride (3-Chlorohexane)	123	1.4163	0.870_{20}^{20}	. . . .	. . . . . .	. . . . . .	. . . . . .	. . . . . .	. . . . . .	. . . . . .	Grignard reagent + O₂ → 3-hexanol $\xrightarrow{CrO_3/H_2SO_4}$ 3-hexanone, 2,4-Dinitrophenylhydrazone, 147–8; Semicarbazone, 110–11

*Derivative data given in order: m.p., crystal color, solvent from which crystallized.

55

TABLE V. ORGANIC DERIVATIVES OF HALIDES
A) Alkyl and cycloalkyl halides 1. Chlorides
a) Liquids (Listed in order of increasing atmospheric b.p.)* (Continued)

No.	Name	Boiling point, °C	n_D^{20}	D_4^{20}	S-Alkyl thiuronium picrate	1-Naphthyl amide	Anilide	Alkyl mercuric halide	Picrate of 2-naphthyl ether	2,4-Dinitrophenyl thio-ether	2,4-Dinitrophenyl sulfone	Miscellaneous
31	2-Hexyl chloride (2-Chlorohexane).......	123–4	1.4142^{21}	0.8694_4^{21}	....	......	91–2	......	......	......	......	
32	1-Chloro-2-ethylbutane...	125–7	1.4230	0.8914	....	......	81–2; 83–4					
33	3-Chloro-2,2,3-trimethyl-butane	133	......	......	......	......	......	......			......	Carbonation of Grignard → acid, 80
34	n-Hexyl chloride........	133	1.420	0.878	157	106	69	125	......	74	97	
35	Cyclohexyl chloride	143	1.462	0.989		188	146	......				6-Nitro-2-mercapto-benzothiazole deriv., 100–1; 2-sulfone, 189
36	5-Chloro-2,3-dimethyl-pentane	152	1.4299	0.8825	....		80–1	......			......	
37	n-Heptyl chloride	159	1.426	0.877	142	95	57	120	......	82	101	
38	Benzyl chloride	179	1.539	1.100	188	166	117	104	123	130	178; 182	Quaternary salt with dimethyl aniline, 110
39	n-Octyl chloride	180; 184	1.431	0.875	134	91	57	115	......	78	98	
40	β-Phenylethyl chloride...	190	......	......			97	......	84	......		
41	4-Methylbenzyl chloride .	192	1.5380	1.0512	....						......	Phthalimide, 120; 117; Carbonation of Grignard → 4-tolylacetic acid, 92
42	α-Phenylethyl chloride...	195	......	......			133					
43	3-Methylbenzyl chloride .	195–6	1.5327^{25}	1.064_{20}	....						......	Phthalimide deriv., 117–8; Carbonation of Grignard → 3-tolylacetic acid, 61
44	2-Methylbenzyl chloride .	197–9										Phthalimide deriv., 148–9; Heating with pyridine → alkyl pyridinium chloride, 183
45	β-Chlorostyrene	197–9	1.571^{25}	1.109	....						......	Br₂ in chl. → dibromo deriv., 32; Oxid. → benzoic acid, 122
46	n-Nonyl chloride........	202	1.434	0.870	131					86	92	
47	2-Chlorobenzyl chloride..	213–4										5-Nitro deriv., 66; Carbonation of Grignard → 2-chlorophenylacetic acid, 94–5
48	4-Chlorobenzyl chloride..	214; 222	......				166	......			......	Oxid. → 4-chlorobenzoic acid, 242
49	3-Chlorobenzyl chloride..	216	......	1.2695_4^{15}								Oxid. → 3-chlorobenzoic acid, 158; 155; Heating with 2,4-dichlorophenol in toluene → 2-(3-chlorobenzyl)-4,6-dichlorophenol, 59–60
50	n-Decyl chloride	223	1.437	0.868	137							
51	4-Isopropylbenzyl chloride	226–9	......	......							......	Carbonation of Grignard → acid, 52
52	n-Undecyl chloride (n-Hendecyl chloride)	241	1.440	0.868	139					......		
53	n-Dodecyl chloride (Lauryl chloride)	243–4	1.4425	0.8673	....			114	......		......	Refluxed with pyridine → alkyl pyridinium chloride, 92
54	Cetyl chloride (Hexadecyl chloride)	286 d.	......	......	155			102				3-Nitrophthalimide deriv., 101; Alkyl saccharin deriv., 98

*Derivative data given in order: m.p., crystal color, solvent from which crystallized.

TABLE V. ORGANIC DERIVATIVES OF HALIDES
A) Alkyl and cycloalkyl halides 1. Chlorides
b) Solids (Listed in order of increasing m.p.)*

No.	Name	Melting point, °C	Boiling point, °C	S-Alkyl thiuronium picrate	1-Naph-thyl amide	Anilide	Alkyl mer-curic halide	Picrate of 2-naph-thyl-ether	2,4-Di-nitro-phenyl thio-ether	2,4-Di-nitro-phenyl sulfone	Miscellaneous
1	**1,3-Bis(chloromethyl)benzene** (*m*-Xylylene dichloride)	32–4	250–5	. . . . . .	. . . . . .	. . . . . .	. . . . . .	. . . . . .	. . . . . .	. . . . . .	Diphthalimide deriv., 237
2	**4-Bromobenzyl chloride**	36–8; 50	236	219	. . . . . .	. . . . . .	. . . . . .	. . . . . .	. . . . . .	. . . . . .	Oxid. → 4-bromobenzoic acid, 251
3	**2,4,6-Trimethylbenzyl chloride**	37	130^{22}	. . . . . .	. . . . . .	. . . . . .	. . . . . .	. . . . . .	. . . . . .	. . . . . .	Hydrolysis → 2,4,6-trimethyl-benzyl alcohol, 88–9; Phthali-mide deriv., 209–10
4	**2,6-Dichlorobenzyl chloride**	39–40	. . . . . .	. . . . . .	. . . . . .	. . . . . .	. . . . . .	. . . . . .	. . . . . .	. . . . . .	Carbonation of Grignard → 2,6-dichlorophenylacetic acid, 157–8
5	**1-Chloro-2,2,3,3-tetramethyl-butane**	52–3	. . . . . .	. . . . . .	. . . . . .	. . . . . .	170–1	. . . . . .	. . . . . .	. . . . . .	Grignard treated with O_2 at −5 → carbinol, 149–50
6	**1,2-Bis(chloromethyl)benzene** (*o*-Xylylene dichloride)	54–5	239–41	. . . . . .	. . . . . .	. . . . . .	. . . . . .	. . . . . .	. . . . . .	. . . . . .	Oxid. → phthalic acid, 200–6
7	**4-Nitrobenzyl chloride**	71	. . . . . .	. . . . . .	. . . . . .	. . . . . .	. . . . . .	. . . . . .	. . . . . .	. . . . . .	Oxid. → 4-nitrobenzoic acid, 241
8	**1,4-Bis(chloromethyl)benzene** (*p*-Xylylene dichloride)	98–100	240–5	. . . . . .	. . . . . .	. . . . . .	. . . . . .	. . . . . .	. . . . . .	. . . . . .	Heating with benzyl alcohol +KOH → dibenzyl ether, 67; Boiling with $Pb(NO_3)_2$ → terephthaldehyde, 115
9	**Triphenylmethyl chloride** (Trityl chloride)	113	. . . . . .	. . . . . .	. . . . . .	. . . . . .	. . . . . .	. . . . . .	. . . . . .	. . . . . .	Boiling with H_2O → triphenyl carbinol, 162

*Derivative data given in order: m.p., crystal color, solvent from which crystallized.

TABLE V. ORGANIC DERIVATIVES OF HALIDES
A) Alkyl and cycloalkyl halides 2. Bromides
a) Liquids (Listed in order of increasing atmospheric b.p.)*

No.	Name	Boiling point, °C	n_D^{20}	D_4^{20}	S-Alkyl thiuronium picrate	1-Naphthyl amide	Anilide	Alkyl mercuric halide	Picrate of 2-naphthyl ether	2,4-Dinitrophenyl thioether	2,4-Dinitrophenyl sulfone	Miscellaneous
1	Methyl bromide	3.5	....	....	224	160	114	172; 160	....	128	185; 189	....
2	Vinyl bromide	16	....	....	....	......	104	....	....	....	....	....
3	Ethyl bromide	38	1.425	1.460	188	126	104	193; 198	104	115	156; 160	....
4	1-Bromopropene	60	1.452	1.4133	....	......	114	....	....	....	....	....
5	Isopropyl bromide	60	1.425	1.314	196;148	......	103	93	92	95	140	....
6	Allyl bromide	71	1.46545	1.398	155	......	114	....	99	71	....	....
7	n-Propyl bromide	71	1.4341	1.353	181; 177	121	92	138	75	84	126	....
8	tert-Butyl bromide	72–3	....	1.211	....	147	128	....	....	....	....	....
9	Isobutyl bromide	91	1.435	1.253	174; 167	125	109	55	84	76	105	....
10	sec-Butyl bromide	91	1.437	1.256	190; 166	129	108	39	85	66	120	....
11	n-Butyl bromide	101	1.440	1.274	180; 177	112	63	136; 129	67	66	92	....
12	tert-Amyl bromide	108	1.442	1.198_4^{18}	....	138	92	....	....	....	....	....
13	Neopentyl bromide	109	....	1.225	....	......	126	....	....	....	....	....
14	DL-2-Pentyl bromide	117; 113	1.442	1.212	....	102–3	93	....	....	....	....	....
15	3-Pentyl bromide	118	1.443	1.211	....	......	124	....	....	....	....	....
16	Isoamyl bromide	120–1	1.442	1.213	179; 173	111	108	80	94	80	124	....
17	n-Amyl bromide (n-Pentyl bromide)	129	1.445	1.219	154	112	96	127; 122	67	80	83	....
18	Cyclopentyl bromide	137	1.489	1.387	....	......	....	....	....	....	....	....
19	2-Hexyl bromide (2-Bromohexane)	146	1.4832^{25}	1.1658	....	......	91–2	....	....	....	....	....
20	n-Hexyl bromide	155; 157	1.448	1.175	157	106	69	127; 119	....	74	97	....
21	Cyclohexyl bromide	165	1.495	1.336	....	188	146	153	....	....	....	....
22	n-Heptyl bromide	180; 174	1.451	1.140	142	95	57	118	....	82	101	....
23	Benzyl bromide	198	....	1.438	188	166	117	119	123	130	178; 182	....
24	n-Octyl bromide	201; 204	1.453	1.112	134	91	57	109	....	78	98	....
25	α-Phenylethyl bromide	205	....	....	....	......	133	....	....	....	....	....
26	β-Phenylethyl bromide	218	1.556	1.359	....	......	97	169	84	....	....	....
27	n-Nonyl bromide	220	1.454	1.090	131	......	....	109	....	86	92	....
28	β-Bromostyrene	221	....	....	....	217	115	91	....	....	....	....
29	n-Dodecyl bromide (Lauryl bromide)	130^6	1.458	1.038	....	......	....	108	....	....	....	....
30	n-Tetradecyl bromide	179^{20}	1.460	1.017	....	......	....	....	....	94	104	m.p. 5

* Derivative data given in order: m.p., crystal color, solvent from which crystallized.

TABLE V. ORGANIC DERIVATIVES OF HALIDES

A) Alkyl and cycloalkyl halides 2. Bromides
b) Solids (Listed in order of increasing m.p.)*

No.	Name	Melting point, °C	Boiling point, °C	S-Alkyl thiuronium picrate	1-Naphthyl amide	Anilide	Alkyl mercuric halide	Picrate of 2-naphthyl ether	2,4-Dinitrophenyl thioether	2,4-Dinitrophenyl sulfone	Miscellaneous
1	*n*-Hexadecyl bromide (Cetyl bromide)	14	201^9	155; 137	......	......	101–2	......	95	105	n_D^{20}: 1.462; D_4^{20}: 1.001
2	**2-Bromobenzyl bromide**	31	......	222	......	......	......	......	......	......	CrO$_3$ → 2-bromobenzoic acid, 150
3	**3-Bromobenzyl bromide**	41	......	205	......	......	......	......	......	......	CrO$_3$ → 3-bromobenzoic acid, 155
4	**2-Nitrobenzyl bromide**	46–7	......	......	......	......	......	......	......	......	Oxid. → 2-nitrobenzoic acid, 146–8
5	**4-Chlorobenzyl bromide**	51	......	194	......	......	......	......	......	......	CrO$_3$ → 4-chlorobenzoic acid, 242
6	**3-Nitrobenzyl bromide**	58–9	......	......	......	......	......	......	......	......	Oxid. → 3-nitrobenzoic acid, 141
7	**4-Bromobenzyl bromide**	62	......	219	......	......	......	......	......	......	CrO$_3$ → 4-bromobenzoic acid, 251
8	**4-Nitrobenzyl bromide**	99	......	......	......	......	......	......	......	......	Oxid. → 4-nitrobenzoic acid, 240

*Derivative data given in order: m.p., crystal color, solvent from which crystallized.

TABLE V. ORGANIC DERIVATIVES OF HALIDES
A) Alkyl and cycloalkyl halides 3. Iodides
a) Liquids (Listed in order of increasing atmospheric b.p.)*

No.	Name	Boiling point, °C	n_D^{20}	D_4^{20}	S-Alkyl thiuronium picrate	1-Naph-thyl amide	Anilide	Alkyl mercuric halide	Picrate of 2-naphthyl ether	2,4-Dinitro-phenyl thioether	2,4-Dinitro-phenyl sulfone	Miscellaneous
1	Methyl iodide	43	1.532	2.282	224	160	114	152; 145	117	128	185; 189	....
2	Vinyl iodide	56	....	....	....	....	104	....	....	....	....	....
3	Ethyl iodide	72	1.514	1.940	188	126	104	186; 182	104	115	156; 160	....
4	Isopropyl iodide	90	1.499	1.703	196; 148		103		92	95	140	....
5	n-Propyl iodide	102–3	1.505	1.743	181; 176	121	92	113	75	84	126	
6	Allyl iodide	103	1.578	1.777	155	121	114	112	99	....	....	
7	tert-Butyl iodide	103; 98	....	....	188	147	128	....	....	....	....	
8	sec-Butyl iodide	120	1.499	1.592	190; 166	129	108	....	85	66	120	
9	Isobutyl iodide	120	1.496	1.602	174; 167	125	109	72	84	76	105	
10	tert-Amyl iodide	128	....	1.479	....	138	92	....	....	....	....	
11	n-Butyl iodide	130	1.499	1.616	180; 177	112; 110	63	117	67	66	92	
12	2-Pentyl iodide	142	1.496	1.510	....	....	93	....	....	....	....	
13	3-Pentyl iodide	142	1.497	1.511	....	....	124	....	....	....	....	
14	Isoamyl iodide	148	1.493	1.503	179; 173	111	108	122	94	80	124	
15	n-Amyl iodide (n-Pentyl iodide)	155	1.496	1.512	154	112	96	110	67	80	83	....
16	Cyclopentyl iodide	166–7	1.5447	1.7096	....	....	....	....	....	....	....	
17	Cyclohexyl iodide	179, sl. d.	....	1.626^{15}_{15}	....	188	146	....	....	....	....	
18	n-Hexyl iodide	179	1.493	1.437	157	106	69	110	....	74	97	....
19	n-Heptyl iodide	204	1.490	1.373	142	95	57	103	....	82	101	....
20	n-Nonyl iodide	220	....	....	131	....	......	......	....	86	92	....
21	n-Octyl iodide	225–6	1.489	1.330	134	....	......	......	....	78	98	....

*Derivative data given in order: m.p., crystal color, solvent from which crystallized.

TABLE V. ORGANIC DERIVATIVES OF HALIDES

A) Alkyl and cycloalkyl halides 3. Iodides

b) Solids (Listed in order of increasing m.p.)*

No.	Name	Melting point, °C	Boiling point, °C	S-Alkyl thiuronium picrate	1-Naph-thyl amide	Anilide	Alkyl mercuric halide	Picrate of 2-naphthyl ether	2,4-Dinitro-phenyl thioether	2,4-Dinitro-phenyl sulfone	Miscellaneous
1	*n*-**Hexadecyl iodide** (Cetyl iodide).........	22	......	155; 137	......	......	82	....	95	105	....
2	**Benzyl iodide**.........................	24	......	188	166	117		123	130	178; 182	....

*Derivative data given in order: m.p., crystal color, solvent from which crystallized.

61

TABLE V. ORGANIC DERIVATIVES OF HALIDES
B) Dihalides and polyhalides (non-aromatic)
1. Fluorides (Listed in order of increasing atmospheric b.p.)*

No.	Name	Boiling point, °C	n_D^{20}	D_4^{20}	Miscellaneous
1	**Perfluorocyclopentane**	22	....	1.648_4^{25}	m.p. 10
2	**1,3-Difluoropropane**	41–2	1.3190^{26}	1.0057_4^{25}	....
3	**Perfluorocyclohexane**	50	....	....	m.p. 49
4	**Perfluoro-*n*-hexane**	57	1.2515^{22}	1.6995_4^{25}	....
5	**Perfluoro-2-methylpentane**	58	1.2564^{22}	1.7326	....
6	**Perfluoro-*n*-heptane**	84	1.2770	1.801_4^{25}	....
7	**Perfluoro-*n*-nonane**	127	1.2865^{25}	1.860_4^{25}	....
8	**Perfluoro-*n*-decane**	150	1.2890^{25}	1.873_4^{25}	m.p. 36
9	**Perfluoro-*n*-undecane** (Perfluoro-*n*-hendecane)	161	1.2960^{25}	1.919_4^{25}	m.p. 57

*Derivative data given in order: m.p., crystal color, solvent from which crystallized.

62

TABLE V. ORGANIC DERIVATIVES OF HALIDES
B) Dihalides and polyhalides (non-aromatic)
2. Chlorides a) Liquids (Listed in order of increasing atmospheric b.p.)*

No.	Name	Boiling point, °C	n_D^{20}	D_4^{20}	Miscellaneous
1	Dichloromethane (Methylene chloride)	41	1.4237	1.336	6-Nitro-2-mercaptobenzothiazole deriv., 232–3; Di-(2-naphthyl) ether, 133; S-Alkyl *bis*-(thiuronium picrate), 267
2	*trans*-1,2-Dichloroethylene	48	1.452	1.2569	Br$_2 \rightarrow$ dibromo deriv., 190–5
3	1,1-Dichloroethane	57	1.4164	1.175	1,1-Di-(1-naphthyl)ether, 117
4	*cis*-1,2-Dichloroethylene	60	1.4428[25]	1.282	Br$_2 \rightarrow$ dibromo deriv., 190–5
5	Chloroform..	61	1.446	1.489	Gives carbylamine test with primary amines
6	2,2-Dichloropropane	70	1.4117	1.093	....
7	1,1,1-Trichloroethane	74	1.4380	1.349	....
8	Carbon tetrachloride	77	1.4630	1.595	....
9	Ethylene dichloride (1,2-Dichloroethane)	84	1.4443	1.256	1,2-Di-(2-naphthyl) ether, 217
10	1,1,2-Trichloroethylene	87	1.4773	1.464	HgO + NaOEt + KCN in al. shaken 1 hr. at 40–60 $\rightarrow$ mercury *bis*-(trichloroethylenide), Hg(—CCl=CCl$_2$)$_2$, 83, eth.
11	1,2-Dichloropropane	96	1.4388	1.155	1,2-Di-(2-naphthyl) ether, 152; 1,2-Diphenyl ether, 32
12	1-Bromo-2-chloroethane	106–7	....	....	6-Nitro-2-mercaptobenzothiazole deriv., 202–3; Di-(2-naphthyl)ether, 217
13	1,1,2-Trichloroethane	114	1.4707	1.443	....
14	1,1,2,2-Tetrachloroethylene (Perchloroethylene)	121	1.5055	1.623	With paraformaldehyde + conc. H$_2$SO$_4 \rightarrow \alpha,\alpha$-dichloro-$\beta$-hydroxypropionic acid, 88–9
15	1,2-Dichlorobutane	123–4	1.440	....	6-Nitro-2-mercaptobenzothiazole deriv., 164–5
16	1,3-Dichloropropane	125	1.449	1.189$_4^{18}$; 1.177$_4^{25}$	1,3-Di-(1-naphthyl) ether, 103–4; 1,3-Di-(2-naphthyl) ether, 148–9; 1,3-Diphenyl ether, 60
17	1,3-Dichloro-2-methylpropane	135–6	1.4627[19]	1.131$_{20}^{20}$	....
18	1-Bromo-3-chloropropane	143–4	1.4861	1.594	1,3-Di-(1-naphthyl) ether, 103–4; 1,3-Di-(2-naphthyl) ether, 148–9; 1,3-Diphenyl ether, 60
19	1,1,2,2-Tetrachloroethane...........................	146	1.4942	1.600	....
20	1,2,3-Trichloropropane	158	1.4585	1.417	....
21	Pentachloroethane.................................	161	1.504	1.681	
22	Benzalchloride	207; 214	1.5515	1.295[16]	Oxid. $\rightarrow$ benzoic acid, 122; Hydrolysis $\rightarrow$ benzaldehyde, 2,4-Dinitrophenylhydrazone 237, Semicarbazone, 222
23	Benzotrichloride....................................	221	....	1.374[17]	Hydrolysis $\rightarrow$ benzoic acid, 122
24	2-Chlorobenzalchloride (2-Chlorobenzylidene chloride) ..	228–9	1.5670[16]	1.399$_{15}^{15}$	Oxid. $\rightarrow$ 2-chlorobenzoic acid, 141; Hydrolysis $\rightarrow$ 2-chlorobenzaldehyde, 2,4-dinitrophenylhydrazone, 213; 209
25	3-Chlorobenzalchoride (3-Chlorobenzylidene chloride)...	237–40	....	....	Oxid. $\rightarrow$ 3-chlorobenzoic acid, 158; Hydrolysis $\rightarrow$ 3-chlorobenzaldehyde, 2,4-dinitrophenylhydrazone, 256; 248
26	4-Chlorobenzalchloride (4-Chlorobenzylidene chloride) ..	237	....	....	Oxid. $\rightarrow$ 4-chlorobenzoic acid, 240; Hydrolysis $\rightarrow$ 4-chlorobenzaldehyde, 47, 2,4-dinitrophenylhydrazone, , 265

* Derivative data given in order: m.p., crystal color, solvent from which crystallized.

TABLE V. ORGANIC DERIVATIVES OF HALIDES
B) Dihalides and polyhalides (non-aromatic) 2. Chlorides
b) Solids (Listed in order of increasing m.p.)*

No.	Name	Melting point, °C	Boiling point, °C	Miscellaneous
1	**3,4-Dichlorobenzotrichloride**	26	. . . .	Hydrolysis → 3,4-Dichlorobenzoic acid, 202
2	**DDT** (2,2-Bis-(4-chlorophenyl)-1,1,1-trichloroethane). . .	108	260	Heating with Cl$_2$ + trace PCl$_3$ in CCl$_4$ → 1,1,1-tetrachloro deriv., 91–2; Nitration → nitro deriv., 148; AlCl$_3$ + benzene → 1,1,2,2-tetraphenylethane, 211
3	**γ-Benzene hexachloride** (Gammexane, 666).	112	. . . .	. . . .
4	**α-Benzene hexachloride**	157	288	Heat above m.p. → HCl + 1,2,4-trichlorobenzene, 17, b.p. 213, mononitro deriv., 56, dinitro, 103
5	**Hexachloroethane**	187 subl.	185	. . . .
6	**β-Benzene hexachloride**	310	. . . .	Unreactive to boiling pyridine; Unattacked by boiling HNO$_3$ or H$_2$SO$_4$

*Derivative data given in order: m.p., crystal color, solvent from which crystallized.

TABLE V. ORGANIC DERIVATIVES OF HALIDES
B) Dihalides and polyhalides (non-aromatic)
3. Bromides a) Liquids (Listed in order of increasing atmospheric b.p.)*

No.	Name	Boiling point, °C	n_D^{20}	D_4^{20}	Miscellaneous
1	**Dibromomethane** (Methylene bromide)	98–9	1.538	2.496	6-Nitro-2-mercaptobenzothiazole deriv., 232–3; S-Alkyl *bis*-(thiuronium picrate), 267
2	**1,1-Dibromoethane**	112	1.5128	2.055	6-Nitro-2-mercaptobenzothiazole deriv., 145–6; 1,1-Di-(1-naphthyl) ether, 117
3	**1,2-Dibromoethane**	132	1.5379	2.179	m.p. 10; 6-Nitro-2-mercaptobenzothiazole deriv., 201–2; 1,2-Di-(2-naphthyl) ether, 217
4	**DL-1,2-Dibromopropane**	141–2	1.5203	1.933	6-Nitro-2-mercaptobenzothiazole, 194–5; 1,2-Di-(2-naphthyl) ether, 152; 1,2-Diphenyl ether, 32
5	**1,2-Dibromo-2-methylpropane**	149	1.512	1.783	. . . .
6	**1,2-Dibromo-1-butene**	150	. . . . . .	1.887	. . . .
7	**Bromoform**	150–1	1.598	2.890[0]	m.p. 8
8	**1,3-Dibromopropene**	156	1.538[25]	2.097[0]	. . . .
9	**1,1-Dibromo-2-methylpropene**	156–7	1.530	1.866_{20}^{20}	. . . .
10	**2,3-Dibromobutane**	157	1.515	1.792	. . . .
11	**1,2-Dibromobutane**	166	. . . . . .	1.820	6-Nitro-2-mercaptobenzothiazole deriv., 164–5
12	**1,3-Dibromopropane**	167–8	1.523	1.982	1,3-Di-(1-naphthyl) ether, 103–4; 1,3-Di-(2-naphthyl) ether, 148–9; 1,3-Diphenyl ether, 60
13	**1,3-Dibromo-2-butene**	168–9	1.548	1.877	. . . .
14	**1,3-Dibromobutane**	174	1.507	1.820[0]	. . . .
15	**1,1,2-Tribromoethane**	189	1.5933	2.6211	. . . .
16	**1,4-Dibromobutane**	197–8	. . . . . .	1.847[0]	*p*-toluidine (3 moles) $\xrightarrow{\text{heat}}$ N-4-tolylpyrrolidine, 42, dil. al.
17	**1,2,3-Tribromopropane**	220	1.582	2.402	. . . .
18	**1,5-Dibromopentane**	221	1.514[15]	1.694_4^{25}	6-Nitro-2-mercaptobenzothiazole deriv., 132–3; S-Alkyl *bis*-(thiuronium picrate), 247
19	**1,1,2,2-Tetrabromoethane**	243–4	1.638	2.967	. . . .
20	**1,8-Dibromooctane**	270–2	1.501[15]	1.468[15]	m.p. 15–6; S-Alkyl *bis*-(thiuronium picrate), 214
21	**1,9-Dibromononane**	285–8	. . . . . .	1.415[15]	m.p. −2.5; S-Alkyl *bis*-(thiuronium picrate), 193

*Derivative data given in order: m.p., crystal color, solvent from which crystallized.

TABLE V. ORGANIC DERIVATIVES OF HALIDES
B) Dihalides and polyhalides (non-aromatic)
3. Bromides b) Solids (Listed in order of increasing m.p.)*

No.	Name	Melting point, °C	Boiling point, °C	Miscellaneous
1	**1,7-Dibromoheptane**	42	263	S-Alkyl *bis*-(thiuronium picrate), 208
2	**Carbon tetrabromide**	92	190	. . . .

*Derivative data given in order: m.p., crystal color, solvent from which crystallized.

TABLE V. ORGANIC DERIVATIVES OF HALIDES
B) Dihalides and polyhalides (non-aromatic)
4. Iodides a) Liquids (Listed in order of increasing atmospheric b.p.)*

No.	Name	Boiling point, °C	n_D^{20}	D_4^{20}	Miscellaneous
1	**Di-iodomethane** (Methylene iodide)	181	1.7425	3.325	6-Nitro-2-mercaptobenzothiazole deriv., 232–3; Di-(2-naphthyl) ether, 133; S-Alkyl *bis*-(thiuronium picrate), 267
2	**1,3-Di-iodopropane**	224	1.6423	2.5755	1,3-Di-(1-naphthyl) ether, 103–4; 1,3-Di-(2-naphthyl) ether, 148–9; 1,3-Diphenyl ether, 60

* Derivative data given in order: m.p., crystal color, solvent from which crystallized.

TABLE V. ORGANIC DERIVATIVES OF HALIDES
B) Dihalides and polyhalides (non-aromatic)
4. Iodides b) Solids (Listed in order of increasing m.p.)*

No.	Name	Melting point, °C	Boiling point, °C	Miscellaneous
1	1,2-Di-iodoethane	81	. . . . . .	6-Nitro-2-mercaptobenzothiazole deriv., 202–3; 1,2-Di-(2-naphthyl) ether, 217
2	Iodoform	119	. . . . . .	Comp. with quinoline, 65

*Derivative data given in order: m.p., crystal color, solvent from which crystallized.

TABLE V. ORGANIC DERIVATIVES OF HALIDES
C) Aryl halides 1. Fluorides (Listed in order of increasing atmospheric b.p.)*

No.	Name	Boiling point, °C	Melting point, °C	n_D^{20}	D_4^{20}	Nitro derivative		Sulfonamide		Miscellaneous
						M.P.	Position of nitro groups	M.P.	Position of sulfona-mide group	
1	**1,3-Difluorobenzene**	82	.....	1.4404^{18}	1.1473_4^{25}	74	1,3	.....	....	....
2	**Fluorobenzene**	87	.....	1.466	1.024	.....	....	125	4	....
3	**1,4-Difluorobenzene**	88	.....	1.4423^{18}	1.1632_4^{25}	.....	....	.....	....	Boiling with NaOH → 4-fluorophenol, 48, b.p. 186–8, n_D^{56}: 1.5010, D^{56}: 1.1889
4	**1,2-Difluorobenzene**	92	−34	1.4451^{18}	1.1496_4^{25}	.....	....	.....	....	....
5	**2-Fluorotoluene**	114	.....	....	....	.....	....	105	5	Oxid. → 2-fluorobenzoic acid, 127
6	**3-Fluorotoluene**	116	.....	....	....	.....	....	174	6	Oxid. → 3-fluorobenzoic acid, 124
7	**4-Fluorotoluene**	117	.....	1.496	0.998	.....	....	141	2	Oxid. → 4-fluorobenzoic acid, 182
8	**1-Fluoronaphthalene**	214	.....	1.594	1.134	.....	....	.....	....	Picrate, 113
9	**2-Fluoronaphthalene**	....	60	....	....	.....	....	.....	....	Picrate, 101

*Derivative data given in order: m.p., crystal color, solvent from which crystallized.

TABLE V. ORGANIC DERIVATIVES OF HALIDES

C) Aryl halides 2. Chlorides a) Liquids (Listed in order of increasing atmospheric b.p.)*

No.	Name	Boiling point, °C	Melting point, °C	n_D^{20}	D_4^{20}	Nitro derivative M.P.	Nitro derivative Position of nitro groups	Sulfonamide M.P.	Sulfonamide Position of sulfona-mide group	Miscellaneous
1	Chlorobenzene..........	132	......	1.525	1.107	52	2,4	144	4	2,4-Dinitrobenzenesulfenyl chloride adduct, 123–4
2	2-Chlorotoluene	159	......	1.524	1.082	63	3,5	128	5	Oxid. → 2-chlorobenzoic acid, 141
3	3-Chlorotoluene	162	......	1.521	1.072	91	4,6	185	6	Oxid. → 3-chlorobenzoic acid, 158
4	4-Chlorotoluene	162	7	1.521	1.071	38	2	143	2	Oxid. → 4-chlorobenzoic acid, 240
5	1,3-Dichlorobenzene.....	173	......	1.546	1.288	103	4,6	182	6	....
6	1-Chloro-2-ethylbenzene..	178; 180	......	1.5218	1.057	......	......	......	......	Oxid. → 2-chlorobenzoic acid, 141
7	1,2-Dichlorobenzene.....	179	......	1.552	1.305	110	4,5	135; 140	4	....
8	1-Chloro-3-ethylbenzene..	184	......	1.5199	1.053	......	......	......	......	Oxid. → 3-chlorobenzoic acid, 158
9	1-Chloro-4-ethylbenzene..	184; 180–1	......	1.5175	1.045	......	......	......	......	Oxid. → 4-chlorobenzoic acid, 240
10	2-Chloro-1,4-dimethyl-benzene	184–5	2	......	1.059^{20}_{20}	77; 101	5; 5,6	155	5'	Sulfonyl chloride, 50
11	1-Chloro-2-vinylbenzene (o-Chlorostyrene)......	189	......	1.5649	1.100					Polymerizes on heating with benzoyl peroxide
12	1-Chloro-2,3-dimethyl-benzene	190	......							Oxid. → 3-chloro-2-methylbenzoic acid, 159
13	1-Chloro-2-isopropyl-benzene	191	......	1.5168	1.0341					Oxid. → 2-chlorobenzoic acid, 141
14	1-Chloro-2,4-dimethyl-benzene	192; 187	......	1.5230^{25}	1.0598^{20}_{20}	42	6	195	6	Oxid. $\xrightarrow{CrO_3/H_2SO_4}$ 4-chloro-3-methylbenzoic acid, 209–10; Oxid. $\xrightarrow{aq.\ KMnO_4}$ 4-chloroisophthalic acid, 294–5
15	1-Chloro-4-vinylbenzene (p-Chlorostyrene)......	192	......	1.5660	1.0868					Polymerizes on heating with peroxide
16	1-Chloro-3,4-dimethyl-benzene	194–5	−6	......	1.069^{15}_{15}	63	5	207	5	$Cl_2 \xrightarrow{Fe}$ 1,2-dichloro-4,5-dimethyl-benzene, 76
17	1-Chloro-4-isopropyl-benzene (p-Chloro-cumene).............	198	......	1.5117	1.0208	......	......	91	....	Oxid. → 4-chlorobenzoic acid, 240
18	2,6-Dichlorotoluene	199	......	1.5510	1.2686	50; 121	3; 3,5			Chlorosulfonic acid in chl. → 3-sulfonyl chloride, 54–6; 60; Oxid. → 2,6-di-chlorobenzoic acid, 139
19	2,5-Dichlorotoluene	199	4–5	......	1.2535^{20}_{20}	50–1; 100–1	4; 4,6	......	....	Oxid. $\xrightarrow{dil.\ HNO_3}$ 2,5-dichlorobenzoic acid, 154
20	2,4-Dichlorotoluene	200	......	1.549	1.249	104	3,5	......	....	Oxid. → 2,4-dichlorobenzoic acid, 164
21	3,5-Dichlorotoluene	201	......	......	....	61–2; 99–100	2; 2,6	168–9	2	Oxid. → 3,5-dichlorobenzoic acid, 188
22	2-Chloro-1,3,5-trimethyl-benzene	204–6	......	1.5212^{30}	1.0337^{30}	178	4,6	165–6	....	Oxid. $\xrightarrow{aq.\ KMnO_4}$ 2-chlorobenzene tricarboxylic acid, 285 (anh.), 278 (hyd.)
23	2,3-Dichlorotoluene	207	......	1.5511		51; 71–2	4; 4,6			Oxid. $\xrightarrow{alk.\ KMnO_4}$ 2,3-dichloro-benzoic acid, 163
24	3,4-Dichlorotoluene	209	......	1.5471	1.2526	63; 91–2	6; 2,6	......	......	Oxid. → 3,4-dichlorobenzoic acid, 206
25	1,2,4-Trichlorobenzene...	213	17	......	....	56; 103	5; 3,5	>200	......	Sulfonyl chloride, 31–4
26	2-Chloro-4-isopropyl-1-methylbenzene (2-Chloro-p-cymene)......	217	......	1.5178^{17}	1.015^{17}_4	109–10	5,6	......	......	Boiling with dil. HNO_3 → 3-chloro-4-methylbenzoic acid, 196
27	3-Chloro-4-isopropyl-1-methylbenzene (3-Chloro-p-cymene)......	217	......	1.5179^{18}	1.018^{18}_4	102–3; 106	2,6	......		....
28	1-Chloronaphthalene	259	......	1.633	1.191	180	4,5	......	......	Picrate, 137
29	3-Chlorobiphenyl	284–5	16	......	....	202–3	4,4'	......	......	Oxid. → 3-chlorobenzoic acid, 158; 155

*Derivative data given in order: m.p., crystal color, solvent from which crystallized.

No.	Name	Melting point, °C	Boiling point, °C	Nitro derivative M.P.	Position of nitro groups	Sulfonamide M.P.	Position of sulfonamide group	Miscellaneous
1	2-Chlorobenzotrichloride	29	283	....	....	....	....	Hydrolysis → 2-chlorobenzoic acid, 142
2	2,4,6-Trichlorotoluene..............	33–4; 38	....	54;50; 178–80	3; 3,5	....	....	Oxid. → 2,4,6-trichlorobenzoic acid, 160–1
3	2-Chlorobiphenyl	34	273	....	....	....	....	Oxid. → 2-chlorobenzoic acid, 141
4	1,2-Dichloronaphthalene	35	296	169	*di*	....	....	n_D^{48}: 1.6337; D_4^{48}: 1.3147; Oxid. $\xrightarrow{\text{CrO}_3/\text{ac. a.}}$ 5,6-dichloro-1,4-naphthoquinone, 181
5	2,3,4-Trichlorotoluene..............	41	231[761]	60; 140–1	5 or 6; 5,6	....	....	Oxid. → 2,3,4-trichlorobenzoic acid, 186–7
6	1,2,3,4-Tetrachlorobenzene	44–5	254	63–5; 151	5; 5,6	....	....	....
7	3,4,5-Trichlorotoluene..............	44–5	245[768]	81–2; 163–4	2; 2,6	....	....	Oxid. → 3,4,5-trichlorobenzoic acid, 203; $\text{Cl}_2 \xrightarrow{\text{Al/Hg}}$ 2,3,4,5-tetrachlorotoluene, 97–8
8	2,3,5-Trichlorotoluene..............	45–6	232	58–9; 149–50	4 or 6; 4,6	....	....	Oxid. $\xrightarrow{\text{dil. HNO}_3}$ 2,3,5-trichlorobenzoic acid, 162
9	1,6-Dichloronaphthalene	48	....	119	4	216	4	....
10	1,2,3,5-Tetrachlorobenzene	50–1	246	40–1; 161–2	4; 4,6	....	....	....
11	1,2,3-Trichlorobenzene	52–3	218–9	56; 92–3	4; 4,6	226–30	4	Sulfonyl chloride, 65
12	1,4-Dichlorobenzene	53	173	54	2	180; 186	2	....
13	4,4'-Dichlorodiphenylmethane	55	337	198–9	3,3'	....	....	Oxid. $\xrightarrow{\text{CrO}_3/\text{ac. a.}}$ 4,4'-dichlorobenzophenone, 145
14	2-Chloronaphthalene	56; 61	265	175	1,8	126	....	Picrate, 81
15	2,2'-Dichlorobiphenyl	60	....	203–5	5,5'	....	....	....
16	1,3-Dichloronaphthalene	61	291[775]	150 and 158	*di*	....	....	Oxid. $\xrightarrow{\text{dil. HNO}_3}$ phthalic acid, 200–6
17	1,3,5-Trichlorobenzene	63	208	68	2	210–2	2	Sulfonyl chloride, 35–40
18	1,7-Dichloronaphthalene	63–4	286	138–9	....	226	4	Sulfonyl chloride, 118
19	1-Bromo-4-chlorobenzene	67	197	72	2	....	....	....
20	1,4-Dichloronaphthalene	68	286[740]	92	8	244	6	Oxid. $\xrightarrow{\text{CrO}_3/\text{ac. a.}}$ 5,8-dichloro-1,4-naphthoquinone, 173–4; Boiling $\text{HNO}_3(D = 1.3) →$ 3,6-dichlorophthalic acid, 194; 185
21	2,5-Dichloro-1,4-dimethylbenzene (2,5-Dichloro-*p*-xylene)	68	224	....	....	....	....	Oxid. → 2,5-dichloroterephthalic acid, 306
22	4-Chlorobiphenyl	77	293	....	....	....	....	Oxid. → 4-chlorobenzoic acid, 240
23	2,4,5-Trichlorotoluene..............	82	230[715]	89–90; 226–7	3; 3,6	....	....	Oxid. → 2,4,5-trichlorobenzoic acid, 168
24	Pentachlorobenzene.................	86; 84	276	143; 146	6	....	....	....
25	1,8-Dichloronaphthalene	89	....	....	....	228	4	Sulfonyl chloride, 141
26	1,5-Dichloronaphthalene	107	....	142	8	204	3	Oxid. $\xrightarrow{\text{CrO}_3/\text{ac. a.}}$ 3-chlorophthalic acid, 185–7; Picrate, 87
27	2,7-Dichloronaphthalene	114–5	....	141–2	*mono*	218	3	Oxid. $\xrightarrow{\text{dil. HNO}_3}$ 4-chlorophthalic acid, 157
28	2,6-Dichloronaphthalene	135–6	285	....	....	269	4	Sulfonyl chloride, 136; Cl_2 in chl. → 1,2,6-trichloronaphthalene, 92; Oxid. $\xrightarrow{\text{CrO}_3/\text{ac. a.}}$ 1,4-naphthoquinone deriv., 148–9
29	1,2,4,5-Tetrachlorobenzene	140	245	99; 232	3; 3,6	....	....	Chlorosulfonic acid → hexachlorobenzene, 229
30	4,4'-Dichlorobiphenyl	149	....	....	....	....	....	Oxid. → 4-chlorobenzoic acid, 240

*Derivative data given in order: m.p., crystal color, solvent from which crystallized.

No.	Name	Melting point, °C	Boiling point, °C	Nitro derivative		Sulfonamide		Miscellaneous
				M.P.	Position of nitro groups	M.P.	Position of sulfona-mide group	
31	**5,6,7,8-Tetrachlorotetralin**	174	180²⁶	....	....	....	....	Br₂ in CS₂ → 1,2-dibromo-5,6,7,8-tetra-chloronaphthalene, 142
32	**1,2,3,4-Tetrachlorotetralin**	182; 187	....	....	....	....	....	Oxid. $\xrightarrow{CrO_3/ac.\ a.}$ 2,4-dichloro-1-naphthol, 106–7; Boiling HNO₃ → phthalic acid, 200–6
33	**Octachloronaphthalene**	198; 200	442	....	....	....	....	Oxid. $\xrightarrow{fuming\ HNO_3}$ hexachloro-1,4-naphthoquinone, 222; SbCl₅ in CCl₄ → cherry-red color
34	**9,10-Dichloroanthracene** (*meso*-Di-chloroanthracene)	209–10, yel.	....	....	....	279	2	Sulfonyl chloride, 221–5; Oxid. → 9,10-anthraquinone, 286; Maleic anh. adduct, 258–9
35	**Hexachlorobenzene**	229, subl.; 226	309	....	....	....	....	Boiling with fuming HNO₃ + conc. H₂SO₄ → tetrachloro-1,4-benzoquinone (chloroanil), 290

*Derivative data given in order: m.p., crystal color, solvent from which crystallized.

72

No.	Name	Boiling point, °C	Melting point, °C	n_D^{20}	D_4^{20}	Nitro derivative M.P.	Position of nitro groups	Sulfonamide M.P.	Position of sulfona-mide group	Miscellaneous
1	**Bromobenzene**............	156	......	1.560	1.494	70–2	2,4	166; 161	4	1-Naphthylamide, 161; 2,4-Dinitroben-zenesulfenyl chloride adduct, 140–1
2	**2-Bromotoluene**...........	182	......	......	1.425	82	3,5	146	5	Oxid. → 2-bromobenzoic acid, 150
3	**3-Bromotoluene**...........	184	......	......	1.410	103	4,6	168	6	Oxid. → 3-bromobenzoic acid, 155
4	**1-Bromo-2-ethylbenzene**......	199	......	1.5486	1.355	......	....	......	....	Oxid. → 2-bromobenzoic acid, 150
5	**1-Bromo-4-ethylbenzene**......	205	......	1.5448	1.342	......	....	......	....	Oxid. → 4-bromobenzoic acid, 251
6	**1-Bromo-2-vinylbenzene** (*o*-Bromostyrene)...........	210	......	1.5927	1.4160	......	....	......	....	Polymerizes on heating with benzoyl peroxide
7	**1-Bromo-2-isopropylbenzene** ..	210	......	1.5408	1.3020	......	....	......	....	Oxid. → 2-bromobenzoic acid, 150
8	**1-Bromo-4-vinylbenzene** (*p*-Bromostyrene)...........	212	......	1.5947	1.398	......	....	......	....	Polymerizes on heating with benzoyl peroxide; Oxid. → 4-bromobenzoic acid, 251
9	**1-Bromo-2,3-dimethylbenzene** .	217	......	......	......	......	....	......	....	Oxid. → 3-bromophthalic acid, 188
10	**1,3-Dibromobenzene**........	219	......	1.606	1.952	61	4	190	6	....
11	**1-Bromo-4-isopropylbenzene** ..	219	......	1.5361	1.2854	......	....	......	....	Oxid. → 4-bromobenzoic acid, 251
12	**1,2-Dibromobenzene**........	219	......	1.609	1.956	114	4,5	176	4	....
13	**2-Bromocymene**	234	......	......	1.267	97	....	......	....	Anilide, 143
14	**2,5-Dibromotoluene**	236	......	......	1.811	......	....	......	....	Oxid. → 2,5-dibromobenzoic acid, 157
15	**3,4-Dibromotoluene**	240	......	......	1.81	......	....	......	....	Oxid. → 3,4-dibromobenzoic acid, 235
16	**1-Bromonaphthalene**........	281	......	1.658	1.484	85	4	191–3	4	Picrate, 134; Carbonation of Grignard → 1-naphthoic acid, 162
17	**2-Bromobiphenyl**.......:...	297	......	......	......	......	....	......	....	Oxid. → 2-bromobenzoic acid, 150

*Derivative data given in order: m.p., crystal color, solvent from which crystallized.

No.	Name	Melting point, °C	Boiling point, °C	Nitro derivative		Sulfonamide		Miscellaneous
				M.P.	Position of nitro groups	M.P.	Position of sulfona-mide group	
1	4-Bromotoluene	28–9	184	......	....	......	....	Oxid. → 4-bromobenzoic acid, 251
2	2-Bromonaphthalene	59	281	......	....	208	8	Picrate, 86; 79; 2,4,7-Trinitrofluorenone adduct, 138–40
3	1,2-Dibromonaphthalene........	67	......	......	....	......	....	Oxid. → 3,4-dibromophthalic acid, 196
4	1,4-Dibromonaphthalene........	82	......	......	....	......	....	Oxid. → 3,6-dibromophthalic acid, 135
5	1,4-Dibromobenzene	89	219	84	2,5	195	2	....
6	4-Bromobiphenyl	89	310	......	....	......	....	Oxid. → 4-bromobenzoic acid, 251
7	1,3,5-Tribromobenzene	120	271	......	....	222	2	....
8	4,4'-Dibromobiphenyl	164	......	......	....	......	....	Oxid. → 4-bromobenzoic acid, 251
9	1,2,4,5-Tetrabromobenzene......	180	......	168	3	......	....	....

* Derivative data given in order: m.p., crystal color, solvent from which crystallized.

TABLE V. ORGANIC DERIVATIVES OF HALIDES
C) Aryl halides 4. Iodides a) Liquids (Listed in order of increasing atmospheric b.p.)*

No.	Name	Boiling point, °C	Melting point, °C	n_D^{20}	D_4^{20}	Nitro derivative		Sulfonamide		Miscellaneous
						M.P.	Position of nitro groups	M.P.	Position of sulfona-mide group	
1	Iodobenzene.................	188–7	......	1.620	1.831	171	4	......	....	Br₂ → 1-Bromo-4-iodobenzene, 91
2	3-Iodotoluene	204	......	.....	1.698	108	4,6	......	....	Oxid. → 3-iodobenzoic acid, 187
3	2-Iodotoluene	211	......	.....	1.698	103	6	......	....	Oxid. → 2-iodobenzoic acid, 162
4	1-Iodo-4-isopropylbenzene	236–8	......	.....	.....	.....	....	......	....	Cl₂ in chl. → dichloride (ArICl₂), 110
5	1-Iodonaphthalene	305	......	.....	.....	.....	....	......	....	Picrate, 128

*Derivative data given in order: m.p., crystal color, solvent from which crystallized.

No.	Name	Melting point, °C	Boiling point, °C	Nitro derivative		Sulfonamide		Miscellaneous
				M.P.	Position of nitro groups	M.P.	Position of sulfona-mide group	
1	**4-Iodotoluene**	35	211	. . . . . .	. . . .	. . . . . .	. . . .	HNO₃ at 200° → 4-iodobenzoic acid, 270
2	**1-Iodo-2,4,5-trimethylbenzene**	37	256–8	. . . . . .	. . . .	. . . . . .	. . . .	Cl₂ in chl. → dichloride (ArICl₂), 66
3	**1,3-Di-iodobenzene**	40	285	. . . . . .	. . . .	. . . . . .	. . . .	. . . .
4	**2-Iodonaphthalene**	55	309	. . . . . .	. . . .	. . . . . .	. . . .	Picrate, 95
5	**4-Iodobiphenyl**	114	320 d.	. . . . . .	. . . .	. . . . . .	. . . .	Cl₂ in chl. → dichloride (ArICl₂), 102
6	**1,4-Di-iodobenzene**	129	289	171	2,5	. . . . . .	. . . .	. . . .

*Derivative data given in order: m.p., crystal color, solvent from which crystallized.

EXPLANATIONS AND REFERENCES TO TABLE VI

Phenylurethane.

$$\text{ROH} \;+\; C_6H_5N{=}C{=}O \;\rightarrow\; C_6H_5NHCOOR$$

Phenylurethane
(Phenylcarbamate)

From the dry alcohol with phenylisocyanate without solvent.

For directions and examples see: Linstead, pp. 34–35; Shriner, p. 211; Vogel, p. 264; B. T. Dewey and N. F. Witt, *Ind. Eng. Chem., Anal. Ed.*, **12**, 459 (1940); **14**, 648 (1942).

From the dry alcohol with phenylisocyanate in petrol ether.

See: Wild, pp. 55–57.

1-Naphthylurethane (α-Naphthylcarbamate). *

$$\text{ROH} \;+\; 1\text{-}C_{10}H_7N{=}C{=}O \;\rightarrow\; 1\text{-}C_{10}H_7NHCOOR$$

1-Naphthylurethane
(α-Naphthylcarbamate)

From the dry alcohol with 1-naphthylisocyanate without solvent.

For directions and examples see: Cheronis, pp. 475–479; Linstead, pp. 34–35; Shriner, p. 211; Vogel, p. 264; V. T. Bickel and H. E. French, *J. Amer. Chem. Soc.*, **48**, 747 (1926); H. E. French and A. F. Wirtel, *J Amer. Chem. Soc.*, **48**, 1736 (1926).

From the dry alcohol with 1-naphthylisocyanate in petrol ether.

See: Cheronis, pp. 476–477; Wild, pp. 55–57.

p-Xenylurethane (4-Biphenylylurethane).

$$\text{ROH} \;+\; p\text{-}C_6H_5C_6H_4N{=}C{=}O \;\rightarrow\; p\text{-}C_6H_5C_6H_4NHCOOR$$

p-Xenylurethane
(4-Biphenylylcarbamate)

From the alcohol with *p*-xenylisocyanate in toluene.

For directions and examples see: G. T. Morgan and A. E. J. Pettet, *J. Chem. Soc.*, 1124 (1931); B. Witten and E. E. Reid, *J. Amer. Chem. Soc.*, **69**, 2470 (1947).

From the alcohol with *p*-xenylisocyanate in a benzene—petrol ether mixture.

See: M. J. van Gelderen, *Rec. Trav. chim.*, **52**, 969 (1933).

p-Nitrobenzoate. *

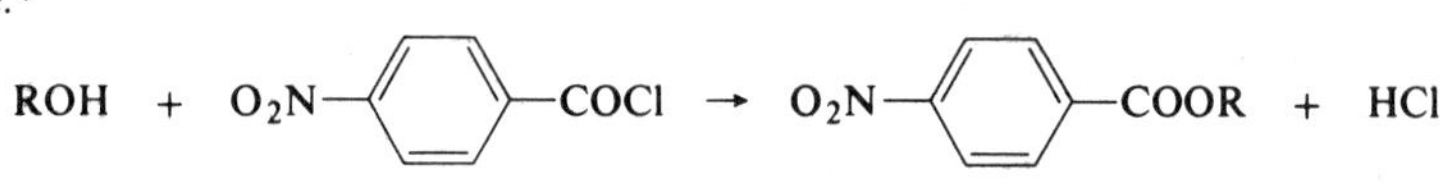

$$\text{ROH} \;+\; O_2N{-}\!\!\bigcirc\!\!{-}COCl \;\rightarrow\; O_2N{-}\!\!\bigcirc\!\!{-}COOR \;+\; HCl$$

p-Nitrobenzoate

From the alcohol in excess and *p*-nitrobenzoyl chloride.

For directions and examples see: Cheronis, pp. 467–469, 471; Shriner, p. 212; Vogel, p. 263; Wild, p. 52; M. D. Armstrong and J. E. Copenhaver, *J. Amer. Chem. Soc.*, **65**, 2252 (1943).

From an aqueous solution of the alcohol with *p*-nitrobenzoyl chloride in a ligroin-benzene mixture.

See: Cheronis, pp. 468–469, 472.

From the alcohol with *p*-nitrobenzoyl chloride in pyridine.

See: Shriner, p. 212; Wild, p. 52; L. F. King, *J. Amer. Chem. Soc.*, **61**, 2383 (1939).

From the alcohol with *p*-nitrobenzoyl chloride in aqueous sodium hydroxide.

See: Wild, p. 52.

From the alcohol with *p*-nitrobenzoyl chloride in an aqueous solution of sodium acetate and potassium hydroxide at low temperature.

See: Wild, p. 53; F. A. Menalda, *Rec. Trav. chim.*, **49**, 967 (1930); H. Henstock, *J. Chem. Soc.*, 216 (1933).

3,5-Dinitrobenzoate. *

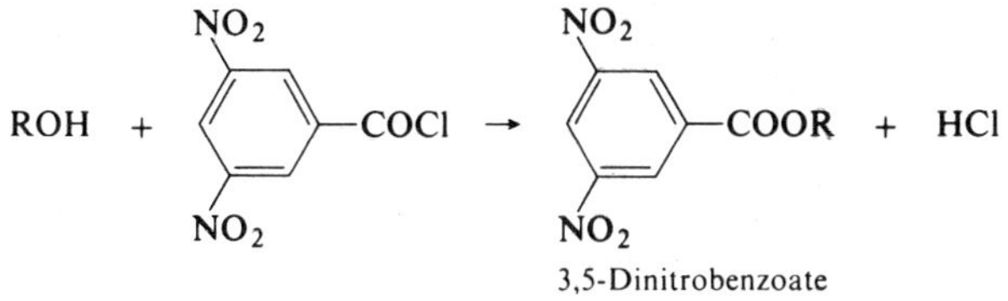

$$\text{ROH} \;+\; \underset{NO_2}{\overset{NO_2}{\bigcirc}}{-}COCl \;\rightarrow\; \underset{NO_2}{\overset{NO_2}{\bigcirc}}{-}COOR \;+\; HCl$$

3,5-Dinitrobenzoate

*Derivatives recommended for first trial.

WARNING: This is not an instruction manual. References should be consulted for the preparation of derivatives.

From the alcohol in excess with 3,5-dinitrobenzoyl chloride.

For directions and examples see: Cheronis, pp. 467–470; Shriner, pp. 212–213; Vogel, p. 262; G. B. Malone and E. E. Reid, *J. Amer. Chem. Soc.*, **51**, 3424 (1929).

From an aqueous solution of the alcohol with 3,5-dinitrobenzoyl chloride in a ligroin-benzene mixture.

See: Cheronis, pp. 468–469, 472.

From the alcohol with 3,5-dinitrobenzoyl chloride and pyridine in benzene.

See: Linstead, p. 34; Wild, p. 53; T. Reichstein, *Helv. chim. Acta*, **9**, 799 (1926); W. M. D. Bryant, *J. Amer. Chem. Soc.*, **54**, 3758 (1932).

From the alcohol with 3,5-dinitrobenzoyl chloride and a catalytic amount of pyridine in isopropyl or *n*-butyl ether.

See: Cheronis, pp. 469, 471.

From the alcohol with 3,5-dinitrobenzoyl chloride in pyridine.

See: Cheronis, p. 469; Shriner, pp. 212–213; Vogel, pp. 262–263.

From the alcohol with 3,5-dinitrobenzoyl chloride in aqueous potassium hydroxide.

See: Linstead, p. 34.

From the alcohol in aqueous sodium hydroxide and potassium acetate with 3,5-dinitrobenzoyl chloride in a benzene-ligroin mixture.

See: Wild, pp. 53–54; W. N. Lipscomb and R. H. Baker, *J. Amer. Chem. Soc.*, **64**, 179 (1942).

*Hydrogen phthalate.**

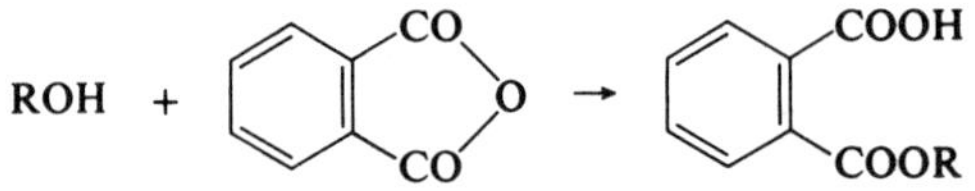

$$ROH \ + \ \text{(phthalic anhydride)} \ \rightarrow \ \text{(alkyl hydrogen phthalate)}$$

Alkyl hydrogen
phthalate

$$R_3COH \ + \ C_2H_5MgBr \ \rightarrow \ R_3COMgBr \ + \ C_2H_6$$

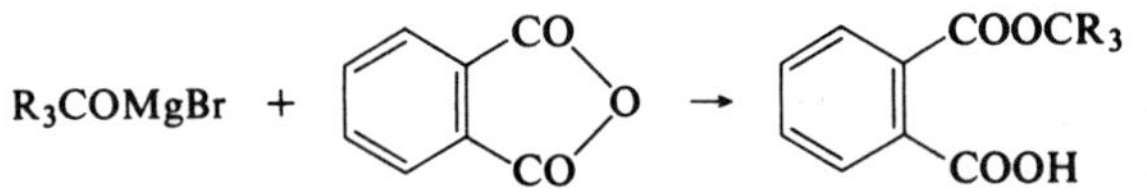

$$R_3COMgBr \ + \ \text{(phthalic anhydride)} \ \rightarrow \ \text{(tert-alkyl hydrogen phthalate)}$$

tert-Alkyl hydrogen
phthalate

From the alcohol with phthalic anhydride.

For directions and examples see: E. E. Reid, *J. Amer. Chem. Soc.*, **39**, 1250 (1917); J. F. Goggans and J. E. Copenhaver, *J. Amer. Chem. Soc.*, **61**, 2909 (1939).

From the alkoxymagnesium halide derived from a tertiary alcohol (prepared from the alcohol with ethylmagnesium bromide) with phthalic anhydride in ether or an ether-dioxan mixture.

See: W. A. Fessler and R. L. Shriner, *J. Amer. Chem. Soc.*, **58**, 1384 (1936).

*Hydrogen 3-nitrophthalate.**

$$ROH \ + \ \text{(3-nitrophthalic anhydride)} \ \rightarrow \ \text{(main product)} \ + \ \text{(trace)}$$

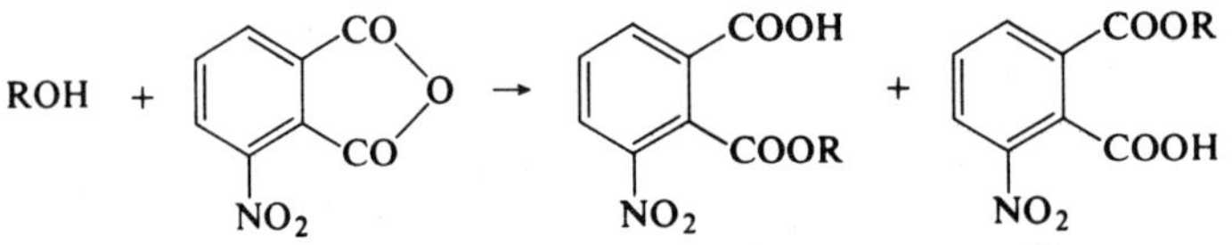

Main product   Trace

Hydrogen 3-nitrophthalates
(3-Nitrophthalic acid monoalkyl esters)

From the alcohol with 3-nitrophthalic anhydride.

For directions and examples see: Cheronis, pp. 473–474; Linstead, p. 35; Shriner, p. 213; Vogel, p. 265; Wild, p. 59; G. M. Dickinson, L. H. Crosson and J. E. Copenhaver, *J. Amer. Chem. Soc.*, **59**, 1094 (1937); B. H. Nicolet and J. Sacks, *J. Amer. Chem. Soc.*, **47**, 2348 (1925); A. J. Veraguth and H. Diehl, *J. Amer. Chem. Soc.*, **62**, 233 (1940).

From a high boiling alcohol with 3-nitrophthalic anhydride in toluene.

See: Linstead, p. 35; Shriner, p. 213; Vogel, p. 265; Wild, p. 59; G. M. Dickinson, L. H. Crosson and J. E. Copenhaver, *J. Amer. Chem. Soc.*, **59**, 1094 (1937).

*Derivatives recommended for first trial.
WARNING: This is not an instruction manual. References should be consulted for the preparation of derivatives.

Pseudosaccharin ether (Pseudosaccharin derivative).

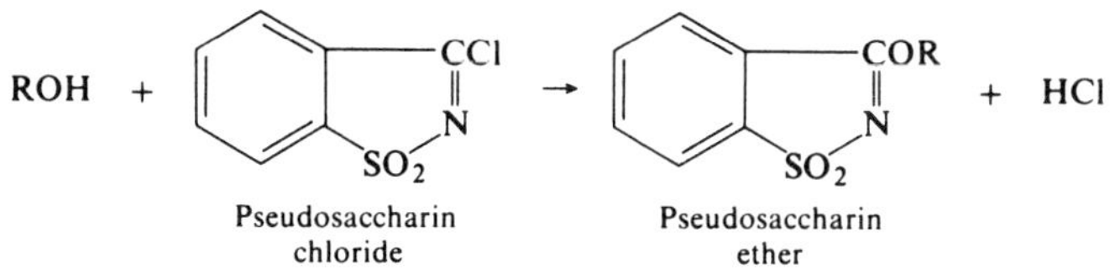

| Pseudosaccharin chloride | | Pseudosaccharin ether |

From the alcohol with pseudosaccharin chloride without solvent.
For directions and examples see: Vogel, p. 266; Wild, pp. 60–61; J. R. Meadoe and E. E. Reid, *J. Amer. Chem. Soc.*, **65**, 457 (1943).
From the alcohol with pseudosaccharin chloride in chloroform.
See: H. Böhme and H. Opper, *Z. Anal. Chem.*, **139**, 255 (1953).
From the alcohol with pseudosaccharin chloride and a catalytic amount of pyridine in chloroform.
See: Cheronis, p. 482; H. Böhme and H. Opper, *Z. Anal. Chem.*, **139**, 255 (1953).

Allophanate

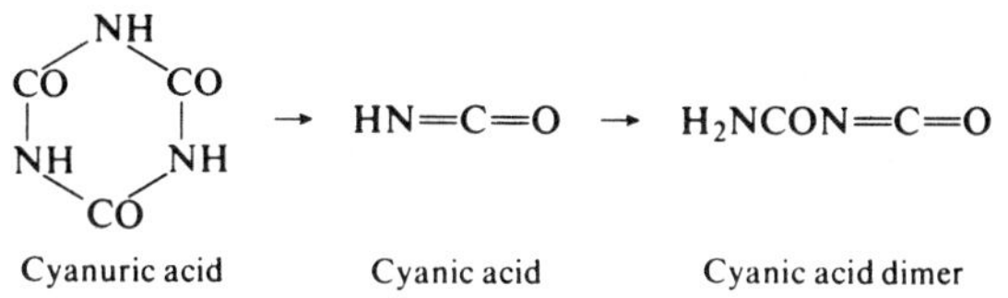

| Cyanuric acid | Cyanic acid | Cyanic acid dimer |

$$ROH + H_2NCON=C=O \rightarrow H_2NCONHCOOR$$
Allophanate

From the alcohol with cyanic acid (prepared from the depolymerization of cyanuric acid).
For directions and examples see: Linstead, p. 36; A. Behál, *Compt. rend.*, **168**, 945 (1919); M. A. Spielman, J. D. Barnes and W. J. Close, *J. Amer. Chem. Soc.*, **72**, 2520 (1950); H. W. Blohm and E. I. Becker, *J. Amer. Chem. Soc.*, **72**, 5342 (1950); *Chem. Revs.*, **51**, 471 (1952).
From the alcohol with sodium cyanate and dry hydrochloric acid in dioxane.
See: E. S. Lane, *J. Chem. Soc.*, 2764 (1951).

Benzoate. *

$$ROH + C_6H_5COCl \rightarrow C_6H_5COOR + HCl$$
Benzoate

Especially for polyhydric alcohols.
From the alcohol with benzoyl chloride.
For directions and examples see: Shriner, p. 212.
From the alcohol with benzoyl chloride in anhydrous pyridine.
See: Cheronis, pp. 481–482; Shriner, p. 212; Vogel, pp. 243, 447.
From the alcohol with benzoyl chloride in aqueous sodium hydroxide.
See: Vogel, p. 447.

Acetate.

$$ROH + (CH_3CO)_2O \rightarrow CH_3COOR + CH_3COOH$$
$$R_3COH + CH_3COCl \rightarrow CH_3COOCR_3 + HCl$$
Acetate

Especially for polyhydric alcohols.
From the alcohol with acetic anhydride and sodium acetate.
For directions and examples see: Linstead, pp. 35, 39; Shriner, p. 212.
From the alcohol with acetic anhydride in pyridine.
See: Shriner, p. 212.
From the alcohol (especially a tertiary alcohol) with acetyl chloride in the presence of magnesium.
See: A. Spassow, *Chem. Ber.*, **70B**, 1926 (1937).
NOTE: For additional information regarding directions and examples for the preparation of derivatives of polyhydric alcohols see explanations and references to Table XIX, p. 326.

*Derivatives recommended for first trial.
WARNING: This is not an instruction manual. References should be consulted for the preparation of derivatives.

TABLE VI. ORGANIC DERIVATIVES OF ALCOHOLS

a) Liquids (Listed in order of increasing atmospheric b.p.)*

No.	Name	Boiling point, °C	Melting point, °C	n_D^{20}	D_4^{20}	Phenyl-urethane	1-Naph-thyl-urethane	4-Nitro-benzoate	3,5-Dinitro-benzoate	Hydrogen 3-nitro-phthalate	Hydro-gen phthalate	Miscellaneous
1	**Methanol** (Methyl alcohol)............	64.65	f.p.: −97	1.3306^{15}	0.7915	47, al.	124, lgr.	96, dil. al.	108 (cor.), al.	153 (cor.)	82.5 (cor.)	Pseudosaccharin ether, 182 (cor.)
2	**Ethanol** (Ethyl alcohol) ..	78.32	f.p.: −117.3	1.3610	0.7894	52	79, lgr.	57, al.	93, al.	158 (cor.), w.	48	Pseudosaccharin ether, 219 (cor.)
3	**2-Propanol** (Isopropyl alcohol)............	82.4	−89.5	1.37927	0.78507	75–6, lt. pet.	106	110.5, lt. pet.; 108	123, pet. eth.	154 (cor.), w.	......	Pseudosaccharin ether, 137 (cor.)
4	*d,l*-**3-Buten-2-ol** (Methyl vinyl carbinol)	94–6	......	......	......	......	......	......	......	43–4	......	Allophanate, 152; Constant boil. mixt. with 21.76% w., b.p.: 80
5	**2-Propen-1-ol** (Allyl alcohol)............	97.1	......	1.41345	0.8540	70	108	28	49–50	124	......	....
6	**1-Propanol** (*n*-Propyl alcohol)............	97.1	......	1.38499	0.80359	57, pet.	80; 76	35, pet.	74, pet. eth.	145.5 (cor.), w.	54.1–4 (cor.), pet. eth.-bz. (9:1)	Pseudosaccharin ether, 124.5 (cor.)
7	**2-Butanol** (*d,l-sec*-Butyl alcohol; Ethyl methyl carbinol)............	99.5	......	1.39495^{25}	0.80692	64.5, pet.	97	25–6, dil. al.	76	131 (cor.)	59–60	Pseudosaccharin ether, 65.5 (cor.)
8	**2-Methyl-2-butanol** (*tert*-Amyl alcohol)	102.3	−8.55	1.4052	0.80889	42, pet. eth.	72	85	116; 117–8	......	......	......
9	**2-Fluoroethanol**	105	......	1.3633^{25}	....	......	128	......	......	......	......	......
10	**2-Methyl-1-propanol** (Iso-butyl alcohol)........	108.1	......	1.3939^{25}	0.80196	86, lgr.	104	69	87	180.5 (cor.)	65, pet. eth.	Pseudosaccharin ether, 100 (cor.)
11	**3-Buten-1-ol**	122.5–3.5^{755}	......	....	....	23.4–4.5	......	......	......	......	......	....
12	*d,l*-**3-Methyl-2-butanol** (*sec*-Isoamyl alcohol; *d,l*-Isopropyl methyl carbinol)............	114; *d*: 110–2	......	1.3973	0.8180	68	109	......	......	127	39; *d*: 34; *l*: 34	*d*: $[\alpha]_D^{20}$: +5.34, in al.
13	**3-Pentanol** (*sym-sec*-Amyl alcohol; Diethyl car-binol)	116.1	......	1.4103	0.82037	48–9	95, lgr.	17	101; 99; 97	121	......	....
14	**1-Butanol** (*n*-Butyl alcohol)............	117.6; 116	−90.2	1.3974^{25}	0.80960	61	71	70; 64; 35–6	64; 62.5	147 (cor.)	73.1–.5 (cor.)	Pseudosaccharin ether, 96 (cor.)
15	*d,l*-**2-Pentanol** (*sec*-Amyl alcohol)............	119.85	......	1.4060	0.80919	......	74.5; 76; *d*: 88–91	17	62	102–3	60–1; *d*: 34; *l*: 34	Pseudosaccharin ether, 38 (cor.)
16	**3,3-Dimethyl-2-butanol** (*d,l*-Pinacolyl alcohol; *tert*-Butyl methyl carbinol)............	120.4	5.3	1.4148	0.8185	77–8, pet. eth.	......	......	107, yel.-wh., pet. eth.	......	85–6, lt. pet.	....
17	**2,3-Dimethyl-2-butanol** (Dimethyl isopropyl carbinol)............	120.5	−14	1.4140	0.8208	65–6, pet. eth.	101	......	111, yel., bz.-pet. eth.	......	......	......
18	**3-Methyl-3-pentanol**	123	−22	1.4166^{25}	0.82334$_4^{25}$	43.5	83.5	......	96.5, yel., pet. eth.; 62.5	......	......	Allophanate, 152 (cor.)

*Derivative data given in order: m.p., crystal color, solvent from which crystallized.

TABLE VI. ORGANIC DERIVATIVES OF ALCOHOLS
a) Liquids (Listed in order of increasing atmospheric b.p.)* (Continued)

No.	Name	Boiling point, °C	Melting point, °C	n_D^{20}	D_4^{20}	Phenyl-urethane	1-Naph-thyl-urethane	4-Nitro-benzoate	3,5-Dinitro-benzoate	Hydrogen 3-nitro-phthalate	Hydro-gen phthalate	Miscellaneous
19	**2-Methyl-2-pentanol** (Dimethyl *n*-propyl carbinol)............	123; 121	−103; −108	1.4113	0.81341	....	....	....	72	....	....	Benzoate, 182–3, al.; Allophanate, 128
20	**2-Methoxyethanol** (Methyl cellosolve; Ethylene glycol mono-methyl ether)........	124.5	......	1.40238	0.9647	....	112.5–3.0	50.5, dil. al.	....	129, dil. al.	....	Diphenyl ure-thane, 51
21	**2-Methyl-3-pentanol** (Ethyl isopropyl carbinol)............	127.5	......	1.4168	0.82487	50	....	....	85, yel., pet. eth.	150.7	70; 69–71, ra-cemic	....
22	**1-Chloro-2-propanol**	127	......	....	....	....	....	....	77	....	....	
23	**2-Methyl-1-butanol** (Active amyl alcohol; *d-sec*-Butyl carbinol) ...	128.9	......	1.4107	0.8193	31	82, lgr.	....	70	157–8, w.	....	$[\alpha]_D^{20}$: −5.756
24	**2-Chloroethanol** (Ethylene chlorohydrin)........	131	......	....	....	51	101	....	....	98	....	
25	**d,l-4-Methyl-2-pentanol** (Isobutyl methyl car-binol)	132	......	1.4011	0.80713	143, et. ac.	88	26	65, yel., pet. eth.	....	....	
26	**3-Methyl-1-butanol** (*prim*-Isoamyl alcohol).............	132	−117	1.40851[15]	0.80918	56–7, lgr.	68	21	61	166.3 (cor.), 30% al.; 165–6, w.	....	Pseudosaccharin ether, 64 (cor.)
27	**d,l-2-Chloro-1-propanol** ..	133.4	......	1.436	1.103	....	....	....	76	....	....	Alkali + heat → propylene oxide, b.p. 35
28	**3-Methyl-2-pentanol** (*sec*-Butyl methyl carbinol) .	134.2[749]	......	....	....	....	72	....	43.5, yel., pet. eth.; 41	....	....	
29	**2-Ethoxyethanol** (Ethyl-ene glycol monoethyl ether)...............	135	......	1.40797	0.9297	....	67.3–.5	....	75, al.	118–8.6 (anh.); 94.2–4 (mono-hyd.), w.-al.	....	Diphenyl ure-thane, 43
30	**3-Hexanol** (Ethyl *n*-propyl carbinol).......	136	......	1.4159	0.81851	....	....	....	97, yel.-wh., pet. eth.	....	76–7, pet. eth.	....
31	**2,2-Dimethyl-1-butanol** (*tert*-Amyl carbinol) ...	136.7	......	1.4208	0.82834	65–6	80–1, lgr.	....	....	51, yel., pet. eth.	....	Pseudosaccharin ether, 68–9, lt. pet.
32	**1-Pentanol** (*n*-Amyl alcohol)..............	138 (cor.)	−78.5	1.40994	0.81479	46	68	11	46.4	136 (cor.)	75.5	Pseudosaccharin ether, 62 (cor.)
33	**d,l-2-Hexanol** (*n*-Butyl methyl carbinol).......	138–9[745]	......	1.4126[25]	0.80977[25]₄	....	60.5	40	38.5	....	*d*: 29	3,5-Dinitrophenyl urethane, 40
34	**2,4-Dimethyl-3-pentanol** .	140	......	1.42259	0.8288	95, eth.-pet. eth.; 96–9	95; 99	155	....	150–1	....	Camphor-like odor
35	**Cyclopentanol**.........	140.85	......	1.4530	0.94688	132.5, al.	118	....	....	....	....	
36	**2-Isopropoxyethanol** (Ethylene glycol mono-isopropyl ether)	141.5[736]	......	1.40954	0.9030	....	....	....	....	....	....	Triphenylmethyl ether, 71.0–.5, me. al.

*Derivative data given in order: m.p., crystal color, solvent from which crystallized.

TABLE VI. ORGANIC DERIVATIVES OF ALCOHOLS·
a) Liquids (Listed in order of increasing atmospheric b.p.)* (Continued)

No.	Name	Boiling point, °C	Melting point, °C	n_D^{20}	D_4^{20}	Phenyl-urethane	1-Naph-thyl-urethane	4-Nitro-benzoate	3,5-Dinitro-benzoate	Hydrogen 3-nitro-phthalate	Hydro-gen phthalate	Miscellaneous
37	**3-Ethyl-3-pentanol** (Triethyl carbinol)	142	....	1.4305	0.83889	....	....	....	....	....	......	Camphor-like odor; Allo-phanate, 152 (cor.)
38	**2,3-Dimethyl-1-butanol** ..	145	....	1.4195	$0.8297_4^{20.5}$	28–9	....	....	51.5, pa. yel., pet. eth.	....	....	....
39	**3-Hydroxy-2-butanone** (*d,l*-Acetoin; Acetyl methyl carbinol).......	145	−72	1.4178	0.9861_4^{30}	....	....	....	....	....	?	Semicarbazone, 185, al.; 202; 2,4-Dinitro-phenylhydra-zone, 318, or., PhNO₂-tol.
40	**1-Hydroxy-2-propanone** (Acetol; Acetyl car-binol)	146	−17	1.4295	1.0824_{20}^{20}	....	....	....	....	....	......	Semicarbazone, 196, al.; 2,4-Di-nitrophenylhy-drazone, 128.5 (cor.), or., al.
41	**2-Methyl-1-pentanol** (2-Methyl-*n*-amyl alcohol)	148.0	....	1.4190	0.8208	....	75–6	....	50.5, yel., pet. eth.	145; 141, bz.	......	....
42	**2-Ethylbutanol**	148.9	....	1.4224	0.83345	....	....	....	51.5, pet. eth.	....	......	....
43	**2-Bromoethanol** (Ethylene bromohydrin)........	149d.	....	....	....	....	86	....	....	....	......	
44	**2-*n*-Propoxyethanol** (Ethylene glycol mono-*n*-propyl ether).......	150.0[736]	....	1.41328	0.9112	....	....	....	....	....	......	
45	**Trichloroethanol**........	151	19	....	....	87	120	71, al.	142.3	....	......	Urethane, 64–5
46	**3-Methyl-1-pentanol**	151–2; 153.7–4.1	....	1.4188	0.8242	....	58; *d,l*: 40–1; *d*: 38–40; *l*: 37–8	....	38, yel., pet. eth.	....	......	
47	**4-Methyl-1-pentanol** (Isoamyl carbinol; Isohexyl alcohol)	152–3	....	1.4153	0.8131	48 (cor.)	....	....	72, pet. eth.; 69.8 (cor.)	138.5–40, bz.-pet. eth.	......	
48	***d,l*-4-Heptanol** (Di-*n*-propyl carbinol)......	156	−41.5	1.4205	0.8183	....	78–80	35	64	....	60	....
49	**1-Hexanol** (*n*-Hexyl alcohol)..............	157.5	−51.6; −46.1	1.41778	0.81893	42	59; 62	5	58.4 (cor.); 60–1	124 (cor.); 123	25	Pseudosaccharin ether, 60 (cor.)
50	***d,l*-2-Heptanol** (*n*-Amyl methyl carbinol; *sec*-Heptyl alcohol)	158.7	....	1.4210	0.8167	....	54	....	49.4	....	57.5; *d,l*: 76.5	....
51	**2-Isobutoxyethanol** (Ethylene glycol mono-isobutyl ether)	159.3[746]	....	1.41428	0.8900	....	....	....	....	....	......	
52	**2-*sec*-Butoxyethanol** (Ethylene glycol mono-*sec*-butyl ether).......	159.3[746]	....	1.41606	0.8966	....	....	....	....	....	......	
53	**2,4-Dimethyl-1-pentanol** .	159.8	....	1.427	0.793	....	....	....	154–5, bz.-pet. eth.	....	......	*p*-Xenylurethane, 74–5, pet.

*Derivative data given in order: m.p., crystal color, solvent from which crystallized.

No.	Name	Boiling point, °C	Melting point, °C	n_D^{20}	D_4^{20}	Phenyl-urethane	1-Naph-thyl-urethane	4-Nitro-benzoate	3,5-Dinitro-benzoate	Hydrogen 3-nitro-phthalate	Hydro-gen phthalate	Miscellaneous
54	3-Chloro-1-propanol (3-Chloropropyl alcohol)	161.2	......	....	....	38	76	....	77	....	....	....
55	2-Methyl-1-hexanol.....	164–5	......	1.4250	0.8270	....	....	....		131–2, wh., pet.	......	p-Xenylurethane, 88.0–.5, pet.
56	2-Ethyl-1-pentanol (2-Ethyl-n-amyl alcohol)..	164–6	......	....	....	....	....	....		127–8, bz.-pet.	......	p-Xenylurethane, 77–77.5, pet.
57	d,l-4-Methyl-1-hexanol..	165; 173	......	1.4219	0.8239	....	50	....		149	......	Odor of Amyl alcohol
58	d,l-cis-2-Methylcyclo-hexanol (cis-Hexa-hydro-o-cresol).......	165.3	−9.3	1.4640	0.9340	90–1; 93–4	....	51–2; 55–6	98–9	....	103–4; 104–5	....
59	4-Hydroxy-4-methyl-2-pentanone (Diacetone alcohol).............	166	......	....	0.9306[25]	....	....	48	55	....	....	Oxime, 57.5–8.5, lgr.-eth.
60	d,l-trans-2-Methyl-cyclohexanol......... (trans-Hexahydro-o-cresol)...............	167.4	21	1.4611	0.9235	105; mixt. cis + trans: 90–105	....	65; mixt. cis + trans: 35–6	114–5; mixt. cis + trans: 85–90	....	124–5; mixt. cis + trans: 95–6	....
61	2-n-Butoxyethanol (Ethyl-ene glycol mono-n-butyl ether)..........	170–6[743]	......	1.4177[26]	0.9188	62	....	....		120.0–.6	......	4-Nitrophenyl-urethane, 58.7–9.1, CCl₄
62	2-Aminoethyl alcohol (Ethanolamine).......	171	......	....	....	....	....	....				N-1-Naphthyl-urea, 186 (cor.); Picrate, 160
63	2,6-Dimethyl-4-heptanol (Di-isobutyl carbinol)..	171.4–3.4	......	1.4242	0.8129[20][20]	61–2, lgr.-al.	....	....			118	p-Xenylurethane, 118; Allo-phanate, 156
64	Furfuryl alcohol (2-Furyl carbinol).............	172; 170	......	1.4863	1.1351[20][20]	45	129–30, lgr.; 133	76	80–1	....	85	Urethane, 50; Pseudosaccharin ether, 55
65	d,l-cis-3-Methylcyclo-hexanol (cis-Hexa-hydro-m-cresol).......	173–4	......	1.4572	0.919	87–8	128–9	65	91–2	....	82–3	....
66	d,l-cis-4-Methylcyclo-hexanol (cis-Hexahydro-p-cresol)..............	173–4[750]	......	1.4549	0.914	118–9	....	94	134	....	72–3	....
67	d,l-trans-4-Methylcyclo-hexanol (trans-Hexa-hydro-p-cresol).......	173–4.5[745]	......	1.4534	0.913	124–5; mixt. cis + trans: 112–5	....	67	139–40; mixt. cis + trans: 125–30	....	119–25, ac. a.	....
68	d,l-trans-3-Methylcyclo-hexanol (trans-Hexa-hydro-m-cresol).......	174–5	......	1.4550	0.9145	93–4; mixt. cis + trans: 75–85	122	58	97–8; mixt. cis + trans: 80–5	....	93–4	....
69	2,6-Dimethylcyclohexanol	174–5[748]	......	1.4619	0.9115; 0.9235	158	....	....				
70	cis-2,5-Dimethylcyclo-hexanol.............,..	175	......	1.4522[17]	0.9096[17][17]	....	....	....			......	Allophanate, 157–8
71	trans-2,4-Dimethylcyclo-hexanol..............	175	......	1.4560	0.900	96	....	....			......	Acetate, b.p.: 198[765]
72	1,3-Dichloro-2-propanol	176	......	....	....	73	115	....			......	....

*Derivative data given in order: m.p., crystal color, solvent from which crystallized.

TABLE VI. ORGANIC DERIVATIVES OF ALCOHOLS
a) Liquids (Listed in order of increasing atmospheric b.p.)* (Continued)

No.	Name	Boiling point, °C	Melting point, °C	n_D^{20}	D_4^{20}	Phenyl-urethane	1-Naph-thyl-urethane	4-Nitro-benzoate	3,5-Dinitro-benzoate	Hydrogen 3-nitro-phthalate	Hydro-gen phthalate	Miscellaneous
73	3-Bromo-1-propanol (Triethylene bromohydrin)	176d.	. . . . . .	. . . .	. . . .	. . . . . .	73	. . . . . .	. . . . . .	. . . . . .	. . . . . .	. . . .
74	cis-2,4-Dimethylcyclo-hexanol	176	. . . . . .	1.4582	0.907	. . . . . .	. . . . . .	. . . . . .	. . . . / . .	. , ...	. . . .
75	1-Heptanol (n-Heptyl alcohol)	176.8	−34.6; −33.8	1.4245	0.82242	60; 65	62	10	46; 47	127 (cor.)	16.5–17.5	Pseudosaccharin ether, 55 (cor.)
76	trans-2,5-Dimethylcyclo-hexanol	177	. . . . . .	1.4545^{17}	0.9079_{17}^{17}	. . . . . .	. . . . . .	. . . . . .	. . . . . .	. . . . . .	. . . . . .	Allophanate, 125
77	2,2-Dimethylcyclohexanol	177	8	1.4648	0.9225	85	. . . . . .	. . . . . .	. . . . . .	. . . . . .	. . . . . .	. . . .
78	Tetrahydrofurfuryl alcohol	$177–8^{743}$	. . . . . .	1.45167	1.0544	61, pet. eth.	. . . . . .	46–8	83–4	. . . . . .	. . . . . .	Diphenylurethane, 81, me. al.
79	2-Methyl-1,2-propanediol (Isobutylene glycol)	178	. . . . . .	1.4358^{17}	0.999_4^{14}	bis: 140.5	. . . . . .	. . . . . .	. . . . . .	. , ...	. . . . . .	. . . .
80	d,l-2-Octanol	179	. . . . . .	1.4265	0.8205	oil	63–4; 62.5	28	32	. . . . , . .	55; d,l: 75	. . . .
81	2,2-Dibromoethanol	179–81	. . . . . .	. . . .	. . . .	. . . . . .	. . . . . .	. . . . . .	. . . . . .	. , ...	. . . . . .	Urethane, 90–1
82	1,3,5-Trimethylcyclo-hexanol	181	. . . . . .	$1.454^{16.3}$	$0.8876_4^{16.8}$	. . . . . .	. . . . . .	. . . . . .	. . . . . .	. , ...	. . . . . .	. . . .
83	2,3Butanediol (2,3-Butylene glycol)	meso: 181.7^{742}; d,l: 176.7^{742}	meso: 34.4; d,l: 7.6	meso: 1.43637	meso: 1.0433	meso: bis: 201	. . . . . .	. . . . . .	. . . . . .	. . . . . .	. . . . . .	Dibenzoate: d,l: 53–4; meso: 75.5–6.2
84	Cyclohexyl carbinol (Hexahydrobenzyl alcohol)	182	. . . . . .	1.4649	0.9280	. . . . . .	. . . . . .	. . . . . .	. . . . . .	. . . . . .	. . . . . .	Acetate, b.p.: $199–201^{740}$
85	2,3-Dichloropropanol	182	. . . . . .	. . . .	. . . .	73	93	37–8	. . . . . .	. . . . . .	. . . . . .	2-Naphthylure-thane, 99
86	4-Methyl-1-heptanol	182.7	. . . . . .	. . . .	. . . .	. . . . . .	. . . . . .	. . . . . .	. . . . . .	133	. . . . . .	Pseudosaccharin ether, 34 (cor.)
87	2-Ethyl-1-hexanol	184.6	. . . . . .	1.4328	0.8328	33–4	60–1	. . . . . .	. . . . . .	108	. . . . . .	p-Xenylurethane, 80, pet.; Pseudo-saccharin ether, 53.5 (cor.)
88	3,3-Dimethylcyclohexanol	185^{754}	11–2	1.4606^{15}	0.9128_4^{14}	. . . . . .	. . . . . .	83	. . . . . .	. . . . . .	. . . . . .	Acetate, b.p.: $194–5^{750}$; o-Nitrobenzoate, 62
89	cis-3,5-Dimethylcyclo-hexanol	187	. . . . . .	1.454^{21}	0.9109_4^{21}	. . . . . .	. . . . . .	. . . . . .	. . . . . .	. . . . . .	. . . . . .	Acetate, b.p.: 201–2
90	trans-3,5-Dimethyl-cyclohexanol	d,l: 187	. . . . . .	1.4579	d: 0.9146; l: 0.9166	. . . . . .	. . . . . .	. . . . . .	. . . . . .	. . . . . .	. . . . . .	Acetate, d,l; b.p., 196; d, $[\alpha]_D^{26}$: +4.55; l, $[\alpha]_D^{17}$: −7.74
91	d,l-1,2-Propanediol (α-Propylene glycol)	187.4	. . . . . .	1.43162^{25}	1.0354_4^{23}	bis: 153; 143–4	. . . . . .	. . . . . .	. . . . . .	. . . . . .	. . . . . .	Monostearate, 59.5; Distearate, 72.3
92	3,4-Dimethylcyclohexanol	189	. . . . . .	1.458^{16}	0.9073_4^{16}	119	. . . . . .	. . . . . .	. . . . . .	. . . . . .	. . . . . .	. . . .
93	2,4,5-Trimethylcyclo-hexanol	cis: 191–3; trans: 196	. . . . . .	. . . .	. . . .	cis: 83.5, al.; trans: 95, al.	. . . . . .	. . . . . .	. . . . . .	81–3.5, eth.-lgr.	. . . . . .	. . . .
94	1,3,3-Trimethylcyclo-hexen-6-ol	193 (cor.)	. . . . . .	. . . .	0.9310_4^{13}	. . . . . .	. . . . . .	. . . . . .	. . . . . .	. . . . . .	. . . . . .	Acetate, b.p.: 206–7
95	2,3,6-Trimethylcyclo-hexanol	$193–5^{747}$	. . . . . .	. . . .	0.9119_4^{17}	. . . . . .	. . . . . .	. . . . . .	. . . . . .	. . . . . .	. . . . . .	. . . .

*Derivative data given in order: m.p., crystal color, solvent from which crystallized.

TABLE VI. ORGANIC DERIVATIVES OF ALCOHOLS

a) Liquids (Listed in order of increasing atmospheric b.p.)* (Continued)

No.	Name	Boiling point, °C	Melting point, °C	n_D^{20}	D_4^{20}	Phenyl-urethane	1-Naph-thyl-urethane	4-Nitro-benzoate	3,5-Dinitro-benzoate	Hydrogen 3-nitro-phthalate	Hydro-gen phthalate	Miscellaneous
96	2-(2-Methoxyethoxy)-ethanol (Diethylene glycol monomethyl ether)........	194	......	1.4244	1.035_{20}^{20}	......	....	92	....	91.4–2.2 (anh.); 87–90 (mono-hyd.), w.-al.	......	4-Nitrophenyl-urethane, 73.5; 76
97	5-Nonanol...........	194^{743}	......	1.4289^{18}	....	....	......	......	....	......	45	Allophanate, 158
98	1-Octanol (n-Octyl alcohol)........	195	−16; −16.7	1.4274^{25}	0.8249	74;72	67	12	61–2	128 (cor.)	22	Pseudosaccharin ether, 46 (cor.)
99	2-Methyl-2,4-pentanediol	196; 198	......	$1.42976^{16.7}$	0.9240_4^{17}	......	......	......	......	......	......	Odor of pinacol; Heating with 2% HBr → diene, b.p.: 75.5–76.0
100	2-(2-Ethoxyethoxy)-ethanol (Diethylene glycol monoethyl ether)........	196^{763}	......	1.4298	1.023_{20}^{20}	......	....	oil	oil	oil	......	4-Nitrophenyl-urethane, 65.8–6.3
101	Glycol (1,2-Ethanediol)..	197.85	−12.6	1.43192	1.11361	di: 157	di: 176	140; 141	di: 169	......	......	bis-4-Nitro-phenylurethane, 135.5
102	d,l-2-Nonanol	198.2	......	1.4290^{25}	0.81910_4^{25}	......	55.5, lt. pet.	......	42.8 (cor.)	......	42–4, d,l: 58–9	....
103	l-Linalool (l-Linalyl alcohol).............	199	......	1.46238	0.8622	65–6	53	70	......	......	......	$[\alpha]_D$: −3 to −17
104	Benzyl alcohol	205.5	−15.3	1.53955	1.04540	77; 75.5–76, pet. eth.	134	85	113	176	106; 104	Pseudosaccharin ether, 130 (cor.)
105	d,l-1,3-Butanediol (d,l-1,3-Butylene glycol........	207.5; 204	......	$1.44252^{19.5}$	1.0053	122–3; d: 115–6	184					Diphenyl-urethane, l: 127–8
106	d,l-2-Decanol (Methyl n-octyl carbinol)......	211	......	d: 1.4344	d: 0.8250	......	69, lt. pet.				48–9; d: 38–9	....
107	1-Nonanol (n-Nonyl alcohol)........	213.5	......	1.43105	0.8271	60; 69; 62–4	65.5	60; 66	52.2	125 (cor.)	42.5	Pseudosaccharin ether, 49 (cor.)
108	1,3-Propanediol (Tri-methylene glycol)......	214.7; 210–2	−30	1.43983	1.0538	di: 137	di: 164	di: 119	di: 178			Dibenzoate, 57; 59
109	3-Methylbenzyl alcohol (3-Tolyl carbinol).....	217	......	....	0.9157^{17}	......	116					
110	α,4-Dimethylbenzyl alcohol (α-Methyl-4-tolyl carbinol).......	219	......	....	$0.9668_4^{15.5}$	96, pet. eth.	......					
111	1-Phenyl-n-propyl alcohol (d,l-Phenylethyl carbinol).............	219	......	1.5257	1.0056_{20}^{20}	......	102	59–60; 56.5–7.8				
112	2,3-Dibromo-1-propanol	219d.	......	....	....	84	....	59–60				3,5-Dinitro-phenylurethane, 71
113	2-Phenethyl alcohol (2-Phenylethanol).......	219.8	−25.8	1.5240	1.0235_4^{25}	78; 79–80, al.	119	61.5–2 (cor.); 62–3, al.	108	123	188–9	....
114	d,l-α-Terpineol	221	35; d,l: 37–8	1.4834	0.9337	112–3, me. al.; d,l: 110	152; 147	139, me. al.	78–9, lgr.	......	117–8, ac. a.	Commercial liquid, lilac-like odor

*Derivative data given in order: m.p., crystal color, solvent from which crystallized.

No.	Name	Boiling point, °C	Melting point, °C	n_D^{20}	D_4^{20}	Phenyl-urethane	1-Naph-thyl-urethane	4-Nitro-benzoate	3,5-Dinitro-benzoate	Hydrogen 3-nitro-phthalate	Hydrogen phthalate	Miscellaneous
115	**Citronellol**	222; 118[17]	. . . .	. . . .	. . . .	. . . .	. . . .	. . . .	. . . .	. . . .	. . . .	Oxid. → Adipic acid, 89; Rose-like odor
116	**α-Isopropylbenzyl alcohol** (d,l-Isopropyl phenyl carbinol)	222–4	. . . .	$1.51932^{18.7}$	0.9790_{20}^{20}	. . . .	116–7	. . . .	. . . .	. . . .	. . . .	Oxid. → Iso-propylphenyl ketone, b.p.: 222
117	**d,l-2-Undecanol** (d,l-2-Hendecanol; Methyl n-nonyl carbinol)	228–9	. . . .	. . . .	0.8263^{18}	. . . .	. . . .	. . . .	. . . .	. . . .	49–50	. . . .
118	**2-(2-n-Butoxyethoxy)-ethanol** (Diethylene glycol mono-n-butyl ether)	228–30	. . . .	1.4341	0.957_{20}^{20}	. . . .	. . . .	. . . .	. . . .	. . . .	. . . .	4-Nitrophenyl-urethane, 54.5–5.3
119	**1,4-Butanediol** (Tetra-methylene glycol)	230; 235	19.0–.5	1.4467	1.0171	di: 183–3.5, chl.; 180	di: 199, xyl.	di: 175, ac. a.	. . . .	. . . .	. . . .	Dibenzoate, 81–2, eth.
120	**Geraniol**	230	. . . .	1.4766	0.8894	. . . .	47–8	35	62–3	117	47, lgr.	. . . .
121	**1-Decanol** (n-Decyl alcohol)	231	5.99; 6.4	1.43682	0.8292	59.6, bz., then al.	73	30.2, al.	57.7	122.8 (cor.)	38 (cor.)	Pseudosaccharin ether, 47.5 (cor.)
122	**2-Phenoxyethanol** (Ethylene glycol monophenyl ether)	237; 245	. . . .	1.534	1.102^{22}	. . . .	. . . .	. . . .	. . . .	112–3	. . . .	Benzoate, 64; 4-Toluene-sulfonate, 80, al.
123	**3-Phenylpropanol** (Hydrocinnamyl alcohol) . .	237.4; 235	. . . .	1.53565	1.0079	45; 47–8, al.	. . . .	45–6; 47	92	117	. . . .	4-Nitrophenyl-urethane, 104, pet. eth.
124	**1,5-Pentanediol** (Penta-methylene glycol)	238–9	. . . .	1.4499	0.9939_{20}^{20}	di: 174–5 (cor.), abs. al.	di: 147	di: 104–5, bz.-al.	. . . .	. . . .	. . . .	. . . .
125	**1-Undecanol** (1-Hende-canol; n-Undecyl alcohol)	243	15.85; 14.3	. . . .	. . . .	62, al.; 52	. . . .	99.5, al.	55	123.3 (cor.)	43.8–4.1	Allophanate, 156; Pseudosaccharin ether, 58–5 (cor.)
126	**Diethylene glycol** (β,β'-Dihydroxydiethyl ether)	244.5	f.p.: −10.45	1.4475	1.1212_{15}^{15}	. . . .	149	151 (cor.); 149, ac. a.	. . . .	. . . .	. . . .	. . . .
127	**2-Methoxybenzyl alcohol** (Saligenin-2-methyl ether)	247	. . . .	1.549^{17}	1.0495_{15}^{15}	. . . .	135–6	. . . .	. . . .	. . . .	. . . .	Allophanate, 180; Benzoate, 59, lgr.
128	**2-Benzyloxyethanol** (Ethylene glycol mono-benzyl ether)	265.0	. . . .	1.5225	1.0700_{20}^{20}	. . . .	. . . .	. . . .	. . . .	. . . .	. . . .	Triphenylmethyl ether, 76–7, eth.
129	**n-Hexyl phenyl carbinol** .	275	. . . .	1.501	0.946	75	. . . .	. . . .	. . . .	. . . .	. . . .	. . . .
130	**Triethylene glycol** (Ethylene glycol di-(β-hydroxyethyl)ether)	285; 165[14]	−9.4	1.4578^{15}	1.1274_4^{15}	. . . .	. . . .	. . . .	. . . .	. . . .	. . . .	bis-Triphenyl-methyl ether, 142–2.5, acet.
131	**Glycerol** (1,2,3-Tri-hydroxypropane)	290d.	17.9	1.4729	1.26134	tri: 180	tri: 191–2, al.	tri: 188	. . . .	. . . .	. . . .	4-Nitrophenyl-urethane, 216; Tribenzoate, 71–2; 75–6
132	**3,4-Dimethoxybenzyl alcohol** (Veratryl alcohol)	$296–7^{732}$	. . . .	1.555^{17}	1.179_{17}^{17}	118	. . . .	. . . .	. . . .	. . . .	. . . .	Acetate, b.p.: 170^{12}, n_D^{17}: 1.5245; Benzoate, 36–7

*Derivative data given in order: m.p., crystal color, solvent from which crystallized.

No.	Name	Boiling point, °C	Melting point, °C	n_D^{20}	D_4^{20}	Phenyl-urethane	1-Naph-thyl-urethane	4-Nitro-benzoate	3,5-Dinitro-benzoate	Hydrogen 3-nitro-phthalate	Hydro-gen phthalate	Miscellaneous
133	4-Methoxyphenyl methyl carbinol (4-Anisyl methyl carbinol)......	310d. (cor.)	....	1.557	1.0864^{16}	82–3	....	....	....	....	....	Odor of anise; Oxid. → 4-Methoxy-acetophenone, 38
134	cis-Octa-9-decen-1-ol (Oleyl alcohol; cis-Octadecenyl alcohol)...	333–5	....	1.4607	0.8489	oil	β: 44–5, al.	....	....	....	....	Allphanate, 135, chl.; 129, chl.; 4-Nitrophenyl-urethane, 85–91

*Derivative data given in order: m.p., crystal color, solvent from which crystallized.

TABLE VI. ORGANIC DERIVATIVES OF ALCOHOLS
b) Solids (Listed in order of increasing m.p.)*

No.	Name	Melting point, °C	Boiling point, °C	Phenyl-urethane	1-Naph-thyl-urethane	4-Nitro-benzoate	3,5-Di-nitro-benzoate	Hydrogen 3-nitro-phthalate	Hydrogen-phthalate	Pseudo-sac-charine ether	Miscellaneous
1	**1-Phenylethyl alcohol** (*d,l*-Methyl phenyl carbinol)	20; 20.1	202	92; 91–2, lgr.	106	43 (cor.), al.	95; 93	. . . . . .	108; ac. a.	. . . . . .	n_D^{20}: 1.5275; D_4^{20}: 1.0129
2	*trans*-2-Methylcyclohexanol	21	167.4	*d,l*: 105	*d,l*: 155	. . . .	*d,l*: 115	. . . . . .	. . . . . .	. . . . . .	Oxalate: *d, l*: 61
3	**1-Dodecanol** (*n*-Dodecyl alcohol; Lauryl alcohol).	24; 26	259	74	80	45; 42	60	124 (cor.)	50.3 (cor.)	54 (cor.)	. . . .
4	**1,1-Dimethyl-2-phenylethanol** (Benzyl dimethyl carbinol)	24	216	. . . .	. . . .	. . . .	. . . .	. . . . . .	. . . . . .	. . . . . .	n_D^{16}: 1.5174
5	**4-Methoxybenzyl alcohol** (4-Anisyl carbinol)	24–5	259	92 (cor.)	. . . .	. . . .	. . . .	. . . . . .	. . . . . .	. . . . . .	Benzoate, 38; Me. eth., b.p.: 225–6; n_D^{25}: 1.5422; D_{15}^{15}: 1.1129
6	**Cyclohexanol**	25.1	161.1	82	129	50	112–3, al.	160	99	. . . . . .	n_D^{25}: 1.46477; D_4^{30}: 0.94155
7	*tert*-**Butyl alcohol** (Trimethyl carbinol)	25.5	82.5	136, eth.	101	116, al.	142, pet. eth.	. . . . . .	. . . . . .	. . . . . .	n_D^{20}: 1.38779; D_4^{20}: 0.78670
8	**3-Nitrobenzyl alcohol**	27	175–80[3]	. . . .	. . . .	. . . .	. . . .	. . . . . .	. . . . . .	. . . . . .	Benzoate, 71–2; Ox. → 3-nitro-benzoic acid, 140
9	**2,3,3-Trimethylcyclohexanol**	28	197	. . . .	. . . .	. . . .	. . . .	. . . . . .	. . . . . .	. . . . . .	. . . .
10	**Diethanolamine** (β,β'-Dihydroxy-diethylamine)	28	270; 217–8[150]	. . . .	. . . .	. . . .	. . . .	. . . . . .	. . . . . .	. . . . . .	Picrate, 109–10
11	**2,4-Hexadien-1-ol**	30.5–1.5	76[12]	78–9	. . . .	. . . .	85	. . . . . .	. . . . . .	. . . . . .	. . . .
12	**1-Tridecanol**	α: 30.6; β: 28.3	155–6[15]	. . . .	. . . .	37.4 (cor.)	. . . .	124 (cor.)	52.5	66 (cor.)	D_4^{31}: 0.8223.
13	**Cinnamyl alcohol**	33	257	90.0–1.5	114	78; 76.5	121	. . . . . .	. . . . . .	. . . . . .	. . . .
14	**2-Methylbenzyl alcohol** (2-Tolyl carbinol)	36; 35	219	79 (cor.)	. . . .	. . . .	. . . .	. . . . . .	. . . . . .	. . . . . .	. . . .
15	*trans*-**Octa-9-decen-1-ol** (Elaidyl alcohol).	36.7; 35; 34	333; 216[18]	56–7	71	. . . .	. . . .	. . . . . .	. . . . . .	. . . . . .	. . . .
16	*d,l*-**Fenchyl alcohol**	38–9; *d,α*: 45; *l,α*: 47; *l,β*: 3–4	201.5; *d,α*: 201–2	104; *d,α*: 82; *l,α*: 82	149	109; *α*: 108–9; *β*: 94–5; *l,α*: 109; *l,β*: 83	104	95	169; *d,α*: 145; *l,α*: 146; *l,β*: 153	. . . . . .	. . . .
17	**1-Tetradecanol** (Myristyl alcohol)	39; 37.7	170–3[20]	74; 71	82	51.2 (cor.)	67	123.5 (cor.)	60 (cor.)	62 (cor.)	. . . .
18	**1,2,2-Trimethylcyclohexanol**	41 (+$\frac{1}{2}$ H_2O)	81.4–8[20]	. . . .	. . . .	. . . .	. . . .	. . . . . .	. . . . . .	. . . . . .	$n_D^{18.4}$: 1.469; $D_4^{18.4}$: 0.9274
19	**Pinacol** (Tetramethylethylene glycol)	43; 45–6	172	. . . .	. . . .	. . . .	. . . .	. . . . . .	. . . . . .	. . . . . .	Diacetate, 65; Hydrate, 46
20	*l*-**Menthol**	44; 42.5; 35; 33; 31; *d*: 38–40; *d,l*: 34	216	111–2, al.; *d,l*: 103–4	119; 126	61–2	153	. . . . . .	112; 129–31, ac. a.	. . . . . .	Allophanate, 215
21	**1-Pentadecanol**	α: 44; β: 38.9	. . . .	72, bz.	72	45.8 (cor.)	. . . .	122.5 (cor.)	60.4	72 (cor.)	. . . .
22	**1,3,5-Trimethyl-1-cyclohexen-3-ol**	46	87–90[17]	. . . .	. . . .	. . . .	. . . .	. . . . . .	. . . . . .	. . . . . .	$n_D^{19.3}$: 1.4735; $D_4^{20.2}$: 0.9132
23	*d,l*-α-**Propylbenzyl alcohol**	*d*: 49; *l*: 49	168–70[100]	. . . .	99	58	. . . .	. . . . . .	91; 53–4	. . . . . .	. . . .
24	**1,1,1-Trichloroisopropanol**	50–1	161.8[773]	. . . .	. . . .	. . . .	. . . .	. . . . . .	. . . . . .	54	Camphor-like odor
25	**1-Hexadecanol** (Cetyl alcohol) . . .	50; 49.27	190[18]	73	82	58.4 (cor.); 52	66	122 (cor.)	66.8	69.5 (cor.)	. . . .
26	**2,2,6-Trimethylcyclohexanol**	51, al.	186–7[753]	. . . .	. . . .	. . . .	. . . .	. . . . . .	. . . . . .	. . . . . .	n_D^{20}: 1.4600; D_4^{20}: 0.9128

*Derivative data given in order: m.p., crystal color, solvent from which crystallized.

TABLE VI. ORGANIC DERIVATIVES OF ALCOHOLS

b) Solids (Listed in order of increasing m.p.)* (Continued)

No.	Name	Melting point, °C	Boiling point, °C	Phenyl-urethane	1-Naph-thyl-urethane	4-Nitro-benzoate	3,5-Di-nitro-benzoate	Hydrogen 3-nitro-phthalate	Hydrogen-phthalate	Pseudo-sac-charine ether	Miscellaneous
27	3,3,5-Trimethylcyclohexanol	trans: 52; 37	cis: 201–3[750]; trans: 196.5[770]	....	....	....	....	....	....	......	Acetate, cis: b.p.: 209–10; trans: b.p.: 209–10
28	2,2-Dimethyl-1-propanol (tert-Butyl carbinol; Neopentyl alcohol)....................	52–3	113	144, lgr.	100	....	....	....	71	......	....
29	4-Methylbenzhydrol (Phenyl 4-tolyl carbinol)	53; 58; 42	....	....	....	....	....	....	....	.....	Ox. → Phenyl 4-tolyl ketone, 60
30	1-Heptadecanol...............	α: 54	310	....	88.5	53.8 (cor.)	121.5 (cor.)	121.0–.8	66.6–.7 (cor.)	76 (cor.)	....
31	Piperonyl alcohol	58	....	102.5	....	....	....	....	....	......	Benzoate, 66; Allophanate, 176.5
32	4-Methylbenzyl alcohol (4-Tolyl carbinol)....................	59–60	217	79	......	....	117–8	....	....	.....	....
33	1-Octadecanol (Stearyl alcohol) ..	59.5	210.5[15]	79–80	......	64.3 (cor.)	66	119	72.5 (cor.)	74.5 (cor.)	....
34	1-Nonadecanol	62	....	....	....	58.9	....	....	71	80.5	....
35	Eicosanol....................	65	220[3]	....	....	69.4	....	....	77	......	Acetate, 40
36	1-(1-Naphthyl) ethanol (d,l-Methyl 1-naphthyl carbinol)....	66	....	....	....	....	....	....	131–2, bz.	......	....
37	1,2-Diphenylethanol (d,l-Benzyl phenyl carbinol)	67	167[10]	....	....	....	....	....	131 (cor.), eth.-lt. pet.	......	....
38	4,4'-Dimethylbenzhydrol (Di-4-tolyl carbinol)..............	68, al.	....	....	....	....	....	....	....	.....	Carbinyl bromide, 48.5–9, lgr.
39	Benzhydrol (Diphenyl carbinol) ..	68, lgr.	288; 180[20]	139–40, bz.	135–6; 139	131–2	141	......	164–5	.....	Acetate, 41–2; Benzoate. 88–9, al.
40	1-Glyceryl phenyl ether	69, eth.	....	....	....	....	....	....	....	.....	Conc. H$_2$SO$_4$ → pa. red
41	Erythritol (d,l-1,2,3,4-Tetra-hydroxybutane)	72	....	....	....	....	....	....	....	.....	Tetraacetate, 53
42	Dihydroxyacetone (1,3-Di-hydroxy-2-propanone)	72	....	....	....	....	....	....	....	.....	Diacetate, 48; Dibenzoate, 120.5; 2,4-Dinitrophenyl-hydrazone, 277–8
43	2-Nitrobenzyl alcohol..........	74	270; 165[20]	....	....	....	....	....	....	.....	Benzoate, 101–2
44	1,10-Decanediol (Decamethylene glycol)	75.5; 72	....	....	....	....	....	....	....	.....	1,10-Dibromide, 27.4; b.p.: 162–5.5[10]
45	2,2,2-Tribromoethanol	80	92–3[10]	....	....	....	....	....	....	.....	Urethane, 86–7
46	10-Nonadecanol (Myricyl alcohol)	85	....	96	54	....	....	....	....	.....	....
47	Phenacyl alcohol (α-Hydroxy-acetophenone; Benzoyl carbinol)	86	118–20[11]	....	....	128.6	....	....	....	.....	Benzoate, 118.5; 3-Nitrobenzoate, 104.5
48	n-Triacontanol (1-Hydroxytria-contane)	86.5, bz.	....	....	....	....	....	....	....	.....	Acetate, 69, pet. eth.
49	2-Hydroxybenzyl alcohol (Saligenin)..................	86–7	....	....	....	....	....	....	....	.....	2-Benzoate, 66
50	d-Sorbitol	89–93; 112 (anh.)	....	....	....	....	....	....	....	.....	Hexaacetate, 99; Hexabenzoate, 216–7, et. ac.
51	3-Nitrophenacyl alcohol (3-Nitro-benzoyl carbinol)	92.5–3.0, pa. yel.	....	....	....	....	....	....	....	.....	Acetate, 53, eth.-lgr.; Semicarbazone, 214, al.

*Derivative data given in order: m.p., crystal color, solvent from which crystallized.

TABLE VI. ORGANIC DERIVATIVES OF ALCOHOLS
b) Solids (Listed in order of increasing m.p.)* (Continued)

No.	Name	Melting point, °C	Boiling point, °C	Phenyl-urethane	1-Naph-thyl-urethane	4-Nitro-benzoate	3,5-Di-nitro-benzoate	Hydro-gen 3-nitro-phthal-ate	Hydrogen-phthalate	Pseudo-sac-charine ether	Miscellaneous
52	4-Nitrobenzyl alcohol	93	185[12]								Acetate, 78; Benzoate, 94–5
53	4,4',4''-Trimethyltriphenyl carbinol (Tris-p-tolyl carbinol)	96									Et. eth., 111, pet. eth.; $H_2SO_4 \rightarrow$ gr.-red
54	*meso*-Erythritol	121; 120 (cor.)	330								Tetraacetate, 85; 89; Dibenzylidene, 201–2
55	4-Nitrophenacyl alcohol (4-Nitro-benzoyl carbinol)	121									Acetate, 124, et. ac.-lgr.; Phenyl-hydrazone, 178, bz.
56	*d,l*-Benzoin (Benzoyl phenyl carbinol)	137; 133	344	165	140	123					4-Nitrophenyl-urethane, 183; Acetate, 83
57	Cinchol (β-Sitosterol)	137					202–4				Acetate, 134; Benzoate, 145
58	Furoin (Furoyl furyl carbinol)	138–9 (cor.); 135									Acetate, 76–7; Benzoate, 92–3
59	Cholesterol (anh.) (*l*-Cholesterol)	148.5	360d.	168	176	185; 190–3			161		4-Nitrophenyl-urethane, 205; Benzoate, 151–2
60	Triphenylmethanol (Triphenyl carbinol)	161–2, bz.	380								Acetate, 87–8
61	Ergosterol	165		185	202		202, chl.				Acetate, 176; 180, eth.; Benzoate, 168
62	*d*-Mannitol	166; *l*: 163–4; *d,l*-α: 168		303							Hexaacetate, 126, eth.; Benzoate, 149–50; 147–8, al.
63	1,1,1-Tribromo-*tert*-butyl alcohol (Brometone)	167–76, w.-al.									Acetate, 43.4, al.; Benzoate, 27, al.
64	Dulcitol (1,2,3,4,5,6-Hexanehexol)	188.5									Hexaacetate, 171; 168–9, abs. al.; Hexabenzoate, 189–91, eth.-chl.
65	4,4',4''-Triaminotriphenyl carbinol (Pararosaniline base)	205									4,4',4''-Triacetyl, 192, acet.-eth.; Me. eth., 105, eth.; 135, bz.
66	*d*-Borneol ("Borneo camphor")	208; 205; *d,l*: 210.5	212	138–9	132; *iso*: 130; 127	153; *d,l*: 134; 137	154–5		161.4, ac. a.; 165 (cor.)		
67	*meso*-Inositol (1,2,3,4,5,6-Hexa-hydroxycyclohexane)	225 (cor.); 218				86, al.					Hexaacetate, 212, subl., tol.; Hexa-benzoate, 258, al.
68	*d*-Quercitol (Pentahydrocyclo-hexane)	232; 234									Pentabenzoate, 155
69	Pentaerythritol (2,2-Bishydroxy-methyl-1,3-propanediol)	262; 253									Tetraacetate, 84, wh., al.; Tetra-benzoate, 99–101, al.

*Derivative data given in order: m.p., crystal color, solvent from which crystallized.

EXPLANATIONS AND REFERENCES TO TABLE VII

Phenylurethane.

$$ArOH + C_6H_5N{=}C{=}O \rightarrow C_6H_5NHCOOAr$$

Phenylurethane
(Phenylcarbamate)

From the phenol with phenylisocyanate without solvent.

For directions and examples see: Linstead, pp. 34–35; J. B. McKinley, J. E. Nickels and S. S. Sidue, *Ind. Eng. Chem., Anal. Ed.*, **16**, 304 (1944).

From the phenol with phenylisocyanate in kerosene.

See: Cheronis, p. 489.

From the phenol with phenylisocyanate and a catalytic amount of pyridine.

See: Shriner, p. 265.

From the phenol with phenylisocyanate in toluene.

See: O. L. Brady and J. Harris, *J. Chem. Soc.*, **127**, 2175 (1925).

1-Naphthylurethane (α-Naphthylcarbamate). *

$$ArOH + 1{-}C_{10}H_7N{=}C{=}O \rightarrow 1{-}C_{10}H_7NHCOOAr$$

1-Naphthylurethane
(α-Naphthylcarbamate)

From the phenol with 1-naphthylisocyanate without solvent.

For directions and examples see: Cheronis, p. 488; Linstead, pp. 34–35; Vogel, p. 683; Wild, p. 68.

From the phenol with 1-naphthylisocyanate and a catalytic amount of pyridine, triethylamine or trimethylamine in ether.

See: Shriner, p. 211; Vogel, p. 683; Wild, p. 68; H. E. French and A. F. Wirtel, *J. Amer. Chem. Soc.*, **48**, 1736 (1926).

From the phenol with 1-naphthylisocyanate and a catalytic amount of a tertiary aliphatic amine in petrol ether.

See: Cheronis, p. 488; Vogel, p. 684.

p-Nitrobenzoate. *

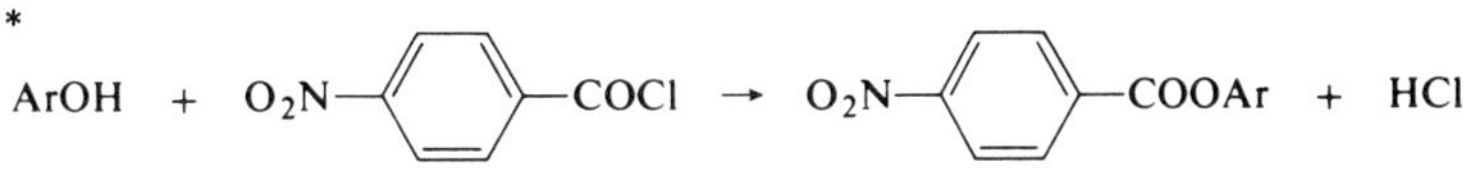

$$ArOH + O_2N{-}\langle\!\!\!\!\bigcirc\!\!\!\!\rangle{-}COCl \rightarrow O_2N{-}\langle\!\!\!\!\bigcirc\!\!\!\!\rangle{-}COOAr + HCl$$

p-Nitrobenzoate

From the phenol with *p*-nitrobenzoyl chloride in pyridine.

For directions and examples see: Vogel, p. 682; Wild, p. 52.

From the phenol with *p*-nitrobenzoyl chloride without solvent.

See: Wild, p. 52.

3,5-Dinitrobenzoate. *

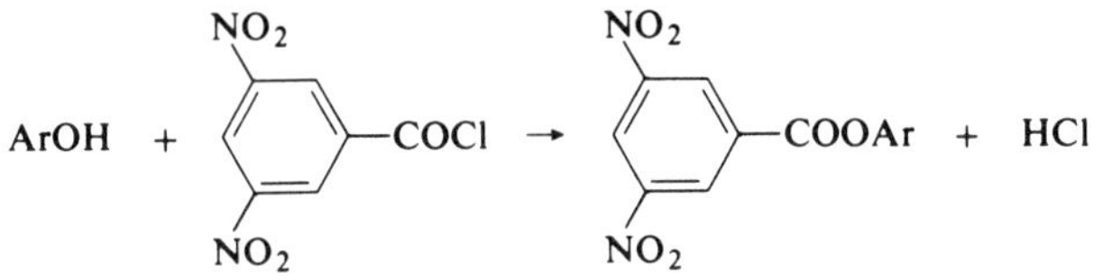

$$ArOH + \underset{NO_2}{\overset{NO_2}{\langle\!\!\!\!\bigcirc\!\!\!\!\rangle}}{-}COCl \rightarrow \underset{NO_2}{\overset{NO_2}{\langle\!\!\!\!\bigcirc\!\!\!\!\rangle}}{-}COOAr + HCl$$

3,5-Dinitrobenzoate

From the phenol with 3,5-dinitrobenzoyl chloride in pyridine.

For directions and examples see: Cheronis, p. 486; Vogel, p. 682; Wild, p. 65; R. C. Brown and R. E. Kremers, *J. Amer. Pharm. Ass.*, **11**, 607 (1922); M. Phillips and G. L. Keenan, *J. Amer. Chem. Soc.*, **53**, 1924 (1931).

From the phenol with 3,5-dinitrobenzoyl chloride without solvent.

See: Shriner, pp. 212–213.

Benzoate.

$$ArOH + C_6H_5COCl \rightarrow C_6H_5COOAr + HCl$$

Benzoate

From the phenol with benzoyl chloride in aqueous sodium hydroxide.

For directions and examples see: Cheronis, pp. 481–482, 487; Linstead, p. 20; Wild, p. 65.

---

*Derivatives recommended for first trial.

WARNING: This is not an instruction manual. References should be consulted for the preparation of derivatives.

From the phenol with benzoyl chloride in pyridine.
See: Linstead, p. 19.

Acetate.

$$ArOH + (CH_3CO)_2O \rightarrow CH_3COOAr + CH_3COOH$$
$$\text{Acetate}$$

From the phenol with acetic anhydride in aqueous sodium hydroxide.
For directions and examples see: Linstead, p. 21; Vogel, p. 682; Wild, p. 64; F. D. Chattaway, *J. Chem. Soc.*, 2495 (1931).
From the phenol with acetic anhydride and sodium acetate.
See: Linstead, p. 21; Wild, p. 64.
From the phenol with acetic anhydride and a catalytic amount of sulfuric acid.
See: Cheronis, p. 487.

p-Phenylazobenzoate.

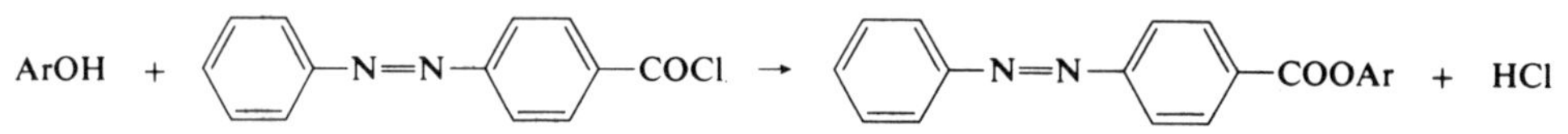

$$ArOH + \langle\!\!\langle \text{—} \rangle\!\!\rangle\text{—N=N—}\langle\!\!\langle \text{—} \rangle\!\!\rangle\text{—COCl} \rightarrow \langle\!\!\langle \text{—} \rangle\!\!\rangle\text{—N=N—}\langle\!\!\langle \text{—} \rangle\!\!\rangle\text{—COOAr} + HCl$$
$$\textit{p}\text{-Phenylazobenzoate}$$

From the phenol with *p*-phenylazobenzoyl chloride in pyridine.
For directions and examples see: Cheronis, p. 486; E. O. Woolfolk and J. M. Taylor, *J. Org. Chem.*, **22**, 827 (1957).

p-Toluenesulfonate.

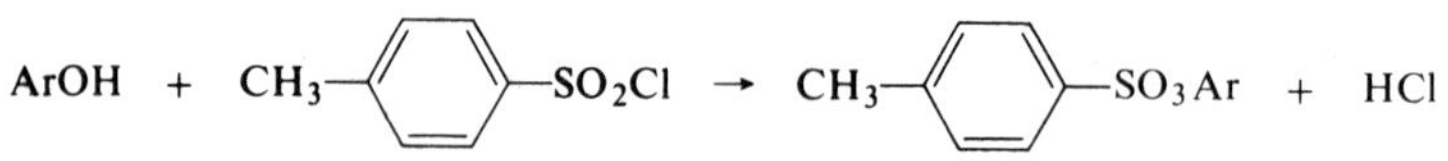

$$ArOH + CH_3\text{—}\langle\!\!\langle \text{—} \rangle\!\!\rangle\text{—SO}_2Cl \rightarrow CH_3\text{—}\langle\!\!\langle \text{—} \rangle\!\!\rangle\text{—SO}_3Ar + HCl$$
$$\textit{p}\text{-Toluenesulfonate}$$

From the phenol with *p*-toluenesulfonyl chloride in pyridine.
For directions and examples see: Linstead, p. 20; Vogel, p. 684; Wild, p. 66.
From the phenol with *p*-toluenesulfonyl chloride in aqueous sodium hydroxide.
See: Linstead, p. 20.
From the phenol with *p*-toluenesulfonyl chloride and sodium hydroxide in aqueous acetone.
See: Wild, p. 66.

Bromo derivative. *

$$ArOH + Br_2 \rightarrow Ar(OH)Br + HBr$$
$$\text{Mono-}$$
$$\text{bromophenol}$$

$$ArOH + nBr_2 \rightarrow Ar(OH)Br_n + nHBr$$
$$\text{Poly-}$$
$$\text{bromophenol}$$

From the phenol in aqueous methanol, in ethanol, in acetone or in dioxane with bromine in aqueous potassium bromide.
For directions and examples see: Cheronis, p. 490; Shriner, p. 264.
From the phenol in aqueous hydrochloric acid with bromine in water.
See: Linstead, p. 19.
From the phenol in glacial acetic acid and bromine.
See: Wild, p. 73.
From the phenol with bromine in carbon disulfide.
See: Vogel, p. 679.
For a discussion on the effect of solvents in the bromination of phenols.
See: N. D. Cheronis, *Micro and Semimicro Methods (Technique of Organic Chemistry)*, Vol. 6, Interscience, New York, 1954, pp. 286–287.

---

*Derivatives recommended for first trial.
WARNING: This is not an instruction manual. References should be consulted for the preparation of derivatives.

*Aryloxyacetic acid.**

$$ArONa \ + \ ClCH_2COOH \ \rightarrow \ ArOCH_2COOH \ + \ NaCl$$

Aryloxyacetic acid

From the phenol in aqueous sodium hydroxide with aqueous chloroacetic acid.

For directions and examples see: Cheronis, pp. 489–490; Linstead, p. 20; Shriner, p. 264; Vogel, p. 683; Wild, p. 72; C. F. Koelsch, *J. Amer. Chem. Soc.*, **53**, 304 (1931); N. V. Hayes and G. E. K. Branch, *J. Amer. Chem. Soc.*, **65**, 1555 (1943).

Aryl 2,4-dinitrophenyl ether.

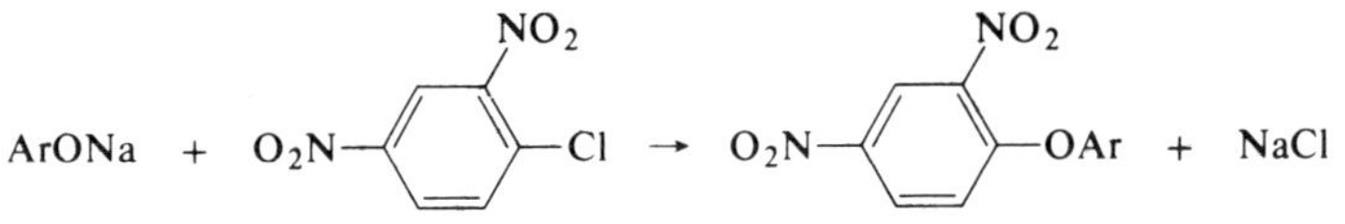

Aryl 2,4-dinitrophenyl
ether

From the phenol in aqueous sodium hydroxide with 2,4-dinitrochlorobenzene in alcohol.

For directions and examples see: Cheronis, pp. 490–491; Vogel, p. 684; Wild, p. 71; R. W. Bost and F. Nicholson, *J. Amer. Chem. Soc.*, **57**, 2368 (1935).

From the phenol with 2,4-dinitrochlorobenzene and aqueous potassium hydroxide.

See: Linstead, pp. 20–21.

NOTE: For additional information regarding directions and examples for the preparation of derivatives of phenols which are similar to those of alcohols (e.g., 1-naphthylurethanes, 3,5-dinitrobenzoates, etc.) see explanations and references to Table VI, p. 77, 78, 79.

*Derivatives recommended for first trial.
 WARNING: This is not an instruction manual. References should be consulted for the preparation of derivatives.

No.	Name	Boiling point, °C	Melting point, °C	n_D^{20}	D_4^{20}	Phenyl-urethane	α-Naphthyl-urethane	p-Nitro-benzoate	3,5-Di-nitro-benzoate	Bromo derivative	p-Toluene sulfonate	Miscellaneous
1	2-Chlorophenol	175.6	7	1.5473^{40}	1.2410^{18}_{15}	121	120	115	143	*mono*: 48–9; *di*: 76	74	Aryloxyacetic acid, 145; 2,4-Dinitrophenyl ether, 99; 4,6-Bis(dimethylaminomethyl) deriv., 62–3; p-Phenylazobenzoate, 120–1
2	2-Bromophenol	195	5	....	1.4924	....	129	....	...,....	95	78	p-Phenylazobenzoate, 126–7
3	2-Chloro-4-methylphenol (2-Chloro-p-cresol)	195–6	.....	1.5200^{27}	1.1785^{27}	....						Benzoate, 71–2; Aryloxyacetic acid, 108; Acetate, b.p. 238
4	2-Hydroxybenzaldehyde (Salicylaldehyde)	197 (cor.)	1.6	1.574	1.1690^{20}_{20}	133	....	128			63–4	Aryloxyacetic acid, 132; Acetate, 39
5	3-Methylphenol (m-Cresol)	203	12	1.540	1.03401	125; 121–2, al.-lgr.	127–8	90	165.4 (cor.), al.	*tri*: 84	51	Aryloxyacetic acid, 103; 2,4-Dinitrophenyl ether, 74; Benzoate, 55
6	2-Ethylphenol	207	....	....	1.0371^{0}	143.4; 141	....	56–7	108	....		Aryloxyacetic acid, 141; Benzoate, 38–9, al.
7	2-Isopropylphenol	212	16	1.5315	1.012	....						Aryloxyacetic acid, 132–3; Methyl urethane, 96–7; 4,6-Dinitro deriv., 53
8	2-Bromo-4-ethylphenol	213–4	....	....							121	....
9	3-Ethylphenol	217	–4	....	1.0250^{0}	137; 138.8		68				Aryloxyacetic acid, 77; Benzoate, 52, 95% al.
10	2-Allylphenol	220	–6	1.5181	1.0255^{15}_{15}	116; 106.0–6.5				6-*mono*: 50		Aryloxyacetic acid, 148.5–50
11	2-Chloro-4,6-dimethylphenol	221–3	....	....		129–30	....	94–5				....
12	Methyl salicylate (Methyl 2-hydroxybenzoate)	224	–8	1.5369	1.184	117, bz.	....	128				Acetate, 52; Benzoate, 92, al.
13	2-Propylphenol	224.6–6.6; 220.0–0.5		1.5280	1.000^{15}_{15}	111, formic a.			96			Aryloxyacetic acid, 99–100
14	2-sec-Butylphenol	227–8; 116^{21}	12–3	1.5288	0.9876	86, lgr.	....					Aryloxyacetic acid, 109.5–110
15	4-Allylphenol	$230–1^{750}$	16	1.5441^{18}	1.033^{18}	....			103.0–3.5			Urethane, 122–3; Acetate, b.p. 238–9
16	Ethyl salicylate (Ethyl 2-hydroxybenzoate)	234	1.3	1.5226	1.131	98–100	....	107–8, yel., bz.				Benzoate, 79–80; 87, al.; 3,5-Dinitro deriv., 92–3
17	2-n-Butylphenol	234–7; 113–5^{14}	....	$1.5180^{25.5}$	0.975	....			97			Aryloxyacetic acid, 104–5; Acetate, 105.5
18	4-Isobutylphenol	236; 235–9	....	1.5319^{25}	0.9796^{20}_{20}	....						Aryloxyacetic acid, 124–5
19	Carvacrol (5-Isopropyl-2-methylphenol)	237.8	1	1.524	0.9760	134–5; 138	116, lgr.	51	83; 76–7	46		Aryloxyacetic acid, 151; p-Xenylurethane, 116, al.
20	Isopropyl salicylate (Isopropyl 2-hydroxybenzoate)	240–2	....	1.50650	1.0729	....						3,5-Dinitro deriv., 101–2, al.

*Derivative data given in order: m.p., crystal color, solvent from which crystallized.

No.	Name	Boiling point, °C	Melting point, °C	n_D^{20}	D_4^{20}	Phenyl-urethane	α-Naph-thyl-urethane	p-Nitro-benzoate	3,5-Di-nitro-benzoate	Bromo derivative	p-Toluene sulfonate	Miscellaneous
21	3-Methoxyphenol (Resorcinol monomethyl ether)	243; 244	−17.5	......	......	......	128–9	......	......	*tri*: 104	......	Aryloxyacetic acid, 118; 111–3, w.; 2,4-Dinitrophenyl ether, 87–8
22	2-Allyl-6-methoxyphenol	250–1; 115[9]	.....	1.5393	......	......	......	96–7	......	......	......	....
23	4-Allyl-2-methoxyphenol (Eugenol)	254.8; 127[15]	−9.1; 16–9	1.5410	1.0664	95.5	122, lgr.	81	130.8 (cor.), al.	*tetra*: 118	85	Acetate, 29, al.; Benzoate, 70, al.; Aryloxyacetic acid, 81; 100; 2,4-Dinitrophenyl ether, 115; N,N-Diphenylurethane, 108
24	Isobutyl salicylate (Isobutyl 2-hydroxybenzoate)	260–2	.....	1.50872	1.0639	......					......	3,5-Dinitro deriv., 72–3, al.
25	*d,l*-1,2,3,4-Tetrahydro-2-naphthol	264[716]	.....	1.5523[17]	1.0715[17]	99	......					Acetate, b.p. 169[34]; Benzoate, b.p. 254–5[40]
26	2-Methoxy-4-propenylphenol (Isoeugenol)	267.5	.....	*cis*: 1.5700; *trans*: 1.5782	*cis*: 1.0851; *trans*: 1.0852	*cis*: 118; *trans*: 152	149–50, lgr.	109	154–8 (cor.), *n*-BuOH			Acetate, 79–80; bz.-lgr.; Benzoate, *cis*, 68; *trans*, 103–4, al.; Aryloxyacetic acid, 116 (94); 2,4-Dinitrophenyl ether, 128
27	*n*-Butyl salicylate (*n*-Butyl 2-hydroxybenzoate)	270–2; 259–60	.−5.9	1.51148	1.0728	......					......	3,5-Dinitro deriv., 60–1, al.; *p*-Nitrobenzyl ether, 92
28	Isoamyl salicylate (Isopentyl salicylate)	276–8	.....	1.50799	1.0535	......					......	3,5-Dinitro deriv., 61–2, al.
29	3-Acetoxyphenol (Resorcinol monoacetate)	283	.....	1.5328	......							Saponification → resorcinol, 110 + ac. a.; Diacetate, b.p. 130–1[7]

*Derivative data given in order: m.p., crystal color, solvent from which crystallized.

TABLE VII. ORGANIC DERIVATIVES OF PHENOLS
b) Solids (Listed in order of increasing m.p.)*

No.	Name	Melting point, °C	Boiling point, °C	Phenyl urethane	α-Naphthyl urethane	p-Nitrobenzoate	3,5-Dinitrobenzoate	Bromo derivative	p-Toluene sulfonate	Acetate	Benzoate	Miscellaneous
1	**2-Benzylphenol (2-Hydroxydiphenylmethane) (Labile form)**	21; stable: 52; 54	312	117–8	......	......	....	....	......	......	......	Me. eth., 30; Urethane, 110–1
2	**4-n-Propylphenol**	22	232	129	......	......	123			b.p. 245–6[745]	38	n_D^{25}: 1.5220
3	**4-n-Butylphenol**	22	248; 138–9[18]	115, al.	......	67–8, yel., al.	92	....		b.p. 138–41[15]	27	$n_D^{25.5}$: 1.5165; D_4^{20}: 0.978; Aryloxyacetic acid, 81
4	**4-n-Amylphenol (4-n-Pentylphenol)**	23	248–53	......	......	......	......			51.0–0.5, al.		n_D^{23}: 1.5272; D_{20}^{20}: 0.9621; Aryloxyacetic acid, 90
5	**3-n-Propylphenol**	26	228	......	......	......	75 (117–8)				......	n_D^{20}: 1.5223; D_4^{20}: 0.9887; Aryloxyacetic acid, 96–7, lgr.
6	**2-Chloro-3,4-dimethylphenol**	27, pet. eth.	....	......	......	......	....			87, aq. al.	......	......
7	**2,4-Dichloro-3-methylphenol (2,4-Dichloro-m-cresol)**	27	240.5–2.5	......	......	......	....		92.0–2.5, al.	......	90.5	Benzenesulfonate, 70, al.
8	**2,4-Dimethylphenol (m-4-Xylenol)**	27.8	211.5 (cor.)	103; 112, CCl₄	135	102; 105	164.6 (cor.), 95% al.	....		37–8, ac. a.		n_D^{14}: 1.5420; D_4^{14}: 1.0276; p-Xenylurethane, 184; Aryloxyacetic acid, 141; p-Phenylazobenzoate, 110–3; 2,4-Dinitrophenyl ether, 102–3
9	**2-Ethoxyphenol**	28	217	......	......	......	....			......	31	Allophanate, 212
10	**2-Acetylphenol (2-Hydroxyacetophenone)** ..	28	215	......	......	......	....			89, al.	87–8, al.	n_D^{20}: 1.5590; D_4^{20}: 1.131; Semicarbazone, 210; Oxime, 118; Phenylhydrazone, 110
11	**2-Methylphenol (o-Cresol)**	31	191–2	141; 143	141–2, lgr.	94	138.4 (cor.), al.	di: 56	54–5, pyr.	......	......	Aryloxyacetic acid, 152; p-Phenylazobenzoate, 110–11.5; 2,4-Dinitrophenyl ether, 90; N,N-Diphenylurethane, 73
12	**2-Methoxyphenol (Guaiacol)**	32; 28.2	205	136, al.	118	93	141.2 (cor.), al.	4,5,6-tri: 116, al.		85, lgr.	57–8	n_D^{20}: 1.5441; $D_{(vac)}^{20.4}$: 1.1287; Aryloxyacetic acid, 116; 2,4-Dinitrophenyl ether, 97
13	**5-Fluoro-2-nitrophenol**	32, lgr.	....	......	......	......	....			......	110–11	Me. eth., 52, lgr.
14	**3-Bromophenol**	33	236	......	108	......	....		52.4	b.p. 149[40]	86	Aryloxyacetic acid, 108; p-Phenylazobenzoate, 125–6
15	**3-Chlorophenol**	33	214	......	158	99	156	....			71	Aryloxyacetic acid, 110; 2,4-Dinitrophenyl ether, 75; p-Phenylazobenzoate, 127–8
16	**2-Bromo-4-chlorophenol** ..	33–4	123[10]	......	......	......	....		....		99–100	Aryloxyacetic acid, 139–40

*Derivative data given in order: m.p., crystal color, solvent from which crystallized.

TABLE VII. ORGANIC DERIVATIVES OF PHENOLS

b) Solids (Listed in order of increasing m.p.)* (Continued)

No.	Name	Melting point, °C	Boiling point, °C	Phenyl ure-thane	α-Naph-thyl-ure-thane	p-Nitro-ben-zoate	3,5-Di nitro-benzoate	Bromo derivative	p-Toluene sul-fonate	Acetate	Benzoate	Miscellaneous
17	4-Methylphenol (p-Cresol)	36	202	115	146	98	188.6 (cor.), al.	di: 49; tetra: 198–9, al.	69–70, al.	. . . . . .	70	p-Phenylazoben-zoate, 134.5–6.5; N,N-Diphenylure-thane, 94; p-Xenyl-urethane, 198
18	2,4-Dibromophenol	36; 40	238–9	. . . . . .	. . . . . .	183.5	. . . .	6-mono: 95–6	120	36	97.5	Aryloxyacetic acid, 153; 2,4-Dinitro-phenyl ether, 135; Me. eth., 61.3; b.p. 272; Et. eth., 53.5
19	4-Methyl-2-nitrophenol (2-Nitro-p-cresol)	36.5, yel., w.-al.	125²²	. . . . . .	. . . . . .	. . . . . .	192	. . . .	. . . . . .	. . . . . .	100–1	Me. eth., 8.5, pa. yel., b.p. 274; Et. eth., b.p. 275–85 d.
20	4-Chlorophenol	37; 43	217	148.5	166	171	186	2-mono: 33–4; 2,6-di: 90	71	7–8	88	Aryloxyacetic acid, 156; 2,4-Dinitro-phenyl ether, 126; p-Phenylazoben-zoate, 153–4; N, N-Diphenylure-thane, 97
21	2,4-Diethylphenol	37–8	219	170–1	. . . . . .	. . . . . .	. . . . . .	. . . .	. . . . . .	. . . . . .	. . . . . .	Aryloxyacetic acid, 67–8
22	3-Fluoro-2-nitrophenol	39, lgr.	. . . .	. . . . . .	. . . . . .	. . . . . .	. . . . . .	. . . .	. . . . . .	. . . . . .	114	Me. eth., 43.5, lgr.
23	2,6-Dichloro-4-methyl-phenol (2,6-Dichloro-p-cresol)	39; 42	120–5¹⁴	. . . . . .	. . . . . .	. . . . . .	. . . . . .	. . . .	. . . . . .	48	9	NH₄ salt, 125; Me. eth., b.p. 234
24	3-Ethoxyphenol (Re-sorcinol monoethyl ether)	40	246–7, pa. yel.; 254–8	. . . . . .	. . . . . .	183.5	. . . .	. . . .	. . . . . .	. . . . . .	97–5	2,4-Dinitrophenyl ether, 114–5; Picrate, 105–6, red, chl.
25	3-Iodophenol	40	. . . .	138	. . . . . .	133	183	. . . .	60–1	38, pet. eth.	72–3, pet. eth.	Aryloxyacetic acid, 115
26	2-Benzoylphenol (2-Hydroxybenzophenone)	41	. . . .	. . . . . .	. . . . . .	124	. . . . . .	. . . .	. . . . . .	. . . . . .	. . . . . .	p-Nitrobenzyl ether, 124–5, acet.; Phenylhydrazone, 155; Semicarba-zone, 250–1; Oxime, 141–3
27	3-Methyl-2-nitrophenol (2-Nitro-m-cresol)	41, yel., pet. eth.	. . . .	. . . . . .	. . . . . .	. . . . . .	. . . . . .	. . . .	. . . . . .	59, al.	79, al.	Me. eth., 54, yel., al.
28	Phenol	41.8; 42	182; 183	126, bz.	132–3, lgr.	127, bz.	145.8 (cor.), al.	tri: 95	95–6, al.	. . . . . .	69	Aryloxybenzoic acid, 99; p-Phenyl-azobenzoate, 148–50; p-Xenylure-thane, 173; N,N-Diphenylurethane, 105
29	3-Fluoro-4-nitrophenol	42, w. or lgr.	173¹²	. . . . .	. . . . . .	. . . . . .	. . . . . .	. . . .	. . . . . .	. . . . . .	118	Me. eth., 56.5
30	Phenyl salicylate (Salol; Phenyl 2-hydroxy-benzoate)	42; 38.8; 28.5 (three forms)	. . . .	111–2, bz., 242	. . . . . .	111	. . . .	. . . .	. . . . . .	99.5	81	N,N-Diphenyl-urethane, 144

*Derivative data given in order: m.p., crystal color, solvent from which crystallized.

TABLE VII. ORGANIC DERIVATIVES OF PHENOLS
b) Solids (Listed in order of increasing m.p.)* (Continued)

No.	Name	Melting point, °C	Boiling point, °C	Phenyl urethane	α-Naphthylurethane	p-Nitrobenzoate	3,5-Dinitrobenzoate	Bromo derivative	p-Toluene sulfonate	Acetate	Benzoate	Miscellaneous
31	2-Iodophenol	43	186–7[160]	122	......	......	....	......	......	98–101	34, pet. eth.	D^{80}: 1.8757; Aryloxyacetic acid, 135; p-Phenylazobenzoate, 126–8; 2,4-Dinitrophenyl ether, 95
32	5-Bromo-2-nitrophenol	44, yel.	....	......	......	......	....	......	......	74.5	......	Me. eth., 85.5; Et. eth., 79.5–80.5, al.
33	2,4-Dichlorophenol	45	210	......	......	......	142–3	68	125	......	97	Aryloxyacetic acid, 141, 135; β-Naphthylurethane, 166; 2,4-Dinitrophenyl ether, 119
34	2-Nitrophenol	45, yel., al.	216	......	113	141	155	di: 117	83	40–1, lgr.	59	D^{40}: 1.2942; Aryloxyacetic acid, 158; 2,4-Dinitrophenyl ether, 142; N,N-Diphenylurethane, 114; p-Phenylazobenzoate, 136.5–7.0
35	5-Chloro-2-hydroxybiphenyl	46	....	......	......	...;..	......	......	......	......	88	....
36	2-Chloro-5-methylphenol (6-Chloro-m-cresol)	46	196	......	......	......	....	......	96	b.p. 122–3[11]	31; 40	Benzenesulfonate, 99
37	4-Bromo-5-isopropyl-2-methylphenol	46, lgr.	....	......	......	53–4	....	......	......	......	......	Me. eth., b.p. 147–50[15]
38	2-tert-Butyl-5-methylphenol (6-tert-Butyl-m-cresol)	46–7	127[11]	......	......	......	....	......	......	b.p. 139[17]	......	Me. eth., 22, b.p. 225–7
39	3-Chlorocatechol (3-Chloro-1,2-dihydroxybenzene)	46–8; 48–50	110–11[11]	......	......	......	....	......	......	......	110–11	2-Me. eth., 31.5–3.0
40	4-Ethylphenol (4-Hydroxyethylbenzene)	47	219	120	128	80–1	132–3	......	......	......	59–60, al.	n_D^{25}: 1.5239; D_{20}^{20}: 1.0123; Aryloxyacetic acid, 97; p-Phenylazobenzoate, 117–8
41	3-Methyl-2,4,6-trichlorophenol (2,4,6-Trichloro-m-cresol)	47, w.	265	......	......	....	....	......	92–3	35; 32, eth.	53	....
42	4-Chloro-2-methylphenol (4-Chloro-o-cresol)	48	222–5	......	......	....	....	......	......	......	71	Aryloxyacetic acid, 115–7; Me. eth., b.p. 213–5
43	2,6-Dibromo-4-methylphenol (2,6-Dibromo-p-cresol)	49; 54	....	......	......	141.2	....	......	......	67	94–5	....
44	Thymol (2-Isopropyl-5-methylphenol)	49.7; 51.5, acet.	233.5	107, aq. al.	160, lgr.	70	103.2, al.	55	71	b.p. 242–3	33	Aryloxyacetic acid, 149; 2,4-Dinitrophenyl ether, 67; p-Xenylurethane, 194; p-Phenylazobenzoate, 85–6

*Derivative data given in order: m.p., crystal color, solvent from which crystallized.

TABLE VII. ORGANIC DERIVATIVES OF PHENOLS

b) Solids (Listed in order of increasing m.p.)* (Continued)

No.	Name	Melting point, °C	Boiling point, °C	Phenyl urethane	α-Naphthyl urethane	p-Nitrobenzoate	3,5-Dinitrobenzoate	Bromo derivative	p-Toluene sulfonate	Acetate	Benzoate	Miscellaneous
45	2-Hydroxy-4-methoxyacetophenone (Peonol)...	52–3, al.								46.5		$n_D^{81.2}$: 1.54322; $D^{81.2}$: 1.310; m-Nitrobenzoate, 109; p-Nitrophenylhydrazone, 238–9, ac. a.
46	2-Benzylphenol (2-Hydroxydiphenylmethane) (stable form)	52; 54; labile: 21–2	312	117.5–8.0, lgr.								Benzyl eth., 38, me. al.
47	2-Chloro-3-methylphenol (2-Chloro-m-cresol)	55–6; 49–50	194						96		55–6	Benzenesulfonate, 58
48	4-Methoxyphenol (Hydroquinone monomethyl ether)	56; 55	243–4							32	87, al.	Aryloxyacetic acid, 110–2
49	3-Methyl-6-nitrophenol (6-Nitro-m-cresol)	56, yel., bz.								48, al.	77	Me. eth., 62; Et. eth., 55, pet. eth.; 50–1
50	3-Bromo-4-methylphenol (3-Bromo-p-cresol)	56	245								75	Me. eth., b.p. 103–5[10]
51	2-Phenylphenol (2-(Hydroxybiphenyl))	56; 67.5 (cor.)	275						64–6, dil. al.	62.5–3, pet. eth.	75–6	p-Phenylazobenzoate, 141–4; 2,4-Dinitrophenyl ether, 113–4
52	2,6-Dibromophenol	56–7	162[21]					93.3		46	68	Me. eth., 13; b.p. 143–5[34]; Et. eth., 40.6
53	4-n-Caproylresorcinol	56–7, tol.-pet. eth.	343–5 d.			89–91, pa. yel., al.						
54	2-Bromo-4-methylphenol (2-Bromo-p-cresol)	56–7	213–4; 102–4[20]						121	b.p. 120[3]		$D^{24.5}_{24.5}$: 1.547
55	5-Bromo-3-methylphenol (5-Bromo-m-cresol)	56–7; 54							83			Me. eth., b.p. 139–40[20]; Picrate, 130
56	2-Cyclohexylphenol	56–7										4,6-Dinitro deriv., 106, al.; 2,4-Dinitrophenyl ether, 76–7
57	2,3-Dichlorophenol	56–7	206				di: 90					Me. eth., 31
58	4,6-Dibromo-2-methylphenol (4,6-Dibromo-o-cresol)	57				136–7					62	
59	3-Hydroxy-6-nitrobiphenyl	57–8, bz.				135	171					2.4-Dinitrophenyl ether, 131; 4-Nitro deriv., 176–8
60	2,3,6-Trichlorophenol	58, pet. eth.									90, al.	
61	2,6-Dichloro-3-methylphenol (2,6-Dichloro-m-cresol)	58	234						100–1, al.		78.0–8.5, al.	
62	2,5-Dichlorophenol	58–9, pet. eth.	212								69	
63	4-Propylcatechol (1,2-Dihydroxy-4-propylbenzene)	60, bz.	175–80[30]									3-Me. eth., b.p. 240–2; Di-me. eth., b.p. 247
64	1,2-Dihydroxynaphthalene (1,2-Naphthalenediol)...	60 (hyd.); 103–4 (anh.)								di: 106		
65	4-Isopropylphenol	61	223–5								71–2	

*Derivative data given in order: m.p., crystal color, solvent from which crystallized.

TABLE VII. ORGANIC DERIVATIVES OF PHENOLS
b) Solids (Listed in order of increasing m.p.)* (Continued)

No.	Name	Melting point, °C	Boiling point, °C	Phenyl urethane	α-Naphthyl urethane	p-Nitrobenzoate	3,5-Dinitrobenzoate	Bromo derivative	p-Toluene sulfonate	Acetate	Benzoate	Miscellaneous
66	5,6,7,8-Tetrahydro-2-naphthol	61.5-2.5	275[705]	......	......	113; 106.5	....			b.p. 158[14]	96	N,N-Diphenylurethane, 114; Cinnamate, 77.5
67	2,3,5-Trichlorophenol	62 (hyg.)	....								103, lgr.	Me. eth., 84, al.
68	2-Methyl-3,5,6-trichlorophenol (3,5,6-Trichloro-o-cresol)	62, ac. a.	....								110, al.	....
69	3,4-Dimethylphenol (o-4-Xylenol)	62-5, w.	225[757]	120, dil. al.	141-2, lgr.	......	181.6 (cor.), al.	tri: 171	......	22	58.5	Aryloxyacetic acid, 162.5; 2,4-Dinitrophenyl ether, 105-6; p-Xenylurethane, 183, al.; Picrate, 83.8, yel.; Me. eth., 204-5; p-Phenylazobenzoate, 104-7
70	2,6-Dinitrophenol	63-4	....						135	....	......	Picrate, 122; Me. eth., 118
71	4-Bromo-3-methylphenol (4-Bromo-m-cresol)	63.5, pet. eth.	118-23[7]	......					84-5	......	83.5	Benzenesulfonate, 79-80; Me. eth., b.p. 108.5[12]
72	4-Bromo-2-methylphenol (4-Bromo-o-cresol)	64	235 (subl.)							b.p. 132[12]	67-8	Et. eth., b.p. 238-40
73	1-Acetyl-2-naphthol	64, lgr.	....								85-6, pyr.	....
74	4-Bromophenol	64; 66.4	238	140	169	180	191	tri: 171	......	22	58.5	Aryloxyacetic acid, 157; 2,4-Dinitrophenyl ether, 141; N,N-Diphenylurethane, 99; p-Phenylazobenzoate, 167.5-8.5
75	2-Methyl-1-naphthol	64-5	....	......						81-2	94-5	Picrate, 133-4
76	4-Methylcatechol (3,4-Dihydroxytoluene)	65, bz.	252	di: 166	......					di: b.p. 260-4	di: 58	Diaryloxyacetic acid, 58; Di-p-xenylurethane, 193
77	3-Bromo-2-nitrophenol	65-7, pet. eth. (anh.); 35 (hyd.), w.							136.5-7.5, al.	......	133	Me. eth., 73
78	4-Chloro-3-methylphenol (4-Chloro-m-cresol)	66; 55	235	......	153-4				98		86	2,4-Dinitrophenyl ether, 112; Benzenesulfonate, 66
79	4-Hydroxy-3-nitrobiphenyl	66	....							85-6, lgr.	111	Me. eth., 91-2
80	4-Methyl-2,3,5-trichlorophenol (2,3,5-Trichloro-p-cresol)	66-7, ac. a.	....							37-8, w.-ac. a.	89, w.-al.	....
81	2,6-Dichlorophenol	67	219-20; 80-5[4]	......							74.0-4.5	Me. eth., b.p. 105-6[20]
82	3,5-Dimethylphenol (m-5-Xylenol)	68	219.5 (subl.)	148; 151	......	109	195.4 (cor.), al.	tri: 166	83, ac. a.	b.p. 130[26]	24	Aryloxyacetic acid, 111; 81; 2,4-Dinitrophenyl ether, 100; p-Phenylazobenzoate, 104.5-6.5; p-Xenylurethane, 150
83	2-Bromo-6-nitrophenol	68, yel.	....	......						39.5-40	......	Me. eth., 67

*Derivative data given in order: m.p., crystal color, solvent from which crystallized.

TABLE VII. ORGANIC DERIVATIVES OF PHENOLS

b) Solids (Listed in order of increasing m.p.)* (Continued)

No.	Name	Melting point, °C	Boiling point, °C	Phenyl ure-thane	α-Naph-thyl-ure-thane	p-Nitro-ben-zoate	3,5-Di-nitro-benzoate	Bromo derivative	p-Toluene sul-fonate	Acetate	Benzoate	Miscellaneous
84	3-Methylcatechol (2,3-Dihydroxytoluene)	68, bz,	....	......	......	......	....	....	....	......	......	2-Me. eth., 39, b.p. 204; Di-Me. eth., b.p. 202–3
85	3,5-Dichlorophenol	68	233	......	......	......	....	tri: 189	116	38	55	....
86	2,6-Di-iodophenol	68	....	......	......	......	....	....	....	107, ac. a.	,......	Me. eth., 35, ac. a.; Et. eth., 41–2, ac. a.
87	2,4,5-Trichlorophenol	68, pet. eth.	....	......	......	......	....	....	....	......	92–3, al.	Aryloxyacetic acid, 157; Me. eth., 77–5, al.
88	5,6,7,8-Tetrahydro-1-naphthol	68.5–9.0; 74–5	264.5–5.0	......	......	......	....	....	....	73–5	46	Me. eth., b.p. 124[10]; Et. eth., b.p. 259[705]
89	2-Bromo-4,6-dichloro-phenol	68–9	268 d.	......	......	......	....	....	82–3	......	......	2,4-Dinitrophenyl ether, 140–1
90	2-Bromo-4-methyl-6-nitrophenol (2-Bromo-6-nitro-p-cresol)	69, yel.	....	......	......	......	....	....	128	110–11	......	....
91	2,4,6-Trichlorophenol	69.5, ac. a.; 68	245	......	......	105–6	....	....	....	b.p. 261–2	75.5, al.	Aryloxyacetic acid, 182–6; 2,4-Dinitrophenyl ether, 136; N,N-Diphenylure-thane, 143; Me. eth., 61–2, al.; Et. eth., 43–4
92	2,4,6-Trimethylphenol	70; 69	220	141–2, lgr.	......	......	....	di: 158	......	......	62, pet. eth.	Aryloxyacetic acid, 142
93	2,3,4,6-Tetrachlorophenol	70	150[15]	......	......	......	....	....	......	65–6	108	Me. eth., 64–5; Et. eth., 55; Benzene-sulfonate, 127
94	1-Chloro-2-naphthol	70, lgr.; 72	....	......	......	......	....	....	......	42–3	99–100	Me. eth., 70–1; Et. eth., 58
95	Methyl 3-hydroxybenzoate	70	280	115–6, bz.	......	......	....	....	......	......	......	....
96	2-Methyl-6-nitrophenol (6-Nitro-o-cresol)	70, w.-al.	....	......	......	......	....	....	66, al.	......	42, al.	Me. eth., 30, pet. eth.; Et. eth., b.p. 249–50, yel.
97	3-Propylcatechol (1,2-Dihydroxy-3-propyl-benzene)	70–2, pet. eth.	....	......	......	......	....	....	......	......	......	3-Me. eth., b.p. 144–6[25]; Di-Me. eth., b.p. 134–7[22]; Aryloxyacetic acid, 132; p-Xenylure-thane, 196
98	2,4,5-Trimethylphenol (Pseudocumenol)	71	232	110	......	......	35	....	......	34.0–4.5, pet. eth.	63, al.	Aryloxyacetic acid, 132; p-Xenylure-thane, 196
99	4,6-Dichloro-3-methyl-phenol (4,6-Dichloro-m-cresol)	72	235–6; 110[18]	......	......	......	....	....	104–5, al.	......	57.5, al.	n_D^{20}: 1.5722; Ben-zenesulfonate, 86, al.
100	2,4-Di-iodophenol	72, w.	....	......	......	......	....	....	165–7 (cor.)	70–1, w.-al.	98	Me. eth., 68, w.-al.; Et. eth., 46, me. al.; 51
101	2-Chloro-4,5-dimethyl-phenol	72	....	......	......	......	....	....	......	......	43	....
102	3,5-Dimethylcatechol (4,5-Dihydroxy-m-xylene)	73–4, w.	....	......	......	......	....	....	......	di: 161, ac. a.	......	4-Me. eth., b.p. 227–8

*Derivative data given in order: m.p., crystal color, solvent from which crystallized.

TABLE VII. ORGANIC DERIVATIVES OF PHENOLS
b) Solids (Listed in order of increasing m.p.)* (Continued)

No.	Name	Melting point, °C	Boiling point, °C	Phenyl ure-thane	α-Naph-thyl ure-thane	p-Nitro-ben-zoate	3,5-Di-nitro-benzoate	Bromo derivative	p-Toluene sul-fonate	Acetate	Benzoate	Miscellaneous
103	**5-Chloro-2-methylphenol** (5-Chloro-o-cresol)	73–4	225	......	......	......	....	tri: 190	110	....	53–4	Me. eth., b.p. 206–8; Et. eth., b.p. 210–20
104	**2,5-Dibromophenol**	73–4	....						110	....	....	
105	**3-Iodo-2-nitrophenol**	73.5, w.	....							102.5		Me. eth., 83–4
106	**Ethyl 3-hydroxybenzoate** ..	73.8, bz.	295; 282							35	58, al.	....
107	**1,3-Dibromo-2-naphthol** ..	75	....							102	......	
108	**2,5-Dimethylphenol** (p-2-Xylenol)	75, al.-eth.	212	160–1, bz.; 162; 166	172–3, lgr.	87	137.2 (cor.)	tri: 178	......		61	Aryloxyacetic acid, 118; p-Xenylurethane, 162; p-Phenylazobenzoate, 95.5–7.5; Picrate, 81–2, or., al.
109	**2,3-Dimethylphenol** (o-3-Xylenol)	75, w.-al.	193.5	......								Aryloxyacetic acid, 187; p-Phenylazobenzoate, 134–6; Me. eth., 29, b.p. 199; Et. eth., 10, b.p. 212.5
110	**8-Hydroxyquinoline** (Oxine)	75–6, dil. al.	266.6^{752}	......		174–5	....		115	b.p. 280	118–20, al.	Picrate, 203–4; Methiodide, 143 d. (hyd.)
111	**4-(Dimethylamino)phenol** .	76	....						130	78	......	
112	**3-Chloro-4-hydroxybiphenyl**	76–7; 80	....								110–11; 95–7	2,4-Dinitrophenyl ether, 109–11
113	**3-Bromo-2,6-dichlorophenol**	76.5, lgr.	264–70^{751}	......							102	Me. eth., b.p. 260–5^{750}
114	**2-Methyl-4,5,6-trichlorophenol** (4,5,6-Trichloro-o-cresol)	77, pet. eth.	....							45, w.-me. al.	......	Me. eth., 51.5, al.
115	**2-Bromo-4-methyl-3-nitrophenol** (2-Bromo-3-nitro-p-cresol)	77, yel., w.	....							81	......	Me. eth., 74
116	**3-(Diethylamino)phenol** ..	78	276–80	......							22–3	Methylurethane, 85–6; Methiodide, 140–3
117	**3-Phenylphenol** (3-Hydroxybiphenyl).	78; 75	>300	......					52.5	......	60–1, al.	Et. eth., 34
118	**4-Bromo-2,6-dinitrophenol**	78, yel.	....						136, al.	110.5, bz.	154, al.	Me. eth., 88; Et. eth., 66
119	**4-Chloro-2-iodophenol**	78		128						57	88; 84	
120	**2,4-Diaminophenol** (4-Hydroxy-m-phenylenediamine)	78–80; unstable										Me. eth., 68; Et. eth., 67.8; 4,N-Acetyl, 249; N,N'-Diacetyl, 220–2; O,N,N'-Triacetyl, 180–2; N,N'-Dibenzoyl, 253–4; Picrate, 120 d., yel.
121	**4-Methyl-3-nitrophenol** (3-Nitro-p-cresol)	79, yel., eth.	....						91	....	......	Me. eth., 17, b.p. 266–7
122	**2,3,4,6-Tetramethylphenol** (Isodurenol)	79–81	230–50	178–9, wh., w.-al.						71–2, wh., w.-al.		....
123	**2-Bromo-4,5-dimethylphenol**	80, pet. eth.	....	......							51	Me. eth., b.p. 86^3; o-Nitrobenzoate, 151–2

*Derivative data given in order: m.p., crystal color, solvent from which crystallized.

TABLE VII. ORGANIC DERIVATIVES OF PHENOLS
b) Solids (Listed in order of increasing m.p.)* (Continued)

No.	Name	Melting point, °C	Boiling point, °C	Phenyl ure-thane	α-Naph-thyl-ure-thane	p-Nitro-ben-zoate	3,5-Di-nitro-benzoate	Bromo derivative	p-Toluene sul-fonate	Acetate	Benzoate	Miscellaneous
124	5-Bromo-2-methylphenol (5-Bromo-o-cresol)	80	....	....	....	....	....	....	....	....	41	....
125	4-Iodo-2-nitrophenol	80–1	....	....	....	....	....	....	....	....	102–3	Me. eth., 98; Et. eth., 80
126	4-Hydroxy-3-methoxy-benzaldehyde (Vanillin)..	81	285	116–7	....	....	....	....	115	102	78	Aryloxyacetic acid, 187; 2,4-Dinitro-phenyl ether, 131; 2,4-Dinitrophenyl-hydrazone, 271 d.
127	3,5-Dibromophenol	81	....	....	....	....	....	....	....	53	77	Me. eth., 140
128	4-Chloro-2,6-dinitrophenol	81	....	....	....	....	....	....	....	110–11	......	Me. eth., 66; Et. eth., 54–5
129	4-Methyl-2-naphthol	81–2	....	....	....	....	....	....	....	117–8	......	....
130	5-Chloro-2,3-dimethyl-phenol	81–2	....	....	....	....	....	....	....	......	88, al.	....
131	3-Methyl-2,4,6-tribromo-phenol (2,4,6-Tribromo-m-cresol).............	81.5–2.0, al.	....	....	....	....	....	....	113–4, al.	68, al.	84–5, al.	p-Phenylazoben-zoate, 130–2
132	2-Hydroxy-1-naphthalde-hyde................	82	192[27]	....	....	....	....	....	....	87, al.; tri: 124, al.	......	Me. eth., 84; Et. eth., 115; Oxime, 157; Picrate, 120
133	3,4-Di-iodophenol........	83	....	....	....	....	....	....	....	123	....
134	2-Hydroxyazobenzene (2-Benzeneazophenol)	83	....	....	....	....	....	....	–20	93, pet. eth.	Me. eth., 41; Et. eth., 44; Cu deriv., 225–6, al.
135	5-Propylresorcinol (1,3-Dihydroxy-5-propyl-benzene; Divarinol).....	83–4, bz., (anh.); 51, w.	....	....	....	....	....	....	....	di: 12–5	......	Di-Me. eth., b.p. 147[29]
136	2,3,4-Trichlorophenol	83.5, lgr.	....	....	....	....	....	....	....	141, al.	Me. eth., 69.5, al.
137	4-Benzylphenol (4-Hy-droxydiphenylmethane) .	84	321; 308	....	....	....	....	....	....	mono: 87, pet.	2,4-Dinitrophenyl ether, 75.6; Benzyl eth., 49.5, al.
138	4-Chloro-2,3-dimethyl-phenol	84	....	....	....	....	....	....	....	102	....
139	2,4-Dimethyl-1-naphthol ..	84–5	169–70[10]	174–5	....	....	....	....	....	......	Me. eth., b.p. 150–1[12]; Picrate, 143–4, dk. red
140	4-Methyl-1-naphthol	84–5	....	....	....	....	....	....	....	81	....
141	1-Bromo-2-naphthol......	85	....	....	....	....	....	....	....	56	Me. eth., 85
142	3-Bromo-2-naphthol......	85	....	....	....	....	....	....	....	94	Me. eth., 77–8
143	2-Nitroresorcinol (1,3-Dihydroxy-2-nitro-benzene)	85, or.-red, w.-al.	....	....	....	....	....	....	....	di: 63	......	Di-Me. eth., 131, yel., al.; Di-Et. eth., 106–7
144	3-(Dimethylamino)phenol (3-Hydroxydimethyl-aniline)	85	265–8; 138[10]	....	....	....	....	....	....	36.5; b.p. 160[5]	94	Picrate, 162; Methylurethane, 87; Ethylurethane, 150; 99–100; Me. eth., b.p. 237; Et. eth., b.p. 247
145	3-Hydroxy-2-nitrobiphenyl	85–6, bz.; 81–2, yel., al.	....	....	....	....	....	....	....	61.5–2.5	131.0–2.5	Benzenesulfonate, 130–1; 4-Nitro deriv., 126–7; 6-Nitro deriv., 214; 4,6-Dinitro deriv., 168–70
146	2-Hydroxybenzyl alcohol (Saligenin)	86–7, w.	....	....	....	....	....	....	....	......	di: 51, 70% al.	Aryloxyacetic acid, 120, w.

*Derivative data given in order: m.p., crystal color, solvent from which crystallized.

TABLE VII. ORGANIC DERIVATIVES OF PHENOLS

b) Solids (Listed in order of increasing m.p.)* (Continued)

No.	Name	Melting point, °C	Boiling point, °C	Phenyl ure-thane	α-Naph-thyl-ure-thane	p-Nitro-ben-zoate	3,5-Di-nitro-benzoate	Bromo derivative	p-Toluene sul-fonate	Acetate	Benzoate	Miscellaneous
147	**4,6-Dinitro-2-methylphenol** (4,6-Dinitro-o-cresol) ...	86.5	....	......	......	......	....	......	......	95–6	135; 132	....
148	**3-Nitrocatechol** (1,2-Dihydroxy-3-nitroben-zene)	86.5, yel., pet. eth.								di: b.p. 103–4[1]	2-mono: 66	1-Me. eth., 62, yel.; 2-Me. eth., 102–3; Di-Me. eth., 64–5, al.
149	**4-Chloro-2-nitrophenol** ...	86–7	....	......	......	......	....	......	......	47–8	......	Me. eth., 98; Et. eth., 61–2
150	**2,4,5-Tribromophenol**	87, CH$_2$Cl$_2$-pet. eth.	....	......	......	......	....	......	......	......	99	Me. eth., 105; o-Br-p-toluenesulfonate, 107–8, al.
151	**4-Bromocatechol** (4-Bromo-1,2-dihydroxybenzene) ..	87									di: 111	1-Me. eth., 65
152	**4-(Methylamino)phenol** ...	87, bz.							135, bz.-lgr.	43, pet. eth.	173–4, 50% al.	Aryloxyacetic acid, 213–4; Me. eth., 37
153	**2-Methyl-3,4,5-tribromo-phenol** (3,4,5-Tribromo-o-cresol)	89, pet.	....	......	......	......	....	......	......	......	......	....
154	**2-Amino-6-methylphenol** (6-Amino-o-cresol)	89, w.							89; 90	78–9	......	N-Acetyl, 100–1
155	**N-Benzylidene-2-amino-phenol**	89								93–6	......	Et. eth., b.p. 215–6[20]
156	**3-Nitro-2,4,6-tribromo-phenol**	89–90, lgr.	....	......	......	......	....	......	146–7, al.	......	......	Me. eth., 82, al.; Et. eth., 79, eth.
157	**2-Amino-6-chloro-4-methylphenol** (2-Amino-6-chloro-p-cresol)	89–90									......	N,O-Diacetyl, 162–3
158	**1,3-Dimethyl-2-naphthol** ..	89–90	....	197	......	......	....	......	85–6	......	......	Picrate, 132–3
159	**2-Propylhydroquinone** (1,4-Dihydroxy-2-propyl-benzene)	90, bz.										Di-Me. eth., b.p. 240–6
160	**4-Chlorocatechol** (4-Chloro-1,2-dihydroxy-benzene)	90–1	136[8.5]							di: b.p. 145–7[7]	di; 96–7, eth.	Di-Me. eth., b.p. 242.4
161	**3-Chloro-4,6-dimethyl-phenol**	90–1	....	......	......	......	....	......	......	......	......	....
162	**2-Methyl-3,4,6-tribromo-phenol** (3,4,6-Tribromo-o-cresol)	91, pet.	....	......	......	......	....	......	......	76–7, ac. a.	85, 133, bz.	Me. eth., 71, al.
163	**5-Chloro-2,4-dinitrophenol**	92	....	......	......	......	....	......	......	69	......	Me. eth., 105; Et. eth., 112; 6-Nitro deriv., 113–5
164	**4-Chloro-2,6-dibromo-phenol**	92							107–8			2,4-Dinitrophenyl ether, 145–6; Me. eth., 74
165	**4-Bromo-2-nitrophenol** ...	92; 89	....	......	......	......	....	......	......	75	......	Me. eth., 88; Et. eth., 47; Benzene-sulfonate, 83–4
166	**4-tert-Amylphenol**	92–3	260–5	108	......	......	....	......	55	......	61	....
167	**4-Hydroxyphenylethyl alcohol** (Tyrosol)	93, chl.	310; 156[15]							β-mono: 59, eth.-lgr.; di: b.p. 187[18]	di: 111, al.	4-Et. eth., 40

*Derivative data given in order: m.p., crystal color, solvent from which crystallized.

No.	Name	Melting point, °C	Boiling point, °C	Phenylurethane	α-Naphthylurethane	p-Nitrobenzoate	3,5-Dinitrobenzoate	Bromo derivative	p-Toluene sulfonate	Acetate	Benzoate	Miscellaneous
168	**4-Iodophenol**	93–4, w.	....	148, bz.	......	....	....	....	99, me. al.	32	119	Aryloxyacetic acid, 156; N,N-Di-phenylurethane, 127; 2,4-Dinitro-phenyl ether, 156
169	**1-Naphthol (α-Naphthol)**	94	278–80	177–8, al.	152, lgr.	143; 140	217.4 (cor.), yel., al.	2,4-*di*: 105	89	48–9, al.	56, al.	Aryloxyacetic acid, 193.5; p-Xenyl-urethane, 190; 2,4-Dinitrophenyl ether, 128; p-Phenylazo-benzoate, 118–9
170	**2-Iodo-4-nitrophenol**	94; 86–7	....	....	......	....	....	....		68	......	Me. eth., 97; Et. eth., 96
171	**2,4,6-Tribromophenol (Bromol)**	95, HCOOH; 94, ac. a. (+1 ac. a.)	....	......	153	153	174	*tetra*: 120	113, al.	82; 87, ac. a.	81, al.	Aryloxyacetic acid, 200; N,N-Di-phenylurethane, 153; 2,4-Dinitro-phenyl ether, 137–8; p-Phenylazo-benzoate, 116–9
172	**2,2'-Stilbenediol (2,2'-Dihydroxystilbene)**	α: 95, al.; β: 197, al.	....								α: *di*: 107–8	β: Di-Me. eth., 136
173	**6-Chloro-1-naphthol**	95	....							47	......	Picrate, 165
174	**3-Bromo-4-hydroxybi-phenyl**	95	....							74–5	93–4	Benzenesulfonate, 102–3
175	**1,3,6-Trihydroxynaph-thalene (1,3,6-Naph-thalenetriol)**	95								*tri*: 112–3		Me. eth., 103–4
176	**2,3,4-Tribromophenol**	95, w.-HCOOH	....									Me. eth., 106
177	**2,3,5-Trimethylphenol**	95–6	233	174, pet. eth.						241	50, pet. eth.	....
178	**2-Naphthyl salicylate (Betol)**	95.5, stable; 93.5, labile	....	268, yel., ac. a.	......					136, al.	......	
179	**3-Amino-2,4,6-trichloro-phenol**	95.5–6.0, lgr.	....									N-Acetyl, 185.0–6.5, tol.
180	**3-Acetylphenol (3-Hydroxyacetophenone)**	96	296; 153[5]	......						44.0–4.5	52–3	D[109]: 1.099; n_α^{109}: 1.5348; Me. eth., b.p. 240; Semi-carbazone, 194–6
181	**5-Iodo-2-nitrophenol**	96, yel., pet. eth.								95	122	Me. eth., 92; Et. eth., 86–7
182	**2-Methoxy-5-propenyl-phenol**	96; 92	147[19]							101	......	Et. eth., 49–50
183	**2-Methyl-4-nitrophenol (4-Nitro-o-cresol)**	96, yel., bz.; 30–40 (+1 H₂O), w.	186–90	....	......				107, al.	......	128	Me. eth., 64, al.; Et. eth., 71, w.-al.
184	**2-(Methylamino)phenol**	96–7; 86–7, pet. eth.	....	......							157–9	N-Benzoyl, 160–1; Me. eth., 33.0–3.5
185	**3-Nitrophenol**	97	194[70]	129	167	174	159	*di*: 91	112–3	55–6	95	D[100]: 1.2797; Aryloxybenzoic acid, 156; 2,4-Dinitrophenyl ether, 136; p-Phenylazo-benzoate, 160.5–2.5

*Derivative data given in order: m.p., crystal color, solvent from which crystallized.

No.	Name	Melting point, °C	Boiling point, °C	Phenyl urethane	α-Naphthylurethane	p-Nitrobenzoate	3,5-Dinitrobenzoate	Bromo derivative	p-Toluene sulfonate	Acetate	Benzoate	Miscellaneous
186	2,3-Dibromo-5,6-dimethyl-phenol	97, aq. al.	....	.....	.....	.....	.....	.....	......	78, pet. eth.	153, al.	....
187	5-Methyl-1-naphthol	97–8	....	.....	.....	.....	.....	.....	......		77–8	....
188	3-Acetylcatechol (2,3-Dihydroxyacetophenone)	97–8, yel., w.	....	.....	.....	.....	.....	.....	......	di: 109, bz.	......	1-Me. eth., 152–3; Di-Me. eth., 48; Oxime, 96–7; Semicarbazone, 166–7
189	2-Cyanophenol	98	....	.....	.....	.....	.....	.....	......	106, pet. eth.		$D_4^{99.6}$: 1.1052; $n_\alpha^{99.6}$: 1.53716
190	3-Chloro-4,5-dimethyl-phenol	98	....	.....	.....	.....	.....	.....	......	42, al.		....
191	2,5-Di-iodophenol	99, pet. eth.	....	.....	.....	.....	.....	.....	......	70, ac. a.	......	
192	4-tert-Butylphenol	100	237	148.5	110	.....	.....	50; di: 64–7	109–10	......	81–2	Aryloxyacetic acid, 86.5; 2,4-Dinitrophenyl ether, 108–10; Benzenesulfonate, 70–1
193	3,4,5-Trichlorophenol	101, lgr.; 91	271–7^{746}	.....	.....	.....	.....	...·.		120, al.	Me. eth., 130, b.p. 256–61; m-Nitrobenzenesulfonate, 176
194	3,5-Dibromo-2-methyl-phenol (3,5-Dibromo-o-cresol)	101; 98–101	....	.....	.....	.....	.....	.....	......		91–3	....
195	4,6-Dinitro-3-methylphenol (4,6-Dinitro-m-cresol)	101; 73–4	....	.....	.....	.....	.....	.....	110–11	......	95	Me. eth., 115; Et. eth., 97
196	2-Acetyl-1-naphthol	102, pa. grn., al; 98, br.-yel., bz.	325, sl. d.	.....	.....	.....	.....	.....	......	107.5, al.	128, al.	....
197	2-Methyl-3,4,5-trinitro-phenol (3,4,5-Trinitro-o-cresol)	102, or.-yel., acet.	....	.....	.....	.....	.....	.....	......			Me. eth., 111–2, w.-al.
198	4-Methyl-2,3,6-tribromo-phenol (2,3,6-Tribromo-p-cresol)	102, pet.	....	.....	.....	.....	.....	.....	......	77, lgr.	......	
199	1-Nitro-2-naphthol	103, yel., al.	....	.....	.....	.....	.....	.....	......	61, pet. eth.	......	m-Nitrobenzenesulfonate, 176, ac. a.; Et. eth., 104–5, yel., al.
200	3,3'-Dihydroxydiphenyl-methane	103, yel., al.	....	.....	.....	.....	.....	.....	......	di: 57.5–8.5, lgr.		....
201	4-Chloro-2-naphthol	104								56		
202	3,5-Di-iodophenol	104, w.	....	.....	.....	.....	.....	.....	......	79, me. al.	93	Me. eth., 85, pet. eth.; Et. eth., 30, me. al.
203	2-Bromo-4-methyl-5-nitro-phenol (2-Bromo-5-nitro-p-cresol)	104, yel.	....	.....	.....	.....	.....	.....	......	121		Me. eth., 94, yel., eth.
204	3-Hydroxybenzaldehyde (3-Formylphenol)	104; 108 (cor.)	240	158–60	.....	.....	.....	.....	......	b.p. 203	38; 48.5–9.0	Aryloxyacetic acid, 148; 2,4-Dinitrophenylhydrazone, 257d.; Semicarbazone, 198
205	5-Methyl-2-naphthol	104–5	....	.....	.....	.....	.....	.....	......		107–8	Picrate, 156–7

*Derivative data given in order: m.p., crystal color, solvent from which crystallized.

TABLE VII. ORGANIC DERIVATIVES OF PHENOLS
b) Solids (Listed in order of increasing m.p.)* (Continued)

No.	Name	Melting point, °C	Boiling point, °C	Phenyl urethane	α-Naphthyl urethane	p-Nitrobenzoate	3,5-Dinitrobenzoate	Bromo derivative	p-Toluene sulfonate	Acetate	Benzoate	Miscellaneous
206	3-Hydroxy-4-nitrobiphenyl	104–5, al.				157	199					
207	Catechol (Pyrocatechol; 1,2-Dihydroxybenzene)	105	245.6	di: 169	175	mono: 159; di: 169, al.	di: 152	tetra: 192–3, wh.-vlt.		mono: 57–8; di: 65	mono: 181; 131; di: 84, al.-eth.	Aryloxyacetic acid, 136–8; Monobenzenesulfonate monoacetate, 86, me. al.; Dibenzenesulfonate, 155–6, acet.
208	2,4-Dibromo-1-naphthol	105; 111								92–3		Me. eth., 54–5, al.; sym.-TNB add. comp., 97; Picrate, 97, yel.
209	2,4-Dichloro-5-nitrophenol	105–6									111–2	m-Nitrobenzoate, 154; o-Nitro-p-toluenesulfonate, 143
210	Chlorohydroquinone	106								mono: 62; di: 72; 99		
211	4,6-Dinitro-2-iodophenol	106–7, w.							149	113		
212	1,6-Dibromo-2-naphthol	106–7 (+1 ac. a., 84)								125		Me. eth., 102; Et. eth., 94
213	2-Amino-5-chloro-4-methylphenol (2-Amino-5-chloro-p-cresol)	106–7										N-Acetyl, 115, aq. al.; Me. eth., 106, lgr.
214	4-Chlororesorcinol (4-Chloro-1,3-dihydroxybenzene)	106–7; 89	259; 147[18]						di: 46–7	di: 66		3-Me. eth., 79–80; Di-Me. eth., b.p. 135–7[17]
215	2-Hydroxypyridine (α-Pyridone)	106–7, bz.	280–1			120				158–9; 53	b.p. 150–60[0.09]	42	Picrate, 176–7; Benzyl eth., 42
216	2-Phenoxyphenol (2-Hydroxydiphenyl ether)	106–7	151–5[11]							b.p. 358–60	48.5	Me. eth., 79, lgr.
217	5-Methylresorcinol (Orcinol; 3,5-Dihydroxytoluene)	106.5–8; 56–8 (+1 H$_2$O)	287–90	154	160, lgr.	214	190	tri: 104		di: 25	di: 88, al.	Aryloxyacetic acid, 217; p-Xenylurethane, 196; 2,4-Dinitrophenyl ether, 153–4
218	6-Amino-4-chloro-2-methylphenol (6-Amino-4-chloro-o-cresol)	107								2,3-di: 196		
219	2,4-Dichloro-1-naphthol	107–8								74–6		Me. eth., 58
220	1,2-Dihydroxynaphthalene (1,2-Naphthalenediol; β-Naphthohydroquinone)	108; 105.5								di: 104–6; 109, ac. a.	di: 106	Diaryloxyacetic acid, 104–6; 1-Me. eth., 90.5; Di-Me. eth., 31
221	1,2,3,4-Tetrahydroanthranol	108, lgr.								109, al.	142	Me. eth., b.p. 197[14]
222	4-Methyl-5,6,7,8-tetrahydro-2-naphthol	108				114–6					89	
223	4-Acetylphenol (4-Hydroxyacetophenone)	109								54		Semicarbazone, 199; 2,4-Dinitrophenylhydrazone, 261.5 (cor.), br., al.
224	3-Methyl-2,4,6-trinitrophenol (2,4,6-Trinitro-m-cresol)	109–10, yel., al.								135, pa. yel., bz.	140	Di-Me. eth., 155, al.; Di-Et. eth., 36–7, w.-al.

*Derivative data given in order: m.p., crystal color, solvent from which crystallized.

TABLE VII. ORGANIC DERIVATIVES OF PHENOLS

b) Solids (Listed in order of increasing m.p.)* (Continued)

No.	Name	Melting point, °C	Boiling point, °C	Phenyl urethane	α-Naphthylurethane	p-Nitrobenzoate	3,5-Dinitrobenzoate	Bromo derivative	p-Toluene sulfonate	Acetate	Benzoate	Miscellaneous
225	**2-Iodo-6-nitrophenol**	109–10	....	,........	....	....	....	....	....	96–7	....	Me. eth., 96–7
226	**Resorcinol** (1,3-Dihydroxy-benzene)	110 (sta-ble); 108–8.5 (labile)	280.8 (cor.); 275.9	*di*: 164, chl.	....	*di*: 182; 175	*di*: 201	*tri*: 112	*di*: 80–1, acet.-dil. al.	57–8, dil. al.	*mono*: 135–6; *di*: 117, dil. al.	Aryloxyacetic acid, 175; 195; 2,4-Dini-trophenyl ether, 194; N,N-Di-phenylurethane, 194; Me. eth., 43–4, me. al.
227	**2,2′-Biphenol** (2,2′-Dihydroxybiphenyl)	110; 109; tol.	326	*di*: 145, dil. al.	....	....	....	*di*: 188	190	*di*: 95, xyl.	*di*: 101, al.	Di-Me. eth., 155, al., Di-Et. eth., 36–7, w.-al.
228	**Bromohydroquinone**......	110	....	....	....	....	....	*di*: 186	....	*di*: 72	....	
229	**4-Hydroxy-2′-nitro-biphenyl**..............	110–1; 116	....	....	....	....	....	....	122		156–7	Aryloxyacetic acid, 160–1; Benzene-sulfonate, 106, yel., al.; Me. eth., 60.0–0.5; Et. eth., 51; 5-nitro deriv., 151–2
230	**7-Methyl-1-naphthol**	110–11	....	....	....	....	....	....		39–41	....	Picrate, 164–5
231	**1-Methyl-2-naphthol**	111	....	....	....	....	....	....		66	116–7	Picrate, 163–4
232	**2-Chloro-4-nitrophenol** ...	111, w.	....	....	....	....	....	....		63	....	Me. eth., 98; Et. eth., 82; 142
233	**2-Amino-6-nitrophenol**....	111–2, aq. al.	....	....	....	....	....	....		2-*mono*: 102–3 (hyd.); 122 (anh.)	....	Me. eth., 198
234	**2,4,6-Tribromoresorcinol** (1,3-Dihydroxy-2,4,6-tri-bromobenzene)	112, w.	....	....	....	....	....	....		*mono*: 114, CS₂; *di*: 108	*mono*: 120, chl.-pet.-eth.	Me. eth., 104; Di-Me. eth., 68–9, w.-al.
235	**4′,5-Dimethyl-2-hydroxy-azobenzene** (2-p-Toluene-azo-p-cresol)..........	112–3, tol.	....	....	....	....	....	....		91, yel., ac. a.	95, yel., al.	Et. eth., 43, ac. a.; Propionate, 62, lgr.
236	**4-Hydroxyphenanthrene** (4-Phenanthrol)	112–3.5, pet. eth.	....	....	....	....	....	....		58–9, al.	....	Me. eth., 68, me. al.
237	**2,2′-Dihydroxy-3,3′-dimethylbiphenyl**	113, pet. eth.	....	....	....	....	....	....			*di*: 147, me. al.	....
238	**2,6-Dinitro-4-iodophenol** ..	113, w.	....	....	....	....	....	....	138		175	....
239	**2-Chloro-4,6-dinitrophenol**	113; 110	....	....	....	....	....	....	155		....	....
240	**4,4′-Dihydroxy-2,2′-dimethylbiphenyl**	114	....	....	....	....	....	....		*di*: 75	*di*: 127	....
241	**2-Bromo-4-nitrophenol** ...	114	....	....	....	....	....	....		62; 86	131–2	Me. eth., 106; Et. eth., 98, yel.
242	**4-Nitrophenol**	114	....	156	150–1	159	186; 188 (+1 ac. a.)	2,6-*di*: 142	97	81–2, w.-al.	142.5	Aryloxyacetic acid, 187; 2,4-Dinitro-phenyl ether, 120; N,N-Diphenylure-thane, 112; p-Phenylazoben-zoate, 203–6
243	**2,4-Dinitrophenol**	114	....	....	....	139	....	6-*mono*: 118	121	72	132	2,4-Dinitrophenyl ether, 248
244	**2,3,5-Tri-iodophenol**	114, bz.-lgr.	....	....	....	....	....	....		123	....	Et. eth., 121

*Derivative data given in order: m.p., crystal color, solvent from which crystallized.

TABLE VII. ORGANIC DERIVATIVES OF PHENOLS

b) Solids (Listed in order of increasing m.p.)* (Continued)

No.	Name	Melting point, °C	Boiling point, °C	Phenyl urethane	α-Naphthyl urethane	p-Nitrobenzoate	3,5-Dinitrobenzoate	Bromo derivative	p-Toluene sulfonate	Acetate	Benzoate	Miscellaneous
245	4-Hydroxy-3-methoxybenzyl alcohol	115								4-mono: 51; di: 48, bz.-lgr.	4-mono: 90, et. ac.-al.; di: 121	4-Et. eth., 56-7
246	1-Hydroxyfluorenone	115, yel.								130-1, aq. al.	128-9	Me. eth., 141.5-2.5; Oxime, 169-70; Phenylhydrazone, 173-4
247	Ethyl 4-hydroxybenzoate	115; 116	297-8								94, eth.	
248	4-Chloro-3,5-dimethylphenol	115-6								47-8		
249	3,5-Dimethyl-2,4-dinitrophenol	115-6; 106						171		148	156	
250	4-Bromo-1,5-dihydroxynaphthalene (4-Bromo-1,5-naphthalenediol)	116								di: 138		Di-Me. eth., 115
251	3-Benzoylphenol (3-Hy-)	116, al.										Oxime, anti: 76, bz.; syn: 126 (on heating anti)
252	4-Hydroxybenzaldehyde	116-7									90	Aryloxyacetic acid, 198; 2,4-Dinitrophenylhydrazone, 270-1
253	3-Bromo-1,2-dihydroxynaphthalene (3-Bromo-1,2-naphthalenediol)	117								di: 160		Naphthalene add. comp., 100
255	Phloroglucinol (1,3,5-Trihydroxybenzene)	117 ($+2H_2O$); 217-9 (anh.)			283			tri: 151		tri: 104	tri: 185	Picrate, 101-3
256	2,4'-Dihydroxydiphenylmethane	117-8, w.-al.								di: 70, ac. a.	di: 108	Di-Me. eth., 26; Di-Et. eth., 60, w.-al.
257	2,3,5,6-Tetramethylphenol (Durenol)	118, wh., pet.	249			4-mono: 118, or., dil. al.						
258	4-Amino-2-methyl-6-nitrophenol (4-Amino-6-nitro-o-cresol)	118, al.								4-mono: 217, yel., al.		
259	2,4-Dibromo-6-nitrophenol	118, ac. a.						140		89		Me. eth., 76-7, yel.; Et. eth., 46
260	2-Methyl-5-nitrophenol (5-Nitro-o-cresol)	118, yel., lgr.						123-4, al.		74		Me. eth., 74, al.; Et. eth., 61, al.
261	2-Bromo-4,6-dinitrophenol	118-9, yel.						157		104.5	94, aq. al.	Me. eth., 48, yel.
262	2-Bromo-5-nitrophenol	118.5-21, pet. eth.						131.5-2.5, al.				Me. eth., 104, al.
263	2-Amino-4-methyl-6-nitrophenol (2-Amino-6-nitro-p-cresol)	119; 110, br., al.										N-Acetyl, 143, yel., al.
264	3-Amino-2,4,6-tribromophenol	119, pet. eth.						146-7, al.				O,N,N-Triacetyl, 136

*Derivative data given in order: m.p., crystal color, solvent from which crystallized.

No.	Name	Melting point, °C	Boiling point, °C	Phenyl urethane	α-Naphthyl urethane	p-Nitrobenzoate	3,5-Dinitrobenzoate	Bromo derivative	p-Toluene sulfonate	Acetate	Benzoate	Miscellaneous
265	2-Methylresorcinol (1,3-Dihydroxy-2-methylbenzene; 2,6-Dihydroxytoluene)	119–20, bz.	271 (cor.)	......	......	......	....	....	....	......	di: 105–6, me. al.	Di-Me. eth., 39
266	4-Acetylcatechol (3,4-Dihydroxyacetophenone)	119.2–.7; 116	....	......	......	......	....	....	di: 144–5, et. ac.	4-mono: 58; di: 91; 88	di: 118, al.	Oxime, 184 d., et. ac.; 1-Me. eth., 91; 2-Me. eth., 115; Di-Me. eth., 51
267	2-Chloro-5-nitrophenol	119.5, w.	....	......	......	......	....	....	....	82	127–8	Me. eth., 83; Et. eth., 64.5, al.
268	5-Methyl-1,2,3-trihydroxybenzene (3,4,5-Trihydroxytoluene; 5-Methylpyrogallol)	120 (subl.), bz.	....	......	......	......	....	....	....	tri: 99	......	3,5-Di-Me. eth., 36, al.
269	9-Hydroxyanthracene (9-Anthrol; Anthranol)	120, yel.	....	......	......	......	....	....	....	126–31	286–8	....
270	6-Bromo-2-methyl-4-nitrophenol (6-Bromo-4-nitro-o-cresol)	120 d., yel., lgr.	....	......	......	......	....	....	....	137	......	
271	2,2'-Dihydroxy-4,4'-dimethylbiphenyl	120	....	......	......	......	....	....	....	......	di: 148, al.-acet.	....
272	4-Nitro-2-naphthol	120, yel., pet. eth.	....	......	......	......	....	....	122, pa. yel., al.	......	......	m-Nitrobenzenesulfonate, 149, ac. a.; Me. eth., 100–3, br., bz.-al.
273	4-Chloro-1-naphthol	120–1; 116–7, al. or chl.	....	......	......	......	....	....	....	44	....	Picrate, 171; Carbonate, 228
274	2-Chloro-3-nitrophenol	120.5, w.	....	......	......	......	....	....	....	51.5	94	Me. eth., 94; Et. eth., 51, me. al.
275	4-Chloro-3,5-dibromophenol	121	....	......	......	......	....	....	....	......	132	Me. eth., 82.5
276	3,4-Dimethyl-1-naphthol	121.5–3.0, lgr.	205–10^{15}	......	......	222–4	....	....	....	89.5–91	......	Turns red in air; Picrate, 168
277	3-Aminophenol (3-Hydroxyaniline)	122	....	......	143	179	....	....	....	......	......	N-Acetyl, 148; N-p-Toluenesulfonyl, 157; N-Phenylthiourea, 156
278	2-Amino-3-chlorophenol	122	....	......	......	......	....	....	....	......	......	N-Acetyl, 123; N-Benzoyl, 123; HNO₃ salt, 137
279	4-Bromo-2-naphthol	122	....	......	......	......	....	....	....	61	......	Me. eth., 64
280	4-Nitroresorcinol (1,3-Dihydroxy-4-nitrobenzene)	122, yel., CCl₄	178–9^{11}	......	......	......	....	....	....	di: 90–1, al.	1-mono: 124, ac. a.; 3-mono: 189, ac. a.; di: 110	Di-Et. eth., 85
281	2,4,6-Trinitrophenol (Picric acid)	122 (subl. on slow htng.; exp. on rapid htng.)	....	......	......	......	....	....	....	76	......	Naphthalene add. comp., 149–51

*Derivative data given in order: m.p., crystal color, solvent from which crystallized.

TABLE VII. ORGANIC DERIVATIVES OF PHENOLS
b) Solids (Listed in order of increasing m.p.)* (Continued)

No.	Name	Melting point, °C	Boiling point, °C	Phenyl urethane	α-Naphthyl urethane	p-Nitro benzoate	3,5-Di nitro benzoate	Bromo derivative	p-Toluene sul fonate	Acetate	Benzoate	Miscellaneous
282	3-Hydroxyphenanthrene (3-Phenanthrol)	122–3, al.	....	....	....	....	....	....	....	114–5, aq. al.	....	Me. eth., 63, me. al.; Et. eth., 46, me. al.; Picrate, 124–5, red, al.
283	2,4-Dichloro-6-nitrophenol	122–3	....	....	....	....	....	....	....	77	....	3-Nitrobenzoate, 149–50
284	2-Naphthol (β-Naphthol)	123	286	155–6, al.	156–7, lgr.	169	210.2 (cor.), al.	84	125, al.	71–2; 70	106–7	Aryloxyacetic acid, 95; 2,4-Dinitrophenyl ether, 95; N,N-Diphenylurethane, 141; p-Phenylazobenzoate, 190–3
285	2,3,4,5-Tetrabromophenol	123, aq. al.	....	....	....	....	....	225–6	....	110.5, aq. ac. a.	133, al.	....
286	2,4-Dimethyl-2-methoxyphenol	123	....	....	....	....	....	....	137–8	114	....	Et. eth., 91
287	2-Nitro-4,5,6-tribromophenol	123, yel., bz.	....	....	....	....	....	....	....	....	....	Me. eth., 109, al.; Et. eth., 74
288	1,4-Dichloro-2-naphthol	123–4	....	....	....	....	....	....	....	90–1	....	....
289	4-Butyl-2-methylphenol (4-Butyl-o-cresol)	124	127–9[15]	....	....	....	....	....	....	268–70	....	....
290	3,3'-Biphenol (3,3'-Dihydroxybiphenyl)	124, w.	....	....	....	....	....	....	....	di: 82.5, dil. al.	di: 92	Di-Me. eth., 36, w.-al., b.p. 328
291	1,3-Dihydroxynaphthalene (1,3-Naphthalenediol)	124, w.	....	....	....	....	....	....	....	di: 56, w.-ac. a.	....	sym-Trinitrobenzene add. comp., 174.5, red
292	3-Iodo-4-nitrophenol	124, yel., pet. eth.	....	....	....	....	....	....	....	73–7	119	Me. eth., 69–70
293	2-Methylhydroquinone (2,5-Dihydroxytoluene)	124–5, bz.	....	....	....	....	....	84	125	mono: 92, pet. eth.; di: 49; 45, w.	di: 119–20	Aryloxyacetic acid, 153; Di-Et. eth., 24–5, b.p. 247–9
294	4-Hydroxybenzyl alcohol (α,4-Dihydroxytoluene)	124.5–5.5	....	....	....	....	....	....	....	α-mono: 84; di: 75	α-mono: 88–9	....
295	4,6-Dimethylresorcinol (4,6-Dihydroxy-m-xylene)	124.5–5.0, w. (+1 w.)	276–9	....	....	....	....	....	....	di: 45, al.; b.p. 285–7	....	Di-Me. eth., 76; Di-Et. eth., 75, al.
296	4-Benzyl-1-naphthol	125–6	....	....	....	....	....	....	....	87–8	103	....
297	Pentamethylphenol	126	267	215	....	....	....	....	....	273	127	Me. eth., 163–4
298	3,5-Dinitrophenol	126; 122	....	....	....	....	....	....	....	126–7	....	Me. eth., 105–6; Et. eth., 97
299	7-Chloro-2-naphthol	126.5	....	....	....	....	....	....	....	104.5	....	....
300	4-Chloro-3-nitrophenol	126.5, w.	....	....	....	....	....	....	....	83.5	96–7	Me. eth., 98, al.; Et. eth., 47.5, al.
301	2-Nitro-3,4,6-tribromophenol	127, pa. yel., w.-HCOOH	....	....	....	....	....	....	....	118	....	Me. eth., 72, w.-HCOOH
302	2-Nitro-1-naphthol	127–8, yel., al.	....	....	....	....	....	....	....	118	....	Me. eth., 80; Et. eth., 84, yel., lgr.
303	1,3-Dibromo-2,4-dihydroxynaphthalene (1,3-Dibromo-2,4-naphthalenediol)	128–9, ac. a.	....	....	....	....	....	186, CS₂	....	4-mono: 148; di: 125, al.	....	....

*Derivative data given in order: m.p., crystal color, solvent from which crystallized.

No.	Name	Melting point, °C	Boiling point, °C	Phenyl urethane	α-Naphthyl urethane	p-Nitrobenzoate	3,5-Dinitrobenzoate	Bromo derivative	p-Toluene sulfonate	Acetate	Benzoate	Miscellaneous
304	4-Iodo-2-naphthol	128.5								59		Me. eth., 67
305	4-Bromo-1-naphthol	129								51		
306	3-Methyl-4-nitrophenol (4-Nitro-m-cresol)	129, w.								34, al.	74	Me. eth., 55, lgr.; Et. eth., 45, al.
307	3-Hydroxypyridine (β-Pyridone)	129								b.p. 210; 92⁹	50.0–0.5	Hydrochloride, 105–7; Picrate, 200–1
308	4-Hydroxy-3-nitroazobenzene	129, lgr.								120.5, ac. a.	132, bz.	Me. eth., 107
309	3-Amino-2-methylphenol (3-Amino-o-cresol)	129, w.								108		Turns br. in air
310	6-Bromo-2-naphthol	129–30								103		Me. eth., 108
311	8-Nitro-1-naphthol	130										m-Nitrobenzene-sulfonate, 166, ac. a.
312	4-Amino-2-nitrophenol	131, dk. red										Me. eth., 243; Et. eth., 170, N-Acetyl, 157–8, yel.
313	Methyl 4-hydroxybenzoate	131		134–5, bz.						85	135	....
314	5-Methyl-1,2,4-trihydroxybenzene (2,4,5-Trihydroxytoluene)	131–2, bz.								tri: 114–5, al.		4-Me. eth., 124, w.; 4-Et. eth., 131 (subl.), bz., Tri-me. eth., 55, w.-me. al.
315	5-Chloro-1-naphthol	131–2, w. or CS₂								53		Picrate, 160
316	4-Cyclohexylphenol	132		145.5		137, al.	168 (cor.)			35	118.5, me. al.	....
317	Pyrogallol (1,2,3-Trihydroxybenzene)	133	309	tri: 173		tri: 230	tri: 205	di: 158		di: 110–11; tri: 165, 173	mono: 140; di: 108; tri: 90, al.	Tris-N,N-Diphenylurethane, 212
318	2-Amino-4,6-dimethylphenol	134–5, al.										N-Acetyl, 96, aq. al.; O,N-Dibenzoyl, 153.5; Me. eth., b.p. 239–40
319	4-Amino-5-isopropyl-2-methyl-6-nitrophenol (4-Amino-5-isopropyl-6-nitro-o-cresol)	134–5, yel., al.									1-mono: 280–3; di: 222–5, bz.	....
320	4,6-Dibromo-2-naphthol	134–5								128	128–9	Me. eth., 103; Et. eth., 98
321	2,3-Dichloro-1,4-dihydroxynaphthalene	135; 155–6, aq. al.								di: 239–40	di: 252	Di-Me. eth., 107–8; Dipropionate, 166–7; Dibutyrate, 128
322	4-Benzoylphenol (4-Hydroxybenzophenone)	135								81, me. al.	115; 94–5	2,4-Dinitrophenylhydrazone, 242.4 (cor.); Semicarbazone, 194

*Derivative data given in order: m.p., crystal color, solvent from which crystallized.

TABLE VII. ORGANIC DERIVATIVES OF PHENOLS
b) Solids (Listed in order of increasing m.p.)* (Continued)

No.	Name	Melting point, °C	Boiling point, °C	Phenyl ure-thane	α-Naph-thyl-ure-thane	p-Nitro-ben-zoate	3,5-Di-nitro-benzoate	Bromo derivative	p-Toluene sul-fonate	Acetate	Benzoate	Miscellaneous
323	**2-Amino-4-methylphenol** (2-Amino-p-cresol)	135, w.	. . . . .	. .ᵣ . .	. . . . . .	. . . . . .	. . . . . .	. . . . . .	. . . . . .	. . . . . .	. . . . . .	N-Benzoyl, 191, al.; O,N-Dibenzoyl, 190–1, al.; O,N-Diacetyl, 128–9; Me. eth., 93–4, pet. eth.
324	**3-Amino-4,6-dichloro-phenol**	135–6, w.	. . . . . .	. . . . .	. . . . . .	. . . . . .	. . . . . .	113–4	. . . . . .	. . . . . .	N-Acetyl, 233–6; Me. eth., 51
325	**2,6-Dinitrohydroquinone** . .	135–6 (anh.)								4-*mono*: 95–6; *di*: 135–6	4-*mono*: 150–1	4-Me. eth., 102; Di-Me. eth., 95–6; 112
326	**1,4-Dimethyl-2-naphthol** . .	135–6								77–8	124–5	. . . .
327	**Trichlorohydroquinone** . . .	136, w.								*di*: 153 (subl.)	. . . . . .	Di-Et. eth., 68.5, al.
328	**5-Iodo-3-nitrophenol**	136, w.								110	100.5	Me. eth., 84
329	**Trichlorophloroglucinol** . . .	136, al.								*tri*: 167–8, ac. a.	. . . . . .	Di-Me. eth., 93–5; Tri-Me. eth., 130–1, al.
330	**1,6-Dihydroxynaphthalene** (1,6-Naphthalenediol) . . .	137–8, bz.								*di*: 73, al.	*di*: 103–4	Di-Me. eth., 60–1, pet. eth.; Di-Et. eth., 83, lgr.; 2-Naphthylamine add. comp., 110.5
331	**2,4-Dinitro-1-naphthol**	138								. . . . . .	174	Me. eth., 97; Et. eth., 92
332	**4-Amino-2,6-dimethyl-phenol**	138 d., bz.										N-Acetyl, 136–7, aq. al.; O,N-Di-acetyl, 160; Me. eth., 66, w.
333	**2-Amino-3-bromophenol** . .	138							120–1, al.			Me. eth., 65; Hydrochloride, 225
334	**2-Amino-4-chlorophenol** . .	138 (unstable)						115	73–4			N-Acetyl, 185; O,N-Dibenzoyl, 157–8; Me. eth., 82–3
335	**1,4,6-Trihydroxynaphtha-lene** (1,4,6-Naphthalene-triol)	138–40								94.5	. . . . . .	. . . .
336	**2,6-Dibromo-3,4,5-tri-hydroxybenzoic acid** (Dibromogallic acid)	139 d. (+1H₂O)								*tri*: 168	*tri*: 95–6	Triacetate of Me. eth., 150–2
337	**2-Hydroxy-2'-nitro-biphenyl**	139–40				116	180	3,5-*di*: 149	100	. . . . . .	116	3-Nitrobenzenesul-fonate, 161; 4-Nitrobenzenesul-fonate, 147; 2,4-Dinitrophenyl ether, 118; Me. eth., 82; 3,5-Di-nitro deriv., 123
338	**4-Phenyl-1-naphthol**	140									73–4	. . . .
339	**1,3-Dihydroxy-2-methyl-naphthalene** (2-Methyl-1,3-naphthalenediol)	140								118	. . . . . .	
340	**1,2,4-Trihydroxybenzene** . .	140–5, eth.								*tri*: 96–7, wh., abs. al.	*tri*: 120, al.	Tri-Et. eth., 34, al.; Picrate, 96
341	**2-Amino-5-iodophenol**	141								. . . . . .	. . . . . .	N-p-Toluenesul-fonyl, 175–6

*Derivative data given in order: m.p., crystal color, solvent from which crystallized.

No.	Name	Melting point, °C	Boiling point, °C	Phenyl urethane	α-Naphthylurethane	p-Nitrobenzoate	3,5-Dinitrobenzoate	Bromo derivative	p-Toluene sulfonate	Acetate	Benzoate	Miscellaneous
342	**4-Hydroxy-2-nitrobiphenyl**	141–3								169	105–6	Me. eth., 72
343	**1,8-Dihydroxynaphthalene** (1,8-Naphthalenediol)	142, ac. a.; 140, w.								di: 155, ac. anh.	di: 174–5	Di-Me. eth., 50, pet. eth.; Picrate, 135–7; 2-Naphthylamine add. comp., 124
344	**2-Amino-4-nitrophenol**	142–3 (anh.); 80–90 (hyd.)				122			122, yel., al.			N-Acetyl, 279; N-Benzoyl, ca. 200 d.; Me. eth., 124–5; Et. eth., 97–8
345	**3,4-Dihydroxyphenanthrene** (Morphol)	143, pet. eth.								di: 159, eth.		Me. eth., 62–3; Di-Me. eth., 45, me. al.
346	**3-Chloro-1-naphthol**	143; 134–5, lgr.								69, lgr.	118–9	Me. eth., b.p. 162–4[18]
347	**2-Isopropyl-5-methylhydroquinone** (Thymoquinol)	143; 139.5	290	232–3, al.	147–8, al.					di: 73–5	141–2, al.	
348	**2,6-Dibromo-4-nitrophenol**	144						128–9		181		
349	**3,4,5-Tribromocatechol**	144 (+1H₂O)								di: 120		Di-Me. eth., 86–7
350	**3-Amino-4-methylphenol** (3-Amino-p-cresol)	144										N-Acetyl, 178; O,N-Diacetyl, 128–9; N-Benzenesulfonyl, 183; Me. eth., 47, w.
351	**8-Nitro-2-naphthol**	144–5, yel.								101–2, w.-al.		m-Nitrobenzenesulfonate, 144–6, ac. a.; Me. eth., 69; Et. eth., 72–3, yel., pet. eth.
352	**4-Benzoylresorcinol** (2,4-Dihydroxybenzophenone)	144–6								di: 78		
353	**1-Hydroxyacenaphthene** (1-Acenaphthenol)	144.5-5.5 (cor.); 148		137						b.p. 166–8[5]		
354	**4-Amino-2,3,6-trinitrophenol**	145 d., ac. a.										N-Acetyl, 178–9; N-Benzoyl, 205, ac. a.; Me. eth., 138–9, al.
355	**4-Benzoylcatechol** (3,4-Dihydroxybenzophenone)	145; 134									di: 95	Me. eth., 131–2; Di-Me. eth., 103–4
356	**3-Bromo-5-nitrophenol**	145								99		Me. eth., 88
357	**3,4-Dihydroxybiphenyl** (4-Phenylcatechol)	145								di: 77.5-8.0		
358	**2,4,6-Tri-iodoresorcinol**	145, CS₂								di: 170		
359	**2,4'-Dihydroxychalcone**	145								di: 94–5	di: 120	4'-Me. eth., 148 d., al.
360	**2,6-Diamino-4-methylphenol** (4-Hydroxy-3,5-toluenediamine)	146										N,N'-Diacetyl, 225–7, dil. al., 1,2,6-Triacetyl, 228, al.
361	**5-Aminoresorcinol** (3,5-Dihydroxyaniline)	146–52										N-Benzoyl, 139; Di-Me. eth., 46; Picrate, 167–70 d., yel., aq. al.

*Derivative data given in order: m.p., crystal color, solvent from which crystallized.

TABLE VII. ORGANIC DERIVATIVES OF PHENOLS

b) Solids (Listed in order of increasing m.p.)* (Continued)

No.	Name	Melting point, °C	Boiling point, °C	Phenyl ure-thane	α-Naph-thyl-ure-thane	p-Nitro-ben-zoate	3,5-Di-nitro-benzoate	Bromo derivative	p-Toluene sul-fonate	Acetate	Benzoate	Miscellaneous
362	4-Acetylresorcinol (Resacetophenone; 2,4-Dihydroxyacetophenone)	147								3-*mono*: 119–20; 4-*mono*: 74; *di*: 38	3-*mono*: 67; 4-*mono*: 106–7	Semicarbazone, 216; 2,4-Dinitrophenylhydrazone, 218; Oxime, 199; Phenylhydrazone, 159
363	3-Chloro-5-nitrophenol	147								84	78	Me. eth., 101; Et. eth., 47, al.
364	5-Nitro-2-naphthol	147, yel., w.										*m*-Nitrobenzene-sulfonate, 106, ac. a.; Et. eth., 115, yel., al.
365	2-Methyl-3-nitrophenol (3-Nitro-o-cresol)	147, yel., w.							94, al.			Me. eth., 52–3, w.-me. al.
366	2-Chloro-4-hydroxybenzal-dehyde	147–8								52	97	Semicarbazone, 214; Oxime, 194; *p*-Nitrophenyl-hydrazone, 288 d.
367	1,5-Dibromo-4,8-di-hydroxynaphthalene	147.5								*di*: 131		
368	5-Acetylresorcinol (3,5-Dihydroxyacetophenone)	148								*di*: 91–2		Semicarbazone, 205–6; *p*-Nitro-phenylhydrazone, 236–7
369	2,4-Dinitroresorcinol	148							*mono*: 126–7	*di*: 119–20	*di*: 182–4	Aryloxyacetic acid, 155; Me. eth., 108; Di-Et. eth., 57
370	4-Propionylphenol (4-Hydroxypropiophenone)	148								62, lgr.	107.5	2,4-Dinitrophenyl-hydrazone, 229
371	9,10-Dihydroxyphenan-threne (9,10-Phenan-threnediol)	148								*mono*: 168–70, *di*: 202	*di*: 216–7	
372	3,4,5-Trihydroxyphenan-threne (3,4,5-Phenan-threnetriol)	148, w.								*tri*: 138, bz.-pet. eth.		Tri-me. eth., 90, me. al.
373	4-Hydroxypyridine (γ-Pyridone)	148.5 (anh.); 65 (+1 H₂O)	>350							140–50	81	Picrate, 240; Methiodide, 108–9
374	3-Nitrosalicylic acid	148.5–9.0										Amide, 155; 145
375	3-Acetamidophenol (3-Hydroxyacetanilide)	148–9, w.								99.5–100.5		
376	2-Amino-3,6-dimethyl-phenol	149–50, bz.										N-Benzoyl, 210–11; O,N-Dibenzoyl, 178–9
377	2,6-Dimethylhydroquinone	149–51, xyl.										4-Me. eth., 77, pet. eth.
378	2,4'-Dihydroxybenzo-phenone	150								84.5		
379	5-Amino-2-bromophenol	150 d.						135–6				
380	2-Amino-5-bromophenol	150										O,N-Dibenzoyl, 133–4; H₂SO₄ salt, 239–40
381	1-Hydroxyanthracene (1-Anthrol)	150–3, br., al.								128–30		Me. eth., 70; Et. eth., 69
382	2-Amino-4-chloro-6-nitro-phenol	152										N-Acetyl, 150–60, yel.

*Derivative data given in order: m.p., crystal color, solvent from which crystallized.

No.	Name	Melting point, °C	Boiling point, °C	Phenyl ure-thane	α-Naph-thyl-ure-thane	p-Nitro-ben-zoate	3,5-Di-nitro-benzoate	Bromo derivative	p-Toluene sul-fonate	Acetate	Benzoate	Miscellaneous
383	**4-Hydroxyazobenzene** (4-Benzeneazophenol)	152, al.								89; 84–5, yel., al.	136–8, yel., al.	Hydrochloride, 169; HNO$_3$ → 2,4-Dini-trophenol, 113; Propionate, 75, red
384	**Tribromophloroglucinol**. . .	152–3 (anh.), w.								*mono*: 169, bz.-pet. eth.; *tri*: 181–3, al.		Me. eth., 123, bz.; Tri-Me. eth., 145, al.; Di-Et. eth., 63–5, w.-ac. a.; Tri-Et. eth., 102–4, ac. a.
385	**4-Amino-2-chlorophenol** . .	153							116–7, aq. al.			N-Acetyl, 144; O,N-Diacetyl, 124; Me. eth., 62
386	**2,2′-Dihydroxy-5,5′-dimethylbiphenyl**	153–4, w.								*di*: 88		Diformate, 61, 70% al.
387	**2-Amino-5-chlorophenol** . .	154, aq. al.										O,N-Dibenzoyl, 140, al.; Me. eth., 46; Hydrochloride, 226 d.
388	**1,2,4-Trihydroxynaph-thalene** (1,2,4-Naph-thalenetriol)	154								*tri*: 134–5		. . . .
389	**6-Hydroxybiphenyl-2-carboxylic acid**	154 (anh.)							177, ac. a.	88–9, al.	121; 150	Benzenesulfonate, 104–5; Butyrate, 59–60
390	**4-Amino-3-nitrophenol**. . . .	154, dk. red							134, al.	185		N-Acetyl, 218, yel., w.; O,N-Diacetyl, 146; O-*m*-nitro-benzenesulfonate, 184
391	**2-Azoxyphenol** (2,2′-Di-hydroxyazoxybenzene) . .	154–5								*di*: 150, bz.	*di*: 108, al.	Di-Me. eth., 81; Di-Et. eth., 102
392	**3,5-Stilbenediol** (3,5-Di-hydroxystilbene; Pino-sylvyn)	155.5–6.0, ac. a.								*di*: 100–1, me. al.	*di*: 150–1, ac. a.-me. al.	Me. eth., 122–3, ac. a.; Di-Me. eth., 56–7, me. al.
393	**1-Hydroxyphenanthrene** (1-Phenanthrol)	156, eth.								135–6, al.		Me. eth., 105, me. al.; Picrate, 182, or.-red, me. al.
394	**4-Iodo-3-nitrophenol**	156, yel., al.								107.5		Me. eth., 62; Et. eth., 63.5
395	**1,4,5-Trichloro-2-naphthol**	157–8, ac. a.								129		
396	**9-Hydroxyphenanthrene** (9-Phenanthrol)	158, bz; 153								77–8, al.	99–100	Me. eth., 95–6, me. al.; Picrate, 185, red; Propionate, 95, ac. a.
397	**5-Nitroresorcinol**	158, w.								*di*: 105		Me. eth., 141–2, yel.; Di-Me. eth., 89, eth.-et. ac.; Et. eth., 80, w.
398	**4,4′-Dihydroxydiphenyl-methane**	158, w.								*di*: 69–70, al.	*di*: 156, al.	Di-Me. eth., 52; Di-Et. eth., 38–9
399	**2,4,6-Tri-iodophenol**	158–9, w.-al.				181				156, bz.	137	Me. eth., 98–9, bz.; Et. eth., 83, eth.

*Derivative data given in order: m.p., crystal color, solvent from which crystallized.

No.	Name	Melting point, °C	Boiling point, °C	Phenyl ure-thane	α-Naph-thyl-ure-thane	p-Nitro-ben-zoate	3,5-Di-nitro-benzoate	Bromo derivative	p-Toluene sul-fonate	Acetate	Benzoate	Miscellaneous
400	**Salicylic acid** (2-Hydroxy-benzoic acid)	158.3	211[20]	.....	.....	205, me. al.	.....		.....	135, wh.	132	Aryloxyacetic acid, 191; Amide, 142; Anilide, 136; p-Toluidide, 156
401	**4-Amino-2,3,6-trichloro-phenol**	159, al.		....						153, yel.	......	N-2,4-Dinitro-phenyl, 211, or.-red
402	**4-Amino-3-chlorophenol** ..	160		....							......	N-Acetyl, 121
403	**6-Amino-2,4-dinitro-3-methylphenol** (6-Amino-2,4-dinitro-m-cresol)	160, al.		....								N-Acetyl, 225, yel.
404	**2,2'-Dihydroxychalcone**...	160–1								di: 85.5–6.0	di: 114	2-Me. eth., 112, al.; 2-Et. eth., 61, al.
405	**4-Amino-6-nitroresorcinol**	160–1 d., eth.-lgr.								......	......	N-Acetyl, 261, yel., ac. a.; Di-Me. eth., 136–7, red. aq. al.
406	**4,4'-Dihydroxy-3,3'-di-methylbiphenyl**	160–1								di: 131, al.; 135.5	185, ac. a.	....
407	**2,3-Dihydroxynaphthalene** (2,3-Naphthalenediol)...	160–1, w.									di: 235	Me. eth., 108; Di-Me. eth., 116.5, lgr., Et. eth., 109–10; Di-Et. eth., 96–7; 2-Naphthyl-amine add. comp., 168
408	**1,2-Dihydroxyanthracene** (1,2-Anthracenediol)....	160–2								di: 157.0–7.5, al.-ac. a.		....
409	**6-Retenol** (6-Hydroxy-retene)...............	161, xyl.		....					110.5–11	134–5	......	Picrate, 152–2.5, red, al.
410	**5-Amino-2-methylphenol** (5-Amino-o-cresol)	161, w.							111–2, aq. al.		......	N-Acetyl, 225; N,N-Diacetyl, 132–3; O,N-Di-benzoyl, 162; Me. eth., 58
411	**4,4'-Dihydroxytriphenyl-methane**..............	161, w.-al.		....						di: 109–10	......	Di-Me. eth., 100–1, chl.-me. al.
412	**3-Hydroxphthalic acid**...	161 d.								114–6	148	....
413	**1,2,3,4-Tetrahydroxy-benzene** (Apionol; Phenetrol)............	161, pink, et. ac.								tetra: 142	tetra: 191–2	1,4-Di-Me. eth., 106; Tetra-Me. eth., 89
414	**5-Amino-2-nitrophenol**....	162, or.-yel., w.										N-Acetyl, 221, yel., ac. a.; O,N-Di-acetyl, 149, w.
415	**1,3,4-Trichloro-2-naphthol**	162								133.5–4.0, ac. a.	......	....
416	**2-Amino-5-methylphenol** (6-Amino-m-cresol).....	162 d.								......	......	N-Benzoyl, 169, acet.-pet. eth.; O,N-Dibenzoyl, 162–3, me. al.; Me. eth., 171, 50% al.
417	**1-Amino-2,4-dihydroxy-naphthalene**...........	162 (at 130 → vlt.)		....								O,O,N-Triacetyl, 155–6, bz.

*Derivative data given in order: m.p., crystal color, solvent from which crystallized.

No.	Name	Melting point, °C	Boiling point, °C	Phenyl urethane	α-Naphthyl urethane	p-Nitro benzoate	3,5-Dinitro benzoate	Bromo derivative	p-Toluene sulfonate	Acetate	Benzoate	Miscellaneous
418	2,4'-Biphenol (2,4'-Dihydroxybiphenyl)	162–3	342	......	......	......	......	......	......	di: 94, al.	......	Di-Me. eth., 70
419	2,5-Dimethylresorcinol (2,6-Dihydroxy-p-xylene)	163, bz.	277–80	......	......	......	......	......	......	di: 69, al.	......	Me. eth., 118–21, bz.
420	2-Amino-3,5-dimethylphenol	163, bz.		......	......	......	......	......	......	186–7	......	O,N-Diacetyl, 87–8; N-Benzoyl, 211–2, al.; O,N-Dibenzoyl, 148–9, me. al.; Hydrochloride, 270–80, dil. HCl
421	4-Nitro-1-naphthol	164, w.		......	......	......	......	......	......	......	......	m-Nitrobenzenesulfonate, 135; Me. eth., 81, yel., bz.; 85–6; Et. eth., 120, al.; 116–7
422	3,5-Dinitrocatechol (1,2-Dihydroxy-3,5-dinitrobenzene)	164		......	......	......	......	......	......	120; di: 112–4; 124, al.	......	1-Me. eth., 123; 2-Me. eth., 80; Di-Me. eth., 102, al.; 1-Et. eth., 155, al.; Di-Et. eth., 78; 94–5
423	2,2'-Dihydroxy-6,6'-dimethylbiphenyl	164		......	......	......	......	......	......	di: 87, al.	di: 136, al.	......
424	2-Amino-3,4-dihydroxynaphthalene	164		......	......	......	......	......	......	di: >200 d.	......	N-Acetyl, 170 d.; 3-O,N-Diacetyl, 195 d., acet.
425	2,6-Dibromohydroquinone	164		......	......	......	......	......	......	di: 117	......	
426	2-Benzoylphloroglucinol (2,4,6-Trihydroxybenzophenone)	165		......	......	......	......	......	......	......	tri: 125–6	2,4-Di-Me. eth., 83; 2,6-Di-Me. eth., 178–9
427	5-Amino-3-nitrophenol	165, yel.		......	......	......	......	......	......	......	......	N-Acetyl, 260–70, et. ac.
428	2-Methoxy-4-nitrophenol	165 d., yel., chl.		......	......	......	......	......	......	156–8	188, yel., al.	Me. eth., 105–6
429	3-Amino-4,5-dimethylphenol	165, eth., br.; (173–5, subl.)		......	......	......	......	......	......	......	......	N-Acetyl, 191 (sinters, 184); O,N-Diacetyl, 157, al., O,N,N-Triacetyl, 100–1, al.; N-Benzoyl, 195–6
430	1,2,3,5-Tetrahydroxybenzene	165		......	......	......	......	......	......	tri: 74	......	1,3-Di.-Me. eth., 159; 83; 1,2,3-Tri-Et. eth., 105
431	4-Phenylphenol (4-Hydroxybiphenyl)	165	305–8	167.5	......	......	......	......	177, ac. a.; 179, al.-acet.	88–9; 87–8, al.	150–1, al.	p-Phenylazobenzoate, 213.5–4.0; 2,4-Dinitrophenyl ether, 118
432	4-Amino-2-bromophenol	165; 155		......	......	......	......	......	......	......	......	N-Benzoyl, 145; O,N-Dibenzoyl, 192
433	Benzeneazocatechol (3,4-Dihydroxyazobenzene)	165 d., dk. red, al.		......	......	......	......	......	......	......	......	3-Me. eth., 70–1, red, lgr.; Di-Me. eth., 53–4, red, lgr.; 44–5
434	4-Amino-2-chloro-3-nitrophenol	165.5 d., bz.		......	......	......	......	......	......	......	......	N-Acetyl, 184–5; Et. eth., 74, or.

* Derivative data given in order: m.p., crystal color, solvent from which crystallized.

TABLE VII. ORGANIC DERIVATIVES OF PHENOLS

b) Solids (Listed in order of increasing m.p.)* (Continued)

No.	Name	Melting point, °C	Boiling point, °C	Phenyl urethane	α-Naphthylurethane	p-Nitrobenzoate	3,5-Dinitrobenzoate	Bromo derivative	p-Toluene sulfonate	Acetate	Benzoate	Miscellaneous
435	4-Amino-2,5-dinitrophenol	166–7, al.	....	....	......	....	....	......	....	....	......	N-Acetyl, 144–5; Me. eth., 153, bz.-lgr., red; Et. eth., 139
436	4-Amino-2,6-dinitro-3-methylphenol (4-Amino-2,6-dinitro-m-cresol)	167, red, 50% al.	....	....	......	....	....	......	....	....	......	N-Acetyl, 231 d., ac. a.; Et. eth., 96–7; Hydrochloride, 200 d., dil, HCl
437	2-Benzamidophenol (2-Hydroxybenzanilide	167 d.	....	....	......	....	....	......	109–10, al.	134–40, al.	......	Me. eth., 60
439	2,3,4-Trichloro-1-naphthol	168, lgr.	....	....	......	....	....	......	....	123–4	......	....
440	2-Hydroxyphenanthrene (2-Phenanthrol)	168, al.	....	....	......	....	....	......	....	142–3	139–40, al.	Et. eth., 112, al.; Picrate, 156, red
441	1,5-Di-(2-hydroxyphenyl)-1,4-pentadiene-3-one	168	....	....	......	....	....	......	....	di: 128, al.	135, al.	Di-Me. eth., 125, al.; Di-Et. eth., 89, al.
442	3,5-Diaminophenol........	168–70	....	....	......	....	....	......	....	....	......	3,5-Diacetyl, 195
443	4-Acetamidophenol (4′-Hydroxyacetanilide	169	....	....	......	....	....	......	....	150–1	......	....
444	2-Amino-4,6-dinitrophenol (Picramic acid)........	169, dk. red, al.	....	....	......	....	....	......	....	....	......	N-Acetyl, 201; N-Benzoyl, 230; 220; N-p-Toluenesulfonyl, 191
445	4-Amino-2-chloro-5-nitro-phenol	169.5 d.	....	....	......	....	....	......	....	....	......	N-Acetyl, 166, yel.; Et. eth., 128.5, or.
446	3,3′-Dihydroxybenzo-phenone	170	....	....	......	....	....	......	....	89–90	101–2	....
447	1,4-Dihydroxy-2-methyl-naphthalene (2-Methyl-1,4-naphthohydro-quinone)	α: 170; β: 60, ac. a.	....	....	......	....	....	......	....	di: 113, al.	181	....
448	4-Amino-2,6-dinitrophenol (Isopicramic acid)	170, br., w.	....	....	......	....	....	......	....	....	......	N-Acetyl, 182; N-Benzoyl, 263; 250; Me. eth., 212; Et. eth., 172
449	Benzeneazoresorcinol (2,4-Dihydroxyazo-benzene)	170, dk. red	....	....	......	....	....	......	....	di: 104, or.-red, al.	......	Di-Me. eth., 92, red, al.; Di-Et. eth., 70, yel.-red, al.
450	3,4-Diaminophenol.......	170–2; 167–8; unstable	....	....	......	....	....	......	....	....	......	N,N′-Diacetyl, 205–7; 3,4-Dibenzoyl, 203–5; 1,3,4-Tribenzoyl, 225; Et. eth., 71–2, b.p. 294–6
451	5-Nitro-1-naphthol	171, dk. yel.-red, w.	....	....	......	....	....	......	....	114, w.-al.	109, me. al.	Me. eth., 96–7, yel., pet. eth.
452	Hydroquinone (1,4-Di-hydroxybenzene)	171; 172	286	di: 224; 205–7	......	di: 258, al.	di: 317	di: 186	mono: 98–9, bz.; di: 159, 25% al.	di: 123, w.	di: 199, 204 (cor.), tol.	Aryloxyacetic acid, 250; 2,4-Dinitrophenyl ether, 243–6; N,N-Diphenylurethane, 250

*Derivative data given in order: m.p., crystal color, solvent from which crystallized.

TABLE VII. ORGANIC DERIVATIVES OF PHENOLS

b) Solids (Listed in order of increasing m.p.)* (Continued)

No.	Name	Melting point, °C	Boiling point, °C	Phenyl urethane	α-Naphthyl urethane	p-Nitrobenzoate	3,5-Dinitrobenzoate	Bromo derivative	p-Toluene sulfonate	Acetate	Benzoate	Miscellaneous
453	2-Azophenol (2,2'-Dihydroxyazobenzene)	172, yel., bz.	....	....	......	....	....	....	....	di: 150, or.-red	......	Di-Me. eth., 153, or.; Di-Et. eth., 131, red
454	2,3,4-Trihydroxyacetophenone (Gallacetophenone)	173; 192.0–2.5								2,4-di: 107–8; 3,4-di: 78–81; tri: 85	......	Semicarbazone, 225 d.; Oxime, 162–3; Picrate, 133
455	3,5-Dinitrosalicylic acid	173–4 (anh.)								......	163	Amide, 181; Anilide, 180 (subl.); 194
456	2-Aminophenol (2-Hydroxyaniline)	174								......	175	N-Acetyl, 209; 201; N-Benzenesulfonyl, 141; N-p-Toluenesulfonyl, 146
457	3-Benzamidophenol (3-Hydroxybenzanilide)	174, tol.								......	153	Et. eth., 103
458	4-Amino-2-methylphenol (4-Amino-o-cresol)	175, bz.	....	....	......	....	....	....	109–10, bz.-lgr.	......		N-Acetyl, 179; O,N-Dibenzoyl, 194, ac. a.; Me. eth., 59.0–9.5; 92–3, aq. al.
459	1,6,7-Trihydroxynaphthalene (1,6,7-Naphthalenetriol)	175								tri: 143–4	......	....
460	4-Nitrocatechol	176, yel., w.	....	....	......	....	....	....	....	di: 98	di: 156, al.	Di-Me. eth., 96, w.-al.; Di-Et. eth., 73–5, pa. yel.
461	1,4-Dihydroxynaphthalene (1,4-Naphthalenediol; 1,4-Naphthohydroquinone)	176; 192								di: 128–30, al.	di: 169, ac. a.	Me. eth., 131; Di-Me. eth., 85, CS_2
462	1,7-Dihydroxynaphthalene (1,7-Naphthalenediol)	178, bz.	....	203–4	......	182–3	....	....	....	di: 108, bz.	di: 101.5; 113–5	Di-Et. eth., 67
463	1,2-Dihydroxyphenanthrene (1,2-Phenanthrenediol)	178, w.-al.								di: 147, me. al.	......	Di-Me. eth., 100–2, lgr.
464	4-Amino-6-isopropyl-3-methylphenol (4-Amino-6-isopropyl-m-cresol)	178–9, bz.	....	....	......	....	....	....	....		178–9	N-Benzoyl, 178–9; O,N-Dibenzoyl, 166–7, aq. al.; Hydrochloride, 255
465	1,8,9-Trihydroxyanthracene (1,8,9-Anthracenetriol; Anthralin)	178–80; 176–7								tri: 209–10	......	....
466	4-Amino-3-methylphenol (4-Amino-m-cresol)	179, 50% al.	....	....	......	....	....	....	....		92, pet. eth.	N-Acetyl, 138; Hydrochloride, 215; Me. eth., 29–30
467	2,5-Dihydroxyphenanthrene (2,5-Phenanthrenediol)	180, xyl.								di: 144, w.-ac. a.	......	Di-Me. eth., 117, ac. a.
468	9,10-Dihydroxyanthracene (9,10-Anthradiol)	180, yel.	....	....	......	....	....	....	....	di: 260, ac. a.	di: 292, yel. xyl.-chl.	Di-Me. eth., 202, bz.; Di-Et. eth., 148, bl. fluor., al.

*Derivative data given in order: m.p., crystal color, solvent from which crystallized.

No.	Name	Melting point, °C	Boiling point, °C	Phenyl urethane	α-Naphthylurethane	p-Nitrobenzoate	3,5-Dinitrobenzoate	Bromo derivative	p-Toluene sulfonate	Acetate	Benzoate	Miscellaneous
469	1,2,5,8-Tetrahydroxynaphthalene (1,2,5,8-Naphthalenetetrol)	180 d.	....	......	......	......	......	......	......	tetra: 202	....	....
470	4-Hydroxy-3-iodo-5-methoxybenzaldehyde (5-Iodovanillin)	180	....	......	......	......	......	......	......	105–6	135.5–6.5	Oxime, 178–9; Semicarbazone, 187–8 d.
471	6-Nitro-1-naphthol	181–2	....	......	......	......	......	......	......	121	....	....
472	4-Amino-3,5-dimethylphenol	181.2, chl.	....	......	......	......	......	......	......	......	......	N-Acetyl, 178–80; N-Benzyl, 104–5; Me. eth., 43, pet. eth.
473	2-Amino-4-nitroresorcinol	182, br., aq. al.	....	......	......	......	......	......	......	......	......	N-Acetyl, 213, yel.
474	3-Azoxyphenol (3,3'-Dihydroxyazoxybenzene)	183	....	......	......	......	......	......	......	di: 102, 50% al.	di: 75, ac. a.	Di-Me. eth., 49–50; 47.6
475	N-Benzylidene-4-aminophenol	183	....	......	......	......	......	......	......	92	144	Me. eth., 62; Et. eth., 76 (71); Hydrochloride, 167–77
476	4-Aminophenol (4-Hydroxyaniline)	184 (subl.)	....	......	......	178.5 (cor.)	......	......	......	168	......	O,N-Diacetyl, 150; 2,4-Dinitrobenzoyl, 204.5 (cor.); N-p-Toluenesulfonyl, 253
477	1,9-Dihydroxyphenanthrene (1,9-Phenanthrenediol)	184–5, bz.	....	......	......	......	......	......	......	di: 154–5, w.-al.	......	9-Me. eth., 131–2, bz.-pet. eth.; Di-Me. eth., 113–4, me. al.
478	4,6-Diacetylresorcinol (Resodiacetophenone)	185, al.	....	......	......	......	......	......	......	di: 120	mono: 214–5; di: 118	Di-Me. eth., 171.5; Dioxime, 242; Phenylhydrazone, 233
479	4-Amino-2-naphthol	185	....	......	......	......	......	137	......	......	......	O,N-Dibenzoyl, 309
480	7-Hydroxy-4-methylcoumarin (4-Methylumbelliferone)	185–6, al.	....	155–6	......	143	......	......	......	150, al.	159–60, al.	Me. eth., 159; m-Nitrobenzoate, 210–11; Picrate, 108
481	3-Amino-4-nitrophenol	185–6, or., w.	....	......	......	......	......	......	......	......	......	N-Benzoyl, 166; Me. eth., 131; Et. eth., 105–6
482	1,2,6-Trihydroxynaphthalene (1,2,6-Naphthalenetriol)	188	....	......	......	......	......	......	......	tri: 262	......	....
483	α,2,4-Trihydroxyacetophenone (ω-Hydroxyresacetophenone)	189	....	......	......	......	......	......	......	tri: 129	α-mono: 200	α-Me. eth., 136; p-Nitrophenylhydrazone, 205 d.; Oxime, 105–7
484	2,7-Dihydroxynaphthalene (2,7-Naphthalenediol)	190; 185–6, w.	....	......	......	......	......	150, chl.	......	mono: 171–2, me. al.; di: 136, w.	mono: 199, me. al.; di: 139, al.	Aryloxyacetic acid, 149; N,N-Diphenylurethane, 176; Me. eth., 117; Di-Me. eth., 139; Di-Et. eth., 104, al.
485	1,4,5,8-Tetrahydroxynaphthalene (1,4,5,8-Naphthalenetetrol)	190	....	......	......	......	......	......	......	tetra: 277–9	......	....

*Derivative data given in order: m.p., crystal color, solvent from which crystallized.

No.	Name	Melting point, °C	Boiling point, °C	Phenyl ure-thane	α-Naph-thyl-ure-thane	p-Nitro-ben-zoate	3,5-Di-nitro-benzoate	Bromo derivative	p-Toluene sul-fonate	Acetate	Benzoate	Miscellaneous
486	**1,5-Diacetyl-2,3,4-tri-hydroxybenzene (4,6-Diacetylpyrogallol; Gallodiacetophenone)...**	190–1, w.	....	......	......	......	....	....		*mono*: 207–9	*tri*: 189	Tri-Me. eth., 73–4
487	**3,9-Dihydroxyacridine....**	190–2, lt. br. → dk. in air, al.	....	......	......	......	....	....		....	....	9-Me.-3-Et. eth., 144, yel., w.; In al. → grn. fluor.
488	**Pentachlorophenol**	190.2							145	149–50	164–5; 159	Aryloxyacetic acid, 196
489	**5-Amino-2-naphthol**	191								....	....	O,N-Diacetyl, 187; O,N-Dibenzoyl, 223
490	**1,4-Dihydroxynaphthalene (1,4-Naphthalenediol)...**	192	....	......	......	......	....	....		*di*: 128–30	*di*: 169	....
491	**5-Amino-1-naphthol**	192								....	....	O,N-Dibenzoyl, 276
492	**Tetrabromocatechol**	192–3								*di*: 215–6	*di*: 197–8, bz.-lgr.	Me. eth., 162–3; Di-Me. eth., 151–2; 118–20
493	**6-Hydroxyquinoline**	193, al.							98	36–8	230–1, ac. a.	Methiodide, 236 d.; Picrate, 235–6
494	**3-Methyl-2,4,5,6-tetra-bromophenol (2,4,5,6-Tetrabromo-*m*-cresol)...**	194, ac. a.								165–6	153–4	Me. eth., 145–6, al.; Et. eth., 108, eth.
495	**1,5-Dichloro-4,8-dihy-droxynaphthalene**.......	194, ac. a.								*4-mono*: 148–60, ac. a.; *di*: 154; 143, acet.	*4-mono*: 157–8, ac. a.; *di*: 179; acet.	....
496	**1,6-Dinitro-2-naphthol**	195 d.	....	......	......	......	....	....	181	......	......	Me. eth., 204; 198; Et. eth., 144, yel.; Alc. NH₃ at 160° → 1,6-di-nitro-2-naphthyl-amine, 248; Oxid. → 4-nitro-phthalic acid, 165
497	**5,6-Dihydroxyace-naphthene (5,6-Acenaph-thenediol)**............	196–9, bz.	....	......	......	......	....	....		*di*: 194–5	......	....
498	**1,2,7-Trihydroxynaphtha-lene (1,2,7-Naphthalene-triol)**	197								181–2	......	....
499	**4-Methyl-2,3,5,6-tetra-bromophenol (2,3,5,6-Tetrabromo-*p*-cresol)...**	199								156		....
500	**2-Hydroxyquinoline**	199									......	2-Ph. eth., 69
501	**2-Amino-4-methyl-5-nitro-phenol (2-Amino-5-nitro-*p*-cresol)**	199–200 d.										N-Acetyl, 242, ac. a.; Me. eth., 132, yel.
502	**6-Amino-1-naphthol**	199.5	....	......	......	......	....	....		......	......	O,N-Diacetyl, 130; N-Benzoyl, 203; O,N-Dibenzoyl, 230
503	**Hexahydroxybenzene**	200 d.								*hexa*: 203	*hexa*: 313	....

*Derivative data given in order: m.p., crystal color, solvent from which crystallized.

No.	Name	Melting point, °C	Boiling point, °C	Phenyl ure-thane	α-Naph-thyl-ure-thane	p-Nitro-ben-zoate	3,5-Di-nitro-benzoate	Bromo derivative	p-Toluene sul-fonate	Acetate	Benzoate	Miscellaneous
504	Methylenedi-2-naphthol (2,2'-Dihydroxy-1,1'-dinaphthylmethane)	200, ac. a.	....	....	....	....	....	....	....	di: 214, al.	....	Di-Me. eth., 144–7, al.; Picrate, 178–9, red-br.
505	3-Hydroxybenzoic acid ...	200	....	....	....	....	....	....	....	131	....	Aryloxyacetic acid, 206; Amide, 170; p-Bromophenacyl ester, 176
506	Methyl gallate (Methyl 3,4,5-trihydroxyben-zoate)	200–1	....	....	....	....	....	....	....	tri: 120; 120–2, al.	tri: 139, al.	....
507	3-Hydroxyquinoline......	200–1, bz.								90	......	......	Picrate, 240–5
508	7-Amino-2-naphthol......	201; 208	....	....	....	....	....	....	....		177	N-Acetyl, 232; O,N-Diacetyl, 156; N-Benzoyl, 243–6; O,N-Dibenzoyl, 181
509	4-Amino-3-methyl-2-nitro-phenol (4-Amino-2-nitro-m-cresol).............	201, al.	....	....	....	....	....	....	....		......	O,N-Diacetyl, 127–8
511	2-Acetamidophenol (2-Hy-droxyacetanilide)......	201–3; 209, aq. al.	....	....	....	....	....	....	....	122	140	O,N-Diacetyl, 77
512	2-Acetylhydroquinone (2,5-Dihydroxyaceto-phenone)..............	202	....	....	....	....	....	....	....	di: 68	di: 113	p-Nitrophenylhy-drazone, 215–6; Oxime, 149–50
513	2,8-Dihydroxyphenan-threne (2,8-Phenan-threnediol)	202, w.-al.	....	....	....	....	....	....	....	di: 125, al.	....	....
514	4-Hydroxy-4'-nitro-biphenyl	203; 200–1	....	....	....	....	....	....	159, bz.	138–9, lgr.	208–10, ac. a.	Me. eth., 111, yel., al.; 3,5-Dinitro deriv., 197–8
515	3,5-Dimethoxy-4-hydroxy-benzoic acid	205									191	229–32	....
516	4-Hydroxycoumarin (Benzotetronic acid)	206; 232–3									103	......	Me. eth., 124, w.
517	2,3,5-Trihydroxyaceto-phenone..............	206–7, yel., ac. a.									tri: 106–7, lgr.	tri: 106–7	p-Nitrophenylhy-drazone, 241–2 d., w.-al.
518	2,4,5-Trihydroxyaceto-phenone..............	206–7, red	....	....	....	....	....	....	....	2,4-di: 165–6, bz.		....
519	6-Chloro-3-hydroxy-4-methylbenzoic acid	206–8									......	146	Amide, 239–40; Anilide, 222
520	8-Amino-2-naphthol......	207 d.	....	....	....	....	....	....	....		......	O,N-Diacetyl, 178; O,N-Dibenzoyl, 208
521	3-Azophenol (3,3'-Di-hydroxyazobenzene)	207, yel.									di: 144, yel., al.	di: 188, w.-al.	Di-Me. eth., 73–4; Di-Et. eth., 91, yel.
522	2-Amino-5-nitrophenol....	207–8, or.; 201–2, w.	....	....	....	....	....	....	188, yel., al.		......	N-Acetyl, 271–2; O,N-Diacetyl, 187; Me. eth., 139
523	2-Methyl-3,4,5,6-tetra-bromophenol (3,4,5,6-Tetrabromo-o-cresol) ...	208	....	....	....	....	....	....	....	154	......	....
524	2,6-Dichloro-3,4,5-tri-bromophenol..........	209	....	....	....	....	....	....	....		202	Me. eth., 143–4

*Derivative data given in order: m.p., crystal color, solvent from which crystallized.

TABLE VII. ORGANIC DERIVATIVES OF PHENOLS
b) Solids (Listed in order of increasing m.p.)* (Continued)

No.	Name	Melting point, °C	Boiling point, °C	Phenyl ure-thane	α-Naph-thyl-ure-thane	p-Nitro-ben-zoate	3,5-Di-nitro-benzoate	Bromo derivative	p-Toluene sul-fonate	Acetate	Benzoate	Miscellaneous
525	4-Hydroxy-3-methoxy-benzoic acid (Vanillic acid)	210 (subl.)	....	......	.....	140–1 d.	....	......	......	110, w.	178, aq. al.	Hydrazide, 207; Phenylhydrazide, 150–2.5
526	4,4'-Dihydroxybenzo-phenone	210	....	......	.....	....	....	......	......	......	156; 152	Me. eth., 151–2; Di-Me. eth., 146; 2,4-Dinitrophenylhy-drazone, 190–2
527	cis-1,2-Dihydroxyace-naphthene (cis-Acenaph-thylene glycol)	212–3, w.	....	......	.....	....	....	......	......	mono: 122–3, al.; di: 130, me. al.	....	....
528	4-Hydroxy-4'-nitroazo-benzene	212–3; 219.0–9.5	....	......	.....	....	....	......	......	147, or.	195, or.	Me. eth., 157.5–8.0
529	6-Amino-2-naphthol	213 d.	....	......	.....	....	....	......	......	......		O,N-Diacetyl, 220
530	2,4-Dihydroxybenzoic acid	213; 216 d.	....	......	.....	....	....	......	......			Amide, 222; Ani-lide, 126–7; p-Nitrophenyl ester, 189
531	Methylphloroglucinol (2,4,6-Trihydroxy-toluene)	214–6, et. ac.	....	......	.....	....	....	......	......	tri: 76, lgr.	......	2-Me. eth., 91 (+1H$_2$O); 117–9 (anh.); 4-Me. eth., 124; Tri-Me. eth., 10–13, b.p. 140–2[18]
532	4-Hydroxybenzoic acid	215; 210	....	......	.....	....	....	......	......	187	221–3	Aryloxyacetic acid, 278; Anilide, 198; p-Toluidide, 204
533	4,6-Dinitroresorcinol	215, yel.	....	......	.....	di: 178	....	......	mono: 135	di: 139	di: 343–4	Me. eth., 113; Di-Me. eth., 157; Et. eth., 77; Di-Et. eth., 133
534	4-Chloro-2,3,5,6-tetra-bromophenol	215	....	......	.....	....	....	......	......	......	203	Me. eth., 161
535	2,6-Dihydroxynaphthalene (2,6-Naphthalenediol)	215; 218	....	......	.....	....	....	......	......	di: 175	di: 215	Di-Me. eth., 50, bz.; Di-Et. eth., 162, al.
536	1,2,4,5-Tetrahydroxy-benzene	215–20	....	......	.....	....	....	......	......	tetra: 226–7	......	2-Me. eth., triacetyl, 142; Tetra-Me. eth., 103
537	4-Azophenol (4,4'-Di-hydroxyazobenzene)	α: 216, grn. (anh.); β: 216, dk. red. (anh.)	....	......	.....	....	....	......	......	di: 198–9, yel., ac. a.	di: 210.5–1.5; 249–51, red-yel., bz.	Di-Me. eth., 160.5–2.5, me. al.; Di-Et. eth., 157–9, yel., al.; 160
538	2-Amino-3-nitrophenol	216–7, red	....	......	.....	....	....	......	136		......	N-Acetyl, 172; Me. eth., 75–6
539	4-Benzamidophenol (4-Hy-droxybenzanilide)	216–7; 227	....	......	.....	....	....	......	......	171	235	Me. eth., 153–4, al.; Et. eth., 173, aq. al.; Benzyl eth., 226–7
540	2,5-Dimethylhydro-quinone (Hydro-phlorone)	217	....	......	.....	....	....	......	......	mono: 117; di: 135	mono: 162–3, pet. eth.; di: 159, me. al.	Me. eth., 90, lgr.

*Derivative data given in order: m.p., crystal color, solvent from which crystallized.

TABLE VII. ORGANIC DERIVATIVES OF PHENOLS
b) Solids (Listed in order of increasing m.p.)* (Continued)

No.	Name	Melting point, °C	Boiling point, °C	Phenyl urethane	α-Naphthyl urethane	p-Nitrobenzoate	3,5-Dinitrobenzoate	Bromo derivative	p-Toluene sulfonate	Acetate	Benzoate	Miscellaneous
541	Phloroglucinol (1,3,5-Trihydroxybenzene)	217–9, rapid htng.; 200–9, slow htng.	....	tri: 190–1	.....	283	tri: 162	tri: 151	......	tri: 104–6, al.	tri: 173–4, al.	Monobenzenesulfonate, 163–4 (anh.); Monobenzenesulfonate, di-acetate, 95–6, bz.; Dibenzenesulfonate, 120–1, bz.; Dibenzenesulfonate monoacetate, 81, me. al.
542	2-Amino-3,5-dinitrophenol	218, yel., al.	....	....	.....	....	....	....	186	......	......	O,N-Di-p-Toluenesulfonyl, 188; N-Acetyl, 171; Me. eth., 181
543	2,2'-Dihydroxy-1,1'-binaphthyl	218	....	....	.....	....	....	....	......	di: 109, al.	mono: 204; di: 160	Dipicrate, 175–6; Di-Me. eth., 190, Di-Et. eth., 90
544	7-Hydroxybenzo[a]pyrene	218–9, yel.	....	....	.....	....	....	....	......	194–5, yel.	191–2, yel.	Me. eth., 183–4, pyr.; p-Nitrobenzyl eth., 252–3
545	Acetylphloroglucinol (2,4,6-Trihydroxyacetophenone; Phloracetophenone)	219, w.; 222	....	....	.....	....	....	tri: 103	......	2-mono: 168; 4-mono: 210–11; tri: 117–8	......	2-Me. eth., 205–7; 4-Me. eth., 139–40; Tri-Me. eth., 103; Tri-Et. eth., 75, aq. al.
546	1,1'-Dihydroxy-2,2'-binaphthyl	220	....	....	.....	....	....	....	......	di: 169	......	Di-Me. eth., 122, lgr.
547	3,5-Dihydroxypyrene	220 d., ac. a.	....	....	.....	....	....	....	......	di: 155	......	Di-Me. eth., 177–8
548	3,6-Dihydroxyphenanthrene (3,6-Phenanthrenediol)	221, w.-al.	....	....	.....	....	....	....	......	di: 124.5, al.	......	3-Me. eth., 135–6, w.-me. al.; Di-Me. eth., 104–5, w.-me. al.
549	2,3-Dimethylhydroquinone (3,6-Dihydroxy-o-xylene)	221, sl. d., w.	....	....	.....	....	....	....	......	mono: 174–5, acet.-pet. eth.; di: 182, acet.-pet. eth.	......	Di-Et. eth., 68–9
550	3-Hydroxy-2-naphthoic acid	222	....	....	.....	....	....	....	......	184–6		Amide, 218; Anilide, 244; p-Toluidide, 222
551	4-Amino-6-chloro-3-methylphenol (4-Amino-6-chloro-m-cresol)	223–5 d.	....	....	.....	....	....	....	......	tri:	tri:	O,N-Diacetyl, 162; O,N-Dibenzoyl, 220
552	4-Azoxyphenol (4,4'-Dihydroxyazoxybenzene)	224 d.	....	....	.....	....	....	....	......	di: 163, or., al.	mono: 200, al.; 212, bz.; di: 187–90	Di-Me. eth., 118–9, yel.; Di-Et. eth., 137–8

*Derivative data given in order: m.p., crystal color, solvent from which crystallized.

TABLE VII. ORGANIC DERIVATIVES OF PHENOLS

b) Solids (Listed in order of increasing m.p.)* (Continued)

No.	Name	Melting point, °C	Boiling point, °C	Phenyl ure-thane	α-Naph-thyl-ure-thane	p-Nitro-ben-zoate	3,5-Di-nitro-benzoate	Bromo derivative	p-Toluene sul-fonate	Acetate	Benzoate	Miscellaneous
553	**5-Hydroxyquinoline**	224							85			Hydrochloride, 240; Methiodide, 224; Picrate, 187
554	**2-Amino-4-chloro-5-nitrophenol**	225 d., yel.										N-Acetyl, 193; Me. eth., 132
555	**1,2,3,4-Tetrahydroxy-naphthalene (1,2,3,4-Naphthalenetetrol)**	225								*tetra*: 220		
556	**1,8-Dihydroxyanthracene (1,8-Anthracenediol; Chrysazol)**	225, yel., al.-w.								*di*: 184, et. ac.		Di-Me. eth., 198, al.; Di-Et. eth., 139, al.
557	**4-Amino-6-nitrocatechol**	228, yel.										O,O,N-Triacetyl, 207, ac. a.
558	**5-Hydroxycoumarin**	229								88–9; 84		Me. eth., 85–7
559	**2-Hydroxy-5-nitro-benzoic acid**	229–30										Amide, 225; Anilide, 224
560	**Pentabromophenol**	229.5; 225–6								197; 171		Me. eth., 173–4; Et. eth., 136
561	**2,6-Dihydroxyphenan-threne (2,6-Phenanthrene-diol)**	234, w.-al.								*di*: 122–3, al.	*di*: 252–3	Di-Me. eth., 87, me. al.
562	**3-Amino-2-naphthol**	235										O,N-Diacetyl, 188; O,N-Dibenzoyl, 184
563	**5-Hydroxy-1-naphthoic acid**	235								202	241	
564	**2,3-Dihydroxyacridine (2,3-Acridinediol)**	235 d.										Di-Me. eth., 107, yel.-wh., al.
565	**Tetrachlorohydroquinone**	236–7								*di*: 245	*di*: 233	
566	**7-Hydroxyquinoline**	238–40, al., (br. at 200)							116		88–9, al.	Methiodide, 251 d., al.; Picrate, 244–5
567	**1,7-Dihydroxyanthrone (Euxanthone)**	240								7-*mono*: 160, al.; *di*: 185, bz.	*di*: 221–2; 214	7-Me. eth., 130–5
568	**1,6-Dihydroxypyrene (1,6-Pyrenediol)**	240 d.; sinters at 175										Sol. red with grn. fluor.; In alkali red soln. with bl. fluor.; Zn dust → pyrene, 149–50
569	**4-Amino-2,5-dimethyl-phenol**	242 d., al.										N-Acetyl, 177–9, al.; Et. eth., 69.5
570	**3,8-Dihydroxyphenan-threne (3,8-Phenanthrene-diol)**	247, lt. red, w.-al.								*di*: 184, al.		Di-Me. eth., 117, me. al.
571	**3-Hydroxy-1-naphthoic acid**	248								169–70	222–3	Amide, 209–11; Anilide, 112–3
572	**2,5-Dihydroxypyridine (2,5-Pyridinediol)**	248								5-*mono*: 156		Hydrochloride, 106 (hyd.); 154 (anh.)
573	**1,4-Dihydroxyisoquino-line (1,4-Isoquinoline-diol)**	>250, ac. a. turns red at 200								4-*mono*: 207–8		4-Me. eth., 171, acet.-pet. eth.
574	**2,3-Dihydroxyquinoline (3-Hydroxycarbostyril; 2,3-Quinolinediol)**	257–8; >300								3-*mono*: 211	3-*mono*: 286–7; *di*: 45–6, pet. eth.	

*Derivative data given in order: m.p., crystal color, solvent from which crystallized.

126

No.	Name	Melting point, °C	Boiling point, °C	Phenyl urethane	α-Naphthylurethane	p-Nitrobenzoate	3,5-Dinitrobenzoate	Bromo derivative	p-Toluene sulfonate	Acetate	Benzoate	Miscellaneous
575	**1,5-Dihydroxynaphthalene** (1,5-Naphthalenediol)...	265; 258								*di*: 159–61, dil. al.	*di*: 235; 242, pyr.	Di-Me. eth., 183–4; Di-Et. eth., 130, w.-al.; 2-Naphthylamine add. comp., 229.5
576	**2,7-Dihydroxyphenanthrene** (2,7-Phenanthrenediol)...............	265, w.-al.								*di*: 181.5, al.		Di-Me. eth., 169–70, me. al.
577	**Phenolphthalein**.........	265 (cor.); 261		*di*: 135, bz.						*di*: 143, al.	*di*: 169, bz.-lgr.	
578	**1,5-Dihydroxyanthracene** (Rufol; 1,5-Anthracenediol)................	265 d., yel.								*di*: 198, et. ac.		Di-Me. eth., 224, me. al.; Di-Et. eth., 179, al.
579	**4,4'-Biphenol** (4,4'-Dihydroxybiphenyl)......	274–5, al.							*di*: 189–90, bz.	*di*: 161, dil. al.; 164 (cor.)	*di*: 241, ac. a.	Aryloxyacetic acid, 274; Di-Me. eth., 173 (subl.); Di-Et. eth., 176
580	**1-Amino-2-naphthol**......	276 d.										O,N-Diacetyl, 206; O,N-Dibenzoyl, 235
581	**2,7-Dihydroxyanthracene** (2,7-Anthracenediol)....	280–5 d., bz., turns dk. at 250								282		Di-Me. eth., 216–7, ac. a.; Di-Et. eth., 192–3
582	**2,3-Dihydroxyanthracene** (2,3-Anthracenediol)....	282 d., yel.								*di*: 175		Di-Me. eth., 204, al.
583	**4,4'-Dihydroxystilbene** (4,4'-Stilbenediol)......	284, ac. a.								*di*: 213		Di-Me. eth., 214–5; Di-Et. eth., 208
584	**3,5'-Dimethoxy-5,7,4'-trihydroxyflavonol** (Syringetin)..........	288–9, pa. yel., ac. a.								*tetra*: 224–6		4'-Benzyl eth., 240–1
585	**2,7-Dihydroxy-4-methylquinoline**..............	290–300, w.-al. (+1H$_2$O); turns br. at 280								*7-mono*: 250–4, al.	*7-mono*: 288, al.	
586	**2,6-Dihydroxyanthracene** (Flavol; 2,6-Anthracenediol)................	295–300 d., al.; turns dk. at 270								*di*: 260–1, ac. a.		Di-Me. eth., 255–6, ac. a.; Di-Et. eth., 230–1
587	**Bi-α-naphthol** (4,4'-Dihydroxy-1,1'-binaphthyl)	300; 250								*di*: 217		Di-Me. eth., 252; Di-Et. eth., 211
588	**2,8-Dihydroxyacridine** (2,8-Acridinediol)......	>300, turns red at 275										Di-Me. eth., 138–9; Di-Et. eth., 142–3
589	**2,6-Dibromo-1,5-dihydroxynaphthalene**.....	>300; 224 d. turns dk. at 200								*1-mono*: 273; *di*: 228	*di*: 262, pyr.	1-Acetate, 5-benzoate, 164; Di-Me. eth., 161; Di-Et. eth., 148
590	**3,7-Dihydroxyacridine** (3,7-Acridinediol)......	324, pa. yel., w.-al.										In al. sol. → grn. fluor.
591	**3,8-Dihydroxypyrene** (3,8-Pyrenediol).......	330, Tri-cl-bz.-ph. hydraz.; turns dk. at 280								*di*: 224, ac. a.		Di-Me. eth., 244, cl-bz.

*Derivative data given in order: m.p., crystal color, solvent from which crystallized.

TABLE VII. ORGANIC DERIVATIVES OF PHENOLS
b) Solids (Listed in order of increasing m.p.)* (Continued)

No.	Name	Melting point, °C	Boiling point, °C	Phenyl ure-thane	α-Naph-thyl-ure-thane	p-Nitro-ben-zoate	3,5-Di-nitro-benzoate	Bromo derivative	p-Toluene sul-fonate	Acetate	Benzoate	Miscellaneous
592	**1,3-Dihydroxyacridone** ...	370	....	......	......	......	....	....	......	*mono*: 200, yel.	*mono*: 295–7	Me. eth. (i) 203, dk. br.; (ii) 252, yel.; Di-Me. eth., 286–7 d.; Anil., 269–70; Zn dust → acri-dine, 111

*Derivative data given in order: m.p., crystal color, solvent from which crystallized.

EXPLANATIONS AND REFERENCES TO TABLE VIII

Cleavage to alkyl bromide or alkyl iodide.

$$ROR' + 2HBr \rightarrow RBr + R'Br + H_2O$$

Mixture of alkyl
bromides

$$ROR' + 2HI \rightarrow RI + R'I + H_2O$$

Mixture of
alkyl iodides

$$ArOR + HI \rightarrow ArOH + RI$$

Phenol   Alkyl
iodide

From the ether with concentrated hydrochloric acid.

For directions and examples see: Cheronis, p. 543; Linstead, pp. 46–7; Shriner, p. 116; Vogel, p. 316.

NOTE: For directions and examples for preparation of derivatives of alkyl iodides and alkyl bromides formed on cleavage of ethers see explanations and references to Table V, pp. 52, 53, 54.

Alkyl 3,5-dinitrobenzoate. *

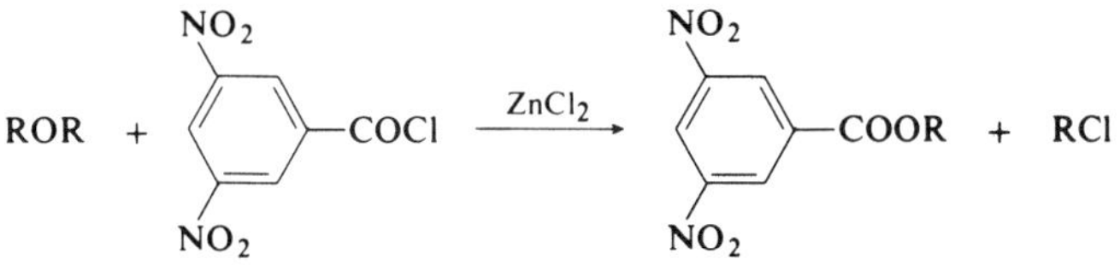

$ROR + $ (3,5-dinitrobenzoyl chloride with NO_2 groups) $—COCl \xrightarrow{ZnCl_2}$ (product) $—COOR + RCl$

Alkyl 3,5-
dinitrobenzoate

From a symmetrical aliphatic ether with freshly fused zinc chloride and 3,5-dinitrobenzoyl chloride.

For directions and examples see: Cheronis, pp. 542, 543; Linstead, p. 46; Shriner, p. 239; Vogel, p. 316; Wild, p. 96; H. W. Underwood, O. L. Baril and G. C. Toone, *J. Amer. Chem. Soc.*, **52**, 4087 (1930).

Bromo derivative.

$$ArOR \xrightarrow{Br_2} Ar(OR)Br$$

Bromoaryl
ether

$$ArOR \xrightarrow{nBr_2} Ar(OR)Br_n$$

Polybromoaryl
ether

From alkyl aryl or diaryl ether with bromine in glacial acetic acid or chloroform.

For directions and examples see: Cheronis, p. 545; Shriner, p. 240.

From the aromatic ether with bromine in alcohol, acetic acid, ether, chloroform or petrol ether.

See: Wild, pp. 98–9; 101; H. W. Underwood, O. L. Baril and G. C. Toone, *J. Amer. Chem. Soc.*, **52**, 4087 (1930).

Sulfonamide. *

$$ArOR \xrightarrow{ClSO_2OH} Ar(OR)SO_2Cl \xrightarrow{(NH_4)_2CO_3} Ar(OR)SO_2NH_2$$

Sulfonyl   Sulfonamide
chloride

The sulfonyl chloride is prepared from the aromatic ether with chlorosulfonic acid in chloroform or without solvent. The sulfonamide is obtained from the sulfonyl chloride with ammonium carbonate and/or aqueous ammonia.

For directions and examples see: Cheronis, pp. 545, 546; Linstead, pp. 47, 50; Shriner, p. 241; Vogel, p. 672; Wild, pp. 27, 101; E. H. Huntress and F. H. Carten, *J. Amer. Chem. Soc.*, **62**, 511, 603 (1940).

---

*Derivatives recommended for first trial.

WARNING: This is not an instruction manual. References should be consulted for the preparation of derivatives.

Picric acid and 1,3,5-trinitrobenzene addition complexes.

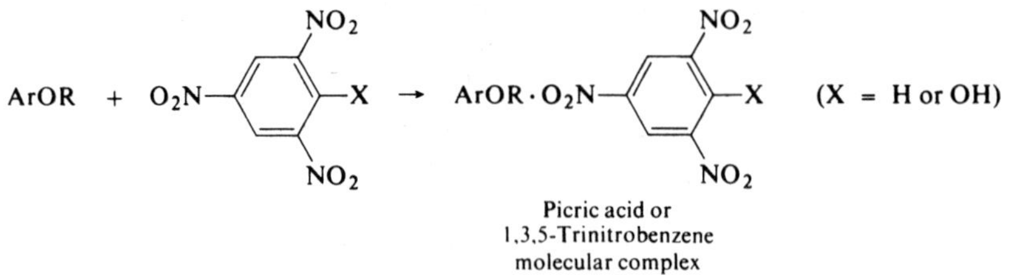

$$\text{ArOR} \; + \; O_2N\text{—}\underset{NO_2}{\overset{NO_2}{\bigcirc}}\text{—X} \; \rightarrow \; \text{ArOR} \cdot O_2N\text{—}\underset{NO_2}{\overset{NO_2}{\bigcirc}}\text{—X} \qquad (X = H \text{ or } OH)$$

Picric acid or
1,3,5-Trinitrobenzene
molecular complex

From the aromatic ether with the aromatic polynitro compound in chloroform.

For directions and examples see: Cheronis, pp. 545, 547; Linstead, pp. 47, 50; Shriner, p. 241; Vogel, p. 672; Wild, p. 100; O. L. Baril and G. A. Megrdichian, *J. Amer. Chem. Soc.*, **58**, 1415 (1936); E. K. Andersen, *Acta Chem. Scand.*, **8**, 157 (1954).

From the aromatic ether with picric acid in ethanol.

See: V. H. Dermer and O. C. Dermer, *J. Org. Chem.*, **3**, 289 (1938).

NOTE: For additional information regarding directions and examples for the derivatization of aromatic ethers (nitration, side-chain oxidation, etc.) see explanations and references to Table IV, pp. 32, 33, 34.

*Derivatives recommended for first trial.
WARNING: This is not an instruction manual. References should be consulted for the preparation of derivatives.

TABLE VIII. ORGANIC DERIVATIVES OF ETHERS
a) Liquids (Listed in order of increasing atmospheric b.p.)*

No.	Name	Boiling point, °C	Melting point, °C	n_D^{20}	D_4^{20}	Picrate	Sulfonamide	Nitro derivative	Bromo derivative	1,3,5-Trinitrobenzene addition compound	3,5-Dinitrobenzoate	Miscellaneous
1	Ethylene oxide (Epoxyethane)	10.7	−111.7	1.3614^4	0.89713_4^0							HBr → Ethylene bromohydrin, b.p.: 149
2	Ethyl methyl ether	10.8; 10			0.7260_4^0							
3	Furan	31.27	−85.6	1.42157	0.9366							Maleic anhydride → 3,6-Endoxo-Δ^4-tetrahydrophthalic anhydride, 125d.; 118d., abs. eth.
4	Diethyl ether (Ethyl ether)	34.60	−116.3, stab.; −123.3, unst.	1.3526	0.71352						93	Iodide, b.p.: 72
5	Propylene oxide (1,2-Epoxypropane)	35		1.466	0.830							Heating with dil. H₂SO₄ → d.l-propylene glycol, b.p.: 187.4
6	Ethyl vinyl ether	35.75	−115.8	1.3768	0.7589							Dil. acid → al. + acetaldehyde
7	Methyl n-propyl ether	39		1.3579	0.7356_4^{13}							
8	Allyl methyl ether	46							β,γ-di: b.p.: 185, D_4^{20}: 1.8329			
9	Ethyl isopropyl ether	53–4			0.7211 (0.745_4^0)							Heating with 1% H₂SO₄ (sealed tube) → al. + isopropyl alcohol
10	tert-Butyl methyl ether	55.2		1.3689	0.7405							Constant boil. mixt. with w., b.p.: 52.6, with 4% w.
11	2,3-Epoxybutane	cis: 58–9^{745}; trans: 53–4^{741}			cis: 0.8226_4^{25}; trans: 0.8010_4^{25}							Normal crude mixt. is 65% trans + 35% cis
12	Chloromethyl methyl ether	59		1.3974	1.015	163						
13	α-Butylene oxide (1,2-Epoxybutane)	61–2		1.385^{17}	0.837^{17}							
14	Ethyl n-propyl ether	63.6	<−79	1.36948	0.7386							Constant boil. mixt. with al., b.p.: 61.2, with 25% al.
15	2-Methylfuran (Sylvan)	64		1.434	0.913							
16	Tetrahydrofuran	65		1.407	0.889							
17	Allyl ethyl ether	66–7^{742}		1.3881	0.7651				β,γ-di: b.p.: 193–5			Heating with 2% H₂SO₄ → al. + allyl alcohol
18	Di-isopropyl ether (Isopropyl ether)	67.5	−60	1.3688	0.726						123; 120–1, CCl₄	

*Derivative data given in order: m.p., crystal color, solvent from which crystallized.

TABLE VIII. ORGANIC DERIVATIVES OF ETHERS
a) Liquids (Listed in order of increasing atmospheric b.p.)* (Continued)

No.	Name	Boiling point, °C	Melting point, °C	n_D^{20}	D_4^{20}	Picrate	Sulfonamide	Nitro derivative	Bromo derivative	1,3,5-Trinitrobenzene addition compound	3,5-Dinitrobenzoate	Miscellaneous
19	n-Butyl methyl ether	70	−115.5	1.3728; 1.3736	0.7455; 0.774	......	......	......	......	......	......	Oxid. by alkaline KMnO₄ at 35–40° → ac. a. + methoxyacetic acid
20	tert-Butyl ethyl ether	73.1 (cor.)	......	1.3760	0.7404						......	Constant boil. mixt. with w., b.p.: 65.2, with 6% w.
21	Tetrahydrosylvan	79	......	1.407	0.855							
22	Chloromethyl ethyl ether	80; 83d.	......	1.40398	1.014							
23	Ethyl isobutyl ether	81.1 (cor.)		1.3739^{25}	0.7323$_4^{25}$							
24	sec-Butyl ethyl ether	81.2 (cor.)	......	1.3802	0.7503							
25	Isopropyl n-propyl ether	83	......	1.376	0.7370							
26	Ethylene glycol dimethyl ether	84.7	......	1.37965	0.8665						......	......
27	Dihydropyran	86	......	1.440	0.923	......	......	......	......	......	......	......
28	tert-Amyl methyl ether	86.3	......	1.3885	0.7703	......						Constant boil. mixt. with w., b.p.: 73.8, with 9% w.; Constant boil. mixt. with me. al., b.p.: 62.3, with 50% me. al.
29	Tetrahydropyran	88	......	1.421	0.881	......	......	......	......	......	......	......
30	Di-n-propyl ether (n-Propyl ether)	90.1	−122	1.38829	0.74698	......	......	......	......	......	74	Constant boil. mixt. with w., b.p.: 75.4; Constant boil. mixt. with n-propyl alcohol, b.p.: 85.8
31	n-Butyl ethyl ether	92.3 (cor.)	−124	1.3820	0.7505	......	......	......	......	......	......	......
32	2,5-Dimethylfuran	94	......	1.4363$^{21.6}$	0.888$_4^{20.1}$	......	......	penta: 180, chl.	......	......	......	Maleic anhydride → 3,6-Endoxo-3,6-dimethyl-Δ⁴-tetrahydrophthalic anhydride, 78, eth.
33	α-Chloroethyl ethyl ether	98	......	1.404	0.966	......	......	......	......	......	......	......
34	n-Amyl methyl ether	99–100	......	1.3873	0.761							
35	tert-Amyl ethyl ether	101	......	1.3912	0.7657	......	......	......	......	......	......	Constant boil. mixt. with 13% w., b.p.: 81.2
36	1,4-Dioxane	101.4	11.8	1.4232	1.03361	......	......	......	65–6	......	......	Iodine derivative, 84–5; Constant boil. mixt. with 48 mole % dioxane, b.p.: 82.8

*Derivative data given in order: m.p., crystal color, solvent from which crystallized.

No.	Name	Boiling point, °C	Melting point, °C	n_D^{20}	D_4^{20}	Picrate	Sulfon-amide	Nitro derivative	Bromo derivative	1,3,5-Tri-nitro-benzene addition compound	3,5-Dinitro-benzoate	Miscellaneous
37	Ethylene glycol mono-ethyl monomethyl ether (1-Ethoxy-2-methoxyethane)....	102	....	1.38677	0.8529	....	....	....	....	....	....	
38	Cyclopentyl methyl ether	105	....	1.4206	0.862	....	....	....	....	....	....	
39	β-Chloroethyl ethyl ether	107	....	1.411	0.989	....	....	....	....	....	....	
40	n-Butyl isopropyl ether	108[738]	....	1.3889$_{5461}^{24.9}$	0.7594[15]	....	....	....	....	....	....	Boil. HI → n-butyl iodide + isopropyl iodide
41	α-Epichlorohydrin ...	115–7	....	1.438	1.181	....	....	....	....	....	....	
42	α,α'-Dichloroethyl ether	116; 114	....	1.4183[24]	1.138$_4^{12}$	....	....	....	....	....	....	
43	n-Amyl ethyl ether ...	118	....	1.3927	0.762	....	....	....	....	....	....	
44	Di-sec-butyl ether	121	....	1.3928[25]	0.760	....	....	....	b.p.: 90–1; n_D^{25}: 1.250	....	75.5	
45	Cyclopentyl ethyl ether	122	....	1.423	0.853	....	....	....	....	....	....	
46	Di-isobutyl ether (Iso-butyl ether).......	123	....	....	0.7616$_{15}^{15}$	....	....	....	....	....	87; 84.5–5.5	
47	Ethylene glycol mono-methyl mono-n-propyl ether (1-Methoxy-2-n-propoxyethane)....	124.5	....	1.39467	0.8472	....	....	....	....	....	....	
48	n-Hexyl methyl ether .	126	....	1.3972	0.772	....	....	....	....	....	....	
49	2-Methoxy-1-propanol	130[758]	....	....	....	....	....	....	....	....	97	α-Naphthylure-thane, 60
50	Cyclohexyl methyl ether	134	....	1.435	0.875	....	....	....	....	....	....	
51	Ethylene glycol mono-ethyl ether ("Cello-solve"; 2-Ethoxy-ethanol)	134.8; 135.1	....	1.40797	0.9297; 0.9311	....	....	....	....	....	75	Miscible with w., with al. and with eth.; Diphenyl-urethane, 43; Xan-thate, 202.5 (cor.), acet.-abs. eth. Phenylurethane, 226
52	3-Ethoxy-2-methyl-2-butanol	141	....	....	....	....	....	....	....	....	....	
53	n-Hexyl ethyl ether ..	142	....	1.4008	0.772	....	....	....	....	....	....	
54	Di-n-butyl ether (Butyl ether).......	142.4; 144	−98	1.3989	0.76829	....	....	....	....	....	62–3; 64	....
55	Cyclohexyl ethyl ether	149	....	1.435	0.864	....	....	....	....	....	....	
56	Anisole (Methoxyben-zene; Methyl phenyl ether)............	153.8; 155 (43[10])	−37.5	1.52211	0.99393	79–81, unst. in. air.	113; 110–1, al.	2,4-di: 86.9, al.; 95.5	2,4-di: 61, al.	....	87	....
57	3-Methoxy-2-methyl-1-propanol........	155	....	1.4140[27]	....	....	....	....	....	....	64	
58	Diethylene glycol dimethyl ether......	162.0	−75	1.4099	0.9440$_{20}^{20}$	....	....	....	....	....	....	

*Derivative data given in order: m.p., crystal color, solvent from which crystallized.

TABLE VIII. ORGANIC DERIVATIVES OF ETHERS
a) Liquids (Listed in order of increasing atmospheric b.p.)* (Continued)

No.	Name	Boiling point, °C	Melting point, °C	n_D^{20}	D_4^{20}	Picrate	Sulfonamide	Nitro derivative	Bromo derivative	1,3,5-Tri-nitro-benzene addition compound	3,5-Dinitro-benzoate	Miscellaneous
59	Furfuryl alcohol (2-Furancarbinol).....	170	....	1.4868	1.1351	....	......	......	....	....	80–1, pyr.	p-Nitrobenzoate, 76; N-Phenyl-urethane, 45
60	Ethylene glycol mono-n-butyl ether (n-Butyl "cellosolve")......	171^{743}	....	1.4177	0.9188	....	......	......	172	......	oil	3-Nitrophthalate, 120
61	Benzyl methyl ether ..	170–1 (cor.)	......	1.5008	0.9649	115–6	......					....
62	2-Methoxytoluene (2-Methyl anisole; Methyl 2-tolyl ether; 2-Cresyl methyl ether)............	171	......	1.505	0.9853	116; 113–4, pa. yel.	137, al.	3,5-di: 69, pa. yel., me. al.	5-mono: 63–4, al.	......	......	Oxid. → o-Methoxybenzoic acid, 101
63	Phenyl ethyl ether (Phenetole)........	172	−33	1.5080; 1.5074	0.9666	92	150	p-mono: 58	....			....
64	Di-isoamyl ether (Iso-amyl ether).......	172.5		1.409	0.778	......	......	......	......	....	60–1	Constant boil. mixt. with w., b.p.: 97.2
65	4-Methoxytoluene (4-Methylanisole; Methyl 4-tolyl ether; 4-Cresyl methyl ether)............	173; 176	....	1.512	0.970	88–9, yel.-or.	182, al.	......				Oxid. → p-Anisic acid, 184–6; 184, w.
66	3-Methoxytoluene (3-Methylanisole; Methyl 3-tolyl ether; 3-Cresyl methyl ether)............	173; 177 (cor.)	....	1.513	0.972	113–4, yel.-or.	129–30, al.	2-mono: 54–5, pet. eth.; 2,4,6-tri: 92, al.	....			Oxid. → m-Methoxybenzoic acid, 110
67	Tetrahydrofurfuryl alcohol...........	117	....	1.45167	1.0544	....	......				83–4	p-Nitrobenzoate, 46–8; N-Phenyl-urethane, 61, pet. eth.
68	Phenyl isopropyl ether	178	....	1.4992	0.975	....					....	conc. H$_2$SO$_4$ + ac. a. → o-Isopropylphenol, b.p.: 213–4, m.p.: 130
69	β,β'-Dichloroethyl ether	178	....	1.4568	1.220	....						....
70	2-Ethoxytoluene (2-Cresyl ethyl ether; Ethyl 2-tolyl ether)..	184	....	1.505	0.953	117.5–8.5, pa. yel.	148–9, al.	di: 51	....		....	Oxid. → o-Ethoxy-benzoic acid, 25; 19.0–.5, well dried
71	Benzyl ethyl ether (Homophenetole) ..	184–6 (cor.)	....	1.4958	0.9478	....						Refluxed in bz. + P$_2$O$_5$ → Ethylene + Diphenyl-methane, 25.1
72	Di-n-amyl ether (n-Amyl ether)	187.5	−69.3	1.416	0.78298	....	......				42–3	....
73	Diethylene glycol diethyl ether	188		1.411	0.906	....	......					
74	Phenyl n-propyl ether (n-Propoxybenzene)	188; 189.3 (cor.)	....	1.5014; 1.5011	0.9494$^{20}_{20}$	....	116–7, al.					

* Derivative data given in order: m.p., crystal color, solvent from which crystallized.

TABLE VIII. ORGANIC DERIVATIVES OF ETHERS
a) Liquids (Listed in order of increasing atmospheric b.p.)* (Continued)

No.	Name	Boiling point, °C	Melting point, °C	n_D^{20}	D_4^{20}	Picrate	Sulfonamide	Nitro derivative	Bromo derivative	1,3,5-Trinitrobenzene addition compound	3,5-Dinitrobenzoate	Miscellaneous
75	4-Ethoxytoluene (4-Cresyl ethyl ether; Ethyl 4-tolyl ether)..	190.5	....	1.505	0.949	110–1, or.-yel.	138.0–.5, al.	....	....	....	....	Oxid. → p-Ethoxybenzoic acid, 198; 195.0–.5, al.
76	3-Ethoxytoluene (3-Cresyl ethyl ether; Ethyl 3-tolyl ether)..	190.5	....	1.506	0.949	114–5, or.-yel.	110–1, al.					Oxid. → m-Ethoxybenzoic acid, 137
77	Diethylene glycol monomethyl ether...	194	....	1.4244	1.035_{20}^{20}							p-Nitrophenylurethane, 73.5
78	3-Chloroanisole	194	....				131					....
79	2-Chloroanisole	195		1.5433^{25}	1.1865_4^{25}			95				
80	Diethylene glycol monoethyl ether	196		1.4298	1.023_{20}^{20}						oil	p-Nitrophenylurethane, 66
81	4-Chloroanisole	200			$1.1851_4^{12.8}$		151	2-mono: 95				
82	n-Butyl phenyl ether.. (n-Butoxybenzene)..	206	....	1.5049	....	110–2, pa. yel., chl.	103–4, al.					
83	2-Chlorophenetole ...	208	17				133	82				
84	2-Bromoanisole	210					140	106				
85	Benzyl isobutyl ether .	210–2 (cor.)	....	1.4826	0.9233							
86	p-Bromoanisole	215; 216			1.494_4^9		148	88				
87	Methyl thymyl ether..	216			0.954_4^9			tri: 92				
88	Triethylene glycol dimethyl ether......	216	−47	1.4233	0.9871_{20}^{20}							
89	1,3-Dimethoxybenzene (Resorcinol dimethyl ether)............	217 (cor.)	−58; −52	1.4233	1.0552_{25}^{25}	56–8, or.-yel., unst. in air	166–7, al.	2,4-di: 72, pa. yel., al.; 4,6-di: 157, al.; 2,4,6-tri: 123–4, pa. red, al.	4,6-di: 140, al.			
90	2-Bromophenetole ...	218	....	....	....		135	98				
91	Benzyl n-butyl ether..	219–21 (cor.)	....	1.4833	0.9227							
92	Creosol (4-Methyl-catechol 2-methyl ether)............	221	5.5	1.5353^{25}	1.0919_4^{25}	112, yel.						
93	n-Butyl 2-tolyl ether (2-Butoxytoluene)..	223	....		0.9437_0^0		95–6, al.					
94	2-Methoxyaniline (2-Anisidine)......	225	5	....	1.0978_{15}^{15}						....	N-Formyl, 83.5; N-Acetyl, 87–8
95	Di-n-hexyl ether (n-Hexyl ether).......	$228–9^{761}$	....		0.7936						54.5–5.5	....
96	Safrole (4-Allyl-1,2-methylenedioxy-benzene).........	233	11	1.5383	1.100	104.0–5.5, or.-red		tri: 108; penta: 169–70, bz.	51			
97	4-Bromophenetole ...	233; 229	12	....	....		145	47				

*Derivative data given in order: m.p., crystal color, solvent from which crystallized.

135

No.	Name	Boiling point, °C	Melting point, °C	n_D^{20}	D_4^{20}	Picrate	Sulfonamide	Nitro derivative	Bromo derivative	1,3,5-Tri-nitro-benzene addition compound	3,5-Dinitro-benzoate	Miscellaneous
98	**Resorcinol diethyl ether**	235	12.4	. . . .	. . . .	109	184	. . . .	*tri*: 69	. . . .	. . . .	. . . .
99	**Eugenol methyl ether** (4-Allyl-1,2-di-methoxybenzene). . .	244	. . . .	1.5360	1.0336	114–5, red-br., chl.	7	. . . .	*tri*: 78, abs. al.	. . . .	. . . .	. . . .
100	**2-Iodophenetole**	246	. . . .	. . . .	1.800	84	. . . .	. . . .	*tri*: 110	. . . .	. . . .	. . . .
101	*trans*(β)-**Isosafrole** (1,2-Methylene-dioxy-4-propylben-zene)	248	6.8	1.5782	1.122	74–5, dk. red, chl.	. . . .	. . . .	*di*: 52–3, eth.; *tri*: 109–10, pet. eth.	85–6, brt. scar.	. . . .	. . . .
102	**3-Methoxyaniline** (3-Anisidine).	251	. . . .	. . . .	. . . .	169d., yel.	. . . .	. . . .	. . . .	. . . .	. . . .	N-Formyl, 57; N-Acetyl, 81; N-*p*-Toluenesulfonyl, 68
103	**Di-*n*-heptyl ether** (*n*-Heptyl ether). . . .	263; 260	. . . .	1.427	0.8056_{20}^{20}	. . . .	. . . .	. . . .	. . . .	. . . .	47	. . . .
104	**Isoeugenol methyl ether**	264	16–7	1.5692	1.0528	42–5, dk. red, chl.	. . . .	. . . .	*di*: 101.0–.5, abs. eth.	69–70, brt. scar.	. . . .	Oxid. → Veratric acid, 181
105	**Tetraethylene glycol dimethyl ether**	266; 275	. . . .	1.432	1.009	. . . .	. . . .	. . . .	. . . .	. . . .	. . . .	. . . .
106	**Methyl 1-naphthyl ether** (1-Methoxy-naphthalene)	271 (cor.)	< –10	1.6940^{25}	1.09159	129.5–30.5; yel.-or., chl.	156–7, al.	2-*mono*: 80; 4-*mono*: 85, yel., al.	4-*mono*: b.p.: 181–2; 5-*mono*: 67.5–8.0; *x*-*mono*: 46, al.; 2,4-*di*: 54–5, al.	139–40; 137–8, yel.	. . . .	. . . .
107	**2-Nitroanisole**.	277	10	1.562	1.254	. . . .	. . . .	. . . .	. . . .	. . . .	. . . .	Reduct. → *o*-anisidine, b.p.: 225
108	**Ethyl 1-naphthyl ether** (1-Ethoxynaph-thalene).	280.5 (cor.)	5.5	1.5973^{25}	1.074	118.5–9.0 (cor.)	164–5, al.	2-*mono*: 84; 4-*mono*: 116–7, al.	4-*mono*: 48, al.	125.5, yel.	. . . .	. . . .
109	**Dibenzyl ether** (Benzyl ether).	290–300d.	3.6	. . . .	1.0428	77–8, or.-yel., chl.	. . . .	. . . .	*di*: 107–8, al.	. . . .	112	. . . .
110	**Isoamyl 1-naphthyl ether**	317.5 (cor.)	< –10	$1.57049^{14.2}$	$1.00689_4^{14.2}$	96.0–7.0	. . . .	. . . .	. . . .	. . . .	. . . .	. . . .

*Derivative data given in order: m.p., crystal color, solvent from which crystallized.

TABLE VIII. ORGANIC DERIVATIVES OF ETHERS
b) Solids (Listed in order of increasing m.p.)*

No.	Name	Melting point, °C	Boiling point, °C	n_D^{20}	D_4^{20}	Picrate	Sulfon-amide	Nitro derivative	Bromo derivative	1,3,5-Tri-nitro-benzene addition compound	3,5-Dinitro-ben-zoate	Miscellaneous
1	**4-Chlorophenetole** (1-Chloro-4-ethoxybenzene)	21	212	1.5227^{19}	1.1231^{20}_{20}	....	134	....	2,6-*di*: 54	......	......	....
2	**Veratrole** (1,2-Dimethoxy-benzene)	22.5	207; 205	1.5287^{21}	1.080	56-7, red	135-6, al.	95	4,5-*di*: 92-3			
3	**Anethole** (1-Methoxy-4-propenylbenzene)	22.5, al.	235	1.558	0.989^{28}_4	69-70d., or.-red, al.	....		*di*: 67, eth.; 65; 62-4; *tri*: 108, pet. eth.			
4	**4-Methoxybenzyl alcohol** (Anisyl alcohol)	24	151^{27}; 138^{14}	....	....	....	....	....	....	......	......	Phenylurethane, 93; *p*-Nitroben-zoate, 94
5	***n*-Amyl 2-naphthyl ether**	24.5	327.5 (cor.)	1.5587^{30}	....	66.5-7.0, or., h. al.	159	*di*: 135	*di*: 58	......	......	....
6	**4-Iodophenetole** (1-Ethoxy-4-iodobenzene)	27	252	....	....	....	....	96				
7	**Diphenyl ether** (Phenyl ether)	28	259	1.5826^{24}	1.073	110	*di*: 159, al.	4,4'-*di*: 144.4, al.; 2,4,2',4'-*tetra*: 195-7, pa. yel., ac. a.	4,4'-*di*: 54-5, al.			
8	**Isoamyl 2-naphthyl ether**	28.0-.5	321.0 (cor.)	....	....	93.5-4.0, al.	....	....				
9	**2-Methoxyphenol** (Guaia-col; Catechol mono-methyl ether)	28.2	205	1.5441	$1.1287^{20.4}_{vac.}$	86-7	....		4,5,6-*tri*: 116, al.	......	141.2 (cor.), al.	....
10	**2-Methoxybiphenyl** (2-Biphenyl methyl ether)	29, pet. eth.	274	....	....	....	....	5-*mono*: 95-6, pa. yel., me. al.	....			
11	**β-Bromoethyl phenyl ether**	32	......	....	....	....	....	....	56			
12	**Isobutyl 2-naphthyl ether**	33	304	....	....	84-5						
13	**Didodecyl ether** (Dilauryl ether)	33; 28-30	$190-5^1$	....	....	....						
14	**2-Ethoxybiphenyl** (2-Bi-phenyl ethyl ether)	34	132^6	....	....	....						
15	***sec*-Butyl 2-naphthyl ether**	34	298.5 (cor.)	....	....	86						
16	**3-Ethoxybiphenyl** (3-Bi-phenyl ethyl ether)	35	158^8	....	....	....						
17	**3-Nitrophenetole**	35	284	....	....	....	....	....	....	......	......	Reduct. → *m*-Phenetidine, (Picrate, 158)
18	***n*-Butyl 2-naphthyl ether**	35.5	309 (cor.)	......	....	67	....	....	....	......	......	....
19	**Ethyl 2-naphthyl ether** (Neonerolin)	36; 37	282 (cor.)	1.5932^{47}	1.064	101	161-3, al.	....	1-*mono*: 66, pet. eth.; 1,6-*di*: 94, pet. eth.	......	......	....
20	**3-Aminodiphenyl ether**	37, lgr.	315	......	....	....	....	....	....	......	......	N-Hydrochloride, 141, 139; N-Acetyl, 83, lgr.

*Derivative data given in order: m.p., crystal color, solvent from which crystallized.

No.	Name	Melting point, °C	Boiling point, °C	n_D^{20}	D_4^{20}	Picrate	Sulfonamide	Nitro-derivative	Bromo derivative	1,3,5-Trinitrobenzene addition compound	3,5-Dinitrobenzoate	Miscellaneous
21	3-Nitroanisole	39	258	......	1.373^{18}	....	....	....	....	......	......	Reduct. → m-Anisidine, (Picrate, 169d.)
22	Isopropyl 2-naphthyl ether	40	285			95						
23	2-Naphthyl n-propyl ether	40	297			81						
24	Catechol diethyl ether (1,2-Diethoxybenzene)	43, dil. al.	217			69–71, red-br., unst. in air	3,4-di: 162–3, al.	tri: 122				
25	bz-Tetrahydro-6-methoxy-quinoline	43	130	1.5718^{50}								
26	2,4,6-Trichlorophenetole	44	246					di: 100				
27	8-Methoxyquinoline	45	175^{29}			162						
28	2-Aminodiphenyl ether	47	173^{14}									Acetate, 81
29	Pyrogallol trimethyl ether (1,2,3-Trimethoxybenzene)	47, dil. al.	241			78.5–80.0, yel.	2,3,4-tri: 123–4	5-mono: 106, ac. a.	mono: oil; di: oil; 4,5,6-tri: 73–4	81, pa. yel.		
30	4-Iodoanisole	52	139									
31	Phloroglucinol trimethyl ether (1,3,5-Trimethoxybenzene)	52–3, al.	255.5 (cor.)						2-mono: 96–7, dil. al.; 2,4-di: 129–30, al.; 2,4,6-tri: 145, al.			
32	Hydroquinone monomethyl ether	52.5	$244^{754.2}$									
33	4-Nitroanisole	54	274	1.5707^{60}	1.233_4^{20}							Reduct. → p-Anisidine, 57
34	Hydroquinone dimethyl ether (1,4-Dimethoxybenzene)	56, 75% al.	213 (cor.)			47–8, or.-red, unst. in air	148, al.	2-mono: 72, yel.; 2,3-di: 177; 2,5-di: 202	di: 142, ac. a.	di: 86.5, red		
35	4-Methoxyaniline (4-Anisidine)	57	246		1.071_4^{55}							N-Formyl, 81; N-Acetyl, 130–2, w.; N-Benzoyl, 216–7
36	4-Cyclohexylphenyl methyl ether	59	116^4									
37	2,4,6-Trichloroanisole	60						di: 95				
38	1,3-Diphenoxypropane (Trimethylene glycol diphenyl ether)	61, al.	338–40 (cor.)				4,4'-di: 245–55, al.					
39	Catechol dibenzyl ether (1,2-Dibenzyloxy-benzene)	63–4, wh., me. al.						4-mono: 98, pa. yel., al.				
40	1-Phenyl-2-phenoxy-methanol	64										p-Nitrobenzoate, 84
41	α-Glyceryl phenyl ether	70	187^{15}									
42	2,4,6-Tribromophenetole	72						79				

*Derivative data given in order: m.p., crystal color, solvent from which crystallized.

TABLE VIII. ORGANIC DERIVATIVES OF ETHERS

TABLE VIII. ORGANIC DERIVATIVES OF ETHERS
b) Solids (Listed in order of increasing m.p.)* (Continued)

No.	Name	Melting point, °C	Boiling point, °C	n_D^{20}	D_4^{20}	Picrate	Sulfonamide	Nitro-derivative	Bromo derivative	1,3,5-Trinitrobenzene addition compound	3,5-Dinitrobenzoate	Miscellaneous
43	Hydroquinone diethyl ether (1,4-Diethoxybenzene) ..	72	......	......	......	......	......	mono: 49, yel.; 2,3-di: 130, yel., al.; 2,5-di: 176, yel., al.	......	86.5	......	......
44	Methyl 2-naphthyl ether (Nerolin).............	73 (cor.), eth.	273	......	......	116.5–7.0, dk. yel., 113.0–3.5	150–1, al.	1-mono: 128; 1,6,8-tri: 215 d.	x-mono: 62–3, pet. eth.; 1-mono: 83–4; 3-mono: 77–8; 6-mono: 108	93.5, yel.	......	....
45	2,4,5-Tribromophenetol ...	73	......	......	......	......	......	79	......	......	......	......
46	4-Ethoxybiphenyl (4-Biphenyl ethyl ether)	76; 74	188[13]	......	......	......	......		......	......	......	......
47	Benzyl 1-naphthyl ether ...	77 (cor.)	200[12]	......	......	85–100 (cor.)	......		......	......	......	......
48	2-Phenyl-2-phenoxy-ethanol	81	......	......	......	......	......		......	......	......	p-Nitrobenzoate, 87
49	4-Aminodiphenyl ether	83.5; 84, w.	189[14]	......	......	......	......		......	......	......	N-Acetyl, 127; N-HCl, 122
50	Biphenylene oxide (Dibenzofuran)	86, wh., al.	288 (cor.)	......	......	94	......	3-mono: 181–2; di: 245, ac. a.	......	96, yel.	......	....
51	4-Methoxybiphenyl (4-Biphenyl methyl ether; 4-Phenylanisole)	90; 89	......	......	......	......	3-mono: 91–2, al.; 3,5-di: 137–8, yel., al.; 3,4'-di: 171	3-mono: 79; 4'-mono: 144, pet.; 3,4'-di: 134; 3,5-di: 87, pet.	......	......	......	......
52	1,2-Diphenoxyethane (Ethylene glycol diphenyl ether)...............	98, al.	......	......	......	......	4,4'-di: 228–9, al.	2',4'-di: 215.2 (cor.), pa. yel., acet.	di-p: 134–5, al.	......	......	......
53	Benzyl 2-naphthyl ether (2-Benzyloxynaphthalene)..	101.5 (cor.), al.	d.	......	......	123.0 (cor.)	......		......	......	......	......
54	Anisoin (4,4'-Dimethoxy-benzoin)	113	......	......	......	......	......		......	......	......	Methyl ether, 52–3, yel., CCl₄; Ethyl ether, 103–4, al.-w.
55	Hydroquinone dibenzyl ether (1,4-Dibenzyloxy-benzene)	128–9, al.	......	......	......	......	......	83	......	......	......	......

*Derivative data given in order: m.p., crystal color, solvent from which crystallized.

TABLE VIII. ORGANIC DERIVATIVES OF ETHERS
b) Solids (Listed in order of increasing m.p.)* (Continued)

No.	Name	Melting point, °C	Boiling point, °C	n_D^{20}	D_4^{20}	Picrate	Sulfon-amide	Nitro-derivative	Bromo derivative	1,3,5-Tri-nitro-benzene addition com-pound	3,5-Dinitro-ben-zoate	Miscellaneous
56	**Anisil** (4,4'-Dimethoxy-benzil)...............	133, yel.	......	....	....	....	....	....	....	......	......	Monoxime, 133; *syn*-Dioxime, 217; *anti*-Di-oxime, 195, bz.; Disemicarba-zone, 254–5, dil. ac. a.; Dihydra-zone, 118
57	**Antiarol** (5-Hydroxy-1,2,3-trimethoxybenzene).....	148, w.	......	....	....	....	....	....	....	......	......	Acetyl, 74, al.; Methyl ether, 47, b.p.: 271
58	**Anhalamine** (6,7-Di-methoxy-8-hydroxy-1,2,3,4-tetrahydroiso-quinoline)............	187–8, al.	......	....	....	234–6	....	....	....	......	......	Dibenzoyl, 128–9; N-Benzoyl, 167–8
59	**7-Methoxyquinoline**......	210	287[758]	......	....	229	....	....	....	......	......	....

*Derivative data given in order: m.p., crystal color, solvent from which crystallized.

*Phenylhydrazone.**

$$RCHO + H_2NNHC_6H_5 \rightarrow RCH{=}NNHC_6H_5 + H_2O$$

$$RR'CO + H_2NNHC_6H_5 \rightarrow RR'C{=}NNHC_6H_5 + H_2O$$

Phenylhydrazone

From the carbonyl compound with phenylhydrazine in methanol or ethanol.
For directions and examples see: Cheronis, pp. 497–8; Shriner, p. 131.
From the carbonyl compound with phenylhydrazine in aqueous acetic acid.
See: Wild, p. 111.
From the carbonyl compound with phenylhydrazine in methanol in the presence of acetic acid.
See: Cheronis, p. 511.
From the carbonyl compound in alcohol with phenylhydrazine hydrochloride and sodium acetate in water.
See: Vogel, p. 721.

*p-Nitrophenylhydrazone.**

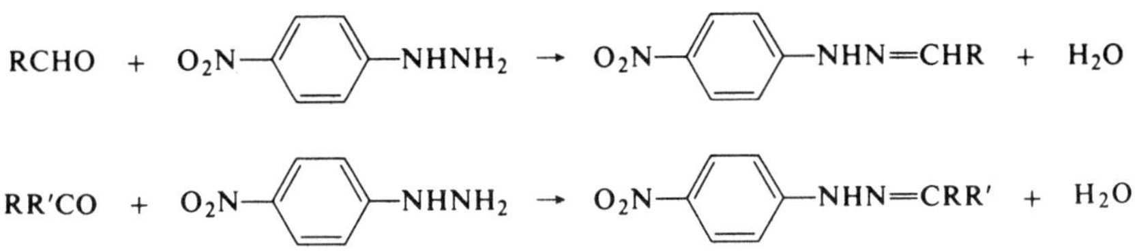

$$RCHO + O_2N{-}C_6H_4{-}NHNH_2 \rightarrow O_2N{-}C_6H_4{-}NHN{=}CHR + H_2O$$

$$RR'CO + O_2N{-}C_6H_4{-}NHNH_2 \rightarrow O_2N{-}C_6H_4{-}NHN{=}CRR' + H_2O$$

p-Nitrophenylhydrazone

From the carbonyl compound with *p*-nitrophenylhydrazine and a catalytic amount of acetic acid in alcohol.
For directions and examples see: Shriner, pp. 131, 219; Vogel, p. 722; Wild, p. 112.
From the carbonyl compound in alcohol or water with *p*-nitrophenylhydrazine in aqueous acetic-hydrochloric acids.
See: G. Petit, *Bull. Soc. Chim. France*, 141 (1948).

*2,4-Dinitrophenylhydrazone (DNP-derivative).**

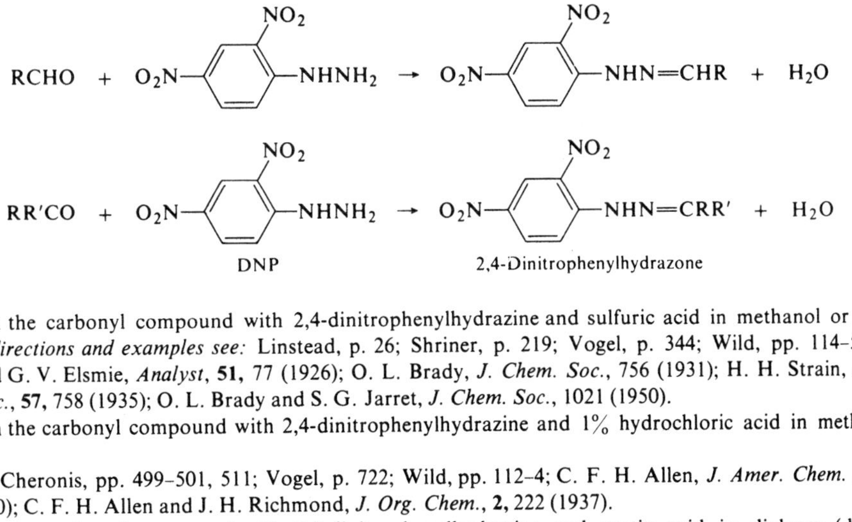

$$RCHO + O_2N{-}(NO_2)C_6H_3{-}NHNH_2 \rightarrow O_2N{-}(NO_2)C_6H_3{-}NHN{=}CHR + H_2O$$

$$RR'CO + O_2N{-}(NO_2)C_6H_3{-}NHNH_2 \rightarrow O_2N{-}(NO_2)C_6H_3{-}NHN{=}CRR' + H_2O$$

DNP   2,4-Dinitrophenylhydrazone

From the carbonyl compound with 2,4-dinitrophenylhydrazine and sulfuric acid in methanol or ethanol.
For directions and examples see: Linstead, p. 26; Shriner, p. 219; Vogel, p. 344; Wild, pp. 114–5; O. L. Brady and G. V. Elsmie, *Analyst*, **51**, 77 (1926); O. L. Brady, *J. Chem. Soc.*, 756 (1931); H. H. Strain, *J. Amer. Chem. Soc.*, **57**, 758 (1935); O. L. Brady and S. G. Jarret, *J. Chem. Soc.*, 1021 (1950).
From the carbonyl compound with 2,4-dinitrophenylhydrazine and 1% hydrochloric acid in methanol or ethanol.
See: Cheronis, pp. 499–501, 511; Vogel, p. 722; Wild, pp. 112–4; C. F. H. Allen, *J. Amer. Chem. Soc.*, **52**, 2955 (1930); C. F. H. Allen and J. H. Richmond, *J. Org. Chem.*, **2**, 222 (1937).
From the carbonyl compound with 2,4-dinitrophenylhydrazine and acetic acid in diglyme (diethylene glycol dimethyl ether).
See: H. J. Shine, *J. Org. Chem.*, **24**, 1790 (1959).
From the carbonyl compound in 95% ethanol with 2,4-dinitrophenylhydrazine and concentrated hydrochloric acid in diglyme (diethylene glycol dimethyl ether).
See: Cheronis, p. 501; H. J. Shine, *J. Org. Chem.*, **24**, 252 (1959); *J. Chem. Ed.*, **36**, 575 (1959).

---

*Derivatives recommended for first trial.
WARNING: This is not an instruction manual. References should be consulted for the preparation of derivatives.

From the carbonyl compound in ethanol with 2,4-dinitrophenylhydrazine in 85% phosphoric acid.
See: Vogel, p. 344; G. D. Johnson, *J. Amer. Chem. Soc.*, **73**, 5888 (1951); **75**, 2720 (1953).
From the carbonyl compound with 2,4-dinitrophenylhydrazine and sulfuric acid in isopropyl alcohol.
See: N. R. Campbell, *Analyst*, **61**, 391 (1936).
From the carbonyl compound with 2,4-dinitrophenylhydrazine in pyridine.
See: E. A. Braude and C. J. Timmons, *J. Chem. Soc.*, 3131 (1953).

Semicarbazone.*

$$RCHO + H_2NNHCONH_2 \rightarrow RCH{=}NNHCONH_2 + H_2O$$

$$RR'CO + H_2NNHCONH_2 \rightarrow RR'C{=}NNHCONH_2 + H_2O$$

$$RR'CO + (CH_3)_2C{=}NNHCONH_2 \rightarrow RR'C{=}NNHCONH_2 + (CH_3)_2CO$$
Semicarbazone

From the carbonyl compound with aqueous semicarbazide hydrochloride and sodium acetate.
For directions and examples see: Cheronis, pp. 503–504, 512; Shriner, p. 218; Vogel, p. 344; Wild, p. 121; A. Michael, *J. Amer. Chem. Soc.*, **41**, 417 (1919).
From the carbonyl compound in ethanol with aqueous semicarbazide hydrochloride and sodium acetate.
See: Linstead, p. 27; Shriner, p. 218; Wild, p. 122; R. L. Shriner and T. A. Turner, *J. Amer. Chem. Soc.*, **52**, 1267 (1930).
From the carbonyl compound and acetone semicarbazone in acetic acid.
See: B. Angla, *Ann. Chim. Anal. Chim. Appl.*, **22**, 10 (1940).

Thiosemicarbazone.*

$$RCHO + H_2NNHCSNH_2 \rightarrow RCH{=}NNHCSNH_2 + H_2O$$

$$RR'CO + H_2NNHCSNH_2 \rightarrow RR'C{=}NNHCSNH_2 + H_2O$$
Thiosemicarbazone

From the carbonyl compound with thiosemicarbazide and sodium acetate in water, alcohol or acetic acid.
For directions and examples see: Cheronis, pp. 503, 512; Wild, p. 128; F. J. Wilson and R. Burns, *J. Chem. Soc.*, **121**, 873 (1922); W. Baird, R. Burns and F. J. Wilson, *J. Chem. Soc.*, 2527 (1927); M. Busch, *J. prakt. Chem.*, **124**, 301 (1930); P. P. T. Sah and T. C. Daniels, *Rec. Trav. Chim.*, **69**, 1545 (1950).

Phenylsemicarbazone.*

$$RCHO + H_2NNHCONHC_6H_5 \rightarrow RCH{=}NNHCONHC_6H_5 + H_2O$$

$$RR'CO + H_2NNHCONHC_6H_5 \rightarrow RR'C{=}NNHCONHC_6H_5 + H_2O$$
Phenylsemicarbazone

From the carbonyl compound with phenylsemicarbazide in alcohol or acetic acid.
For directions and examples see: P. P. T. Sah and T. -S. Ma, *J. Chinese Chem. Soc.*, **2**, 32 (1934), *C.A.*, **28**, 3713 (1934).

Oxime.*

$$RCHO + NH_2OH \rightarrow RCH{=}NOH + H_2O$$

$$RR'CO + NH_2OH \rightarrow RR'C{=}NOH + H_2O$$
Oxime

From the carbonyl compound with hydroxylamine hydrochloride and pyridine in ethanol or without solvent.
For directions and examples see: Cheronis, p. 513; Shriner, p. 254; Vogel, p. 345; J. B. Buck and W. S. Ide, *J. Amer. Chem. Soc.*, **53**, 1536 (1931); W. E. Bachmann and C. H. Boatner, *J. Amer. Chem. Soc.*, **58**, 2097 (1936); W. E. Bachmann and M. X. Barton, *J. Org. Chem.*, **3**, 300 (1938).
For a modification of the above method in aqueous alcohol.
See: W. M. D. Bryant and D. M. Smith, *J. Amer. Chem. Soc.*, **57**, 57 (1935).
From the carbonyl compound with hydroxylamine hydrochloride and sodium hydroxide in methanol or aqueous ethanol.

---

*Derivatives recommended for first trial.
WARNING: This is not an instruction manual. References should be consulted for the preparation of derivatives.

See: Cheronis, p. 513; Shriner, p. 255; Vogel, p. 721; Wild, p. 121.

From the carbonyl compound with hydroxylamine hydrochloride and potassium hydroxide in 95% ethanol.

See: Shriner, p. 255.

From the carbonyl compound with hydroxylamine hydrochloride and sodium or potassium acetate in water or aqueous ethanol.

See: Linstead, p. 27; Vogel, pp. 343, 345; J. S. Buck and W. S. Ide, *J. Amer. Chem. Soc.,* **53,** 1536 (1931).

From the carbonyl compound with hydroxylamine hydrochloride and sodium carbonate or bicarbonate in water or aqueous ethanol.

See: Wild, p. 120.

Dimethone derivative (Methone derivative).*

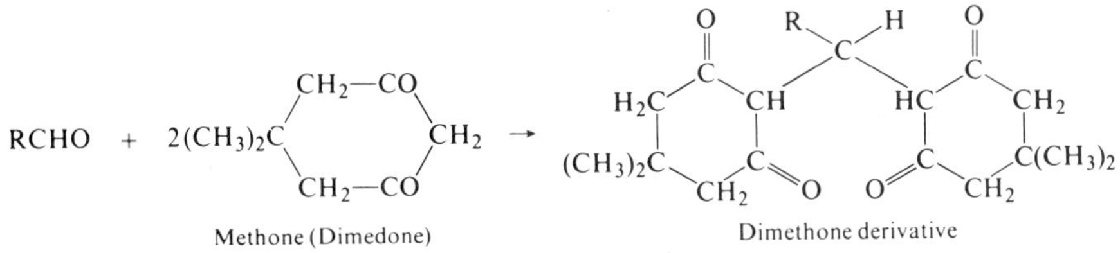

$$RCHO + 2(CH_3)_2C \begin{array}{c} CH_2-CO \\ \\ CH_2-CO \end{array} CH_2 \rightarrow$$

Methone (Dimedone) → Dimethone derivative

This derivative is specific for aldehydes only.

From the aldehyde and methone (dimedone; 5,5-dimethyl-1,3-cyclohexanedione; dimethyl dihydroresorcinol) in aqueous ethanol or methanol.

For directions and examples see: Cheronis, p. 505; Linstead, p. 27; Shriner, p. 220; Vogel, p. 333; Wild, pp. 136–7; D. Vorlander, *Z. Anal. Chem.,* **77,** 241 (1929); *Z. Angew. Chem.,* **42,** 46 (1929); W. Weinberger, *Ind. Eng. Chem., Anal. Ed.,* **3,** 365 (1931).

From the aldehyde with methone and a catalytic amount of piperidine in aqueous ethanol.

See: E. C. Horning and M. G. Horning, *J. Org. Chem.,* **11,** 95 (1946).

Anhydride of dimethone derivative (substituted octahydroxanthene).*

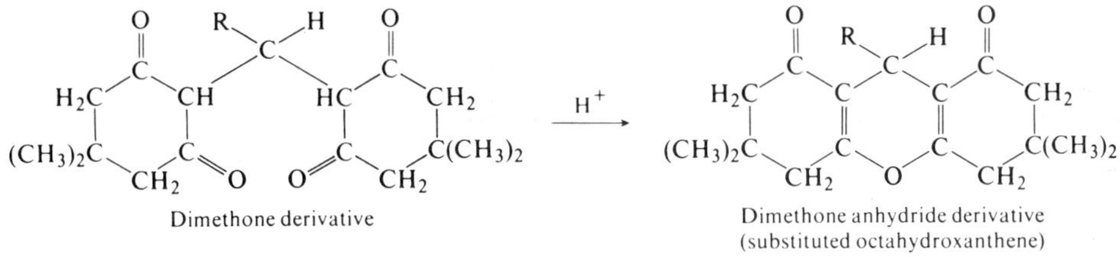

Dimethone derivative $\xrightarrow{H^+}$ Dimethone anhydride derivative (substituted octahydroxanthene)

From the dimethone derivative with acetic anhydride.

For directions and examples see: Cheronis, p. 505; Vogel, p. 333.

From the dimethone derivative and a catalytic amount of hydrochloric acid in water or in ethanol.

See: Cheronis, p. 505; Linstead, p. 27; Shriner, p. 220; Vogel, p. 333; Wild, p. 137; E. C. Horning and M. G. Horning, *J. Org. Chem.,* **11,** 95 (1946).

o-Dianisidine spot test.

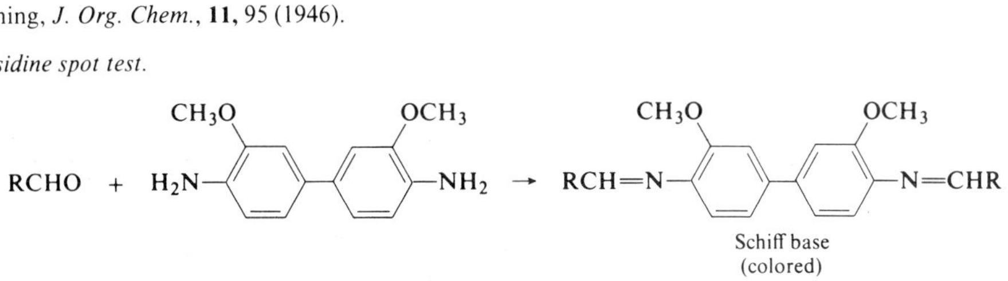

$$RCHO + H_2N-\text{(CH}_3O)(OCH_3)\text{-biphenyl}-NH_2 \rightarrow RCH=N-\text{...}-N=CHR$$

Schiff base (colored)

This test is usually applicable to aldehydes only.

From the aldehyde and a saturated solution of *o*-dianisidine (4,4'-diamino-3,3'-dimethoxybiphenyl) in glacial acetic acid.

For directions and examples see: F. Feigl, *Spot Tests in Organic Analysis,* 6th Ed., Elsevier Publishing Co., New York, 1960, p. 225; R. Wasicky and O. Frehden, *Mikrochim. Acta,* **1,** 55 (1927).

*Derivatives recommended for first trial.

WARNING: This is not an instruction manual. References should be consulted for the preparation of derivatives.

TABLE IX. ORGANIC DERIVATIVES OF ALDEHYDES
a) Liquids 1) Listed in order of increasing atmospheric b.p.*

No.	Name	Boiling point, °C	Melting point, °C	n_D^{20}	Semi-carba-zone	2,4-Di-nitro-phenyl-hydra-zone	p-Nitro-phenyl-hydra-zone	Phenyl-hydra-zone	Oxime	Dimeth-one deriv. (Dime-done deriv.)	Dimeth-one anhy-dride	Miscel-laneous	o-Dianisidine spot test		
													Cold	Hot	Limit, γ
1	Formaldehyde (Methanal)	−21	−91	....	169	167, yel., al.	181–2, yel., bz.	145	oil	189, al.; 191.4	......	....	pa. yel.	or. br.	50
2	Trifluoroacetalde-hyde	−20	......	......	151										......
3	Acetaldehyde (Ethanal).......	20.2	−123.5	1.3392[18]; 1.3316	162–3	stable: 168, al.; un-stable: 157; mix-ture: 148	128.5	57; 99	47	139, al.	175–6, al.	Thio-semicar-bazone, 146	or.	dk. br.	30
4	Propionaldehyde (Propanal).......	48–9	−81	1.364	89, bz.-lgr.; 154, w.	148, or.; 150, red; 155	125, yel., 50% al.	oil	40	154–6, al.	143	Picrate, 156–7	dk. ol. gn.	red	20
5	Glyoxal	50	15	....	270	328	311	180	178	mono: 186; di: 228	mono: 224	Phenyl-osazone, 169–70	......	......	......
6	Acrolein (Acralde-hyde)	52.4	−87.7	1.4025	171, w.	165	150–1	50–1, hot lgr., pyra-zoline	......	192, 50% al.	163, al.	....	red br.	vlt. br.	0.1
7	Propynal (Propargyl aldehyde).......	55	......	......	......	......	......	......	......	......	......	Cu deriv., 160	......	......	......
8	2,2,2-Trifluoro-propionaldehyde ..	56[745]	......	......	......	151									
9	Isobutyraldehyde...	64	−65.9	1.3730	125.6	187, or.-yel., al.; 182	130–1, or.-yel., al.	oil	oil	154	144	....			
10	2-Methyl-2-propenal (Methacrolein) ...	73.5	......	1.4191	198	206	......	74, py-razo-line	......						
11	n-Butyraldehyde (Butanal).......	74.7	−97.1	1.38433	95.5, lgr.; 106	123, al.	87, yel., al.; 93–5, red	93–5	b.p. 152[715]	134; 142	141	....			
12	Trimethylacetalde-hyde (Pivaldehyde)	75	3; 6	1.3791	190	210, yel.	......	......	41						
13	Chloroacetaldehyde	85–6	......	....	134–5d; 148, al.	......	......	......	oil						
14	2-Chloropropion-aldehyde........	86	......	1.431[17]	......	......	......	......	......			Hydrate, b.p. 80.5–81	......		
15	Dichloroacetalde-hyde	89.5–90.5	......	....	155–6, using only 1 equiv-alent of re-agent	......	......	......	b.p.: 67–9[17], using only 1 equiv-alent of re-agent			....	......		

*Derivative data given in order: m.p., crystal color, solvent from which crystallized.

144

TABLE IX. ORGANIC DERIVATIVES OF ALDEHYDES
a) Liquids 1) Listed in order of increasing atmospheric b.p.* (Continued)

No.	Name	Boiling point, °C	Melting point, °C	n_D^{20}	Semi-carba-zone	2,4-Di-nitro-phenyl-hydra-zone	p-Nitro-phenyl-hydra-zone	Phenyl-hydra-zone	Oxime	Dimeth-one deriv. (Dime-done deriv.)	Dimeth-one anhy-dride	Miscel-laneous	o-Dianisidine spot test		
													Cold	Hot	Limit, γ
16	Methoxyacetalde-hyde	92	......	1.3950	....	124–5	115	......	....	....	....	....	....	....	.....
17	3-Methylbutanal (Isovaleraldehyde)	92.5	−51	1.39225	107	123, yel.-or., al.	110–1, al.	oil	48.5	154–5, al.	173 (cor.)	Thio-semicar-bazone, 52–3	.....	....	.....
18	2-Methyl-1-butanal (α-Methylbutyr-aldehyde)	92–3	20, tri-	1.3942	103–5, bz.-pet. eth.	120	......	......	......	......	......	......	......	......	......
19	Trichloroethanal (Chloral; Tri-chloroacetalde-hyde)	98	−57.5	1.45572	90d.	131	131, yel.	......	56	....	....	Hydrate, 51.7	......	....	.....
20	Pentanal (Valeral-dehyde)	103.4	−91.5	1.3947	....	98, yel., al.; 107	......	......	52, pet. eth.	104.5	113	Thio-semicar-bazone, 65	......	....	.....
21	tert-Butylacetalde-hyde	103	......	1.4150	....	147	......	......	......	......	......	......	......	......	......
22	2-Butenal (Croton-aldehyde)	104	−69	1.4362$^{20.5}$	199	190, crim., bz.-lt. pet.	184–5	56	119	183	163, sint.; 167	Phenyl-semicar-bazone, 126–7	dk. red	dk. br.-red	2
23	Dimethylethylacet-aldehyde	104	......	....	....	....	......	......	......	......	......	......	......	......	......
24	Ethoxyacetaldehyde	106	......	1.3956	....	116–7, me. al.	113–4, al.	......	......	......	......	......	......	......	......
25	2-Isopropylacrolein	107–9	......	1.4223	....	165	......	......	......	......	......	......	......	......	......
26	2-Butynal	105–110^{755}	......	1.446^{19}	....	136	......	......	......	......	......	......	......	......	......
27	Methylisopropyl-acetaldehyde	114	......	1.3998^{25}	....	124	......	......	......	......	......	......	......	......	......
28	2-Bromoisobutyr-aldehyde	115	......	1.4518^{25}	....	....	......	......	......	......	......	Decom-poses in w.	......	......	......
29	Diethylacetaldehyde (2-Ethylbutyralde-hyde)	116; 117	......	1.4025	99, bz.-lt. pet.	95, pa.-or., lt. pet.; 129–30, al.	......	......	......	102, me. al.	......	......	......	......	......
30	Methyl-n-propyl-acetaldehyde	116^{737}	......	....	102	103	......	......	......	......	......	......	......	......	......
31	2-Methyl-2-butenal	116–9	......	....	216	....	......	......	......	......	......	......	......	......	......
32	n-Propoxyacetalde-hyde	119^{748}	......	....	....	86	......	......	......	......	......	......	......	......	......
33	Isobutylacetalde-hyde (Isocapro-aldehyde)	121^{743}	......	....	127	99	......	......	b.p. 103^{35}	......	......	......	......	......	......
34	Paraldehyde (Acet-aldehyde trimer)	124.4^{752}	12.6	1.4049	......	....	......	......	......	......	......	Dilute acid → Acetal-dehyde, b.p. 20.2	dk. ol. grn.	dk. red br.	4
35	2-Pentenal	125	......	....	180	....	123	......	......	......	......	......	......	......	......
36	3-Methoxyisobutyr-aldehyde	129	......	1.4030^{27}	....	102	......	......	......	......	......	......	......	......	......

*Derivative data given in order: m.p., crystal color, solvent from which crystallized.

No.	Name	Boiling point, °C	Melting point, °C	n_D^{20}	Semicarbazone	2,4-Dinitrophenylhydrazone	p-Nitrophenylhydrazone	Phenylhydrazone	Oxime	Dimethone deriv. (Dimedone deriv.)	Dimethone anhydride	Miscellaneous	o-Dianisidine spot test Cold	Hot	Limit, γ
37	3-Chloropropionaldehyde.........	130–1	......	1.475^{15}	....	....	....	....	....	....	....	Trimer, 35.5, dil. HCl-abs. al.; b.p. 170–5^{12-5}	......	....	....
38	Hexanal (Capro-aldehyde).......	131	......	1.4068	106, bz.-pet. eth.	104, or.-yel.	....	....	51, pet. eth.-me. al.	108.5, dil. al.	....	Phenyl-semicarbazone, 135–6	......	....	......
39	Ethylisopropylacetaldehyde........	133.5	......	1.4086^{25}	....	121	....	....	....	....	....		......	....	......
40	3,3-Dimethylpentanal........	134	......	1.4292	....	102									
41	3-Methyl-2-butenal (3-Methylcrotonaldehyde).......	135	......	1.4526	223	182	....	....							
42	Cyclopentanecarboxaldehyde......	136	....	....	124										
43	2-Methylpenten-2-al-1 (3-Ethyl-2-methylacrolein)...	136.8	......	1.4488	207	159, red, al.	....	58–60	48–48.8				......	....	......
44	Tetrahydrofurfural .	$142–3^{779}$	......	1.4473; 1.43658	166	134	....	....	....	....		Conc. HCl → brt. red col.; α-Benzyl-α-phenyl-hydrazone, 67, me. al.	......	....	......
45	5-Methylhexanal...	144^{750}	......	1.4114	117	117	....	....					...	...	...
46	3-Furaldehyde.....	144^{732}	......	1.4945	211	....	......	149.5					...	...	...
47	1-Cyclopentenylformaldehyde.....	146	......	1.4828^{21}	208	....	188	......							
49	2-Chloro-2-butenal (2-Chlorocrotonaldehyde).......	147–50	......	1.478^{23}	....	....	....	....				Cyano-hydrin, b.p. 137–8^{26}, n_D^{21}: 1.4762			
50	2-Hexenal........	150	......	1.4470^{13}	176	....	139	......				....			
51	3-Hexenal........	150	......		147							....			
52	Heptanal (Enanthaldehyde).......	155	−45	1.4125	109, al.	108, yel., al.	73	......	57	135	112	....	red-br.	red	9
53	Ethylisobutylacetaldehyde........	155	......		98										
54	Di-n-propylacetaldehyde	161	......	1.4142^{15}	101	....	......	b.p. 126^{47}							

*Derivative data given in order: m.p., crystal color, solvent from which crystallized.

TABLE IX. ORGANIC DERIVATIVES OF ALDEHYDES

a) Liquids 1) Listed in order of increasing atmospheric b.p.* (Continued)

No.	Name	Boiling point, °C	Melting point, °C	n_D^{20}	Semicarbazone	2,4-Dinitrophenylhydrazone	p-Nitrophenylhydrazone	Phenylhydrazone	Oxime	Dimethone deriv. (Dimedone deriv.)	Dimethone anhydride	Miscellaneous	o-Dianisidine spot test Cold	Hot	Limit, γ
55	2-Furancarboxaldehyde (Furfural)	161.7	−36.5	1.52608	202	212–4, yel.; 230 (cor.); red; mixture: 185	54	97	α: 75–6, pet. eth.; β: 91–2, al.	160d.	162–5	Phenylsemicarbazone, 180–1	dk. red-vlt.	dk. bl.-vlt.	0.02
56	Hexahydrobenzaldehyde	162	......	1.4495[19]	173; 176, w.	172	......	......	90–1, pet. eth.	......	......	Oxime-HCl, 107–8d.	......		
57	2-Ethylhexanal-1 (n-Butylethylacetaldehyde)	163	......	1.4150	254d.	114–5, dil. al.; 120–1, yel., al.	......	......	......	......	......	......	......		
58	2,2,3-Trichloro-n-butyraldehyde (n-Butylchloral; Crotonchloral)	164.5–5.5	......	1.47554	......	......	......	......	65	......	......	NH₃ → Butylchloral ammonia, 62	......		
59	Butanedial (Succinaldehyde)	169–70d	......	1.4254	......	280	......	......	di: 172	......	......	Polymer, 65	......		
60	Octanal (n-Octaldehyde; Caprylaldehyde)	171	......	1.42167	98, dil. me. al.; 101	106, yel., al.; 96	80, brt. yel.	......	60, me. al.	90, dil. al.	101	Thiosemicarbazone, 94–94.5	......		
61	2-Ethyl-3-n-propylacrolein	173	......	1.4518[22]	150–1; 153	124–5; 122									
62	3-Fluorobenzaldehyde	173	......	......	......		202	114	63	......	......	......			
63	2,2,2-Tribromoethanal (Bromal)	174, yel.	......	......	......		......	......	115	......	......	Monohydrate, 53.5	no reac.	dk. grn.	40
64	4-Fluorobenzaldehyde	174.5[752]	......	......	......		212	147	syn: 116–7; anti: 86	......	......	......			
65	2-Fluorobenzaldehyde	175	−44.5	......	......		205	90	63	......	......	......			
66	Benzaldehyde	179	−26; f.p.: −55.6	1.5446	222; 233–5, r. htng.	237, or, al.	190, red, al.; 234–6; 262	158; 154–5	α: 35 (stable); β: 130, eth.	193	200	Phenylsemicarbazone, 180–1	or.	red-or.	3
67	Nonanal (Pelargonaldehyde)	185	......	1.4273	100; 84, me. al.	100 (cor.), yel., al.	......	......	64, pet. eth.	86	......	Phenylsemicarbazone, 131–2	......		......
68	5-Methylfurfural	187	......	1.5147[25]	211*	212 (cor.)	130, red	147–8	syn: 112; anti: 51–2	......	......	......			
69	Glutaraldehyde	187–9d.	......	1.4330[25]	......		169	......	di: 175; 178, w.						
70	Phenylethanal (Phenylacetaldehyde)	194	33	1.53191	153, dil. al.; 156	121, grn.-yel., al.; 110	......	58, lgr.; 62–3	97–8, eth.; 100	165	126	....	dk. br.-red	dk. br.	polym.

*Derivative data given in order: m.p., crystal color, solvent from which crystallized.

No.	Name	Boiling point, °C	Melting point, °C	n_D^{20}	Semicarbazone	2,4-Dinitrophenylhydrazone	p-Nitrophenylhydrazone	Phenylhydrazone	Oxime	Dimethone deriv. (Dimedone deriv.)	Dimethone anhydride	Miscellaneous	o-Dianisidine spot test		
													Cold	Hot	Limit, γ
71	2-Hydroxybenzaldehyde (Salicylaldehyde)........	197 (cor.)	−7; f.p.: 1.6	1.574	231	248, red, abs. al.; 252d., lt. red, ac. a.	227, red-br., al.	142	57; 63	......	208, 70% al.	p-Nitrobenzoate, 128	or.	or.	5
72	2-Thiophenecarboxaldehyde........	198	......	1.5950[16]	....	242	......	119; 139	....	......	......	....	......	......	......
73	3-Methylbenzaldehyde (3-Tolualdehyde)........	199	......	1.5413[21]	204; 223–4	212; 194	157	91, lgr.; 84	60, lgr.	172	206	....	dk. or.-red	ch. red	5
74	2-Methylbenzaldehyde (2-Tolualdehyde)........	200	......	1.5481	209, al.; 212; 218	193–4, red, ac. a.	222, red, al.	101; 105–6; 111	49	167	215	....	dk. or.-red	ch. red	5
75	4-Methylbenzaldehyde (4-Tolualdehyde)........	204–5	......	1.5454	234, al.; 215	232.5–4.5 (cor.), or.-yel, al., PhNO₂	200.5 (cor.), dk. red, ac. a.	112–3, al.; 121	79–80; 110	......	......	....	dk. or.-red	ch. red	5
76	d-Citronellal (d-Rhodinal).....	207	......	1.4485	83–4, chl., ppt. by lgr; 91–2	78, yel., al.	......	......	oil	77–9, dil. al.	173	....	dk. grn.	brt. red	10
77	Decanal (Capraldehyde)..........	207–9	......	1.4287	102	104, yel.	......	......	69, dil. me. al.	91.7, dil. al.	......	Thiosemicarbazone, 99–100	pa. ol.	dk. br.	200
78	2-Chlorobenzaldehyde........	213–4	11	1.56708	146, yel.; 225, pyr.; 229–30, me. al.	213.6 (cor.); 209, or. red, xyl.	237–8, red, al.; 241, br.-red; 249, or.	86	α: 75–6, al.; β: 101–3	205d., al.	224–6 (cor.), al.	....	or.	or.	......
79	Phenoxyethanal (Phenoxyacetaldehyde; Glycolaldehyde phenyl ether)	215d.	......	1.5380[21]	145	....	......	86, pa. yel., al.	95, pet. eth.	....	......	....	......	......	......
80	3,5-Dimethylbenzaldehyde........	220–2	9	1.5385	201–2	....	......	......	......	......	......	Oxid. → acid, 170, al.	......	......	......
81	3-Phenylpropionaldehyde (Hydrocinnamaldehyde) .	224	......	......	127, al.	149, yel., al.	122–3, yel., dil. al.	......	93–4.5, dil. al.; 97 (cor.)	......	......	....	......	......	......
82	Citral a. (Geranial).	228d.	......	1.48752	164, me. al.	108–10, red-or., al.; 116	......	......	143–5	....	......	....	dk. red	red blk	0.1
83	Citral b. (Neral) ...	228d.	......	1.4900	HCl: 171; mixture: 132, NaOAc	96, red-or., al.	......	......	....	....	......	....	dk. red	red blk.	0.1

*Derivative data given in order: m.p., crystal color, solvent from which crystallized.

TABLE IX. ORGANIC DERIVATIVES OF ALDEHYDES
a) Liquids 1) Listed in order of increasing atmospheric b.p.* (Continued)

No.	Name	Boiling point, °C	Melting point, °C	n_D^{20}	Semicarbazone	2.4-Dinitrophenylhydrazone	p-Nitrophenylhydrazone	Phenylhydrazone	Oxime	Dimethone deriv. (Dimedone deriv.)	Dimethone anhydride	Miscellaneous	o-Dianisidine spot test		
													Cold	Hot	Limit, γ
84	2,6-Dimethylbenzaldehyde	228^{742}	11	....	158	....	....	....	....	....	....		......	....	.....
85	3-Methoxybenzaldehyde (3-Anisaldehyde)	230	3–4	1.5538	233d.	....	171	76	39–40 pet. eth.; 112	......	......	Phenylthiosemicarbazone, 153	dk. or	red br.	0.4
86	3-Bromobenzaldehyde	234–6	......	....	205	....	220	141	72	......	......	....	....	....	.....
87	4-Isopropylbenzaldehyde (Cumaldehyde)	236	.....	1.5301	211, me. al.	241, red, bz.; 243, red, ac. a.; 244–5, al.-chl.	190, al.	129, al.	α: 52, al.; β: 111	170–1, al.	172–3	....	dk. red	ol. yel.	3
88	3-Ethoxybenzaldehyde	245.5	.....	1.5408	....	....	....	....	....	......	......	....	....	....	.....
89	4-Methoxybenzaldehyde (4-Anisaldehyde)	248	2.5	1.5731	210; 203	253–4d., red, ac. a.; 250, red, xyl.	160, red-vlt.	120–1, wh., dil. al.	α': 64–5, bz. α: 4–5 (from α' on fusion); β: 133, bz.	144–5 (cor.), al.	243 (cor.), al.	....	dk. or.	red-br.	0.4
90	3-Phenylpropenal (Cinnamaldehyde)	252d.	–7.5	1.61949	215–6, w.	255d., red, ac. a.	195, red, al.	168, yel., dil. al.	α: 64–5, lgr.; β: 138.5, bz.	213 (cor.), al.; 161, al.	175, al.	....	dk. ch. red	ch. red	0.05
91	4-Ethoxybenzaldehyde	255; 249	13–4	....	202d., al.; 208	....	....	....	syn: 157; anti: 118	....	....		....	....	.....
92	3,4-Diethoxybenzaldehyde (Protocatechualdehyde diethyl ether)	277–80	.....						98			Oxid. → acid, 165	....	....	.....
93	Diphenylacetaldehyde	315–6d	.....	....	162	....	.....	.....	α: 120; β: 106	....		Oxid. → Benzophenone, 48			

*Derivative data given in order: m.p., crystal color, solvent from which crystallized.

TABLE IX. ORGANIC DERIVATIVES OF ALDEHYDES
a) Liquids 2) Reduced pressure b.p. only (listed in order of increasing semicarbazone m.p.)*

No.	Name	Boiling point, °C	Melting point, °C	n_D^{20}	Semicarbazone	2,4-Dinitrophenylhydrazone	p-Nitrophenylhydrazone	Phenylhydrazone	Oxime	Dimethone deriv. (Dimedone deriv.)	Dimethone anhydride	Miscellaneous	o-Dianisidine spot test Cold	Hot	Limit, γ
1	7-Methyloctanal	94[120]	.....	.....	80	100	.....	.....	.....	.....	.....	.....	....	....	.....
2	3-(2-Furyl)propionaldehyde	70[14]	.....	1.4470	80	.....									
3	2-Methyloctanal	83[20]	.....	.....	80	.....									
4	2,3-Dichloro-n-butyraldehyde	58–60[20]	.....	1.4618[21]	96–7	.....				oil					
5	Octanal (n-Octaldehyde)	81[32]	.....	1.4217	98; 101	106, yel.	80	.....	.....	59–60	89.8	.....			
6	Undecanal (Hendecanal)	120[20]	−4	1.4324[23]	103, me. al.	104, yel.	.....	.....	72, wh., me. al.	.....	.....	Timer, 47–8			
7	Tridecanal (n-Tridecylaldehyde)	136[8]	15	.....	106, al.	108	.....	.....	80.5, dil. al.	.....	.....	Trimer, 61.5, eth.	....		
8	2-Hydroxypropionaldehyde	114[9]	.....	.....	114, w.	.....	127	.....							
9	2-n-Amylcinnamaldehyde (2-n-Pentylcinnamaldehyde; Jasminaldehyde)	161–3[19]	.....	1.5381	118	164, red, al.	.....	.....	74, al.-w.						
10	2-Methyl-3-phenylpropionaldehyde	90[6]	.....	.....	123	.....									
11	2-Hydroxy-2-methyl hexanal (n-Butylmethylglycolaldehyde)	87–8[35]	.....	.....	143	.....									
12	Phenoxyacetaldehyde	83[5]	.....	1.5360	146	138	.....	.....	95						
13	2-Ethyl-2-hexenal	73[20]	.....	.....	152	125									
14	2-Ethyl-3-hexenal	84[52]	.....	.....	156	.....									
15	Cyclohexylacetaldehyde	58[10]	.....	1.4509[25]	159	125									
16	2-Nonenal	126[21]	.....	1.4426	165	126	113								
17	2-Heptenal	85[14]	.....	1.4314	169	.....	116								
18	2,3,6-Trimethylbenzaldehyde	114[10]	.....	.....	169	.....	.....	.....	126						
19	3,5-Dimethylhexahydrobenzaldehyde	71[14]	.....	.....	171										
20	2-Hydroxy-2-phenylpropionaldehyde (Methylphenylglycolaldehyde)	101[4]	.....	.....	182–3										
21	2,4,6-Trimethylbenzaldehyde	98[6]; 128[15]	.....	1.5524	188										
22	2-Hydroxy-2-phenylbutyraldehyde (Ethylphenylglycolaldehyde)	110–11[5]	.....	.....	188										
23	2-Hydroxybutyraldehyde (Aldol)	83[20]	.....	.....	194	.....	109–11, red-yel., dil. al.	*	.....	syn: 112; anti: 51–2 me. al.	146–8, 30% me. al.	126	4-Bromophenylhydrazone, 127–8	....	....	
24	1,2,3,4-Tetrahydro-2-naphthaldehyde	92[0.5]	.....	.....	197	.....									
25	2-(1-Naphthyl)propionaldehyde	132[2]	.....	.....	204	.....									

* Derivative data given in order: m.p., crystal color, solvent from which crystallized.

TABLE IX. ORGANIC DERIVATIVES OF ALDEHYDES

a) Liquids 2) Reduced pressure b.p. only (listed in order of increasing semicarbazone m.p.)* (Continued)

No.	Name	Boiling point, °C	Melting point, °C	n_D^{20}	Semi-carba-zone	2,4-Di-nitro-phenyl-hydra-zone	p-Nitro-phenyl-hydrazone	Phenyl-hydra-zone	Oxime	Di-meth-one deriv. (Dime-done deriv.)	Di-meth-one anhy-dride	Miscellaneous	o-Dianisidine spot test		
													Cold	Hot	Limit, γ
26	**1,6-Hexanedial** (Adipic dialdehyde)	94[12]; 70[3]	. . . . . .	1.4350	*di*: 206	. . . . . .	. . . .	. . . . . .	*di*: 185–6, w.	. . . . . .	. . . . .	. . . .	. . . .	. . . .	. . .
27	**2-Methylcinnamalde-hyde**	124[14]	. . . . . .	1.6057[17]	208, al.-w.	. . . . . .	. . . .	. . . . . .	. . . . . .	. . . . .	. . . .	. . . .	. . . .	. . .
28	**Phenylglyoxal**	108[15]	. . . . . .	. . . .	*mono*: 208–9d., yel., al. *bis*: 229d.	. . . . . .	309	. . . . . .	. . . . . .	. . . . .	91 (mono-hyd.) w.; 2-Thio-semicarba-zone, 170, yel. al.	. . . .	. . . .	. . .
30	**Cyclohexenecarbox-aldehyde**	70[13]	. . . . . .	1.4921[17]	213	. . . . . .	. . . .	. . . . . .	99	. . . . .	. . . .	. . . .	. . . .	. . .
31	**2-Phenoxybenzaldehyde**	153[1]	. . . . . .	. . . .	215	. . . . . .	. . . .	. . . . . .		. . . . .	. . . .	. . . .	. . . .	. . .

*Derivative data given in order: m.p., crystal color, solvent from which crystallized.

No.	Name	Boiling point, °C	Melting point, °C	n_D^{20}	Semi-carba-zone	2,4-Di-nitro-phenyl-hydra-zone	p-Nitro-phenyl-hydra-zone	Phenyl-hydra-zone	Oxime	Di-meth-one deriv. (Dime-done deriv.)	Di-meth-one anhy-dride	Miscellaneous	o-Dianisidine spot test Cold	Hot	Limit, γ
1	2-Chloroacrolein	29–31[17]	. . . . . .	1.463	. . . . .	. . . . . .	. . . . . .	. . . . . .	. . . . .	. . . . . .	. . . . .	Diethylacetal, b.p. 158–60	. . . .	. . . .	. . . .
2	4-Chloro-n-butyraldehyde	50–1[13]	. . . . . .	1.44662[8.5]	. . . . .	134–5	110	. . . . .	74.5	. . . . . .	. . . . .		. . . .	. . . .	. . . .
3	d,l-2,3-Dichloropropion-aldehyde.	48[14]	. . . . . .	1.4762	. . . . .	. . . . . .	. . . . . .	. . . . . .	. . . . .	. . . . . .	. . . . .	Dimethylacetal, b.p. 78–82[13], n_D^{18}: 1.144	. . . .	. . . .	. . . .
4	2-Heptynal	54[13]	. . . . . .	1.4521[17]	. . . . .	74	. . . . . .	. . . . . .	. . . . .	. . . . . .	. . . . .		. . . .	. . . .	. . . .
5	2,4-Hexadienal (Sorbalde-hyde)	65[11]	. . . . . .	1.5372[22]	. . . . .	. . . . . .	. . . . . .	102	160	. . . . . .	. . . . .		. . . .	. . . .	. . . .
6	4-Hydroxy-n-butyr-aldehyde.	68[8]	. . . . . .	1.4403	. . . . .	118	. . . . . .	. . . . . .	. . . . .	. . . . . .	. . . . .		. . . .	. . . .	. . . .
7	3-Hydroxy-2-isopropyl-propionaldehyde	84[10]	. . . . . .	. . . . . .	. . . . .	126	. . . . . .	. . . . . .	. . . . .	. . . . . .	. . . . .		. . . .	. . . .	. . . .
8	3-Hydroxy-3-methyl-n-butyraldehyde.	67[13]	. . . . . .	. . . . . .	. . . . .	. . . . . .	142	. . . . . .	. . . . .	. . . . . .	. . . . .		. . . .	. . . .	. . . .
9	4-Methoxy-2-methyl-n-butyraldehyde	66[55]	. . . . . .	1.4280[25]	. . . . .	88	. . . . . .	. . . . . .	. . . . .	. . . . . .	. . . . .		. . . .	. . . .	. . . .
10	5-Methyl-2-thiophene-carboxaldehyde.	114[25]	. . . . . .	1.5782[29]	. . . . .	. . . . . .	. . . . . .	126	. . . . .	. . . . . .	. . . . .		. . . .	. . . .	. . . .
11	3-Methyl-2-thiophene-carboxyaldehyde.	114[25]	. . . . . .	1.5833[25]	. . . . .	. . . . . .	. . . . . .	149	. . . . .	. . . . . .	. . . . .		. . . .	. . . .	. . . .
12	4-Octenal.	84[13]	. . . . . .	1.4463[25]	. . . . .	108	. . . . . .	. . . . . .	. . . . .	. . . . . .	. . . . .		. . . .	. . . .	. . . .
13	Phenylpropargyl alde-hyde	116–7[17]	. . . . . .	1.6032[25]	. . . . .	. . . . . .	. . . . . .	. . . . . .	108, lgr.	. . . . . .	. . . . .		. . . .	. . . .	. . . .
14	2-Phenylpropionaldehyde .	76[4]	. . . . . .	. . . . . .	. . . . .	135	. . . . . .	. . . . . .	. . . . .	. . . . . .	. . . . .		. . . .	. . . .	. . . .
15	3-Pyridinecarboxaldehyde (Nicotinaldehyde).	99[26]	. . . . . .	. . . . . .	. . . . .	. . . . . .	. . . . . .	. . . . . .	158	. . . . . .	. . . . .		. . . .	. . . .	. . . .
16	2,2,4-Trichloro-n-butyr-aldehyde.	. . . . . .	f.p.-78	. . . . . .	. . . . .	. . . . . .	. . . . . .	. . . . . .	. . . . .	. . . . . .	. . . . .	HNO₃ → acid, 73–5	. . . .	. . . .	. . . .
17	2,4,6-Trihydroxybenzalde-hyde (Phloroglucinalde-hyde)	. . . . . .	d.	. . . . . .	. . . . .	. . . . . .	. . . . . .	. . . . . .	195d., (hyd.), w.	. . . . . .	. . . . .	2,4,6-Triacetate, 156–7, al.; 2-Benzoate, 198–200, chl.	. . . .	. . . .	. . . .
18	4-Vinylbenzaldehyde (4-Formylstyrene).	93[14]	. . . . . .	1.5960[25]	. . . . .	. . . . . .	. . . . . .	131	. . . . .	. . . . . .	. . . . .	. . . .	. . . .	. . . .	. . . .

*Derivative data given in order: m.p., crystal color, solvent from which crystallized.

No.	Name	Melting point, °C	Boiling point, °C	Semi-carbazone	2,4-Di-nitro-phenyl-hydrazone	p-Nitro-phenyl-hydrazone	Phenyl-hydrazone	Oxime	Dimethone deriv. (Dime-done deriv.)	Di-meth-one anhy-dride	Miscellaneous	o-Dianisidine spot test		
												Cold	Hot	Limit, γ
1	**3-Chlorobenzaldehyde**.	17–8	213–4	228, pyr.; 230, me. al.	248, dk. red, xyl.; 256, or.-yel.	216, dil. al.	134–5, abs. al.	α, anti: 70–1, al.; β, syn: 118	. . . . .	. . . . .	$n_D^{20.2}$: 1.55908	. . . . .	. . . . .	. . . . .
2	**2,3,5,6-Tetramethyl-benzaldehyde**	20	135[11]	270d.	. . . .	. . . .	. . . . .	125						
3	**2-Ethoxybenzaldehyde** (Salicylaldehyde ethyl ether)	20–2; 6–7	247–9	219, al.	. . . .			57–9, pet. eth.			Diacetate, 88–9, ac. anh.			
4	**Tetradecanal** (Myrist-aldehyde)	23–3.5	166[24]	106.5, dil. al.	108	95, brt. yel.	. . . . . .	82.5–3.5, dil. al.			Trimer, 65			
5	**Pentadecanal**	24–5	160[14]	106.5, al.	106–7, yel., pyr.-al.	94–5, yel., al.	. . . . . .	86, dil. al.			Trimer, 69–70			
6	**Hexadecanal** (Palmit-aldehyde)	34	. . . . . .	107, dil. al.; 108–9	108	96.5, yel., eth.	. . . . . .	88, yel.			Trimer, 73; Thiosemi-carbazone, 106–9			
7	**1-Naphthaldehyde**	34	292; 162[18]	221	. . . .	224	80	98; 90						
8	**Phenylacetaldehyde** . . .	34	195	156; 163	121	151	mono: 63; 58; di: 101–2	99; 103	165	. . . . .				
9	**4-Methoxy-1-naphthal-dehyde**	34, wh.	200[11]	. . . .	. . . .		113				Azine, 185, yel., al.			
10	**(5-Hydroxymethyl) furfural**	35–6	115–20[0.5]	195d.; al, recr. tol.-lgr.	184, red	185, dk. red, al.	140–1, tol.	77–8; 108						
11	**Heptadecanal** (Margaric aldehyde) . .	35–6; 63	. . . . . .	. . . .				89.5, et. ac.			Trimer, 77–8, lt. pet.			
12	**3,4-Methylenedioxy-benzaldehyde** (Piperonal)	37	263	230; 234; 237	265d., xyl.; 266d., red, ac. a.	199–200, red	102–3, yel., al.; 99; 106	syn: 146, me. al.; anti: 112, w.	177–8; 193, yel., al.	220 (cor.)	. . . .	brt. red	dk. red	4
13	**2-Iodobenzaldehyde** . . .	37	129[14]	206		. . . .	79	108						
14	**Octadecanal** (Stearaldehyde)	38	. . . . . .	108–9	101; 110	101, yel., me. al.	. . . . . .	89			Thiosemicar-bazone, 111			
15	**2-Methoxybenzalde-hyde** (o-Anisalde-hyde; Salicylalde-hyde methyl ether) . .	38–9	243–6 (cor.)	215d., al.	253.5 (cor.), red, xyl.	204–5, br. red	. . . . . .	92, dil. al.			n_D^{20}: 1.5598	. . . . .	. . . . .	. . . . .
16	**2-Aminobenzaldehyde** .	40	. . . . . .	. . . .	. . . .	220	221	135						
17	**4-Diethylaminobenz-aldehyde**	41	172[7]	241d., al.	. . . .		103, yel.-br.	93						
18	**Dodecanal** (Lauralde-hyde)	2 forms: a) 42–3; b) 11	238	103; 106	106, yel.	90	. . . . . .	76–7, eth.; 77–8, me. al.	. . . . . .	. . . . .	Thiosemicar-bazone, 100	. . . . .	. . . . .	. . . . .

*Derivative data given in order: m.p., crystal color, solvent from which crystallized.

TABLE IX. ORGANIC DERIVATIVES OF ALDEHYDES
b) Solids (Listed in order of increasing m.p.)* (Continued)

No.	Name	Melting point, °C	Boiling point, °C	Semicarbazone	2,4-Dinitrophenylhydrazone	p-Nitrophenylhydrazone	Phenylhydrazone	Oxime	Dimethone deriv. (Dimedone deriv.)	Dimethone anhydride	Miscellaneous	o-Dianisidine spot test		
												Cold	Hot	Limit, γ
19	3,4-Dichlorobenzaldehyde	43–4	247–8	....	....	276–7, or.	......	syn: 120, al.; on fusing → anti: 114–5; 118–9	......	....	....	......		....
20	3-Phenylcinnamaldehyde	44	210[14]	214–5	196	....	173, yel.	....						
21	2,4,5-Trimethylbenzaldehyde	44	120[10]	243	....		127	....						
22	2-Nitrobenzaldehyde	44	......	256	265	263	156	anti: 102; syn: 154, bz.	......	....	....	grn. br.	red br.	5
23	3,4-Dimethoxybenzaldehyde (Veratraldehyde)	44; 58	285	177	261–3 (cor.), or., PhNO₂; 264–5	....	121, al.	94–5, lgr.	173					
24	4-Chlorobenzaldehyde	48	214.5–6.5	230, pyr., 233, me. al.	254 (cor.), or.	237, dk. br., al.	127–7.5, lt. yel., dil. al.	α: 110; β: 146	......					
25	2-Pyrrolecarboxaldehyde	50	217–9	183.5, w.	....	182–3, red, xyl.	139, lgr.	164, bz.		......	n_D^{16}: 1.5939	......		
26	Benzylglycolaldehyde	52	121[4]	137	....	....	......	......			Benzoate, 70			
27	Furfural diacetate	52, eth.	220	......										
28	4-Chloro-2-hydroxybenzaldehyde	52.5	......	212, pa. yel., ac. a.	....	257, or., ac. a.	......	155, col., al.						
29	Quinoline-4-carboxaldehyde	51–3, tol. (anh.); 84–4.5 (monohyd.)	123[4]	......	....	261–2, yel., al.	......	181–2, me. al.	......	......	Picrate, 179	....		
30	2-Ethyl-4-hydroxybenzaldehyde	53	145[1]	......										
31	2-(2-Furyl)-acrolein	54, lgr.	95[9]	219.5	....		132, pet. eth.	110–1						
32	2,3-Dimethoxybenzaldehyde (o-Veratraldehyde)	54	137[12]	231d.	....		138	99, al.-w.						
33	9-Hydroxynonanal	54	120[0.1]	......										
34	2,3-Diphenylpropionaldehyde	54	170[11]	125										
35	3-Benzyloxybenzaldehyde	54	218[20]	......										

* Derivative data given in order: m.p., crystal color, solvent from which crystallized.

TABLE IX. ORGANIC DERIVATIVES OF ALDEHYDES

No.	Name	Melting point, °C	Boiling point, °C	Semi-carba-zone	2,4-Di-nitro-phenyl-hydra-zone	p-Nitro-phenyl-hydrazone	Phenyl-hydra-zone	Oxime	Dimeth-one deriv. (Dime-done deriv.)	Di-meth-one anhy-dride	Miscellaneous	o-Dianisidine spot test		
												Cold	Hot	Limit, γ
36	3-Chloro-2-hydroxy-benzaldehyde (3-Chlorosalicylalde-hyde)	54.5–5.5	......	240–3, 50% ac. a.	....	....	.....	167–8, dil. al.	......	.....	5-Nitro deriv., 129, yel., dil. al.	.....	....	.....
37	Octatrienal	55	......	......	....	....	.....	......	......	.....		.....	....	.....
38	Isoquinoline-1-carbox-aldehyde..........	55.5	......	197	....	....	171–2	......	......	.....		.....	....	.....
39	Phthalaldehyde	56	......	......	....	....	di: 191	......	......	.....		brt. yel. ppt.	brt. yel. ppt.	.....
40	2,3,5-Trichlorobenz-aldehyde..........	56, col., dil. al.	......	......	....	....	.....	......	......	.....	Oxid. KMnO₄ acid, 162–3	.....		
41	2-Hydroxy-5-methyl-benzaldehyde (5-Methylsalicylalde-hyde)	56, dil. al.	217–8	......	....	....	149, yel., al.	105, w.	......	.....	Diacetate, 94, al.	.....		
42	3-Iodobenzaldehyde...	57	......	226	....	212	155	62	......	.....				
43	4-Bromobenzaldehyde.	57	......	228; 229	128; 257	207–8	113	syn: 157; anti: 111	......	.....				
44	3-Nitrobenzaldehyde..	58	......	246	293d.	247	120; 124	120; 122	......	.....				
45	2,5-Dichlorobenz-aldehyde..........	58	231–3	......	....	....	104–5, al.	127.5–8, dil. al.	......	.....				
46	2,4,6-Trichlorobenz-aldehyde..........	58–9	......	......	....	....	.....	......	......	.....				
47	2-Phenanthraldehyde..	59; 59.5	......	282	....	....	.....	175	......	.....				
48	Paraisobutyraldehyde (2,4,6-Tri-isopropyl-1,3,5-trioxan)	59–60	195 (cor.), sl. de-polym.	......	....	....	.....	......	......	.....	See: Isobutyr-aldehyde, b.p. 64			
49	1-Hydroxy-2-naphthal-dehyde	59–60, gm.-yel., al.-w.	......	......	....	....	.....	145, bz.	......	.....				
50	2-Naphthaldehyde	60, w.	150¹⁵	245, al.	270	230	205–6 d., al.; 217–8	156, dil. al.	......	.....				
51	4-Phenylbenzaldehyde.	60	......	243d., al.	239d., scar., xyl.	....	189d.	149–50	......	.....				
52	3-Methoxy-1-naphthal-dehyde	60, pet. eth.	......	200, al.-w.	....	197, red, ac. a.	.....	102, al.-w.	......	.....				
53	4-Ethoxy-3-methoxy-benzaldehyde	64	......	......	....	....	.....	......	......	.....				
54	3,5-Dichlorobenz-aldehyde...........	65	235–40⁷⁴⁸	......	....	....	.....	106.5, yel., pet. eth.	112	.....				
55	2,3-Dichlorobenz-aldehyde..........	65–7	......	......	....	....	.....	......	......	.....				
56	5-Methoxy-1-naphthal-dehyde	66, yel., pet. eth.	......	246, ac. a.-w.	....	246, red, ac. a.-w.	.....	104, w.	......	.....				

*Derivative data given in order: m.p., crystal color, solvent from which crystallized.

TABLE IX. ORGANIC DERIVATIVES OF ALDEHYDES

b) Solids (Listed in order of increasing m.p.)* (Continued)

No.	Name	Melting point, °C	Boiling point, °C	Semi-carbazone	2,4-Dinitrophenylhydrazone	p-Nitrophenylhydrazone	Phenylhydrazone	Oxime	Dimethone deriv. (Dimedone deriv.)	Dimethone anhydride	Miscellaneous	o-Dianisidine spot test		
												Cold	Hot	Limit, γ
57	Dibenzofuran-2-carboxaldehyde	68	. . . . . .	. . . . . .	. . . . .		162	. . . . . .	. . . . .	. . . . .	. . . . .	. . . . .	. . . .	. . . .	. . . .
58	2,6-Dichlorobenzaldehyde	70–1	. . . . . .	. . . . . .							o-Nitrophenylhydrazone, 154; p-Bromophenylhydrazone, 142	. . . . .	. . . .	. . . .	. . . .
59	2,4-Dimethoxybenzaldehyde (β-Resorcylaldehyde dimethyl ether)	71, dil. al.; 69	165[10]	. . . . . .		. . . . .		106, w.			5-Nitro deriv., 188–9, me. al.	. . . . .	. . . .	. . . .	. . . .
60	Quinoline-2-carboxaldehyde	71, pet. eth. (anh.); 51 (monohyd.), w.	. . . . . .		250, yel.; 225, subl.		204, yel., al.	188			. . . .				
61	4-Ethoxy-1-naphthaldehyde	72	. . . . . .	. . . . . .	. . . . .	. . . . .	. . . . .	. . . . .			Hydrazone, 160–182, dk. red; Azine, 209, yel., PhNO₂	. . . . .	. . . .	. . . .	. . . .
62	4-Aminobenzaldehyde .	72	. . . . . .	153			156	124			. . . .	or. br.	red br.	0.4
63	2,4-Dichlorobenzaldehyde	72; 74.5	. . . . . .	. . . . . .				136–7			Oxime HCl, 133.5	. . . . .	. . . .	. . . .	. . . .
64	4-Dimethylaminobenzaldehyde	74	. . . . . .	222	325	182	148	185			. . . .	. . . .	. . . .	. . . .
65	4-Methylthiazole-5-carboxaldehyde	75; 72.5	118[21]	. . . . . .			159; 161								
66	Quinoline-6-carboxaldehyde	75–6 (anh.); 55 (hyd.)	. . . . . .	239, yel., al.			185, red, al.	191, yel., al.			Methiodide, 218, yel., al.				
67	3,4,5-Trimethoxybenzaldehyde (Gallaldehyde trimethyl ether)	78; 75	163–5[10]	219–20	. . . . . .	201–2	. . . . . .	83–4			. . . .	. . . .	. . . .	. . . .
68	4-Iodobenzaldehyde . . .	78	. . . . . .	224	257	201	121	. . . . . .							
69	3-Phenanthraldehyde . .	80	. . . . . .	275	. . . . . .	. . . . . .	. . . . .	145							
70	4-Hydroxy-3-methoxybenzaldehyde (Vanillin)	80–1, w.	285d.	230; 240d.	271d. (cor.), red, ac. ac.; 268	227, ac. a.; 223	105, bz.	117, w.; 122	196–8 (cor.), al.	228	2,4-Dinitrophenyl ether, 131	brt. or. red	ch. red	3
71	2-Hydroxy-1-naphthaldehyde	82, al.	192[27]	240, yel., me. al.	. . . . . .	. . . . . .	. . . . .	157	. . . . . .	. . . .	Picrate, 120	or.	brk. red	10
72	Stilbene-2-carboxaldehyde	83		. . . . . .									. . . .	. . . .
73	2-Methoxy-1-naphthaldehyde	84, al.	200–1[11]	. . . . . .	. . . . . .		. . . . .	. . . . .			Azine, 255–6, yel., PhNO₂	. . . . .	. . . .	. . . .

*Derivative data given in order: m.p., crystal color, solvent from which crystallized.

No.	Name	Melting point, °C	Boiling point, °C	Semi-carba-zone	2,4-Di-nitro-phenyl-hydra-zone	p-Nitro-phenyl-hydrazone	Phenyl-hydra-zone	Oxime	Dimeth-one deriv. (Dime-done deriv.)	Di-meth-one anhy-dride	Miscellaneous	o-Dianisidine spot test Cold	Hot	Limit, γ
74	2,3,6-Trichlorobenz-aldehyde	86–7	. . . . . .	. . . . . .	. . . . . .	. . . . . .	. . . . . .	. . . . . .	. . . . . .	. . . .	Ac. anh. + ac. a. + NaOAc → 2,3,6-tri-chlorocin-namic acid, 189, ac. a.	. . . . . .	. . . .	. . . .
75	Isophthalaldehyde	89	. . . . . .	252–4, al.	. . . . . .	. . . . . .	242	180	. . . . . .	. . . .		. . . .		
76	3,4,5-Trichlorobenz-aldehyde	90–1, al.	. . . . . .	252–4, al.	. . . . . .	342d., or., PhNO₂	147	. . . . . .	. . . . . .	. . . .	2-Nitro deriv., 118.5–9.0; Oxid. alk. KMnO₄ → 3,4,5-tri-chloroben-zoic acid, 210	. . . .	. . . .	. . . .
77	Phenylglyoxal hydrate	91	. . . . . .	α: 217d.	. . . . . .	309	di: 152	α: 129; di: 168	. . . . . .	. . . .		. . . .	. . . .	. . . .
78	2,3,4-Trichlorobenz-aldehyde	91	. . . . . .	. . . . . .	. . . . . .	. . . . . .	. . . . . .	. . . . . .	. . . . . .	. . . .	Ac. anh. + ac. a. + NaOAc → 2,3,4-tri-chlorocin-namic acid, 185	. . . .	. . . .	. . . .
79	Quinoline-8-carbox-aldehyde	94–5, dil. al.	. . . . . .	238–9, bz.	. . . . . .	. . . . . .	176, yel., al.	115, dil. al.	. . . . . .	. . . .				
80	2-Phenylcinnamalde-hyde	94, al.; 95	195–200¹⁷	188–9, al.; 195	. . . . . .	. . . . . .	125–6, yel., ac. a.; 141	165–6, al.	. . . . . .	. . . .				
81	3,5-Dichloro-2-hy-droxybenzaldehyde (3,5-Dichlorosalicyl-aldehyde)	95–6	. . . . . .	227d., ac. a.	. . . . . .	. . . . . .	153, pa. yel., al.	195–6, al.-w. (4:1)	. . . . . .	. . . .	Ac. anh. + ac. a. + NaOAc → dichloro-coumarin, 160, bz.			
82	Hydroxyacetaldehyde (Glycolaldehyde) . . .	96–7	. . . . . .	. . . . . .	. . . . . .	. . . . . .	162		. . . . . .	. . . .	Phenylosa-zone, 178–9, yel., eth.; p-Nitrophenyl-osazone, 311	. . . .	. . . .	. . . .
83	3-Chloro-n-butyr-aldehyde (Trimer) . . .	96–7	28–33¹³	. . . . . .	. . . . . .	. . . . . .			. . . . . .	. . . .	. . . . . .	. . . .	. . . .	. . . .
84	2,2-Dimethyl-3-hy-droxypropionaldehyde	97	85¹⁵											
85	2,3,4,6-Tetrachloro-benzaldehyde	97–8	. . . . . .											
86	Benzaldehyde-2-carboxylic acid (2-Formylbenzoic acid; Phthalaldehydic acid)	98–9 (hyd.); 240–50 (anh.)	. . . . . .	202	. . . . . .	. . . . . .		120, w.						
87	3-Hydroxy-2-naphthal-dehyde	99–100	. . . . . .	>270, me. al.	. . . . . .	. . . . . .	246–8	207d.						

*Derivative data given in order: m.p., crystal color, solvent from which crystallized.

No.	Name	Melting point, °C	Boiling point, °C	Semicarbazone	2,4-Dinitrophenylhydrazone	p-Nitrophenylhydrazone	Phenylhydrazone	Oxime	Dimethone deriv. (Dimedone deriv.)	Dimethone anhydride	Miscellaneous	o-Dianisidine spot test Cold	Hot	Limit, γ
88	5-Chloro-2-hydroxybenzaldehyde	99–100	105[12]	286–7, ac. a.			150–2	128, w.; 123–4						
89	9-Phenanthraldehyde	101		223		265		157						
90	3-Hydroxybenzaldehyde	104; 108 (cor.), w.	240	198; 199	259, scar., xyl.; 260d., red, al.	221–2, dil. ac. a.	130–1.5, tol.; 147, recr. bz.	90; 88				dk. br. red	dk. ch. red	4
91	9-Anthraldehyde	105		219, yel., al.			207, or., al.	187						
92	4-Nitrobenzaldehyde	106		221; 211	320	249	159; 153	anti: 133; 129; syn: 182–4				or. br.	red br.	1
93	2,3,4,5-Tetrachlorobenzaldehyde	106–6.5												
94	2,3-Dihydroxybenzaldehyde	108		226d.			167							
95	2-Chloro-5-hydroxybenzaldehyde	110.5–1.5, ac. a.		236, pa. yel.			250–1, red, dil. al.		146–7, abs. al.					
96	1-Phenanthraldehyde	111.5						189						
98	2,4,5-Trichlorobenzaldehyde	112–3, al.									Ac. anh. + ac. a. + NaOAc → 2,4,5-trichlorocinnamic acid, 200–1			
99	3-Hydroxy-2,4,6-trichlorobenzaldehyde	113–6.5, 50% ac. a.				272–3d., yel. or.		170–2, dil. al.						
100	2-Ethoxy-1-naphthaldehyde	115, al.		214–5, yel., al.			91				Azine, 184, yel., PhNO₂-al.			
101	Metaldehyde	115; 246; (polymers)									Dil. a. → acetaldehyde, b.p. 20.2			
102	4-Hydroxybenzaldehyde	116–7, w.		224; 280d.	280d., purp., ac. a.; 260 (monohyd.), red, w.	266	177–8, al.; 184, slow htng.	72; 112 (anh.)	188–90 (cor.); 184	246		dk. or. red	ch. red	5
103	Terephthalaldehyde	116; 118	245			di: 281	di: 278d.; 154	di: 200						
104	2,4,6-Trimethoxybenzaldehyde	118						201–3, me. al.						

*Derivative data given in order: m.p., crystal color, solvent from which crystallized.

TABLE IX. ORGANIC DERIVATIVES OF ALDEHYDES
b) Solids (Listed in order of increasing m.p.)* (Continued)

No.	Name	Melting point, °C	Boiling point, °C	Semi-carba-zone	2,4-Di-nitro-phenyl-hydra-zone	p-Nitro-phenyl-hydrazone	Phenyl-hydra-zone	Oxime	Dimeth-one deriv. (Dime-done deriv.)	Di-meth-one anhy-dride	Miscellaneous	o-Dianisidine spot test		
												Cold	Hot	Limit, γ
105	1-Bromo-2-naphthaldehyde	118	......	......	......	......	......	......	......	......	Oxid. → acid, 186	......	......	....
106	4-Chloro-3-hydroxybenzaldehyde	121	......	238–9, pa. yel.	....	226–7, vlt.-red, dil. al.	......	126 (anh.); 106–10d. (mono-hyd.)	......	......				
107	Pyrene-3-carboxaldehyde	126	......	......	......	......	......	......	......					
108	1,2,3,4-Tetrahydro-phenanthrene-9-carboxaldehyde	129	......	......	......	......	......	......						
109	4,6-Dichloro-3-hydroxybenzaldehyde	129–30	......								2-Nitro deriv., 157			
110	2,4-Dihydroxybenz-aldehyde (β-Resorcyl-aldehyde)	135–6, yel., w.	......	260d.	286d., brt. red, AmOH	....	156–60d.	191, w.						
111	3-Chloro-4-hydroxybenzaldehyde	139 (cor.)	......	210d., yel., v. dil. ac. a.				144–5, w.						
112	2-Chloro-3-hydroxybenzaldehyde	139–9.5	......	236–7, pa. yel.	....	244–5, or. red, al.	......	149, dil. al.						
113	2,6-Dichloro-3-hydroxybenzaldehyde	140–2	......					174–5, dil. al.						
114	2,4-Dichloro-3-hydroxybenzaldehyde	141, ac. a.				277–8, or. red	......	188, al.						
115	d,l-Glyceraldehyde (dimer)	142, 40% me. al.	......	160d.	166–7 (cor.), 50% me. al.	....	......	117–8	197 (cor.), 50% al.; 203	172, 50% al.				
116	2-Chloro-4-hydroxybenzaldehyde	147–8, w.	......	214, yel., al.	284d., dk. red, al.			194, al.						
117	3,4-Dihydroxybenz-aldehyde (Proto-catechualdehyde)	153–4, w.	......	230d.	275d., dk. red, me. al.	....	175–6d., w.; 121–8	157, xyl.	145d., al.	.....	Dibenzoate, 96–7, al.	......	......	....
118	3,5-Dihydroxybenz-aldehyde (α-Resor-cylic aldehyde)	156–7	......	223–4										
119	3,5-Dichloro-4-hy-droxybenzaldehyde	158–9 (cor.); 156, dil. al.	......	236–7d. (cor.), grn.-yel., ac. a.				185, dil. al.						
120	Hydroxypyruvic aldehyde	160	......	......			......	135						
121	Diphenylglycol-aldehyde	163	......	242	....	....	......	124						
122	Benzaldehyde-3-carboxylic acid (3-Formylbenzoic acid)	175, w.	......	265			164	188d.						

*Derivative data given in order: m.p., crystal color, solvent from which crystallized.

TABLE IX. ORGANIC DERIVATIVES OF ALDEHYDES
b) Solids (Listed in order of increasing m.p.)* (Continued)

No.	Name	Melting point, °C	Boiling point, °C	Semi-carbazone	2,4-Dinitro-phenyl-hydrazone	p-Nitro-phenyl-hydrazone	Phenyl-hydrazone	Oxime	Dimethone deriv. (Dimedone deriv.)	Dimethone anhydride	Miscellaneous	o-Dianisidine spot test Cold	Hot	Limit, γ
123	2-Hydroxybenzalde-hyde-3-carboxylic acid (3-Formyl-salicylic acid)......	179	......	......	....	....	188, al.	193, yel., w.	......	.....	....	.....	.....	.....
124	4-Hydroxy-1-naphthal-dehyde	181, yel., w.	......	224	....	....			......	.....	Hydrazone, 220–36, dk. red; Azine, 236, yel., PhNO₂	.....	.....	.....
125	Indole-3-carboxalde-hyde	195; 198	......	......	....	....	198				....			
126	Pentachlorobenz-aldehyde	202.5	......	......	....	....	152.5 (cor.), yel., al.	201 (cor.), bz.	......					
127	3,4-Benzypyrene-5-carboxaldehyde	203	......	......	....	....	......	......						
128	3,4,5-Trihydroxybenz-aldehyde (Gallalde-hyde)	212d., (mono-hyd.)				226; 234–6d.	......	195–200d.	...					
129	4-Hydroxybenzalde-hyde-3-carboxylic acid (5-Formyl-salicylic acid)......	248–9	......	......	....	....	219, al.	179	......	.....				
130	Benzaldehyde-4-carboxylic acid (4-Formylbenzoic acid).	256, w., subl.	......	......	....		226	208–10	......					.....

*Derivative data given in order: m.p., crystal color, solvent from which crystallized.

TABLE X. ORGANIC DERIVATIVES OF KETONES
a) Liquids 1) (Listed in order of increasing atmospheric b.p.)*

No.	Name	Boiling point, °C	Melting point, °C	n_D^{20}	D_4^{20}	Semi-carbazone	2,4-Di-nitrophenyl-hydrazone	p-Nitro-phenyl-hydrazone	Phenyl-hydrazone	Oxime	Miscellaneous
1	Acetone (2-Propanone)	56	−95	1.3592	....	190, w.	126; 128, yel., al.	148 9, yel., al.	42	59	Thiosemicar-bazone, 179
2	3-Buten-2-one (Methyl vinyl ketone)	81	......	1.4095[22]	....	141; 140	....	....	....	....	....
3	2-Butanone (Ethyl methyl ketone)	80; 82	−86.4	1.3791	0.804	**146**	116 7; 115, yel., al.	128 9, yel., w.-al.	oil	b.p. 152	Phenylsemicar-bazone, 168
4	3-Butyn-2-one (Ethynyl methyl ketone) ...	86	......	......	....	181	143	....	....	....	....
5	2,3-Butanedione (Biacetyl)	88, gr.-yel.	f.p. −2.4	1.3927	....	mono: 235 (cor.), w.; di: 278 9, ac. a.	di: 314 5 (cor.), red-or., PhNO₂	mono: 230, or.-yel.	mono: 134, yel., dil. al.; di: 243d., yel., bz.	mono: 76; di: 245-6 (cor.); 234-5, subl., dil. al.	
6	2-Methyl-3-butanone (Isopropyl methyl ketone)	94.3	......	1.3879	0.8046	113 4; 112 3, al.	120; 117, or.-yel., al.-chl.	108 9, or.-yel., al.	oil	oil	....
7	2-Methyl-1-buten-3-one (Iso-propenyl methyl ketone)	97[7.11]	......	1.4232; 1.4235	....	173	181				
8	Cyclobutanone	100	......	1.4189[25]	....	146	....				
9	3-Pentanone (Diethyl ketone)	102	−39.8	1.3922	....	138 9	156, pa.-or., al.	144, or.-yel., 50°₀ al.	oil	b.p. 165	
10	2-Pentanone (Methyl n-propyl ketone)	102.3	......	1.3902; 1.39012	0.80639	112; 106	143 4, yel.-or., al.	117	oil	b.p. 167	....
11	1-Penten-3-one (Ethyl vinyl ketone)	102[7.10]	......	1.4192	....	129	....				
12	3,3-Dimethyl-2-butanone (tert-Butyl methyl ketone; Pinacolone)	106	−49.8	1.3960; 1.3956	0.8114	157 8	125, or.-yel., al.; fusion → 131		oil	75; 79	
13	1-Methoxy-2-propanone (Methoxymethyl methyl ketone)	115[7.56]	......	1.3981	....	....	163; 159	111; 109			
14	1-Methoxy-3-butanone (1-Methoxyethyl methyl ketone) ...	116[7.89]	......	1.3936	....	141	....				
15	4-Methyl-2-pentanone (Isobutyl methyl ketone)	116.8	......	1.3956	0.8008	132; 135	95, or.-red, al.	....		b.p. 176	
16	3-Methyl-2-pentanone (sec-Butyl methyl ketone)	118	......	1.3990	....	94 5, pet. eth.	71.2	....		oil, b.p. 89[20]	
17	1-Chloro-2-propanone (Chloro-acetone)	119	......	......	....	150; 164d.	125			b.p. 171[730]	
18	2-Methyl-1-penten-3-one (Ethyl isopropenyl ketone)	119[7.51]	......	1.4270[24]	....	161	....				
19	1,1-Dichloro-2-propanone (1,1-Dichloroacetone)	120	......	......	1.305[18/15]	163	....				
20	2,4-Dimethyl-3-pentanone (Di-isopropyl ketone)	124	......	1.4001	0.8108	160 (cor.); 149	88; 85 6, or.; 94 8	....			
21	Methyl neopentyl ketone	125; 122	......	1.4018[25]	....	....	100				
22	3-Hexanone (Ethyl n-propyl ketone)	125	......	1.4007	0.81491[22]	113	130	....		b.p. 86[17]	Phenylsemicar-bazone
23	2,2-Dimethyl-3-pentanone (tert-Butyl ethyl ketone)	125[729]	......	1.4052	....	....	144				
24	2-Hexanone (n-Butyl methyl ketone)	128	......	1.40069	0.81127	125 (cor.); 121, rapid htng.	106, red-or., al.; 110	88	oil	49	Thiosemicar-bazone, 110

*Derivative data given in order: m.p., crystal color, solvent from which crystallized.

161

TABLE X. ORGANIC DERIVATIVES OF KETONES

a) Liquids 1) (Listed in order of increasing atmospheric b.p.)* (Continued)

No.	Name	Boiling point, °C	Melting point, °C	n_D^{20}	D_4^{20}	Semi-carbazone	2,4-Di-nitrophenyl-hydrazone	p-Nitro-phenyl-hydrazone	Phenyl-hydrazone	Oxime	Miscellaneous
25	4-Methyl-3-penten-2-one (Iso-propylideneacetone; Mesityl oxide)	130	......	1.44397	0.86532	α: 164; β: 133–4, bz.	200, red, al.; 203, red, ac. a.	132–4, or.-yel., al.	142	β: 48–9, me. al.	....
26	3,3-Dimethyl-2-pentanone (tert-Amyl methyl ketone)	130[733]	......	1.4100	....	....	112	....		....	
27	Cyclopentanone	130.7	−51.3	1.4366; 1.4370	0.94869	210; 203; 216–7, rapid htng.	146, or., ac. a.; 142, or.-yel., al.	154	55, lt. pet.	56.5, pet. eth	....
28	5-Hexen-2-one (Allylacetone)	132	......	1.4174[25]	....	102	108				
29	1-Methoxy-2-butanone (Ethyl methoxymethyl ketone)	133[757]	......	1.4063	....	....	198				
30	2,2,4-Trimethyl-3-pentanone (tert-Butyl isopropyl ketone)	135		1.4065		132	....			144	
31	5-Methyl-3-hexanone (Ethyl isobutyl ketone)	135[735]	......	1.407		152					
32	2-Methyl-1-penten-4-one	135–45d.				192					
33	1-Bromo-2-propanone (Bromo-acetone)	136				135d.				36	
34	2-Methyl-3-hexanone (Isopropyl n-propyl ketone)	136	......	1.4075		119					
35	4-Methyl-3-hexanone (sec-Butyl ethyl ketone)	136	......	1.402		137	78				
36	2-Methoxy-3-pentanone (Ethyl 1-methoxyethyl ketone)	136[750]	......	1.4019		120					
37	Cyclobutyl methyl ketone	136		1.4283[28]		149					
38	3-Methyl-2-hexanone	137				70					
39	3-Methyl-1-hexen-5-one	138		1.4197[25]		112					
40	1-Chloro-2-butanone (Chloro-methyl ethyl ketone)	138	......	1.4372							
41	3-Methyl-1-penten-4-one	138				201				75–6	
42	3,4-Dimethyl-2-pentanone	138		1.4094		113					
43	4-Hexen-3-one	139		1.4388		157					
44	2,4-Pentanedione (Acetylacetone)	139	−30	1.4465[25.6]	0.976	mono: 122; di: 209	209, yel., al.			di: 149, al.	
45	2-Methylcyclopentanone	139		1.4364		184; 182				b.p. 103[22]	
46	3-Ethyl-2-pentanone	139[746]		1.4073		99					
47	3-Hydroxy-3-methyl-2-butanone (Acetyl diethyl carbinol)	140				165				87	
48	4-Methyl-2-hexanone	142; 139	......	1.4057[25]		120; 128					
49	1-Propoxy-2-propanone (Iso-propoxymethyl methyl ketone)	142	......	1.4004		....	142; 144				
50	d-3-Methylcyclopentanone	143		1.4340[19]		184–5				α: 91–2; β: 67–9	[α]_D^{12}: + 132.9
51	3,4-Dimethyl-4-penten-2-one	144				114					
52	4-Heptanone (Di-n-propyl ketone)	144	−34.0	1.4069	0.8175	132, pet. eth.	75, yel.-or., al.			b.p. 193	
53	2,4-Dimethyl-3-hexanone (sec-Butyl isopropyl ketone)	145	......	1.4059; 1.4080		....	71				
54	3-Hydroxy-2-butanone (d, l-Acetoin)	145; 148	−72; 15	1.4178	0.9861[30]	185, al.; 202	di: 318, or., PhNO_2-tol.				Phenylosazone, 243d., yel., bz.
55	d,l-3-Methylcyclopentanone	145[755]	......	1.4329		185					
56	1-Methoxy-3-methyl-2-butanone (Isopropyl methoxymethyl ketone)	145[748]	......	1.4078	....	....	163				

*Derivative data given in order: m.p., crystal color, solvent from which crystallized.

TABLE X. ORGANIC DERIVATIVES OF KETONES
a) Liquids 1) (Listed in order of increasing atmospheric b.p.)* (Continued)

No.	Name	Boiling point, °C	Melting point, °C	n_D^{20}	D_4^{20}	Semi-carbazone	2,4-Di-nitrophenyl-hydrazone	p-Nitro-phenyl-hydrazone	Phenyl-hydrazone	Oxime	Miscellaneous
57	2,2-Dimethyl-3-hexanone (tert-Butyl n-propyl ketone)	145[738]	......	1.4107	....	....	124; 116	....	....		
58	1-Hydroxy-2-propanone (Acetol)	146	−17	1.4295	....	196, al.	128.5 (cor.), or., al. 116	173	....		
59	4-Chloro-3-methyl-2-butanone (α-Chloroisopropyl methyl ketone)	146	......	1.4390	....	....					
60	1-Hepten-4-one	146–7	......	....	....	110, w.-al.	....	....	....	b.p. 92–3[13]	
61	3,4-Dimethyl-3-penten-2-one	147	......	1.4506[14]	....	200					
62	1-Ethoxy-2-butanone (Ethoxy-methyl ethyl ketone)	147[752]	......	1.4068	....	....					
63	2,5-Dimethyl-3,4-hexanedione (Di-isobutyryl).............	148	......	1.42057	....	....				mono: 125; di: 172	
64	3-Heptanone (n-Butyl ethyl ketone)	148	......	1.4092	....	101; 103; 152				....	
65	5-Methyl-4-hexen-3-one.........	148	......	1.4496[15]		163					
66	5-Methyl-5-hexen-2-one (Meth-allylacetone)..............	149	......	1.4285[25]	....	137					
67	2-Methyl-4-heptanone (Isobutyl n-propyl ketone)..........	150[750]	......	....	....	124					
68	4,4-Dimethyl-3-hexanone (tert-Amyl ethyl ketone)...........	150–2	......	....	....	98					
69	2-Heptanone (n-Amyl methyl ketone)	151.2	−35.5	1.40069	....	123, al.; 127	89, yel.-or., al.; 74	....	207	....	
70	3-Ethyl-5-hexen-2-one	152	......	1.4260[25]			53				
71	5-Hepten-2-one (Crotylacetone) ..	153	......	1.4280[25]	0.8446	105; 97					
72	1-Methoxy-2-pentanone (Meth-oxymethyl n-propyl ketone)	153[745]	......	1.4119	....	....					
73	3,3-Dimethylcyclopentanone	153[748]	......	....	....	178					
74	2,2,4,4-Tetramethyl-3-pentanone (Di-tert-butyl ketone)	154	......	1.4392; 1.4194							
75	1-Bromo-2-butanone (Bromo-methyl ethyl ketone)	155; 50[12]	......	1.4670							
76	Cyclopentyl methyl ketone.......	155	......	....	....	143					
77	2,2,5,5-Tetramethylcyclo-pentanone	155	......	1.4280							
78	1-Methoxy-3-hexanone (1-Meth-oxyethyl n-propyl ketone)	155[746]	......	1.4091	....	169; 170					
79	Cyclohexanone	156	−16.4	1.4507	....	166–7	160; 162, yel. al. 80	146–7, 90% al.	81–2, 50% al.	91, lgr.	
80	4-Methyl-6-hepten-3-one	156	......	....		....					
81	2-Hepten-4-one...............	156–7	......	....		147, w.-me. al.					
82	2,3-Hexanedione.............	158	......	....	....	....			....	di: 175	
83	3,4-Dimethyl-2-hexanone........	158; 155	......	....	....	120; 118; 126					
84	3,4-Dimethyl-3-hexen-2-one	158	....	1.4476[15]	....	142					
85	2,2,4-Trimethyl-3-hexanone (tert-Butyl isobutyl ketone).....	158	......	....		145					
86	2-Ethyl-1-hexen-3-one	158[742]	......	1.4408[18]	....	119					
87	3,3-Dimethyl-1-methoxy-2-butanone (tert-Butyl methoxy-methyl ketone).	159[743]	......	1.4193							
88	1-Isopropoxy-3-methyl-2-butanone	160	......	....	....	....	88			....	
89	2-Methyl-3-cyclopentenone.......	161	......	1.4771	....	220				127	

*Derivative data given in order: m.p., crystal color, solvent from which crystallized.

TABLE X. ORGANIC DERIVATIVES OF KETONES
a) Liquids 1) (Listed in order of increasing atmospheric b.p.)* (Continued)

No.	Name	Boiling point, °C	Melting point, °C	n_D^{20}	D_4^{20}	Semi-carbazone	2,4-Di-nitrophenyl-hydrazone	p-Nitro-phenyl-hydrazone	Phenyl-hydrazone	Oxime	Miscellaneous
90	1-Ethylcyclopentanone	161⁷⁵⁵	......	......	....	189	....	....	....	....	....
91	3-Methyl-2-heptanone	162	......	1.415	....	82					
92	4,5-Dimethyl-5-hexen-3-one	162⁷⁵⁰	......	....	....	110					
93	3,5-Dimethyl-4-heptanone (Di-sec-butyl ketone)	162; 170–3				83–4					
94	6-Methyl-3-heptanone (Ethyl isoamyl ketone)	163; 160	......			132					
95	2-Methoxy-3-methyl-2-pentanone (sec-Butyl methoxymethyl ketone)	164⁷⁵⁷	......	1.4162		....					
96	1-Methoxy-4-methyl-2-pentanone (Isobutyl methoxymethyl ketone)	164⁷⁵¹	......	1.4140							
97	2-Methylcyclohexanone	165.1; 166	−14.0	1.4885	0.92500	191; 197d., al., rapid htng.	135.5–7.0, al.; 137 (cor.)	132	b.p. 220³⁵⁻⁴⁰	43, eth.	........,
98	4-Hydroxy-4-methyl-2-pentanone (Diacetone alcohol)	166; 164				....	202–3	....	....	58	3,5-Dinitro-benzoate, 55
99	4,5-Dimethyl-4-hexen-3-one	166⁷⁵⁰	......	....	....	209					
100	2,2-Dimethyl-3-heptanone (n-Butyl tert-butyl ketone)........	166⁷⁴⁵	......	1.4167	....	145					
101	2,6-Dimethyl-4-heptanone (Di-isobutyl ketone; Isovalerone) ...	168.0	......	1.4173²⁵	....	122; 126	66, or.-red; 92	....			
102	2-Methyl-4-octanone (n-Butyl isobutyl ketone).............	168				132	....				
103	2,5-Dimethyl-4-heptanone (sec-Butyl isobutyl ketone)	169; 167				133					
104	d-3-Methylcyclohexanone	169		1.4456²¹		180, me. al.	....	....	....	43	$[\alpha]_D^{15}$: +13.38
105	d, l-3-Methylcyclohexanone	168; 169.6	−73.5	1.4430; 1.4463	0.91535	179, me. al.; 191.4d., rapid htng.	155, yel.	119	94, w.-al.	....	
106	1-Methoxy-2-hexanone (n-Butyl methoxymethyl ketone)........	169⁷⁴⁴	......	1.4173	....						
107	4-Octanone (n-Butyl n-propyl ketone)	170	......	....	....	96					
108	Methyl acetoacetate	170	−40.6	1.41964	1.0765	152	....				
109	2,2-Dimethylcyclohexanone......	170; 171		1.4482	....	201; 193	140–2				
110	6-Methyl-2-heptanone (Isohexyl methyl ketone)	171	......	1.4146	....	154	77	....			
111	trans-2,4-Dimethylcyclohexanone.	171	......	1.4429¹⁶	....	136					
112	4-Methylcyclohexanone	171.25	−40.6	1.4445	0.91562	199, me. al.; 203.5d., rapid htng.	....	128.5, yel., al.	109–10, al.	37–9	
113	d,l-2,5-Dimethylcyclohexanone ...	171–3	......	1.4446	....	α: 122; β: 173				111, al.	
114	2-Octanone (Hexyl methyl ketone)	173	−21.5	1.41518; 1.4154	0.81853	122–3 (cor.), pet. eth.-al.	58, or., al.	92–3, yel., al.			
115	5-Ethyl-3-heptanone	173	......	....	....	134					
116	d-2,5-Dimethylcyclohexanone	173–4	......	....	....	176–7	....	....	....	97–8	$[\alpha]_D^{20}$: +11.6
117	3-Ethyl-2-methylcyclopentanone ..	174				170, al.	....	....	....	....	....

*Derivative data given in order: m.p., crystal color, solvent from which crystallized.

TABLE X. ORGANIC DERIVATIVES OF KETONES
a) Liquids 1) (Listed in order of increasing atmospheric b.p.)* (Continued)

No.	Name	Boiling point, °C	Melting point, °C	n_D^{20}	D_4^{20}	Semi-carbazone	2,4-Dinitrophenyl-hydrazone	p-Nitrophenyl-hydrazone	Phenyl-hydrazone	Oxime	Miscellaneous
118	2,6-Dimethylcyclohexanone	174		1.4500; 1.4470							
119	2-Isopropylcyclopentanone	174		1.4395[29]		202					
120	Acetoxyacetone	174–5; 74[18]		1.4150	1.0749	145, me. al.		144, yel., bz.	60d., eth.	b.p. 144[20]	
121	2,4-Heptanedione (n-Butyryl-acetone)	174–5									Cu salt, 165; 161, pa. bl.
122	3-Methyl-3-hepten-2-one	175				164					
123	cis-2,4-Dimethylcyclohexanone	176		1.4430[25]		200; 190				98–9	
124	4-Ethyl-4-hydroxy-3-hexanone	178[742]				177					
125	2,3-Dimethylcyclohexanone	178–9		1.4505		203–4					
126	2,2,6-Trimethylcyclohexanone	179[767]		1.4480		209	141				
127	3,3-Dimethylcyclohexanone	179[748]		1.4482[17]		219					
128	5-Ethyl-4-hepten-3-one	179[740]				105					
129	3-Ethyl-4-methylcyclopentanone	180				208–9, w.-al.				oil, b.p. 117[11]	
130	Cyclohexyl methyl ketone	180		1.4514		177		154		60	
131	trans-3,5-Dimethylcyclohexanone	d, l: 180–1		1.4475[21]	d,l: 0.897; d: 0.9083; l: 0.9074	d,l: 193–4; d: 193–4; l: 189				d,l: oil, b.p. 116–8[14]	d: $[\alpha]_D^{20}$: +4.65 l: $[\alpha]_D^{20}$: −7.91
132	5-Hydroxy-4-octanone (Butyroin)	180–90					99				
133	Ethyl acetoacetate	181				133; 129d.	93				
134	Cycloheptanone	181; 182				163	148	137		23	
136	cis-3,5-Dimethylcyclohexanone	182–3		1.4407	0.890	202–3				74	
137	2-Propylcyclopentanone	183		1.4429		214d., al.				oil, b.p. 109–11[9]	
138	2,2,6,6-Tetramethylcyclohexanone	184[772]	15	1.4473							
139	3-Methyl-2,4-hexanedione	184; 183									Cu salt, 177
140	5-Nonanone (Di-n-butyl ketone)	186–7	f.p.-5.9	1.421[15]	0.8222	90, al.					
141	3,4-Dimethylcyclohexanone	187		1.4520; 1.4507	0.906	189					
142	3-Nonanone (Ethyl n-hexyl ketone)	187[751]				112					
143	2,5-Dimethylcyclohexen-3-one	189–90		1.4753[22]		165, me. al.				92–3, me. al.; 169, al.	
144	Methyl 2-pyridyl ketone (2-Acetyl-pyridine)	190								121	
145	3-Propylcyclopentanone	190–1		1.4456[12]		178–9, me. al.				oil, b.p. 121–2[12]	
146	3-Ethylcyclohexanone	192		1.4537; 1.4511		182; 175					
147	1,5-Dimethylcyclohexen-4-one	192–3; 194								102	
148	2,5-Hexanedione (Acetonyl-acetone)	194	−9	1.428; 1.449	0.97370	mono: 185d.; di: 224	di: 257, pyr.	di: 210–2, red., al.	di: 120, dil. al.	mono: b.p. 130[11]; di: 137	

*Derivative data given in order: m.p., crystal color, solvent from which crystallized.

No.	Name	Boiling point, °C	Melting point, °C	n_D^{20}	D_4^{20}	Semi-carbazone	2,4-Di-nitrophenyl-hydrazone	p-Nitro-phenyl-hydrazone	Phenyl-hydrazone	Oxime	Miscellaneous
149	d-Fenchone	195–6	......	1.46355[18]	0.947[19]	184; 172	140	....	b.p. 202–3[18]	d or l: α+: 165; β+: 123; d,l: α+: 159; β+: 129	Hydrazone, 56–7
150	2-Nonanone (n-Heptyl methyl ketone)	195.3	–8	1.42072	0.82133; 0.82217	118–9, al.	....				
151	1-Acetyl-4-methylcyclohexanone	195–7	......	1.4509[18]	....	α: 159, me. al.; β: 175	....			57–9	....
152	Methyl levulinate	196.0	....	1.42333	1.04945	143	142, al.		96; 105, al.	....	
153	4-Fluoroacetophenone	196	......	1.5081[25]	....	219					
154	d,l-2-Ethyl-5-methylcyclo-hexanone	197	......	1.4485	....	178–81				80, w.-al.	
155	1-Acetyl-2-methylcyclohexanone	197–200				172–3					
156	2-n-Propylcyclohexanone	198–9[748]		1.4558[13]	....	133d., w.-al.				67–8	
157	1-Acetylcyclohexene	200	......	1.4892	....	220				59	
158	3-(Trifluoromethyl)acetophenone	202	....	....	....	....					
159	β-Thujone	202; 76[10]				174	114				
160	Acetophenone (Methyl phenyl ketone)	205; 202	20	1.541; 1.5339	1.02810	198–9 (cor.), 50% al.; 203	238–40, al.; 249–50, or.-red., ac. a.	184–5, or.-red	105, wh., al., → dk.	60	
161	2-Ethyl-4-methylcyclohexanone	205[747]	......	1.4452							
162	Ethyl levulinate	206	......	1.42288	1.01114	148	102		104	....	....
163	4-Decanone	206–7				51–2					
164	1,5-Dimethylcyclohexen-3-one	208–9	......	1.4819[22]	....	179–80, yel., al.; 168–71			76–8	....	Thiosemicar-bazone, 195d.
165	l-Menthone	209; 207	–6.6	1.4505	....	189; 187; 184	146, or., al.		53	59, eth.	....
166	2-Decanone (Methyl n-octyl ketone)	211; 215.5	14; f.p. 3.1	1.42523	0.82370	124; 126, pet. eth.					
167	Methyl 4-pyridyl ketone	212	....	....	....	....				142	
168	4-n-Propylcyclohexanone	212[740]	.....	1.4514[25]	....	180					
169	2-Acetylthiophene (Methyl 2-thienyl ketone)	213	10.5	1.5666	....	190, bz.	....	181	96	81	
170	2-Methylacetophenone (Methyl 2-tolyl ketone)	214; 216		1.5320		205, al.; 210	159, yel., al; 161			61	
171	6-Bromo-2-hexanone	214[720]		1.4713		81				....	
172	1,5,5-Trimethylcyclohexen-3-one (Isophorone)	215	......	1.4789[21.5]	0.9255[20.5]	199.5d., al.; 191	....		68, dil. al.	79.5, pet. eth.; 76	
173	n-Propyl 2-pyridyl ketone	217–8		....	....	173–4			82	48	Picrate, 75
174	Propiophenone (Ethyl phenyl ketone)	218; 220	20; 18.6	1.5270	1.0105	173–4 (cor.), al.; 182, rapid htng.	190–1, red, bz.; 189		....	54; 53, pet. eth.	....
175	Methyl 3-pyridyl ketone	220; 218		....	....	....			137	113	....
176	3-Methylacetophenone (Methyl 3-tolyl ketone)	220	......	1.5306	1.007	198; 203	207		....	55; 57, al.	....

*Derivative data given in order: m.p., crystal color, solvent from which crystallized.

TABLE X. ORGANIC DERIVATIVES OF KETONES

a) Liquids 1) (Listed in order of increasing atmospheric b.p.)* (Continued)

No.	Name	Boiling point, °C	Melting point, °C	n_D^{20}	D_4^{20}	Semi-carbazone	2,4-Di-nitrophenyl-hydrazone	p-Nitro-phenyl-hydrazone	Phenyl-hydrazone	Oxime	Miscellaneous
177	Isobutyrophenone (Isopropyl phenyl ketone)	222; 217	......	1.5190	$0.9863_4^{16.9}$	181, al.	163, or.-red, dil. ac. a.	....	73	94, lt. pet.	....
178	Acetyl benzoyl ketone	222, yel.	......	1.537^{10}	....	di: 229–32	....	di: 256	α: 143	α, mono: 166; β, mono: 114; di: 240	....
179	5-Ethyl-1-methylcyclohexene-3-one	223–7	......	....	....	162–8d., al.	....	....	....	....	Thiosemicar-bazone, 150–1
180	4[8]-p-Menthen-3-one (Pulegone)	224; 221–2	......	1.48705^{18}	....	174; 175–6	142			119	....
181	Pivalophenone (tert-Butyl phenyl ketone)	224^{750}	......	1.5082; 1.5102	....	150	194–5			167	
182	1-Phenyl-2-butanone (Benzyl ethyl ketone)	226	......	....	....	135; 146					
183	6-Undecanone (6-Hendecanone; Di-n-amyl ketone)	228 (cor.)	15	1.42875	0.82471	oil				oil	
184	3-Chloroacetophenone	228	......	....	....	232	....	176		88	
185	Ethyl 1-thienyl ketone	228	......	....	....	167				55–6	
186	2-Undecanone (2-Hendecanone; Methyl n-nonyl ketone)	228	12.1; 12.7	1.42899	0.82564	122.0–.5	63, al.	90–1, yel., al.	....	44–5	
187	2,4-Dimethylacetophenone	228; 234–5	......	1.5381; 1.5340	....	185–7				63–4, pet. eth.	
188	2-Chloroacetophenone	229	......	1.685^{25}	....	160				113	
189	1-Phenoxy-2-propanone (Phenoxy-acetone)	229–30; 120^{19}	......	1.5228	1.0903	173; 176 (cor.), 50% al.					
190	n-Propyl 4-pyridyl ketone	229–31	......	....	....	....	....	....	....	....	Picrate, 96
191	n-Butyrophenone (Phenyl n-propyl ketone)	230; 218–21	11.5–13.0	1.5196; 1.5203	....	187–8, al.; 191	190, or.-red, dil. ac. a.			50, abs. eth.	
192	d-Carvone	230	......	1.49952	0.9608	162–3; 142–3; d, l: 154–6	191, red, ac. a.	174–5, red-br.	....	d, α: 72–3, al.; d, β: 56–7; l, α, (–): 72; l, β, (+): 57–8; d, l: 93–4	$[\alpha]_D^{20}$: +62.9
193	2,5-Dimethylacetophenone	230	......	1.5291; 1.5306	....	168–9	....			....	....
194	4-Chloroacetophenone	232; 236	12	....	....	204; 160; 146	231	239	114	95	....
196	4-Phenyl-2-butanone (Methyl-β-phenylethyl ketone)	235	......	....	....	142				87	
197	Isovalerophenone (Isobutyl phenyl ketone)	236	......	....	....	210				76; 64.5	
198	3,5-Dimethylacetophenone	236–7	......	1.5276^{25}	....			179–80, yel., ac. a.	....	114, me. al.	....
199	2-Methoxyacetophenone (2-Acetylanisole)	239; 245	......	1.5395	1.089	183	....		114, al.	83; 96.0–.5, pet.	
200	3-Methoxyacetophenone (3-Acetylanisole)	240; 252	......	$1.5583^{15.4}$	$1.0993_4^{15.4}$	196	....				
201	5-Phenyl-3-pentanone	244	......	1.5125	....	80					
202	5-Isopropyl-2-methylacetophenone (2-Acetyl-p-cymene)	245	......	1.51849	0.9654_{20}^{20}	147	140–2, clearing at 160	....	....	91–2.5	....

*Derivative data given in order: m.p., crystal color, solvent from which crystallized.

TABLE X. ORGANIC DERIVATIVES OF KETONES
a) Liquids 1) (Listed in order of increasing atmospheric b.p.)* (Continued)

No.	Name	Boiling point, °C	Melting point, °C	n_D^{20}	D_4^{20}	Semi-carbazone	2,4-Di-nitrophenyl-hydrazone	p-Nitro-phenyl-hydrazone	Phenyl-hydrazone	Oxime	Miscellaneous
203	α-Bromopropiophenone.........	245–50	......	1.5686^{25}	....	....	....	....	....	....	....
204	3,4-Dimethylacetophenone.......	246–7; 251	......	1.5400	....	233–4	....	....	....	85	....
205	2,4,5-Trimethylacetophenone	246–7	......	....	....	204	....	....	....	85–6	....
206	n-Propyl 3-pyridyl ketone	246–52	......	1.5128	....	169–70	....	....	182	....	Picrate, 104
207	n-Valerophenone (n-Butyl phenyl ketone)	248.5; 242	......	1.5150	0.988_{20}^{20}	160, w.-al.	166, brt. red, ac. a.	161.5–2.5, or.-red, al.	162	52.0–.5, pet. eth.	....
208	2-Aminoacetophenone	250–2d.	20	....	....	290d., al.	....	....	108, al.	109, subl., w.	....
209	2,5-Dichloroacetophenone	251	14	....	....	....	....	....	....	130	....
210	4-Isopropylacetophenone	252–4	......	....	....	....	....	....	....	....	....
211	1,1,1-Tribromoacetone..........	255d.	......	....	....	....	....	....	....	....	....
212	Ethyl benzoylacetate	265	......	....	....	125	....	....	....	....	....
213	n-Enanthophenone (n-Hexyl phenyl ketone)	283.3	16.4	1.50760_{He}^{15}	0.95155	119, dil. al.	....	127–8	....	55	....
214	3-Phenylcyclohexanone	$287–8^{736}$	......	....	....	167, al.	....	....	....	128–9, al.	....
215	1-Acetylnaphthalene (Methyl 1-naphthyl ketone)...........	302	......	1.629	....	288.5–9.5; 232–3	....	....	146	140; 137.5	....
216	Ethyl 1-naphthyl ketone........	305–7	......	1.6109	....	....	....	....	....	58	Picrate, 77–8, al.; 79
217	2-Benzoylpyridine (Phenyl 2-pyridyl ketone).............	317	......	1.6056	....	....	199	....	136, yel., al.	150; 165	Picrate, 130, al.
218	2,4,5-Trimethylbenzophenone	328	......	....	1.0332_4^{18}	....	....	....	....	....	....
219	2,4,4'-Trimethylbenzophenone....	340	......	....	....	....	....	....	....	132, al.	....
220	α-Methylstyryl phenyl ketone (Dypnone)	340–5 sl. d.	......	....	1.108_0^{20}	151, bz.	....	....	....	syn: 134, al.; anti: 78	....
221	1,5-Diphenyl-3-pentanone (Di-benzylacetone)	352; 348	13–4	....	....	....	....	....	....	95–6	....

* Derivative data given in order: m.p., crystal color, solvent from which crystallized.

TABLE X. ORGANIC DERIVATIVES OF KETONES
a) Liquids 2) (Reduced pressure b.p. only) (Listed in order of increasing semicarbazone m.p.)*

No.	Name	Semi-carbazone	Boiling point, °C	n_D^{20}	D_4^{20}	Miscellaneous
1	1-Chloro-2-methyl-3-pentanone	70	64[9]			
2	4-Methyl-2-octanone	70	94[40]			
3	1-Hepten-5-one	82–3, w.-al.	46–7[12]	1.4254[18.3]	0.8487[18.3]	
4	3-Dodecanone	89, w.-al.	134[18]			m.p. 19
5	1,3-Diethoxy-2-propanone (*sym*-Diethoxyacetone)	91	105[35]	1.4202		
6	1-Ethoxy-2-propanone (Ethoxyacetone)	96	36[28]	1.4000		
7	3-Cyclopentyl-2-butanone (α-Cyclopentyl-α-methylacetone)	98	79[17]	1.4470		
8	7-Methyl-1-octen-5-one	101–2	62–3[14]	1.4288[12.5]		
9	Cyclohexyl methoxymethyl ketone	102	111[21]	1.4552[25]		
10	1-Phenoxy-2-butanone (Ethyl phenoxymethyl ketone)	102	100[5]	1.5201		
11	1-Naphthoxyacetone	103	205–8[14]			
12	1-Hepten-6-one	108, w.-al.	41–3[10]	1.4350[18]	0.8673[18]	
13	1-Phenoxy-2-pentanone (Phenoxymethyl *n*-propyl ketone)	108	112[4]	1.5148		
14	3-Octyn-2-one	109	76[15]	1.4446[25]		2,4-Dinitrophenylhydrazone, 88
15	3-Hepten-6-one	109–10, wh.	61–2[20]	1.4290[21]	0.8618[21]	
16	3-Methyl-4-phenyl-2-butanone	112; 114	130[17]	1.5090[19]		
17	3-Methyl-3-hepten-5-one	114	82–6[42]	1.4488[25]		
18	1-Chloro-2-ethyl-3-hexanone	115	92[12]			
19	1,3-Dimethoxy-2-propanone (*sym*-Dimethoxyacetone)	120	78[18]	1.4174		
21	*trans*-3-Hepten-2-one	125; 128	60[16]	1.4421; 1.4430	0.8445	
22	5-Hydroxy-5-methyl-3-heptanone	125	86[14]	1.4386[14]		
23	α-Ethoxyacetophenone	128	122[15]	1.5250		
24	3-Propylpropiophenone (Ethyl 3-propylphenyl ketone)	128	145[20]			
25	α-Methoxyacetophenone	129	126[19]			
26	1-Phenyl-4-hexen-1-one	130	97[1]	1.5270[25]		
27	5-Phenyl-2-pentanone	130	122[6]			
28	2-Methyl-3-octen-6-one	131–2	73–7[19]	1.44533		
29	1-Phenyl-1-hexen-5-one	132, et. ac.	153–5[10]	1.5458[25]		
30	3-Phenyl-1-hexen-5-one	132	153–5[10]	1.5193[25]		2,4-Dinitrophenylhydrazone, 103
31	4-Phenyl-2-pentanone	137	115[13]	1.5124		
32	3-Propyl-3-hexen-2-one	142	72[9]			
33	3-Acetylfuran	150	84[21]			
34	3-Hydroxy-3-methyl-2-pentanone	150	73[50]	1.4200		
35	1-Cyclopentyl-2-propanone (1-Cyclopentylacetone)	150	67[12]			
37	*cis*-3-Hepten-2-one	152	70[15]	1.4505[22]	0.8555[22]	
38	3-Hydroxy-3-methyl-2-heptanone	152	84[19]			
39	*d*-2-Ethyl-5-methylcyclohexanone	152–4	83–4[18]		0.9016[15]	[α]D: +8.5
40	5-Hydroxy-2-pentanone	155	86[10]	1.4350[25]		
41	3-Phenyl-2-butanone	158	107[22]	1.5092		
42	3-Phenyl-3-hexen-5-one	158	138[14]			
43	Dicyclopentyl ketone	162	112[12]			
44	2-Ethylcyclohexanone	162; 163	76[20]	1.4522		2,4-Dinitrophenylhydrazone, 162
45	2,3-Dimethyl-2-hepten-6-one	163	76[13]			
46	3-*n*-Propylcyclohexanone	169	42[0.7]	1.4530		
48	2-Cyclohexenone	172; 168	68[22]	1.4879		2,4-Dinitrophenylhydrazone, 163; 117
49	2-Chloropropiophenone (2-Chlorophenyl ethyl ketone)	173	106[12]			
50	*d,l*-1-Acetyl-3-methylcyclohexanone	174–5	99–100[38]			
51	3-*n*-Propyl-2-cyclohexenone	175	60[0.4]	1.4876[25]		2,4-Dinitrophenylhydrazone, 156
52	2-Bromoacetophenone	177	112[10]			2,4-Dinitrophenylhydrazone, 189

*Derivative data given in order: m.p., crystal color, solvent from which crystallized.

TABLE X. ORGANIC DERIVATIVES OF KETONES

TABLE X. ORGANIC DERIVATIVES OF KETONES
a) Liquids 2) (Reduced pressure b.p. only) (Listed in order of increasing semicarbazone m.p.)* (Continued)

No.	Name	Semi-carbazone	Boiling point, °C	n_D^{20}	D_4^{20}	Miscellaneous
53	2-Methyl-3-butenyl phenyl ketone	177	100[2.1]	1.5223[25]		
54	4-Methoxycyclohexanone	178	85[14]	1.4560		2,4-Dinitrophenylhydrazone, 150
55	5,5-Dimethyl-3-hexen-2-one	178	79[40]	1.4430		
56	Ethyl 2-methylstyryl ketone	178	152[14]			
57	2-Bromopropiophenone (2-Bromophenyl ethyl ketone)	179	118[11]			
58	3-Isopropyl-2-cyclohexenone	179	60[0.3]	1.4842		2,4-Dinitrophenylhydrazone, 155
59	2-Ethylacetophenone	180	118[29]	1.5249		
60	3-Pyridylacetone	185	123[1]			
61	l-6-Isopropyl-3-cyclohexenone	185	98–100[10]	1.484		$[\alpha]_D^{18}$: −64.5; 2,4-Dinitrophenyl-hydrazone, 137–8; p-Nitro-phenylhydrazone, 168–9
62	4-n-Butylacetophenone	185	141[14]			
63	3-Phenyl-2-hexen-5-one	185	138[14]			
64	3-Ethyl-2-cyclohexenone	186	57[0.9]	1.4913		
65	3-Methyl-3-phenyl-2-butanone	186	77[15]	1.5083		
66	2-Methyl-3-octen-5-one	187–8	68–78[24]	1.4748		
67	4-Isopropylcyclohexanone	188; 188–9	91[13]	1.4560		p-Nitrophenylhydrazone, 123–4
68	4,4,6-Trimethyl-2-cyclohexen-1-one	188; 185–7	73–5[13]			
69	2-Acetyl-5-methylfuran	191	73[8]			
71	3-Phenyl-2-pentanone		110[18]	1.5051		
72	4-Phenylhexahydroacetophenone (Methyl 4-phenylcyclohexyl ketone)	191	121[1–2]			
73	2,6,6-Trimethylcycloheptanone	191–2	85.5[12]	1.4568[18]	0.9095[18]	
74	Acetyl phenyl carbinol	194	137			2,4-Dinitrophenylhydrazone, 170; 126; Oxime, 113
75	2-Tetralone	194	131[11]	1.5555[25]		m.p. 18; Oxime, 88
76	3-Isopropylcyclohexanone	195	51[1]	1.4540		
77	1-Propionylcyclohexene	195; 189	102[14]			Oxime, 78
78	α-Thienylacetone (1-(α-Thienyl)-2-propanone)	195	106[12]	1.5366[14]		
79	5,5-Dimethyl cyclohexen-3-one	195	88.5[32]			H_2SO_4 → red → vlt. → col.
80	2-Acetylbiphenyl	197	105[1]			
81	3-Methyl-2-cyclohexen-1-one	199; 201	78[14]	1.4945		2,4-Dinitrophenylhydrazone, 176; 178
82	1-Acetyl-2,2-dimethylcyclohexene	201	118[49]	1.4810[25]		
83	1,1-Dimethyl-2-tetralone	204	96[0.5]	1.538		
84	2-Methyl-1-tetralone	205; 195	138[16]	1.5447		
85	6-Propionyltetralin	209	163[11]	1.5508[29]		
86	3-Methyl-2-n-propylcyclopentanone	210	58[2]	1.4778		
87	4-Methyl-1-tetralone	211	111[1]			
88	1-Acetylcyclopentene	211	74[12]			
89	2-Acetyl-5-methylthiophene	217	83[2]	1.5622		
90	1-Tetralone	217, yel., al.	170[49]			Oxime, 102, prisms; 88–9, needles, me. al.
91	Neopentyl phenyl ketone	218	116[11]	1.5078		Oxime, 114
92	3-Methyl-2,5-hexanedione	220	71[10]	1.4260		
93	cis-1-Decalone	220d.	116[18]	1.4939		
94	3-Acetylbiphenyl	223	138[1]	1.6140[25]		
95	1,2-Dimethyl cyclohexen-3-one	225d.	118–9[12]			
96	3-Chloroacetophenone	232	113[11]	1.5494		
97	3-Bromoacetophenone	233	132[17]	1.5755		
99	6-Acetyltetralin	234	156[10]	1.5591[25]		
100	2,3-Dimethyl-2-cyclopentenone	250	92[25]	1.4830		

*Derivative data given in order: m.p., crystal color, solvent from which crystallized.

TABLE X. ORGANIC DERIVATIVES OF KETONES

a) Liquids 2) (Reduced pressure b.p. only) (Listed in order of increasing semicarbazone m.p.)* (Continued)

No.	Name	Semi-carbazone	Boiling point, °C	n_D^{20}	D_4^{20}	Miscellaneous
101	1-Ethyl-2-methyl-3-cyclohexenone	250	105^{19}	. . . .	. . . .	. . . .
102	3-Acetylthianaphthene	250	137^{3}	. . . .	. . . .	. . . .
103	2-Oxopropionaldehyde (Methylglyoxal; Pyruvic aldehyde).	*di*: 254	52^{12}	. . . .	. . . .	*bis*-2,4-Dinitrophenylhydrazone, 299–300, red, $PhNO_2$; Dioxime, 157, al.

*Derivative data given in order: m.p., crystal color, solvent from which crystallized.

TABLE X. ORGANIC DERIVATIVES OF KETONES
b) Solids (Listed in order of increasing m.p.)*

No.	Name	Melting point, °C	Boiling point, °C	Semi-carbazone	2,4-Di-nitrophenyl-hydrazone	p-Nitro-phenyl-hydrazone	Phenyl-hydrazone	Oxime	Miscellaneous
1	**2-Aminoacetophenone**	20	250–2d.	290d., al.	. . . .	. . . .	108, al.	109, subl., w,	. . . .
2	**2-Dodecanone** (*n*-Decyl methyl ketone)	20.5	246–7	122–3, dil. al.					n_D^{30}: 1.42855; D_4^{30}: 0.81982
3	*n*-**Amyl phenyl ketone** (*n*-Pentyl phenyl ketone)	24.7	265.2	131.5, 50% al.; 133 (cor.)	168 (cor.), ac. a.				n_D^{25}: 1.50272
4	**3,5-Dichloroacetophenone**	26	134–6[17]	. . . .				138	. . . .
5	**Benzyl methyl ketone** (Phenyl-acetone)	27	216.5 (cor.)	199–9.5, al.; 188	156	145	86–7, lgr.; 83	68–70	n_D^{20}: 1.5168
6	**4-Methylacetophenone**	28	226	204–5, al.; 197	260.4 (cor.), scar., ac. a.	198	97, al.	87–8, pet. eth.	n_D^{20}: 1.5348; D_4^{20}: 1.003
7	**2-Hydroxyacetophenone**	28	215	210	210–12; 212–3	. . . .	110	118	. . . .
8	**Phorone** (Di-isopropylidene-acetone)	28, yel.-gr.	198	221, w.; 186	118			48	Tetrabromide, 88–9, al.
9	**2-Tridecanone** (Methyl *n*-undecyl ketone; *n*-Hendecyl methyl ketone)	28	263	123, al.; 126; 117	69, or.-yel.	101–2	. . . .	56–7, al.-pet. eth.	n_D^{30}: 1.43175
10	**Furfuralacetophenone**	29, yel.-red	317d.		169, scar.				
11	**Ethyl 2-furyl ketone**	30; 28	183	189					
12	**4-Cyclohexylcyclohexanone**	30–31; 29.2	100[0.1]	216	137			101–2; 104–5	
13	**2-(1′-Hydroxycyclopentyl)-cyclo-pentanone**	31	99[3]	. . . .				78	
14	**7-Tridecanone** (Di-*n*-hexyl ketone)	31–2	255; 264		96				
15	**2-Acetylfuran** (2-Furyl methyl ketone)	32; 33	169–73	150, me. al.; 148	220	185–6, red, w.-al.	86, yel., w.-al.	104, eth.-pet. eth.; 92	n_D^{20}: 1.5017; D^{20}: 1.098
16	**Levulinic acid** (3-Acetyl propionic acid)	33	245–6	. . . .	206 (cor.), or.-yel., ac. a.	174–5	108, bz.	45–6	. . . .
17	**2-Tetradecanone** (*n*-Dodecyl methyl ketone)	33–4, dil. al.	. . . .	115–6, al.	. . . .	. . . .			
18	**Methyl 1-naphthyl ketone** (1-Acetylnaphthalene)	34	302	222.5–4	. . . .	. . . .	146	136	n_D^{20}: 1.6257; Picrate, 116, yel.
19	**1,3-Diphenyl-2-propanone** (1,3-Diphenylacetone; Dibenzyl ketone)	34; 35; 30	330	145–6, abs. al.; 125–6, dil. al.	100		121, al.; 128–9	125; 123	. . . .
20	**2,2,6,6-Tetramethyl-4-piperidone** .	34.9, red, dry eth.; 58 (mono-hyd.), eth.	205–6	219–20, al.	. . . .			153, al.	. . . .
21	**4-Chloropropiophenone**	36; 35	118[2]	177; 175–6	. . . .		. . . .	62–3	. . . .
22	**2-Phenylcyclopentanone**	37	126–7[10]	218d.					
23	**Furfuralacetone**	38; 39	116[10]	. . . .	241 (cor.)	. . . .	131–2, al.	. . . .	. . . .
24	**4-Methoxyacetophenone**	38; 37	258	197–8, dil. al.	220 (cor.), red; 231.8 (cor.)	195–5.5, or., al.	142, yel., al.	86–7, wh., pet. eth.	
25	**1-Phenyl-1-hepten-3-one** (*n*-Butyl styryl ketone)	38–9; 40	159–67[11]	. . . .	. . . .	. . . .	98, yel.	. . . .	Dimer, 175–6

*Derivative data given in order: m.p., crystal color, solvent from which crystallized.

TABLE X. ORGANIC DERIVATIVES OF KETONES

b) Solids (Listed in order of increasing m.p.)* (Continued)

No.	Name	Melting point, °C	Boiling point, °C	Semi-carbazone	2,4-Di-nitrophenyl-hydrazone	p-Nitro-phenyl-hydrazone	Phenyl-hydrazone	Oxime	Miscellaneous
26	**4,4-Dimethylcyclohexanone**	38–41	73[14]	204	....	....	106–7	....	n_D^{24}: 1.4537; D_4^{20}: 0.932
27	**3,4-Methylenedioxypropio-phenone** (Propiopiperone)	39	....	187–8	....	....	97	104	....
28	**2-Hydroxybenzophenone**	39, w.-al.; 153	250[560]	....	....	....	155, al.	*syn*: 141, bz.; *anti*: 143, bz.	....
29	**2-Methoxybenzophenone** (2-Anisyl phenyl ketone)........	39	....	....	....	....	....	145–8, dil. al.; fu-sion → 130	
30	**3-Bromopropiophenone**........	40	....	183	....	....	....	115	....
31	**Benzalacetone**	41	212	187	227; 223	166	157	115	Thiosemicarbazone, 148
32	**1-Indanone** (α-Hydrindone)	42; 38	241–2[739]	233; 239	258	234–5, ac. a.	130–1; 134–5, me. al.; 124–8	146; 144, bz.-pet. eth.	....
33	**2,4-Dichloroacetophenone**	42	235–40	208	....	....	....	152	n_D^{20}: 1.5640
34	**3-Aminopropiophenone**........	42, yel.	168–9[15]	196–7	....	....	....	112; 112–3	N-*p*-Toluenesulfonyl deriv., 97, al.
35	**2-Bromobenzophenone**	42	345	....	....	....	....	133	....
36	**8-Pentadecanone** (Di-*n*-heptyl ketone).....................	42	178	....	....	....	....	120	
37	**4-Phenyl-3-buten-2-one** (Methyl styryl ketone)...............	42	262	186, al.; 198; 142	227, red, ac. a.; 223, or.-red, al.	165–7, red, al.	156–7, yel., al.; 159	115–6, 60% al.; 87	H_2SO_4 → or.-red
38	**3-Chlorobenzyl phenyl ketone**....	43	....	....	....	....	....	102	....
39	**8-Acetylguanine**..............	43.5	116[0.7]	....	253	....	....	....	
40	**2-Benzoylfuran** (2-Furyl phenyl ketone).....................	44	150[3]	....	....	....	....	122	
41	**1,3-Dichloro-2-propanone** (1,3-Dichloroacetone)........	45	175; 173	....	....	....	....	....	n_D^{46}: 1.47144; D_4^{46}: 1.3826
42	**2-Acetylquinoline**	46	....	....	....	....	....	54	....
43	**3-Chloropropiophenone**........	46	....	179–80	....	....	....	....	
44	**4-Bromopropiophenone**........	46	140[2]	171	....	....	....	90–1	
45	**Phenyl *n*-undecyl ketone** (*n*-Hendecyl phenyl ketone; Laurophenone).............	47; 44	....	94.5–95	....	....	....	63–63.5	
46	**2-Aminopropiophenone**	47, pet. eth.	....	190d., al.	....	....	....	88–9, w.	Hydrochloride, 184–5; N-Acetyl, 70–1
47	**Benzophenone**	48; 49	306 (cor.)	164–5, al.; 167	238–9, or.-yel., ac. a.; 229	154–5, yel., al.; 144, red, al.	137–8, al.	142–3, me. al.; 144; 140	D_{50}^{50}: 1.0976
48	**2,4,6-Heptanetrione** (Diacetyl-acetone)	49	121[10]	*mono*: 203	....	....	*di*: 142	2,6-*di*: 68.5	n_D^{20}: 1.4930; D_{40}^{40}: 1.0681
49	**5-Phenoxy-2-pentanone** (Methyl 3-phenoxypropyl ketone)......	50	121[2]	108–10	110	....	....	....	
50	**9-Heptadecanone** (Di-*n*-octyl ketone)....................	50–50.5	250–3	....	....	54	....	111–2	
51	**Phenacyl bromide** (ω-Bromo-acetophenone)...............	50; 51	....	146	212–3, yel., or.	....	....	89.5; 97	
52	**4-Bromoacetophenone**..........	51; 50.5	225	208	230; 237 (cor.)	....	126	128; 129	
53	**3-Bromophenacyl bromide**	51, lgr.	174[14]	163–4d., al.	....	....	....	....	
54	**Ethynyl phenyl ketone**..........	51.	....	....	214	....	....	....	

*Derivative data given in order: m.p., crystal color, solvent from which crystallized.

TABLE X. ORGANIC DERIVATIVES OF KETONES

b) Solids (Listed in order of increasing m.p.)* (Continued)

No.	Name	Melting point, °C	Boiling point, °C	Semi-carbazone	2,4-Di-nitrophenyl-hydrazone	p-Nitro-phenyl-hydrazone	Phenyl-hydrazone	Oxime	Miscellaneous
55	3,4-Dimethoxyacetophenone (Acetoveratrone)............	51, w.-al.	286–8	218, w.-al.	206–7	227	131	140, w.-al.	....
56	Diphenylacetoin..............	52	....	169	....	....	....	....	4-Nitrobenzoate, 84
57	Methyl 2-naphthyl ketone (2-Acetylnaphthalene)..........	53–4, al.; 56	301	234–5; 237	262d., red, ac. a.	....	176–7; 171	149; 145–6	Picrate, 82
58	Chloromethyl 2-phenylethyl ketone....................	54	244.5	156	147; 146	....	....	89	
59	2-Furyl-2-thenoylmethane.......	55.5	195[6]	....	....	....	....	....	Cu salt, 274
60	Phenyl 2-thienyl ketone (2-Benzoylthiophene)	56	300	195–7	....	....	....	93	....
61	2-Nonadecanone (n-Heptadecyl methyl ketone)	56	....	124–5; 125.5–6	....	....	....	77	
62	4-n-Caproylresorcinol (2,4-Di-hydroxy-n-caproylbenzene)....	56–7	243–5d.	....	....	....	....	190–1d., 50% al.	....
63	2,2′-Dichlorobenzoin...........	57	....	....	....	....	....	....	
64	3-Propionylphenanthrene	57	....	....	....	....	....	53.6–4.7	Picrate, 113
65	9-Propionylphenanthrene	57	....	....	....	....	....	....	Picrate, 107
66	Benzalacetophenone (Phenyl styryl ketone; Chalcone)......	58, pa. yel., al.; 57–8	345	α: 168; β: 170, yel.; γ: 179–80d.	244d., or.-red, ac. a.; 245 (cor.)	....	120	140; 68	Picrate, 93–7; Dimers, 124; 178; 195; 225–6
67	2-Indanone	58; 58–9	....	218; 212–15 (dec.)	....	232 (dec.)	....	155	
68	Phenacyl chloride (ω-Chloro-acetophenone)...............	59	244	156; 149	213–4d.; 214–5d.	....	....	89	
69	3-Phenyl-2,4-pentanedione	60	134[20]	....	....	....	....	....	Cu salt, 224
70	Mesitylacetone	60	130[10]	205; 197	....	....	....	....	
71	Ethyl 2-naphthyl ketone	60	312–4	202	....	....	....	133, w.-al.	
72	Difurfuralacetone	60, yel.	....	....	....	....	121–2	....	
73	Desoxybenzoin (Benzyl phenyl ketone)....................	60, al.	321 (cor.)	148, dil. al.	204 (cor.), or.	163, red-br.; 160	116, yel., al.	98, al.	
74	4-Methylbenzophenone (Phenyl 4-tolyl ketone)..............	60; 55	326 (cor.)	121–2, al.	202.4 (cor.); 199–200, or.	....	109, wh., ac. a.	154, less soluble in w.-ac. a.; 115, more soluble in w.-ac. a.	
75	1-Phenyl-1,3-butanedione (Benzoylacetone; Methyl phenacyl ketone)............	61	261–2	....	151, pa. yel., al.	100–1, me. al.	150–3	....	
76	1,1-Diphenylacetone	61, al.	....	170	....	....	131, bz.	165	
77	2,4′-Dibromobenzophenone	62, pet. eth.	381–4 sl. d.	....	....	....	....	141–2	
78	5-Isopropyl-1,3-cyclohexanedione	62	....	....	....	....	....	....	
79	Benzyl 3-chlorophenyl ketone....	62	....	....	....	....	....	120	
80	4-Methoxybenzophenone (4-Anisyl phenyl ketone)........	62–4, al.	354	....	180, dk. or.	198–9, al.	132; 90	α: 140–1; 137–8; β: 115–6	
81	2-Phenylcyclohexanone.........	63, al.; 60	160[15]	190	139	....	....	169	....
82	4-Methoxybenzil	63	....	....	....	....	....	124	
83	1-Acetyl-2-hydroxynaphthalene ..	64	....	....	....	....	....	....	Benzoate, 85–6, pyr.
84	11-Heneicosanone (Di-n-decyl ketone)....................	64, w.-al.	....	....	....	....	....	27.5	
85	Benzoylformic acid (Phenylgly-oxylic acid)	66	147–51[12]	....	196–7d. (cor.), yel.	....	....	α: 127, eth.; β: 145d., w.	Thiosemicarbazone, 188–9 (cor.), yel.
86	2,2′-Dimethylbenzophenone (Di-2-tolyl ketone).............	67	....	....	190	....	....	105	....

*Derivative data given in order: m.p., crystal color, solvent from which crystallized.

No.	Name	Melting point, °C	Boiling point, °C	Semicarbazone	2,4-Dinitrophenylhydrazone	p-Nitrophenylhydrazone	Phenylhydrazone	Oxime	Miscellaneous
87	1,5-Diphenyl-1,5-pentanedione (1,3-Dibenzoylpropane)	67.5; 62–3						di: 165–6d.	
88	3,5-Dibromoacetophenone	68, al.; 65	198[15]	268d., w.-ac. a.			109–10, yel., al.		
89	Cinnamalacetone	68, eth.		186, yel., al.	222–3, vlt.-red, ac. a.; 218–20, br.-red, chl.-me. al.		180, yel., al.	153, al.; 152	
90	Benzoyl-2-furoylmethane	68	169[3]						Cu salt, 248
91	12-Tricosanone (Di-n-undecyl ketone; Di-n-hendecyl ketone; Laurone)	69.5		179				39–40, al.	
92	Diphenyl triketone	70; 69, yel., lgr.							Heating with excess phenylhydrazine → 4-Benzene-azo-1,3,5-triphenylpyrazole, 156–7, yel.-red, al.
93	2-Chlorobenzyl phenyl ketone	71						86	
94	Dihydroxyacetone	72			277–8	160		84	Diacetate, 48; Dibenzoate, 120.5; Dimer, 78–81
95	3-Acetylphenanthrene	72		230				193–4	Picrate, 125–6
96	4-Methoxybenzalacetone (Anisalacetone)	73, me. al.			229 (cor.), red, ac. a.			119–20	
97	Benzylacetophenone	73		144				87	
98	Phenoxymethyl phenyl ketone (α-Phenoxyacetophenone)	74	187[8]	187					
99	9-Acetylphenanthrene	74	170[1]	201				154–5	Picrate, 107–8
100	1-Naphthyl phenyl ketone	75.5–6.0	225[15]	385	α: 246–7, red; β: 243–4, or.; mixt.: 220			161	
101	9-Acetylfluorene	75.5					139		
102	2-Benzofuryl methyl ketone	76; 72	136[11]	207			154		
103	Benzyl 4-methoxyphenyl ketone	77						118	
104	4-Methoxybenzalacetophenone (Anisalacetophenone; 4-Methoxychalcone)	77, yel., al.		α: 168, al.; β: 190, al.					Picrate, 87, or.
105	2-Naphthoxyacetone	78; 77		203			154	123	
106	4-Phenylcyclohexanone	78		212; 229d., al.				110	
107	Benzoyl-2-thenoylmethane	78	201[4]						Cu salt, 278
108	4-Chlorobenzophenone	78			185		106	β: 105–6	
109	1,4-Cyclohexanedione	79	132[20]	mono: 221–2; di: 231	240			188	
110	Di-n-tridecyl ketone (Myristone)	79						57	
111	Phenacyl phenyl ketone (Dibenzoylmethane; ω-Benzoylacetophenone)	keto: 81; enol: 78, al.		205			mono: 105	mono: 165	Dibromo deriv., 94–5, eth.
112	3-Nitroacetophenone	81		257	228		128; 135	132	
113	4-Bromobenzophenone	82		350	230		126	α: 116–7; β: 110–1	
114	1-Benzoylpropionic acid	82–3d.					100–4, br., bz.		

*Derivative data given in order: m.p., crystal color, solvent from which crystallized.

TABLE X. ORGANIC DERIVATIVES OF KETONES

b) Solids (Listed in order of increasing m.p.)* (Continued)

No.	Name	Melting point, °C	Boiling point, °C	Semi-carbazone	2,4-Di-nitrophenyl-hydrazone	p-Nitro-phenyl-hydrazone	Phenyl-hydrazone	Oxime	Miscellaneous
115	Fluorenone..................	83, yel., bz.	341.5	....	283–4	269	151–2, yel., al.	195–6 (cor.)	....
116	4-Iodoacetophenone	85, eth.	153[18]	....	....	....	....	....	....
117	Di-*n*-Heptadecyl ketone	88.5, lgr.; 89	....	....	....	....	....	67; 62–3	....
118	4,4'-Dimethylbenzophenone (Di-4-tolyl ketone)	95, al.	335	143–4	218–9	....	100, yel., al.	163, al.	Hydrazone, 108–10
119	Benzil (Dibenzoyl)	95, yel.	347	*mono*: 174–5 d.; *di*: 243–4d., al.	*di*: 189, yel., al.; 185	*mono*: 192–3, dk. or., ac. a.; *di*: 290, yel., pyr.-eth.	*mono*: 134, yel., al.; *di*: 235, chl. rapid htng.	*α: mono*: 137–8; 140, bz.; *di*: 237	....
120	*β,β*-Diphenylpropiophenone.....	96; 92	....	....	....	....	....	133	....
121	3-Hydroxyacetophenone........	96; 95	296	189–91	261	....	....	....	....
122	4-Chlorophenacyl bromide	96–8	....	....	....	....	....	....	Acetate, 72
123	2,3-Dihydroxyacetophenone (3-Acetylcatechol)............	97–8, dk. yel., bz.-lgr.	....	166–7	....	....	....	96–7	Diacetate, 109, bz.; Di-Me. eth., b.p. 143–4[14] 143–4[14]
124	2-Naphthylglyoxal	98, (hyd.), w.; 109	183[20]	....	....	....	....	....	Diacetate, 150, bz.-pet. eth.; osazone, 184
125	3-Aminoacetophenone.........	98–9, pa. yel., al.	....	196d., w.	....	....	....	192–4, w.-al.	Hydrazone, 98, al.
126	2-Benzoylacrylic acid	99 (anh.); 64 (mono-hyd.)	....	190	....	....	197	168d.	Hydrazone, 185–6, al.
127	Di-2-thenoylmethane..........	100	....	....	....	....	....	....	Cu salt, 263
128	Di-1-naphthyl ketone..........	100	....	....	....	....	....	200	Picrate, 121.5–2.0
129	1,3-Dibenzoylbenzene	101–2, al.	....	....	....	....	....	*mono*: 201; *di*: 70–3	....
130	2-Acetyl-1-hydroxynaphthalene ..	102, gr.-yel., al.; 98, yel., bz.	325 sl. d.	245–50, pa. yel.	....	....	136–7, wh., dil. al.	168–9	Acetate, 107.5; Benzoate, 128, al.
131	Cinnamacetophenone	102, yel., al.	....	....	222, red, ac. a.; 218–9d.	*α*: 135, al.	....	....	....
132	1,3-Cyclohexanedione.........	104	....	....	....	....	....	156	....
133	4-Tolil (4,4'-Dimethylbenzil)	104–5	....	....	....	....	....	225	....
134	2-Propionylphenanthrene	105; 104	....	....	....	....	....	....	Picrate, 107
135	2-Aminobenzophenone	105–6, pa. yel., al.	....	....	....	....	....	156, alk.-stab; 127, a.-stab.	....
136	Benzoylnitromethane..........	106	....	....	....	....	105–5.5, yel., al.	96, w.	....
137	4-Aminoacetophenone	106, w.	294	250, yel. al.	266–7; 263	....	....	147–8, al.	4-Toluenesulfonamide, 203
138	Benzalacenaphthenone........	107, yel., w.-al.	....	....	....	....	....	48	....
139	Benzyl 4-chlorophenyl ketone	108	....	....	....	....	....	123	....
140	4-Bromophenacyl bromide	108–9	....	....	....	....	....	115	Acetate, 72
141	4-Hydroxyacetophenone (4-Acetylphenol)............	109	....	199	210, br., al.	....	151, wh. → yel.	145; 143–4, bz.	Acetate, 54; Benzoate, 134–5, al.
142	*trans*-1,2-Dibenzoylethylene.....	110	....	....	....	....	....	211	....
143	Piperonalacetone.............	110–1, pa. yel.	....	*α*: 217, al.; *β*: 168, bz.	....	....	163	186, al.	....

*Derivative data given in order: m.p., crystal color, solvent from which crystallized.

TABLE X. ORGANIC DERIVATIVES OF KETONES

b) Solids (Listed in order of increasing m.p.)* (Continued)

No.	Name	Melting point, °C	Boiling point, °C	Semi-carbazone	2,4-Di-nitrophenyl-hydrazone	p-Nitro-phenyl-hydrazone	Phenyl-hydrazone	Oxime	Miscellaneous
144	2-Acetyldibenzothiophene	112		235					
145	1,5-Diphenyl-3-pentadienone (Dibenzalacetone)	112; 111		187–90, al.	180, red, ac. a.	173, yel., bz.	152–3; 147–8, yel., al.	142–4	Picrate, 114
146	4,4'-Dimethoxybenzoin (Anisoin)	113, dil. al.		185 (cor.), w.-al.					Acetate, 94–5, al.-pet. eth.
147	1,4-Diacetylbenzene	114	130^3					240	
148	3,4-Dihydroxyacetophenone (4-Acetylcatechol)	116, w.	127–33^{11}					184d., et. ac.	3,4-Diacetate, 91
149	3-Hydroxybenzophenone	116, al.						syn: 76; anti: 126, bz.	
150	α-Hydroxyacetophenone (Phenacyl alcohol; Benzoyl carbinol)	117–8	118^{11}	146–6.5, al.			112, lgr.-eth.	70	Acetate, 49, eth.; Benzoate, 118, dil. al.
151	7-Acenaphthenone	121 (cor.), al.					90, dk., al.	175, al.; 183–4, bz.; di: 222d.	Picrate, 113
152	4-Phenylacetophenone (4-Acetyl-biphenyl; Methyl 4-xenyl ketone)	121, al.	325–7		241.5–2, red-or.			186–7, al.	
153	Piperonalacetophenone (3,4-Methylenedioxychalcone)	122, yel., al.		α: 203–5, abs. al.					Dibromide, 152, bz.-lgr. (1:1); Picrate, 126–8
154	9-Hydroxyxanthene (Xanthydrol)	122–4d.							Heat → Dixanthyl ether, 219; Dixanthyl, 204, lgr.
155	4-Aminobenzophenone	124, w.-al.						168, al.; 127, w.-al.	Hydrazone, 139–40, yel., al.
156	4-Phenylphenacyl bromide	124–5							Acetate, 111
157	2-Naphthoin	126						172	
158	4-Phenylphenacyl chloride	126–7							Acetate, 111
159	Vanillalacetone (4-Hydroxy-3-methoxystyryl methyl ketone)	129, yel., al.			230 (cor.), red		127–8, yel.		
160	Dianisalacetone	129, yel., bz.-pet. eth.			82–3			147–8	
161	4,4'-Dimethoxybenzil (Anisil)	133, yel.		di: 254–5, dil. ac. a.				mono: 133; syn, di: 217; anti, di: 195, bz.	Dihydrazone, 118
162	d,l-Benzoin	133, al.; 129	344	α: 205–6, w.	245, yel., al.; 234		α: 158–9, bz.-lgr.; β: 106	α: 151–2, bz.; β: 99	Acetate, 83, al.; Benzoate, 124–5, 75% al.
163	cis-1,2-Dibenzoylethylene	134						di: 210–1d.	
164	3,4,5-Tribromoacetophenone	134–5, al.		265d., ac. a.			129–34d., yel., pet. eth.		
165	4-Hydroxybenzophenone (4-Benzoylphenol)	134–5, w.		194, bz.	242.4 (cor.), or.		144, pet. eth.	81; Heat → 152	Acetate, 81, al.; Benzoate, 94–5; 115
166	1-Furoin	135; 138–9 (cor.)			216–7, or.-red, al.		79–81, lgr.-bz.	α: 161, al.; β: 102, pa. yel., eth.	Acetate, 76–7; Benzoate, 92–3
167	Mesityl phenyl ketone	137			232				
168	4-Chlorobenzyl phenyl ketone	138						96	

*Derivative data given in order: m.p., crystal color, solvent from which crystallized.

No.	Name	Melting point, °C	Boiling point, °C	Semi-carbazone	2,4-Di-nitrophenyl-hydrazone	p-Nitro-phenyl-hydrazone	Phenyl-hydrazone	Oxime	Miscellaneous
169	α-Anisal-α'-cinnamalacetone....	139, red, al.	....	....	....	....	Pyrazo-line, 155–6, yel., al.	....	Dibromide, 139–40, CS₂; Tetrabromide, 155–6, CS₂
170	4-Aminopropiophenone.........	140, w.	....	....	....	....	....	153, al.	N-Acetyl deriv., 161, w.
171	3,3'-Dibromobenzophenone	141	....	....	....	....	....	181–2d.	....
172	2-Acetylphenanthrene..........	143	....	260	....	....	187–8	....	....
173	Dicinnamalacetone	144, yel., abs. al.	....	....	195.7 (cor.), dk. red	....	166, yel., al.	....	Light → d.
174	1,2-Dibenzoylethane	147	....	....	di: 265	....	mono: 116; di: 179	204	....
175	2,4-Dihydroxyacetophenone (Resacetophenone)..........	147; 144	....	218; 214–20d.	206–8	....	156–8	202–3	2,4-Diacetate, 38; 2,4-Dibenzoate, 81
176	3,5-Dihydroxyacetophenone.....	147–8, w.	....	205–6, al.	....	236–7, red, w.-ac. a.	....	....	3,5-Diacetate, 91–2, lgr.
177	4,4'-Dichlorobenzophenone	147–8	....	....	238–40	....	....	135	....
178	1,2-Dibenzoylbenzene	148	....	....	....	....	....	mono: 150	....
179	9-Benzoylanthracene (9-Anthra-phenone)	148, yel., bz.	....	....	....	....	....	....	H₂SO₄ → brief blue color
180	4-Hydroxypropiophenone.......	148	....	....	229	....	....	....	....
181	5,5-Dimethyl-1,3-cyclo-hexanedione (Methone; Dimedone)................	148–9	....	....	....	....	....	mono: 115; di: 176	....
182	2,3,4,2'-Tetrahydroxybenzo-phenone	149 (anh.); 100 (hyd.), yel., w.	....	....	....	....	....	....	2,3,4,2'-Tetraacetate, 118, al.
183	Anthrone	154, ac. a.	....	....	....	....	....	....	Al. sol. → bl. fluorescence
184	1,4-Dibenzoylbenzene	161, al.	....	....	....	....	....	mono: 212–3; di: 235	....
185	Furil (2,2'-Bifuroyl)	165, yel., bz.	....	....	....	....	mono: 82–3, yel.; di: 184, yel., lgr.	α, mono: 106; β, mono: 97–8; α, di: 100; 166; β, di: 188–90	....
186	Benzanthrone.................	170, yel., al.	....	....	....	....	....	....	H₂SO₄ → or.-red sol., gr. fluorescence
187	Quinhydrone	171, dk. gr., subl.	....	....	....	....	152	161	....
188	2,3,4-Trihydroxyacetophenone (Gallacetophenone).........	172, w.	....	225, rapid htng.	....	....	....	162–3	2,3,4-Triacetate, 85; Picrate, 133
189	Xanthone (Diphenylene ketone oxide)...................	174	350	....	....	....	152	161	....
190	4,4'-Bis(dimethylamino)benzo-phenone	174	....	....	....	....	174–5	233	Hydrazone, 150; Picrate, 156
191	4,4'-Dibromobenzophenone	177	395	....	....	....	....	150–2	Hydrazone, 92–4
192	d,l-Camphor	d, l: 178; d: 179	209; 205	247–8d. (cor.); 236–7, al.	d, l: 164; d: 177, or., al.	217	233	d: 118–9	d: [α]₀²⁰: + 44; Hydrazone, 55
193	3-Acetylindazole.............	182, yel., ac. a.	....	....	>320, red, PhNO₂	....	....	222, bz.-al.	N-Acetyl deriv., 123, ac. a.
194	3,4,5-Trihydroxyacetophenone...	187–8, w.	....	216–7, al.	....	260d., red, w.-ac. a.	....	....	3,4,5-Triacetate, 111–2, lgr.

*Derivative data given in order: m.p., crystal color, solvent from which crystallized.

TABLE X. ORGANIC DERIVATIVES OF KETONES
b) Solids (Listed in order of increasing m.p.)* (Continued)

No.	Name	Melting point, °C	Boiling point, °C	Semi-carbazone	2,4-Di-nitrophenyl-hydrazone	p-Nitro-phenyl-hydrazone	Phenyl-hydrazone	Oxime	Miscellaneous
195	3-Acetylindole	190–1, bz.	. . . .	. . . .	. . . .	. . . .	. . . .	144–7, w.	N-Acetyl deriv., 151, subl., pet. eth.-bz.; Picrate, 183, yel., pet. eth.; Diacetyl deriv., 165–6, bz.
196	2,5,2′,6′-Tetrahydroxybenzo-phenone	200–2d., w.	. . . .	. . . .	. . . .	. . . .	. . . .		2,5,2′,6′-Tetraacetate, 118–9, al.
197	2,5-Dihydroxyacetophenone (Quinacetophenone)	202, yel.-gr., w.	. . . .	. . . .	. . . .	215–6	. . . .	149–50, tol.	2,5-Diacetate, 68, ac. a.
198	2,4,5-Trihydroxyacetophenone. . .	206–7, red	. . . .	. . . .	. . . .	. . . .	. . . .		2,4,5-Triacetate, 165–6, bz.
199	2,3,5-Trihydroxyacetophenone. . .	206–7, yel., ac. a.	. . . .	. . . .	. . . .	241–2d., w.-al.	. . . .		2,3,5-Triacetate, 106–7, lgr.
200	2,4,6-Trihydroxyacetophenone (Phloracetophenone)	219, anh., w.	. . . .	. . . .	. . . .	. . . .	. . . .		2,4,6-Triacetate, 103; 2,4,6-Tribenzoate, 117–8
201	2,3-(3′,4′,5′-Triphenylcyclo-pentadieno)-indone	222	. . . .	. . . .	. . . .	. . . .	246–7	. . . .	. . . .
202	3,4,3′4′-Tetrahydroxybenzo-phenone	227–8, w.	. . . .	. . . .	. . . .	. . . .	. . . .	145, al.	. . . .
203	Ninhydrin (Triketohydrindene hydrate)	243; 241d.	. . . .	. . . .	. . . .	di: 207–8, or.-red, al.	201		Warm aqueous sol. of α-amino acids → intense bl., vlt., etc.; At 125–30, loses w., turns red.
204	Phenacridone	304–5, yel., ac. a.	. . . .	. . . .	. . . .	. . . .	. . . .		N-Benzyl deriv., 188–9, yel., al.

*Derivative data given in order: m.p., crystal color, solvent from which crystallized.

EXPLANATIONS AND REFERENCES TO TABLE XI

The derivatives of quinones are usually similar to those of ketones. Therefore, for directions and examples for their preparation see explanations and references to Tables 9 and 10, pages 141, 142, 143.

The derivatives listed as *phenylhydrazones, p-nitrophenylhydrazones* and *2,4-dinitrophenylhydrazones* of quinones in most cases are not real substituted phenylhydrazones, but either addition compounds or hydroxy derivatives of variously substituted aromatic azo compounds.

*Semicarbazone.**

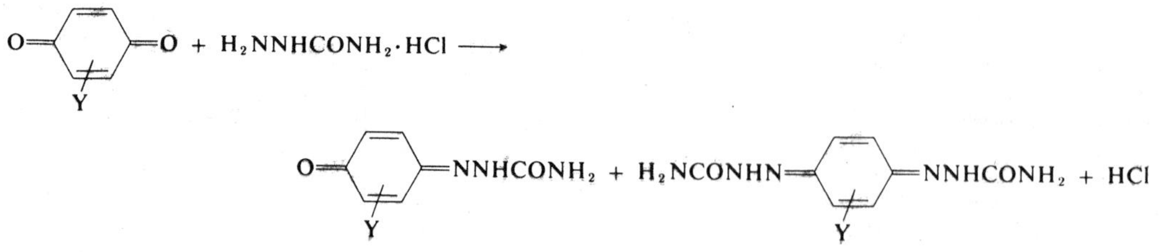

$$O={\Large\bigcirc}=O + H_2NNHCONH_2 \cdot HCl \longrightarrow$$
(Y)

$$O={\Large\bigcirc}=NNHCONH_2 + H_2NCONHN={\Large\bigcirc}=NNHCONH_2 + HCl$$
(Y)   (Y)

Monosemicarbazone   Disemicarbazone

From the quinone with semicarbazide hydrochloride in water.
For directions and examples see: Linstead, p. 30; Vogel, p. 749.

*Oxime.**

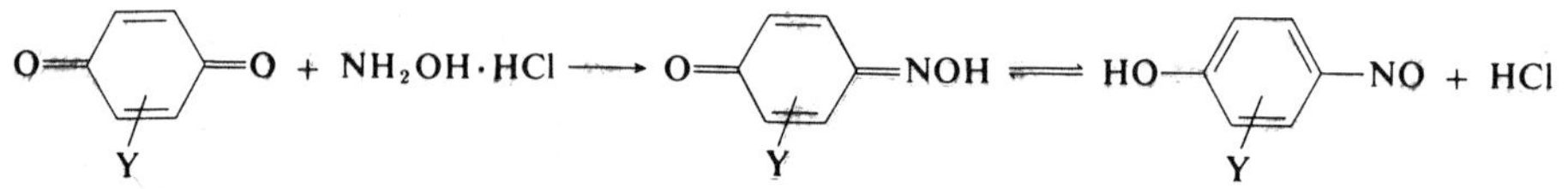

$$O={\Large\bigcirc}=O + NH_2OH \cdot HCl \longrightarrow O={\Large\bigcirc}=NOH \rightleftharpoons HO-{\Large\bigcirc}-NO + HCl$$
(Y)   (Y)   (Y)

Monooxime   Substituted *p*-nitrosophenol

From the quinone with hydroxylamine hydrochloride in water.
For directions and examples see: Linstead, p. 30.

---

*Derivatives recommended for first trial.
WARNING: This is not an instruction manual. References should be consulted for the preparation of derivatives.

TABLE XI. ORGANIC DERIVATIVES OF QUINONES
(Listed in order of increasing m.p.)*

No.	Name	Melting point, °C	Boiling point, °C	Semi-carbazone	2,4-Di-nitrophenyl-hydrazone	p-Nitro-phenyl-hydrazone	Phenyl-hydrazone	Oxime	Miscellaneous
1	**2,3,5-Trimethyl-1,4-benzoquinone**	32, yel., eth.	....	252–3 d., yel.	....	....	....	1-*mono*: 181–2, yel., al.; 4-*mono*: 134, yel.	....
2	**2-Isopropyl-5-methyl-1,4-benzoquinone** (Thymoquinone) .	45.5, or.-yel.	232	*mono*: 201–2d., yel., al.; *di*: 237, yel.	*mono*: 179–80, dk. red, al.	....	93	1-*mono*: 160–2, pa. yel., chl.	....
3	**2,3-Dimethyl-1,4-benzoquinone** (*o*-Xylo-*p*-quinone)..........	55 (subl.), yel.	....	....	....	....	....	*mono*: 166, yel.	....
4	**2-Bromo-1,4-benzoquinone**......	56	....	....	....	....	....	1-*mono*: 184, or.; 4-*mono*: 196	....
5	**2-Chloro-1,4-benzoquinone**......	57, yel.-red	....	4-*mono*: 185d.	....	....	....	1-*mono*: 184, pa. grn.-yel.; 4-*mono*: 148d.	....
6	**2-Methyl-1,4-benzoquinone** (*p*-Toluquinone)	67.6–68.4	....	4-*mono*: 178–9, yel., al.; *di*: 240d., or.-red	*di*: 269, PhNO₂	....	130	*mono*: 134–5d., w.; *di*: 220d., yel.-wh.	....
7	**2,6-Dimethyl-1,4-benzoquinone** (*m*-Xylo-*p*-quinone)	68–71, yel.	....	....	....	....	....	1-*mono*: 175, yel., al.-w.; 4-*mono*: 170–1, yel., bz.	....
8	**4-Chloro-1,2-benzoquinone**......	78, pa. yel.-red, hexane	....	....	....	....	....	*di*: 128, br.	....
9	**2,5-Dimethyl-1,4-naphthoquinone**	94, yel., me. al.	....	....	....	....	*mono*: 226, red, ac. a.	....	....
10	**Dunnione**	98–9, or.-red, w.	....	*mono*: 232–3, w.-me. al.	266–8, or.	....	....	....	$[\alpha]_D^{18}$: +310° in chl.
11	**2-Methyl-1,4-naphthoquinone** ...	106, yel., me. al.	....	....	4-*mono*: 299d.	....	....	*mono*: 160; *di*: 166–8	Benzoyl chloride + Zn dust → 1,4-dibenzyloxy-2-methylnaphthalene, 180.0–0.5, col., al.
12	**Quinone** (1,4-Benzoquinone)	116, yel.; 113	....	*mono*: 166, yel.; 165–6d., red; 178; *di*: 243d., red.	*mono*: 185.6, br., al.; *di*: 231	....	152	240	Picrate, 79; Quinhydrone, 171
13	**2-Chloro-1,4-naphthoquinone**....	117, yel., w.	....	....	....	....	....	4-*mono*: 200 d.; 198, pa. yel., bz.	....
14	**1,4-Naphthoquinone** (*α*-Naphtho-quinone)..................	117–8, yel., al.	....	*mono*: 247, grn.-yel., ac. a.	*mono*: 278, yel., pyr.	*mono*: 277–9, or.-red, PhNO₂	*mono*: 205–6d., dk. vlt., bz.	....	

*Derivative data given in order: m.p., crystal color, solvent from which crystallized.

No.	Name	Melting point, °C	Boiling point, °C	Semi-carbazone	2,4-Dinitro-phenyl-hydrazone	*p*-Nitro-phenyl-hydrazone	Phenyl-hydrazone	Oxime	Miscellaneous
15	2,5-Dimethyl-1,4-benzoquinone .. (*p*-Xylo-*p*-quinone)..........	125, yel., al.	....	....	....	....	122–4, yel.; 154–5, or.	*mono*: 168, yel., w.; *di*: 272, yel., al., 254	Monobenzoylphenyl-hydrazone, 122–4, yel., lgr.
16	2,6-Dibromo-1,4-benzoquinone ..	131, yel., al.	....	4-*mono*: 225d., yel., al.	....	....	....	4-*mono*: 170d., br.	....
17	2,6-Diphenyl-1,4-benzoquinone ..	137–8, red	....	....	....	....	....	242–4d.	
18	2,5-Dihydroxy-3-*n*-dodecyl-1,4-benzoquinone (Embelin)	143, or.-red, eth.-bz.	....	*di*: 236	....	....	*di*: 189–90	*tetra*: 175	Diacetate, 54; Dibenzoate, 97–8
19	1,2-Naphthoquinone (*β*-Naphtho-quinone)..................	145–7d., red, eth.; 120	....	1-*mono*: 184d., yel., al.	....	1-*mono*: 250–1; 2-*mono*: 236, dk. red, ac. a.	2-*mono*: 138, dk. red, al.	1-*mono*: 109.5; 2-*mono*: 162–4d., *di*: 169, yel., al.	....
20	3,7-Dimethyl-1,2-naphthoquinone	151–2, red, al.	....	....	....	....	....	2-*mono*: 222d., or.	....
21	5-Hydroxy-1,4-naphthoquinone (Juglone) ....,...	153–4, or., bz.	....	....	....	....	....	*mono*: 167.0–7.5, red, ac. a.; *di*: 225 (exp.), dk. br., ac. a.	Acetate, 154–5
22	3-Chloro-1,2-naphthoquinone....	172, red, chl.	....	....	....	....	....	1-*mono*: 167–8, or.	....
23	1,8-Dihydroxy-2-methyl-9,10-anthraquinone (2-Methylchry-sazin)	175	....	....	....	....	....	....	Diacetate, 205
24	2-Methyl-9,10-anthraquinone....	177–9; 177, pa. yel.	....	....	....	....	....	....	Diacetate, 217, pa. yel., ac. a.
25	3,5-Dihydroxy-2-methyl-1,4-naphthoquinone (Droserone) ...	181, pa. yel., al.	....	....	....	....	....	*di*: 151	Diacetate, 119, me. al.
26	2,3,4-Trihydroxy-9,10-phenan-thraquinone	185d., br.-red	....	*mono*: 270d., br.-red, al.	....	....	....	....	Phenazine, 255d., br., al.
27	6-Bromo-1,4-dihydroxy-9,10-anthraquinone (6-Bromo-quinizarin)................	185.5, red-br., bz.	....	....	....	....	....	....	Di-Me. eth., 176.5, or.-yel., al.; Diacetate, 220.5, yel., al.
28	1,2-Anthraquinone............	185–90d., or.-br.	....	....	....	....	....	1-*mono*: 188d., or.-br.; 2-*mono*: 200d., or.-br.	....
29	4-Chloro-1,2-naphthoquinone....	188, red-br., bz.	....	....	....	....	....	2-*mono*: 157, pa. yel.	....
30	7-Isopropyl-1-methyl-9,10-phenanthraquinone (Retene-quinone)...................	197, or., al.	....	*mono*: 200, yel., pyr.	....	*mono*: 222–3, red, ac. a.	*mono*: 160, or., bz.-al.	*mono*: 128.5; 130–1 (cor.), yel., al.	....

*Derivative data given in order: m.p., crystal color, solvent from which crystallized.

No.	Name	Melting point, °C	Boiling point, °C	Semi-carbazone	2,4-Dinitro-phenyl-hydrazone	p-Nitro-phenyl-hydrazone	Phenyl-hydrazone	Oxime	Miscellaneous
31	Camphorquinone	199, yel., dil. al.	....	3-mono (α): 236d., al.	mono: 36; di: 190	239	183–90, pa. yel., al.; 170	mono: α: 153; β: 114–5; di: (four forms): α: 201d.; β: 248d.; γ: 136; δ: 194d.	3-p-Bromophenylhydrazone, 215–6, ac. a.; Hydrazone, 182
32	1-Hydroxy-9,10-anthraquinone	200, or.-red, al.; 193	subl.	....	....	....	....	....	Acetate, 176–9, yel., al.
33	1,4-Dihydroxy-9,10-anthra-quinone (Quinizarin)	200–2 (cor.), red, ac. a.; 195	....	....	....	....	....	....	Diacetate, 207.8, yel., pyr.; 200–1, yel., ac. anh.
34	9,10-Phenanthraquinone	206–7.5, or.-yel.; 208, or.	>360; subl. → or.-red	mono: 220d.	mono: 312–3d., dk. red	mono: 245, red, xyl.	mono: 165, dk. red, al.	mono: 158, grn.-yel., al.; di: 202d.	Conc. H₂SO₄ → dull grn.
35	1,4-Anthraquinone	218d., yel.; turns dark at 200–10	....	....	....	....	....	233, br.; turns dark at 205	....
36	4-Chloro-1,2,3-trihydroxy-9,10-anthraquinone	233, yel.	....	....	....	....	....	....	Triacetate, 187, yel.; Conc. H₂SO₄ → red
37	2-Bromo-9,10-phenanthraquinone	233–4, red-yel., ac. a.	....	....	....	....	....	mono: 163–4, or.	....
38	1-Bromo-9,10-phenanthraquinone	233–4, yel.	....	....	....	....	....	mono: 213d.	....
39	Chrysoquinone (Chrysene-quinone)	239.5, red	....	....	....	....	....	mono: 161, or.	Conc. H₂SO₄ → bl.
40	1,2,8-Trihydroxy-9,10-anthra-quinone (2-Hydroxychrysazin)	239–40, red, ac. a.	....	....	....	....	....	....	Triacetate, 224, yel.; 2-Me. eth., 220, or., chl.-me. al.; 2,8-Di-Me. eth., 193, br.-yel., chl.-me. al.; 1,2,8-Tri-Me. eth., 157, yel., me. al.
41	1-Amino-9,10-anthraquinone	251, or.-red	....	....	....	....	....	....	N-Acetyl, 218, or.-red; N-Benzoyl, 255, grn.; N-p-Toluenesulfonyl, 228–9
42	3-Amino-9,10-phenanthraquinone	254, dk. red-br., al.	....	....	....	....	....	mono: 247d., red-br.	....
43	1,2,4-Trihydroxy-9,10-anthra-quinone	259, dk. red, abs. al.	....	....	....	....	....	....	2-Me. eth., 232–3, red, bz.; 2,4-Di-Me. eth. 186–9, or.; 2-Acetate, 179–80, or., al.; Triacetate, 198–200 (sinters 193), pa. yel.
44	Acenaphthenequinone	261 (cor.), yel., ac. a.	....	mono: 192–3, ac. a.; di: 271, al.	....	mono: 247, or.-red, ac. a.	mono: 179, or.-red, al., di: 219, dk. yel., al.	mono: 230, dil. al.; 220d.	....

* Derivative data given in order: m.p., crystal color, solvent from which crystallized.

No.	Name	Melting point, °C	Boiling point, °C	Semi-carbazone	2,4-Dinitro-phenyl-hydrazone	p-Nitro-phenyl-hydrazone	Phenyl-hydrazone	Oxime	Miscellaneous
45	**1,3-Dihydroxy-4-methyl-9,10-anthraquinone** (4-Methylpurpuroxanthin)	265–6, or., bz.	....	....				....	Di-Me. eth., 162, yel., chl.; Diacetate, 181–2, yel., ac. a.
46	**2-Bromo-1,4-dihydroxy-9,10-anthraquinone** (2-Bromoquinizarin)	265–8, br.-red	....						Diacetate, 226–9, yel.
47	**3-Bromo-9,10-phenanthraquinone**	268, dk.-yel., ac. a.	....	*mono:* 242d.			*mono:* 177, red	*mono:* 198; *di:* 212d., grn.	....
48	**Aceanthrenequinone** (3,4-Benzacenaphthenequinone)	270, red, bz.	....				*mono:* 203, or., bz.	*mono:* 251d., yel., ac. a.	subl.
49	**1,2,5-Trihydroxy-9,10-anthraquinone** (Hydroxyanthrarufin)	273–4, red, ac. a.	....					....	2-Me. eth., 229, yel., al.; 1,2-Di-Me. eth., 231, or., al.; 1,2,5-Tri-Me. eth., 203–4, yel., al.; Triacetate, 228–9, yel., al.
50	**1,5-Dihydroxy-9,10-anthraquinone** (Anthrarufin)	280 (subl.), pa. yel.	379–81					....	Diacetate, 245d., pa. yel., ac. a.
51	**Chloranilic acid** (2,5-Dichloro-3,6-dihydroxy-1,4-benzoquinone)	283–4, red, w. ($+2H_2O$)	....						Di-Me. eth., 141–2, red; Di-Et. eth., 107, red; Diacetate, 182.5, yel.
52	**9,10-Anthraquinone**	286	382; 376.8 (cor.)					*mono:* 224, pa. yel., (rapid htng.)	Diacetate, 260, col., ac. a.
53	**Chloranil** (2,3,5,6-Tetrachloro-1,4-benzoquinone)	290, yel., ac. a., (slow htng., sealed tube)	subl.	....					SO_2—Tetrachlorohydroquinone; In w.-alkali sol. → alkali salts of chloranilic acid
54	**Alizarin** (1,2-Dihydroxy-9,10-anthraquinone)	290, or., al.	430	....					2-Benzoate, 214–6, al.; 2-*p*-Bromobenzoate, 195, yel.; Diacetate, 184, yel., al.; Di-Me. eth., 215
55	**2-Amino-9,10-phenanthraquinone**	>300, dk. vlt., w.; sinters at 205–10	....						N-Acetyl, 324, dk. red-vlt., $PhNO_2$; N-Benzoyl, 297–8, br.-red, $PhNO_2$
56	**3-Aminoalizarin** (3-Amino-1,2-dihydroxy-9,10-anthraquinone)	>300, dk. red, ac. a.	....						N-Acetyl, 238–40, yel.-br.; Monobenzoyl, 275, dk. yel.; Dibenzoyl, 252, yel.
57	**1,4-Diamino-5,8-dihydroxy-9,10-anthraquinone** (5,8-Diaminoquinizarin)	>300, br.-vlt., $PhNO_2$	....						N,N′-Dibenzoyl, 284–5, br.-vlt., xyl.; N,N′-Diphenyl, 258–60, dk. bl., bz.-lgr.; 1,4-Di-Me. eth., 250d., vlt.-blk., ac. a.
58	**Dianthraquinone** (9,9′-Dianthranyl-10,10′-quinone)	>300, yel.	....						Conc. H_2SO_4 → vlt.-red; CrO_3 → Anthraquinone; Zn dust + ac. a. → dianthranol, 230 (enol), 250 (keto)

*Derivative data given in order: m.p., crystal color, solvent from which crystallized.

No.	Name	Melting point, °C	Boiling point, °C	Semi-carbazone	2,4-Dinitro-phenyl-hydrazone	p-Nitro-phenyl-hydrazone	Phenyl-hydrazone	Oxime	Miscellaneous
59	**2-Amino-9,10-anthraquinone**	306; 303–6, red, al.	. . . .	. . . .	. . . .	. . . .	. . . .	. . . .	N-Acetyl, 262, yel., N,N-Diacetyl, 258, yel., ac. a.; N-Benzoyl, 227–8, yel., ac. a.
60	**2-Hydroxy-9,10-anthraquinone** . .	305, yel., al.	306	. . . .	. . . .	. . . .	. . . .	. . . .	Acetate, 159–60, al.; Benzoate, 202–4, ac. a.
61	**1,2,3-Trihydroxy-9,10-anthra-quinone** (Anthragallol)	313–4d., br.-or. (290, subl.)	. . . .	. . . .	. . . .	. . . .	. . . .	. . . .	Triacetate, 181–2, yel., al.; 188–9, pyr.; 2,3-Di-p-toluenesulfonate, 196–8, yel., pyr.; Tri-Me. eth., 167–9, grn.-yel., bz.-pet.; Triacetate, 181–2, yel., ac. a.; Tribenzoate, 213–5, pa. yel., al.-bz.
62	**1,2,6-Trihydroxy-9,10-anthra-quinone** (Flavopurpurin)	>330, (>160, subl.)	. . . .	. . . .	. . . .	. . . .	. . . .	. . . .	2,6-Di-Me. eth., 239, yel.; 1,2,6-Tri-Me. eth., 225–6, yel.; Diacetate, 238; Tri-acetate, 202–3
63	**1,2,7-Trihydroxy-9,10-anthra-quinone** (Anthrapurpurin)	369, or., al.	. . . .	. . . .	. . . .	. . . .	. . . .	. . . .	2-Acetate, 296–8, yel., al.; 2,7-Diacetate, 192–3, yel., al.-ac. a.; Triacetate, 223, pa. yel., ac. a.; Tri-Me. eth., 201, yel., al.

*Derivative data given in order: m.p., crystal color, solvent from which crystallized.

EXPLANATIONS AND REFERENCES TO TABLES XII, XIII AND XIV

The derivatives of three classes of compounds (carboxylic acids, acyl halides and acid anhydrides) are essentially the same as those of carboxylic acids, and are prepared either directly from the acid or *via* the acyl halide. All of them appear therefore under the same title.

Hydrolysis of acid halide or acid anhydride to the corresponding carboxylic acid.

$$RCOCl + H_2O \longrightarrow \underset{\text{Acid}}{RCOOH} + HCl$$

$$(RCO)_2O + H_2O \xrightarrow{\text{NaOH}} 2RCOONa \xrightarrow{H^+} \underset{\text{Acid}}{RCOOH}$$

From the acyl halide in water.
For directions and examples see: Wild, p. 180.
From the acyl halide with aqueous sodium hydroxide.
See: Vogel, p. 369; Wild, p. 180.
From the acid anhydride with water.
See: Vogel, p. 376; Wild, p. 184; A. C. D. Rivett and N. V. Sidgwick, *J. Chem. Soc.*, 97, 1677 (1910).
From the acid anhydride with aqueous sodium hydroxide.
See: Linstead, pp. 16–7; Wild, p. 184.

Amide. *

$$RCOOH \xrightarrow{SOCl_2} \underset{\substack{\text{Acid} \\ \text{chloride}}}{RCOCl} \xrightarrow{NH_3} RCONH_2 + NH_4Cl$$

$$RCOOH + NH_3 \longrightarrow RCONH_2$$

$$(RCO)_2O + NH_3 \longrightarrow \underset{\text{Amide}}{RCONH_2}$$

Acid chloride is prepared from the acid and thionyl chloride. Amide is formed on addition of aqueous ammonia.
For directions and examples see: Cheronis, p. 440; Shriner, p. 200; Vogel, p. 361; Wild, p. 181.
From the acid chloride in benzene with aqueous ammonia.
See: D. Swern, J. M. Stutzman and E. T. Roe, *J. Amer. Chem. Soc.*, 71, 3017 (1942).
By passing gaseous ammonia through a benzene or ether solution of the acyl chloride.
See: Linstead, p. 14; Wild, p. 182.
From the neat acid with gaseous ammonia.
See: J. A. Mitchell and E. E. Reid, *J. Amer. Chem. Soc.*, 53, 1879 (1931).
From the acid anhydride with aqueous ammonia.
See: Wild, p. 184, 185.

Anilide. *

$$RCOOH \xrightarrow{SOCl_2} RCOCl \xrightarrow{C_6H_5NH_2} RCONHC_6H_5 + C_6H_5NH_3{}^+Cl^-$$

$$RCOOH + C_6H_5NH_2 \longrightarrow RCONHC_6H_5 + H_2O$$

$$(RCO)_2O + C_6H_5NH_2 \longrightarrow \underset{\text{Anilide}}{RCONHC_6H_5} + C_6H_5NH_3{}^+RCOO^-$$

From the acid chloride (prepared from the acid and thionyl chloride) and aniline in benzene or in ether.
For directions and examples see: Cheronis, p. 445; Linstead, p. 14; Shriner, pp. 98, 200–1; Vogel, pp. 361, 369, 458; Wild, p. 182; P. W. Robertson, *J. Chem. Soc.*, 115, 1210 (1919).
From the acid chloride with aniline in aqueous sodium hydroxide.
See: Wild, pp. 181, 219.
From the acid and aniline at high temperatures.
See: Vogel, p. 362.

*Derivatives recommended for first trial.
WARNING: This is not an instruction manual. References should be consulted for the preparation of derivatives.

From the sodium salt of the acid with aniline and concentrated hydrochloric acid.
See: Shriner, p. 201; Wild, p. 154.
From the acid anhydride with aniline without solvent.
See: Linstead, p. 17; Vogel, p. 377; Wild, p. 185.
From the acid anhydride with aniline in benzene.
See: Linstead, p. 15; Wild, p. 185.

p-Toluidide. *

$$RCOOH \xrightarrow{SOCl_2} RCOCl \xrightarrow{p\text{-}CH_3C_6H_4NH_2} RCONHC_6H_4CH_3\text{-}p + p\text{-}CH_3C_6H_4NH_3{}^+Cl^-$$

$$RCOOH + p\text{-}CH_3C_6H_4NH_2 \longrightarrow RCONHC_6H_4CH_3\text{-}p + H_2O$$

$$(RCO)_2O + p\text{-}CH_3C_6H_4NH_2 \longrightarrow RCONHC_6H_4CH_3\text{-}p + p\text{-}CH_3C_6H_4NH_3{}^+RCOO^-$$

From the acid chloride with *p*-toluidine in ether or benzene.
For directions and examples see: Cheronis, pp. 441, 444, 458; Linstead, p. 14; Shriner, pp. 200–1; Vogel, p. 361.
From the acid and *p*-toluidine at high temperatures.
See: Cheronis, pp. 441, 442–3; Vogel, p. 362.
From the sodium salt of the acid, *p*-toluidine and concentrated hydrochloric acid.
See: Shriner, p. 201; Wild, p. 154.
From the acid anhydride with *p*-toluidine without solvent.
See: Cheronis, p. 459; Linstead, p. 17.
From the acid anhydride with *p*-toluidine in benzene.
See: Wild, p. 185.

1- and 2-Naphthylamide. *

$$RCOOH \xrightarrow{SOCl_2} RCOCl \xrightarrow{1\text{- or }2\text{-}C_{10}H_7NH_2} RCONHC_{10}H_7 + C_{10}H_7NH_3{}^+Cl^-$$

Naphthylamide
(1- or 2-)

From the acid chloride with the naphthylamine.
For directions and examples see: Cheronis, p. 446; P. W. Robertson, *J. Chem. Soc.*, **115**, 1210 (1919).

p-Nitrobenzyl ester. *

$$RCOONa + p\text{-}NO_2C_6H_4CH_2X \rightarrow RCOOCH_2C_6H_4NO_2\text{-}p + NaX \quad (X = Cl, Br, I)$$

p-Nitrobenzyl ester

From an aqueous solution of the sodium salt of the acid, with the *p*-nitrobenzyl halide in ethanol.
For directions and examples see: Cheronis, pp. 447, 448; Shriner, p. 200; Vogel, p. 362; Wild, pp. 144–5.
From an aqueous solution of the sodium salt of the acid with *p*-nitrobenzyl bromide in acetone.
See: F. F. Blicke and F. D. Smith, *J. Amer. Chem. Soc.*, **51**, 1947 (1929).
From the sodium or the potassium salt of the acid and *p*-nitrobenzyl bromide in 1:2 water-ethanol.
See: E. E. Reid, *J. Amer. Chem. Soc.*, **39**, 124 (1917).
From the sodium or the potassium salt of the acid and *p*-nitrobenzyl chloride or iodide in 1:2 water-ethanol.
See: J. A. Lyman and E. E. Reid, *J. Amer. Chem. Soc.*, **39**, 701 (1917).

p-Bromophenacyl ester. *

$$RCOONa + p\text{-}BrC_6H_4COCH_2Br \longrightarrow RCOOCH_2COC_6H_4Br\text{-}p + NaCl$$

p-Bromophenacyl
bromide

$$RCOOH + p\text{-}BrC_6H_4COCHN_2 \xrightarrow{CuCl_2} RCOOCH_2COC_6H_4Br\text{-}p + N_2$$

p-Bromodiazoaceto-
phenone

p-Bromophenacyl ester

From the sodium salt of the acid and *p*-bromophenacyl bromide in aqueous ethanol.

*Derivatives recommended for first trial.
WARNING: This is not an instruction manual. References should be consulted for the preparation of derivatives.

For directions and examples see: Cheronis, pp. 447, 448; Linstead, p. 14; Shriner, p. 200; Vogel, p. 362; Wild, p. 146.

From the sodium salt of the acid (neutralization with sodium carbonate) with *p*-bromophenacyl halide in 1:2 water-ethanol.

See: W. L. Judefind and E. E. Reid, *J. Amer. Chem. Soc.*, **41**, 1043 (1920).

From the sodium salt of the acid (neutralization with sodium hydroxide) with *p*-bromophenacyl bromide in 95% ethanol.

See: R. M. Hann, E. E. Reid and G. S. Jamieson, *J. Amer. Chem. Soc.*, **52**, 818 (1930); C. G. Moses and E. E. Reid, *J. Amer. Chem. Soc.*, **54**, 2101 (1930).

From the acid and *p*-bromodiazoacetophenone in dioxane in the presence of catalytic amounts of cupric chloride.

See: J. L. E. Erickson, J. M. Dechary and M. R. Kesling, *J. Amer. Chem. Soc.*, **73**, 5301 (1951).

p-Phenylphenacyl ester.*

$$RCOONa + p\text{-}C_6H_5C_6H_4COCH_2Br \longrightarrow RCOOCH_2COC_6H_4C_6H_5\text{-}p + NaBr$$

p-Phenylphenacyl bromide

$$RCOOH + p\text{-}C_6H_5C_6H_4COCHN_2 \xrightarrow{\text{CuCl}_2} RCOOCH_2COC_6H_4C_6H_5\text{-}p + N_2$$

p-Phenyldiazoaceto-
phenone

p-Phenylphenacyl ester

From the sodium salt of the acid (neutralization with sodium carbonate) and *p*-phenylphenacyl bromide in aqueous alcohol.

For directions and examples see: Linstead, p. 14; Vogel, p. 363; N. L. Drake and J. Bronitsky, *J. Amer. Chem. Soc.*, **52**, 3715 (1930).

From the sodium salt of the acid (neutralization with sodium hydroxide) and *p*-phenylphenacyl bromide in aqueous alcohol.

See: Shriner, p. 200; N. L. Drake and J. P. Sweeney, *J. Amer. Chem. Soc.*, **54**, 2059 (1932).

For dibasic acids: from the acid, ethylamine and *p*-phenylphenacyl bromide in aqueous ethanol.

See: Wild, p. 147; N. L. Drake and J. P. Sweeney, *J. Amer. Chem. Soc.*, **54**, 2059 (1932).

From the acid and *p*-phenyldiazoacetophenone in dioxane in the presence of catalytic amounts of cupric chloride.

See: J. L. E. Erickson, J. M. Dechary and M. R. Kesling, *J. Amer. Chem. Soc.*, **73**, 5301 (1951).

Methyl ester.

$$RCOOH + CH_3OH \xrightarrow{\text{H}_2\text{SO}_4} RCOOCH_3 + H_2O$$

$$RCOOH + CH_2N_2 \longrightarrow RCOOCH_3 + N_2$$

Methyl ester

From the acid with methanol and a catalytic amount of sulfuric acid.

For directions and examples see: Linstead, p. 16; Vogel, p. 383.

From the acid and diazomethane in ether.

See: B. Eistert, in *Newer Methods of Preparative Organic Chemistry*, Interscience, New York, 1948, p. 513.

Ethyl ester.

$$RCOOH + C_2H_5OH \longrightarrow RCOOC_2H_5 + H_2O$$

$$RCOOAg + C_2H_5I \longrightarrow RCOOC_2H_5 + AgI$$

$$RCOOH \xrightarrow{\text{SOCl}_2} RCOCl \xrightarrow{\text{C}_2\text{H}_5\text{OH}} RCOOC_2H_5 + HCl$$

Ethyl ester

From the acid and ethanol in the presence of a catalytic amount of sulfuric acid.

For directions and examples see: Vogel, pp. 383, 385, 386, 387.

From the silver salt of the acid with ethyl iodide.

See: Vogel, p. 388.

*Derivatives recommended for first trial.
WARNING: This is not an instruction manual: References should be consulted for the preparation of derivatives.

From the acid chloride and ethanol.

See: Vogel, p. 389.

NOTE: The same methods can be used for the formation of other esters.

*S-Benzylthiuronium salt.**

$$RCOONa \ + \ [C_6H_5CH_2SC(NH_2)_2]^+Cl^- \ \rightarrow \ [C_6H_5CH_2SC(NH_2)_2]^+RCOO^- \ + \ NaCl$$

S-Benzylthiuronium chloride   S-Benzylthiuronium salt

From the sodium or the potassium salt of the acid and S-benzylthiuronium chloride in water.

For directions and examples see: Linstead, p. 15; Vogel, p. 36; Wild, p. 149; S. Veibel and H. Lillelund, *Bull. Soc. Chim.* [5], **5**, 1153 (1938), S. Veibel and K. Ottung, *Bull. Soc. Chim.* **6**, 1434 (1939).

From the sodium or the potassium salt of the acid in water or in aqueous ethanol with an ethanolic solution of S-benzylthiuronium chloride.

See: Cheronis, p. 449; Shriner, p. 202; J. J. Donleavy, *J. Amer. Chem. Soc.,* **58**, 1004 (1936).

Phenylhydrazide.

$$RCOOH \ + \ H_2NNHC_6H_5 \ \rightarrow \ RCONHNHC_6H_5 \ + \ H_2O$$

Phenylhydrazide

From the acid with phenylhydrazine without solvent.

For directions and examples see: Shriner, p. 201; Wild, p. 152; G. H. Stempel and G. S. Schaffel, *J. Amer. Chem. Soc.,* **64**, 470 (1942).

From the acid with phenylhydrazine in benzene.

See: Shriner, p. 201; Wild, p. 152.

*Derivatives recommended for first trial.

WARNING: This is not an instruction manual. References should be consulted for the preparation of derivatives.

TABLE XII. ORGANIC DERIVATIVES OF CARBOXYLIC ACIDS

a) Liquids 1) (Listed in order of increasing atmospheric b.p.)*

No.	Name	Boiling point, °C	Melting point, °C	n_D^{20}	D_4^{20}	p-Toluidide	Anilide	p-Bromophenacyl ester	Amide	Methyl ester	Ethyl ester	Miscellaneous
1	Thioacetic acid	93	....	....	1.0744^{10}	130	76	....	108	......	....	
2	Formic acid	100.7	8.4	1.37137	1.22026	53	50	140; 135	.....	......	....	p-Nitrobenzyl ester, 31
3	Acetic acid (Ethanoic acid)	118.2	16.6	1.36976; 1.3721	1.04926	153; 147	114	86.0	82	......	....	p-Nitrobenzyl ester, 78
4	Difluoroacetic acid	134–5	....	....		......	......	....	52	......	....	
5	Acrylic acid	141; 140	13	1.4224	1.0621^{16}_4	141	104–5, w.	....	84–5, pet. eth.			
6	Propionic acid (Propanoic acid)	141	−20.8	1.3868	0.99336	126; 123	106	63.4	81	......	....	p-Nitrobenzyl ester, 31
7	Propiolic acid	144d.	18	....	1.139^{15}_{15}	......	87	....	61–2			
8	Isobutyric acid (Isobutanoic acid)	154.7	−46.1	1.3920	0.94791	108.5–9.5	105	76.8	128; 129			
9	Methacrylic acid	161	16	1.429	1.015	......	......		102–6			p-Bromoanilide, 116
10	n-Butyric acid (n-Butanoic acid)	162.5; 164	−5.5; −8	1.3983; 1.3979	0.95790	75	96; 97	63	115–6			p-Nitrobenzyl ester, 35
11	Pyruvic acid (α-Oxopropionic acid)	165d.; 80^{25}	13.6	1.4138	1.2668^{15}_4	109; 130	104, subl.	....	124–5; 145			2,4-Dinitrophenylhydrazone, 218, yel., al.
12	Vinylacetic acid (3-Butenoic acid)	169; 163	−35	1.4221	1.0094	......	58		73			....
13	Isocrotonic acid (cis-(β)-Crotonic acid; cis-2-Butenoic acid)	169	15	1.4456	1.0265	132	101–2	81	101–2			
14	d,l-2-Methylbutanoic acid (Ethylmethylacetic acid)	176–7; 174	....	1.4052	0.9382^{20}_{20}	92.5–3.0	110	55	112			
15	Isovaleric acid (3-Methylbutanoic acid)	176.5	−30.0	1.4043	0.92623	106–7	109.5 (cor.)	68.0	135; 137			
16	n-Amylpropiolic acid (1-Heptyne-1-carboxylic acid)	180–220d.	f.p.: 2–5	....		68, bz.			91			Nitrile, b.p.: 194–6; o-Toluidide, 60, pet. eth.
17	3,3-Dimethylbutanoic acid (tert-Butylacetic acid)	184; 96^{26}	6.7	1.4096	0.9124	134	132, et. ac.-pet. eth.	....	132	b.p.: 126		....
18	d,l-α-Chloropropionic acid	186	....	....		124	92		80			
19	Cyclopropanecarboxylic acid	186; 182–4	17; 18–9	1.43901	1.0885	......	......		125		b.p.: 134; n_D^{20}: 1.41902; D_4^{15}: 0.96078	....
20	n-Pentanoic acid (n-Valeric acid)	186.4	−34.5	1.4086	0.93922	74	63	75	106	......		....
21	2,2-Dimethylbutanoic acid (Dimethylethylacetic acid)	187; 190	−15.0	1.4141; 1.4145	0.9276	83.0–.5	92; 90–1		103		....	p-Phenylphenacyl ester, 86
22	Allylacetic acid (4-Pentenoic acid)	188–9	....	1.4341^7; 1.4283	0.9843^{18}_4	......	......		94, b.p.: 230		b.p.: 144–6	....
23	Cyclopropylacetic acid	190^{750}	....	1.4320^{25}	....							p-Phenylphenacyl ester, 83
24	d,l-2,3-Dimethylbutanoic acid (Isopropylmethylacetic acid)	191.7	−1.5	1.4146	0.9275	112.6	78.4	....	132			p-Phenylphenacyl ester, 74
25	Dichloroacetic acid	194	5–6	1.4659	1.5634	153	118	99	98, subl.	......	....	

*Derivative data given in order: m.p., crystal color, solvent from which crystallized.

TABLE XII. ORGANIC DERIVATIVES OF CARBOXYLIC ACIDS

a) Liquids 1) (Listed in order of increasing atmospheric b.p.)* (Continued)

No.	Name	Boiling point, °C	Melting point, °C	n_D^{20}	D_4^{20}	p-Toluidide	Anilide	p-Bromophenacyl ester	Amide	Methyl ester	Ethyl ester	Miscellaneous
26	**Cyclobutanecarboxylic acid** ..	195	1.4403[25]	1.0599	....	......	......	....	152–3	b.p.: 136.0 –.5	b.p.: 159–62	....
27	**2-Ethylbutanoic acid** (Diethylacetic acid)	195	−31.8	1.4132	0.9239	116.2	127.5	....	112; 107	......		
28	**d,l-2-Methylpentanoic acid** (Methyl-n-propylacetic acid)	195–6	......	1.4136	0.9230	81	95		79.6			
29	**d,l-3-Methylpentanoic acid** ...	197.5	−41.6	1.4159	0.9262	74.8	87; 88	....	124.9			
30	**4-Methylpentanoic acid** (Iso-caproic acid; Isobutylacetic acid)	199.1[752]	−33	1.4144	0.9225	63.0	112.0; 110.5; 111.5	77.3	120–1			
31	**Methoxyacetic acid** (Glycolic acid methyl ether)	204; 203	......	1.41677	1.1768	......	58, pet. eth.		96.5–7.0; 92–4			....
32	**2-Ethyl-2-methylbutanoic acid** (Diethylmethylacetic acid) ..	204	......	1.4256	....	....	......	....	78			
33	**Hexanoic acid** (n-Caproic acid)	205.35	−3.9; f.p.: −1.5–2	1.41635	0.93568	74–5	94–5	72.0	100; 101		b.p.: 166–7	
34	**Ethoxyacetic acid** (Glycolic acid ethyl ether)	206–7	......	1.41937	1.1021	32, eth.	95; 92	104.8	80–2			
35	**5-Methylhexanoic acid**	207[752]		1.4220	....	......	75		103			
36	**2-Ethylpentanoic acid** (Ethyl-n-propylacetic acid) ..	209	......	......	....	129	94	....	104–5			
37	**2-Methylhexanoic acid** (n-Butylmethylacetic acid).	209.6	......	1.4189[25]	....	85	98		73; 70–2.5			
38	**α-Chloroisovaleric acid**	20–2	......	......	....	....	......	....			b.p.: 178–9	Nitrile, b.p.: 154–5; Chloride, b.p.: 149
39	**α-Bromobutanoic acid**	217d.	......	......	....	92	98	....	112; 108			....
40	**4-Methylhexanoic acid**	217–8[754]		1.4211	0.9194	......	76.5		98			
41	**2,2-Dimethylhexanoic acid** ...	218	......	......	....	......	......	....	89			
42	**4-Ethyl-4-methylbutanoic acid** (active-Amylacetic acid).	221	......		0.9149				b.p.: 158–64	b.p.: 173–9	$[\alpha]_D^{15}$: +7.6 in me. al.	
43	**2-Chloro-n-valeric acid** (2-Chloropentanoic acid)	222	......	......	....	....	......	....	b.p.: 160	b.p.: 185–6	Nitrile, b.p.: 160	
44	**n-Heptanoic acid** (n-Heptoic acid)	223.0	−7.46	1.4234	0.91808	81	70; 65	72.0	96; 96.5	......	....	
45	**2-Ethylhexanoic acid** (α-Ethylcaproic acid)	228	......	......	....	....	......	....	102		p-Phenylphenacyl ester, 53–4; 49.5–50	
46	**Cyclohexylacetic acid**	237							172			
47	**n-Caprylic acid** (n-Octanoic acid)	237; 239.3	16.3	1.4268	0.90884	70	57	67.4	110; 106		b.p.: 207–8[753]	....
48	**Pelargonic acid** (n-Nonanoic acid)	254.4	12.3	1.43446[15] He, yel.	0.90552	84	57	68.5	99			
49	**d-Citronellic acid** (2,6-Dimethyl-1-octene-8-carboxylic acid)	257	......		0.9308	......	......	....	84–5		b.p.: 113–5[12]; $[\alpha]_D^{16}$: +0.3	$[\alpha]_D$: +21; Nitrile, b.p.: 230, D^{20}: 0.8645
50	**2-Phenylpropionic acid**	265	......						92			
51	**4-Acetylbutanoic acid** (γ-Acetobutyric acid)	275d.; 195–200[65]	13–4	......		123, w.	......		114, chl.		......	Semicarbazone, 175d. (+1 H_2O), w.; Oxime, 104–5. bz.

*Derivative data given in order: m.p., crystal color, solvent from which crystallized.

TABLE XII. ORGANIC DERIVATIVES OF CARBOXYLIC ACIDS

a) Liquids 2) (Reduced pressure b.p. only) (Listed in order of increasing amide m.p.)*

No.	Name	Amide	Boiling point, °C	Melting point, °C	n_D^{20}	D_4^{20}	p-Tolui-dide	Anilide	p-Bromo-phenacyl ester	Methyl ester	Ethyl ester	Miscellaneous
1	3-Ethoxypropionic acid ...	51	120[17]	....	1.4216	....	....	....	....	....	....	....
2	3-Heptynoic acid	67	102[2]	14	1.4635[25]	....	....	....	....	....	....	....
3	2-Heptynoic acid	68–9, al.	135[20]	....	1.4619	0.978	....	....	....	b.p.: 91–3[19]; n_D^{20}: 1.4455; D_4^{20}: 0.937	....	....
4	trans-Oleic acid	75–6	216[5]; 250 (super-heated steam)	α: 13.36; β: 16.25	1.4597	....	42.5	41	40; 46	....	....	....
5	2-Fluoropropionic acid....	76	60[8]	....	....	....	....	....	....	....	....	....
6	2-Azidoisovaleric acid (2-Triazoisovaleric acid).	78–9, bz.	82[0.1]	....	....	1.0638[33/33]	.....	....	....	....	b.p.: 82[16]; D_{20}^{20}: 1.0295	....
7	d,l-Lactic acid..........	78.5–9.0 (cor.), bz.-al. (3:1)	122[15]	18	....	....	107	58.5–9.0, w.	112.8	144–8	154	....
8	d,l-2-Azidopropionic acid (d,l-2-Triazopropionic acid)	80, bz.	121.5[20]	....	....	....	....	....	....	....	b.p.: 70[16]; n_D^{25}: 1.428–57; D_{23}^{23}: 1.065	Explodes on heating
9	2-Ethyl-3-Hexenoic acid ..	80	132[19]	....	....	....	....	....	....	....	....	....
10	4-Phenoxybutanoic acid...	80	197[18]	....	....	....	....	....	....	....	....	....
11	2-Methoxypropionic acid..	81	89[10]	....	....	....	....	....	....	....	....	....
12	l-Citronellic acid (2,6-Dimethyl-1-octen-8-carboxylic acid)...........	84–5	117.9[0.6]	....	1.4563[24]	0.9274[25]	93–4	76	....	b.p.: 86[1.1]	....	$[α]_D^{24}$: –6.6
13	2-Ethyl-4-methylpentanoic acid (Ethylisobutylacetic acid)	89	115[20]	....	....	....	....	....	....	....	....	....
14	2-Octynoic acid	90	133[10]	....	1.4595	....	....	60	....	....	....	....
15	6-Methyloctanoic acid	91	149[23]	....	1.4337	....	....	....	....	....	....	....
17	3-Methylhexanoic acid ...	98	112[16]	....	1.4222	....	....	....	....	....	....	....
18	2,3-Dimethylpentanoic acid	102	92[15]	....	....	....	....	....	....	....	....	....
19	2-Cyanopropionic acid....	105; 81	142–5[11]	....	....	....	....	....	....	....	b.p.: 192–3	....
20	7-Methyloctanoic acid	106	105[2]	....	....	....	....	....	....	....	....	....
21	1-Chlorocyclohexane carboxylic acid	110, me. al.-w.	138–40[13]	....	....	....	....	....	....	....	....	Ethylamide, 53
22	2-Cyanobutanoic acid	113	153–5[15]	....	....	....	....	....	....	....	b.p.: 207–9	....
23	Methylneopentylacetic acid	123	108[14]	....	....	....	....	....	....	....	....	....
24	2-Isopropylbutanoic acid (2-Ethyl-3-methylbutanoic acid)	135	105[15]	....	....	....	....	....	....	....	....	....
25	5-Cyclopentylpentanoic acid	136	123[4.5]	....	....	....	....	....	....	....	....	....
26	2-Methylcyclopentane-carboxylic acid	148	107[9]	....	1.4504[22]	....	....	....	....	....	....	....
27	3,4,4-Trimethylpentanoic acid	167	98[4]	....	1.4320[21]	....	....	....	....	....	....	....
28	cis-4-Methylcyclohexane-carboxylic acid	175	130[13]	....	....	....	....	....	....	....	....	....
29	Cyclopentanecarboxylic acid	179	123[27]	....	....	....	....	....	....	....	....	....

*Derivative data given in order: m.p., crystal color, solvent from which crystallized.

No.	Name	Melting point, °C	Boiling point, °C	p-Toluidide	Anilide	p-Nitrobenzyl ester	p-Bromophenacyl ester	Amide	Methyl ester	Ethyl ester	Miscellaneous
1	β-Bromobutyric acid (β-Bromobutanoic acid)	20	122[16]	....	....	....	....	92–3	....	b.p.: 183–4	....
2	trans-β-Ethyl-α-methylacrylic acid	24	112[12] cis: 94[10]	....	....	....	91; cis: 46	80	....	....	n_D^{20}: 1.4578; cis: n_D^{25}: 1.4485
3	d,l-α-Azidobutyric acid (d,l-α-Triazobutyric acid)	24	81[0.2]	....	....	....	....	38–9, bz.-pet. eth.	....	b.p.: 64[7], D_{20}^{20}: 1.038	....
4	Undecylenic acid (10-Undecen-1-oic acid; 10-Hendecen-1-oic acid)	24.5	275	....	....	....	....	87	....	....	Cu salt, 232–4; Pb salt, 80
5	2-Ethoxybenzoic acid (Salicylic acid ethyl ether)	24.5–5.5	300d.	....	....	....	....	132	....	....	....
6	d,l-α-Bromopropionic acid	25.7	203.5	125	99; 100	......	......	123	b.p.: 145–50	b.p.: 159–60d.	....
7	n-Undecylic acid (n-Undecanoic acid; n-Hendecanoic acid)	28.5; α: 13.4; β: 16.3	280; 284	80	71	......	68.2	103	....	....	....
8	α-Chloroisobutyric acid (α-Chloroisobutanoic acid)	31	118[50]	....	69–70, al.	......	......		b.p.: 133–5	b.p.: 148–9	....
9	α-Azidoisobutyric acid (α-Azidoisobutanoic acid; α-Triazoisobutyric acid)	31	75[0.2]	....	....	......	......	93–4	....	b.p.: 71[16], D_{20}^{20}: 1.0344	D_{33}^{33}: 1.1433
10	Cyclohexanecarboxylic acid (Hexahydrobenzoic acid)	31; 30–1	233	....	146 (cor.)	......	......	185–6	....	....	....
11	α-Ketobutyric acid (2-Oxobutanoic acid)	31	78[25]	....	....	......	......	117	....	....	n_D^{20}: 1.3975; p-Nitrophenylhydrazone, 194
12	Fluoroacetic acid	31–2	167–9	....	....	......	......	108	....	....	
13	Capric acid (n-Decanoic acid)	31.5	268–70	78	70	......	67, al.; 66	108; 100.1; 98; 99	b.p.: 224	b.p.: 243–5	n_D^{40}: 1.42855
14	Bromochloroacetic acid	31.5	215 sl. d.	....	....	......	......	126; 117	....	b.p.: 174d.	Phenyl ester, 46.5, b.p.: 266
15	2-Hexenoic acid	32	....	....	110	......	......		....	....	
16	n-Butylmethylglycolic acid	33	....	....	....	......	......	58	....	....	
17	cis-13-Docosenoic acid (Erucic acid)	33–4	264[15]	75–8	55	......	62.5; 61.0	84	....	....	D: 0.860[55]
18	Levulinic acid (γ-Ketovaleric acid; β-Acetylpropionic acid)	33–5 deliq.	245–6	108–9, w.	102, w.	61	84	107–8d.	....	....	Oxime, 96
19	Pivalic acid (Trimethylacetic acid)	35.5	163–4	119–20	132–3; 128 (cor.)	......	75–6	155–7; 153–4, et. ac.-pet. eth.	....	....	
20	d,l-α-Methylhydrocinnamic acid (α-Benzylpropionic acid)	36.5	272	130; d: 115–6	....	......	......	107–8; d: 113–4	....	....	
21	1-Cyclohexenylcarboxylic acid	38	107[3]	....	....	......	......	128	....	....	
22	n-Hexylmethylglycolic acid	40	....	....	....	......	......	59	....	....	
23	5-Acetyl-n-valeric acid (δ-Acetylpentanoic acid)	40–2; 31–2	250–3[280]	....	....	......	......		....	....	Semicarbazone, 144–6, ac. a.
24	d,l-α-Campholytic acid (1,5,5-Trimethylcyclopenten-4-carboxylic acid)	40.5	162–5[45]; l: 240–3	....	....	......	......	103, w.	b.p.: 200	....	Nitrile, b.p.: 200–5
25	β-Chloropropionic acid	41, w.; 39, lgr.	204	....	....	......	......		b.p.: 155–7, D^0: 1.198	b.p.: 162, D_4^{20}: 1.1086, n_D^{20}: 1.42537	Nitrile, b.p.: 175–6, $D^{18.5}$: 1.1443
26	d,l-α-Ethylphenylacetic acid (d,l-α-Phenylbutanoic acid)	42	270	....	....	......	......	85–7; 83	....	....	....

*Derivative data given in order: m.p., crystal color, solvent from which crystallized.

No.	Name	Melting point, °C	Boiling point, °C	p-Toluidide	Anilide	p-Nitrobenzyl ester	p-Bromophenacyl ester	Amide	Methyl ester	Ethyl ester	Miscellaneous
27	**α-Ethylpimelic acid**	43	223^{17}	....	145	......	......	....	....	....	....
28	**Tridecylic acid** (*n*-Tridecanonic acid)	43; 41.6	312; 177^{10}	88	80	......	75.0	100	....	....	....
29	**Lauric acid** (*n*-Dodecanoic acid)	44; 42	299	87	78	......	76	100; 99	....	....	....
30	*d,l*-**α-Bromoisovaleric acid**	44	230d.	124	116	......	....	133, bz.	b.p.: 174	b.p.: 186	....
31	**Elaidic acid** (*trans*-Oleic acid) ..	44–5; 51	234^{15}	....	....	......	65	93–4; 89–90	....	....	*p*-Phenylphenacyl ester, 73.5; *p*-Chlorophenacyl ester, 56
32	**4-Cyanobutanoic acid** (γ-Cyanobutyric acid)	45	....	....	....	......	....	69–70, sealed tube	....	b.p.: 245	....
33	**Dimethylneopentylacetic acid** ..	45	230^{732}	....	....	......	....	71	....	....	....
34	*trans*-**2-Methyl-2-butenoic acid** (Angelic acid)	45–6	185 (cor.)	....	126, bz.	......	....	127–8	....	....	Isobutyl ester, b.p.: 177; 2-Naphthylamide, 135, bz.; Heating 2 hours in sealed tube → tiglic acid, 64–5
35	**Dibromoacetic acid**..........	48	232–5	....	....	......	....	156	....	....	....
36	**α-Bromoisobutyric acid** (α-Bromoisobutanoic acid)	48–9	198–200	92.5, al.	83, al.-w.	......	....	148	....	....	*o*-Toluidide, 63
37	*tert*-**Butylpropiolic acid**	48–9	110^{10}	....	....	......	....		b.p.: 66^{13}, D^0: 0.9209	b.p.: 75^{15}, D^0: 0.9209	....
38	**Hydrocinnamic acid** (β-Phenylpropionic acid)	48.7; 40	279–80 (cor.)	135	98; 96	36.3	104	105; 82	....	....	*p*-Phenylphenacyl ester, 95
39	**β-Cyanopropionic acid**	48–50	....	....	....	......	....	97, sealed tube	b.p.: 215, n_D^{20}: 1.42427, D^{20}: 1.0792	b.p.: 220^{754} D^{20}: 1.0353	....
40	**Benzylpyruvic acid**	49–50 ($+\frac{1}{2}$ H₂O), w.	....	....	....	......	....	180	....	....	Semicarbazone, 175d.; Oxime, 65; Phenylhydrazone, 144–5
41	**Bromoacetic acid**	50	208	....	131	88	....	91	b.p.: 144d.	b.p.: 168–9	....
42	**2-Pentynoic acid** (Ethylpropiolic acid)...................	50	100^{10}	....	....	......	....	146	....	....	....
43	**γ-Phenylbutyric acid**	52	290	....	....	......	....	84	....	....	....
44	*n*-**Pentadecylic acid** (*n*-Pentadecanoic acid).............	52.3	212^{16}	....	78	39.5–40 (cor.)	77.2	102.5	....	....	....
45	**β-Campholenic acid**	53.5	245	....	....	......	....	86	....	222–5	Nitrile, 225, D^{20}: 0.9093
46	**Myristic acid** (Tetradecanoic acid).....................	53.9	202^{16}	93	84	......	81	103	....	....	....
47	**Trichloroacetic acid**	57–8	197.5	113	97; 94	80	....	141	b.p.: 153.8	b.p.: 168	Phenylhydrazide, 123
48	**α-Acetoxypropionic acid** (O-Acetyllactic acid)	57–60; 39–40	167–70^{78}	....	....	......	....	....	....	....	Nitrile, b.p.: 172–3
49	**β-Acetylglutaric acid**	58	....	....	....	......	....	*mono*: 141–2, al.-eth.	89	....	....
50	*sec-n*-**Amylmalonic acid** (2-Ethylbutane-1,1-dicarboxylic acid; *sec-n*-Pentylmalonic acid)...................	58, bz.	....	....	*di*: 219–20	......	....	....	....	*di*: b.p.: 243–5	....

*Derivative data given in order: m.p., crystal color, solvent from which crystallized.

TABLE XII. ORGANIC DERIVATIVES OF CARBOXYLIC ACIDS
b) Solids (Listed in order of increasing m.p.)* (Continued)

No.	Name	Melting point, °C	Boiling point, °C	p-Toluidide	Anilide	p-Nitrobenzyl ester	p-Bromophenacyl ester	Amide	Methyl ester	Ethyl ester	Miscellaneous
51	*trans*-Brassidic acid	59.7	256[10]	....	78	......	94.2	94	....	....	....
52	5-Phenylpentanoic acid	60	....	....	90	......	....	109	....	....	....
53	β-Cyclohexylacrylic acid	60	154[11]	....	....	......	....	159	....	....	....
54	β-Chloroisocrotonic acid	61	195 (subl.)	....	108	......	....	110	b.p.: 142	b.p.: 161	....
55	**Margaric acid** (*n*-Heptadecanoic acid)	61.2	231[16]	....	....	48.5–9.0 (cor.)	82.6	108; 106	....	....	....
56	Chloroacetic acid	α: 61.3; β: 56.2; γ: 52.5	189	162	136–7	......	104	121	b.p.: 130	b.p.: 145–6	....
57	β-Bromopropionic acid	62.5	....	....	....	......	....	111	b.p.: 80[27], D[17]: 1.4897	b.p.: 70[12], D[15]: 1.2609	2-Naphthylamide, 174
58	**Palmitic acid** (Hexadecanoic acid)	62.7	222[16]	98	90.6, al.	42.5	86; 82	106–7; 105.3, al.	....	....	....
59	*cis*-2-Methyl-2-butenoic acid (Tiglic acid)	64.5–5.0	198.5 (cor.)	70.0–1.5	77, pet. eth.	64	68	75–6, bz.	....	....	....
60	**Cyanoacetic acid**	66	....	....	198–9	......	....	119–20	b.p.: 200	b.p.: 207	Nitrile, 29–30, b.p.: 218–9
61	**Benzoylformic acid**	66	....	....	....	......	....	91	....	....	Nitrile, 32–3, b.p.: 206–8; 2,4-Dinitrophenylhydrazone, 196–7d. (cor.); Phenylhydrazone, 64
62	**Acetoxyacetic acid**	66–8, bz.	145[12]	....	89–90, w.	......	....	....	....	b.p.: 179, D[17]: 1.0993	....
63	**2,3-Dibromopropionic acid**	67, stab.; 51, unst.	160[20]	....	....	......	....	130	....	....	....
64	**3,3-Dimethylacrylic acid**	67	106[20]	....	....	......	....	108	....	....	....
65	**2-Furylacetic acid**	67	....	....	85	......	....	....	....	....	....
66	**3,3,4,4-Tetramethylpentanoic acid**	67	....	....	....	......	....	138	....	....	....
67	**4-Ketocyclohexanecarboxylic acid** (4-Oxocyclohexanecarboxylic acid)	67–8, bz.-pet. eth.	....	....	....	......	....	....	b.p.: 140[20]	b.p.: 158[40]	Semicarbazone, 200d.; Oxime, 147, eth.
68	**d,l-2-Phenyllactic acid**	68 (+½ H₂O), w.; 94 (anh.); d: 116–7, w.; l: 115–6, bz.	....	....	....	......	....	101–2, dichloroethylene; l: 62.5–3.5, bz.	....	....	d,l-Et. eth., 60–2, lgr.; d-Quinine salt, 216d., al.; l-1-Menthyl ester, 55.5–6.0
69	*d*-Chaulmoogric acid (*d*-ω-Cyclopentyltridecanoic acid)	68.5	247–8[20]	100	89	......	....	106, al.	22	b.p.: 230[20], D₄[15]: 0.9064	[α]_D: +62 in chl.
70	**Stearic acid** (Octadecanoic acid)	70–1; 69.6	....	102	95.5, al.	......	92	109; 108.4, al.	....	....	....
71	*trans*-Crotonic acid (*trans*-2-Butenoic acid)	72, w.	189 (cor.)	132, bz.	118, w.; 115	67.4	95–6	159–60, bz.	b.p.: 121	b.p.: 138, D₄[20]: 0.9175, n_D[20]: 1.42524	....

*Derivative data given in order: m.p., crystal color, solvent from which crystallized.

195

No.	Name	Melting point, °C	Boiling point, °C	p-Toluidide	Anilide	p-Nitro-benzyl ester	p-Bromo-phenacyl ester	Amide	Methyl ester	Ethyl ester	Miscellaneous
72	γ-Bromocrotonic acid.........	74, lgr.	....	....	....	....	....	101	b.p.: 87[15], D_4^{19}: 1.490, n_D^{19}: 1.498	b.p.: 97–8[15], D_4^{16}: 1.402, n_D^{16}: 1.490	....
73	Caproylacetic acid	74d.	....	....	....	....	....	100	b.p.: 118[19], D_4^0: 0.9916	b.p.: 127[19], D^0: 0.9721	Nitrile, b.p.: 127–8[14], D^{15}: 0.9914
74	3-Ketocyclohexanecarboxylic acid (3-Oxocyclohexane-carboxylic acid)............	75–6, bz.	195–7[20]	....						b.p.: 138[18]	Semicarbazone, 183–4, al.; Oxime, 170d., w.; Phenylhydra-zone, 125, yel.
75	2-Thienylacetic acid	76	....	....	....	....	....	148			
76	sec-Butylmalonic acid (Iso-pentane-1,1-dicarboxylic acid).....................	76	....	....	....	....	....	di: 242	di: b.p.: 217–8[748]	di: b.p.: 245–50[762]	....
77	Phenylacetic acid	76.5, subl.	256.5 (cor.)	135–6	117–8	65	89	156	....		
78	Eicosanoic acid (Arachidic acid)......................	77; 75	204[1]	96	92	......	89	108–9			
79	Glycolic acid (Hydroxyacetic acid).....................	78–9; 80	....	143, w.	97, w.	106.8	138	120, al.-et. ac.		....	On prolonged heating at 100° → anh., 128–30
80	α-Hydroxyisobutyric acid (2-Hydroxyisobutanoic acid; Dimethylglycolic acid)	79	212	132–3, w.	136, w.	80.5	98, acet.	....			
81	α-Methylcinnamic acid	81; 74	....	....	....	....	....	128			
82	2-Ketocyclohexanecarboxylic acid (2-Oxocyclohexane-carboxylic acid).............	81–2, eth.	....							b.p.: 107–8[12]; 159–60[100]	Alcoholic sol. + FeCl₃ → blue color
83	n-Docosanoic acid (Behenic acid).....................	81–2	....	....	101–2	....	....	111	54	50	....
84	β-Iodopropionic acid	82; 85	....	....	....	....	....	101; 142			
85	α-Benzoylpropionic acid.......	82–3, bz.-pet. eth.	....	....	137–8, al.	....	....	145–6			Phenylhydrazone, 100–4, br., bz.
86	Iodoacetic acid	83	....	....	....	....	....	95			
87	γ-Chlorocrotonic acid	83	117–8[13]	....	....	....	....	130–2, w.		b.p.: 191–3[750]	Nitrile, b.p.: 73[15], D^0: 1.1495
88	Lignoceric acid (Tetracosanoic acid).....................	84	....	....	....	....	....	91		....	p-Chlorophenacyl ester, 100
89	β-Methyladipic acid	85; 91	223[18]	......	200						
90	α-Benzoylbutyric acid (α-Benzoylbutanoic acid).......	85–7	....	....	....	....	....	148–9		b.p.: 168–71[19]	Nitrile, b.p.: 134–5[3]
91	d,l-α-Bromophenylacetic acid ..	86; 84	....	....	....	....	....	148; 144			Nitrile, 29, b.p.: 242d.
92	(4-Methoxyphenyl)acetic acid..	87; 84	....	....	....	....	....	189			
93	Dineopentylacetic acid	88	....	....	....	....	....	140			
94	Dibenzylacetic acid..........	89	....	175, abs. al.	155, abs. al.	....	....	128–9, bz.			
95	(2-Tolyl)acetic acid	90; 88	....	....	....	....	....	161			
96	α-Thienylglyoxylic acid	91	....	....	....	....	....	88			
97	Δ⁵-Campholytic acid (4,5,5-Trimethylcyclopentene-1-carboxylic acid)	91	....	....	....	....	....	90, lgr.			
98	Citraconic acid (Methylmaleic acid)	92d.; 92–3; 91d., eth.-lgr.	....	mono: 170–1, yel., eth.	mono: 153; di: 175.5, al.	di: 70.6	....	di: 185–7d.	di: b.p.: 210–1	di: b.p.: 231	....

*Derivative data given in order: m.p., crystal color, solvent from which crystallized.

No.	Name	Melting point, °C	Boiling point, °C	p-Toluidide	Anilide	p-Nitrobenzyl ester	p-Bromophenacyl ester	Amide	Methyl ester	Ethyl ester	Miscellaneous
99	2-Bromobenzoylformic acid	93–101	......	......	......	......	......	136–7, w.	....	......	Nitrile, 62–4, yel.; Oxime, 162–4d.
100	β-Chlorocrotonic acid.........	94	206–11 sl. d.	......	123–4	......	......	100–1	b.p.: 64–7[14], D_4^{22}: 1.555, n_D^{20}: 1.463	b.p.: 180, 184; D_4^{20}: 1.1062, n_D^{20}: 1.459	1-Naphthylamide, 169–70
101	Phenyl-n-propylglycolic acid ...	94	......	......	......	......	......	132	....	......	....
102	(2-Chlorophenyl)acetic acid....	95, w.	......	170	138.5	......	......	175, w.	....	......	Nitrile, 25, b.p.: 251; o-Toluidide, 174
103	(4-Tolyl)acetic acid	95; 91	159[15]	......	......	......	......	185	....	......	....
104	o-Chlorohydrocinnamic acid ...	96.5, w.	......	......	......	......	......	119, bz.	b.p.: 255	......	Nitrile, b.p.: 267–8
105	2-Hydroxy-3-phenylpropionic acid	97; 96	......	......	......	......	......	112	....	......	....
106	1,2,3,4-Tetrahydro-2-naphthoic acid	97	......	......	......	......	......	139	....	......	....
107	Glutaric acid (1,3-Propanedicarboxylic acid)..........	98	302–4	di: 218	di: 223–4	di: 69	di: 136.8	di: 175–6	....	......	....
108	3-Phenoxypropionic acid	98	......	......	......	......	......	119	....	......	....
109	α-Crotonic acid..............	99	212	......	......	......	......	112	161	176	Nitrile, b.p.: 136
110	Phenoxyacetic acid...........	98–9; 99–100	285d.	......	99, al.	......	148.5	101.5	....	......	....
111	2-Benzofurylacetic acid	99	......	......	......	......	......	164	....	......	....
112	1-Naphthylglycolic acid	99; 124–5	......	......	......	......	......	135	....	......	....
113	Citric acid	100 (+1 H_2O); 153 (anh.)	......	tri: 189, al.	tri: 192	tri: 102	tri: 148	tri: 210–5d., w.	....	......	....
114	2-Methoxybenzoic acid (o-Anisic acid; Salicylic acid methyl ether) .	100–1	200	......	......	......	113	129	....	......	....
115	l-Malic acid (Hydroxysuccinic acid).....................	100–1	......	di: 206–7	di: 197	mono: 87.2; di: 124.5	di: 179	di: 156–7; d,l: 162–3	....	......	....
116	Oxalic acid	101 (+2 H_2O) (rapid htng.); 189.5 (anh.); subl. at 150–60	......	mono: 169; di: 268	mono: 148–9; di: 254; 246, bz.	di: 204	......	mono: 219; di: 419d.	....	......	....
117	Acetylpyruvic acid (2,4-Diketo-n-valeric acid; 2,4-Dioxo-pentanoic acid).............	101, bz.	......	......	......	......	......	131–2d., al.	63–4	......	....
118	n-Butylmalonic acid (Pentane-1,1-dicarboxylic acid)	101	......	......	di: 193	......	......	di: 200	....	di: b.p.: 235–40	Mononitrile, 122.5–6.5, w., subl.
119	α-Cyanohydrocinnamic acid (Benzylcyanoacetic acid).....	101–2	......	......	......	......	......	130	....	b.p.: 176–85[21]	....
120	2-Chloro-6-methylbenzoic acid .	102, w.	......	......	......	......	......	167	....	......	Nitrile, 82–3, pet. eth.
121	Aleuritic acid (9,10,16-Trihydroxypalmitic acid)	102, w.	......	......	......	......	......	......	63–4	......	Hydrazide, 139–40; Azide, 50d., al.

* Derivative data given in order: m.p., crystal color, solvent from which crystallized.

No.	Name	Melting point, °C	Boiling point, °C	p-Toluidide	Anilide	p-Nitrobenzyl ester	p-Bromophenacyl ester	Amide	Methyl ester	Ethyl ester	Miscellaneous
122	(2-Bromophenyl)acetic acid....	103–4; 109	....	....	....	......	......	186–7	....	....	Nitrile, b.p.: 145–7[14]
123	Benzylacetic acid	103–4d.	....	....	107–8	......	......	113	....	....	Nitrile, 80–1; l-Menthyl ester, 41
124	Pimelic acid...............	104–5, subl.	223[15]	di: 206, al.	mono: 108–9; di: 155–6, me. al.-w.	......	di: 136.6	di: 175	....	....	
125	2-Toluic acid (2-Methylbenzoic acid)	104–5; 107–8	259[751]	144	125	90.7	57	142.8 (cor.)	....	....	
126	Allylmalonic acid	105, eth.	....	....	...,....	46, al.	......	....	....	di: b.p.: 222–3	Mononitrile, b.p.: 223; Dinitrile, b.p.: 217–8
127	(4-Chlorophenyl)acetic acid....	105–6; 104	....	190	164–5, al.			175, al.	....	32; b.p.: 260	o-Toluidide, 190, bz.: Nitrile, 30, b.p.: 265–7
128	Δ²-Cyclogeranic acid (1,5,5-Trimethylcyclohexene-6-carboxylic acid)	106, lgr.	138[11]	....	....			120–1, bz.-pet. eth.	....	b.p.: 101–2[10]	....
129	d-Campholic acid (d-1,2,2,3-Tetramethylcyclopentane-1-carboxylic acid)	106; d,l: 109	255	....	91			80; d,l: 90	b.p.: 208	b.p.: 220	Nitrile, 73; Anhydride, 56; d,l: 66
130	Atropic acid (1-Phenylacrylic acid)...............	106–7, w.	....	....	134	......		121–2, w.		b.p.: 124[16], n_D[16]: 1.52605	....
131	l-Campholic acid	106–7	250	....	....	......		78–9	b.p.: 211	b.p.: 228	Anhydride, 57–8
132	Azelaic acid (Heptane-1,7-dicarboxylic acid)..........	106.5	>360 sl. d.; 237[15]	di: 201–2	mono: 107–8, dil. al.; di: 186–7	di: 43.8	di: 130.6	mono: 93–5; di: 175	....	....	
133	Methylneopentylglycolic acid ..	109	....	....	....			116	....	....	
134	trans-4-Methylcyclohexane-carboxylic acid	111	....	....	....			226	....	....	
135	cis-α-Chloroallocinnamic acid ..	111	....	....	138–9, al.-w.			134, bz.	b.p.: 153–4[28]	b.p.: 157–8[10], D_4[25]: 1.1569 n_D[25]: 1.5525	
136	Ethylmalonic acid...........	111	....	....	150	75	......	di: 214	....	....	
137	3-Toluic acid (3-Methylbenzoic acid)...............	111–3; 110–1	263, subl.	118	126	86.6	108	94; 97	....	....	
138	O-Benzoyllactic acid (Lactic acid benzoate)..............	112						124	....	b.p.: 288	Nitrile, b.p.: 269–70; 1-Naphthylamide, 155; 2-Naphthylamide, 177
139	2,4,6-Triethylbenzoic acid	113	....	....	....			156	....	....	....
140	2-Phenylbenzoic acid	113	....	....	....			177	....	....	....
141	(1-Naphthyl)glyoxylic acid	113	....	....	....			151	....	....	....
142	Bromomalonic acid...........	113d.	....	di: 217, ac. a.	....			di: 181, al.	di: b.p.: 215–25	di: b.p.: 233–5d.	Dinitrile, 65–6
143	(4-Bromophenyl)acetic acid....	114, subl.	....	....	....			192–4	....	30	Nitrile, 46–7
144	2-Acetylbenzoic acid (Acetophenone-o-carboxylic acid)...	114–5	....	....	....			116.5, w.	....	....	Oxime, 159; 2,4-Dinitrophenylhydrazone, 186

*Derivative data given in order: m.p., crystal color, solvent from which crystallized.

No.	Name	Melting point, °C	Boiling point, °C	p-Toluidide	Anilide	p-Nitro-benzyl ester	p-Bromo-phenacyl ester	Amide	Methyl ester	Ethyl ester	Miscellaneous
145	**Pyrotartaric acid** (Methyl-succinic acid)	115	. . . .	164	*mono*: 159, et. ac.; 123, chl.; *di*: 200	. . . . . .	. . . .	*di*: 225	. . . .	. . . .	. . . .
146	**2-Phenoxypropionic acid**	115–6; 112–3	. . . .	115	117; 118–9	. . . . . .	. . . .	132–3; 130	. . . .	. . . .	. . . .
147	**3-Benzoylpropionic acid**	116	. . . .		150; 145	. . . . . .	. . . .	145–6, w.	. . . .	18–9	Semicarbazone, 181d.
148	**Benzylmalonic acid**	117d.; 121	. . . .		*di*: 217	*di*: 119.5	. . . .	*di*: 225	. . . .		Dinitrile, 91; 79
149	*d,l*-**Tropic acid** (3-Hydroxy-2-phenylpropionic acid)	117–8; *d*: 130						169			
150	**Cuminic acid** (4-Isopropyl-benzoic acid)	117–8, al.						133	b.p.: 263–4		Nitrile, b.p.: 243–4[784]
151	*d,l*-**Mandelic acid** (α-Hydroxy-phenylacetic acid)	118; *d*: 133; *l*: 134	. . . .	172, al.	151–2, al.	123–4		133–4 (cor.)		43–4	
152	*l*-**Arabonic acid**	118–9, al.	. . . .	200	204			136, me. al.			*o*-Toluidide, 172
153	α-**Chlorodiphenylacetic acid** . . .	118–9d., bz.-lgr.			88			115	. . . .	43–4	Anhydride, 219
154	*d,l*-**Citramalic acid** (*d,l*-2-Hydroxy-2-methylsuccinic acid)	119	. . . .					*mono*: 140–1	*di*: b.p. 112[15]	. . . .	Me. eth., 90–2; Et. eth., 81–3
155	**Anilinomalonic acid**	119d, al.-lgr.			*mono*: 157d., w.; *di*: 162; 246–7, ac. a.			*di*: 156	*di*: 68	*di*: 45, al.	. . . .
156	**4-Chloromandelic acid**	119–22; 112–3						122–3			Nitrile, 43; Me. eth., 85–8, bz.-pet. eth.
157	**(3-Nitrophenyl)acetic acid**	120	. . . .					110	. . . .		. . . .
158	*cis*-**2-Bromoallocinnamic acid** . .	120						129	b.p.: 111[0.6], D$_4^{20}$: 1.4726	b.p.: 173–4[30], D$_4^{25}$: 1.3713	
159	**3-Furoic acid** (3-Furancar-boxylic acid)	121						169			
160	**1-Cyclopentenylcarboxylic acid** .	121		122	126						
161	**Cetylmalonic acid** (Heptade-cane-1,1-dicarboxylic acid) . . .	121.5–2.0, ac. a.						*mono*: 130–50d., lgr.-al.	*di*: 44, eth.	*di*: 22	
162	*cis*-**1,3-Cyclopentanedicar-boxylic acid**	122; *trans*: 161						226			
163	*d,l-trans*-**Camphenic acid** (*d,l-trans*-Camphene-camphoric acid)	122–3, ac. a.			*di*: 165, ac. a.			*di*: 231–2, ac. a.			
164	**Benzoic acid**	122.4; at 100, subl.	249	158	160, boil. 50% al.	89	119.0	130	b.p.: 199.6	b.p.: 212.6	. . . .
165	**3,3,3-Trichlorolactic acid**	124			164			96			
166	**3-Nitrosalicylic acid**	125 (hyd.)						145			
167	**Diethylmalonic acid**	125				*di*: 91		*mono*: 146; *di*: 224			
168	**1,14-Tetradecanedicarboxylic acid**	126			163						

*Derivative data given in order: m.p., crystal color, solvent from which crystallized.

No.	Name	Melting point, °C	Boiling point, °C	p-Toluidide	Anilide	p-Nitro-benzyl ester	p-Bromo-phenacyl ester	Amide	Methyl ester	Ethyl ester	Miscellaneous
169	**2,4-Dimethylbenzoic acid**	127 (anh.); 90 (hyd.)	......	......	141	......	......	179–81	....	....	
170	*cis*-**2-Chloroallocinnamic acid**	127	......	......	......	......	......	112			
171	**2-Benzoylbenzoic acid** (Benzo-phenone-2-carboxylic acid)	128; 91 (+1 H$_2$O), w.	......	......	195	100.4	......	165 (cor.)	52	......	
172	**1,10-Decanedicarboxylic acid**	128	......	......	......	......	......	185			
173	**2-Thenoic acid** (2-Thiophene-carboxylic acid)	129	......	......	......	......	......	180			
174	**4-Bromopyromucic acid** (4-Bromofuran-2-carboxylic acid)	129	......	......	......	......	......	155–6		29; b.p.: 235–6	....
175	**Maleic acid** (*cis*-Butenedioic acid)	130 (+30% Fumaric a.); 137 (pure)	......	*di:* 142, eth.	*mono:* 198; 187, yel., al.; *di:* 187, al.	*di:* 91 (cor.)	168–70; 190	*mono:* 172–3, w.; 153 sl. d.; *di:* 260; 181, me. al.			Heated at 160 → anh., 60, b.p.: 202
176	**Tribromoacetic acid**	131; 135	245d.	......	......	......	......	122			
177	**(1-Naphthyl)acetic acid** (1-Naphthaleneacetic acid)	131; 135	......	......	155, al.; 159.6	......	......	180–1, al.	....	....	
178	*trans*-α-**Bromocinnamic acid**	131–2	......	......	......	......	......	119	23	b.p.: 294–6	....
179	**2,5-Dimethylbenzoic acid**	132	......	......	140	......	......	186	....	....	
180	*cis*-β-**Chloroallocinnamic acid**	132	......	142	134.5	......	......	76	34	b.p.: 265 sl. d.	
181	*trans*-**Cinnamic acid**	133	300	168	153; 109	116.8	145.6	147–8	....	....	Nitrile, 20–1, b.p.: 255–6
182	**Chloromalonic acid**	133	......	*di:* 118, w.	......	......	*di:* 170	*di:* b.p.: 206–8^{772}	*di:* b.p.: 222	Di-*p*-bromo-anilide, 239
183	**Sebacic acid** (Decanedioic acid; Octane-1,8-dicarboxylic acid)	33, subl.	243^{15}	*di:* 201	*mono:* 122–3; *di:* 201–2	*di:* 73.5; 72.6	*di:* 147	*mono:* 170; *di:* 210; 208	....	....	Phenylhydrazide, 194
184	**2-Furoic acid** (2-Furancar-boxylic acid; Pyromucic acid)	133–4; 132	230–2	170.5, al.	123.5, al.	133.5	138.5	142–3	....	34, b.p.: 195	....
185	**Malonic acid** (Propanedioic acid)	134.8–.9	......	*mono:* 156d.; *di:* 252–3, al.	*mono:* 132; *di:* 230; 227–8, al.	*di:* 85.5	......	*mono:* 106–10; *di:* 170, w.-al.	....	*di:* b.p.: 199	Phenylhydrazide, 194
186	**O-Acetylsalicylic acid** (Aspirin)	135, rapid htng.	140d.	......	136	90.5	......	138	....	....	Phenacyl ester, 105
187	β-**Campholytic acid** (1,5,5-Tri-methylcyclopentene-2-carboxylic acid)	135	247–9; 255–6	114	104, al.-w.	......	......	130	b.p.: 203–4	b.p.: 214	....
188	**2-Anilinoisovaleric acid**	135, w.	......	......	......	......	......	102–3	....	b.p.: 275–80	
189	**Acetone-1,3-dicarboxylic acid**	135d., et. ac.	......	......	*di:* 155, al.	......	......	......			Oxime, 53–4; w.; Acids or alkalis → acetone, b.p. 56 + CO$_2$
190	**d.l-cis-Camphenic acid** (d,l,cis-Camphenecamphoric acid)	135–7	......	......	*di:* 212	......	......	*di:* 225			
191	**Phenylpropiolic acid**	136–7, subl.	......	142	128; 126; 125	83	......	99–100; 109	....	....	Melts under w. at 80

*Derivative data given in order: m.p., crystal color, solvent from which crystallized.

TABLE XII. ORGANIC DERIVATIVES OF CARBOXYLIC ACIDS

b) Solids (Listed in order of increasing m.p.)* (Continued)

No.	Name	Melting point, °C	Boiling point, °C	p-Toluidide	Anilide	p-Nitro-benzyl ester	p-Bromo-phenacyl ester	Amide	Methyl ester	Ethyl ester	Miscellaneous
192	*trans*-Glutaconic acid	136–8	....	....	*mono*: 167; *di*: 228	......	....	....	....	....	Acetic anhy-dride → anh., 88
193	3-Ethoxybenzoic acid	137	....	....	....	......	....	139.0–.5	....	....	....
194	Methylmalonic acid	137; 138d.	....	*mono*: 145d.; *di*: 228; 214	....	......	....	217; 206	....	....	....
195	*trans*-α-Chlorocinnamic acid ...	137–8	....	116, al.	118, al.	......	....	121–2	33	b.p.: 209^{75}, D$_4^{25}$: 1.1719, n$_D^{25}$: 1.5705	....
196	3-Thenoic acid (3-Thiophene-carboxylic acid)	138	....	....	....	130	....	180	....	....	....
197	*cis*-Cyclobutane-1,2-dicar-boxylic acid	138	....	....	....	......	....	*di*: 228, w.	*di*: b.p.: 225	*di*: b.p.: 238–42^{720}	Anhydride, 75; 71–3
198	2-Pyridinecarboxylic acid (Picolinic acid)	138	....	....	....	......	....	107	....	....	....
199	(3-Chloromethyl)benzoic acid ..	138, w.	....	....	....	......	....	124	....	b.p. 168–9^{25}	Nitrile, 67, al., b.p.: 258–60
200	5-Chloro-2-nitrobenzoic acid ...	139, w.	....	....	164, eth.	......	....	154, eth.	48.5, me. al.	....	Methylamide, 134, al.-w.; Di-methylamide, 104.5
201	Anhydrocamphoronic acid	139	....	....	202–3	......	....	α: 138; β: 45	....	....	....
202	Butane-1,1,4-tricarboxylic acid .	139–40, bz.-et. ac.	....	....	*mono*: 177	......	....	....	....	*tri*: b.p.: 175–6^{18}, D^{15}: 1.0726	....
203	*meso*-Tartaric acid	140	....	....	*mono*: 193–4, pa. yel., w.	93	....	*di*: 187; 189–90, dil. me. al.	....	....	Diphenylhydra-zide, 245
204	3-Nitrobenzoic acid	140	....	162	154	141	132	143	78.5; 70	47; 40–1	....
205	3-Bromo-4-toluic acid (2-Bromo-4-methylbenzoic acid).	140	....	....	....	......	....	137, subl.	....	....	Nitrile, 47
206	2-Chloro-4-nitrobenzoic acid ...	140–2	....	....	168	......	....	172, al.	73–5	....	....
207	(2-Nitrophenyl)acetic acid	141; 138	....	....	....	......	....	161	....	....	....
208	Furanacrylic acid (β-(2-Furyl)-acrylic acid)	141	286	....	....	......	....	168–9	....	....	....
209	2-Anilinobutyric acid	141	....	....	92, al.	......	....	123, w.	....	26, b.p.: 278	Nitrile, 39
210	(2-Naphthyl)acetic acid (2-Naphthaleneacetic acid)	141–2; 143	....	....	....	......	....	200; 205	....	....	....
211	4-Chloro-2-nitrobenzoic acid .	142, w.	....	....	....	......	....	172, al.	41–3	....	Nitrile, 98
212	*trans*-β-Chlorocinnamic acid ...	142	....	122–5	128	......	....	118	29	b.p.: 293	....
213	2-Chlorobenzoic acid	142; 140	....	131	114; 118, pet. eth.	106	106	142; 202	b.p.: 234	b.p.: 243	....
214	(2-Bromophenoxy)acetic acid ..	142.5, al.	....	....	....	......	....	151, al.	....	b.p.: 160–70^{16}	....

*Derivative data given in order: m.p., crystal color, solvent from which crystallized.

No.	Name	Melting point, °C	Boiling point, °C	*p*-Toluidide	Anilide	*p*-Nitro-benzyl ester	*p*-Bromo-phenacyl ester	Amide	Methyl ester	Ethyl ester	Miscellaneous
215	**Suberic acid** (Octanedioic acid; Hexane-1,6-dicarboxylic acid)	144; 139–41	....	*di*: 218; 219	*mono*: 128–9; *di*: 186–7	*di*: 85	*di*: 144.2	*mono*: 125–7; *di*: 216–7	....	*di*: b.p.: 282–6	....
216	**Asaronic acid** (2,4,5-Tri-methoxybenzoic acid)	144, bz.-pet. eth.	*ca.* 300	....	154.5	....	....	184.5	97.5, yel.	72, yel.	Nitrile, 112–4, al.
217	**(2-Chlorophenoxy)acetic acid**	145–6, w.	....	....	121	....	....	149.5	b.p.: 186–8	32	
218	**2-Nitrobenzoic acid**	146	....	....	155	112	107	176	b.p.: 275; 269, D_4^{20}: 1.286	30, b.p.: 148–50[10]	....
219	**Phthalonic acid**	146	....	....	*mono*: 176; *di*: 208	....	....	α: 179d.; β: 155d.	....	....	Phenylhydrazone, 171–2
220	**(2-Hydroxyphenyl)acetic acid**	147; 149; 141	....	....	....	....	....	118			
221	**2-Anilinovaleric acid** (2-Anilinopentanoic acid)	147–8, al.-w.	....	....	....	....	....	99, eth.-pet. eth.			Nitrile, 51, pet. eth.
222	**Diphenylacetic acid**	148	....	172–3	180	....	....	167.5–8.0			
223	**Diglycolic acid**	148; 142	....	*mono*: 148, w.	*mono*: 118; *di*: 152, eth.-al. (2:1)	....	....	*mono*: 135			
224	**Oxanilic acid**	148–9	....	....	*di*: 154	....	....	228	....	....	
225	**(4-Hydroxyphenyl)acetic acid**	148–50; 148, w.	....	....	....	....	....	175			Benzoate of amide, 167–9
226	**2-Bromobenzoic acid**	150	....	....	141	110	102	155	b.p.: 243–4	b.p.: 254–5	
227	**Benzilic acid** (α-Hydroxy-diphenylacetic acid)	150	....	189–90	174–5	99.5	152	153, chl.; 154–5	74–5	34	Acetate, 98, ac. a.
228	**Citric acid** (2-Hydroxypropane-1,2,3-tricarboxylic acid)	153 (slow htng.)	....	*tri*: 189, al.	*tri*: 192, al.-w.	*tri*: 102	*tri*: 148	*tri*: 210–5d.	....	....	Triphenyl ester, 124
229	**(4-Nitrophenyl)acetic acid**	153	....	....	198	......	207	198			
230	**2,5-Dichlorobenzoic acid**	153	....	....	....	....	....	155			
231	**Phenylmalonic acid**	153	....	....	....	....	....	233			
232	**Adipic acid** (Butane-1,4-dicarboxylic acid)	153–4 (cor.)	216[15]	241	*mono*: 151–3, w.; *di*: 240–1, al.	106	154.5; 152.6	*mono*: 125–30, w.; *di*: 220	3, b.p.: 162[10]	*di*: 8, b.p.: 112[10], f.p.: 0	Diphenyl ester, 105–6, al.-w.
233	**(4-Bromophenoxy)acetic acid**	153–4, al.	....	....	....	....	....			54, al.	Phenyl ester, 73, al.
234	**Phenylpyruvic acid**	154	....	....	....	....	....		....	....	Oxime, 159
235	**3-Bromobenzoic acid**	155	....	....	136	105	120	155	31–2	b.p.: 254–5	....
236	**2,4,6-Trimethylbenzoic acid**	155; 153	....	....	....	....	....	188			
237	**2-Chloro-4-methylbenzoic acid**	155–6	....	....	....	....	....	182			Nitrile, 61–2, subl.
238	**(4-Chlorophenoxy)acetic acid**	155–6, w.; 158	....	....	125	....	136	133	b.p.: 177–80	49	....
239	**3-(1-Naphthyl)propionic acid**	156	....	....	....	....	....	104			
240	**Tartronic acid** (Hydroxy-malonic acid)	156–8d.	....	....	....	....	....	*di*: 198, dil. al.; 195–6d.			
241	**Benzoylpyruvic acid**	156–8d. (+1 H_2O), al.-w.	....	....	....	....	....	138d.	59; 62	46	1-Oxime, 98–100d. (+1 H_2O)

*Derivative data given in order: m.p., crystal color, solvent from which crystallized.

No.	Name	Melting point, °C	Boiling point, °C	p-Toluidide	Anilide	p-Nitro-benzyl ester	p-Bromo-phenacyl ester	Amide	Methyl ester	Ethyl ester	Miscellaneous
242	**Cyclobutane-1,1-dicarboxylic acid**	157, w.; 158	....	....	*di*: 214–5	....	....	*di*: 275–7	....	b.p.: 218^{762}; *di*: b.p.: 222–6	Dihydrazide, 109–10, al.-w.
243	**3-Chlorobenzoic acid**	158; 155	....	....	122–5, al.	107	116	134	21, b.p.: 231	b.p.: 245	....
244	**Salicylic acid** (2-Hydroxy-benzoic acid)	158.3; subl. at 76	....	156	136	97–8	140	142; 139	−8.6, b.p.: 223.3	1.3, b.p.: 234; 231.5	
245	**1-Naphthoic acid**	161–2 (cor.)	....	....	162–3; 164	....	135.5	202; 205	....	....	....
246	**2-Iodobenzoic acid**	162	....	....	141	111	143	110	184	....	....
247	**2-Anilinopropionic acid**	162, w.	....	....	127, al.	....	....	144	....	b.p.: 272	Nitrile, 92, al.; N-Acetyl, 143, w.
248	**4-Dibenzothienylacetic acid**	162	....	....	....	....	....	206	....	....	
249	**Alloxanic acid**	162–3d., eth.	....	....	....	....	....	191, w.	171, et. ac.	115, acet.-chl.	Phenylamide, 99, eth.
250	**5-Chloro-3-nitrosalicylic acid** (5-Chloro-2-hydroxy-3-nitro-benzoic acid)	163	....	....	....	....	....	199	....	91, al.	
251	**2-Benzofurylacetic acid**	163	....	....	....	....	....	210	....	....	
252	**Cholanic acid**	164, ac. a.	....	....	....	....	....	175	....	93–4, 80% al.	[α]$_D^{14}$: +21.74 in chl.; Propyl ester 56–7; Butyl ester, 53
253	**4-Nitrophthalic acid**	165	....	*mono*: 172	192	....	....	200d.	....	....	
254	**Itaconic acid** (Methylene-succinic acid)	165	....	....	*mono*: 151.5, eth.	*di*: 90.6	*di*: 117.4	*di*: 191.2–.8, al.	....	....	
255	**5-Bromosalicylic acid** (5-Bromo-2-hydroxybenzoic acid)	165	....	....	222	....	....	232	61, b.p.: 264–6	50	....
256	**6-Chloro-3-nitrobenzoic acid**	165, w.	....	....	....	....	....	178, w.	73, me. al.	28–9	Nitrile, 105–6
257	**3,4-Dimethylbenzoic acid**	166; 164	....	....	104; 108	....	....	130	....	....	
258	**Tricarballylic acid** (Propane-1,2,3-tricarboxylic acid)	166	....	....	*tri*: 252, PhNO$_2$	....	*tri*: 138.2	*tri*: 205–7d.	....	....	
259	**Mesitylenic acid** (3,5-Dimethyl-benzoic acid)	166	....	....	....	....	....	133	....	....	
260	**d,l-Phenylsuccinic acid**	167–8; 84 (anh.); d,l: 173–4	....	*mono* (α): 175; *mono* (β): 168–9	*mono* (α): 175; *mono* (β): 171; *di*: 222	....	....	*mono* (α): 158–9; *mono* (β): 145; *di*: 211	....	....	
261	**Mesitylacetic acid**	168	....	....	....	....	....	210	....	b.p.:	
262	**3-Chloro-4-hydroxybenzoic acid**	169–70, w.; 164–5	....	....	....	....	....	180–2	106–7	77–8	Nitrile, 155
263	**d-Tartaric acid**	169–71	....	....	*mono*: 180d.; 194 (cor.), ac. a.; *di*: 263–4d., al.	*di*: 163	*di*: 204	*mono*: 171–2; *di*: 196d., al.	....	....	Phenylhydrazide, 240

*Derivative data given in order: m.p., crystal color, solvent from which crystallized.

No.	Name	Melting point, °C	Boiling point, °C	p-Toluidide	Anilide	p-Nitrobenzyl ester	p-Bromophenacyl ester	Amide	Methyl ester	Ethyl ester	Miscellaneous
264	Azobenzene-3-carboxylic acid ..	170–1, or., al.	....	....	....	.....	....	198–9, or., al.	58, me. al.	....	....
265	2,2-Diphenylpropionic acid	171; 175	....	....	....	.....	....	149			
266	8-Chloro-1-naphthoic acid	171–2, al.-w.	....	....	....	.....	....	207.5, red, al.	....	50	....
267	4-Bromo-2,5-dimethylbenzoic acid	171.5–2.5, lgr.	....	....	....	.....	....	209–10	....	....	Nitrile, 103–4
268	5-Chlorosalicylic acid (5-Chloro-2-hydroxybenzoic acid)...................	172, w.	....	....	....	.....	....	226–7	50, b.p.: 249d.	25	Nitrile, 165–7; Phenyl ester, 81–3; Me. eth., 81–2; Et. ester, 118
269	4-Chloro-2-methylbenzoic acid .	172	....	....	....	.....	....	183	....	b.p.: 258	Nitrile, 67
270	2,4-Dibromobenzoic acid	174	....	....	....	.....	....	198	....	....	....
271	3-Aldehydeobenzoic acid (3-Formylbenzoic acid) `........	175	....	....	....	.....	....	190d.	53	b.p.: 278	Nitrile, 79–81, eth.; Semicar-bazone, 265; Phenylhydra-zone, 164
272	3-Thianaphthenecarboxylic acid	175	....	....	173	.....	....	198	....	....	
273	Apiolic acid (2,5-Dimethoxy-3,4-methylenedioxybenzoic acid)...................	175, w.	....	....	....	.....	....		71–2, w.	....	Nitrile, 135.5, al.-w.
274	Allomucic acid (2,3,4,5-Tetra-hydroxyadipic acid)........	176d., w.	....	....	....	.....	....	175–6, w.; di: 209d., w.	....	di: 139–41, al.	Polyphenylhydra-zide, 218d., al.
275	8-Bromo-1-naphthoic acid	178, bz.	....	....	151, al.	.....	....	179–80	33, pet. eth.	52, pet. eth.	....
276	3-Phenanthrylacetic acid	178	....	....	....	.....	....	176	....	....	
277	Acetylenedicarboxylic acid	179	....	....	....	.....	....	di: 294d.	....	....	
278	4-Toluic acid (4-Methylbenzoic acid)	179–80, subl.; 182	275 (cor.)	160; 165	144–5; 148; 140	104.5	153	160; 158			
279	6-Bromo-3-nitrobenzoic acid ...	180	....	....	166, al.	.....	....	197–8	82	66	Nitrile, 117, subl.
280	5-Bromo-2,4-dimethylbenzoic acid	180–1	....	....	....	.....	....	197.5–8.5	....	....	Nitrile, 88–9
281	Veratric acid (3,4-Di-methoxybenzoic acid).......	181 (anh.)	....	....	154	.....	....	164			
282	N-Benzoylanthranilic acid (2-Benzamidobenzoic acid) ...	181	....	....	279	.....	....	218–9	100	98	Nitrile, 156
283	4-Chloro-3-nitrobenzoic acid ...	181–2	....	....	131	.....	....	156, al.	83, me. al.	59, yel.	Nitrile, 100–1
284	3,5-Dinitrosalicylic acid (3,5-Dinitro-2-hydroxybenzoic acid)	182 (anh.); 174 (+1 H₂O)	....	....	....	.....	....	181			
285	4-Fluorobenzoic acid	182; 182.6	....	....	....	.....	....	154; 154.5	....	....	Nitrile, 35
286	4-Chloropicolinic acid (4-Chloropyridine-2-carboxylic acid)...................	182d.	....	....	....	.....	....	158; 152–4	57–8	....	Phenyl ester, 68, pet. eth.
287	2,4-Dinitrobenzoic acid	183	....	....	....	142	158	203	....	....	
288	2-Naphthoic acid............	184; 185.5	....	192, al.	171, bz.; 173	.....	....	192–3, al.; 195			
289	3-Bromosalicylic acid (3-Bromo-2-hydroxybenzoic acid)...................	184	....	....	....	.....	....	165	....	....	Nitrile, 49–50
290	2-Anilinoisobutyric acid (2-Anilinoisobutanoic acid).....	184–5, w.	....	....	155, al.	.....	....	136			Nitrile, 93–4, al.
291	4-Anisic acid (4-Methoxy-benzoic acid)..............	184–6; 184.2 (cor.)	275–80	186	169–71	132	152	167; 162–3, w.			

*Derivative data given in order: m.p., crystal color, solvent from which crystallized.

TABLE XII. ORGANIC DERIVATIVES OF CARBOXYLIC ACIDS
b) Solids (Listed in order of increasing m.p.)* (Continued)

No.	Name	Melting point, °C	Boiling point, °C	p-Toluidide	Anilide	p-Nitro-benzyl ester	p-Bromo-phenacyl ester	Amide	Methyl ester	Ethyl ester	Miscellaneous
292	(2-Carboxyphenyl)acetic acid (Homophthalic acid)	185; 180	......	....	....	......	......	228	....	....	....
293	Acetylanthranilic acid	185, ac. a.	......	....	167–8, al.	......	......	177, al.	....	....	Nitrile, 133, w.; N-Methylamide, 172, al.
294	Succinic acid (Butanedioic acid; Ethane-1,2-dicarboxylic acid)	185; 182.8	235d.	mono: 179–80; di: 254.5–5.5; 260	mono: 148.5; di: 230, al.	di: 88	di: 211.0	mono: 157; di: 260d., w.	....	....	....
295	5-Bromopyromucic acid (5-Bromofuran-2-carboxylic acid)	186, w.	......	....	....	......	......	144–5	....	b.p.: 234	Hydrazide, 135.5–6.0; Azide, 66–7
296	Hippuric acid	187	......	....	208	136	151	183	....	....	....
297	3-Iodobenzoic acid	187	......	....	....	121	128	186	....	....	....
298	5-Bromo-2-toluic acid (4-Bromo-2-methylbenzoic acid)	187, subl.	......	....	....	......	......	180	....	....	Nitrile, 70
299	2-Cyanobenzoic acid (Phthalic acid mononitrile)	187; 192	......	....	....	......	......	173	151	70	....
300	3-Nitroanisic acid (4-Methoxy-3-nitrobenzoic acid)	187	......	....	163	......	......	....	....	....	....
301	Fluorene-2-acetic acid	187	......	....	....	......	......	266	....	....	....
302	Coumarin-3-carboxylic acid	187d., w.	......	....	250	......	......	236	116–7	94	Nitrile, 182
303	d-Camphoric acid (1,2,2-Trimethylcyclopentane-1,3-dicarboxylic acid)	187.5–8.0; l: 187; d,l: 202; 208	......	(α): 212–4; (β): 190–6	mono (α): 204; 209–10; mono (β): 196; di: 226; di, l: 226	65.5	......	mono (α-amide-β-acid): 176; mono (β-amide-α-acid): 182–3; di: 192–3	(α): 77; (β): 86; di: b.p.: 263–4	(α): 47–8; (β): 57; di: b.p.: 285–6	....
304	3-Bromophthalic acid	188	......	....	....	......	......	.	....	mono: 127–8	Anhydride, 132–4
305	4-Bromo-3,5-dinitrobenzoic acid	188, al.	......	....	....	......	......	188, pa. yel., al.-w.	125, me. al.-w.	118, al.-w.	....
306	Butane-1,2,3,4-tetracarboxylic acid (low melting form)	189, w.	......	....	187 (rapid htng.), al.-w.	......	......	di: 181d., dil. H_2SO_4 tetra: 310d., w.	tetra: 75–6, w.	di: 168, w.	Heating → monoanh. of high melting form
307	Anthroxanic acid	190; 196d.	......	....	....	......	......	211–2, w.	70	64–5	....
308	α-Chrysenic acid (o-2-Naphthylbenzoic acid)	190	......	....	....	......	......	169–70	63	....	....
309	l-Ascorbic acid	190d.; d,l: 168–9	......	....	....	......	......	....	....	....	$[\alpha]_D^{23}$: +48 in me. al.; Diphenylhydrazone, 178d., red; Di-p-nitrophenylhydrazone, 262d., al.; Di-2,4-dinitrophenylhydrazone, 282d., br.-red

*Derivative data given in order: m.p., crystal color, solvent from which crystallized.

TABLE XII. ORGANIC DERIVATIVES OF CARBOXYLIC ACIDS

b) Solids (Listed in order of increasing m.p.)* (Continued)

No.	Name	Melting point, °C	Boiling point, °C	p-Toluidide	Anilide	p-Nitrobenzyl ester	p-Bromophenacyl ester	Amide	Methyl ester	Ethyl ester	Miscellaneous
310	Chlorofumaric acid	191–2, ac. a.			186, al.	di: 138.5			di: b.p.: 224	di: b.p.: 250 sl. d.	Ethyl ester amide, 102
311	N-Methylacetylanthranilic acid	192–3					155				N-Methylamide, 171–2; N-Ethylamide, 140
312	Coumarilic acid (Coumarone-2-carboxylic acid)	192–3, w.	310–5 sl. d.		159			159		27	Nitrile, 36; Phenyl ester, 101
313	Dimethylmalonic acid	193, subl.				83.6		di: 269			
314	trans-Aconitic acid	194–5d. (cor.); cis: 125 → trans on heating			di: 189; cis, mono: 170d., al.		tri: 186	tri: 250 → br.; 260 → sinters			Heat → Itaconic acid, 165
315	Benzylidenemalonic acid	195–6d.						di: 189–90	di: 44	85; di: 32	Mononitrile, 183; Dinitrile, 87
316	4-Ethoxybenzoic acid	198; 195–6			169; 170; 172			202			
317	trans-3-Nitrocinnamic acid	199; cis: 138				174	178; 173	196			
318	Chrysodiphenic acid (2-Phenyl-naphthalene-1,2'-dicarboxylic acid)	199						1-mono: 275; 2'-mono: 220	1-mono: 171.5, me. al.; 2'-mono: 124; di: 90		
319	3,4-Dihydroxybenzoic acid (Protocatechuic acid)	199–200d.			166	188		212	134.5, w.		
320	3-Hydroxybenzoic acid	200, subl.		163, dil. al.	156–7, w.; 155	106–8	176; 176.1–.4	170; 167, w.			
321	Phthalic acid (Benzene-1,2-dicarboxylic acid)	200–6; 191 (sealed tube); 230 (rapid htng.)		mono: 150 (slow htng.); 160–5 (rapid htng.); di: 201	mono: 170; di: 253–5	di: 155.5	di: 152.8	mono: 149; di: 220			
322	3,4-Dichlorobenzoic acid	201–2; 208–9						133			
323	(4-Chloromethyl)benzoic acid	203						173			Nitrile, 79–80, al., b.p.: 263
324	5-Bromo-2-nitro-4-toluic acid (2-Bromo-4-methyl-5-nitro-benzoic acid)	203; 200						191		61	Nitrile, 132
325	4-Bromo-3-nitrobenzoic acid	203–4			156, or.-yel., al.			156	104	74	Nitrile, 120
326	d,l-Tartaric acid	203–4 (+1 H$_2$O); 205–6 (anh.)			di: 235–6	di: 147.6		di: 226, w.-me. al.			
327	cis-Apocamphoric acid	204, w.; trans: 190–1, w.			mono: 212						Anhydride, 178, al.
328	3,5-Dinitrobenzoic acid	204–5			234	157	159	183			

*Derivative data given in order: m.p., crystal color, solvent from which crystallized.

No.	Name	Melting point, °C	Boiling point, °C	p-Toluidide	Anilide	p-Nitro-benzyl ester	p-Bromo-phenacyl ester	Amide	Methyl ester	Ethyl ester	Miscellaneous
329	**Mesaconic acid** (Methylfumaric acid)	204.5 (cor.), subl.	....	*mono* (α): 196; *di*: 212, al.	*mono* (α): 202; *mono* (β): 163; *di*: 185.7	*di*: 134 (cor.)	....	*mono* (α): 222; *mono* (β): 174; *di*: 176.5	....	....	....
330	**5-Bromo-3-nitro-4-toluic acid** (6-Bromo-4-methyl-2-nitro-benzoic acid).............	206	....	....	....	....	....	171	....	....	Nitrile, 130, subl.
331	**Anthracene-9-carboxylic acid** (*meso*-Anthroic acid)........	207, pa. yel., al.	....	....	....	....	....	111, yel.	....	....	Nitrile, 170–2, lgr.
332	**Vanillic acid**	207; 210	....	....	140d.	....	....	....	....	44, b.p.: 293	....
333	*trans*-**2-Coumaric acid** (*trans*-2-Hydroxycinnamic acid)......	207–8d., subl., w.	....	....	152.5	....	....	209d.	....	....	Acetate, 154–5; 146, bz.
334	**Oxamic acid**	210	....	....	148–9	....	....	419d.	....	....	....
335	**Pentamethylbenzoic acid**	210	....	....	....	....	....	206	....	....	....
336	**4-Coumaric acid** (4-Hydroxy-cinnamic acid)	210–3; 206 (anh.)	....	....	....	....	....	194	137; 126	....	Acetate, 200–5
337	*trans*-**2-Chlorocinnamic acid** ...	212, yel., al.	....	....	176	....	....	168	10.5, b.p.: 278–9	b.p.: 162[12]	Nitrile, 40
338	**2,4-Dihydroxybenzoic acid** (β-Resorcylic acid).........	213d. (rapid htng.); 216d.; 217	....	....	126–7	188–9	....	222	....	....	Loses H_2O of crystallization at 100. Easy loss of CO_2 gives m.p. varying from 194 to 236.
339	**2-Bromo-3,5-dinitrobenzoic acid**	213	....	....	....	....	....	216, pa. yel., al.-w.	109, me. al.-w.	74, al.	....
340	**4-Dibenzofurylacetic acid**	214	....	....	....	....	....	212	....	....	....
341	**Mucic acid**..................	214d.; (varies with htng. rate), 223–255	....	....	310	225	....	*mono*: 192d.; *di*: 220	....	....	....
342	**3-Chloroanisic acid** (3-Chloro-4-methoxybenzoic acid)......	214–5	....	....	....	....	....	193	94–5	....	....
343	**4-Hydroxybenzoic acid**	215; 213–4; 210	....	203–4, al.	196–7, yel., w.	180–2	191.5 (cor.); 184	162 (+1 H_2O), w.	....	....	....
344	**Piperic acid**	216	....	....	145	....	....	....	....	....
345	**3-Chloro-2-naphthoic acid**	216–7, me. al.-w.	....	....	....	....	....	237	58, me. al.	50	....
346	**3-Nitrophthalic acid**	218	....	*di*: 226	*di*: 234	189	....	*di*: 201d.	....	....	
347	**Acenaphthene-5-carboxylic acid**	219, bz.	....	....	....	....	....	198	....	....	Nitrile, 110–1
348	**4-Cyanobenzoic acid** (Terephthalic acid mono-nitrile)	219; 214	....	....	179	189	....	223	62	54	....
349	**4-Phenylbenzoic acid**	221	....	....	....	....	....	223	....	....	
350	**3-Hydroxy-2-naphthoic acid** ...	222–3 (cor.)	....	221–3	243–4, ac. a.; 249 (cor.)	....	....	217–8 (cor.), yel., al.	....	....	

*Derivative data given in order: m.p., crystal color, solvent from which crystallized.

TABLE XII. ORGANIC DERIVATIVES OF CARBOXYLIC ACIDS

b) Solids (Listed in order of increasing m.p.)* (Continued)

No.	Name	Melting point, °C	Boiling point, °C	p-Toluidide	Anilide	p-Nitrobenzyl ester	p-Bromophenacyl ester	Amide	Methyl ester	Ethyl ester	Miscellaneous
351	4-Hydroxy-2-naphthoic acid	225–6	......	206	......	......	......	217–8	......	......	......
352	5-Bromo-3-nitro-2-toluic acid (4-Bromo-2-methyl-6-nitrobenzoic acid)	226	......	......	......	......	......	235	......	......	Nitrile, 106–7, subl.
353	9-Fluorenecarboxylic acid	227; 230; 225	......	......	......	......	......	251	......	......	......
354	Biphenyl-2,2'-dicarboxylic acid (2,2'-Diphenic acid)	227; 233; 229	......	......	mono: 176; di: 229–30, al.	di: 187; 182.6	......	mono: 193; 190–1; di: 212, w.	......	......	......
355	Methyliminodiacetic acid	227d.	......	......	......	......	......	mono: 169; di: 169	......	......	......
356	2,4,6-Trinitrobenzoic acid	228	......	......	......	......	......	264d.	......	......	......
357	Piperonylic acid	229; 228	......	......	......	......	......	169, al.	......	......	......
358	5-Nitrosalicylic acid	229–30	......	......	224	......	......	225	......	......	......
359	4-Chloro-3-hydroxy-2-naphthoic acid	231, yel.	......	......	......	......	......	225	116, yel.	......	......
360	1-Phenanthroic acid	232	......	......	......	......	......	284	......	......	......
361	3-Pyridylacrylic acid	233	......	......	......	......	......	148	......	......	......
362	4-Bromo-3-hydroxy-2-naphthoic acid	233–5d., yel., al.-ac. a.	......	......	161–2	......	......	......	......	......	Acetate, 183
363	4-Chloro-1-hydroxy-2-naphthoic acid	234, al.	......	143–4	180–1	......	......	......	120–1	92–3	o-Toluidide, 148–9; m-Toluidide, 188–9
364	3-Chloro-2-nitrobenzoic acid	235, w.	......	......	186	......	......	......	......	......	......
365	Benzophenone-2,4-dicarboxylic acid	235, w.	......	......	......	......	......	di: >288	di: 107	......	......
366	5-Bromo-2-hydroxy-3-toluic acid (5-Bromo-2-hydroxy-3-methylbenzoic acid)	236	......	......	125, al.-w.	......	......	75–8	109	75	......
367	2-Thianaphthenecarboxylic acid	236	......	......	......	......	......	177	......	......	......
368	Butane-1,2,3,4-tetracarboxylic acid (high melting form)	236–7 (slow htng.)	......	......	di: 168, acet. (slow htng.)	......	......	di: 169d.	tetra: 63–4, lgr.	......	Di-imide, 320d., w.
369	7-Bromo-1-naphthoic acid	237 (cor.), 60% al.	......	......	202, al.-w.	......	......	247, 50% al.	55 (cor.), 60% me. al.	46	......
370	3-Pyridinecarboxylic acid	237–8; 235; 232	......	150	85; 132, bz.-lgr.; 265, w.	......	......	128; 122	......	......	......
371	trans-2-Nitrocinnamic acid	240; cis: 146–7	......	......	......	132	141	185	......	......	......
372	2-Chloroquinoline-3-carboxylic acid	240	......	......	......	......	......	200–1	......	......	......
373	4-Nitrobenzoic acid	241	......	204; 192	211; 204	168	137	201; 198	96	57	......
374	Azobenzene-4-carboxylic acid	241, red, al.	......	......	......	......	......	224–5, red	123–4, or., me. al.	86–7, or., red, al.	Nitrile, 120–1, br., bz.; Propyl ester, 64, red, lgr.
375	4-Chlorobenzoic acid	243; 240	......	......	194, al.	129.5, al.	126	179; 170	44	b.p.: 238	......
376	7-Chloro-1-naphthoic acid	243, 60% al.	......	......	185, al.-w.	......	......	237, 50% al.	54, 60% al.	......	......
377	3-Chlorocinchonic acid (2-Chloroquinoline-4-carboxylic acid)	244, al.	......	......	202, al.	......	......	334–5, al.-w.; 276–8 (after fusion)	89–90, acet.	64.5	......

* Derivative data given in order: m.p., crystal color, solvent from which crystallized.

No.	Name	Melting point, °C	Boiling point, °C	p-Toluidide	Anilide	p-Nitro-benzyl ester	p-Bromo-phenacyl ester	Amide	Methyl ester	Ethyl ester	Miscellaneous
378	5-Chloro-1-naphthoic acid	245; 241–2 subl.	....	....	....	....	....	239	....	42	Nitrile, 145
379	Azobenzene-2,2'-dicarboxylic acid	245, dk. yel., al.						*mono*: 215d., red-br., et. ac.; *di*: 294d., red-br., ac. a.	*di*: 101, red, me. al.	*di*: 85, pa. red, al.	....
380	Anthracene-1-carboxylic acid (α-Anthroic acid)..........	245, yel., al.; 252	....	....	....	....	....	260, al.	108, ac. a.	....	Nitrile, 126, yel.; Phenyl ester, 207–9, yel.
381	2-Amino-9,10-anthraquinone-1-carboxylic acid.............	250–2, or.-red						300, or., PhNO₂			
382	4-Bromobenzoic acid	251–3	....	197	180	....	189–90, w.	....	....	p-Phenylphenacyl ester, 193	
383	9-Phenanthroic acid	251; 253	....	....	....	....	....	233	....	....	....
384	4-Bromocinnamic acid	251–3	....	183	....	....	....	80	....	....
385	Cinchoninic acid (Quinoline-4-carboxylic acid)	253–4 (+1 or 2H₂O)	....	....	....	....	181	24	13, b.p.: 173¹⁵	Nitrile, 102
386	Gallic acid (3,4,5-Trihydroxy-benzoic acid)..............	253–4d.; 222–40d.	....	207	141	134	189	....	....	....
387	1-Acenaphthoic acid	256	....	....	....	....	....	228	....	....	....
388	2-Phenanthroic acid	260	....	....	....	....	....	243	....	....	....
389	Cinchomeronic acid (Pyridine-3,4-dicarboxylic acid)	260d., w.	....	*di*: 199–206	....	....	3-*mono*: 200d.; 4-*mono*: 170d., w.; *di*: 163–5d.	3-*mono*: 182; 4-*mono*: 154–72; *di*: 141	4-*mono*: 131–3, bz.; *di*: b.p.: 172²¹	Imide, 229–30, subl.
390	5-Bromo-1-naphthoic acid	261; 256	....	....	....	....	....	241	....	48–9	Nitrile, 147, subl.
391	Chelidonic acid (γ-Pyrone-2,6-dicarboxylic acid)..........	262	....	....	....	....	245	*di*: 122.5	227; *di*: 63	p-Phenylphenacyl ester, 195–8d.
392	4-Iodobenzoic acid	270; 265	....	210	141	146	217	....	....	....
393	5-Chloro-2-naphthoic acid	270, al.	....	202.5	....	....	186–7	81	45	Nitrile, 144
394	3-Phenanthroic acid	270	....	....	....	....	....	234	....	....	....
395	Quinoline-3-carboxylic acid	272	....	....	....	....	....	198	....	....	....
396	1-Chloroanthraquinone-2-carboxylic acid	272, pa. yel., al.	....	248–9, pa. yel., bz.-ac. a.	....	....	317, yel.	161.5, yel., acet.; 155	142, yel., al.	Benzyl ester, 135–6, yel., al.
397	Anthracene-2-carboxylic acid (β-Anthroic acid)..........	281, yel., al.	....	....	....	....	293–5, yel., al.	....	134–5	....
398	*trans*-4-Nitrocinnamic acid.....	285	....	....	186	191	204; 217	....	....	....
399	Fumaric acid (*trans*-Butanedioic acid)	286–7; (sealed tube); >200, subl.; 293–5	....	*mono*: 233.0–4.5; *di*: 313–4, ac. a.	150.8	....	270; 300–2 subl.; *di*: 266d.	*di*: 102, b.p.: 192	*mono*: 66; *di*: b.p.: 218	At 230 → maleic anh., 56
400	Muconic acid...............	289d. (slow htng.); 306 (rapid htng.)	....	....	....	....	*di*: 240d.	....	....	*trans-trans*: 296–8; *cis-cis*: 195

* Derivative data given in order: m.p., crystal color, solvent from which crystallized.

No.	Name	Melting point, °C	Boiling point, °C	p-Toluidide	Anilide	p-Nitro-benzyl ester	p-Bromo-phenacyl ester	Amide	Methyl ester	Ethyl ester	Miscellaneous
401	9,10-Anthraquinone-2-carboxylic acid	290–2, yel., ac. a.	......	......	258–60	......	......	280, ac. a.-bz.	170	147	......
402	9,10-Anthraquinone-1-carboxylic acid	293–4, pa. yel., ac. a.	......	......	288–9, pa. yel., PhNO₂	......	......	280, pa. yel., al.	189, pa. yel., me. al.	169, yel., al.	Nitrile, 247, yel., ac. a.
403	Bromoterephthalic acid (2-Bromobenzene-1,4-dicarboxylic acid)	299	......	......	......	......	......	di: 270	1-mono: 145; 4-mono: 164; di: 54	......	......
404	Terephthalic acid (Benzene-1,4-dicarboxylic acid)	300, subl. without melting	......	......	di: 334–7, PhNO₂	di: 263.5	di: 225	di: >225	......		
405	Chloroterephthalic acid (2-Chlorobenzene-1,4-dicarboxylic acid)	>300, w.	......	......	......	......	......	di: >300	di: 60		
406	4-Pyridinecarboxylic acid (Isonicotinic acid)	324	......	......	......	......	......	156	......		
407	9,10-Anthraquinone-2,3-dicarboxylic acid	240–2, yel., ac. a.						mono: >340, br., ac. a.	......	......	Anhydride, 290
408	Isophthalic acid (Benzene-1,3-dicarboxylic acid)	348, subl.	......	......	......	202.5	179.1	mono: 280; di: 280	......	......	Ba salt (+6 H₂O) very soluble—differentiates from Terephthalic acid.
409	Benzophenone-4,4'-dicarboxylic acid	subl. <360	......	......	......	......	......	di: >300	di: 224; 231	......	Dinitrile, 204–5
410	Trimesic acid (Benzene-1,3,5-tricarboxylic acid)	380 (cor.)	......	......	tri: 118–20d., ac. a.	......	tri: 197 (sealed tube)	365d. (cor.)	tri: 143–4, me. al.	tri: 132–3, al.; 133 after sintering at 127	......

* Derivative data given in order: m.p., crystal color, solvent from which crystallized.

TABLE XIII. ORGANIC DERIVATIVES OF ACYL HALIDES
I. Acyl Fluorides (Listed in order of increasing b.p.) *

No.	Name	Boiling point, °C	Melting point, °C	n_D	Density g/ml	Acid B.p., °C	Acid M.p., °C	Amide	Anilide	p-Toluidide	2-Naphthyl amide	Miscellaneous
1	**Acetyl fluoride**	20–1	. . . . .	. . . .	1.002^{15}	118	. . . .	82	114	147	134	. . . .
2	**Propionyl fluoride.**	44–6	. . . . .	. . . .	. . . .	141	. . . .	81	106	126	. . . . . .	. . . .
3	**Fluoroacetyl fluoride**	50.5–51	. . . . .	. . . .	. . , ...	167–9	31–2	108	. . . .	. . . .	. . . . . .	. . . .
4	**Trichloroacetyl fluoride**	66–8	. . . . .	. . . .	. . . .	197	57–8	141	97	113	. . . . . .	. . . .
5	*n*-**Butyryl fluoride**	67	. . . . .	. . . .	. . . .	162.5	. . . .	115	96	75	125	. . . .
6	**Chloroacetyl fluoride**	73–5	. . . . .	. . . .	. . . .	. . . . . .	63	120	137	162	117–8	. . . .
7	**Phthaloyl difluoride**	224–6	42–3	. . . .	. . . .	. . . . . .	206	220 (*di*)	253 (*di*)	201 (*di*)	. . . . . .	. . . .
8	**Phenylacetyl fluoride**	88–9^{17}	. . . . .	. . . .	. . . .	. . . . . .	76	156	118	136	159	. . . .

ᵛ Derivative data given in order: m.p., crystal color, solvent from which crystallized.

TABLE XIII. ORGANIC DERIVATIVES OF ACYL HALIDES
II. Acyl Chlorides a) Liquids 1) (Listed in order of increasing atmospheric b.p.)*

No.	Name	Boiling point, °C	Melting point, °C	n_D	Density g/ml	Acid B.p., °C	Acid M.p., °C	Amide	Anilide	p-Toluidide	2-Naphthyl amide	Miscellaneous
1	Acetyl chloride	51–2	......	1.3897²⁰	1.105²⁰₄	118	......	82	114	147	134	....
2	Oxalyl chloride..........	64	−12	1.434¹³	1.488¹³·⁴₄	......	101 (dih-yd.)	419d.	246	268	....	....
3	Fluoroacetyl chloride	72–3	......	....	....	167–9	31–2	108	....			
4	Acrylyl chloride	76	.....	1.4343²⁰	1.114²⁰₄	140	....	85	105	141		
5	Propionyl chloride	80		1.4051²⁰	1.065²⁰₄	141	......	81	106	126		
6	Isobutyryl chloride	92		1.4079²⁰	1.017²⁰₄	154.5	......	128	105	107		
7	Methacrylyl chloride	95–6		1.4435	....	160.5	15–6	102–6	....			
8	Vinylacetyl chloride	98				163		72–3	58			
9	n-Butyryl chloride	101–2		1.4121²⁰	1.028²⁰₄	162.5	......	115	96	75		
10	Pivalyl chloride...........	105–6					35	154	129	120		
11	Dichloroacetyl chloride	108				194	......	98	118	153		
12	Chloroacetyl chloride.....	108–10		1.454²⁰	1.3997¹⁸₄	189	63	120	137	162		
13	DL-α-Chloropropionyl chloride	110–11		1.440²⁰	1.285²⁰₄	185–6	......	80	92	124		
14	Methoxyacetyl chloride	113				204		97	58			
15	DL-Ethylmethylacetyl chloride	115–6				176	......	112	110	93		
16	Isovaleryl chloride	115		1.4136²⁴·³	0.985²⁴·³₄	176	......	135	109–10	107	138.5	....
17	Acetylglycyl chloride	115–8		....	....	......	206	137	....			Hydrazide, 115; Me. ester, 58–9
18	Trichloroacetyl chloride....	118		1.470²⁰	1.620²⁰₄	197	57–8	141	97	113		
19	Cyclopropane carbonyl chloride...............	120			1.152²⁰₀	186	18	125				
20	Ethoxyacetyl chloride	123–4				207	......	80–2				
21	trans-Crotonyl chloride	126		1.46¹⁸	1.08²⁰₄	......	72	161	118	132		
22	n-Pentanoyl chloride (n-Valeryl chloride)	126		1.420²⁰	1.0004²⁰₄	186	......	106	63	74	112	
23	Allylacetyl chloride	128			1.074¹⁶	188–9	......	94				
24	Bromoacetyl chloride	133–5			1.908⁰	208	50	91	131		134	
25	Cyclobutane carbonyl chloride	137; 142–3				195		153				
26	β-Methoxypropionyl chloride	138		1.424		107¹⁰		50.5				
27	Diethylacetyl chloride	140		1.4234		190		107				
28	β-Chloropropionyl chloride .	144		1.455	1.331¹³	......	42	....	119	121		
29	Isocaproyl chloride (4-Methylpentanoyl chloride)	147			0.9725²⁰₄	199	......	121	112	63		
30	α-Acetoxypropionyl chloride (O-Acetyl lactoyl chloride).	150 part. d.	.....	1.4241¹⁷	1.192	......	57–60; 40					
31	DL-α-Bromobutyryl chloride	150–2		....	....	217d.	−4	112	98	92		
32	n-Hexanoyl chloride (n-Caproyl chloride).......	153		1.426²⁰	0.975²⁰₄	205	......	100	95	75	107	
34	Furoyl chloride	173–4		....	....		133–4	142–3	124	107	......	
35	n-Heptanoyl chloride (Enanthoyl chloride)	175		1.4345¹⁵	0.963²⁰₄	223	......	96	70 (65)	81	101	
36	Hexahydrobenzoyl chloride (Cyclohexane carboxylic acid chloride)	183–4		1.4766¹⁵; 1.4711²⁰	1.096¹⁵₄		29–30	185	143–4			
37	3-Fluorobenzoyl chloride ...	189; 204		....	....		124	130				
38	Succinyl dichloride	190d.	20	1.473¹⁵	1.395¹⁵₄	186		260 (di)	230 (di)	255 (di)		
39	4-Fluorobenzoyl chloride ...	193	9	....	....		183	154.5	....			

*Derivative data given in order: m.p., crystal color, solvent from which crystallized.

No.	Name	Boiling point, °C	Melting point, °C	n_D	Density g/ml	Acid		Amide	Anilide	p-Toluidide	2-Naphthyl amide	Miscellaneous
						B.p., °C	M.p., °C					
40	n-Octanoyl chloride (n-Capryloyl chloride)	196	.....	....	0.949_4^{20}	239	16	110; 106	57	70	103	.....
41	Benzoyl chloride	197	−1	1.558^{15}	1.212_4^{20}	.....	122	130	163	158	.....	.....
42	Diethyl malonyl dichloride	197	.....	1.5537^{20}	1.2187_{15}^{15}	.....	125	224 (di)	....	....	.....	.....
43	2-Fluorobenzoyl chloride	206	4	....	....	.....	126.5	116	....	....	.....	.....
44	Phenylacetyl chloride	210	.....	1.533^{20}	1.1685_4^{20}	.....	76	156	118	136	159	.....
45	n-Nonanoyl chloride (Pelargonyl chloride)	215	.....	....	0.946_4^{15}	255	12	99	57	84	103	.....
46	Glutaryl dichloride	218	.....	1.473^{20}	1.324_4^{20}	302	97–8	175–6 (di)	224	....	.....	.....
47	4-Chlorobenzoyl chloride	222	16	1.579_4^{20}	1.362_4^{20}	.....	240	179; 170	194	....	.....	.....
48	Hydrocinnamoyl chloride (β-Phenylpropionyl chloride)	225 d.	.....	....	1.135_{21}^{21}	.....	48	105	98, pet. eth.	135	.....	.....
49	3-Chlorobenzoyl chloride	225	.....	....	....	.....	158	134	122	....	.....	.....
50	Phenoxyacetyl chloride	225–6	.....	....	....	.....	98–9	101.5	101	....	.....	.....
51	4-Methylbenzoyl chloride (4-Toluyl chloride)	225–6	−3.9	1.545^{20}	1.1686_4^{20}	.....	179–80	160	145	160; 165	.....	.....
52	n-Decanoyl chloride	232	.....	....	....	268–70	31	108; 98	70	78	104	.....
53	2-Chlorobenzoyl chloride	233	.....	....	....	.....	142	142	118	131	.....	.....
54	3-Methoxybenzoyl chloride	242–4	.....	....	....	.....	110; 105	....	....	....	.....	Benzylamine salt of acid, 112
55	3-Bromobenzoyl chloride	243; 239	.....	....	....	.....	155	155	136	....	.....	Hydrazide, 151
56	2-Bromobenzoyl chloride	245	11	....	....	.....	150	155–6	141	....	.....	Hydrazide, 153
57	2-Methoxybenzoyl chloride	254	.....	....	....	.....	....	129	131	....	.....	Phenyl ester, 59
58	4-Methoxybenzoyl chloride (Anisoyl chloride)	262–3 sl. d.	22	1.58^{20}	1.261_4^{20}	.....	184	162–3	169; 163	186	.....	Anisidide, 202
59	Phthaloyl dichloride	276	15–6	1.569^{20}	1.406_4^{20}	.....	200–6	220 (di)	253–5 (di)	201 (di)	.....	.....
60	3-Nitrobenzoyl chloride	278	35	....	....	.....	140	143	154	162	.....	.....
61	1-Naphthoyl chloride	297.5	20	....	....	.....	161	202	....	....	.....	Piperidide, 85–7

*Derivative data given in order: m.p., crystal color, solvent from which crystallized.

TABLE XIII. ORGANIC DERIVATIVES OF ACYL HALIDES
II. Acyl Chlorides a) Liquids
2) (Reduced pressure b.p. only) (Listed in order of increasing m.p. of the corresponding amides)*

No.	Name	Boiling point, °C	Melting point, °C	n_D	Density g/ml	Acid B.p., °C	Acid M.p., °C	Amide	Anilide	p-Toluidide	2-Naphthyl amide	Miscellaneous
1	β-Ethoxypropionyl chloride	78^{52}	......	....	....	120^{17}	....	51	....	....	....	....
2	Azidoacetyl chloride	50^{20}	......	....	....	......	16	58	....	....	....	....
3	Oleyl chloride	163^2	......	....	....	......	16	75–6	41	42.5	....	....
4	γ-Phenoxybutyryl chloride	155^{20}	......	....	....	......	64–5; 60	80	....	....	....	....
5	γ-Phenylbutyryl chloride	$140–2^{12}$	......	....	....	290	52	84.5	....	....	....	....
6	ω-Undecenoyl chloride (ω-Undecylenoyl chloride; ω-Hendecenoyl chloride)	128^{14}	......	....	....	275	24.5	87	....	....	....	....
7	Benzoylformyl chloride	125^9	......	....	....	......	64–6	91	....	....	....	2,4-Dinitrophenyl-hydrazone of acid, 196–7, yel.
8	Iodoacetyl chloride	$49–52^{15}$	......	....	2.25^{25}	......	83	95	143–4	....	....	....
9	β-Iodopropionyl chloride	81^{15}	......	....	....	......	82; 85	101; 142	....	....	....	....
10	Palmitoyl chloride	194^{17}	11–2	....	....	......	63	106–7	90	98	109	....
11	Myristoyl chloride	174^{16}	1–3	....	....	......	54; 58	107	84	93	108	....
12	Phenylpropiolyl chloride	$115–6^{17}$	......	....	....	......	136–7	108–9; 99–100	126	142	....	....
13	Dodecanoyl chloride (Lauroyl chloride)	145^{18}	−17	1.446^{20}	....	299	44	110; 102	78	87	106	....
14	α-Phenoxybutyryl chloride	$128–31^{38}$	......	....	....	258	82–3; 99	111; 123	93–4	....	....	Phenyl ester, 48–9
15	Cyanoacetyl chloride	$57^{0.5}$	......	....	....	......	66	119–20	198–9	....	....	....
16	Nicotinyl chloride	90^{15}	......	....	....	......	235	122	85	....	....	....
17	Dibenzylacetyl chloride	202^{18}	......	....	....	......	89	129	155	....	....	....
18	α-Phenoxypropionyl chloride	115^{20}	......	....	....	......	115–6; 112–3	132	117	115	117	....
19	DL-α-Bromoisovaleryl chloride	59^{15}	......	....	....	......	44	133	116	124	145	....
20	3-Ethoxybenzoyl chloride	$135–40^{16}$	27–8	....	....	......	137	139	....	....	....	....
21	α-Bromoisobutyryl chloride	52^{30}	......	1.475^{23}	....	......	48–9	148	83	92.5	135	....
22	4-Isopropylbenzoyl chloride	121^{10}	......	....	....	......	256–8	153	....	....	....	....
23	Benzilic acid chloride (α-Hydroxydiphenylacetyl chloride)	$193–5^{27}$	......	....	....	......	150	154–5	175	190	....	Me. ester, 74–5
24	1-Naphthoxyacetyl chloride	194^{10}	......	....	....	......	190	155	144	....	....	4-Phenetidide, 145–6
25	Hexahydrophenylacetyl chloride (Cyclohexylacetyl chloride)	$98–100^{23}$	......	....	....	244–6	33	171–2	....	....	....	....
26	Azelayl dichloride	166^{18}; $140^{0.4}$	......	....	....	......	106.5	175 (di)	186–7 (di)	191 (di)	....	....
27	2-Nitrobenzoyl chloride	148^9	20	....	....	......	146	176	155	....	....	....
28	Mesaconyl dichloride (Methylfumaryl di-chloride)	$64–5^{14}$	......	....	....	......	240.5	177 (di)	186 (di)	212	....	....
29	1-Naphthylacetyl chloride	188^{23}	......	....	....	......	131	180–1; 154	....	....	....	....
30	2,4,6-Trimethylbenzoyl chloride	$155–6^{18}$	......	1.5263^{25}	1.0967^{25}_4	......	152	188	....	....	....	....
31	3-Formylbenzoyl chloride	130^{20}	......	....	....	......	175	190	....	....	....	Me. ester, 53; Semicarbazone of acid, 265
32	4-Ethoxybenzoyl chloride	160^{20}	......	....	....	......	198	202	170	....	....	....
33	Sebacoyl dichloride	182^{16}	......	1.4684	1.1212^{20}_4	......	134.5	210 (di)	198 (di)	....	....	....

*Derivative data given in order: m.p., crystal color, solvent from which crystallized.

TABLE XIII. ORGANIC DERIVATIVES OF ACYL HALIDES
II. Acyl Chlorides a) Liquids
2) (Reduced pressure b.p. only) (Listed in order of increasing m.p. of the corresponding amides)* (Continued)

No.	Name	Boiling point, °C	Melting point, °C	n_D	Density g/ml	Acid B.p., °C	Acid M.p., °C	Amide	Anilide	p-Toluidide	2-Naphthyl amide	Miscellaneous
34	**Adipyl dichloride**	130–2[18]	. . . . .	. . . .	. . . .	. . . . . .	153	220 (*di*)	240–1	241	. . . .	Di-N-methyl-amide, 152–3
35	**Benzylmalonyl dichloride**. . .	141[15]	. . . . .	. . . .	. . . .	. . . . . .	117d.	225 (*di*)	217 (*di*)	. . . .	. . . .	. . . .
36	**Phenylmalonyl dichloride** . .	122[15]	. . . . .	. . . .	. . . .	. . . . . .	152–3	233	. . . .	. . . .	. . . .	Di-Me. ester, 51
37	*trans*-**Aconityl trichloride** (1,2,3-Propylenetricarboxylic acid trichloride) . .	155–7[20]	. . . . .	. . . .	. . . .	. . . . . .	194–5	260 (*tri*) (sinters)	. . . .	. . . .	. . . .	. . . .
38	**Fumaryl dichloride**	63[13]	. . . . .	1.5004[18]	1.408[20][4]	. . . . . .	300–2	266 (*di*)	314 (*di*)	. . . .	. . . .	. . . .

*Derivative data given in order: m.p., crystal color, solvent from which crystallized.

TABLE XIII. ORGANIC DERIVATIVES OF ACYL HALIDES
II. Acyl Chlorides b) Solids (Listed in order of increasing m.p.)*

No.	Name	Boiling point, °C	Melting point, °C	n_D	Density g/ml	Acid B.p., °C	Acid M.p., °C	Amide	Anilide	p-Toluidide	2-Naphthyl amide	Miscellaneous
1	Salicyloyl chloride	92^{15}	19–20	. . . .	. . . .	. . . . . .	158	142	136	156	189	. . . .
2	Stearoyl chloride	$202-3^6$	23	. . . .	. . . .	. . . . . .	70–1	109	95	102	112	. . . .
3	2-Iodobenzoyl chloride.		35–40; 30–1	. . . .	. . . .	. . . . . .	162	184	. . . .	. . . .	. . . .	
4	*trans*-Cinnamoyl chloride . .	258	35–6	1.6202^{37}	1.1632^{37}	. . . . . .	133	147–8	151	168	. . . .	
5	4-Bromobenzoyl chloride . . .	245–7	42	. . . .	. . . .	. . . . . .	251–3	189–90	197			Hydrazide, 164
6	Isophthaloyl dichloride.	276	43–4	1.570^{47}	1.388^{47}_4	. . . . . .	345–7	280 (di)	. . . .			Di-Me. ester, 68; Dihydrazide, 220
7	2-Naphthoyl chloride	304–6	43	. . . .	. . . .	. . . . . .	184–5	192				Piperidide, 88–90
8	2,4-Dinitrobenzoyl chloride.		46	. . . .	. . . .	. . . . . .	183	203	. . . .			Me. ester, 70
9	4-Formylbenzoyl chloride . .	258	48	. . . .	. . . .	. . . . . .	256	. . . .				Me. ester, 63; Phenylhydrazone of acid, 226
10	4-Nitrophenylacetyl chloride	. . . . . .	48	. . . .	. . . .	. . . . . .	153	198	198			. . . .
11	2-Naphthoxyacetyl chloride.	. . . . . .	54	. . . .	. . . .	. . . . . .	156	147	145	. . . .	. . . .	4-Phenetidide, 164–5; Et. ester, 48–9
12	Diphenylacetyl chloride	. . . . . .	56–7	. . . .	. . . .	. . . . . .	148	168	180	173	191–2	. . . .
13	*trans*-2-Nitrocinnamoyl chloride	. . . . . .	64.5				240	185	. . . .			Me. ester, 73
14	3,5-Dinitrobenzoyl chloride .	. . . . . .	68–9; 74				204–5	183	234	. . . .		Me. ester, 108; Et. ester, 93
15	4-Nitrobenzoyl chloride	$150-2^{15}$	75				241	201	211	204		. . . .
16	3-Nitrophthaloyl dichloride .	. . . . . .	77				218	201 (di)	234 (di)	226 (di)	. . . .	. . . .
17	Benzylidene malonyl dichloride	. . . . . .	77				195–6	189 (di)	. . . .	. . . .	. . . .	Di-Me. ester, 45
18	Fluorene-9-carboxylic acid chloride	. . . . . .	77				230–2	251	. . . .	. . . .		Me. ester, 63
19	Terephthaloyl dichloride . . .		83–4					>250 (di)	334–7 (di)	. . . .	. . . .	Di-1-naphthyl-amide, 334
20	4-Iodobenzoyl chloride		83; 77–8				270; 265	218	210	. . . .	. . . .	. . . .
21	Diphenylcarbamyl chloride (Diphenylaminoformyl chloride)	. . . . . .	86	. . . .	. . . .	. . . . . .		189				Me. ester, 86; Et. ester, 72, lgr.
22	2,2′-Diphenic acid dichloride	. . . . . .	94				228–9	212				
23	α,α-Diphenylpropionyl chloride	. . . . . .	95–6				173–4	149				Benzyl ester, 71–2
24	Phenanthrene-2-carboxylic acid chloride	. . . . . .	101				259–60	242–3	217–8	. . . .		. . . .
25	Phenanthrene-9-carboxylic acid chloride	. . . . . .	102				252	232; 226	218			. . . .
26	Diphenyl-4-carbonyl chloride (4-Phenylbenzoyl chloride)	. . . . . .	114–5				228	223				Me. ester, 117–8; Et. ester, 46
27	Phenanthrene-3-carboxylic acid chloride	. . . . . .	116–7				269	233; 227	216–7			. . . .
28	*trans*-4-Nitrocinnamoyl chloride	. . . . . .	124				286	217				Me. ester, 161
29	Fluorenone-4-carboxylic acid chloride	. . . . . .	128, yel.				227, yel.	230; 225	. . . .	. . . .		Oxime of acid, 263; Me. ester, 132; Et. ester, 103
30	Fluorenone-1-carboxylic acid chloride	. . . . . .	140, yel.	. . . .	. . . .	. . . . . .		229–30	. . . .	. . . .		Oxime of acid, 230; Me. ester, 86–9; Et. ester, 84–6

*Derivative data given in order: m.p., crystal color, solvent from which crystallized.

No.	Name	Boiling point, °C	Melting point, °C	n_D	Density g/ml	Acid B.p., °C	Acid M.p., °C	Amide	Anilide	p-Toluidide	2-Naphthyl amide	Miscellaneous
31	Azobenzene-4,4′-dicar-boxylic acid dichloride	....	144–5, red	....	....	......	330d.	....	....	....	....	Di-Me. ester, 242; Di-Et. ester, 146
32	9, 10-Anthraquinone-2-car-boxylic acid chloride	....	147	....	....	......	290, yel.	280	258–60	....	....	Me. ester, 170
33	Di-(1-naphthyl) acetyl chloride	....	167–9	....	....	......	228.5	....	....	....	....	....
34	9, 10-Anthraquinone-2,6-di-carboxylic acid dichloride .	....	197–8	....	....	......	>400	>370	....	....	....	....
35	9,10-Anthraquinone-1,4-di-carboxylic acid dichloride .	....	203–5	....	....	......	>300	....	....	....	....	....
36	9,10-Anthraquinone-1,5-di-carboxylic acid dichloride .	....	260–3	....	....	......	>390	....	....	....	....	Di-Me. ester, 236; Di-Et. ester, 155, yel.

*Derivative data given in order: m.p., crystal color, solvent from which crystallized.

217

TABLE XIII. ORGANIC DERIVATIVES OF ACYL HALIDES
III. Acyl Bromides a) Liquids 1) (Listed in order of increasing atmospheric b.p.)*

No.	Name	Boiling point, °C	Melting point, °C	n_D	Density g/ml	Acid B.p., °C	Acid M.p., °C	Amide	Anilide	p-Toluidide	2-Naphthyl amide	Miscellaneous
1	Oxalyl dibromide	64	.....	.....	.....	.....	101 (hyd.)	419d. (di)	254 (di)	268 (di)	.....	.....
2	Acetyl bromide	81	.....	1.4538^{16}	1.6625^{16}_4	118	.....	82	114	147	132	.....
3	Propionyl bromide	103	.....	.....	.....	141	.....	81	106	126	.....	.....
4	Chloroacetyl bromide	127	.....	.....	.....	.....	63	120	137	162	117–8	.....
5	n-Butyryl bromide	128	.....	.....	.....	162.5	.....	115	96	75	125	.....
6	Isovaleryl bromide	138–40	.....	.....	.....	176	.....	135	.....	107	138.5	.....
7	Trichloroacetyl bromide	143	.....	.....	1.90^{15}_{15}	197	57–8	162.5	95–7	113	.....	4-Nitroanilide, 146–7
8	Bromoacetyl bromide	150	.....	.....	2.425	208	50	91	131	.....	134	.....
9	DL-α-Bromopropionyl bromide	154–5	.....	.....	2.061^{16}_4	204	25.7	123	99; 110	.....	.....	.....
10	α-Bromoisobutyryl bromide	162–4	.....	.....	.....	198–200	48–9	148	83	92.5	135	.....
11	DL-α-Bromobutyryl bromide	172–4	.....	.....	.....	127^{25}	−4	112; 108	.....	.....	.....	.....
12	n-Hexanoyl bromide (n-Caproyl bromide)	175–6	.....	.....	.....	205	.....	100	95	75	107	.....
13	DL-α-Bromoisovaleryl bromide	184–94	.....	.....	.....	.....	44	133	116	124	145	.....
14	Benzoyl bromide	218–9	.....	.....	1.570^{15}	.....	122	130	163	158	.....	.....

*Derivative data given in order: m.p., crystal color, solvent from which crystallized.

TABLE XIII. ORGANIC DERIVATIVES OF ACYL HALIDES
III. Acyl Bromides a) Liquids
2) (Reduced pressure b.p. only) (Listed in order of increasing m.p. of the corresponding amides)*

No.	Name	Boiling point, °C	Melting point, °C	n_D	Density g/ml	Acid B.p., °C	Acid M.p., °C	Amide	Anilide	p-Toluidide	2-Naphthyl amide	Miscellaneous
1	3-Methylbenzoyl bromide	137[52]	.....	....	....	......	111	94; 97	126	118	....	....
2	n-Pentanoyl bromide (n-Valeryl bromide)	64[66]	.....	....	....	186.5	....	106	63	74	....	....
3	3-Chlorobenzoyl bromide	145[40]	.....	....	....	......	158; 155	134	122		....
4	2-Chlorobenzoyl bromide	144[37]	.....	....	....	......	140	142	114; 118	131	....	....
5	2-Methylbenzoyl bromide	135[37]	.....	....	....	......	104–5	143	125	144		
6	2-Bromobenzoyl bromide	167[18]	.....	....	....	......	150	155	141	....	
7	Phenylacetyl bromide	150–5[50]	.....	....	....	......	76	156	117–8	135–6	159	....
8	4-Methylbenzoyl bromide	147[42]	.....	....	....	......	179–80	160	145; 148	160; 165		
9	4-Methoxybenzoyl bromide	185[27]	.....	....	....	......	184–6	167; 163	169–71	186	....	....
10	4-Chlorobenzoyl bromide	142[27]	.....	....	....	......	240	179; 170	194	....	....
11	4-Bromobenzoyl bromide	136[18]	.....	....	....	......	251	189	197	....	....
12	Succinyl dibromide	105–6[13]	.....	....	....	......	186	260 (di)	230 (di)	255 (di)	....	....

*Derivative data given in order: m.p., crystal color, solvent from which crystallized.

TABLE XIII. ORGANIC DERIVATIVES OF ACYL HALIDES
III. Acyl Bromides b) Solids (Listed in order of increasing m.p.)*

No.	Name	Boiling point, °C	Melting point, °C	n_D	Density g/ml	Acid B.p., °C	Acid M.p., °C	Amide	Anilide	p-Toluidide	2-Naphthyl amide	Miscellaneous
1	3-Nitrobenzoyl bromide....	....	43	....	....	......	140	143	154	162	....	....
2	trans-Cinnamoyl bromide ..	....	48	....	....	......	133	148	151; 153	168	....	....
3	4-Iodobenzoyl bromide.....	....	55	....	....	......	270; 265	217	210	....	....	....
4	3,5-Dinitrobenzoyl bromide.	....	60	....	....	......	204–5	183	234	....	....	....
5	4-Nitrobenzoyl bromide....	....	64	....	....	......	241	201; 198	211	203	....	....
6	Phthaloyl dibromide.......	....	80	....	....	......	206	220 (di)	253 (di)	201 (di)	....	....

*Derivative data given in order: m.p., crystal color, solvent from which crystallized.

TABLE XIII. ORGANIC DERIVATIVES OF ACYL HALIDES
IV. Acyl Iodides. Liquids 1) (Listed in order of increasing atmospheric b.p.)*

| No. | Name | Boiling point, °C | Melting point, °C | n_D | Density g/ml | Acid | | Amide | Anilide | p-Toluidide | 2-Naphthyl amide | Miscellaneous |
						B.p., °C	M.p., °C					
1	Acetyl iodide............	108	......	....	1.98^{17}	118	....	82	114	147	134	....
2	Propionyl iodide..........	127	......	....	....	141	....	81	106; 103	126	....	....
3	n-Butyryl iodide	146–8	......	....	....	162.5	....	115	96	75	125	......,......

*Derivative data given in order: m.p., crystal color, solvent from which crystallized.

TABLE XIII. ORGANIC DERIVATIVES OF ACYL HALIDES
IV. Acyl Iodides. Liquids
2) (Reduced pressure b.p. only) (Listed in order of increasing m.p. of the corresponding amides)*

No.	Name	Boiling point, °C	Melting point, °C	n_D	Density g/ml	Acid		Amide	Anilide	p-Toluidide	2-Naphthyl amide	Miscellaneous
						B.p., °C	M.p., °C					
1	Dichloroacetyl iodide	55[15]	......	1.5754	....	194	....	98	118	153	....	....
2	Chloroacetyl iodide	37[4]	......	1.5903	....	......	63	120	137; 134	162	117–8	....
3	Benzoyl iodide	109[10]	......	....	....	......	122	130	163	158	....	....
4	Trichloroacetyl iodide	74[30]	......	1.5711	....	197	57–8	141	97; 94	113	....	....

*Derivative data given in order: m.p., crystal color, solvent from which crystallized.

222

TABLE XIV. ORGANIC DERIVATIVES OF ACID ANHYDRIDES
a) Liquids 1) (Listed in order of increasing atmospheric b.p.)*

No.	Acid anhydride	Boiling point, °C	Melting point, °C	n_D	Density g/ml	Acid B.P.	Acid M.P.	Amide	Anilide	p-Toluidide	2-Naphthyl-amide	Miscellaneous
1	Trifluoroacetic	39	.....	1.269^{25}	1.490^{25}_{4}	72	.....	75	88	....	....	....
2	Perfluoropropionic	72	.....	1.273^{25}	1.571^{25}_{4}	96	.....	95	....	....	....	....
3	Perfluoro-n-butyric	108	.....	1.285^{20}	1.665^{20}	120	.....	105	93	....	....	....
4	Acetic	140	−73	1.3904^{20}	1.0811^{20}	118	16	82	114	153	....	....
5	n-Propionic...............	167	−45	1.404^{20}	1.017^{15}	141	.....	81	106	126 (124)	....	....
6	Perfluoro-n-caproic (Perfluoro-n-hexanoic)	176	.....	1.295^{20}	1.769^{25}_{4}	157	.....	117	....	....	....	....
7	Isobutyric	182	.....	....	0.957^{17}	154	.....	128	105	107	....	....
8	Pivalic (Trimethylacetic).....	190	.....	....	....	164	35	154	129	120	....	....
9	n-Butyric..................	198	.....	....	0.978^{15}	162	.....	115	96	75 (73)	125	....
10	Citraconic (Methylmaleic) ...	214	7–8	$1.471^{21.5}$	1.238^{25}_{4}	.....	92d.	185–7 (di)	175 (di)	....	....	....
11	Isovaleric	215	.....	....	....	176	.....	135 (137)	....	107	138	....
12	Dichloroacetic	216d.	.....	....	....	194	.....	98	118	153	....	....
13	Valeric (Pentanoic)	218	.....	....	0.922^{17}_{4}	186	.....	106	63	74	112	....
14	Crotonic	248	.....	1.4745^{20}	1.0397^{20}_{4}	189	72	161 (158)	118 (115)	132	....	....
15	Caproic (n-Hexanoic)	254–7 (245)	.....	1.4297^{20}	0.922^{20}_{4}	205	.....	100	95 (92)	75 (73)	107	....
16	n-Heptanoic	258	.....	1.4335^{15}	0.9175^{20}	223	.....	96	70 (65)	81	101	....
17	α-Methylglutaric	272–5	.....	....	....	.....	79	....	175–6 (di); mono: (2 forms) 114 or 100	174–5 (di); mono: (2 forms) 126 or 98–9	227–8 (di), 115–9 (mono)	....
18	Caprylic (n-Octanoic)	280–5	−1	1.436^{17}	0.9065^{17}_{4}	239	16	110 (106)	57 (55)	70	103	....
19	cis-Hexahydroisophthalic	304	.....	....	....	.....	187–9	....	298–9 (di)	....	....	....

*Derivative data given in order: m.p., crystal color, solvent from which crystallized.

TABLE XIV. ORGANIC DERIVATIVES OF ACID ANHYDRIDES

a) Liquids 2) (Reduced pressure b.p. only) (Listed in order of increasing m.p. of the corresponding amide derivative)*

No.	Acid anhydride	Boiling point, °C	Melting point, °C	n_D	Density g/ml	Acid B.P.	Acid M.P.	Amide	Anilide	p-Toluidide	2-Naphthyl-amide	Miscellaneous
1	DL-α-Bromobutyric........	148–52^{10}	......	....	....	127^{25}	−4	112	....	....	....	4-Nitrophenyl ester, 48–9; 2-Naphthyl ester, 54
2	DL-α-Bromopropionic.......	120^5 (123–4^{10})	......	....	....	204	26	123	....	....	....	....

* Derivative data given in order: m.p., crystal color, solvent from which crystallized.

TABLE XIV. ORGANIC DERIVATIVES OF ACID ANHYDRIDES
b) Solids (Listed in order of increasing m.p.)*

No.	Acid anhydride	Melting point, °C	Boiling point, °C	Acid B.P.	Acid M.P.	Amide	Anilide	p-Toluidide	2-Naphthyl-amide	Miscellaneous
1	**Oleic**	22	......	......	16	76	41	43	169	....
2	**Capric** (*n*-Decanoic)	24	......	268–70	31	108; 98	70	78	104	D_D^{20}: 0.8596; n_D^{20}: 1.4234
3	**β-Ethyl-β-methylglutaric**	25	185²⁰	......	87	....	105 (*mono*)	....	....	1-Naphthylamide, 126
4	**Hexahydrobenzoic**	25	280–3	232	29–30	185–6	....	....	....	
5	**α,α-Dimethylsuccinic** (*unsym.*-Dimethylsuccinic)	29	220	......	141	....	....	....	....	α-Me. ester, 41; β-Me. ester, 52; Anil, 87
6	*cis*-**Hexahydrophthalic**	32	145¹⁸	......	192	....	....	....	....	Conc. HCl at 180 → *trans* form, 221
7	**DL-Methylsuccinic**	37	244–8	......	115 (112)	225 (*di*)	123, chl. (*mono*); 159, et, ac, (*mono*)	164 (*mono*)	155 (*mono*)	Anil, 109–10
8	*n*-**Undecanoic** (*n*-Hendecanoic) .	37	......	284	30	103; 99	71	80	....	
9	**2-Methylbenzoic** (*o*-Toluic)	39	......	......	104–5	143	125	144	....	
10	**β-Methylglutaric**	41	276–8	......	87	....	200 (*di*); 121 (117) (*mono*)	*mono:* 135	143 (*mono*)	
11	**Bromoacetic**	41–2	......	208	50	91	131	....	134	
12	**Lauric** (*n*-Dodecanoic)	42	......	299	44 (42)	110; 100	78	87	106	
13	**Benzoic**	42	360	......	122	130	163	158	....	
14	*trans*-α,β-**Dimethylsuccinic**	43	......	......	198 (208)	238 (*di*); 165–7 (*mono*)	....	....	....	Imide, 78
15	**Iodoacetic**	46	......	......	83	95	143–4	....	....	
16	**Chloroacetic**	46	......	189	63	121	134	162	117–8	
17	*n*-**Tridecanoic**	50	......	312	44	100	80	88	....	
18	**DL-Phenylsuccinic**	54	204–6²²	......	168	209–10 (*di*); 158–9 (α-); 144–5 (β-)	222 (*di*); 175 (α-); 170–1 (β-)	175 (α-); 168–9 (β-)	....	Imide, 90
19	**Myristic** (*n*-Tetradecanoic)	54	......	202¹⁶	54	107;103	84	93	108	D_4^{20}: 0.8502, n_D^{20}: 1.4335
20	**Glutaric**	56	......	200²⁰	97	*di:* 175–6	224	218	....	
21	**Maleic**	56; 52–4	198	......	130	181 (172) (*mono*); 266 (*di*)	173–5 (*mono*); 187 (*di*)	*di:* 142	....	
22	**Suberic** (*dimer*) (Octanedioic) .	56–7	......	......	144 (141)	127 (*mono*); 217 (*di*)	128 (*mono*); 186 (*di*)	*di:* 218	....	
23	**α-Bromoisobutyric**	63–5	198–200	......	48–9	148	83	92	135	1-Naphthylamide, 116
24	**Palmitic** (*n*-Hexadecanoic)	64	......	222¹⁶	63	106–7	90	98	109	D_4^{20}: 0.847; n_D^{20}: 1.4357
25	**Margaric** (*n*-Heptadecanoic) ...	67	......	231¹⁶	61	108	....	....	....	
26	**Itaconic** (Methylenesuccinic) ..	67–8	......	......	165	*di:* 192	190; 185	....	....	
27	**Sebacic** (*dimer*) (Decanedioic) ..	68	......	243¹⁵	133	210 (*di*); 170 (*mono*)	201 (*di*), 122 (*mono*)	201	....	
28	**Stearic** (*n*-Octadecanoic)	70	......	......	70	109	95	102	112	
29	**3-Methylbenzoic** (*m*-Toluic)....	71	......	......	111–3	94	126	118	....	Hydrazide, 97
30	**Phenylacetic**	72	......	......	76–7	156	118	136	159	
31	**2-Bromobenzoic**	75–6	......	......	150	155–6	....	....	....	Hydrazide, 153
32	**Arachidic** (*n*-Eicosanoic)	77–8	......	......	77	108–9	92	96	112	
33	**2-Chlorobenzoic**	79	......	......	142; 140	142	114; 118	131	....	
34	*cis*-α-**Methylglutaconic**	85	......	......	118	....	148 (*mono*)	....	....	
35	*cis*-β-**Methylglutaconic**	86	......	......	147–9	....	143 (*mono*)	....	....	Mono-Et. ester, 73
36	*cis*-α,β-**Dimethylsuccinic**	87	......	......	129;122	148–9 (*mono*); 244 (*di*)	222 (*di*)	....	....	Imide, 111; 101; Anil, 146
37	**3,5-Dichlorophthalic**	89	......	......	164	....	....	....	....	Imide, 208; N-Phenyl-imide, 150
38	**4-Methylphthalic**	92	295	......	152	188 (*di*)	....	....	....	Imide, 196
39	**3-Chlorobenzoic**	95	......	......	158; 155	134	122	....	....	
40	**4-Methylbenzoic** (*p*-Toluic)	95	......	......	179–80	160	145	160	....	
41	**Diphenylacetic**	98	......	......	148	167–8	180	....	....	Me. ester, 60

*Derivative data given in order: m.p., crystal color, solvent from which crystallized.

No.	Acid anhydride	Melting point, °C	Boiling point, °C	Acid B.P.	Acid M.P.	Amide	Anilide	p-Toluidide	2-Naphthyl-amide	Miscellaneous
42	**4-Chlorophthalic**...........	99	......	......	157	....	....		....	Imide, 210–11, Di-Me. ester, 37; Anil, 174
43	**Anisic** (4-Methoxybenzoic)	99	......	......	184–6	167; 163	169–71	186	....	....
44	**DL-Benzylsuccinic**	102	......	......	161	....	....		....	Imide, 97–8; Dihydrazide, 146
45	**β-Phenylglutaric**...........	105	......	......	140	....	171 (168) (*mono*)	154 (*mono*)	....	Imide, 174; Di-Me. ester, 86–7
46	**4-Ethoxybenzoic**	108	......	......	198	202	170	....	....	Hydrazide, 124
47	**α-Benzylcinnamic**	108–9	......	......	158	....	....		....	Me. ester, b.p. 278; Et. ester, 38–9
48	**3,5-Dinitrobenzoic**	109	......	......	204–5	183	234		....	......
49	**4-Bromophthalic**...........	113; 109	......	......	173–5; 166	....	....		....	Di-Me. ester, 40
50	**3-Methylphthalic**...........	114–5; 110	......	......	157	....	....		....	Imide, 189–90
51	**4-Nitrophthalic**	119	......	......	165	200d.	192	*mono:* 172	....	....
52	**Succinic**	120	261	......	186	157 (*mono*); 260 (*di*)	148 (*mono*); 230 (*di*)	180 (*mono*); 255 (*di*)	....	....
53	**Nicotinic** (3-Pyridine-carboxylic)	123	......	......	237–8	128	85	150	....	
54	**3-Chlorophthalic**...........	124–5	......	......	186	....	....		....	Imide, 118–20 (sealed tube)
55	**4-Iodophthalic**.............	125–6	......	......	182; 185	....	....		....	Imide, 224–4
56	**3,4-Dimethylphthalic**	126	......	......	201	....	....		....	Imide, 240–1; Methyl-imide, 98–9
57	**3-Bromophthalic**	132–4	......	......	188; 178	....	....		....	Mono-Et. ester, 127–8
58	**Phthalic**...................	132	......	......	206; 200	149 (*mono*); 220 (*di*)	170 (*mono*); 253–5 (*di*)	*mono:* 160	....	
59	**3-Iodobenzoic**	134	......	......	187	187			....	Me. ester, 54–5
60	**2-Naphthoic** (β-Naphthoic)	135	......	......	184	192–3	171–2	192	....	....
61	**2-Nitrobenzoic**.............	135	......	......	146	176	155		....	....
62	**Cinnamic**..................	136	......	......	133	148	151; 153	168	....	....
63	*trans*-**DL-Hexahydrophthalic acid**	140	......	......	221	*mono:* 196	....		....	Mono-Me. ester, 96; Di-Me. ester, 33
64	**Homophthalic** (2-Carboxy-phenylacetic).............	141	......	......	180–1	230 (2-), 185 (α-)	231		....	α-Me. ester, 96–8; 2-Me. ester, 143–5; α-Et. ester, 107–8; Imide, 233
65	**1-Naphthoic** (α-Naphthoic)	146	......	......	162	202	163		....	Piperidide, 85–7
66	**3-Bromobenzoic**	148–9	......	......	155	155	....		....	Hydrazide, 151
67	**3-Iodophthalic**	159–61	......	......	206	....	....		....	Di-Me. ester, 89; Di-Et. ester, 70; Imide, 238
68	**2,4-Dinitrobenzoic**	160	......	......	183	203	....		....	
69	**3-Nitrobenzoic**..............	160; 163	......	......	140	143	154	162	....	
70	**3-Nitrophthalic**	162	......	......	218	201 (*di*)	234 (*di*)	226 (*di*)	....	
71	**3,5-Dinitrophthalic**	163–4; 161	......	......	226	....	....		....	Et. ester, 187; Di-Et. ester, 73
72	**4,5-Dichlorophthalic**.........	188	313	......	200; 188	....	....		....	Mono-Et. ester, 133–4
73	**4-Nitrobenzoic**.............	189	......	......	241	201; 198	211; 204	204; 192	....	....
74	**4-Chlorobenzoic**	194	......	......	240	179; 170	194		....	....
75	**3,6-Dichlorophthalic**.........	194–5	339	......	194–5	....	....		....	Mono-Et. ester, 130–1; Di-Et. ester, 60; Imide, 242; Anil, 191
76	**3,4-Di-iodophthalic**..........	198	......	......	212–3	....	....		....	Anil, 270
77	**β-Phenylglutaconic**	206	......	......	154–5	138 (*mono*)	174 (*mono*)	184 (*mono*)	....	Mono-Et. ester, 78; Imide, 256–7
78	**4,5-Dimethylphthalic**	208			123;196	....	....		....	Methylimide, 150; Ethylimide, 89

* Derivative data given in order: m.p., crystal color, solvent from which crystallized.

TABLE XIV. ORGANIC DERIVATIVES OF ACID ANHYDRIDES

No.	Acid anhydride	Melting point, °C	Boiling point, °C	Acid B.P.	Acid M.P.	Amide	Anilide	p-Toluidide	2-Naphthyl-amide	Miscellaneous
79	2,2'-Diphenic...............	217	......	......	229	191 (mono); 212 (di)	176 (mono); 230 (di)	....	....	H₂SO₄ at 100-120 → Fluorenone-4-carboxylic acid, 227
80	4-Bromobenzoic	218	......	......	251	189	197	....	....	....
81	D-Camphoric................	221	......	......	188	177 (mono); 193 (di)	209 (204) (mono); 226 (di)	α: 212–4; β: 190–6	....	....
82	4-Iodobenzoic	228	......	......	270; 267	217–8	....	....	....	Me. ester, 114
83	Tetrachlorophthalic	256; 249	......	......	250 d.	....	....	....	....	Mono-Me. ester, 142; Mono-Et. ester, 94–5; Imide, 338–9; 2-Naphthylimide, 287; Anil, 268–9
84	1,8-Naphthalenedicarboxylic ...	274	......	......	274	....	250–82 (di)	....	....	Heat with aq. NH₃ → 1,8-Naphthalimide, 300; N-Phenylimide, 202; Di-Me. ester, 102–3
85	Tetrabromophthalic	280	......	......	266	....	....	....	....	Mono-Me. ester, 267; Imide, > 380, yel.; Anil, 279–80; p-Tolil, 280; 2-Naphthylimide, 306–8
86	Tetraiodophthalic	318; 325, yel.	......	......	324–7	....	....	....	....	Mono-Me. ester, 298

*Derivative data given in order: m.p., crystal color, solvent from which crystallized.

EXPLANATIONS AND REFERENCES TO TABLE XV

*Hydrolysis of amide or imide to the corresponding carboxylic acid and amine.**

$$RCONHR' \ + \ H_2O \ + \ HCl \ \rightarrow \ RCOOH \ + \ NH_3R'^+Cl^-$$

Acid $\qquad \downarrow OH^-$

$$NH_2R'$$

Amine

$$RCONHR' \ + \ NaOH \ \rightarrow \ RCOONa \ + \ NH_2R'$$

$\downarrow H^+$ $\qquad$ Amine

$$RCOOH$$

Acid

From the amide with aqueous hydrochloric acid.

For directions and examples see: Cheronis, pp. 607, 608; Vogel, pp. 404, 808.

From the amide with 85% or 100% phosphoric acid.

See: Cheronis, p. 609; G. Berger and S. C. J. Olivier, *Rec. Trav. chim.*, **46**, 600 (1927); W. M. Dehn and K. E. Jackson, *J. Amer. Chem. Soc.*, **55**, 4284 (1933).

From the amide with 70% sulfuric acid.

See: Wild, p. 193.

From the amide with aqueous sodium hydroxide.

See: Cheronis, p. 609; Vogel, pp. 404, 799; Wild, p. 193.

NOTE: For directions and examples for preparation of derivatives of carboxylic acids formed on hydrolysis of amides and imides see explanations and references to Tables XII, XIII and XIV, p. 186, 187, 188, 189.

For directions and examples for preparation of derivatives of amines formed on hydrolysis of amides and imides see explanations and references to Table XVIII, p. 291, 292, 293, 294.

*N-Xanthylamides.**

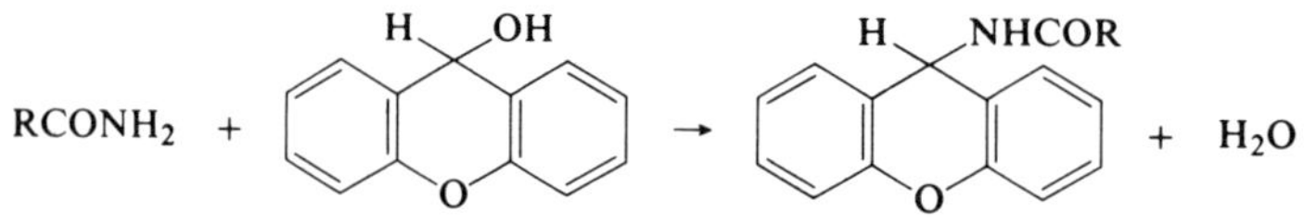

N-Xanthylamide

From the amide with xanthydrol in glacial acetic acid.

For directions and examples see: Cheronis, p. 610; Linstead, p. 66; Shriner, p. 222; Vogel, p. 405; Wild, p. 195; R. F. Phillips and B. M. Pitt, *J. Amer. Chem. Soc.*, **65**, 1355 (1943); W. Andriani, *Rec. Trav. chim.*, **35**, 180 (1916).

From the amide with xanthydrol in ethanol-water-acetic acid mixture.

See: Shriner, p. 222; Wild, p. 195; R. F. Phillips and B. M. Pitt, *J. Amer. Chem. Soc.*, **65**, 1355 (1943).

*Hg salt (Hg derivative).**

$$RCONH_2 \ + \ HgO \ \rightarrow \ (RCONH)_2Hg \ + \ H_2O$$

Mercuric salt

From the amide with mercuric oxide in methanol or ethanol.

For directions and examples see: Cheronis, pp. 610, 611; Wild, p. 197; J. W. Williams, W. T. Rainey and R. S. Leopold, *J. Amer. Chem. Soc.*, **64**, 1738 (1942).

From the amide with mercuric oxide in water.

See: Vogel, p. 405.

From the amide with yellow mercuric oxide without solvent.

See: Cheronis, p. 611; Wild, p. 196; J. W. Williams, W. T. Rainey and R. S. Leopold, *J. Amer. Chem. Soc.*, **64**, 1738 (1942).

Oxalate.

$$RCONH_2 \ + \ (COOH)_2 \ \rightarrow \ RCONH_2 \cdot (COOH)_2$$

Amide oxalate

From the amide with anhydrous oxalic acid in the presence of ethyl acetate.

*Derivatives recommended for first trial.

WARNING: This is not an instruction manual. References should be consulted for the preparation of derivatives.

For directions and examples see: Cheronis, p. 611; Wild, p. 196; C. A. MacKenzie and W. T. Rawles, *Ind. Eng. Chem., Anal. Ed.*, **12,** 737 (1940).

N-Acylphthalimide (Phthalimide derivative).

$$RCONH_2 \; + \; \text{Phthaloyl chloride} \; \rightarrow \; \text{N-Acylphthalimide} \; + \; 2\,HCl$$

From the amide with phthaloyl chloride in toluene or without solvent.

For directions and examples see: Cheronis, p. 611; T. W. Evans and W. M. Dehn, *J. Amer. Chem. Soc.*, **51,** 3651 (1929).

*Derivatives recommended for first trial.
WARNING: This is not an instruction manual. References should be consulted for the preparation of derivatives.

TABLE XV. ORGANIC DERIVATIVES OF AMIDES AND IMIDES
a) Liquids (Listed in order of increasing b.p.)*

No.	Name	Boiling point, °C	Melting point, °C	n_D^{20}	D_4^{20}	Derived acid				Derived amine				Miscellaneous
						M.P., °C	B.P., °C	p-Nitro benzyl ester	p-Bromo-phenacyl ester	M.P., °C	B.P., °C	Acet-amide	Benz-amide	
1	N,N-Dimethylformamide .	153; 76[39]	− 61	1.42938[22, 4]	0.9484[22, 4]	8.4	100.7	31	140; 135	. . . .	7	. . . . .	41	. . . .
2	N,N-Diethylformamide...	176–8; 68[15]	. . . . . .	. . . .	0.908[16]	8.4	100.7	31	140; 135	. . . .	56	. . . . .	42	. . . .
3	N-Methylformamide	180–5; 131[90]	− 3.8; − 5.4	1.4310[25]	1.011[19]	8.4	100.7	31	140; 135	. . . .	− 6	28	80	. . . .
4	Formamide.	193; 195d.	2.55	. . . .	. . . .	8.4	100.7	31	140; 135	NH₃	. . . . .	. . . . .	Xanthyl deriv., 184; Oxalate, 107.4–7.7
5	N-Ethylformamide	197–9	. . . . . .	. . . .	0.952[21]	8.4	100.7	31	140; 135	. . . .	16.5; 19	. . . . .	71	. . . .
6	N-Formylpiperidine (Form-N-piperidide) . . .	222	. . . . . .	. . . .	. . . .	8.4	100.7	31	140; 135	. . . .	106	. . . . .	48	. . . .
7	N-Acetylpiperidine (Aceto-N-piperidide) . . .	226	. . . . . .	. . . .	. . . .	166	118.2	78	86.0	. . . .	106	. . . . .	48	. . . .
8	N-Methylformanilide	243–4; 249–51; 128–9[15]	12.5	. . . .	1.0928[23]	8.4	100.7	31	140; 135	. . . .	196	102	63	. . . .
9	N-Ethylformanilide	258[728]; 123[11]	. . . . . .	. . . .	1.0549	8.4	100.7	31	140; 135	. . . .	205	54	60	. . . .
10	N-Propylformanilide	267[731] (cor.)	. . . . . .	. . . .	1.044[16]	8.4	100.7	31	140; 135	. . . .	222	47		. . . .
11	N-Isobutylformanilide. . . .	274[731] (cor.)	. . . . . .	. . . .	. . . .	8.4	100.7	31	140; 135	. . . .	227	. . . . .		. . . .
12	N-Isoamylformanilide. . . .	285–6[728]	. . . . . .	. . . .	1.004[16]	8.4	100.7	31	140; 135	. . . .	254.5 (cor.)	. . . . .		. . . .

* Derivative data given in order: m.p., crystal color, solvent from which crystallized.

TABLE XV. ORGANIC DERIVATIVES OF AMIDES AND IMIDES
b) Solids (Listed in order of increasing m.p.)*

No.	Name	Melting point, °C	Xanthylamide	Derived acid M.P., °C	B.P., °C	p-Nitrobenzyl ester	p-Bromophenacyl ester	Derived amine M.P., °C	B.P., °C	Acetamide	Benzamide	Miscellaneous
1	n-Butyranilide	35	......	− 5.5; − 8	162.5;164	......	63		184	114	160	....
2	Oleanilide	41	......	α: 13.36; β: 16.25	250 (superheated steam); 216[5]	......	40; 46		184	114	160	....
3	N-Benzpiperidide (N-Benzoyl piperidine)	48	......	122.4	249	89	119.0	......	106	......	48	....
4	Ethyl urethane (Ethyl carbamate)	49; 48	169	....	....	....	....	NH₃				
5	Formanilide	50; 47	......	8.4	100.7	31	140; 135	......	184	114	160	B.p. 271; Benzyl chloride → benzyl formanilide, 48
6	Malonic acid monoamide (Malonamic acid)	50	......	134.8–.9	....	di: 85.5	....	NH₃		....		
7	N-Propylacetanilide	50	......	16.6	118.2	78	86.0			47		....
8	Difluoroacetamide	52	......	....	134–5	....	....	NH₃				....
9	N-Benzyl-n-caproamide	53	......	− 3.9	203.35	....	72	......	184–5	60	105	
10	Phenyl urethane (Phenyl carbamate)	53	......						184	114	160	
11	Methyl urethane (Methyl carbamate)	54; 52	193					NH₃				
12	N-Ethylacetanilide	54	......	16.6	118.2	78	86.0		205	54	60	B.p. 249
13	n-Butyl urethane (n-Butyl carbamate)	54	......					NH₃				
14	N-Benzylisovaleramide	54	......	− 30	176.5	68.0	135; 137	......	184–5	60	105	
15	Acetoacetamide	54	......					NH₃				
16	Isobutyl urethane (Isobutyl carbamate)	55	148					NH₃				
17	N-Methyl-2-acetotoluidide	56	......	16.6	118.2	78	86.0		208	56	66	
18	Carprylanilide	57;55	......	16.3	237; 239.3		67.4		184	114	160	
19	Pelargonanilide	57	......	12.3	254.4	......	68.5	......	184	114	160	
20	N-Benzylacetanilide	58	......	16.6	118.2	78	86.0	37	298	58	107	....
21	Methoxyacetanilide	58	......		204; 203				184	114	160	
22	d,l-Lactanilide	59	......	18	122[15]		112.8		184	114	160	
23	N-Ethylbenzanilide	60	......	122.4	249	89	119.0	......	205	54	60	
24	n-Propyl urethane (n-Propyl carbamate)	60	......					NH₃		....		
25	N-Benzylformamide	60	......	8.4	100.7	31	140; 135	......	184–5	60	105	
26	N-Benzylacetamide	61	......	16.6	118.2	78	86.0	......	184–5	60	105	
27	Propiolamide	61–2	......	18	144d.	....	....	NH₃		....		
28	n-Valeranilide (n-Pentananilide)	63	......	− 34.5	186.4	....	75	......	184	114	160	
29	Isoamyl urethane (Isoamyl carbamate)	64	145					NH₃		....		
30	Erucanilide	65; 55	......	33–4	264[15]	......	62.5	......	184	114	160	
31	3-Acetotoluidide (N-Acetyl-m-toluidine)	66; 65	......	16.6	118.2	78	86.0	......	203	65	125	
32	N-Methyl-3-acetotoluidide	66	......	16.6	118.2	78	86.0	......	206–7	66	125	....
33	Ethyl oxanilate	66–7	....						184	114	160	....
34	Benzindole	68	......	122.4	249	89	119	52	253	157–8	68	
35	Heptananilide	70; 65	......	− 7.46	223		72	......	184	114	160	
36	Capranilide (n-Decananilide)	70	......	31.3	268.7	....	60	......	184	114	160	
37	n-Undecananilide (n-Hendecananilide)	71	......	28.5; α: 13.4; β: 16.3	280; 284	......	68.2	......	184	114	160	

*Derivative data given in order: m.p., crystal color, solvent from which crystallized.

No.	Name	Melting point, °C	Xanthyl-amide	Derived acid				Derived amine				Miscellaneous
				M.P., °C	B.P., °C	p-Nitro-benzyl ester	p-Bromo-phenacyl ester	M.P., °C	B.P., °C	Acet-amide	Benz-amide	
38	2-Methylhexanamide	72	......	......	209.6	......	......	NH₃		......	......	......
39	N,N-Diphenylformamide	73	......	8.4	100.7	31	140; 135	53–4	......	101	180	
40	Vinylacetanilide	73	......	– 35	169; 163	......	......		184	114	160	
41	Oleamide	76	......	α: 13.36 β: 16.25	250 (super-heated steam); 216[5]	......	40–6	NH₃		......	......	......
42	Thioacetanilide	76	......	......	93	......			184	114	150	......
43	Tiglamide	76	......	64.5–5.0	198.5 (cor.)	64	68	NH₃		......	......	
44	Tiglanilide	77		64.5–5.0	198.5 (cor.)	64	68		184	114	160	
45	4-Methylhexananilide	77		......	217–8[254]				184	114	160	
46	Lauranilide (Dodecan-anilide)	78	......	44; 42	299	......	76		184	114	160	
47	d,l-2,3-Dimethylbutananilide	78	......	– 1.5	191.7	......	......		184	114	160	
48	Pentadecananilide	78	......	52.3	212[16]	39.5–40 (cor.)	77.2		184	114	160	
49	d,l-Lactamide	78.5–9.0; 76	......	18	122[15]	......	112.8	NH₃		......	......	
50	Transbrassidanilide	79		59.7	256[10]	......	94.2		184	114	160	
51	2-Acetophenetidide (N-Acetyl-o-phenetidine)	79	......	16.6	118.2	78	86.0		229	79	104	
52	d,l-2-Methylpentanamide	79.6; 80	......	......	195–6	......	......	NH₃		......	......	
53	Tridecananilide	80	......	43; 41.6	312;177[10]		75.0		184	114	160	
54	d,l-α-Chloropropionamide	80	......	......	186	......	......	NH₃				
55	Propionamide	81;77	214; 211	– 20.8	141	31	63.4	NH₃		......	......	Mercury deriv., 201; Oxalate, 80.8–1.0
56	Acetamide	82	245; 238–40	16.6	118.2	78	86.0	NH₃		......	......	Mercury deriv., 196–7; Oxalate : 127.3; Phthali-mide, 135–6
57	Ethoxyacetamide	82	......	......	206–7	......	104.8	NH₃		......	......	
58	N-Methyl-4-acetotoluidide	83	......	16.6	118.2	78	86.0		210	83		
59	α-Bromoisobutyranilide	83	......	48–9	198–200	......	......		184	114	160	
60	γ-Phenylbutyramide	84		52	290	......		NH₃		......	......	
61	Myristanilide	84		53.9	212[16]	......	81		184	114	160	
62	Acrylamide	85	......	13	141; 140	......		NH₃				
63	Allylurea	85		......	......	......	......		58			
64	Acetoacetanilide	85	......	......	......	......	......		184	114	160	
65	d,l-α-Ethylphenylacetamide (α-Phenylbutyramide)	86; 83		42	270	......	......	NH₃				
66	4-n-Propylacetanilide	87		16.6	118.2	78	86.0		225	87	115	
67	α-Undecylenamide (α-Hendecyleneamide)	87	......	24.5	275	......		NH₃				
68	Propiolanilide	87	......	18	144d.	......	......		184	114	160	
69	3-Bromoacetanilide	87	......	16.6	118.2	78	86.0	18	251	87	120; 136	......
70	d,l-3-Methylpentananilide	87	......	– 41.6	197.5	......	......		184	114	160	
71	n-Butyl oxamate	88	......	189.5 (anh.); 101(+ 1H₂O)	......	di: 204	......	NH₃				
72	2-Chloroacetanilide	88	......	16.6	118.2	78	86.0		209; 207	87	99	
73	D-Chaulmoogranilide	89	......	68.5	247–8[20]	......	......		184	114	160	
74	Palmitanilide	90	......	62.7	222[16]	42.5	86;82		184	114	160	
75	N-Phenylmaleimide	91	......	130	......	di: 91 (cor.)	168–70; 190	......	184	114	160	

*Derivative data given in order: m.p., crystal color, solvent from which crystallized.

TABLE XV. ORGANIC DERIVATIVES OF AMIDES AND IMIDES

b) Solids (Listed in order of increasing m.p.)* (Continued)

No.	Name	Melting point, °C	Xanthyl-amide	Derived acid				Derived amine				Miscellaneous
				M.P., °C	B.P., °C	p-Nitro-benzyl ester	p-Bromo-phenacyl ester	M.P., °C	B.P., °C	Acet-amide	Benz-amide	
76	**Bromoacetamide**	91	. . . . . .	50	208	88	. . . .	NH₃		. . . .	. . . .	
77	**α-Phenylpropionamide**	92	158	. . . .	265	. . . .	. . . .	NH₃		. . . .	. . . .	
78	**Isopropyl urethane** (Isopropyl carbamate)	92	. . . .	. . . .	. . . .	. . . .	. . . .		33	. . . .	. . . .	
79	**Arachidanilide**	92	. . . . .	77; 75	204[1]	. . . .	89		184	114	160	. . . .
80	**d,l-α-Chloropropionanilide**	92	. . . .	. . . .	186	. . . .	. . . .		184	114	160	. . . .
81	**2,2-Dimethylbutananilide**	92	. . . .	− 15.0	187; 190	. . . .	. . . .		184	114	160	. . . .
82	**2-Nitroacetanilide**	92; 94	. . . .	16.6	118.2	78	86.0	71	. . . . . .	92; 94	98; 110	
83	**Maleimide**	93	. . . .	130	. . . .	di: 91	168–70; 190	NH₃		. . . .	. . . .	
						(cor.)						
84	**Elaidamide**	93–4	. . . .	44–5; 51	234[15]	. . . .	65	..	NH₃	. . . .	. . . .	
85	**Transbrassidamide**	94	. . . . . .	59.7	256[10]	. . . .	94.2	NH₃		. . . .	. . . .	
86	**2-Ethylpentananilide**	94	. . . . .	. . . .	209	. . . .	. . . .		184	114	160	. . . .
87	**N-Methyl-N-(1-naphthyl) acetamide**	94	. . . . .	16.6	118.2	78	86.0	. . . . . .	294	94–5	121	
88	**n-Caproanilide** (n-Hexananilide)	95; 92	. . . . . .	− 3.9	205.35	. . . .	72		184	114	160	
89	**N-Butyranilide**	95	. . . .	− 5.5; − 8	162.5; 164	35	63		184	114	160	
90	**N-Benzylpalmitamide**	95	. . . . . .	62.7	222[16]	42.5	86; 82		184–5	60	105	. . . .
91	**Azelaic acid monoamide**	95	. . . . . .	106.5	>360 sl. d.; 237[15]	di: 43.8	di: 130.6	NH₃		. . . .	. . . .	
92	**d,l-2-Methylpentananilide**	95	. . . .	. . . .	195–6	. . . .	. . . .		184	114	160	
93	**Iodoacetamide**	95	. . . .	83	. . . .	. . . .	. . . .	NH₃		. . . .	. . . .	
94	**Stearanilide**	95	. . . . .	70.1; 69.6	. . . .	. . . .	92		184	114	160	
95	**Heptanamide**	96	154–5	− 7.46	223.0	. . . .	72	NH₃		. . . .	. . . .	
96	**Trichlorolactamide**	96	. . . .	124	. . . .	. . . .	. . . .	NH₃		. . . .	. . . .	
97	**Semicarbazide**	96	. . . .	. . . .	. . . .	. . . .	. . . .	1.4	113.5	mono: 67; di (sym): 138	mono: 172–5; di (sym): 241 (cor.)	Gives semicar-bazones with aldehydes and ketones
98	**3-Toluamide**	97; 94	. . . . . .	111–3; 110–1	236, subl.	86.6	108	. . . . . .	. . . . . .	. . . .	. . . .	Mercury deriv., 200
99	**Trichloroacetanilide**	97; 94	. . . .	57–8	197.5	80	. . . .		184	114	160	. . . .
100	**3-Acetophenetidide**	97	. . . .	16.6	118.2	78	86.0		248	37	103	
101	**N-Benzylstearamide**	97	. . . .	70.1; 69.6	. . . .	. . . .	92		184–5	60	105	
102	**Glycollanilide**	97	. . . .	78–9; 80	. . . .	106.8	138		184	114	160	
103	**Methoxyacetamide**	97	. . . .	. . . .	204; 203	. . . .	. . . .	NH₃		. . . .	. . . .	
104	**Hydrocinnamanilide** (β-Phenylpropionanilide)	98; 96	. . . .	48.7; 40	279–80 (cor.)	36.3	104		184	114	160	
105	**α-Hydroxyisobutyramide**	98	. . . .	79	212	80.5	98	NH₃		. . . .	. . . .	
106	**Dichloroacetamide**	98, subl.	. . . .	5–6	194	. . . .	99	NH₃		. . . .	. . . .	
107	**2-Methylhexananilide**	98	. . . .	. . . .	209.6	. . . .	. . . .		184	114	160	
108	**4-Methylhexanamide**	98	. . . .	. . . .	217–8[745]	. . . .	. . . .	NH₃		. . . .	. . . .	
109	**4-Methyl-2-nitroacetanilide** . . .	99; 94	. . . .	16.6	118.2	78	86.0	117	. . . . . .	99	148	
110	**Capramide** (n-Decanamide) . . .	99	148	31.3	268.7	. . . .	67.0	NH₃		. . . .	. . . .	
111	**2-Bromoacetanilide**	99	. . . .	16.6	118	78	86.0	32	250	99	116	
112	**Phenoxyacetanilide**	99	. . . .	98–9; 99–100	285d.	. . . .	148.5	. . . . . .	184	114	160	
113	**Pelargonamide**	99	147.5–8.5	12.3	254.4	. . . .	68.5	NH₃		. . . .	. . . .	
114	**α-Bromopropionanilide**	99; 110	. . . .	25.7	203.5	. . . .	. . . .		184	114	160	. . . .
115	**n-Caproamide** (n-Hexaneamide)	100; 101	160	− 3.9	203.35	. . . .	72	NH₃		. . . .	. . . .	Oxalate, 71.1–.3
116	**Tridecanamide**	100	. . . .	43; 41.6	312; 177[10]	. . . .	75	NH₃		. . . .	. . . .	
117	**Phenylpropiolamide**	100; 109	. . . .	136–7, subl.	. . . .	83	. . . .	NH₃		. . . .	. . . .	

*Derivative data given in order: m.p., crystal color, solvent from which crystallized.

TABLE XV. ORGANIC DERIVATIVES OF AMIDES AND IMIDES
b) Solids (Listed in order of increasing m.p.)* (Continued)

No.	Name	Melting point, °C	Xan-thyl-amide	Derived acid M.P., °C	B.P., °C	p-Nitro-benzyl ester	p-Bromo-phenacyl ester	Derived amine M.P., °C	B.P., °C	Acet-amide	Benz-amide	Miscellaneous
118	N,N-Diphenylacetamide	101	.....	16.6	118.2	78	86.0	53–4	.....	101	180	....
119	β-Iodopropionamide	101 ...	.....	82; 85	....	....	....	NH$_3$				....
120	N,N'-Diacetyltrimethylene-diamine	101	.....	16.6	118.2	78	86.0	.....	136	mono: 126; di: 101	mono: 140; di: 147	....
121	Methylurea	101	230	....	....	....	....		–6	28	80	Picrate, 127d.
122	Phenoxyacetamide	101	.....	98–9; 99–100	285d.	....	148.5	NH$_3$		....	....	....
123	N-Methylacetanilide	102	.....	16.6	118.2	78	86.0	.....	196	102	63	B.p. 237; Conc. HNO$_3$ + H$_2$SO$_4$ → p-Nitro deriv., 153
124	Levulinanilide	102	.....	33–5, deliq.	245–6	61	84	.....	184	114	160	....
125	Pentadecanamide	102	.....	52.3	212[16]	39.5–40 (cor.)	77.2	NH$_3$		....	....	....
126	Isocrotonamide	102	.....	15	169	....	81	NH$_3$		....	....	....
127	Isocrotonanilide	102	.....	15	169	....	81	.....	184	114	160	....
128	n-Undecanamide (n-Hendecanamide)	103; 99	.....	28.5; α:13.4; β:16.3	280–4	....	68.2	NH$_3$		....	....	....
129	3-Benzophenetidide (N-Benzoyl-m-phenetidine)	103	.....	122.4	249	89	119	.....	248	97	103	....
130	N,N-Dicyclohexylacetamide	103	.....	16.6	118.2	78	86.0	20	225 sl. d.	103	153	....
131	3,4-Dimethylbenzanilide	104	.....	166; 164	....	....	....	.....	184	114	160	....
132	2-Benzophenetidide (N-Benzoyl-o-phenetidine)	104	.....	122.4	249	89	119	.....	229	79	104	....
133	Pyruvanilide	104, subl.	.....	13.6	165d; 80[25]	....	....	.....	184	114	160	....
134	N-Cyclohexylacetamide	104	.....	16.6	118.2	78	86.0	.....	134	104	149	....
135	2-n-Propylacetanilide	104–5	.....	16.6	118.2	78	86.0	.....	222–4	104–5	119	....
136	2-Ethylpentanamide	105; 103	.....	....	209	....	....	NH$_3$		....	....	....
137	Isobutyranilide	105	.....	–46.1	154.7	....	76.8	.....	184	114	160	....
138	4-n-Butylacetanilide	105	.....	16.6	118.2	78	86.0	.....	261	105	126	....
139	Acrylanilide	105	.....	13	141; 140	....	....	.....	184	114	160	....
140	β-Phenylpropionamide (Hydrocinnamamide)	105	189	48.7; 40	279–80 (cor.)	36.3	104	NH$_3$		....	....	....
141	Propionanilide	106; 103	.....	–20.8	141	31	63.4	.....	184	114	160	Conc. HNO$_3$ + H$_2$SO$_4$ → p-Nitro deriv., 182
142	Palmitamide	106	142	62.7	222[16]	42.5	86; 82	NH$_3$		....	....	....
143	N-Benzylbenzamide	106	.....	122.4	249	89	119	.....	184–5	60	105	....
144	D-Chaulmoogramide	106	.....	68.5	247–8[20]	....	....	NH$_3$		....	....	....
145	sym-Dimethylurea	106	.....	....	....	....	....		–6	28	80	....
146	n-Valeramide (n-Pentanamide)	106	167	–34.5	186.4	....	75	NH$_3$		....	....	Oxalate, 61.1–.4
147	Myristamide	107; 103	.....	53.9	212[16]	....	81	NH$_3$		....	....	....
148	N-Benzylbenzanilide	107	.....	122.4	249	89	119	37	298	58	107	....
149	Margaramide (Heptadecanamide)	108	.....	61.2	231[16]	48.5–9.0 (cor.)	82.6	NH$_3$		....	....	....
150	Thioacetamide	108	.....	93	....	....	....	NH$_3$		....	....	....
151	Fluoroacetamide	108	.....	31–2	167–9	....	....	NH$_3$		....	....	....
152	Levulinamide	108d.	.....	33–5, deliq.	245–6	61	84	NH$_3$		....	....	....
153	Azelaic acid monoanilide	108	.....	106.5	> 360 sl. d.; 237[15]	di: 143.8	di: 130.6	.....	184	114	160	....
154	Arachidamide	108–9	.....	77; 75	204[1]	....	89	NH$_3$		....	....	....

*Derivative data given in order: m.p., crystal color, solvent from which crystallized.

TABLE XV. ORGANIC DERIVATIVES OF AMIDES AND IMIDES
b) Solids (Listed in order of increasing m.p.)* (Continued)

No.	Name	Melting point, °C	Xanthylamide	Derived acid M.P., °C	Derived acid B.P., °C	p-Nitrobenzyl ester	p-Bromophenacyl ester	Derived amine M.P., °C	Derived amine B.P., °C	Acetamide	Benzamide	Miscellaneous
155	Anthranilamide	109	......	147d.	......	......	......	NH$_3$		......	......	
156	2-Iodoacetanilide	109	......	16.6	118.2	78	86	61; 58	......	109	139	
157	Pimelic acid monoanilide	109	......	104–5, subl.	223^{15}	......	di: 136.6	......	184	114	160	
158	Stearamide	109	139–41	70.1; 69.6	......		92	NH$_3$		......	......	
159	α-Methylhydrocinnamamide	109	......	......	......	......	......	NH$_3$		......	......	
160	Lauramide (Dodecanamide)	170; 102	......	44; 42	299	......	76	NH$_3$		......	......	
161	n-Caprylamide (n-Octanamide)	110; 108	148	16.3	237; 239.3	......	67.4	NH$_3$		......	......	
162	Isovaleranilide	110	......	−30.0	176.5	......	68.0		184	114	160	
163	d,l-2-Methylbutananilide	110	......	......	176–7; 174	......	55		184	114	160	
164	3-Nitrophenylacetamide	110	......	120	......	......	......	NH$_3$		......	......	
165	2-Ethylacetanilide	111	......	16.6	118.2	78	86.0	......	210–1	111	147	
166	β-Bromopropionamide	111	......	62.5	......	......	......	NH$_3$		......	......	
167	3-Aminobenzamide	111	......	174d.	......	......	......	NH$_3$		......	......	
168	2-Ethylbutanamide	112; 107	......	−31.8	195	......	......	NH$_3$		......	......	
169	4-Methylpentananilide (Isocaproanilide)	112; 110	......	−33	199.1^{752}	......	77.3		184	174	160	
170	d,l-2-Methylbutanamide	112	......	......	176–7; 174	......	55	NH$_3$		......	......	
171	2-Acetotoluidide	112	......	16.6	118.2	78	86.0	200	......	110–1^1	146	KMnO$_4$ → Acetylanthranilic acid, 185
172	d-Hydnocarpamide (α-Cyclopentylundecylamide)	112–3	......	60.5	......	......	......	NH$_3$				
173	4-Aminobenzamide	114	......	118d.	......	......	......	NH$_3$				
174	Acetanilide	114 (cor.)	......	16.6	118.2	78	86.0	......	184	114	160	B.p.304; Conc. HNO$_3$ + H$_2$SO$_4$ → p-nitro deriv., 210
175	N-Benzylcrotonamide	114	......	72	189 (cor.)	67.4	95–6	......	184–5	60	105	......
176	Ethyl oxamate	114	......	189.5 (anh.); 101(+ 2H$_2$O) (rapid htng.)	......	di: 204	......	......	16.5; 19	......	71	
177	2-Chlorobenzanilide	114; 118	......	142; 140	......	106	106	......	184	114	160	......
178	Dihydroacetic acid monoanilide	115	......	109	270	......	......	......	184	114	160	
179	n-Butyramide	115	185–7	−5.5; −8	162.5; 164	......	63	NH$_3$		......	......	Mercury deriv., 222–4; Oxalate, 65.9–6.2
180	Methacrylamide	116	......	16	161	......	......	NH$_3$		......	......	
181	α-Bromoisovaleranilide	116	......	44	230d.	......	......	......	184	114	160	
182	trans-α-Crotonanilide	118; 115	......	72, w.	189 (cor.)	67.4	95–6	......	184	114	160	
183	Phenylacetanilide	118	......	76.5, subl.	256.5 (cor.)	65	89	......	184	114	160	Conc. HNO$_3$ → 2,4-dinitrophenylacetic acid, 189
184	Dichloroacetanilide	118	......	5–6	194	......	99	......	184	114	160	
185	N-Ethyl-4-nitroacetanilide	118	......	16.6	118.2	78	86.0	96	......	119	98	
186	Trimesic acid trianilide	118–20d.	......	380 (cor.)	......	......	tri: 197 (sealed tube)	......	184	114	160	
187	3-Iodoacetanilide	119	......	16.6	118.2	78	86.0	33; 27	......	119	157	
188	Cyanoacetamide	120	222–3	66	......	......	......	NH$_3$		......	......	

* Derivative data given in order: m.p.. crystal color, solvent from which crystallized.

TABLE XV. ORGANIC DERIVATIVES OF AMIDES AND IMIDES

b) Solids (Listed in order of increasing m. p.)* (Continued)

No.	Name	Melting point, °C	Xanthylamide	Derived acid M.P., °C	B.P., °C	p-Nitrobenzyl ester	p-Bromophenacyl ester	Derived amine M.P., °C	B.P., °C	Acetamide	Benzamide	Miscellaneous
189	Glycolamide	120	......	78–9; 80	....	106.8	138	NH₃		....	....	....
190	Isocaproamide (Isohexanamide)	120–1	159–60	−33	199.1⁷⁵²	....	77.3	NH₃		....	....	....
191	Chloroacetamide	121	208–9	α:61.3; β:56.2; γ:52.5	189	....	104			....	....	....
192	2-Chlorophenoxyacetanilide	121	......	145–6, w.	245d.	....	....		184	114	160	....
193	Tribromoacetamide	122	......	131; 135	245d.	....	....	NH₃		....	....	....
194	Sebacic acid monoanilide	122	......	33, subl.	243¹⁵	di: 73.5; 72.6	di: 147		184	114	160	....
195	3-Chlorobenzanilide	122–5	......	158; 155	....	107	116		184	114	160	....
196	α-Bromopropionamide	123	......	25.7	203.5	....	....	NH₃		....	....	....
197	Furanilide	123.5	......	133–4; 132	230–2	133.5	138.5		184	114	160	....
198	Pyruvamide	124	......	13.6	165d.; 80²⁵	....	....	NH₃		....	....	....
199	3-Methylpentanamide	125	......	−41.6	197.5	....	....	NH₃		....	....	....
200	4-Chlorophenoxyacetanilide	125	......	155–6, w.; 158	....	....	136		184	114	160	....
201	3-Benzotoluidide (N-Benzoyl-m-toluidine)	125	......	122.4	249	89	119.0		203	65	125	....
202	2-Toluanilide	125	......	104–5; 107–8	259⁷⁵¹	90.7	57		184	114	160	....
203	Acetyl-β-phenylhydrazine	125–6	......	16.6	118.2	78	86.0	19; 23	243	128; di: 107	168; di: 177	....
204	Adipic acid monoamide	125–30	......	153–4 (cor.)	216¹⁵	106	154.5; 152.6	NH₃		....	....	....
205	Succinimide	126	245–7	185; 182.8	235d.	di: 88	di: 211	NH₃		....	....	....
206	3-Toluanilide	126	......	111–3; 110–1	263, subl.	86.6	108		184	114	160	....
207	Angelanilide	126	......	45–6	185 (cor.)	....	....		184	114	160	....
208	β-Resorcylanilide (2,4-Dihydroxybenzanilide)	126–7	......	213d. (rapid htng.) 216; 217	....	188–9	....		184	114	160	....
209	2-Ethylbutananilide	127; 127.5	......	−31.8	195	....	....		184	114	160	....
210	Suberic acid monoamide	127	......	144; 139–41	....	di: 85	di: 144.2	NH₃		....	....	....
211	4-Methoxyacetanilide	127	......	16.6	118.2	78	86.0	58	240	130; 127	154; 157	....
212	Angelamide	127–8	......	45–6	185 (cor.)	....	....	NH₃		....	....	....
213	Phenylpropiolanilide	128; 126	......	136–7, subl.	....	83	....		184	114	160	....
214	Nicotinamide	128; 129; 129–31	......	237–8, subl.	....	....	....	NH₃		....	....	B.p. 150–60⁵·¹⁰⁻⁴; Chloroaurate, 205; N-Ethyl, 188–9; N-isopropyl, 184–6
215	Pivalanilide	128 (cor.); 132–3	......	35.5	163–4	....	75–6		184	114	160	....
216	Suberic acid monoanilide	128–9	......	144; 139–41	....	di: 85	di: 144.2		184	114	160	....
217	Isobutyramide	129; 127	210–1	−46.1	154.7	....	76.8	NH₃		....	....	....
218	2-Methoxybenzamide	129	......	100–1	200	....	113	NH₃		....	....	Mercury deriv., 241
219	2-Bromo-4-nitroacetanilide	129	......	16.6	118.2	78	86.0	105	....	129	160	....
220	Benzamide	130; 129	222.5–3.5; 224	122.4	249	89	119	NH₃		....	....	Mercury deriv., 222; Phthalimide, 168

*Derivative data given in order: m.p., crystal color, solvent from which crystallized.

TABLE XV. ORGANIC DERIVATIVES OF AMIDES AND IMIDES
b) Solids (Listed in order of increasing m.p.)* (Continued)

No.	Name	Melting point, °C	Xanthyl-amide	Derived acid M.P., °C	B.P., °C	p-Nitro-benzyl ester	p-Bromo-phenacyl ester	Derived amine M.P., °C	B.P., °C	Acet-amide	Benz-amide	Miscellaneous
221	3,4-Dimethylbenzamide	130	......	166; 164	....	....	....	NH$_3$				....
222	α,β-Dibromopropionamide	130; 133	......	67(stab.); 50 (un-stab.)	160^{20}	....	....	NH$_3$				....
223	Anthranilanilide	131	......	147	....	....	....		184	114	160	....
224	Bromoacetanilide	131	......	50	208	88	....		184	114	160	....
225	2-Methoxybenzanilide	131	......	100–1	200	....	113		184	114	160	....
226	Nicotinanilide	132, bz.; 85 (+ 2H$_2$O), w.; 265 (anh.)	......	237–8, subl.	....	....	....		184	114	160	....
227	2,2-Dimethylbutanamide	132; 103	......	−15.0	187; 190	....	....		184	114	160	....
228	d,l-2,3-Dimethylbutanamide	132	......	−1.5	191.7	....	....	NH$_3$				....
229	3,3-Dimethylbutananilide	132	......	6.7	184; 96^{26}	....	....		184	114	160	....
230	3,3-Dimethylbutanamide	132	......	6.7	184; 96^{26}	....	....	NH$_3$				....
231	2,5-Dichloroacetanilide	132	......	16.6	118.2	78	86.0	50	......	132	120	....
232	Malonic acid monoanilide	132	......	134.8–.9	....	di: 85.5	....		184	114	160	....
233	Urea (Carbamide)	132.8	265; 274	....	....	....	....	NH$_3$				Phthalimide, 188–90; Picrate, 148
234	2,4-Dimethylacetanilide	133; 130	......	16.6	118.2	78	86.0	......	217	133; 130	192	....
235	Mesityleneamide (3,5-Dimethylbenzamide)	133	......	16.6	....	....	....	NH$_3$				....
236	4-Isopropylbenzamide	133	......	177, al.	....	....	....	NH$_3$				....
237	α-Bromoisovaleramide	133	......	44	230d.	....	....	NH$_3$				....
238	4-Chlorophenoxyacetamide	133	......	155–6, w.; 158	....	....	136	NH$_3$				....
239	d,l-Mandelamide	133–4 (cor.)	......	118	....	123–4	....	NH$_3$				....
240	N-(2-Naphthyl)acetamide	134	......	16.6	118.2	78	86.0	112	......	132	162	Br$_2$ → 1-Bromo deriv., 140
241	3-Chlorobenzamide	134	......	158; 155	....	107	116	NH$_3$				Mercury deriv., 245
242	Phenacetin (4-Aceto-phenetidide)	134	......	16.6	118.2	78	86.0	2–3	248; 254	137	173	10%HNO$_3$ → 3-Nitro deriv., 103
243	Chloroacetanilide	134; 136–7	......	α:61.3; β:56.2; γ:52.5	189	....	104		184	114	160	....
244	2,3-Dimethylacetanilide	135	......	16.6	118.2	78	86.0	......	221–2	135	189	....
245	Isovaleramide	135; 136	182–3	−30.0	176.5	....	68.0	NH$_3$				....
246	Acetyl salicylanilide	136	......	135 (rapid htng.)	140d.	90.5	....		184	114	160	....
247	3-Bromobenzanilide	136	......	155	....	105	120		184	114	160	....
248	Salicylanilide	136	......	158.3 (subl. at 76)	....	97–8	140	......	184	114	160	....
249	α-Hydroxyisobutyranilide	136	......	79	212	80.5	98	......	184	114	160	....
250	N,N-Diacetyltetramethyl-enediamine	137	......	16.6	118.2	78	86.0	27	159	di: 137	di: 177	....
251	Benzo-2-iodonanilide (N-Benzoyl-o-iodoaniline)	139	......	122.4 (subl. at 100)	249	89	119	61; 58	......	109	139	....
252	3-Ethoxybenzamide	139	......	137	....	....	....	NH$_3$				....
253	2,5-Dimethylacetanilide	139	......	16.6	118.2	78	86.0	15.5	213–5	139	140	....
254	3-Aminobenzanilide	140	......	174d.	....	....	....		184	114	160	....

*Derivative data given in order: m.p., crystal color, solvent from which crystallized.

No.	Name	Melting point, °C	Xanthylamide	Derived acid				Derived amine				Miscellaneous
				M.P., °C	B.P., °C	p-Nitrobenzyl ester	p-Bromophenacyl ester	M.P., °C	B.P., °C	Acetamide	Benzamide	
255	2-Toluamide	140; 143	199–200.5	104–5; 107–8	259[751]	90.7	57	NH$_3$	....	....		Mercury deriv., 196
256	Trichloroacetamide	141	.....	57–8	197.5	80	....	NH$_3$				....
257	2-Iodobenzanilide	141	.....	162	....	111	143	......	184	114	160	....
258	2-Bromobenzanilide	141	.....	150	....	110	102	......	184	114	160	....
259	3-Tolylurea	142	.....	....	....	....	....	......	203	65	125	....
260	2-Chlorobenzamide	142	.....	142; 140	....	106	106	NH$_3$				....
261	Salicylamide	142	.....	158.3 (subl. at 76)	....	97–8	140	NH$_3$		....	....	Mercury deriv., 190
262	Furamide...................	142–3	210	133–4; 132	230–2	133.5	138.5	NH$_3$		....	....	
263	3-Nitrobenzamide...........	143; 142	.....	140	....	141	132	NH$_3$		....	....	
264	Iodoacetanilide	143–4	.....	83	....	....	....	......	184	114	160	
265	3,5-Dimethylacetanilide......	144; 140	.....	16.6	118.2	78	86	......	220	144; 140	136	....
266	2-Benzotoluidide (N-Benzoyl-o-toluidine)...............	144	.....	122.4	249	89	119	......	200	110–11	146	KMnO$_4$ → Benzoylanthranilic acid, 177
267	3-Nitrosalicylamide	145 (hyd.)	.....	125	....	....	....	NH$_3$		....	....	
268	2,4-Dichloroacetanilide	145	.....	16.6	118.2	78	86.0	63	......	145	177	
269	α-d,l-Phenylsuccinamide (β form)	145	.....	167–8; 84 (anh.)	....	....	....	NH$_3$		....	....	
270	4-Toluanilide	145; 148	.....	179–80; 182 subl.	275 (cor.)	104.5	153	......	184	114	160	....
271	Diethylmalonic acid monoamide	146	.....	125	....	di: 91	....	NH$_3$				
272	Cyclohexancarboxanilide (Hexahydrobenzanilide).....	146; 131	.....	30–1	233	....	....	......	184	114	160	
273	Phenylurea	147	225	....	....	....	....	......	184	114	160	
274	N,N′-Dibenzoyltrimethylene-diamine	147	.....	122.4	249	89	119	......	136	mono: 126; di: 101	mono: 140; di: 147	
275	Benzo-2-ethylanilide (N-Benzoyl-o-ethylaniline)........	147	.....	122.4	249	89	119	......	210–11	111	147	....
276	2,4,6-Trichloroacetanilide	148	.....	16.6	118.2	78	86.0	78	......	148	172	
277	α-Bromoisobutyramide	148	.....	48–9	198–200	....	....	NH$_3$		....	....	
278	Cinnamamide	148; 142	.....	133	300	116.8	145.6	NH$_3$		....	....	
279	Succinic acid monoanilide	148.5	.....	185; 182.8	235 d.	di: 88	di: 211	......	184	114	160	
280	N-Cyclohexbenzamide	149	.....	122.4	249	89	119	......	134	104	149	
281	Benzylurea	149	.....	....	....	....	....	......	184–5	60	105	
282	Phthalic acid monoamide (Phthalamic acid)...........	149	.....	200–6; 197 (sealed tube); 230 (rapid htng.)	....	di: 155.5	di: 152.8	NH$_3$				
283	β-Benzoylpropionanilide	150; 145	.....	116	....	....	....	......	184	114	160	....
284	Ethylmalonic acid monoanilide .	150	.....	111	....	75	....	......	184	114	160	
285	2-Chlorophenoxyacetamide....	150	.....	145–6, w.	....	....	....	NH$_3$		....	....	
286	Adipic acid monoanilide.......	151–3	.....	153–4 (cor.)	216[15]	106	154.5; 152.6	......	184	114	160	
287	Cinnamanilide	151; 153	.....	133	300	116.8	145.6	......	184	114	160	Acid KMnO$_4$ → Benzoic acid, 122.4

*Derivative data given in order: m.p., crystal color, solvent from which crystallized.

TABLE XV. ORGANIC DERIVATIVES OF AMIDES AND IMIDES

b) Solids (Listed in order of increasing m.p.)* (Continued)

No.	Name	Melting point, °C	Xan-thyl-amide	Derived acid				Derived amine				Miscellaneous
				M.P., °C	B.P., °C	p-Nitro-benzyl ester	p-Bromo-phenacyl ester	M.P., °C	B.P., °C	Acet-amide	Benz-amide	
288	**4-Fluoroacetanilide**	152	......	16.6	118.2	78	86.0	−1	186	152	185	....
289	d,l-Mandelanilide.............	152	......	118	....	123–4	....		184	114	160	
290	**4-Acetotoluidide** (N-Acetyl-p-toluidine)	153; 147	......	16.6	118.2	78	86.0	45	200	147	158	KMnO$_4$ → 4-Acetamido-benzoic acid, 256; Br$_2$ → 3-Bromo deriv, 117
291	**N-Methyl-4-nitroacetanilide**	153	......	16.6	118.2	78	86.0	152	......	153	112	....
292	Veratranilide	154	......	181	....	....	....		184	114	160	
293	**4-Fluorobenzamide**..........	154	......	182; 182.6	....	....	....	NH$_3$		......	......	....
294	**3-Nitrobenzanilide**	154	......	140	....	141	132		184	114	160	
295	**Benzilamide**	154–5; 155	......	150	....	99.5	152	NH$_3$				
296	**3-Nitrosalicylamide**	155; 145	......	125 (+ H$_2$O)	....	....	....	NH$_3$				
297	**2,5-Dichlorobenzamide**	155	......	153	....	....	....	NH$_3$		......	......	....
298	**2-Bromobenzamide**..........	155	......	150	....	110	102	NH$_3$		......	......	Mercury deriv., 242
299	Dibenzylacetanilide	155	......	89	....	....	....		184	114	160	....
300	**2-Nitrobenzanilide**	155	......	146	....	112	107		184	114	160	....
301	**3-Bromobenzamide**..........	155	......	155	....	105	120	NH$_3$		......	......	Mercury deriv., 235
302	**N-(1-Naphthyl) acetanilide**	155; 159.6	......	131; 135	....	....	....		184	114	160	....
303	Phthalonamide (β form)	155d.	......	146	....	....	....	NH$_3$				
304	**3-Nitroacetanilide**	155	......	16.6	118.2	78	86.0		114	mono: 155; di: 76	mono: 155; di: 150	
305	Pimelic acid dianilide........	155–6	......	104–5, subl.	223[15]	....	di: 136.6		184	114	160	
306	**Pivalamide**	155–7; 153–4	......	35.5	163–4	....	75–6	NH$_3$		......	......	
307	**N-Phenylsuccinimide**	156	......	185; 182.8	235d.	di: 88	di: 211		184	114	160	
308	Dibromoacetamide...........	156	......	48	232–5	....	....	NH$_3$				
309	**L-Malamide**	156.5–8.0	......	100–1	....	mono: 87.2; di: 124.5	di: 179	NH$_3$				
310	Phenylacetamide	156; 157	196	76.5, subl.	256.5 (cor.)	65	89	NH$_3$				
311	3-Hydroxybenzanilide	157; 155	......	200, subl.	....	106–8	176; 176.1–.4		184	114	160	
312	**Succinic acid monoamide** (Succinamic acid)...........	157	......	185; 182.8	235d.	di: 88	di: 211	NH$_3$				
313	**N-Acetylindole**	157–8	......	16.6	118.2	78	86	52	253	157–8	68	
314	**d,l-Phenylsuccinamide** (α form)	158	......	167–8	....	....	....	NH$_3$		......	......	
315	**4-Benzotoluidide** (N-Benzoyl-p-toluidine)................	158	......	122.4	249	89	119	45	200	147	158	CrO$_3$ → 4-Benzamido benzoic acid, 278
316	N-(1-Napthyl) acetamide......	159	......	16.6	118.2	78	86.0	50	......	159	160	Br$_2$ → 4-Bromo deriv., 193; Fuming HNO$_3$ →dinitro deriv., 250

*Derivative data given in order: m.p., crystal color, solvent from which crystallized.

No.	Name	Melting point, °C	Xanthyl-amide	Derived acid				Derived amine				Miscellaneous
				M.P., °C	B.P., °C	p-Nitro-benzyl ester	p-Bromo-phenacyl ester	M.P., °C	B.P., °C	Acet-amide	Benz-amide	
317	**4-Toluamide**	159; 160	224–5	179–80; 182, subl.	275 (cor.)	104.5	153	NH$_3$				Mercury deriv., 260
318	Crotonamide	161; 158	......	72, w.	189 (cor.)	67.4	95–6	NH$_3$				
319	N-(1-Naphthyl) benzamide	161	......	122.4	249	89	119	50	......	159	160	
320	N-(2-Naphthyl) benzamide	162	......	122.4	249	89?	119	112	......	132	162	
321	4-Aminoacetanilide	162	......	16.6	118.2	......	86.0	140; 147	267	mono: 162–3; di: 304	mono: 128; di: 300	Azo-β-naphthol deriv., 261
322	4-Hydroxybenzamide	162 (hyd.)	......	215; 213–4; 210	......	180–2	191.5 (cor.); 184	NH$_3$				
323	Benzanilide	163; 160	......	122.4	249	89	119	......	184	114	160	Br$_2$→4-Bromo deriv., 204
324	1-Naphthanilide	163; 164	......	161–2 (cor.)			135.5	......	184	114	160	
325	Trichlorolactanilide	164	......	124				......	184	114	160	
326	Veratramide	164	......	181				NH$_3$				
327	2-Benzoylbenzamide	165	......	128; 91 (hyd.)		100.4		NH$_3$				
328	L-Glutamamide	165	......	211 (rapid htng.); 197 (slow htng.)				NH$_3$				
329	Protocatechuanilide	166	......	199–200d.			188	......	184	114	160	......
330	4-Anisamide	167; 163	......	184–6; 184.2 (cor.)	275–80	132	152	NH$_3$				Mercury deriv., 222
331	4-Bromoacetanilide	167; 168	......	16.6	118.2	78	86.0	66	245	168	204	......
332	Acetylanthranilanilide	167	......	185, ac. a.	......			......	184	114	160	
333	Diphenylacetamide	168	......	148				NH$_3$				
334	α-Benzoyl-β-phenylhydrazine	168	......	122.4	249	89	119	19; 23	243	128	168	
335	2-Furanacrylamide (β-(2-Furyl)-acrylic acid)	168–9	......	141	286			NH$_3$				
336	Piperonylamide	169	......	229; 228				NH$_3$				
337	d,l-Tropamide	169	......	117–8				NH$_3$				
338	Methyliminodiacetic acid monoamide	169	......	227d.				NH$_3$				
339	Methyliminodiacetic acid diamide	169	......	227d.				NH$_3$				
340	4-Hydroxyacetanilide	169	......	16.6	118.2	78	86.0	184; 186	......	mono: 168; di: 150	N-mono: 216–7; N,O-di: 234	
341	4-Anisanilide	169–71	......	184–6; 184.2 (cor.)	275–80	132	152	......	184	114	160	
342	3-Hydroxybenzamide	170; 167	......	200, subl.	......	106–8	176; 176.7–.4	NH$_3$				
343	Sebacic acid monoamide	170	......	33, subl.	243[15]	di: 73.5; 72.6	di: 147	NH$_3$				
344	cis-Aconitanilide	170d.	......	125			tri: 186	......	184	114	160	

*Derivative data given in order: m.p., crystal color, solvent from which crystallized.

No.	Name	Melting point, °C	Xan-thyl-amide	Derived acid				Derived amine				Miscellaneous
				M.P., °C	B.P., °C	p-Nitro-benzyl ester	p-Bromo-phenacyl ester	M.P., °C	B.P., °C	Acet-amide	Benz-amide	
345	**Malonic acid diamide** (Malondiamide)...........	170	270	134.8–.9	....	di: 85.5	....	NH₃	....	....		....
346	**D,L-Phenylsuccinic acid monoanilide** (β form)........	170	......	167–8; 84 (anh.)					184	114	160	
347	**4-Ethoxybenzanilide**	170; 172	......	198; 195–6	....				184	114	160	
348	**2-Naphthylanilide**...........	171; 173		184; 185.5	....				184	114	160	
349	**N,N′-Diacetylethylenediamine** .	172	......	16.6	118.2	78	86.0	8.5	116	di: 172	di: 244	
350	**Benzo-2,4,6-trichloroanilide** (N-Benzoyl-2,4,6-trichloroaniline)...........	172	......	122.4	249	89	119	78	......	148	172	
351	**Azelaic acid diamide**	172	......	106.5	>360 sl. d.; 237¹⁵	di: 43.8	di: 130.6	NH₃		....		
352	**Maleic acid monoamide** (Maleamic acid)...........	172–3; 153 sl.d.	......	137–8; 130 (+3% fumaric acid)	....	di: 91 (cor.)	168–70; 190	NH₃		....		
353	**4-Phenetylurea** (Dulcin)	173	....	....	....			2–3	248; 254	137	173	....
354	**4-Benzophenetidide** .... (N-Benzoyl-p-phenetidine) ...	173	......	122.4	249	89	119	2–3	248; 254	137	173	
355	**Benzylanilide**	174–5	......	150	....	99.5	152	......	184	114	160	
356	**Pimelic acid diamide**	175	......	104–5, subl.	223¹⁵		di: 136.6	NH₃				
357	**d,l-Phenylsuccinic acid monoanilide** (α form)........	175		167–8; 84 (anh.)					184	114	160	
358	**4-Hydroxyphenylacetamide**....	175		148–50; 148, w.				NH₃				
359	**Citraconic acid dianilide**	175.5	......	92–3; 22d.	....	70.6			184	114	160	
360	**Glutaric acid diamide**.........	175–6		98	302–4	di: 69	di: 139.8	NH₃				
361	**2-(4-Toluyl) benzamide**	175–6		139–140	....			NH₃				
362	**2-Nitrobenzamide**............	176; 175		146		112	107	NH₃				
363	**Phthalonic acid monoanilide** ...	176	......	146	....				184	114	160	
364	**N,N-Dibenzoyltetramethylenediamine**...........	177		122.4	249	89	119	27	159	di: 137	di: 177	
365	**Acetylanthranilamide**.........	177		185, ac. a.				NH₃				
366	**2,6-Dimethylacetanilide**.......	177		16.6	118.2	78	86.0	......	215; 218	177	168	
367	**D-Camphoric acid monoamide** .	177		187.5–8.0	....	65.5		NH₃				
368	**Mesaconic acid diamide**.......	177		204.5 (cor.), subl.	....	di: 134 (cor.)		NH₃				
370	**4-Cyanobenzanilide**	179	......	219; 214	....	189	....	......	184	114	160	....
371	**N-Benzylphthalamide**	179	......	200–6; 191 (sealed tube); 230 rapid htng.)	....	di: 155.5	di: 152.8	......	184–5	60	105	....
372	**4-Chloroacetanilide**	179	......	16.6	118.2	78	86.0	72	......	179	192	....
373	**α-Phthalonamide**	179d.	......	146	....	....	....	NH₃		....		

*Derivative data given in order: m.p., crystal color, solvent from which crystallized.

No.	Name	Melting point, °C	Xanthylamide	Derived acid				Derived amine				Miscellaneous
				M.P., °C	B.P., °C	p-Nitrobenzyl ester	p-Bromophenacyl ester	M.P., °C	B.P., °C	Acetamide	Benzamide	
374	**2,4-Dimethylbenzamide**	179–81		127; 90 (+H₂O)				NH₃				
375	**D-Tartaric acid monoanilide**	180d.		169–71		di: 163	di: 204		184	114	160	
376	**α-Acetyl-β-methylurea**	180		16.6	118.2	78	86.0		−6	28	80	
377	**Diphenylacetanilide**	180		148					184	114	160	
378	**3,5-Dinitrosalicylamide**	181		182				NH₃				
379	**1-Naphthylacetamide**	181		131; 135				NH₃				
380	**Maleic acid diamide**	181; 180		137		di: 91 (cor.)	168–70; 190	NH₃				
381	*unsym*-Dimethyl urea	182	225						7		41	
382	**Thiourea**	182						NH₃				
383	**Hippuramide**	183		187		136	151	NH₃				
384	**4-Tolylurea**	183						45	200	147	158	
385	**3,5-Dinitrobenzamide**	183		204–5		157	159	NH₃				
386	**2-Iodobenzamide**	184		162		111	143	NH₃				
387	**4-Iodoacetanilide**	184		16.6	118.2	78	86.0	67–8		184	222	
388	**Benzo-4-fluoroanilide** (N-Benzoyl-*p*-fluoroaniline)	185		122.4	249	89	119	−1	186	152	185	
389	**N,N′-Diacetyl-*o*-phenylene-diamine**	185		16.6	118.2	78	86.0	102		di: 185	di: 301	
390	**2-Nitrocinnamamide**	185		240		132	141	NH₃				
391	**Mesaconic acid dianilide**	185.7		204.5 (cor.)		di: 134 (cor.)			184	114	160	
392	**Citraconic acid diamide**	185–7		92–3; 92d.		di: 70.6		NH₃				
393	**Chlorofumaranilide**	186		191–2		di: 138.5			184	114	160	
394	**3-Iodobenzamide**	186		187		121	128	NH₃				
395	**Suberic acid dianilide**	186–7		144; 139–41		di: 85	di: 144.2		184	114	160	
396	**Maleic acid dianilide**	187		137		di: 91 (cor.)	168–70; 190		184	114	160	
397	**Maleic acid monoanilide**	187		137		di: 91 (cor.)	168–70; 190		184	114	160	
398	**Hippuric acid**	187.5		122.4	249	89	119	Glycine: 228–30; 262d.		206	187.5	Acetamide, 136; Benzamide, 151
399	*unsym*-Diphenylurea	189	180					53–4		101	180	
400	**Aconitic acid dianilide**	189		194–5d. (cor.)			tri: 186		184	114	160	
401	*meso*-Tartaric acid diamide	189–90; 187		140		93		NH₃				
402	**4-Bromobenzamide**	189–90		251–3		180		NH₃				Mercury deriv., 266
403	**Itaconic acid dianilide**	190; 185		165		di: 90.6	di: 117.4		184	114	160	
404	**Picramide**	190		122.5				NH₃				Acetamide, 230; Benzamide, 196
405	**N,N′-Diacetyl-*m*-phenylene-diamine**	191		16.6	118.2	78	86.0	63		mono: 87–9; di: 191	mono: 125; di: 240	
406	**Itaconic acid diamide**	191.2–.8		165		di: 90.6	di: 117.4	NH₃				
407	**Mucic acid monoamide**	192d.		214d.; varies with htng. rate; 223–255		310	225	NH₃				

*Derivative data given in order: m.p., crystal color, solvent from which crystallized.

No.	Name	Melting point, °C	Xan-thyl-amide	Derived acid M.P., °C	B.P., °C	p-Nitro-benzyl ester	p-Bromo-phenacyl ester	Derived amine M.P., °C	B.P., °C	Acet-amide	Benz-amide	Miscellaneous
408	4-Nitrophthalanilide.........	192	......	165	....	....	....	......	184	114	160	....
409	2-Tolylurea..............	192	228	....	....	....	....		200	110–11	146	
410	Benzo-4-chloroaniline (N-Benzoyl-p-chloroaniline) .	192	......	122.4	249	89	119	......	72	179; 172	192	
411	Biuret	192d.		....	....	....	....	NH₃			....	
412	2-Naphthamide.............	192; 195	......	184; 185.5	....	....	....	NH₃				
413	D-Camphoric acid diamide	193	......	187.5–8.0	....	65.5	....	NH₃				
414	4-Chlorobenzanilide.........	194	......	243; 240	....	129.5	126		184	114	160	
415	4-Coumaramide	194	......	210–3; 206 (anh.)	....	....	....	NH₃				
416	2-Benzoylbenzanilide	195	......	128; 91 (+1 H₂O)	....	100.4	....		184	114	160	....
417	3-Nitrocinnamamide	196	......	199	....	174	178; 173	NH₃				
418	D-Tartaric acid diamide	196d.	......	169–71	....	di: 163	di: 204	NH₃				
419	2-Methyl-4-nitroacetanilide ...	196; 202	......	16.6	118.2	78	86.0	130	......	202		
420	L-Malanilide (Hydroxysuccin-anilide)	197	......	100–1	....	mono: 87.2; di: 124.5	di: 179	......	184	114	160	
421	4-Hydroxybenzanilide	198; 196–7	......	215; 213–4		180–2	191.5 (cor.)	......	184	114	160	
422	4-Nitrophenylacetamide......	198	......	153	....	....	207	NH₃		....		
423	4-Nitrophenylacetanilide	198	......	153	....	....	207	147–8	......	215	di: 193.; 203	....
424	Cyanoacetanilide	198–9	......	66					184	114	160	
425	Citric acid trianilide	199; 192 (+1 H₂O)	......	100; 153 (anh.)	....	tri: 102	tri: 148	......	184	114	160	
426	4-Nitrophthalamide	200d.	......	165	....	....	....	NH₃				
427	cis-Aconitic acid dianilide	200	......	125	....	....	tri: 186		184	114	160	
428	Methylsuccinic acid dianilide ..	200	......	115	....	....	....		184	114	160	
429	4-Nitrobenzamide...........	200	232	241	....	168	137	NH₃		....		
430	2-Naphthylacetamide........	200; 205	......	141–2; 143	....	....	....	NH₃				
431	Isatin....................	200–1	......								....	Acetamide, 147
432	3-Nitrophthalic acid diamide ...	201d.	......	218	....	189	....	NH₃				
433	Sebacic acid dianilide........	201	......	33, subl.	243¹⁵	di: 73.5; 72.6	di: 147		184	114	160	
434	1-Naphthoamide............	202	......	161–2 (cor.)	....	....	135.5	NH₃				
435	4-Ethoxybenzamide	202	......	198; 195–6				NH₃		....		
436	2,4-Dinitrobenzamide	203	......	183	....	142	158	NH₃				
437	D-Camphoric acid monoanilide	204	......	187.5–8.0	....	65.5	....		184	114	160	
438	Benzo-4-bromoanilide (N-Benzoyl-p-bromoaniline) .	204	......	122.4	249	89	119	66	245	168	204	....
439	4-Nitrocinnamamide	204; 217	......	285	....	186	191	NH₃		....		
440	N-Phenylphthalimide........	205	......	200–6; 191 (sealed tube); 230 (rapid htng.)	....	di: 155.5	di: 152.8	......	184	114	160	....

*Derivative data given in order: m.p., crystal color, solvent from which crystallized.

No.	Name	Melting point, °C	Xan-thyl-amide	Derived acid				Derived amine				Miscellaneous
				M.P., °C	B.P., °C	p-Nitro-benzyl ester	p-Bromo-phenacyl ester	M.P., °C	B.P., °C	Acet-amide	Benz-amide	
441	Carballylic acid triamide......	207d.; 205– 7d.	......	166	....	....	tri: 138.2	NH$_3$		....	....	....
442	Gallanilide..................	207	......	253–4d.; 222– 40d.	....	141	134	......	184	114	160	....
443	Phthalonic acid dianilide......	208	......	146	....	....	....		184	114	160	
444	Hippuranilide...............	208	......	187	....	136	151		184	114	160	
445	2-Coumaramide.............	209d.	......	207–8, subl.	....	152.5	......	NH$_3$				
446	Sebacic acid diamide........	210; 208	......	133, subl.	243^{15}	di: 73.5; 72.6	di: 147	NH$_3$				....
447	4-Iodobenzanilide...........	210	......	270; 265	....	141	146	......	184	114	160	
448	Citric acid triamide.........	210–5	......	153 (slow htng.)	....	tri: 102	tri: 148	NH$_3$				
449	4-Nitrobenzanilide..........	211; 204	......	241	....	168	137	......	184	114	160	
450	d,l-Phenylsuccinic acid diamide..................	211	......	167–8; 84 (anh.)	......	......	......	NH$_3$				
451	Protocatechuamide..........	212	......	199– 200d.	....	188	......	NH$_3$				
452	2,2'-Diphenic acid diamide....	212	......	227; 233	....	di: 187; 182.6	......	NH$_3$				
453	4-Nitroacetanilide..........	213–4	......	16.6	118.2	78	86.0	147–8	......	215	di: 199; 203	
454	Ethylmalonic acid diamide.....	214	......	111	....	75		NH$_3$				
455	3-Nitrophthalimide..........	216	......	218	....	189		NH$_3$				
456	Suberic acid diamide........	216–7	......	144; 139– 41	....	di: 85	di: 144.2	NH$_3$				
457	Methylmalonic acid diamide...	217; 206	......	137; 138d.	....	....		NH$_3$				
458	4-Iodobenzamide...........	217	......	270; 265		141	146	NH$_3$				
459	Benzylmalonic acid dianilide...	217	......	117d; 121		di: 119.5	....		184	114	160	
460	4-Hydroxy-2-naphthamide....	217–8	......	225–6		....		NH$_3$				
461	Acetylurea.................	218	......	16.6	118.2	78	86.0	NH$_3$				
462	3-Hydroxy-2-naphthamide....	218	......	222–3 (cor.)				NH$_3$				
463	sym.-Di-3-tolylurea..........	218	......						203	65	125	
464	Phthalic acid diamide........	220	......	200–6; 191 (sealed tube); 230 (rapid htng.)		di: 155.5	di: 152.8	NH$_3$				
465	Mucic acid diamide..........	220	......	214d.; varies with htng. rate; 223–255	....	310	225	NH$_3$				
466	Saccharin..................	220	198–9	206	....			NH$_3$				
467	Adipic acid diamide..........	220; 229	......	153–4 (cor.)	216^{15}	106	152.6; 154.5	NH$_3$				
468	d,l-Phenylsuccinic acid dianilide..................	222	......	167–8; 84 (anh.)	....				184	114	160	

*Derivative data given in order: m.p., crystal color, solvent from which crystallized.

No.	Name	Melting point, °C	Xanthylamide	Derived acid M.P., °C	B.P., °C	p-Nitrobenzyl ester	p-Bromophenacyl ester	Derived amine M.P., °C	B.P., °C	Acetamide	Benzamide	Miscellaneous
469	β-Resorcylamide	222	......	213d. (rapid htng.) 216d; 217	....	188–9	....	NH₃				....
470	4-Cyanobenzamide	223	......	219; 214	....	189		NH₃		....	....	
471	Diethylmalonic acid diamide	224	......	125	302–4	di: 91	....	NH₃				
472	Glutaric acid dianilide	224	......	98	....	di: 69	di: 139.8	......	184	114	160	
473	5-Nitrosalicylanilide	224	......	229–30	....	....	....		184	114	160	
474	5-Nitrosalicylamide	225	......	229–30	....	....		NH₃				
475	Benzylmalonic acid diamide	225	......	117d.; 121	....	di: 119.5	....	NH₃				
476	Methylsuccinic acid diamide	225	......	115				NH₃				
477	Malonic acid dianilide	225; 227; 230	......	134.8–.9		di: 85.5			184	114	160	
478	d,l-Tartaric acid monoamide	226	......	203–4 (+1 H₂O); 205–6 (anh.)	....	di: 147.6		NH₃				
479	D-Camphoric acid dianilide	226	......	187.5–8.0	....	65.5	....		184	114	160	....
480	Succinic acid dianilide	230; 226	......	185; 182.8	235d.	di: 88	di: 211	......	184	114	160	Heat above m.p. → succinanil, 155–6 + aniline, b.p. 184
481	2,2'-Diphenanilide	230	......	227; 229; 233		di: 187; 182.6			184	114	160	....
482	Phthalimide	233.5 (cor.); 238	176–7	200–6; 191 (sealed tube); 230 (rapid htng.)	249	89	119	122; 119	......	232	198; 204	....
483	3,5-Dinitrobenzanilide	234	......	204–5	....	157	159		184	114	160	....
484	3-Nitrophthalic acid dianilide	234	......	218		189			184	114	160	
485	Terephthalic acid monoanilide	234–7	......	300, subl. without melting	....	di: 263.5	di: 225		184	114	160	
486	d,l-Tartaric acid monoanilide	236	......	203–4 (+1 H₂O); 205–6 (anh.)	....	....			184	114	160	....
487	N-Benzylacrylamide	237	......	13	141; 140	....	....		184–5	60	105	....
488	Carbanilide (sym-Diphenylurea)	238; 240	......						184	114	160	
489	Muconic acid diamide	240d.	......	289d. (slow htng.); 306 (rapid htng.)	....	....		NH₃		....		
490	Adipic acid dianilide	241	......	153–4 (cor.)	216¹⁵	106	152.6; 154.5	......	184	114	160	....

*Derivative data given in order: m.p., crystal color, solvent from which crystallized.

No.	Name	Melting point, °C	Xan-thyl-amide	Derived acid				Derived amine				Miscellaneous
				M.P., °C	B.P., °C	p-Nitro-benzyl ester	p-Bromo-phenacyl ester	M.P., °C	B.P., °C	Acet-amide	Benz-amide	
491	N,N′-Dibenzoylethylene-diamine	244	. . . . . .	122.4	249	89	119	8.5	116	di: 172	di: 244	. . . .
492	Gallamide	245	. . . . . .	253–4d.; 222–40d.	. . . .	141	134	NH₃		. . . .		. . . .
493	3-Hydroxy-2-naphthanilide . . .	249 (cor.); 244	. . . . . .	222–3 (cor.)	. . . .	. . . .	. . . . . .		184	114	160	. . . .
494	sym-Di-2-tolylurea	250	. . . . . .	. . . .	. . . .	. . . .	. . . . . .		200	110–1	146	. . . .
495	Carballylic acid trianilide	252	. . . . . .	166	. . . .	. . . .	tri: 138.2		184	114	160	. . . .
496	Phthalic acid dianilide	253–5	. . . . . .	200–6; 191 (sealed tube); 230 (rapid htng.)	. . . .	di: 155.5	di: 152.8	. . . . . .	184	114	160	. . . .
497	Oxalic acid dianilide	254	. . . . . .	189.5 (anh.); 101 (+2 H₂O); (rapid htng.)	. . . .	di: 204	. . . . . .	. . . . . .	184	114	160	. . . .
498	Succinic acid diamide	255; 260d.	275	185; 182.8	235d.	di: 88	di: 211	NH₃		. . . .		. . . .
499	2,4,6-Trinitrobenzamide	264d.	. . . . . .	228	. . . .	. . . .	. . . . . .	NH₃		. . . .		. . . .
500	D-Tartaric acid dianilide	264d.	. . . . . .	169–71	. . . .	di: 163	di: 204		184	114	160	. . . .
501	Fumaric acid diamide	266d.	. . . . . .	293–5; 286–7 (sealed tube); 200, subl.	. . . .	150.8	. . . . . .	NH₃		. . . .		. . . .
502	sym-Di-4-tolylurea	268	. . . . . .	. . . .	. . . .	. . . .	. . . . . .	45	200	147	158	. . . .
503	Isophthalic acid monoamide . . .	280	. . . . . .	348, subl.	. . . .	202.5	179.1	NH₃		. . . .		. . . .
504	Isophthalic acid diamide	280	. . . . . .	348, subl.	. . . .	202.5	179.1	NH₃		. . . .		. . . .
505	Acetylenedicarboxylic acid diamide	294d.	. . . . . .	179	. . . .	. . . .	. . . . . .	NH₃		. . . .		. . . .
506	Mucic acid monoanilide	310	. . . . . .	214; varies with htng. rate; 223–255	. . . .	310	225	. . . . . .	184	114	160	. . . .
507	N,N′-Diacetyl p-phenylenedi-amine	310	. . . . . .	16.6	118.2	78	86.0	140; 147	267	mono: 162–3; di: 304	mono: 128; di: 300	. . . .
508	Fumaric acid dianilide	314	. . . . . .	286–7 (sealed tube); 293–5; 200, subl.	. . . .	150.8	. . . . . .		184	114	160	. . . .
509	N,N′-Diacetylbenzidine	317	. . . . . .	16.6	118.2	78	86.0	127	. . . . . .	mono: 199; di: 317	mono: 203–5; di: 352	. . . .

*Derivative data given in order: m.p., crystal color, solvent from which crystallized.

No.	Name	Melting point, °C	Xan-thyl-amide	Derived acid				Derived amine				Miscellaneous
				M.P., °C	B.P., °C	p-Nitro-benzyl ester	p-Bromo-phenacyl ester	M.P., °C	B.P., °C	Acet-amide	Benz-amide	
510	Terephthalic acid dianilide.....	334–7	......	300, subl. without melting	....	di: 263.5	di: 225	......	....	....	....	....
511	N,N'-Dibenzoylbenzidine	352	......	122.4	249	89	119	127	....	mono: 199; di: 317	mono: 203–5; di: 352	....
512	Trimesic acid triamide	365d.	......	380 (cor.)	....	....	tri: 197 (sealed tube)	NH₃		....	....	....
513	Oxalic acid diamide	419d. (sealed tube)	......	189.5 (anh.); 101 (+2 H₂O); (rapid htng.)	....	di: 204	....	NH₃		....	....	....

*Derivative data given in order: m.p., crystal color, solvent from which crystallized.

*Hydrolysis to the corresponding acid and alcohol.**

$$RCOOR' + KOH \rightarrow R'OH + RCOOK$$

Alcohol $\quad \downarrow H^+$

RCOOH

Acid

From the ester with aqueous sodium or potassium hydroxide.
For directions and examples see: Cheronis, p. 539; Linstead, p. 42; Vogel, pp. 390, 391, 786; Wild, p. 187.
From the ester and potassium hydroxide in anhydrous or aqueous diethylene glycol.
See: Cheronis, p. 538; C. E. Redemann and H. J. Lucas, *Ind. Eng. Chem., Anal. Ed.,* **9**, 514 (1937).
From the ester with sodium methoxide in methanol or with sodium ethoxide in ethanol.
See: Linstead, p. 40; Vogel, p. 391.
From an α-hydroxy ester in water without catalyst.
See: A. Findlay and E. M. H. Hickmans, *J. Chem. Soc.,* **95**, 1004 (1909).

Saponification equivalent.

The saponification equivalent (S. E.) measures the number of equivalents of base required for complete hydrolysis of an ester. It is defined as:

$$\text{S. E.} = \frac{\text{Milligrams ester taken for hydrolysis}}{\text{Milliequivalents of KOH required for complete hydrolysis}}$$

For directions and examples see: Cheronis, pp. 975–6; Shriner, p. 235; Vogel, p. 392.
NOTE: For directions and examples for preparation of derivatives of the carboxylic acids formed on hydrolysis of esters see explanations and references to Tables XII, XIII and XIV, pp. 186, 187, 188, 189.
For directions and examples for preparation of derivatives of alcohols formed on hydrolysis of esters see explanations and references to Table VI, pp. 77, 78, 79.

Amide.

$$RCOOR' + NH_3 \rightarrow RCONH_2 + R'OH$$

From the ester with aqueous or alcoholic ammonia.
For directions and examples see: Linstead, p. 42; Wild, p. 188.

Anilide and p-Toluidide.

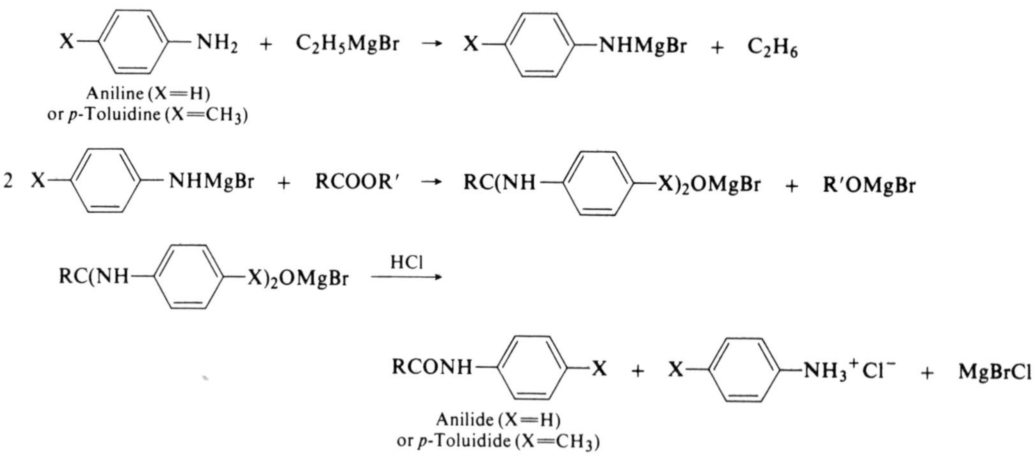

$$X\text{—C}_6H_4\text{—}NH_2 + C_2H_5MgBr \rightarrow X\text{—C}_6H_4\text{—}NHMgBr + C_2H_6$$

Aniline (X=H)
or *p*-Toluidine (X=CH_3)

$$2\ X\text{—C}_6H_4\text{—}NHMgBr + RCOOR' \rightarrow RC(NH\text{—C}_6H_4\text{—}X)_2OMgBr + R'OMgBr$$

$$RC(NH\text{—C}_6H_4\text{—}X)_2OMgBr \xrightarrow{HCl}$$

$$RCONH\text{—C}_6H_4\text{—}X + X\text{—C}_6H_4\text{—}NH_3^+Cl^- + MgBrCl$$

Anilide (X=H)
or *p*-Toluidide (X=CH_3)

From the ester and the N-magnesium bromide derivative of aniline or *p*-toluidine (prepared from the amine and ethylmagnesium bromide) in anhydrous ether.
For directions and examples see: Cheronis, p. 537; Linstead, pp. 42–3; Vogel, p. 394; Wild, p. 190; C. F. Koelsch and D. Tenenbaum, *J. Amer. Chem. Soc.,* **55**, 3049 (1933); D. V. N. Hardy, *J. Chem. Soc.,* 398 (1936).

---

*Derivatives recommended for first trial.
WARNING: This is not an instruction manual. References should be consulted for the preparation of derivatives.

Hydrazide.

$$RCOOR' + H_2NNH_2 \rightarrow RCONHNH_2 + R'OH$$

Hydrazide

From the ester and 90% hydrazine hydrate.
For directions and examples see: Linstead, p. 42; Wild, p. 191.
From the ester and 85% hydrazine hydrate in alcohol.
See: Cheronis, p. 535; Shriner, p. 237; Vogel, p. 395; P. P. T. Sah, *Rec. Trav. chim.*, **59**, 1036 (1940).

*N-(β-Aminoethyl)morpholide.**

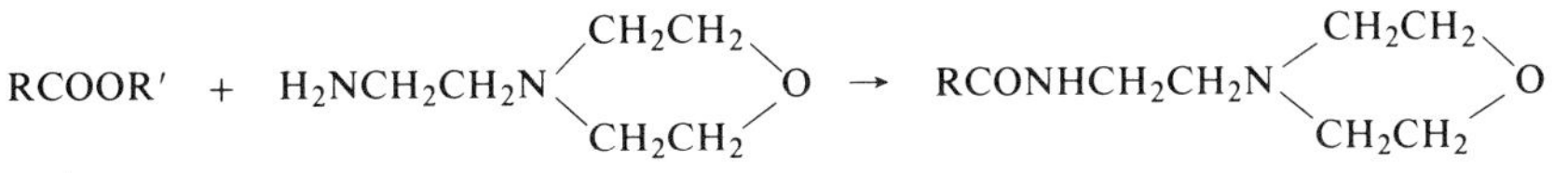

N-(β-Aminoethyl)morpholide

From the ester and N-(β-aminoethyl)morpholine in ethylene glycol or without solvent.
For directions and examples see: Cheronis, p. 536; R. W. Bost and L. V. Mullen, *J. Amer. Chem. Soc.*, **73**, 1967 (1951).

*3,5-Dinitrobenzoate.**

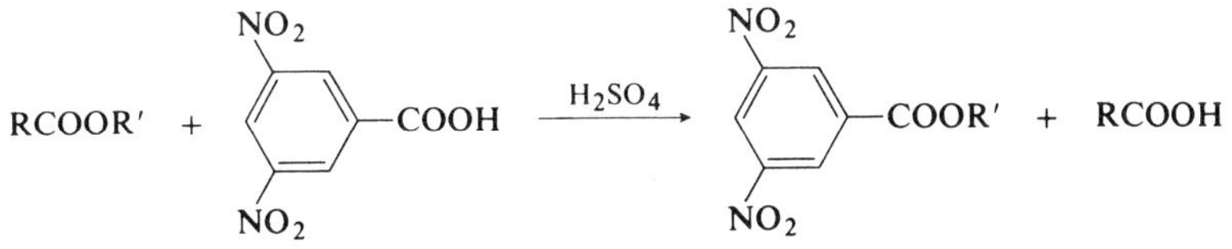

3,5-Dinitrobenzoate

From the ester with 3,5-dinitrobenzoic acid with a catalytic amount of sulfuric acid.
For directions and examples see: Linstead, p. 43; Shriner, p. 238; Vogel, p. 393; W. B. Renfrow and A. Chaney, *J. Amer. Chem. Soc.*, **68**, 150 (1946).
From the ester with 3,5-dinitrobenzoyl chloride and pyridine.
See: Cheronis, p. 538.

*Derivatives recommended for first trial.
WARNING: This is not an instruction manual. References should be consulted for the preparation of derivatives.

TABLE XVI.   ORGANIC DERIVATIVES OF ESTERS

Including esters of inorganic acids
a) Liquids. 1) (Listed in order of increasing b.p.). *

No.	Name	Boiling point, °C	Melting point, °C	n_D^{20}	D_4^{20}	Saponification Equivalent	Acid M.P., °C	Acid B.P., °C	Alcohol M.P., °C	Alcohol B.P., °C	Amide	p-Toluidide	3,5-Dinitrobenzoate	Miscellaneous
1	Ethyl nitrite	17	. . . . . .	. . . .	0.900_4^{15}	75	. . . . . .	. . . . . .	−117.3	78.32	. . . . . .	. . . . .	93, al.	. . . .
2	Methyl formate . .	31.50	−99	1.34648^{15} He (yel)	0.97421	60	8.4	100.7	−97	64.65	2.55	53	108 (cor.), al.	. . . .
3	Ethyl formate. . . .	54.15	−79.4	1.35975	0.92247	74	8.4	100.7	−117.3	78.32	2.55	53	93, al.	. . . .
4	Methyl acetate . . .	57.1	−98.7	1.36170; 1.3639	0.9274; 0.93347	74	16.6	118.2	−97	64.65	82	153; 147	108 (cor.), al.	. . . .
5	Ethyl trifluoro-acetate	60.5	. . . . . .	1.3093^{15}	. . . .	142	−15.25	72.4	−117.3	78.32	. . . . . .	. . . . .	93, al.	. . . .
6	Methyl nitrate . . .	65	. . . . . .	. . . .	1.217_4^{15}	77	. . . . . .	. . . . . .	−97	64.65	. . . . . .	. . . . .	108 (cor.), al.	. . . .
7	Isopropyl formate	71; 68	. . . . . .	. . . .	0.8728	88	8.4	100.7	−89.5	82.4	2.55	53	123, pet. eth.	. . . .
8	Butyl nitrite	75	. . . . . .	. . . .	0.911	103	. . . . . .	. . . . . .	−90.2	117.6; 116	. . . . . .	. . . . .	64; 62.5	. . . .
9	Methyl chloro-formate	75	. . . . . .	1.38675	1.2231	94.5	. . . . . .	. . . . . .	−97	64.65	. . . . . .	. . . . .	108 (cor.), al.	. . . .
10	Ethyl acetate	77.15	−83.6	1.372	0.90055	88	16.6	118.2	−117.3	78.32	82	153; 147	93, al.	. . . .
11	Methyl propionate	79.65	−87.5	1.3779	0.9151	88	−20.8	141	−97	64.65	81; 81.3; 79	126; 123	108 (cor.), al.	. . . .
12	Methyl acrylate . .	80.3	. . . . . .	1.3984	$0.961^{19.2}$	86	13	140; 141	−97	64.65	84–5, pet. eth.	141	108 (cor.), al.	Polymerizes on standing
13	n-Propyl formate .	80.85; 81	−92.9	1.37789	0.9071; 0.918	88	8.4	100.7	. . . . . .	97.1	2.55	53	74, pet. eth.	. . . .
14	tert-Butyl formate	83	. . . . . .	. . . .	. . . .	102	8.4	100.7	25.5	82.5	2.55	53	142, pet. eth.	. . . .
15	Allyl formate	83.6	. . . . . .	. . . .	0.946	86	8.4	100.7	. . . . . .	97.1	2.55	53	49–50	. . . .
16	Ethyl nitrate.	87	−112	. . . .	1.106	91	. . . . . .	. . . . . .	−117.3	78.32	. . . . . .	. . . . .	93, al.	. . . .
17	Isopropyl acetate .	88.9; 91	−73.4	1.3740^{25}	0.872	102	16.6	118.2	−89.5	82.4	82	153; 147	123, pet. eth.	. . . .
18	Dimethyl carbon-ate (Methyl car-bonate).	90.5	. . . . . .	1.3687	1.0702; 1.0694	90	. . . . . .	. . . . . .	−97	64.65	. . . . . .	. . . . .	108 (cor.), al.	. . . .
19	Methyl iso-butyrate	92.6; 92.26	−87.7; −84.7	1.3840	0.8906	102	−46.1	154.7	−97	64.65	128; 129	108.5-9.5	108 (cor.), al.	. . . .
20	Ethyl chloro-formate.	93	. . . . . .	1.3974	1.13519	108.5	. . . . . .	. . . . . .	−117.3	78.32	. . . . . .	. . . . .	93, al.	. . . .
21	sec-Butyl formate	97	. . . . . .	1.384	0.884	102	8.4	100.7	. . . . . .	99.5	2.55	53	76	. . . .
22	tert-Butyl acetate	97.8	. . . . . .	1.386	0.867	116	16.6	118.2	25.5	82.5	82	153; 147	142, pet. eth.	. . . .
23	Isobutyl formate	98.4	−95.8	1.38568	0.88535; 0.8755	102	8.4	100.7	. . . . . .	108.1	2.55	53	87	. . . .
24	Isoamyl nitrite . . .	99	. . . . . .	1.38708^{21}	0.880^{15}	117	. . . . . .	. . . . . .	−117	132	. . . . . .	. . . . .	61	. . . .
25	Ethyl difluoro-acetate	99	. . . . . .	1.3463	. . . .	124	. . . . . .	134–5	−117.3	78.32	52	. . . . .	93, al.	. . . .

*Derivative data given in order: m.p., crystal color, solvent from which crystallized.

TABLE XVI. ORGANIC DERIVATIVES OF ESTERS
Including esters of inorganic acids
a) Liquids. 1) (Listed in order of increasing b.p.)* (Continued)

No.	Name	Boiling point, °C	Melting point, °C	n_D^20	D_4^20	Saponification Equivalent	Acid M.P., °C	Acid B.P., °C	Alcohol M.P., °C	Alcohol B.P., °C	Amide	p-Toluidide	3,5-Dinitrobenzoate	Miscellaneous
26	Methyl meth-acrylate	99; 100–1	−50	1.413	0.936	100	16	161	−97	64.65	102–6	......	108 (cor.), al.	Polymerizes on standing or heating; 4-Bromo-anilide, 116
27	Ethyl propionate	99.1	−73.85	1.3853	0.8889	102	−20.8	141	−117.3	78.32	81; 81.3; 79	126; 123	93, al.	N-(β-Amino-ethyl)mor-pholide, 85
28	Ethyl acrylate	101	......	1.4059^19.4	0.9136^15	100	13	141	−117.3	78.32	84–5, pet. eth.	141	93, al.	Polymerizes on standing or heating
29	Methyl pivalate (Methyl tri-methylacetate)	101	......	1.4228	0.891^0	116	35.5	163–4	−97	64.65	155–7; 153–4, et. ac.-pet. eth.	119–20	108 (cor.), al.	....
30	n-Propyl acetate	101.55	−95	1.38468	0.8834	102	16.6	118.2	....	97.1	82	153; 147	74, pet. eth.	....
31	Methyl n-butyrate	102.3	−84.8	1.3879	0.8982	102	−5.5; −8	162.5; 164	−97	64.65	115–6	75	108 (cor.), al.	....
32	Allyl acetate	104	......	1.40488	0.9276	100	16.6	118.2	....	97.1	82	153; 147	49–50	....
33	Trimethyl ortho-formate (Methyl orthoformate)	105; 102	......	1.3793	0.9676	106	8.4	100.7	−97	64.65	2.55	53	108 (cor.), al.	....
34	Methyl iso-crotonate	106.2–108.2 (cor.)	......	....	....	100	15	169	−97	64.65	101–2	132	108 (cor.), al.	....
35	n-Butyl formate	106.6	−91.9	1.38940	0.8885	102	8.4	100.7	−90.2	117.6; 116	2.55	53	64; 62.5	....
36	Ethyl isobutyrate	109.8; 111	−88.2	1.3903	0.86930	116	−46.1	154.7	−117.3	78.32	128; 129	108.5–9.5	93, al.	Hydrazide, 104, eth.-al.
37	n-Propyl nitrate	110	......	1.3979	1.063	105	....	......	......	97.1	....	......	74, pet. eth.	....
38	Chloromethyl acetate	111	......		1.094^15	108.5	16.6	118.2			82	153; 147	......	
39	Isopropyl propionate	111.3	......		0.8931^0	116	−20.8	141	−89.5	82.4	81; 81.3; 79	126; 123	123, pet. eth.	....
40	sec-Butyl acetate	112.0	......	1.3865^25	0.872; 0.8648^25	116	16.6	118.2		99.5	82	153; 147	76	
41	n-Propyl chloro-formate	113; 115	......	1.40350	1.0901	122.5	....	......		97.1	......	.....	74, pet. eth.	....
42	Methyl isovalerate	116.7	......	1.3900^25	0.8808	116	−30.0	176.5	−97	64.65	135; 137	106–7	108 (cor.), al.	....
43	Isobutyl acetate	117.2; 118	......	1.39008	0.8747	116	16.6	118.2	....	108.1	82	153; 147	87	
44	Ethyl pivalate (Ethyl trimethyl-acetate)	118.15	......	1.39061	0.85467	130	35.5	163–4	−117.3	78.32	155–7; 153–4, et. ac.-pet. eth.	119–20	93, al.	....
45	Ethyl meth-acrylate	118.5^753	......	1.41472	0.91063	114	16,	161	−117.3	78.32	102–6	......	93, al.	Polymerizes on heating; 4-Bromo-anilide, 116

*Derivative data given in order: m.p., crystal color, solvent from which crystallized.

251

TABLE XVI. ORGANIC DERIVATIVES OF ESTERS
Including esters of inorganic acids
a) Liquids. 1) (Listed in order of increasing b.p.)* (Continued)

No.	Name	Boiling point, °C	Melting point, °C	n_D^{20}	D_4^{20}	Saponification Equiv-alent	Acid M.P., °C	Acid B.P., °C	Alcohol M.P., °C	Alcohol B.P., °C	Amide	p-Tolui-dide	3,5-Di-nitro-benzoate	Miscellaneous
46	Methyl crotonate	118.8–119.3	......	....	0.9806⁴	100	72	189 (cor.)	−97	64.65	118, w.; 115	132, bz.	108 (cor.), al.	....
47	Isopropyl iso-butyrate	120.76	......	....	0.84708²¹·³	130	−46.1	154.7	....	82.4	128; 129	108.5–9.5 pet. eth.	123, 104, eth.-al.	Hydrazide, 104, eth.-al.
48	Ethyl n-butyrate	121.6	−100.8	1.40002	0.87917	116	−5.5; −8	162.5; 164	−117.3	78.32	115–6	75	93, al.	....
49	n-Propyl pro-pionate	122.2; 123.4	−75.9	1.39325	0.8809	116	−20.8	141	....	97.1	81; 81.3; 79	126; 123	74, pet. eth.	....
50	tert-Amyl acetate (Dimethylethyl-carbinyl acetate)	124	......	1.392	0.8738¹⁹	130	16.6	118.2	−8.55	102.3	82	153; 147	116; 117–8	....
51	Allyl propionate	124	......	....	....	114	−20.8	141	....	97.1	81; 81.3; 79	126; 123	49–50	....
52	Isoamyl formate	124.2	−93.5	1.39756	0.8820	116	8.4	100.7	−117	132	2.55	53	61	....
53	Ethyl isocrotonate	125.5–126⁷⁴⁹	......	1.42423	0.91820	114	15	169	−117.3	78.32	101–2	132	93, al.	....
54	n-Butyl acetate	126.1	−73.5	1.39614	0.881	116	16.6	118.2	−90.2	117.6; 116	82	153; 147	64; 62.5	....
55	Diethyl carbonate (Ethyl carbon-ate)	126.5	−43.0	1.3852	0.9752	118	....	....	−117.3	78.32	....	....	93, al.	....
56	tert-Butyl iso-butyrate	126.7	......	1.3921	....	144	−46.1	154.7	25.5	82.5	128; 129	108.5–9.5 pet. eth.	142, 104, eth.-al.	Hydrazide, 104, eth.-al.
57	Methyl n-valerate (Methyl n-pentanoate	127.7	−91.0	1.397	0.885	116	−34.5	186.35	−97	64.65	106	74	108 (cor.), al.	....
58	Isopropyl n-butyrate	128	......	....	0.8652¹³	130	−5.5; −8	162.5; 164	−89.5	82.4	115–6	75	123, pet. eth.	....
59	Isobutyl chloro-formate	130; 128.8	......	1.40711¹⁷·⁹ He	....	136.5	....	....	....	108.1	....	....	87	....
60	Methyl methoxy-acetate	130	......	1.39636	1.0511	104	....	203	−97	64.65	96.5–7.0; 92–4	....	108 (cor.), al.	....
61	Methyl chloro-acetate	130; 132	......	1.4221	1.238	108.5	α: 61.3; β: 56.2; γ: 52.5	189	−97	64.65	121	162	108 (cor.), al.	....
62	Ethyl methoxy-acetate	132	......	....	1.0118¹⁵	118	....	203	−117.3	78.32	96.5–7.0; 92–4	....	93, al.	....
63	n-Amyl formate	132.1; 130	−73.5	1.39916	0.8853	116	8.4	100.7 (cor.)	−78.5	138	2.55	53	46.4	....
64	sec-Amyl(3) acetate (Diethyl-carbinyl acetate)	133	......	1.4005	....	130	16.6	118.2	....	116.1	82	153; 147	101; 99; 97	....
65	sec-Amyl(2) acetate (Methyl n-propylcarbinyl acetate)	133.5	......	1.3960	0.8692¹⁸	130	16.6	118.2	....	119.85	82	153; 147	62	....
66	Allyl isobutyrate	134	......	....	....	128	−46.1	154.7	....	97.1	128; 129	108.5–9.5	49–50	Hydrazide, 104, eth.-al.
67	Ethyl isovalerate	134.7	−99.3	1.4009	0.86565	130	−30.0	176.5	−117.3	78.32	135; 137	106–7	93, al.	....
68	n-Propyl iso-butyrate	135	......	1.3959	0.8843⁰	130	−46.1	154.7	....	97.1	128; 129	108.5–9.5 pet. eth.	74, pet. eth.	Hydrazide, 104, eth.-al.

*Derivative data given in order: m.p., crystal color, solvent from which crystallized.

TABLE XVI.   ORGANIC DERIVATIVES OF ESTERS
Including esters of inorganic acids
a) Liquids. 1) (Listed in order of increasing b.p.)* (Continued)

No.	Name	Boiling point, °C	Melting point, °C	n_D^{20}	D_4^{20}	Saponification					Amide	p-Toluidide	3,5-Dinitrobenzoate	Miscellaneous
						Equivalent	Acid		Alcohol					
							M.P., °C	B.P., °C	M.P., °C	B.P., °C				
69	n-Butyl nitrate	136	......	....	1.048⁰	119	......	......	−90.2	117.6; 116	......	......	64; 62.5	....
70	Methyl pyruvate	136.8–138; 134–7	......	....	1.154⁰	102	13.6	165d.	−97	64.65	124–5; 145	109; 130	108 (cor.), al.	2,4-Dinitrophenylhydrazone, 186.5–7.5 (cor.), yel., diox.-me. al.
71	Methyl α-hydroxyisobutyrate	137	......	....		118	79	212	−97	64.65	....	132–3, w.	108 (cor.), al.	....
72	Isobutyl propionate	138; 137	−71.4	1.3975	0.8876⁰	130	−20.8	141	....	108.1	81; 81.3; 79	123–6	87	....
73	Ethyl crotonate	138; 136.7⁷⁴⁹	......	1.42524	0.91752	114	72, w.	189 (cor.)	−117.3	78.32	159–60, bz.	132, bz.	93, al.	....
74	Allyl n-butyrate	142	......	....	....	128	−5.5; −8	162.5; 164	......	97.1	115–6	75	49–50	....
75	Isoamyl acetate (3-Methylbutyl acetate)	142	......	1.40034	0.8674	130	16.6	118.2	−117	132	82	153; 147	61	....
76	Isopropyl isovalerate	142	......	1.3938²⁵	0.8538¹⁷	144	−30	176.5	−89.5	82.4	135; 137	106–7	123, pet. eth.	....
77	n-Propyl n-butyrate	143.8	−95.2	1.4005	0.872	130	−5.5; −8	162.5; 164	......	97.1	115–6	75	74, pet. eth.	....
78	β-Methoxyethyl acetate (Ethylene glycol monomethyl ether acetate; Methyl cellosolve acetate)	144	......	....	1.088	118	16.6	118.2	......	124.5	82	153; 147	......	......
79	Methyl bromoacetate	144d.	......	....	1.657	153	50	208	−97	64.65	91	......	108 (cor.), al.	....
80	n-Butyl chloroformate	145; 139	......	1.417⁸·⁴	1.079	136.5	......	......	−90.2	117.6; 116	......	......	64; 62.5	....
81	β-Chloroethyl acetate	145	......	1.4234	1.178	122.5	16.6	118.2	......	131	82	153; 147	......	......
82	Methyl d,l-lactate	145; 144.8	......	1.4144	1.0931	104	16.8; 18	122¹⁵	−97	64.65	78.5–9.0 (cor.), bz.-al. (3:1)	107	108 (cor.), al.	....
83	Ethyl chloroacetate	145	−26	1.42274	1.158	122.5	α: 61.3; β: 56.2; γ: 52.5	189	−117.3	78.32	121	162	93, al.	....
84	tert-Butyl n-butyrate	145–6.6	......	1.4001¹⁷·⁵	....	144	−5.5; −8	162.5; 164	25.5	82.5	115–6	75	142, pet. eth.	....
85	Triethyl orthoformate (Ethylorthoformate)	145.5	......	1.3922	0.8909	148	8.4	100.7	−117.3	78.32	2.55	53	93, al.	....
86	Ethyl n-valerate (Ethyl n-pentanoate)	145.5	−91.2	1.40094	0.8739	130	−34.5	186.35	−117.3	78.32	106	74	93, al.	....
87	Ethyl α-chloropropionate	146	......	....	1.087	136.5	......	186	−117.3	78.32	80	124	93, al.	Phenylhydrazide, 95

*Derivative data given in order: m.p., crystal color, solvent from which crystallized.

TABLE XVI. ORGANIC DERIVATIVES OF ESTERS
Including esters of inorganic acids
a) Liquids. 1) (Listed in order of increasing b.p.)* (Continued)

No.	Name	Boiling point, °C	Melting point, °C	n_D^{20}	D_4^{20}	Saponification					Amide	p-Toluidide	3,5-Di-nitro-benzoate	Miscellaneous
						Equiv-alent	Acid M.P., °C	Acid B.P., °C	Alcohol M.P., °C	Alcohol B.P., °C				
88	n-Butyl propionate	146.8	−89.6	1.4038[15]	1.401	130	−20.8	141	−90.2	117.6; 116	81; 81.3; 79	126; 123	64; 62.5	....
89	Benzyl chloro-acetate	147	......	1.5246[18]	1.2223[4]	170.5	α: 61.3; β: 56.2; γ: 52.5	189	−15.3	205.5	121	162	113	....
90	Di-isopropyl car-bonate (Isopropyl carbonate).....	147.2 (cor.)	......	1.3932	0.9162	146	....	....	−89.5	82.4	......	......	123, pet. eth.	....
91	Methyl isobutyl-carbinyl acetate .	148	......	....	0.8805[0]	130	16.6	118.2	−97	64.65	82	153; 147	108 (cor.), al.	
92	Methyl ethoxy-acetate	148	......	....	1.0112[15]	118	....	206–7	−97	64.65	80–2	32, eth.	108 (cor.), al.	....
93	Isobutyl iso-butyrate	148.6	−80.65	1.3999	0.87496[0]	144	−46.1	154.7	....	108.1	128; 129	108.5-9.5	87	Hydrazide, 104, eth.-al.
94	n-Amyl acetate (n-Pentyl acetate)........	149.25	−70.8	1.4031	0.8756	130	16.6	118.2	−78.5	138 (cor.)	82	153; 147	46.4	....
95	Ethyl α-hydroxy-isobutyrate.....	150	......	....	....	132	79	212	−117.3	78.32	......	132–3, w.	93, al.	....
96	Methyl glycolate .	151.2	......	....	1.1677[18]	90	78–9; 80	....	−97	64.65	120, al.-et. ac.	143, w.	108 (cor.), al.	....
97	Methyl n-caproate (Methyl n-hexanoate).....	151.25	−71.0	1.405	0.88464	130	−3.9	205.35	−97	64.65	100–1	74–5	123, pet. eth.	....
98	Isopropyl n-valerate (Iso-propyl n-pentanoate)....	153.5	......	1.4009	0.8579	144	−34.5	186.35	−89.5	82.4	106	74	61	
99	Isoamyl chloro-formate.....	154	......	1.41916[15]$_{He}$	1.032[15]	150.5	....	....	−117	132	......	......	93, al.	
100	Ethyl d,l-lactate..	154.5	......	1.410	1.030	118	16.8; 18	122[15]	−117.3	78.32	78.5–9.0 (cor.), bz.-al., (3:1)	107	93, al.	
101	Ethyl pyruvate ...	155	......	0.0596[15.6]	1.408[15.6]	116	13.6	165d.	−117.3	78.32	124–5; 145	109; 130	93, al.	Phenylhydra-zone, 118, dil. al.; 4-Nitro-phenylhy-drazone, 185–7; 2,4-Dinitro-phenylhy-drazone, 154.5–155 (cor.), diox.-al.
102	n-Propyl iso-valerate........	155.5	......	1.40413[17.8]	0.8643[17.8]	144	−30	176.5	....	97.1	135; 137	106–7	74, pet. eth.	....
103	n-Hexyl formate .	155.51	−62.65	1.40898[15] He (yel)	0.88133	130	8.4	100.7	−51.6; −46.1	157.5	2.55	53	58.4 (cor.)	....

*Derivative data given in order: m.p., crystal color, solvent from which crystallized.

TABLE XVI.   ORGANIC DERIVATIVES OF ESTERS

No.	Name	Boiling point, °C	Melting point, °C	n_D^{20}	D_4^{20}	Saponification Equivalent	Acid M.P., °C	Acid B.P., °C	Alcohol M.P., °C	Alcohol B.P., °C	Amide	p-Toluidide	3,5-Dinitrobenzoate	Miscellaneous
104	β-Ethoxyethyl acetate (Ethylene glycol mono-ethyl ether acetate; Ethyl cellosolve acetate)	156.2; 158	......	1.40292	0.9701	132	16.6	118.2	......	135	82	153; 147	75, al.	....
105	Isobutyl n-butyrate	157	......	1.40295[18.4]	0.8620	144	−5.5; −8	162.5; 164	......	108.1	115–6	75	87	
106	Ethyl dichloroacetate	158	......	1.43860	1.2821	157	5–6	194	−117.3	78.32	98 (subl.)	153	93, al.	....
107	Ethyl bromoacetate	159	......	1.451	1.506	167	50	208	−117.3	78.32	91	......	93, al.	
108	Ethyl glycolate	160	......		1.0869[15]	104	78–9; 80	......	−117.3	78.32	120, al.-et. ac.	143, w.	93, al.	
109	Isoamyl propionate	160.2	......	1.4065	0.870	144	−20.8	141	−117	132	81; 81.3; 79	126; 123	61	
110	Ethyl α-bromopropionate	162	......		1.524	181	25.7	203.5	−117.3	78.32	123	125	93, al.	
111	Cyclohexyl formate	162.5[750]	......	1.443	1.010	128	8.4	100.7	25.1	161.1	2.55	53	112–3, al.	
112	β-Bromoethyl acetate	163	......		1.524	167	16.6	118.2	......	149d.	82	153; 147	......	
113	Tetraethyl silicate (Ethyl orthosilicate)	165.5; 168.5	......	1.38619	0.93975	52	......	......	−117.3	78.32	......		93, al.	Gives SiO$_2$ on hydrolysis
114	n-Propyl n-valerate (n-Propyl n-pentanoate)	166.2; 167	−70.7	1.4065	0.8699	144	−34.5	186.35	......	97.1	106	74	74, pet. eth.	....
115	n-Butyl n-butyrate	166.6	−91.5	1.406	0.869	144	−5.5; −8	162.5; 164	−90.2	117.6; 116	115–6	75	64; 62.5	....
116	Ethyl n-caproate (Ethyl n-hexanoate)	167.7	−67.5	1.40727	0.8710	144	−3.9	205.35	−117.3	78.32	100–1	74–5	93, al.	....
117	Ethyl trichloroacetate	168	......	1.450	1.380	191.5	57–8	197.5	−117.3	78.32	141	113	93, al.	Phenylhydrazide, 123
118	Isopropyl d,l-lactate	168; 166–8	......	1.4082[25]	0.998	132	16.8; 18	122[15]	−89.5	82.4	78.5–9.0 (cor.), bz.-al. (3:1)	107	123, pet. eth.	
119	Di-n-propyl carbonate (n-Propyl carbonate)	168.5 (cor.)	......	1.4014	0.9411	146	......	......	......	97.1	......	......	74, pet. eth.	....
120	n-Amyl propionate (n-Pentyl propionate)	168.7	−73.1	1.4096[15]	0.8761[15]	144	−20.8	141	−78.5	138 (cor.)	81; 81.3; 79	126; 123	46.4	
121	Ethylidene diacetate	169	......		1.061[12]	73	16.6	118.2	−12.6	197.85	82	153; 147	169	....
122	Isoamyl isobutyrate	169	......		0.8760[0]	158	−46.1	154.7	−117	132	128; 129	108.5–9.5	61	Hydrazide, 104, eth.-al.
123	Methyl acetoacetate	170	......	1.41964	1.0765[0]	116	......	......	−97	64.65	......	......	108 (cor.), al.	Semicarbazone, 152.5, me. al.
124	Isobutyl isovalerate	171	......	1.40569	0.8534	158	−30	176.5	......	108.1	135; 137	106–7	87	....

*Derivative data given in order: m.p., crystal color, solvent from which crystallized.

TABLE XVI. ORGANIC DERIVATIVES OF ESTERS

TABLE XVI. ORGANIC DERIVATIVES OF ESTERS
Including esters of inorganic acids
a) Liquids. 1) (Listed in order of increasing b.p.)* (Continued)

No.	Name	Boiling point, °C	Melting point, °C	n_D^{20}	D_4^{20}	Saponification Equivalent	Acid M.P., °C	Acid B.P., °C	Alcohol M.P., °C	Alcohol B.P., °C	Amide	p-Toluidide	3,5-Dinitrobenzoate	Miscellaneous
125	Methyl enanthate (Methyl n-heptanoate)	173.8	−55.8	1.412	0.88011	144	−74.7	223	−97	64.65	96; 96.5	81	108 (cor.), al.	....
126	Ethylene glycol diformate	174	......	....	1.193[0]	59	8.4	100.7	−78.5	138 (cor.)	2.55	53	46.4	....
127	sec-Butyl n-valerate (sec-Butyl n-pentanoate)	174.5	......	1.4081	0.8605[20]	158	−34.5	108.35	......	99.5	106	74	76	
128	Cyclohexyl acetate	175	......	1.442	0.970	142	16.6	118.2	25.1	161.1	82	153; 147	112–3, al.	....
129	n-Butyl chloroacetate	175	......	....	1.081	150.5	α: 61.3; β: 56.2; γ: 52.5	189	−90.2	117.6; 116	121	162	64; 62.5	....
130	Furfuryl acetate ..	175–7	......	1.4627	1.118	140	16.6	118.2	......	172; 170	82	153; 147	80–1	....
131	Methyl methylacetoacetate	177.4	......	1.418	1.030	130	......		−97	64.65	......	......	108 (cor.), al.	Semicarbazone, 138, al.
132	n-Heptyl formate .	178.12	......	1.41505[15] He (yel)	0.87841	144	8.4	100.7	−34.6; −33.8	176.8	2.55	53	46; 47	....
133	n-Hexyl acetate ..	178.1	−80.9; −60.9	1.41122[15] He (yel)	0.87336	144	16.6	118.2	−51.6; −46.1	157.5	82	153; 147	58.4 (cor.)	....
134	Isoamyl n-butyrate	178.6	......	1.411	0.864	158	−5.5; −8	162.5; 164	−117	132	115–6	75	61	....
135	Ethyl β-bromopropionate	179	......	1.425	181		62.5		−117.3	78.32	111	......	93, al.	2-Naphthylamide, 174
136	Ethyl acetylglycolate.......	179	......	1.0993[17]	73		......		−117.3	78.32	......	......	93, al.	Hydrolysis → glycolic a. + ac.a. + al.
137	Isobutyl n-valerate (Isobutyl n-pentanoate)....	179	......	1.4099	0.8625	158	−34.5	186.35	......	108.1	106	74	87	....
138	β-Hydroxyethyl formate (Ethylene glycol monoformate)......	180	......	....	1.1989[15]	90	8.4	100.7	−78.5	138 (cor.)	2.55	53	46.4	....
139	Ethyl methylacetoacetate	180.8 (cor.); 187	......	1.419	1.0191	144	......		−117.3	78.32	73, eth.	......	93, al.	Anilide, 138–40; Semicarbazone, 194; 2,4-Dinitrophenyl hydrazone, 56–7
140	Ethyl acetoacetate	181	......	1.41976	1.025	130	......		−117.3	78.32	......	......	93, al.	Semicarbazone, 129; 133, eth.
141	Methyl pyromucate (Methyl 2-furoate)......	181.3	......	1.4860	1.180	126	133–4; 132	230–2	−97	64.65	142–3	170.5, al.	108 (cor.), al.	2,4-Dinitrophenylhydrazone, 93; 96, yel., al.

*Derivative data given in order: m.p., crystal color, solvent from which crystallized.

256

TABLE XVI. ORGANIC DERIVATIVES OF ESTERS
Including esters of inorganic acids
a) Liquids. 1) (Listed in order of increasing b.p.)* (Continued)

No.	Name	Boiling point, °C	Melting point, °C	n_D^{20}	D_4^{20}	Saponification Equivalent	Acid M.P., °C	Acid B.P., °C	Alcohol M.P., °C	Alcohol B.P., °C	Amide	p-Toluidide	3,5-Dinitrobenzoate	Miscellaneous
142	Dimethyl malonate (Methyl malonate)......	181.5	−62	1.41398	1.1539	66	134.8–.9	......	−97	64.65	*mono*: 106–110; *di*: 170, w.-al.	*mono*: 156d.; *di*: 252–3, al.	108 (cor.), al.	Phenylhydrazide, 194
143	Ethyl β-methoxyethyl carbonate	182.6	......	1.4036^{25}	1.0424^{25}	148	......	......	−117.3	78.32	......	......	93, al.	....
144	Methyl cyclohexanecarboxylate (Methyl hexahydrobenzoate)......	183	......	1.45372^{15}	0.9954^{15}	142	30–1	233	−97	64.65	185–6	......	108 (cor.), al.	....
145	Diethyl oxalate (Ethyl oxalate)..	185.19	−41.5; −40.6	1.41043	1.0785	73	189.5 (anh.); 101 (+ 2H₂O)	......	−117.3	78.32	*mono*: 219; *di*: 419d.	*mono*: 169; *di*: 268	93, al.	N-(β-Aminoethyl)-morpholide, 170
146	n-Amyl n-butyrate (n-Pentyl n-butyrate)......	186.4	−72.3	1.412	0.866	158	−5.5; −8	162.5; 164	−78.5	138 (cor.)	115–6	75	46.4	....
147	n-Butyl n-valerate (n-Butyl n-pentanoate).....	186.9	−92.8	1.4123	0.8678	158	−34.5	186.35	−90.2	117.6; 116	106	74	64; 62.5	....
148	β-Hydroxyethyl acetate (Ethylene glycol monoacetate).......	187–9	......	....	....	104	16.6	118.2	−78.5	138 (cor.)	82	153; 147	46.4	....
149	n-Propyl n-caproate (n-Propyl n-hexanoate).....	187.15; 186	−74.0	1.417	0.86719	158	−3.9	205.35	......	97.1	100–1	74–5	74, pet. eth.	....
150	Dimethyl sulfate (Methyl sulfate).	188	−27	1.3874	1.3348^{15}	63	......	......	−97	64.65	......	......	108 (cor.), al.	....
151	n-Butyl lactate...	188	−43	1.4216	0.984_{20}^{20}	146	16.8; 18	122^{15}	−90.2	117.6; 116	78.5–9.0 (cor.), bz.-al. (3:1)	107	64; 62.5	....
152	Ethyl enanthate (Ethyl n-heptanoate)......	188.6	−66.3	1.413	0.86856	158	−7.47	223	−117.3	78.32	96; 96.5	81	93, al.	....
153	Methyl ethylacetoacetate	189.7 (cor.)	......	....	0.989	144	......	......	−97	64.65	95–6, bz.	......	108 (cor.), al.	....
154	Di-isobutyl carbonate (Isobutyl carbonate).....	189.8 (cor.)	......	1.4072	0.9138	174	......	......		108.1	......		87	....
155	n-Hexyl propionate	190	−57.5	1.41621^{15} He (yel)	0.86980	158	−20.8	141	−51.6; −46.1	157.5	81; 81.3; 79	126; 123	58.4 (cor.)	....
156	Ethylene glycol diacetate.......	190.2	−31	1.4150	1.1040	73	16.6	118.2	−78.5	138 (cor.)	82	153; 147	46.4	....
157	Isoamyl isovalerate.......	190.4	......	$1.41300^{18.7}$	0.870	172	−30	176.5	−117	132	135; 137	106–7	61	....
158	n-Heptyl acetate .	192.45	......	1.41653^{15} He (yel)	0.87070^{15}	158	16.6	118.2	−34.6; −33.8	176.8	82	153; 147	46; 47	....
159	Cyclohexyl propionate.......	193^{750}	......	....	0.9718^{0}	156	−20.8	141	25.1	161.1	81; 81.3; 79	126; 123	112–3, al.	....

* Derivative data given in order: m.p., crystal color, solvent from which crystallized.

TABLE XVI. ORGANIC DERIVATIVES OF ESTERS

TABLE XVI. ORGANIC DERIVATIVES OF ESTERS
Including esters of inorganic acids
a) Liquids. 1) (Listed in order of increasing b.p.)* (Continued)

No.	Name	Boiling point, °C	Melting point, °C	n_D^{20}	D_4^{20}	Saponification Equiv-alent	Acid M.P., °C	Acid B.P., °C	Alcohol M.P., °C	Alcohol B.P., °C	Amide	p-Tolui-dide	3,5-Di-nitro-benzoate	Miscellaneous
160	Di-isopropyl oxalate (Iso-propyl oxalate) .	193–4	.....	1.4100	1.0097	87	189.5 (anh.); 101 (+ 2H₂O)	......	−89.5	82.4	mono: 219; di: 419d.	mono: 169; di: 268	123, pet. eth.	....
161	Ethyl β-ethoxy-ethyl carbonate .	194.5	.....	1.5064²⁵	1.0115²⁵	162	......	......	−117.3	78.32	......	......	93, al.	....
162	sec-Octyl acetate .	194.5	.....	1.4141	0.8606¹⁹	172	16.6	118.2		179	82	153; 147	32	....
163	Methyl n-capryl-ate (Methyl n-octanoate).....	194.6	−41	1.417	0.878	158	16.3	237; 239.3	−97	64.65	57	70	108 (cor.), al.	....
164	α-Tetrahydro-furfuryl acetate .	195; 194	.....	1.4350	1.0624²⁵	144	16.6	118.2		177–8⁷⁴³	82	153; 147	83–4	....
165	Methyl levulinate .	196; 191	.....	1.42333	1.04945	130	33–5	245–6	−97	64.65	107–8, al.	108–9, w.	108 (cor.), al.	Semicarba-zone, 142–3; Phenyl-hydrazone, 94–6; 2,4-Dinitro-phenylhyd-razone, 141.5–2.5 (cor.), diox.-al.; Oxime, 96
166	Ethyl cyclo-hexanecar-boxylate (Ethyl hexahydroben-zoate)........	196	.....	1.45012¹⁵	0.9672¹⁵	156	30–1	233	−117.3	78.32	185–6	......	93, al.	....
167	Diethyl methyl-malonate	196	.....	....	1.019¹⁵	87	137; 138d.	......	−117.3	78.32	217; 206	mono: 145d.; di: 228; 214	93, al.	....
168	Phenyl acetate ...	196.7	.....	1.503	1.078	136	16.6	118.2	41.8; 42	182	82	153; 147	145.8 (cor.), al.	....
169	Ethyl ethylaceto-acetate	198	.....	1.422	0.9856	158	......	......	−117.3	78.32	95–6, bz.	......	93, al.	Ketone cleavage → 2-penta-none, b.p. 102
170	n-Octyl formate ..	198.8	−39.1	1.42082¹⁵ He (yel)	0.87435	158	8.4	100.7	−16; −16.7	195	2.55	53	61–2	....
171	2-Ethyl-1-hexyl acetate	199	.....	....	0.8733²⁰₂₀	172	16.6	118.2	......	184.6	82	153; 147		....
172	Methyl benzoate .	199.2	−12.4	1.5164	1.0888	136	122.4	249	−97	64.65	130	158	108 (cor.), al.	....
173	Diethyl malonate (Ethyl malonate)......	199.3	−51.5	1.41618	1.05513	80	134.8–.9	......	−117.3	78.32	mono: 106–10; di: 170, w.-al.	mono: 156d.; di: 252–3, al.	93, al.	Phenylhy-drazide, 194
174	Methyl cyano-acetate	200	−22.5	....	1.0962²⁵	99	66	......	−97	64.65	119–20	......	108 (cor.), al.	....

*Derivative data given in order: m.p., crystal color, solvent from which crystallized.

TABLE XVI. ORGANIC DERIVATIVES OF ESTERS
Including esters of inorganic acids
a) Liquids. 1) (Listed in order of increasing b.p.)* (Continued)

No.	Name	Boiling point, °C	Melting point, °C	n_D^{20}	D_4^{20}	Saponification					Amide	p-Tolui-dide	3,5-Di-nitro-benzoate	Miscellaneous
						Equiv-alent	Acid M.P. °C	Acid B.P. °C	Alcohol M.P. °C	Alcohol B.P. °C				
175	Dimethyl mesaconate.....	203	......	1.45119	1.0914	79	204.5 (cor.)	......	−97	64.65	mono (α): 222; (β): 174; di: 176.5	mono (α): 196; di: 212, al.	108 (cor.)	Dihydrazide, 215d., dil. al.
176	Benzyl formate...	203	......	1.516	1.080	136	8.4	100.7	−15.3	205.5	2.55	53	113	....
177	Vinyl benzoate...	203	......	......	1.065	148	122.4	249	......	......	130	158	......	....
178	Cyclohexyl iso-butyrate.......	204⁷⁵⁰	......	......	0.9489⁰	170	−46.1	154.7	25.1	161.1	128; 129	108.5–9.5	112–3, al.	Hydrazide, 104, al.-eth.
179	Dimethyl maleate	204.4	7.6	1.44156	1.14513¹⁵	72	137	......	−97	64.65	mono: 172–3, w.; 153, sl. d.; di: 181, me. al.	di: 142, eth.	108 (cor.), al.	....
180	α-Tetrahydro-furfuryl pro-pionate.......	204–7	......	1.044		158	−20.8	141		177–8⁷⁴³	81; 81.3; 79	126; 123	83–4	....
181	Ethyl levulinate ..	205.8	......	1.42288	1.01114	144	33–5	245–6	−117.3	78.32	107–8d.	108–9, w.	93, al.	Semicarba-zone, 147–8; Phenylhyd-razone, 103–4; 2,4-Dinitro-phenylhyd-razone, 101–2, diox.-al.; Oxime, 96
182	Ethyl allylaceto-acetate........	206 sl. d.; 211–2 sl. d.	......	1.43¹⁷·⁶	0.9898	170	......	......	−117.3	78.32	......	......	93, al.	Semicarba-zone, 125, w.
183	n-Amyl n-valerate (n-Pentyl n-pentanoate)....	207.4	......	1.4181¹⁵	0.8825⁰	172	−34.5	186.35	−78.5	138 (cor.)	106	74	46.4	....
184	Di-n-butyl car-bonate (n-Butyl carbonate).....	207.5 (cor.)	......	1.4117	0.9238	174	......	......	−90.2	117.6; 116	......	......	64; 62.5	....
185	n-Butyl n-caproate (n-Butyl n-hexanoate) ...	207.74	−63.1; −64.3 He (yel)	1.41877¹⁵	0.86530	172	−3.9	205.35	−90.2	117.6; 116	100–1	74–5	64; 62.5	....
186	n-Hexyl n-butyrate.......	207.88	−78	1.41875¹⁵ He (yel)	0.86519	172	−5.5; −8	162.5; 164	−51.6; −46.1	157.5	115–6	75	58.4 (cor.)	....
187	2-Tolyl acetate ("o-Cresyl acetate")......	208	......		1.048	150	16.6	118.2	31	191–2	82	153; 147	134.8 (cor.), al.	....
188	Diethyl sulfate (Ethyl sulfate) ..	208	......	1.4010¹⁸	1.172²⁵	77	......	......	−117.3	78.32	......	......	93, al.	....
189	n-Propyl n-enan-thate (n-Propyl n-heptanoate) ..	208	−64.8	1.41835¹⁵	0.86556	172	−7.47	223	......	97.1	96; 96.5	81	74, pet. eth.	....
190	Ethyl n-caprylate (Ethyl n-octanoate).....	208.35	α: −43.1; β: −59.2	1.41775	0.8667	172	16.3	237; 239.3	−117.3	78.32	110; 106	70	93, al.	N-(β-Amino-ethyl) mor-pholide, 59

*Derivative data given in order: m.p., crystal color, solvent from which crystallized.

TABLE XVI. ORGANIC DERIVATIVES OF ESTERS
Including esters of inorganic acids
a) Liquids. 1) (Listed in order of increasing b.p.)* (Continued)

No.	Name	Boiling point, °C	Melting point, °C	n_D^{20}	D_4^{20}	Saponification					Amide	p-Tolui-dide	3,5-Di-nitro-benzoate	Miscellaneous
						Equiv-alent	Acid		Alcohol					
							M.P., °C	B.P., °C	M.P., °C	B.P., °C				
191	Isobutyl enanthate (Isobutyl n-heptanoate)	209	......	....	0.8593	186	−7.47	223	....	108.1	96; 96.5	81	87	....
192	Isopropyl levulinate	209.3	......	1.42088	0.98724	158	33.5	245–6	....	82.4	107–8d.	108–9, w.	123, pet. eth.	Semicarba-zone, 141–2; Phenylhyd-razone, 108–9; 2,4-Dinitro-phenylhyd-razone, 88–9 (cor.); 90.9
193	Trimethylene glycol diacetate (1,3-Diacetoxy-propane)	210	......	....	1.069	80	16.6	118.2	−30	214.7; 210–2	82	153; 147	178	....
194	n-Octyl acetate ..	210	......	....	0.8847⁰	172	16.6	118.2	−16; −16.7	195	82	153; 147	61–2	....
195	n-Heptyl pro-pionate	210	−50.9	1.42605¹⁵ He (yel)	0.86786	172	−20.8	141	−34.6; −33.8	176.8	81; 81.3; 79	126; 123	46; 47	....
196	Dimethyl citra-conate	210.5	......	1.44856	1.11531	79	92; 91d. eth.-lgr.	206–11, sl. d.	−97	64.65	100–1	......	108 (cor.), al.	Dihydrazide, 177, w.; 1-Naphthyl-amide, 169–70
197	n-Propyl pyro-mucate (n-Propyl 2-furoate)......	211	......	1.4737²⁵·⁹	1.0745²⁵·⁹	154	133–4; 132	230–2	....	97.1	142–3	170.5, al.	74, pet. eth.	....
198	Ethylene glycol dipropionate....	211	......	....	1.0544¹⁵₁₅	87	−20.8	141	−78.5	138 (cor.)	81; 81.3; 79	126; 123	46.4	
199	Cyclohexyl n-butyrate	212⁷⁵⁰	......	....	0.9572⁰	170	−5.5; −8	162.5; 164	25.1	161.1	115–6	75	112–3, al.	....
!00	3-Tolyl acetate ("m-Cresyl acetate")	212	12	1.4978	1.049	150	16.6	118.2	11.95	202.7	82	153; 147	164.5 (cor.), al.	....
01	Ethyl aceto-pyruvate	213–5	......	1.4757¹⁷	1.1251	158	101, bz.	......	−117.3	78.32	131–2d., al.	......	93, al.	....
02	Ethyl benzoate ...	212.4; 213.2	−34.7	1.50570	1.04684	150	122.4	249	−117.3	78.32	130	158	93, al.	N-(β-Amino-ethyl) mor-pholide, 123.4
!03	4-Tolyl acetate ("p-Cresyl acetate")	212.5	......	1.500	1.051	150	16.6	118.2	36	202	82	153; 147	188.6 (cor,), al.	....
204	Di-n-propyl oxalate (n-Propyl oxalate) .	213.9	−51.7	1.4168	1.0169	87	189.5 (anh.); 101 (+2 H₂O)	......	....	97.1	mono: 219; di: 419d.	mono: 169; di: 268	74, pet. eth.	NH₄OH → Di-n-propyl oxamate, 90–2, me. al.
205	Methyl pel-argonate	214; 213–4	......	....	0.892	172	12.3	254.4	−97	64.65	99	84	108 (cor.), al.	
206	Dimethyl glu-tarate	214⁷⁵¹	−34.7	1.42415	1.0874	80	98	302–4	−97	64.65	di: 175	di: 218	108 (cor.), al.	....

*Derivative data given in order: m.p., crystal color, solvent from which crystallized.

TABLE XVI. ORGANIC DERIVATIVES OF ESTERS

TABLE XVI. ORGANIC DERIVATIVES OF ESTERS
Including esters of inorganic acids
a) Liquids. 1) (Listed in order of increasing b.p.)* (Continued)

No.	Name	Boiling point, °C	Melting point, °C	n_D^{20}	D_4^{20}	Saponification					Amide	p-Toluidide	3,5-Dinitrobenzoate	Miscellaneous
						Equivalent	Acid M.P., °C	Acid B.P., °C	Alcohol M.P., °C	Alcohol B.P., °C				
207	**2,6-Dimethylphenyl acetate** (*vic-m*-Xylenyl acetate)	214–6	......	....	....	164	16.6	118.2	49	203	82	153; 147	158.8 (cor.), al.	....
208	**Methyl 2-toluate** (Methyl 2-methylbenzoate)	215	......	....	1.068	150	104–5; 107–8	259[751]	−97	64.65	142.8 (cor.)	144	108 (cor.), al.	....
209	**Benzyl acetate**	217	......	1.5200	1.055	150	16.6	118.2	−15.3	205.5	82	153; 147	113	N-(β-Aminoethyl) morpholide, 95.2
210	**Diethyl succinate**	217.25	−20.8	1.41975	1.0398	87	185; 182.8	235d.	−117.3	78.32	mono: 157; di: 260d., w.	mono: 179–80; di: 254.5–5.5; 260	93, al.	N-(β-Aminoethyl) morpholide, 174
211	**Diethylene glycol monoethyl ether acetate**	218	......	....	1.013	176	16.6	118.2	....	198	82	153; 147	oil	....
212	**Diethyl fumarate**	218.4; 213–4	0.55	1.44103	1.052	86	286–7 (sealed tube); 233–5; 200, subl.	......	−117.3	78.32	mono: 270; 300–2, subl.; di: 266d.	mono: 233.0–4.5; di: 313–4; ac. a.	93, al.	....
213	**Isopropyl benzoate**	218.5	......	1.4890[25]	1.013	164	122.4	249	−89.5	82.4	130	158	123, pet. eth.	....
214	**Methyl phenylacetate**	220	......	1.507	1.068	150	76.5, subl.	256.5 (cor.)	−97	64.65	156	135–6	108 (cor.), al.	....
215	**l-Linalyl acetate**	220	......	1.4460	0.8951	196	16.6	118.2	....	199	82	153; 147	......	$[\alpha]_D$: −3 to −17; 4-Nitrobenzoate, 70
216	**Methyl 3-toluate** (Methyl 3-methylbenzoate)	221; 215	......	....	1.061	150	111–3; 110–1	263, subl.	−97	64.65	94; 97	118	108 (cor.), al.	....
217	**n-Propyl levulinate**	221.2	......	1.42576	0.98955	158	33–5	245–6	....	97.1	107–8d.	108–9, w.	74, pet. eth.	Semicarbazone, 129–30; Hydrazone, 88–90; Phenylhydrazone, 67–8 (cor.), al.; Oxime, 96
218	**Diethyl d,l-tartronate**	222–5d.	......	....	1.152[15]	88	156–8d.	......	−117.3	78.32	di: 198, dil. al.; 195–6d.	......	93, al.	....

*Derivative data given in order: m.p., crystal color, solvent from which crystallized.

TABLE XVI. ORGANIC DERIVATIVES OF ESTERS

Including esters of inorganic acids
a) Liquids. 1) (Listed in order of increasing b.p.)* (Continued)

No.	Name	Boiling point, °C	Melting point, °C	n_D^{20}	D_4^{20}	Saponification					Amide	p-Tolui-dide	3,5-Di-nitro-benzoate	Miscellaneous
						Equiv-alent	Acid		Alcohol					
							M.P., °C	B.P., °C	M.P., °C	B.P., °C				
219	Diethyl maleate ..	222.7	−17	1.44156	1.066	86	137	......	−117.3	78.32	mono: 172–3, w.; 152–3 sl. d.; di: 181, me. al.	di: 142, eth.	93, al.	....
220	Methyl salicylate .	224	......	1.5369	1.184	152	158.3	......	−97	64.65	142; 139	156	108 (cor.), al.	....
221	Ethyl n-butoxy-ethyl carbonate .	224	......	1.4143²⁵	0.9756²⁵	190	......	......	−117.3	78.32	......	......	93, al.	....
222	sec-Butyl levu-linate	225.8	......	1.42495	0.96698	172	33–5	245–6	......	99.5	107–8d.	108–9, w.	76	Oxime, 96
223	n-Heptyl n-butyrate	225.87	−57.5	1.42279¹⁵, He (yel)	0.86371	186	−5.5; −8	162.5; 164	−34.6; −33.8	176.8	115–6	75	46; 47	....
224	2,4-Dimethyl-phenyl acetate (unsym-m-Xylenyl acetate) .	226 (cor.)	......	1.4990¹⁵	1.0298¹⁵·⁵	164	16.6	118.2	27	211.5 (cor.)	82	153; 147	164.6 (cor.), 95% al.	....
225	Methyl n-caprate (Methyl n-decanoate)	226	......	1.426	0.873	186	31.5	268–70	−97	64.65	108; 100.1	78	108 (cor.), al.	....
226	n-Amyl n-caproate (n-Pentyl n-hexanoate).....	226.16	−50; −47	1.42280¹⁵ He (yel)	0.86349	186	−3.9	205.35	−78.5	138 (cor.)	100–1	74–5	46.4	....
227	n-Butyl n-enan-thate (n-Butyl n-heptanoate) ..	226.2	......	1.42280¹⁵	0.86382	186	−7.47	223	−90.2	117.6; 116	96; 96.5	81	64; 62.5	....
228	n-Hexyl n-valerate (n-Hexyl n-pentanoate)....	226.3	−63.1	1.42286¹⁵	0.86345	186	−34.5	186.35	−51.6; −46.1	157.5	106	74	58.4 (cor.)	....
229	n-Propyl n-caprylate (n-Propyl n-octanoate).....	226.43	−46.2	1.42351¹⁵ He (yel)	0.86591	186	16.3	237; 239.3	......	97.1	110; 106	57	74, pet. eth.	....
230	Ethyl 2-toluate (Ethyl 2-methyl-benzoate)......	227	......	1.507²¹·⁶	1.0325⁴²¹·⁵	164	104–5; 107–8	259⁷⁵¹	−117.3	78.32	142.8 (cor.)	144	93, al.	....
231	Ethyl pelargonate	227	α: −55.0; β: −36.7	1.42200	0.8657	186	12.3	254.4	−117.3	78.32	99	84	93, al.	N-(β-Amino-ethyl) mor-pholide, 61.3
232	l-Menthyl acetate	227	......	......	0.9185	198	16.6	118.2	43	216	82	153; 147	153	....
233	Ethyl phenyl-acetate	227.5	......	1.49921¹⁸·⁵	1.0333	164	76.5, subl.	256.5 (cor.)	−117.3	78.32	156	135–6	93, al.	N-(β-Amino-ethyl) mor-pholide, 88.9
234	n-Octyl propionate	227.9	−41.6	1.42185¹⁵ He (yel)	0.86633	186	−20.8	141	−16; −16.7	195	81; 81.3; 79	126; 123	61–2	....
235	Diethyl itaconate .	228	......	1.4377	1.0467	93	165	......	−117.3	78.32	di: 191.2–.8, al.	......	93, al.	....

*Derivative data given in order: m.p., crystal color, solvent from which crystallized.

TABLE XVI. ORGANIC DERIVATIVES OF ESTERS
Including esters of inorganic acids
a) Liquids. 1) (Listed in order of increasing b.p.)* (Continued)

No.	Name	Boiling point, °C	Melting point, °C	n_D^{20}	D_4^{20}	Saponification Equivalent	Acid M.P., °C	Acid B.P., °C	Alcohol M.P., °C	Alcohol B.P., °C	Amide	p-Toluidide	3,5-Dinitrobenzoate	Miscellaneous
236	Diethyl mesaconate........	229	.....	1.4488	1.0453	93	204.5 (cor.), subl.	......	−117.3	78.32	mono (α): 222; (β): 174; di: 176.5	mono (α): 196; di: 212, al.	93, al.	....
237	Di-isobutyl oxalate (Isobutyl oxalate)......	229	.....	1.4180	0.97373	101	189.5 (anh.); 101 (+2 H₂O)	......	......	108.1	mono: 219; di: 419d.	mono: 169; di: 268	87	....
238	Allyl benzoate ...	230	.....	1.067_4^4	1.0578_{15}^{15}	162	122.4	249	......	97.1	130	158	49–50	....
239	Isobutyl levulinate	230.9	.....	1.42677	0.96770	172	33–5	245–6	......	108.1	107–8d.	108–9, w.	87	Semicarbazone, 112–3; Phenylhydrazone, 84–6; 2,4-Dinitrophenylhydrazone, 55.6; Oxime, 96
240	n-Propyl benzoate	231	......	1.500	1.023	164	122.4	249	......	97.1	130	158	74, pet. eth.	....
241	Diethyl citraconate........	231	.....	1.4442	1.0491	93	92d., eth.-lgr.	206–11 sl. d.	−117.3	78.32	100–1	......	93, al.	1-Naphthylamide, 169–70
242	Methyl 3-chlorobenzoate.......	231	.....	......	......	170.5	158; 155	......	−97	64.65	134	......	108 (cor.), al.	....
243	β-Phenylethyl acetate........	232; 224	.....	1.5108	$1.057^{22.5}$	164	16.6	118.2	−25.8	219.8	82	153; 147	108	....
244	Ethyl β-(2-furyl) acrylate	232	14	1.5286	1.0891^{15}	166	141	286	−117.3	78.32	168–9, w.	......	93, al.	
245	Di-(β-methoxyethyl) carbonate.	232	.....	1.4193^{25}	1.0936^{25}	178	......	......	......	124.5				
246	Di-isoamyl carbonate........	233 (cor.)	.....	1.4174	0.9067	202	......	......	−117	132	......	......	61	
247	Diethyl glutarate.	233.66	−23.8	1.02229	1.42395	94	98	302–4	−117.3	78.32	di: 175–6	di: 218	93, al.	N-(β-Aminoethyl) morpholide, 152.7
248	Ethyl 3-toluate...	234	......	$1.505^{21.4}$	$1.0265^{21.4}$	164	111–3; 110–1	263, subl.	−117.3	78.32	94; 97	118	93, al.	
249	Ethyl salicylate ..	234	.....	1.52542	1.1396	166	158.3; subl. at 76	......	−117.3	78.32	142; 139	156	93, al.	....
250	Methyl 2-chlorobenzoate.......	234	.....	......	......	170.5	142; 144	......	−97	64.65	142; 202	131	108, (cor.), al.	
251	Ethyl 4-toluate...	234.5	......	$1.5089^{18.2}$	$1.0269^{18.2}$	164	179–80, subl.	275 (cor.)	−117.3	78.32	160; 158	160; 165	93, al.	
252	Diethyl bromomalonate	235	.....	....	1.426_{15}^{15}	239	113d.	......	−117.3	78.32	di: 181, al.	di: 217, ac. a.	93, al.	....

*Derivative data given in order: m.p., crystal color, solvent from which crystallized.

TABLE XVI. ORGANIC DERIVATIVES OF ESTERS
Including esters of inorganic acids
a) Liquids. 1) (Listed in order of increasing b.p.)* (Continued)

No.	Name	Boiling point, °C	Melting point, °C	n_D^{20}	D_4^{20}	Equivalent	Acid M.P., °C	Acid B.P., °C	Alcohol M.P., °C	Alcohol B.P., °C	Amide	p-Toluidide	3,5-Dinitrobenzoate	Miscellaneous
253	**Ethylene glycol di-*n*-butyrate** ...	235–7[749]	......	1.42619He	1.0005	101	−5.5; −8	162.5; 164	−78.5	138 (cor.)	115–6	75	46.4	....
254	**Diethyl butylmalonate**	235–40	......	....	1.425	101	......	......	−117.3	78.32	*di:* 200	......	93, al.	....
255	**2,4,6-Trimethylphenyl acetate** (Mesityl acetate)	236	......	....	....	178	16.6	118.2	70; 69	220	82	153; 147	......	
256	**2,5-Dimethylphenyl acetate** (*p*-Xylenyl acetate)	237[768]	......	....	1.0264[15]	164	16.6	118.2	74.5	212	82	153; 147	137.2 (cor.), al.	
257	**n-Butyl levulinate**	237.8	......	1.42905	0.97353	172	33–5	245–6	−90.2	117.6; 116	107–8d.	108–9, w.	64; 62.5	Semicarbazone, 102–3; Phenylhydrazone, 79–81; 2,4-Dinitrophenylhydrazone, 65.8; Oxime, 96
258	**Benzyl n-butyrate**	238–40	......	....	1.033[16]	178	−5.5; −8	162.5; 164	−15.3	205.5	115–6	75	113	....
259	**Methyl hydrocinnamate** (Methyl β-phenylpropionate)	239	......	....	1.0455[0]	164	48.7; 40	279–80 (cor.)	−97	64.65	105; 82	135	108 (cor.), al.	....
260	**n-Propyl salicylate**	239; 249–51	......	1.51610	1.0979	180	158.3	......		97.1	142; 139	156	74, pet. eth.	....
261	**Guaiacol acetate** (2-Methoxyphenyl acetate) .	240	......	1.5101[25]	1.1285[25]	166	16.6	118.2	32; 28.2	205	82	153; 147	141.2 (cor.), al.	....
262	**Isopropyl salicylate**	240–2; 237	......	1.50650	1.0729	180	158.3; subl. at 76	......	−89.5	82.4	142; 139	156	123, pet. eth.	
263	**Dimethyl *l*-malate**	242	......	1.4425	1.2334	81	100–1	......	−97	64.65	*di:* 156–7	*di:* 206–7	108 (cor.), al.	$[\alpha]_D^{20}: -6.85$
264	**Geranyl acetate** ..	242	......	1.4660	0.9174[15]	196	16.6	118.2		230	82	153; 147	62–3	....
265	**Isobutyl benzoate**	242.2 (cor.)	......	....	0.999	178	122.4	249	......	108.1	130	158	87	....
266	**Di-n-butyl oxalate** (*n*-Butyl oxalate)	243; 245.5	−29.6	1.4240	0.98732	101	189.5 (anh.); 101 (+2H₂O)	......	−90.2	117.6; 116	*mono:* 219; *di:* 419d.	*mono:* 169; *di:* 268	64; 62.5	....
267	**Methyl 2-bromobenzoate**	244	......	....	....	215	150	......	−97	64.65	155	......	108 (cor.), al.	
268	**n-Octyl n-butyrate**	244.1	−55.6	1.42674[15] He (yel)	0.86288	200	−5.5; −8	162.5; 164	−16; −16.7	195	115–6	75	61–2	....
269	**Ethyl n-caprate** (Ethyl *n*-decanoate)	244.9	β: −20; γ: −30.6	1.42575	0.8650	200	31.5	268–70	−117.3	78.32	108; 100.1	78	93, al.	N-(β-Aminoethyl) morpholide, 60.1

*Derivative data given in order: m.p., crystal color, solvent from which crystallized.

TABLE XVI. ORGANIC DERIVATIVES OF ESTERS
Including esters of inorganic acids
a) Liquids. 1) (Listed in order of increasing b.p.)* (Continued)

No.	Name	Boiling point, °C	Melting point, °C	n_D^{20}	D_4^{20}	Saponification Equivalent	Acid M.P. °C	Acid B.P. °C	Alcohol M.P. °C	Alcohol B.P. °C	Amide	p-Toluidide	3,5-Dinitrobenzoate	Miscellaneous
270	Diethyl adipate	245; 133.8[15]	−21	1.42765	1.0090	101	153–4 (cor.)	216[15]	−117.3	78.32	*mono:* 125–30, w.; *di:* 220	241	93, al.	N-(β-Amino-ethyl) morpholide, 165
271	Methyl phenoxy-acetate	245	.....	....	1.150[17.5]	166	98–9	285d.	−97	64.65	101.5	.....	108 (cor.), al.	....
272	Thymyl acetate	245	.....	....	1.009[0]	192	16.6	118.2	51.5	233.5	82	153; 147	103.2 (cor.), al.	....
273	Carvacryl acetate	245 (cor.)	.....	1.49128[28]	0.98959[25]	192	16.6	118.2	1	237.5	82	153; 147	83	....
274	Diethylene glycol diacetate (β,β'-Diacetoxy di-ethyl ether)	245–51; 148[26]	.....	1.4348	1.1078[15][15]	95	16.6	118.2	−10.45	244.5	82	153; 147	149, ac. a.	
275	n-Butyl n-caprylate (n-Butyl n-octa-noate)	245.02	−41.9; −43	1.42647[15] He (yel)	0.86278	200	16.3	237	−90.2	117.6; 116	110; 106	70	64; 62.5	....
276	n-Heptyl n-valerate (n-Heptyl n-pentanoate)	245.2	−46.4	1.42536[15] He (yel)	0.86225	200	−34.5	186.35	−34.6; −33.8	176.8	106	74	46; 47	
277	n-Amyl n-enan-thate (n-Pentyl n-heptanoate)	245.4	−49.5	1.42627[15] He (yel)	0.86232	200	−7.47	223	−78.5	138 (cor.)	96; 96.5	81	46.4	
278	n-Hexyl n-Caproate (n-Hexyl n-decanoate)	245.4	−55.25	1.42637[15] He (yel)	0.86216	200	−3.9	205.35	−51.6; −46.1	157.5	100–1	74–5	58.4 (cor.)	....
279	Di-(β-ethoxy-ethyl) carbonate	245.5	.....	1.4239[25]	1.0635[25]	206	....	.....		135	......	.....	75, al.	
280	Diethylene glycol monobutyl ether acetate	246	.....		0.983	204	16.6	118.2		228–30	82	153; 147		
281	Isobutyl phenyl-acetate	247	.....		0.999[18]	192	76.5 (cor.)	256.5 (cor.)		108.1	156	135–6	87	
282	Ethyl hydrocinna-mate (Ethyl β-phenylpro-pionate)	247.2	.....		1.0147	178	40; 48.7	279–80 (cor.)	−117.3	78.32	105; 82	135	93, al.	
283	Di-n-propyl succinate	248; 246	−10.4	1.4252	1.011	101	185; 182.8	235d.	....	97.1	*mono:* 157; *di* 260d., w.	*mono:* 179–80; *di* 254.5-5.5; 260	74, pet. eth.	....
284	Methyl 2-meth-oxybenzoate	248	.....	1.534[19.5]	1.1571[19]	166	100–1	200	−97	64.65	129	.....	108 (cor.), al.	....
285	Methyl undecylen-ate (Methyl hendecylenate)	248	−27.5	1.43928	0.889[15]	198	24.5	275	−97	64.65	87	.....	108 (cor.), al.	....

*Derivative data given in order: m.p., crystal color, solvent from which crystallized.

TABLE XVI. ORGANIC DERIVATIVES OF ESTERS

TABLE XVI. ORGANIC DERIVATIVES OF ESTERS
Including esters of inorganic acids
a) Liquids. 1) (Listed in order of increasing b.p.)* (Continued)

No.	Name	Boiling point, °C	Melting point, °C	n_D^{20}	D_4^{20}	Saponification Equiv-alent	Acid M.P., °C	Acid B.P., °C	Alcohol M.P., °C	Alcohol B.P., °C	Amide	p-Toluidide	3,5-Di-nitro-benzoate	Miscellaneous
286	Isoamyl levulinate	248.8	......	1.43102	0.96136	186	33–5	245–6	–117	132	107–8d.	108–9, w.	61	Semicarba-zone, 91–2; Phenylhyd-razone, 70–2; 2,4-Dinitro-phenylhyd-razone, 50.5; Oxime, 96
287	Diethyl acetone-dicarboxylate...	250d.	......	....	1.113	101	135	......	–117.3	78.32	....	......	93, al.	Dianilide, 155, bz.; Semicarba-zone, 94–5; Cu(OAc)₂ → Cu enolate, 142–3, grn. bz.
288	n-Butyl benzoate .	250.3	–22.4	....	1.000	178	122.4	249	–90.2	117.6; 116	130	158	64; 62.5	....
289	Ethyl phenoxy-acetate	251	......	....	1.104[17.5]	180	98–9	285d.	–117.3	78.32	101.5	......	93, al.	....
290	Methyl 3-meth-oxybenzoate....	252	......	1.52236	1.131	166	109–10	......	–97	64.65	....	......	108 (cor.), al.	α-Phenyl-ethylamide, 128.6–9.0; Benzyl-amide, 111.8–2.8
291	Diethyl l-malate .	253	......	1.4362	1.1290	95	100–1	......	–117.3	78.32	di: 156–7	di: 206–7	93, al.	$[\alpha]_D^{20}$: –10.18
292	n-Amyl levulinate (n-Pentyl levulinate)	253.4	......	1.43192	0.96136	186	33–5	245–6	–78.5	138 (cor.)	107–8d.	108–9, w.	46.4	2,4-Dinitro-phenylhyd-razone, 84.2; Oxime, 96
293	n-Butyl phenyl-acetate	254	......	1.489	0.994	192	76.5, subl.	256.5 (cor.)	–90.2	117.6; 116	156	135–6	64; 62.5	....
294	β-Methoxyethyl benzoate (Methyl "cellosolve" benzoate)	255	......	1.5040[25]	1.0891[25]	180	122.4	249	......	124.5	130	158	......	4-Nitro-benzoate, 50.5, dil. al.
296	Diethyl pimelate .	255	–23.8	1.42985	0.9929	108	105	223[15]	–117.3	78.32	di: 175	di: 206, al.	93, al.	N-(β-Amino-ethyl) mor-pholide, 137.9
297	Ethyl benzoyl-formate.......	256–7	......	1.5190[25]	1.222[25]	178	66	......	–117.3	78.32	91	......	93, al.	Phenylhyd-razone, 64; 2,4-Di-nitro-phenylhyd-razone, 196–7d. (cor.)

*Derivative data given in order: m.p., crystal color, solvent from which crystallized.

TABLE XVI. ORGANIC DERIVATIVES OF ESTERS
Including esters of inorganic acids
a) Liquids. 1) (Listed in order of increasing b.p.)* (Continued)

No.	Name	Boiling point, °C	Melting point, °C	n_D^{20}	D_4^{20}	Saponification					Amide	p-Toluidide	3,5-Dinitrobenzoate	Miscellaneous
						Equivalent	Acid M.P., °C	Acid B.P., °C	Alcohol M.P., °C	Alcohol B.P., °C				
298	Glyceryl triacetate	258	. . . . .	. . . .	1.161^{15}	72.7	16.6	118.2	17.9	290d.	82	153; 147	. . . . .	Tris-4-nitro-benzoate, 188
299	Ethyl 3-methoxy-benzoate	260	. . . . .	1.5161	1.0993	180	109–10	. . . . .	−117.3	78.32	. . . .	. . . . .	93, al.	Benzyl-amide, 111.8–2.8; α-Phenyl-ethylamide, 128.6–9.0
300	β-Ethoxyethyl benzoate ("Cello-solve" benzoate)	$260–1^{738.5}$	. . . . .	1.4969^{25}	1.0585^{25}_{25}	194	122.4	249	. . . .	135	130	158	75, al.	. . . .
301	Isobutyl salicylate	260–2	. . . . .	1.50872	1.0639	194	158.3, subl. at 76	. . . . .	. . . .	108.1	142; 139	156	87	. . . .
302	n-Amyl n-capryl-ate (n-Pentyl n-octanoate)	260.21	−34.8	1.43019^{15} He (yel)	0.86132	214	16.3	237; 239.3	−78.5	138 (cor.)	110; 106	70	46.4	. . . .
303	n-Hexyl n-enan-thate (n-Hexyl n-heptanoate)	260.9	−47.9	1.42939^{15} He (yel)	0.86114	214	−7.47	223	−51.6; −46.1	157.5	96; 96.5	81	58.4 (cor.)	. . . .
304	n-Heptyl n-caproate (n-Heptyl n-hexanoate)	260.97	−34.4	1.42934^{15}; He (yel)	0.86115	214	−3.9	205.35	−34.6; −33.8	176.8	100–1	74–5	46; 47	. . . .
305	Ethyl 2-methoxy-benzoate	261	. . . . .	1.5224	1.1124	261	100–1	200	−117.3	78.32	129	. . . . .	93, al.	. . . .
306	n-Octyl n-valerate (n-Octyl n-pentanoate)	261.1	−42.5	1.42743^{15} He (yel)	0.86148	214	−34.5	186.35	−16; −16.7	195	106	74	61–2	. . . .
307	Isoamyl benzoate .	262.3	. . . . .	1.4950	1.004	192	122.4	249	−117	132	130	158	61	. . . .
308	Dimethyl d-cam-phorate	263	. . . . .	$1.46334^{16.9}$	1.0747	114	187.5–8.0	. . . . .	−97	64.65	mono: (α-amide β-acid), 176; (β-amide-α-acid), 182–3; di: 192–3	α: 212–4; β: 190–6	108 (cor.), al.	. . . .
309	Ethyl undecylenate (Ethyl hendecylenate)	264	. . . . .	1.4449^{23}	0.88271^{15}_{15}	212	24.5	275	−117.3	78.32	87	. . . . .	93, al.	. . . .
310	Isobutyl succinate	265	. . . . .	1.427	0.974	115	185; 182.8	235d.	. . . .	108.1	mono: 157; di: 260d., w.	mono: 179–80; di: 254.5–5.5; 260	87	. . . .

* Derivative data given in order: m.p., crystal color, solvent from which crystallized.

TABLE XVI. ORGANIC DERIVATIVES OF ESTERS
Including esters of inorganic acids
a) Liquids. 1) (Listed in order of increasing b.p.)* (Continued)

No.	Name	Boiling point, °C	Melting point, °C	n_D^{20}	D_4^{20}	Saponification					Amide	p-Tolui-dide	3,5-Di-nitro-benzoate	Miscellaneous
						Equiv-alent	Acid		Alcohol					
							M.P., °C	B.P., °C	M.P., °C	B.P., °C				
311	Ethyl benzoyl-acetate	265 sl. d.; 270 d.	......	1.5498	1.116	192	....	......	−117.3	78.32	....	......	93, al.	Ketone cleavage → aceto-phenone, m.p. 19.65, b.p. 202
312	Di-isoamyl oxa-late (Isoamyl oxalate)	267–8; 262	......	1.427	0.961	115	189.5 (anh.); 101 (+ 2H₂O)	......	−117	132	mono: 219; di: 419d.	mono: 169; di: 268	61	....
313	Dimethyl suberate	268	−5	1.43326	1.0198	101	144; 139–41	......	−97	64.65	mono: 125–7; di: 216–7	di: 218; 219	108 (cor.), al.	....
314	Methyl laurate ...	268	......	1.432	0.870	214	44; 42	299	−97	64.65	100; 99	87	108 (cor.), al.	β-Naphthol → β-naphthyl methyl ether, 72
315	Ethyl 4-methoxy-benzoate (Ethyl anisate)	269	7	1.5254	1.1038	180	184.6; 184.2 (cor.)	275–80	−117.3	78.32	167; 162–3, w.	186	93, al.	N-(β-Amino-ethyl) mor-pholide, 130.6
316	Ethyl laurate	269	−1.7	1.4321	0.8671¹⁹₁₉	228	44; 42	299	−117.3	78.32	100; 99	87	93, al.	....
317	Trimethyl aconitate	270	......	....	....	72	194–5 (cor.) d.	......	−97	64.65	tri: turns br. at 250; sinters at 260	......	108 (cor.), al.	....
318	n-Butyl salicylate	270–2; 268	......	1.51148	1.0728	194	158.3, subl. at 76	......	−90.2	117.6; 116	142; 139	156	64; 62.5	....
319	Ethyl cinnamate..	271	6.70	1.55982	1.0490	176	133	300	−117.3	78.32	147–8	168	93, al.	N-(β-Amino-ethyl) mor-pholide, 121.9
320	Di-n-butyl suc-cinate	274.5	−29.3	1.4298	0.9760	115	185; 182.8	235d.	−90.2	117.6; 116	mono: 157; di: 260d., w.	mono: 179–80; di: 254.5 −5.5; 260	64; 62.5	....
321	Ethyl 2-nitro-benzoate	275	30	....	....	195	146	......	−117.3	78.32	176	......	93, al.	....
322	Triethyl aconitate	275d.	......	1.45562	1.1064	86	194–5 (cor.)	......	−117.3	78.32	tri: turns br. at 250; sinters at 260	......	93, al.	....
323	Di-isopropyl d-tartarate	275	......	....	1.1274	117	169–71	......	−89.5	82.4	mono: 171–2; di: 196d., al.	......	123, pet. eth.	$[\alpha]_D^{20}$: +14.886; Phenylhyd-razide, 240
324	Ethyl 4-ethoxy-benzoate	275	......	....	1.076²¹	194	198; 195–6	......	−117.3	78.32	202	......	93, al.	Hydrazide, 126–7, al.

*Derivative data given in order: m.p., crystal color, solvent from which crystallized.

TABLE XVI. ORGANIC DERIVATIVES OF ESTERS
Including esters of inorganic acids
a) Liquids. 1) (Listed in order of increasing b.p.)* (Continued)

No.	Name	Boiling point, °C	Melting point, °C	n_D^{20}	D_4^{20}	Saponification					Amide	p-Tolui-dide	3,5-Di-nitro-benzoate	Miscellaneous
						Equiv-alent	Acid M.P., °C	Acid B.P., °C	Alcohol M.P., °C	Alcohol B.P., °C				
325	n-Octyl n-caproate (n-Octyl n-hexanoate)	275.2	−28.4	1.43256[15] He (yel)	0.86032	228	−3.9	205.35	−16; −16.7	195	100–1	74–5	61–2	....
326	Isoamyl salicylate	276–8	.....	1.50799	1.0535	208	158.3, subl. at 76	.....	−117	132	142; 139	156	61	....
327	n-Heptyl n-enanthate (n-Heptyl n-heptanoate) ..	277.2	−33.3	1.43183[15] He (yel)	0.86039	228	−7.47	223.0	−34.6; −33.8	176.8	96; 96.5	81	46; 47	....
328	n-Hexyl n-caprylate (n-Hexyl n-octanoate)	277.44	−30.6	1.43230[15] He (yel)	0.86033	228	16.3	237; 239.3	−51.6; −46.1	157.5	110; 106	70	58.4 (cor.)	....
329	Resorcinol di-acetate	278 sl. d.	.....	....	1.179	97	16.6	118.2	110 (stab.); 108–8.5 (labile)	280.8 (cor.)	82	153; 147	di: 201	....
330	Diethyl suberate .	282	5.9	1.43236	1.9807	115	144; 139–41	.....	−117.3	78.32	mono: 125–7; di: 216–7	di: 218–9	93, al.	N-(β-Amino-ethyl) mor-pholide, 157.2
331	Resorcinol mono-acetate	283	.....	....	....	152	16.6	118.2	110 (stab.); 108–8.5 (labile)	280.8 (cor.)	82	153; 147	di: 201	....
332	Dimethyl phthalate (Methyl phthal-ate)..........	283.8	.....	1.5138	1.191	97	200–6; 191 (sealed tube)	.....	−97	64.65	mono: 149; di: 220	mono: 150 (slow htng.); 160–5 (rapid htng.)	108 (cor.), al.	....
333	Diethyl iso-phthalate	286[733]	11.5	....	....	111	348 (subl.)	.....	−117.3	78.32	mono: 280; di: 280	.....	93, al.	....
334	Diethyl d-cam-phorate	286	.....	1.45354[26.2]	1.0298	128	187.5–8.0	.....	−117.3	78.32	mono: (α-amide-β-acid): 176; (β-amide-α-acid): 182–3; di: 192–3	α: 212–4; β: 190–6	93, al.	....
335	Glyceryl tri-propionate	289	.....	....	1.083[19]	86.7	−20.8	141	17.9	290d.	81; 81.3; 79	126; 123	.....	Tris-4-nitro-benzoate, 188

*Derivative data given in order: m.p., crystal color, solvent from which crystallized.

TABLE XVI. ORGANIC DERIVATIVES OF ESTERS
Including esters of inorganic acids
a) Liquids. 1) (Listed in order of increasing b.p.)* (Continued)

No.	Name	Boiling point, °C	Melting point, °C	n_D^{20}	D_4^{20}	Saponification					Amide	p-Toluidide	3,5-Di-nitro-benzoate	Miscellaneous
						Equiv-alent	Acid		Alcohol					
							M.P., °C	B.P., °C	M.P., °C	B.P., °C				
336	**Diethyl phthalate** (Ethyl phthal-ate)	289.5; 298	. . . . . .	1.5019	1.1175	111	200–6; 191 (sealed tube)	. . . . . .	−117.3	78.32	*mono*: 149; *di*: 220	*mono*: 150 (slow htng.); 160–5 (rapid htng.)	93, al.	. . . .
337	**n-Heptyl n-caprylate** (n-Heptyl n-octanoate)	290.6	−10.2	1.43492[15] He (yel)	0.85958	242	16.3	237; 239.3	−34.6; −33.8	176.8	110; 106	70	46; 47	. . . .
338	**n-Octyl n-enan-thate** (n-Octyl n-heptanoate) . .	290.8	−21.5	1.43488[15] He (yel)	0.85961	242	−7.47	223.0	−16; −16.7	195	96; 96.5	81	61–2	. . . .
339	**Diethyl azelate** . . .	291	−18.5	1.43509	0.97294	122	106.5	>360 sl. d.; 237[15]	−117.3	78.32	*mono*: 93–5; *di*: 175	*di*: 201–2	93, al.	N-(β-Amino-ethyl) mor-pholide, 141.3
340	**Triethyl citrate** . .	294	. . . . . .	1.44554	1.1369	92	153 (anh.); 100 (+1 H₂O)	. . . . . .	−117.3	78.32	*tri*: 210–5d., w.	*tri*: 189, al.	93, al.	. . . .
341	**Ethyl myristate** . .	295	α: 11.9; β: 12.3	1.4362	0.8573[25]	256	53.9	202[16]	−117.3	78.32	103	93	93, al.	N-(β-Amino-ethyl) mor-pholide, 76
342	**Di-n-propyl d-tartarate**	297	. . . . . .	. . . .	1.1390	117	169–71	. . . . . .	. . . . . .	97.1	*mono*: 171–2; *di*: 196d., al.	. . . . . .	74, pet. eth.	$[\alpha]_D^{20}$: +12.00; Phenylhyd-razide, 240
343	**Isoamyl succinate**	297	. . . . . .	1.434	0.958	129	185; 182.8	235d.	−117	132	*mono*: 157; *di*: 260d., w.	*mono*: 179–80; *di*: 254.5–5.5; 260	61	. . . .
344	**Di-(β-n-butoxy-ethyl)carbonate** .	297–8	. . . . . .	1.4279[25]	0.9766[65]	262	. . . . . .	. . . . . .	. . . . . .	. . . . . .	170–6[743]	. . . . . .	. . . . . .	. . . .
345	**Diethyl benzyl-malonate**	300	. . . . . .	1.077[15]		125	117d.	. . . . . .	−117.3	78.32	225	. . . . . .	93, al.	. . . .
346	**α-Tetrahydro-furfuryl ben-zoate**	300–2[750]	. . . . . .	. . . .	1.137[20]_0	206	122.4	249	. . . . . .	177–8[743]	130	158	83–4	. . . .
347	**Di-isopropyl phthalate** (Iso-propyl phthalate)	302	. . . . . .	. . . .	1.065[19]	115	200–6; 191 (sealed tube)	. . . . . .	−89.5	82.4	*mono*: 149; *di*: 220	*mono*: 150 (slow htng.); 160–5 (rapid htng.)	123, pet. eth.	. . . .
348	**n-Octyl n-caprylate** (n-Octyl n-octanoate)	306.8	−15.1	1.43698[15] He (yel)	0.85919	256	16.3	237; 239.3	. . . . . .	. . . . . .	110; 106	70	61–2	. . . .

*Derivative data given in order: m.p., crystal color, solvent from which crystallized.

TABLE XVI.   ORGANIC DERIVATIVES OF ESTERS

Including esters of inorganic acids

a) Liquids. 1) (Listed in order of increasing b.p.)* (Continued)

No.	Name	Boiling point, °C	Melting point, °C	n_D^{20}	D_4^{20}	Equivalent	Saponification				Amide	p-Toluidide	3,5-Dinitro-benzoate	Miscellaneous
							Acid		Alcohol					
							M.P., °C	B.P., °C	M.P., °C	B.P., °C				
349	Diethyl sebacate	307	1.3	1.43657	0.9631	129	33, subl.	243[15]	−117.3	78.32	mono: 170; di: 210; 208	di: 201	93, al.	....
350	2-Tolyl benzoate ("o-Cresyl" benzoate)	307	.....	.....	1.114[19]	212	122.4	249	31	191–2	130	158	138.4 (cor.), al.	....
351	Ethyl 1-naphthoate	309	.....	.....	1.1274[15/15]	200	161–2 (cor.)	.....	−117.3	78.32	202; 205	.....	93, al.	....
352	Glyceryl tributyrate	318	.....	.....	1.033[17]	100.7	−5.5; −8	162.5; 164	17.9	290d.	115–6	75	.....	Tris-4-nitrobenzoate, 188
353	Di-n-butyl d,l-tartarate (Di-n-butyl racemate)	320	.....	.....	1.0879[18]	131	205–6 (anh.); 203–4 (+1 H₂O)	.....	−90.2	117.6; 116	di: 226, w.-me. al.	.....	64; 62.5	Dianilide, 235–6
354	Benzyl salicylate	320	.....	.....	....	228	158.3, subl. at 76	.....	−15.3	205.5	142; 139	156	113	....
355	Di-n-butyl phthalate (n-Butyl phthalate)	340.7	.....	1.4900	1.047[20/20]	139	200–6; 191 (sealed tube)	.....	−90.2	117.6; 116	mono: 149; di: 220	mono: 150 (slow htng.); 160–5 (rapid htng.)	64; 62.5	N-(β-Aminoethyl) morpholide, 124
356	Di-n-butyl sebacate	345	.....	.....	0.9329[15]	157	133, subl.	243[15]	−90.2	117.6; 119	mono: 126.5; di: 210; 208	di: 201	64; 62.5	Phenylhydrazide, 194
357	Di-isoamyl phthalate (Isoamyl phthalate)	349	.....	.....	1.024[17]	153	200–6; 191 (sealed tube)	.....	−117	132	mono: 149; di: 220	mono: 150 (slow htng.); 160–5 (rapid htng.)	61	....
358	Tricresyl phosphate	400d.; 275–80[20]	−30	1.5568	1.197[25]	122.7	.....	.....	36	202.32	.....	.....	188.6 (cor.), al.	

*Derivative data given in order: m.p., crystal color, solvent from which crystallized.

TABLE XVI. ORGANIC DERIVATIVES OF ESTERS
Reduced pressure b.p. only
a) Liquids. 2) (Listed in order of increasing m.p. of the corresponding amide)*

No.	Name	Boiling point, °C	Melting point, °C	n_D^{20}	D_4^{20}	Saponification Equivalent	Acid M.P., °C	Acid B.P., °C	Alcohol M.P., °C	Alcohol B.P., °C	Amide	p-Toluidide	3,5-Dinitrobenzoate	Miscellaneous
1	3,5-Dimethylphenyl acetate (*Sym-m-*Xylenyl acetate)	130[26]; 120[11]	......	......	......	164	16.6	118.2	63.2; 68	220.2	82	153; 147	195.4, al.	....
2	Dimethyl azelate	156[20]; 146.2[10]	......	1.43607	1.0069	108	106	>360 sl. d.	−97	64.65	*mono:* 93–5; *di:* 172	*di:* 201–2; 198	108 (cor.), al.	....
3	Dimethyl adipate	107.6[11]	8.5	1.4277	1.0625	87	153–4 (cor.)	216[15]	−97	64.65	*mono:* 125–30, w.; *di:* 220	241	108 (cor.), al.	....
4	*β-n-*Butoxyethyl benzoate (Butyl "cellosolve" benzoate)	156.5–7.0[14.5]; 131.6–2.6[3.0]	......	1.4925[25]	1.0277[25][25]	222	122.4	249	......	170–6[7.13]	130	158	....	4-Nitrophenylurethane, 58.7–9.1, CCl₄
5	Ethyl furoylacetate ...	170[20]; 143[10]	......	1.5055[16]	1.165[17][17]	.....	......	......	−117.3	78.32	159, al.	....	93, al.	Oxime, 131–2, dil., al.
6	Methyl furoylacetate..	144–5[20]; 96–8[1]	......	......	......	.....	......	......	−97	64.65	159, al.		108 (cor.), al.	Semicarbazone, 141–2, bz.-al. (3:1); Oxime, 124–5, bz.
7	Di-*n*-propyl adipate ...	155[16]	−20	1.4314	0.9790	115	153–4	......	......	97.1	*mono:* 161; *di:* 220	*di:* 241	74, pet. eth.	....
8	Dimethyl pimelate	119.3–9.6[10]	−20.6	1.42888	1.0383	94	105	.....	−97	64.65	*di:* 175	*di:* 206, al.	108 (cor.), al.	....
9	Di-*n*-propyl maleate ..	114–7[6]	......	1.444[18.3]	1.026	100	137	.....	.....	97.1	*di:* 181, me. al.	*mono:* 195d., chl.; *di:* 142, eth.	74, pet. eth.	....

*Derivative data given in order: m.p., crystal color, solvent from which crystallized.

TABLE XVI. ORGANIC DERIVATIVES OF ESTERS
b) Solids (Listed in order of increasing m.p.) *

No.	Name	Melting point, °C	Boiling point, °C	Saponification					Amide	p-Toluidide	3,5-Di-nitro-benzoate	Miscellaneous
				Equiv-alent	Acid M.P., °C	Acid B.P., °C	Alcohol M.P., °C	Alcohol B.P., °C				
1	Dimethyl succinate	18.2	196	73	185; 182.8	235d.	−97	64.65	*mono*: 157; *di*: 260d.	*mono*: 179–80; *di*: 254.5–5.5; 260	108 (cor.), al.	n_D^{20}: 1.41965 D_4^{20}: 1.1192
2	Methyl myristate	18.5	323	242	53.9	202[16]	−97	64.65	103	93	108 (cor.), al.	n_D^{45}: 1.428
3	Ethyl piperonylate	18.5	286	194	....	228; 229	−117.3	78.32	169, al.	....	93, al.	....
4	Diethyl *d*-tartarate	18.6	280	103	169–71	......	−117.3	78.32	*mono*: 171–2; *di*: 196d., al.	....	93, al.	n_D^{20}: 1.44677; D_4^{20}: 1.2028; $[\alpha]_{Hg}^{20}$ (grn): +7.87; Phenylhydrazide, 204
5	Phenyl propionate	20	211	150	−20.8	141	41.8; 42	182; 183	81	123; 126	145.8 (cor.), al.	D_{25}^{25}: 1.0467; Tribromo, 95
6	Ethyl margarate	20.6 (β)	....	298	61.2	231[16]	−117.3	78.32	108; 106	....	93, al.	....
7	Methyl 3-chlorobenzoate	21	231	170.5	158; 155	......	−97	64.65	134	....	108 (cor.), al.	....
8	Benzyl benzoate	21	323–4 (cor.)	212	122.4	......	−15.3	205.5	130	158	113	n_D^{21}: 1.5681; D^{19}: 1.1224
9	Di-*n*-butyl *d*-tartarate	22	....	131	169–71	......	−90.2	117.6; 116	*mono*: 171–2; *di*: 196d., al.	....	64; 62.5	D_4^{18}: 1.0886; $[\alpha]_D^{11}$: + 10.09; Phenylhydrazide, 240
10	3,4-Dimethylphenyl acetate	22	235	164	16.6	118.2	62.5	225	82	153; 147	181.6, rods, al.	....
11	Isobutyl stearate	(a) 22.5; (b) 28.9; (two forms)	....	340	70–1	......	....	108.1	109; 108.4, al.	102	87	....
12	Isoamyl stearate	23	....	354	70–1	......	−117	132	109; 108.4, al.	102	61	....
13	Cetyl acetate (*n*-Hexadecyl acetate)	α: 18.5; β: 24.2; 22	....	284	16.6	118.2	49.27	190[18]	82	153; 147	66	....
14	Ethyl palmitate	α: 19.4; β: 24.2	185	284	62.7	222[16]	−117.3	78.32	106–7; 105.3, al.	98	93, al.	....
15	Methyl anthranilate (Methyl 2-aminobenzoate)	24.4	299.8	151	146	......	−117.3	78.32	109	151	93, al.	N-(β-Aminoethyl) morpholide, 126; Picrate, 106
16	Di-*n*-propyl *d,l*-tartarate	25	286[765]	117	203–4 (+1 H₂O); 205–6 (anh.)	......	....	97.1	226, w.-me. al.	....	74, pet. eth.	D_4^{20}: 1.1256
17	Dimethyl sebacate	26.6; 27–8	....	115	133, subl.	243[15]	−97	64.65	*mono*: 170; *di*: 210; 208	*di*: 201	108 (cor.), al.	n_D^{28}: 1.43549; D_4^{28}: 0.98818; Phenylhydrazide, 194

* Derivative data given in order: m.p., crystal color, solvent from which crystallized.

No.	Name	Melting point, °C	Boiling point, °C	Saponification					Amide	p-Toluidide	3,5-Di-nitro-benzoate	Miscellaneous
				Equiv-alent	Acid		Alcohol					
					M.P., °C	B.P., °C	M.P., °C	B.P., °C				
18	Methyl β-(2-furyl) acrylate	27	227	152	141	286	−97	64.65	168–9	. . . .	108 (cor.), al.	. . . .
19	n-Butyl stearate	27.5; 28	. . . .	340	70–1	. . . . . .	−90.2	117.6; 116	109; 108.4, al.	102	64; 62.5	. . . .
21	d-Bornyl acetate	29	226; 221	196	16.6	118.2	204.5–5.5	212	82	153; 147	154	$n_D^{22.6}$: 1.4633; D_4^{15}: 0.991 (undercooled)
22	Methyl margarate	29	. . . .	284	61.2	231[16]	−97	64.65	108; 106	. . . .	108 (cor.), al.	. . . .
23	Eugenyl acetate	30	282	206	16.6	118.2	−9.1	253	82	153; 147	130.8 (cor.), 95% al.	n_D^{20}: 1.52069; D_{15}^{15}: 1.087
24	Methyl palmitate	30	184[12]	270	62.7	222[16]	−97	64.65	106–7; 105.3, al.	98	108 (cor.), al.	n_D^{45}: 1.4317
25	n-Amyl stearate (n-Pentyl stearate)	30	. . . .	354	70–1	. . . . . .	−78.5	138 (cor.)	109; 108.4, al.	102	136 (cor.)	. . . .
26	Ethyl 2-nitrobenzoate. . .	30	275	195	146	. . . . . .	−177.3	78.32	176	. . . .	93, al.	. . . .
27	n-Octadecyl acetate	α: 29.97; β: 31.95	. . . .	312	16.6	118.2	α: 57.95; 59.5	210.5[15]	82	153; 147	66	β-Form exist below 0°; α-Form: seeding with crys. or cooling soln. of the compound.
28	Ethyl 2-naphthoate.	32	304	200	184; 185.5	. . . . . .	−117.3	78.32	192–3; 195, al.	192, al.	93, al.	n_D^{20}: 1.596; D_4^{20}: 1.117
29	Methyl-3-bromo-benzoate	32	. . . .	229	155	. . . . . .	−97	64.65	155	. . . .	108 (cor.), al.	. . . .
30	Methyl 4-toluate.	33	222.5; 217	150	179–80, subl.	275 (cor.)	−97	64.65	160; 158	160; 165	108 (cor.), al.	. . . .
31	Thymyl benzoate	33	. . . .	255	122.4	. . . . . .	51.5	233.5	130	158	103.2; al.	. . . .
32	Di-(β-ethoxyethyl) phthalate.	33	. . . .	155	200–6; 191 (sealed tube)	. . . . . .	. . . .	134.8	mono: 149; di: 220	mono: 150 (slow htng.); 160–5 (rapid htng.) di: 201	75, al.	. . . .
33	Ethyl stearate	α: 30.9; β: 33.5	199[10]	312	70–1	. . . . . .	−117.3	78.32	109; 108.4, al.	102	93, al.	α → β Slowly on rubbing; N-(β-Aminoethyl) morpholide, 58
34	Di-isopropyl d,l-tartarate	34	275[765]	117	203–4 (+ 1H₂O); 205–6 (anh.)	. . . . . .	−89.5	82.4	226, w.-me., al.	. . . .	123, pet. eth.	D_4^{20}: 1.1166
35	Ethyl pyromucate (Ethyl furoate).	34	197	140	133–4; 132	230–2	−117.3	78.32	142–3	170.5, al.	93, al.	n_D: 1.4797; $D_4^{20.8}$: 1.1174 (undercooled)
36	Diethyl 4-nitrophthalate	34	. . . .	133.5	165	. . . . . .	−117.3	78.32	200 d	mono: 172	93, al.	. . . .
37	Ethyl benzilate	34	. . . .	256	150	. . . . . .	−117.3	78.32	153, chl.	189–90	93, al.	. . . .

*Derivative data given in order: m.p., crystal color, solvent from which crystallized.

TABLE XVI. ORGANIC DERIVATIVES OF ESTERS
b) Solids (Listed in order of increasing m.p.)* (Continued)

No.	Name	Melting point, °C	Boiling point, °C	Saponification Equivalent	Acid M.P., °C	Acid B.P., °C	Alcohol M.P., °C	Alcohol B.P., °C	Amide	p-Toluidide	3,5-Dinitrobenzoate	Miscellaneous
38	2,4,5-Trimethylphenyl acetate (Pseudocumenyl acetate)	34–4.5	245–6	178	16.6	118.2	71	232	82	153; 147	....	....
39	Methyl cinnamate	36	261	162	133	300	– 97	64.65	147–8	168	108 (cor.), al.	....
40	Ethyl d,l-mandelate	37	254	180	118	......	– 117.3	78.32	133–4	172, al.	93, al.	....
41	Dimethyl itaconate.....	38	208	79	165	......	– 97	64.65	di: 191.2–.8, al.	....	108 (cor.), al.	n_D^{20}: 1.44413; D_4^{18}: 1.12410
42	Methyl sebacate	38	288d.	216	133, subl.	243^{15}	– 97	64.65	mono: 170; di: 210, 208	di: 201	108 (cor.), al.	Phenylhydrazide, 194
43	Methyl stearate	38.8	214–5^{15}	298	70–1	......	– 97	64.65	109; 108.4, al.	102	108 (cor.), al.	....
44	Benzyl cinnamate	39	....	238	133	300	– 15.3	205.5	147	168	113	....
45	Methyl dibenzylacetate	41	....	254	89	......	– 97	64.65	128–9, bz.	175, abs. al.	108 (cor.), al.	....
46	Phenyl salicylate (Salol)	42	....	214	158.3, subl. at 76	......	41.8; 42	182; 183	142; 139	156	145.8 (cor.), al.	Tribromo deriv. of phenol, 95
47	Benzyl succinate	42	....	208	185; 182.8	235d.	– 15.3	205.5	mono: 157; di: 260d.	mono: 179–80; di: 254.5–5.5; 260	113	....
48	Dibenzyl phthalate	43 -	....	173	200.6; 191 (sealed tube)	......	....	......	mono: 149; di: 220	mono: 150 (slow htng.); 160–5 (rapid htng.); di: 201	113	....
49	Diethyl terephthalate ...	44	302	111	300, subl. without melting	......	– 117.3	78.32	>225	....	93, al.	Dianilide, 334–7, PhNO₂
50	Cinnamyl cinnamate ...	44	....	264	133	300	33	257	147–8	168	121	....
51	Ethyl 2-nitrocinnamate .	44	....	221	240	......	– 117.3	78.32	185	....	93, al.	....
52	Methyl 2-chlorocinnamate	44	....	196.5	212, yel., al.	......	– 97	64.65	168	....	108 (cor.), al.	....
53	Diethyl 3-nitrophthalate	46	....	133.5	218	......	– 117.3	78.32	di: 201d.	di: 226	93, al	N-(β-Aminoethyl) morpholide, 131.9
54	Ethyl 3-nitrobenzoate...	47	296	195	140	......	– 117.3	78.32	di: 187; 189–90, dil. me. al.	....	93, al.	....
55	Dicyclohexyl oxalate ...	47; 42	....	127	189.5 (anh.); 101 (+ 2H₂O)	......	25.15	161.1	mono: 219; di: 419d.	mono: 168; di: 268	112–3, al.	....
56	2-Phenylethyl cinnamate	47–8	....	252	133	300	– 25.8	219.8	147–8	168	108	....

*Derivative data given in order: m.p., crystal color, solvent from which crystallized.

275

No.	Name	Melting point, °C	Boiling point, °C	Saponification					Amide	p-Toluidide	3,5-Dinitro-benzoate	Miscellaneous
				Equiv-alent	Acid		Alcohol					
					M.P., °C	B.P., °C	M.P., °C	B.P., °C				
58	1-Naphthyl acetate	48; 49	......	186	16.6	118.2	94	278-80	82	153; 147	217.4, yel., al.	....
59	Methyl 4-methoxy-benzoate (Methyl anisate)	49; 45	255	166	184-6	275-80	-97	64.65	167; 162-5, w.	186	108 (cor.), al.	....
60	Phenacyl acetate (Benzoylcarbinyl acetate; ω-Acetoxy-acetophenone)	49	......	178	16.6	118.2	86	118-20[11]	82	153; 147	....	
61	Di-3-tolyl carbonate (Di-"m-cresyl" carbonate)	49	......	242	....	......	....	12	203	....	165.4 (cor.), al.	
62	Triphenyl phosphate	49	260[20]	108.7	....	......	41.8; 42	182; 183	....	....	145.8 (cor.), al.	D_4^{20}: 1.185; Tri-bromo deriv. of phenol, 95
63	Dibenzyl d-tartarate	50	......	165	169-71	......	-15.3	205.5	mono: 171-2; di: 196d., al.	....	113	Phenylhydrazide, 240
64	Dibenzyl succinate	51-2	......	149	185; 182.8	235d.	-15.3	205.5	mono: 157; di: 260d.	mono: 179-80; di: 254.5-5.5; 260	113	....
65	Methyl piperonylate	51-2	270-1[777]	180	229; 228	......	-97	64.65	169, al.	....	108 (cor.), al.	....
66	Cetyl palmitate (n-Hexadecyl palmitate)	51.6	......	480	62.7	222[16]	49.27	190[18]	106-7; 105.3, al.	98	66	....
68	Furfuryl diacetate	52	220	99	16.6	118.2	....	......	82	153; 147	....	Hydrolysis → furfural, b.p., 161.7; Semicarbazone, 202
69	Ethylene glycol dilaurate	52	......	213	44; 42	299	-12.6	197.85	100; 99	87	169	....
70	Phenyl stearate	52	......	360	70-1	......	41.8; 42	182; 183	109; 108.4, al.	102	145.8 (cor.), al.	Tribromo deriv. of phenol, 95
71	Methyl d,l-mandelate	53.3	250 sl. d.	166	118	......	-97	64.65	133-4	172, al.	108 (cor.), al.	....
72	Dimethyl tartronate	53.4	......	74	156-8d.	......	-97	64.65	di: 198, dil. al.	....	108 (cor.), al.	....
73	Dimethyl oxalate	54	163.5[262]	59	189.5 (anh.); 101 (+ 2H₂O)	......	-97	64.65	mono: 219; di: 419d.	mono: 168; di: 268	108 (cor.), al.	....
74	Tetraethyl pyromellitate	54	......	91.5	275	......	-117.3	78.32	....	....	93, al.	....
75	Diethyl meso-tartrate	55	......	103	140	......	-117.3	78.32	di: 187; 189-90, dil. me. al.	....	93, al.	Bis-phenylhydrazide, 245

*Derivative data given in order: m.p., crystal color, solvent from which crystallized.

No.	Name	Melting point, °C	Boiling point, °C	Saponification Equiv-alent	Acid M.P., °C	Acid B.P., °C	Alcohol M.P., °C	Alcohol B.P., °C	Amide	p-Toluidide	3,5-Di-nitro-benzoate	Miscellaneous
76	3-Tolyl benzoate ("m-Cresyl" benzoate)	55	314	212	122.4	249	12	203	130	158	165.4 (cor.), al.	....
77	Ethyl 4-nitrobenzoate...	56	186.3	195	241	......	−117.3	78.32	201; 198	204; 192	93, al.	N-(β-Aminoethyl) morpholide, 186.3
78	1-Naphthyl benzoate ...	56	....	248	122.4	249	94	278–80	130	158	217.4, yel., al.	....
79	Cetyl stearate (n-Hexadecyl stearate)...	56.6	....	508	70–1	......	49.27	190[18]	109; 108.4, al.	102	66	
80	Di-isobutyl d,l-tartarate.	58	311	131	203–4 (+1H₂O); 205–6 (anh.)	......	....	108.1	di: 226, w.-me. al.	....	87	
81	Ethyl diphenylacetate...	58	....	240	148	......	−117.3	78.32	167.5–8.0	172–3	93, al.	....
82	Ethyl 2-benzoylbenzoate	58	....	254	128 (anh.); 91 (+1H₂O); w.		−117.3	78.32	165 (cor.); 162	....	93, al.	N-(β-Aminoethyl) morpholide, 150.2
83	Diethyl naphthalate	58–60	....	136	274	......	−117.3	78.32	....		93, al.	....
84	Methyl diphenylacetate .	60	....	226	148	......	−97	64.65	167.5–8.0	172–3	108 (cor.), al.	....
85	Di-2-tolyl carbonate (Di-"o-cresyl" carbonate) .	60	....	242	....	......	30.75	190.8			138.4 (cor.), al.	....
86	Methyl 2-(4-toluyl)-benzoate	61	....	254	139–46		−97	64.65	175–6, al.	....	108 (cor.), al.	....
87	Dimethyl d-tartarate ...	61.5	....	89	169–71		−97	64.65	mono: 171–2; di: 196d., al.	....	108 (cor.), al.	Two other forms, m.p. 48 and 50; Phenylhydrazide, 240
88	Ethylene glycol dimyristate	63.0	....	241	53.9	202[16]	−12.6	197.85	103	93	169	....
89	Dimethyl 4-nitro-phthalate	66	....	119.5	165	......	−97	64.65	200d.	mono: 172	108 (cor.), al.	....
90	Dicyclohexyl phthalate .	66	....	165	200–6; 191 (sealed tube)	......	25.15	161.1	mono: 149; di: 220	mono: 150 (slow htng.); 160–5 (rapid htng.); di: 201	112–3, al.	n_D^{20}: 1.451; D_4^{20}: 1.383
92	Ethyl oxanilate........	66–7	....	193	148–9	......	−117.3	78.32	228	....	93, al.	....
93	Dimethyl isophthalate ..	67–8	....	97	348, subl.	......	−97	64.65	mono: 280; di: 280	....	108 (cor.), al.	....
94	Ethyl 2-(4-toluyl)ben-zoate	68; 69	314; 299	268	139–40	......	−117.3	78.32	175–6, w.	....	93, al.	....
95	Phenyl benzoate	69; 71	314	198	122.4	249	41.8; 42	182; 183	130	158	145.8 (cor.), al.	AlCl₃ → 4-Hydroxy benzophenone; Tri-bromo deriv. of phenol, 95

* Derivative data given in order: m.p., crystal color, solvent from which crystallized.

No.	Name	Melting point, °C	Boiling point, °C	Saponification					Amide	p-Toluidide	3,5-Di-nitro-benzoate	Miscellaneous
				Equiv-alent	Acid		Alcohol					
					M.P., °C	B.P., °C	M.P., °C	B.P., °C				
96	Dimethyl 3-nitro-phthalate............	69	....	133.5	218	......	−97	64.65	*di*: 201d.	*di*: 226	108 (cor.), al.	....
97	Methyl 3-hydroxy-benzoate	70	....	152	200, subl.	......	−97	64.65	170; 167	163, dil. al.	108 (cor.), al.	....
98	Ethylene glycol di-palmitate...........	70.5; 69	....	269	62.7	222[16]	−12.6	197.85	106–7; 105.3, al.	98	169	....
99	2-Naphthyl acetate.....	71	....	186	16.6	118.2	123	285–6	82	153; 147	210.2, al.	....
100	Glyceryl tristearate	71	....	297	70–1	......	17.9	290d.	109; 108.4, al.	102	....	n[80]: 1.4399; D[80][4]: 0.862
101	4-Tolyl benzoate ("p-Cresyl" benzoate)	71	316	212	122.4	249	36	202	130	158	188.6 (cor.), al.	....
102	Glyceryl tribenzoate....	72, lgr.; 76, al.	....	135	122.4	249	17.9	290d.	130	158	....	....
103	Phenyl cinnamate......	72	....	238	133	300	41.8; 42	182; 183	147–8	168	145.8 (cor.), al.	Tribromo deriv. of phenol, 95
104	Ethylene glycol diben-zoate	73	....	135	122.4	249	−12.6	197.85	130	158	*di*: 169	....
105	Methyl 2-nitro-cinnamate	73	....	207	240	......	−97	64.65	185	....	108 (cor.), al.	....
106	Di-isobutyl *d*-tartarate..	73–4; 70	....	131	169–71	......	....	108.1	*mono*: 171–2; *di*: 169d., al.	....	87	Phenylhydrazide, 240
107	Ethyl 3-hydroxy-benzoate	73.8	282	166	200, subl.	......	−117.3	78.32	170; 167	163, dil. al.	93, al.	....
108	Diphenyl phthalate (Phenyl phthalate)	74–5; 70	....	159	200–6; 191 (sealed tube)	......	41.8; 42	182; 183	*mono*: 149; *di*: 220	*mono*: 150 (slow htng.); 160–5 (rapid htng.); *di*: 201	145.8 (cor.), al.	Tribromo deriv. of phenol, 95
109	Methyl 3-hydroxy-2-naphthoate	75	....	202	222–3 (cor.)	......	−97	64.65	217–8 (cor.), yel., al.	221–3	108 (cor.), al.	....
110	Methyl benzilate.......	75	....	242	150	......	−97	64.65	154–5, chl.	189–90	108 (cor.), al.	....
111	Ethylene glycol di-*n*-stearate	76; 73	....	297	70; 69.6	......	−12.6	197.85	109; 108.4, al.	102	169	....
112	Trimethyl citrate	76; 78.9	283–7d.	78	100; 153 (anh.)	......	−97	64.65	*tri*: 210–5d., w.	*tri*: 189, al.	108 (cor.), al.	....
113	Methyl 2-naphthoate ...	77	290	186	184; 185.5	......	−97	64.65	192–3, al.	192, al.	108 (cor.), al.	....
114	Methyl α-phenyl-*n*-butyrate............	77–8	....	178	42	270	−97	64.65	85–7	....	108 (cor.), al.	....

*Derivative data given in order: m.p., crystal color, solvent from which crystallized.

No.	Name	Melting point, °C	Boiling point, °C	Saponification Equivalent	Acid M.P., °C	Acid B.P., °C	Alcohol M.P., °C	Alcohol B.P., °C	Amide	p-Toluidide	3,5-Dinitrobenzoate	Miscellaneous
115	Diphenyl carbonate	78	306	214	....	......	41.8; 42	182; 183	....	....	145.8 (cor.), al.	Phenylhydrazine → N,N'-diphenylcarbazide; Tribromo deriv. of phenol, 95
116	Methyl 3-nitrobenzoate	78	279	181	140	......	−97	64.65	143	162	108 (cor.), al.	....
117	Ethyl 3-nitrocinnamate	79	......	221	199	......	−117.3	78.32	196	....	93, al.	....
118	Isoeugenyl acetate	79	283	206	16.6	118.2	....	267.5	82	153; 147	158.4 (cor.), BuOH	Dibromide, 132–3
119	Methyl 2-benzoylbenzoate	79–80; 52	352	240	128 (anh.); 91 (+1 H₂O), w.	......	−97	64.65	165 (cor.); 162	....	108 (cor.), al.	....
120	Benzyl oxalate	80	......	135	189.5 (anh.); 101 (+2 H₂O)	......	−15.3	205.5	mono: 219; di: 419d.	mono: 169; di: 268	113	....
121	Methyl 4-bromobenzoate	81	......	215	251–3	......	−97	64.65	189–90, w.	....	108 (cor.), al.	....
122	Benzoin acetate	83	......	254	16.6	118.2	133	344	82	153; 147	....	....
123	Pentaerythritol tetraacetate	84	......	76	16.6	118.2	262; 253	......	82	153; 147	....	....
124	Pyrocatechol dibenzoate (Catechol dibenzoate)	84	......	159	122.4	249	105	245.6	130	158	di: 152	....
125	Ethyl 3-hydroxy-2-naphthoate	85	291	216	222–3 (cor.)	......	−117.3	78.32	217–8 (cor.), yel., al.	221–3	93, al.	....
126	Diguaiacol carbonate (Di-(2-methoxyphenyl) carbonate; "Guaiacol carbonate")	87	......	274	....	......	32	205	....	....	141.2 (cor.), al.	Monobromo deriv., 178
127	Dimethyl d,l-tartarate	90 (stab.); 84 (meta-stab.)	282	89	203–4 (+1 H₂O); 205–6 (anh.)	......	−97	64.65	226, w.-me. al.	....	108 (cor.), al.	....
128	Di-2-tolyl oxalate (Di-"o-cresyl" oxalate)	91	......	135	189.5 (anh.); 101 (+2 H₂O)	......	30.75	190.8	mono: 219; di: 419d.	mono: 169; di: 268	138.4 (cor.), al.	....
129	Ethyl 3,5-dinitrobenzoate	94; 93	......	240	204–5	......	−117.3	78.32	183	....	93, al.	N-(β-Aminoethyl) morpholide, 189.5
130	2-Naphthyl salicylate	95.5; 93.5	......	264	158.3 subl. at 76	......	123	285–6	142; 139	156	210.2, al.	....
131	Methyl 4-nitrobenzoate	96	......	181	241	......	−97	64.65	201; 198	204; 192	108 (cor.), al.	....
132	n-Propyl 4-hydroxybenzoate	96	......	180	215; 210	......	....	97.1	162 (+1 H₂O), w.	203–4, al.	123, pet. eth.	....
133	1,2,4-Triacetoxybenzene ("Hydroquinone triacetate")	96–7	......	76	16.6	118.2	140.5	......	82	153; 147	....	....

*Derivative data given in order: m.p., crystal color, solvent from which crystallized.

TABLE XVI. ORGANIC DERIVATIVES OF ESTERS

b) Solids (Listed in order of increasing m.p.)* (Continued)

No.	Name	Melting point, °C	Boiling point, °C	Saponification Equivalent	Acid M.P., °C	Acid B.P., °C	Alcohol M.P., °C	Alcohol B.P., °C	Amide	p-Toluidide	3,5-Dinitrobenzoate	Miscellaneous
134	Ethyl 3,5-dinitrosalicylate	99	......	256	182; 173 (+1 H$_2$O)	......	−117.3	78.32	181	......	93, al.	....
135	Dimethyl fumarate	101.7	193.25	72	286–7 (sealed tube), subl. 200	......	−97	64.65	*mono:* 270; 300–2, subl. *di:* 266d.	......	108 (cor.), al.	$n_D^{110.5}$: 1.40625; $D^{110.5}$: 1.0397
136	Ethyl 5-nitrosalicylate	102	....?..	211	229–30	......	−117.3	78.32	225	......	93, al.	....
137	Dimethyl naphthalate	104	......	122	274	......	−97	64.65			108 (cor.), al.	
138	Di-3-tolyl oxalate (Di-"*m*-cresyl" oxalate)	105	......	135	189.5 (anh.); 101 (+2 H$_2$O)	......	12	203	*mono:* 219; *di:* 419d.	*mono:* 169; *di:* 268	164.5 (cor.), al.	....
139	Phloroglucinol triacetate (1,3,5-Triacetoxybenzene)	105–6	......	76	16.6	118.2	200–9 (slow htng.); 217–9 (rapid htng.)	......	82	153; 147	*tri:* 162	....
140	Diphenyl adipate	106	......	149	153–4 (cor.)	216[15]	......	......	*mono:* 125–30, w.; *di:* 220	241	145.8 (cor.), al.	Tribromo deriv. of phenol, 95
141	Acetylsalicylaldehyde diacetate ("Salicylaldehyde triacetate")	107; 103	......	89	16.6	118.2	→	→	82	153; 147	......	Hydrolysis → salicylaldehyde, b.p. 197 (cor.)
142	2-Naphthyl benzoate	107	......	248	122.4	249	123	285–6	130	158	210.2, al.	....
143	Methyl 3,5-dinitrobenzoate	108	......	226	204–5	......	−97	64.65	183	......	108 (cor.), al.	....
144	Dimethyl mesotartrate	111	......	89	140	......	−97	64.65	*di:* 187; 189–90, dil. me. al.	......	108 (cor.), al.	Bis-phenylhydrazide, 245
145	Di-4-tolyl carbonate (Di-"*p*-cresyl" carbonate)	114	......	242	....	......	36	202			188.6 (cor.), al.	....
146	Ethyl oxamate	114–5	......	117	210	......	−117.3	78.32	419d.	......	93, al.	....
147	Cholesteryl acetate	114	......	416	16.6	118.2	148.5	......	82	153; 147	....	
148	Ethyl 4-hydroxybenzoate	116	......	166	215; 210	......	−117.3	78.32	162 (+1 H$_2$O), w.	203–4, al.	93, al.	N-(β-Aminoethyl) morpholide, 184
149	Resorcinol dibenzoate	117	......	159	122.4	249	110 (stab.); 108–8.5 (labile)	280.8 (cor.)	130	158	*bis:* 201	....
150	Ethyl 3-nitrosalicylate	118	......	211	125 (+1 H$_2$O)	......	−117.3	78.32	145	......	93, al.	....
151	Methyl 5-nitrosalicylate	119	......	197	229–30	......	−97	64.65	225	......	108 (cor.), al.	....

*Derivative data given in order: m.p., crystal color, solvent from which crystallized.

TABLE XVI. ORGANIC DERIVATIVES OF ESTERS

b) Solids (Listed in order of increasing m.p.)* (Continued)

No.	Name	Melting point, °C	Boiling point, °C	Saponification Equiv-alent	Acid M.P., °C	Acid B.P., °C	Alcohol M.P., °C	Alcohol B.P., °C	Amide	p-Toluidide	3,5-Di-nitro-benzoate	Miscellaneous
152	Diphenyl succinate	121	....	135	185; 182.8	235d.	41.8; 42	182; 183	mono: 157; di: 260d.	mono: 179–80; di: 254.5–5.5; 260	148.5 (cor.), al.	Tribromo deriv. of phenol, 95
153	Di-4-tolyl succinate (Di-"p-cresyl" succinate) ..	121	....	149	185; 182.8	235d.	36	202	mono: 157; di: 260d.	mono: 179–80; di: 254.5–5.5; 260	188.6 (cor.), al.	....
154	Hydroquinone diacetate .	124	....	97	16.6	118.2	171	286	82	153; 147	bis: 317	....
155	Methyl 3-nitro-cinnamate	124	....	207	199	......	–97	64.65	196	....	108 (cor.), al.	....
156	Methyl 3,5-dinitro-salicylate..........	127	....	242	182	......	–97	64.65	181; 173 (+1 H₂O)	....	108 (cor.), al.	....
157	Methyl 4-hydroxy-benzoate	131	....	152	215; 210	......	–97	64.65	162 (+1 H₂O), w.	203–4, al.	108 (cor.), al.	....
158	Methyl 3-nitro-salicylate...........	132	....	197	125 (+1 H₂O)	......	–97	64.65	145	....	108 (cor.), al.	....
159	Triethyl trimesate......	133	....	98	380 (cor.)	......	–117.3	78.32	tri: 365d. (cor.)	....	93, al.	....
160	Ethyl 4-nitro-cinnamate	137; 142	....	221	285	......	–117.3	78.32	204; 217	....	93, al.	....
161	Dimethyl terephthalate .	141	....	97	300 (subl. without melting)	......	–97	64.65	di: >225	....	108 (cor.), al.	....
162	Tetramethyl pyromellitate	142	....	77.5	275	......	–97	64.65	....	....	108 (cor.), al.	....
163	Trimethyl trimesate	144	....	84	380 (cor.)	......	–97	64.65	tri: 365d. (cor.)	....	108 (cor.), al.	....
164	Di-4-tolyl oxalate (Di-"p-cresyl" oxalate) ...	148–9	....	135	189.5 (anh.); 101 (+2 H₂O)	......	36	202	mono: 219; di: 419d.	mono: 169; di: 268	188.6 (cor.), al.	....
165	Methyl 4-nitro-cinnamate	161	....	207	285	......	–97	64.65	204; 217	....	108 (cor.), al.	....
166	Diethyl mucate	163–4	....	133	214d.; 223–55	......	–117.3	78.32	mono: 192d.; di: 220	....	93, al.	....
167	Pyrogallol triacetate ...	165; 172	....	84	16.6	118.2	133	309	82	153; 147	tri: 205	....
168	Dimethyl mucate	165–7d.	....	119	214d.; 223–55	......	–97	64.65	mono: 192d.; di: 220	....	108 (cor.), al.	....
169	Methyl gallate	200–1	....	184	253–4d.; 222–40d.	......	–97	64.65	189	....	108 (cor.), al.	....
170	Hydroquinone di-benzoate	204 (cor.); 199	....	159	122.4	249	171; 172	286	130	158	bis: 317	....

*Derivative data given in order: m.p., crystal color, solvent from which crystallized.

EXPLANATIONS AND REFERENCES TO TABLE XVII

*p-Toluenesulfonamide (p-Toluenesulfonyl derivative).**

$$H_2NCHRCOOH \;+\; CH_3-\!\!\langle\ \rangle\!\!-SO_2Cl \;\rightarrow\; CH_3-\!\!\langle\ \rangle\!\!-SO_2NHCHRCOOH$$

p-Toluenesulfonamide

From the amino acid in aqueous sodium hydroxide with *p*-toluenesulfonyl chloride in ether.

For directions and examples see: Cheronis, pp. 453–454; Linstead, pp. 77–78; Shriner, p. 231; Vogel, p. 437; Wild, pp. 169–170; E. Fischer and P. Bergell, *Chem. Ber.*, **35**, 3779, 3784 (1902); E. W. McChesney and W. K. Swann, *J. Amer. Chem. Soc.*, **59**, 1116 (1937).

From the amino acid in aqueous sodium hydroxide with *p*-toluenesulfonyl chloride.

See: J. I. Harris and T. S. Work, *Biochem. J.*, **46**, 582 (1950).

From the amino acid with *p*-toluenesulfonyl chloride and triethylamine in aqueous tetrahydrofuran.

See: D. Theodoropoulos and L. C. Craig, *J. Org. Chem.*, **21**, 1376 (1956).

For an extensive list of references for the preparation of the *p*-toluenesulfonyl derivatives of amino acids *see*: J. P. Greenstein and M. Winitz, *Chemistry of the Amino Acids*, Vol. 2, John Wiley and Sons, New York, 1961, pp. 886–889.

*3,5-Dinitrobenzamide (3,5-Dinitrobenzoyl derivative).**

$$H_2NCHRCOOH \;+\; \begin{array}{c} NO_2 \\ \langle\ \rangle\!\!-COCl \\ NO_2 \end{array} \;\rightarrow\; \begin{array}{c} NO_2 \\ \langle\ \rangle\!\!-CONHCHRCOOH \\ NO_2 \end{array} \;+\; HCl$$

3,5-Dinitrobenzamide

From the amino acid in aqueous sodium hydroxide with 3,5-dinitrobenzoyl chloride.

For directions and examples see: Cheronis, p. 453; Vogel, p. 436; Wild, p. 168; B. C. Saunders, *Biochem. J.*, **28**, 580 (1934); *J. Chem. Soc.*, 1397 (1938); B. C. Saunders, G. J. Stacey and I. G. E. Wilding, *Biochem. J.*, **36**, 368 (1942); B. W. Town, *Biochem. J.*, **35**, 578 (1941).

Benzamide (Benzoyl derivative).

$$H_2NCHRCOOH \;+\; C_6H_5COCl \;\rightarrow\; C_6H_5CONHCHRCOOH \;+\; HCl$$

Benzamide

From the amino acid in aqueous sodium carbonate or bicarbonate and benzoyl chloride.

For directions and examples see: Linstead, p. 77; Vogel, p. 436; Wild, p. 167.

From the amino acid in aqueous sodium hydroxide with benzoyl chloride.

See: Cheronis, p. 453; E. Fischer and P. Bergell, *Chem. Ber.*, **35**, 3779, 3784 (1902); **39**, 597 (1906).

Acetamide (Acetyl derivative).

$$H_2NCHRCOOH \;+\; (CH_3CO)_2O \;\rightarrow\; CH_3CONHCHRCOOH \;+\; CH_3COOH$$

Acetamide

From the amino acid with acetic anhydride in water.

For directions and examples see: Linstead, p. 77; Shriner, p. 226; Wild, p. 167; R. M. Herbst and D. Shemin in *Organic Syntheses*, Coll. Vol. 2, (Ed. A. H. Blatt), John Wiley and Sons, New York, 1943, p. 11.

From the amino acid in aqueous sodium hydroxide with acetic anhydride.

See: Cheronis, p. 454; M. Bergmann and L. Zervas, *Biochem. Z.*, **203**, 288 (1928).

Carbobenzoxamide (Carbobenzoxy derivative; Benzyloxycarbonyl derivative).

$$H_2NCHRCOOH \;+\; C_6H_5CH_2OCOCl \;\rightarrow\; C_6H_5CH_2OCONHCHRCOOH \;+\; HCl$$

Carbobenzoxamide

From the amino acid in aqueous sodium hydroxide with carbobenzoxy chloride (benzyl chloroformate).

For directions and examples see: M. Bergmann and L. Zervas, *Chem. Ber.*, **65**, 1192 (1932); M. Winitz, L. Bloch-Frankenthal, N. Izumiya, S. M. Birnbaum, C. G. Baker and J. P. Greenstein, *J. Amer. Chem. Soc.*, **78**, 2423 (1956).

---

*Derivatives recommended for first trial.

WARNING: This is not an instruction manual. References should be consulted for the preparation of derivatives.

EXPLANATIONS AND REFERENCES TO TABLE XVII (Continued)

For an extensive list of references for the preparation of the carbobenzoxy derivatives of amino acids *see:* J. P. Greenstein and M. Winitz, *Chemistry of the Amino Acids*, Vol. 2, John Wiley and Sons, New York, 1961, pp. 887–895.

*Phenylurethane (Phenylurea derivative).**

$$H_2NCHRCOOH \; + \; C_6H_5N{=}C{=}O \; \rightarrow \; \underset{\text{Phenylurethane}}{C_6H_5NHCONHCHRCOOH}$$

From the amino acid with aqueous potassium hydroxide and phenylisocyanate.
For directions and examples see: Linstead, p. 78; Shriner, p. 211; Wild, p. 171.

*Phenylhydantoin.**

$$C_6H_5NHCONHCHRCOOH \xrightarrow{HCl} \underset{\text{Phenylhydantoin}}{\begin{array}{l} C_6H_5N{-}CO{-}NH \\ \quad\;| \qquad\quad\;\; | \\ \quad CO{-\!-\!-}CHR \end{array}} \; + \; H_2O$$

From the phenylurethane (obtained as described above) in aqueous hydrochloric acid.
For directions and examples see: Cheronis, p. 456.

Rf Values.

For the determination of the Rf values of amino acids in aqueous phenol, in collidine-lutidine and in butanol-acetic acid mixtures *see:* R. J. Block, R. LeStrange and G. Zweig, *Paper Chromatography*, Academic Press, New York, 1952, pp. 51–66; E. Lederer and M. Lederer, *Chromatography*, Elsevier Publishing Co., New York, 1957, pp. 306–311.

NOTE: For additional information regarding directions and examples for the preparation of derivatives of amino acids which are similar to those of amines (e.g., phenylurethane, acetamide, etc.) see explanations and references to Table XVIII, p. 291, 292, 293, 294.

*Derivatives recommended for first trial.
WARNING: This is not an instruction manual. References should be consulted for the preparation of derivatives.

TABLE XVII. ORGANIC DERIVATIVES OF AMINO ACIDS
(Listed in order of increasing decomposition temperatures)* **

No.	Name	Decomp. temp., °C	Specific rotation			Rf values***			p-Toluene-sulfonyl	Phenyl urea	Benzoyl	3,5-Dinitro-benzoyl	Picrate	Miscellaneous
			$[\alpha]_D$	T, °C	Conc. (C) and solvent	Aqueous phenol	Collidine-Lutidine	Butanol-Ac. acid						
1	3-Aminohydro-cinnamic acid	84–5	. . . . . .	. . . .	. . . . . .	. . . . . .	. . . . . .	. . . . . .	. . . . . .	. . . .	. . . . . .	. . . . . .	. . . . . .	Acetyl, 162; Hydrochlo-ride, 191
2	N-Methyl-β-alanine	99–100	. . . . . .	. . . .	. . . . . .	. . . . . .	. . . . . .	. . . . . .	. . . . . .	. . . .	. . . . . .	. . . . . .	. . . . . .	Hydrochloride, 105, aq. al.
3	Aminomalonic acid	109	. . . . . .	. . . .	. . . . . .	. . . . . .	. . . . . .	. . . . . .	. . . . . .	. . . .	61, pet. eth.	. . . . . .	. . . . . .	Formyl; 48; Heat → gly-cine, decom. temp., 228–30; 262
4	2-Aminophenyl-acetic acid . . .	119	. . . . . .	. . . .	. . . . . .	. . . . . .	. . . . . .	. . . . . .	. . . . . .	. . . .	179, al.	. . . . . .	. . . . . .	Acetyl, 158; Formyl, 110
5	2-Amino-1-Naphthoic acid	126	. . . . . .	. . . .	. . . . . .	. . . . . .	. . . . . .	. . . . . .	. . . . . .	. . . .	. . . . . .	. . . . . .	. . . . . .	N-Acetyl, 195–6, al.
6	N-Phenyl-glycine	127	. . . . . .	. . . .	. . . . . .	. . . . . .	. . . . . .	. . . . . .	. . . . . .	195	63	. . . . . .	. . . . . .	Acetyl; 124
7	4-Aminohydro-cinnamic acid .	132	. . . . . .	. . . .	. . . . . .	. . . . . .	. . . . . .	. . . . . .	. . . . . .	194–5	. . . . . .	. . . . . .	. . . . . .	Acetyl; 143 (anh.); 124 (hyd.)
8	L-Ornithine . . .	140	11.5	25	c = 6.5	0.79	0.11	0.15	. . . . . .	190	240 (mono); 189 (di)	. . . . . .	208	α,δ-Dicarbo-benzyloxy, 112–4
9	Anthranilic acid (2-Amino-benzoic acid)	147	. . . . . .	. . . .	. . . . . .	0.85	. . . . . .	. . . . . .	217	181	182	278	104	. . . .
10	3-Aminophenyl-acetic acid . . .	151	. . . . . .	. . . .	. . . . . .	. . . . . .	. . . . . .	. . . . . .	. . . . . .	. . . .	. . . . . .	. . . . . .	. . . . . .	Amide, 164–6, al; Chloro-acetyl, 187–8, al.
11	5-Amino-pentanoic acid (ω-Amino-n-valeric acid) . .	157	. . . . . .	. . . .	. . . . . .	. . . . . .	. . . . . .	. . . . . .	. . . . . .	. . . .	105; 94	. . . . . .	. . . . . .	
12	2-Aminocin-namic acid . . .	158, yel.	. . . . . .	. . . .	. . . . . .	. . . . . .	. . . . . .	. . . . . .	. . . . . .	. . . .	191–3, al.	. . . . . .	. . . . . .	Monoacetyl, 250–1, al.; Diacetyl, 158, lgr.
13	DL-β-Amino-n-valeric acid DL-3-Amino-pentanoic acid)	160–5	. . . . . .	. . . .	. . . . . .	. . . . . .	. . . . . .	. . . . . .	. . . . . .	. . . .	145–6	. . . . . .	. . . . . .	N-β-Naphthal-enesulfonyl, 134
14	2-Amino-4-toluic acid	165	. . . . . .	. . . .	. . . . . .	. . . . . .	. . . . . .	. . . . . .	. . . . . .	. . . .	. . . . . .	. . . . . .	. . . . . .	Acetyl, 279–81
15	3-Aminoben-zoic acid	174	. . . . . .	. . . .	. . . . . .	0.86	. . . . . .	. . . . . .	. . . . . .	270; 264	248	270	. . . . . .	. . . .
16	trans-4-Amino-cinnamic acid	175–6	. . . . . .	. . . .	. . . . . .	. . . . . .	. . . . . .	. . . . . .	. . . . . .	. . . .	274	. . . . . .	. . . . . .	Acetyl, 259–60
17	ω-Aminotri-decylic acid . .	177	. . . . . .	. . . .	. . . . . .	. . . . . .	. . . . . .	. . . . . .	. . . . . .	. . . .	111; 105	. . . . . .	. . . . . .	Benzenesul-fonyl, 120, al.
18	3-Amino-4-toluic acid (Homoanthra-nilic acid)	177	. . . . . .	. . . .	. . . . . .	. . . . . .	. . . . . .	. . . . . .	. . . . . .	. . . .	. . . . . .	. . . . . .	. . . . . .	Amide, 146; Acetyl, 184; Formyl, 186, al.

*Derivative data given in order: m.p., crystal color, solvent from which crystallized.

**Decomposition points of amino acids are only a first doubtful identification as they depend on velocity of heating and other conditions.

***Aqueous phenol: 80% w/w; for basic amino acids 3 vol. —% of a conc. aq. NH₃ has to be present (in a separate vessel) in the chamber, otherwise low values are obtained; Collidine-lutidine mixture: 2,6-lutidine (100 ml.), 2,4,6-collidine (100 ml.), water (100 ml.), diethylamine (3 ml.); Butanol-acetic acid-water: 40 ml.: 10 ml.: 10 ml.

No.	Name	Decomp. temp., °C	[α]_D	T, °C	Conc. (C) and solvent	Rf values*** Aqueous phenol	Collidine-Lutidine	Butanol-Ac. acid	p-Toluene-sulfonyl	Phenyl urea	Benzoyl	3,5-Dinitro-benzoyl	Picrate	Miscellaneous
19	4-Amino-1-naphthoic acid	177	....	....	....	....	....	....			....	....	....	Acetyl, 189; Amide, 175
20	trans-3-Amino-cinnamic acid	181, yel.	....	....	....	....	....	....			229	....	....	Acetyl, 237, al.
21	3-Amino-1-naphthoic acid	181	....	....	....	....	....	....			....	....	....	Acetyl, 254–5
22	N-Ethylglycine.	182	....	....	....	....	....	....			....	....	....	Hydrochloride, ca. 180
23	L-Canavanine .	184	7.9	20	....	0.51	....	....			tri: 186	....	163–4	....
24	L-Glutamine ..	185	....	....	....	0.6	....	....			....	....	....	Carbo-benzyloxy, 137
25	Hippuric acid ..	187												4-Nitrobenzyl ester, 136; 4-Bromo-phenacyl ester, 151
26	4-Aminobenzoic acid........	188	....	....	....	0.81	....	....	26	300	278	290	....	....
27	DL-Canaline ..	190–5									158–60 (di)			γ-Carboben-zyloxy, 208–10
28	Betaine (Tri-methyl-glycine)......	193	....	....	....	....	....	0.43			....	....	....	Formyl, 183
29	DL-β-Amino-butyric acid ..	194	....	....	....	0.78	....	....			154	....	....	
30	DL-Glutamic acid........	199	....	....	....	0.31	0.20	0.3	117	....	153; 155	....	....	Acetyl, 187
31	4-Aminophenyl-acetic acid ...	199–200									205–6, al.			Acetyl, 168–70; Chloroacetyl, 158–60
32	β-Alanine.....	200	....	....	....	0.66	0.22	0.37	168		120	202	....	Carboben-zyloxy, 106
33	L-Isoserine....	200	....	....	....	0.39	....	....			107–9	....	....	....
34	ω-Amino-n-caproic acid (6-Amino-hexanoic acid)	202	....	....	....	....	....	....			45–7	....	....	
35	γ-Aminobutyric acid........	203	....	....	....	0.75	....	....			....	....	....	Hydrochloride, 135; Heat → pyrrolidone, 24, pet. eth.
36	DL-Proline ...	203 (mono-hyd.); 191	....	....	....	0.88	0.28	0.43	170		....	217	135–7	....
37	γ-Amino-n-caproic acid (4-Amino-hexanoic acid)	205–7									150–2			Hydrochloride, 120–1
38	6-Amino-1-naphthoic acid	205–6	....	....	....	....	....	....			....	....	....	Acetyl, 170–2; 252–3
39	1-Amino-2-naphthoic acid	205 r.h.	....	....	....	....	....	....			....	....	....	Heating with conc. HCl → 1-naphthyl-amine, 50

*Derivative data given in order: m.p., crystal color, solvent from which crystallized.

**Decomposition points of amino acids are only a first doubtful identification as they depend on velocity of heating and other conditions.

***Aqueous phenol: 80% w/w; for basic amino acids 3 vol.—% of a conc. aq. NH_3 has to be present (in a separate vessel) in the chamber, otherwise low values are obtained; Collidine-lutidine mixture: 2,6-lutidine (100 ml.), 2,4,6-collidine (100 ml.), water (100 ml.), diethylamine (3 ml.); Butanol-acetic acid-water: 40 ml.: 10 ml.: 10 ml.

TABLE XVII. ORGANIC DERIVATIVES OF AMINO ACIDS
(Listed in order of increasing decomposition temperatures)* ** (Continued)

No.	Name	Decomp. temp., °C	$[\alpha]_D$	T, °C	Conc. (C) and solvent	Aqueous phenol	Collidine-Lutidine	Butanol-Ac. acid	p-Toluene-sulfonyl	Phenyl urea	Benzoyl	3,5-Dinitro-benzoyl	Picrate	Miscellaneous
40	L-Arginine	207	11.8	20	c = 0.87 in 0.5 N-NaOH	0.89	0.17	0.2	....	....	298 (mono); 235 (di)	150	217 (mono); 190 (di)	Monocarbo-benzyloxy, 175
			12.5	20	c = 3.48 in water									
41	L-Glutamic acid	211 r.h.; 197 s.h.	31.2	22.4	c = 1.0 in 6N-HCl	0.31	0.2	0.3	131	....	....	....	....	Acetyl, 199; Carboben-zyloxy, 120
			11.5	18	c = 1.47 in water									
42	5-Amino-1-naphthoic acid	212	....	....										Acetyl, 296, al.
43	Sarcosine	212				0.78	....		102		104	153		Acetyl, 135
44	L-3,5-Di-iodo-tyrosine	213	2.9	20	c = 5.08 in 1.1 N-HCl	0.61	0.55							
45	L-α-Asparagine	213–5	....			0.47								Carboben-zyloxy, 164
46	DL-γ-Amino-n-valeric acid (DL-4-Amino-pentanoic acid)	214 (cor.)									132			....
47	L-Canaline....	214	....			0.77					99 (di)		192–3	....
48	β-Aminoiso-valeric acid ...	217	....											Hydrochloride, 120
49	β-Hydroxy-valine	218	....							182	153 (mono)			2-Naphthalene-sulfonyl, 261
50	L-Proline	220–2	−93.0	20	c = 2.42 in 0.6 N-KOH	0.88	0.28	0.43	130–3	....			154	Phenylhy-dantoin, 144
			−52.6	20	c = 0.57 in 0.5 N-HCl									
51	L-Citrulline ...	222	3.7	20	c = 2 in water	0.63	0.23	0.25	....				206	....
52	7-Amino-1-naphthoic acid	223–4	....											Acetyl, 229
53	L-Lysine......	224	14.6	20	c = 6.5 in water	0.81	0.11	0.14	....	184	235 (mono); 149 (di)		266	Monohydro-chloride, 235; Dihydrochlo-ride, 193; α,ε-Dicarboben-zyloxy, 150
			25.9	22.9	c = 2.0 in 6 N-HCl									
54	β-L-Asparagine	227	....			0.40	0.21	0.19	175	164	189	196	180	Carboben-zyloxy, 165
55	3,5-Diamino-benzoic acid ..	228	....										....	3,5-Diacetyl, 184; Et. ester, 84
56	L-Serine......	228	14.45	25	c = 9.34 in 1 N-HCl	0.36	0.28	0.27						Carboben-zyloxy, 121
			−6.83	20	c = 10.4 in water									
57	Glycine.......	228–30; 262	....	....	....	0.41	0.24	0.26	147	197	187.5	179	202	Carboben-zyloxy, 120
58	DL-Thyroxine .	230 s.h.; 250 r.h.	....			0.86	0.76				210–5			N-Chloro-acetyl, 201; Me. ester, 156
59	DL-β-Hydroxy-norvaline.....	230	....	....						156	170			Phenylhy-dantoin, 154–5

*Derivative data given in order: m.p., crystal color, solvent from which crystallized.

**Decomposition points of amino acids are only a first doubtful identification as they depend on velocity of heating and other conditions.

***Aqueous phenol: 80% w/w; for basic amino acids 3 vol.—% of a conc. aq. NH₃ has to be present (in a separate vessel) in the chamber, otherwise low values are obtained; Collidine-lutidine mixture: 2,6-lutidine (100 ml.), 2,4,6-collidine (100 ml.), water (100 ml.), diethylamine (3 ml.): Butanol-acetic acid-water: 40 ml.: 10 ml.: 10 ml.

TABLE XVII. ORGANIC DERIVATIVES OF AMINO ACIDS
(Listed in order of increasing decomposition temperatures)* ** (Continued)

No.	Name	Decomp. temp., °C	Specific rotation			Rf values***			p-Toluene-sulfonyl	Phenyl urea	Benzoyl	3,5-Dinitro-benzoyl	Picrate	Miscellaneous
			$[\alpha]_D$	T, °C	Conc. (C) and solvent	Aqueous phenol	Collidine-Lutidine	Butanol-Ac. acid						
60	DL-β-Amino-hydrocinnamic acid........	231	......	...			....		....	......	194–6	....	....	Hydrochloride, 218; Formyl, 128–9; Acetyl, 161, al.
61	DL-Homo-aspartic acid (α-Amino-α-methyl suc-cinic acid)....	232	......	...			....		....	......	....	....	....	Amide, 266
62	D-β-Amino-hydrocinnamic acid........	234–5	7.0	20	water		....		....	......	....	....	....	N-Formyl, 142–3
63	L-β-Amino-hydrocinnamic acid........	234–5	−7.5	25	water		....		....	......	....	....	....	N-Formyl, 142–3
64	3-Amino-salicylic acid .	235									189			Acetyl, 215; N-Benzenesul-fonyl, 194
65	DL-Allo-threonine	237	......	...		0.50	0.34	......			176 (mono); 174 (di)			
66	DL-Arginine ..	238				0.89	0.17	0.2	....	......	230 (di, anh.); 176 (di, hyd.)	....	200 (mono); 196 (di)	....
67	4-Dimethyl-aminobenzoic acid........	242	......	...			....		....	......	....	....	....	Amide, 206; Anilide, 182–3
68	β-Amino-β-phenyliso-butyric acid ..	243	......	...			....		....	......	205	....	....	....
69	DL-Isoserine ..	246	......	...		0.39	....	......		184	151			Phenylure-thane, 183–4
70	DL-Serine	246	......	...		0.36	0.28	0.27	213	169	149–50	....	....	Carboben-zyloxy, 125
71	4-Hydroxy-phenylglycine .	248									117			Monoacetyl, 203; Diacetyl, 174–5; Amide, 135
72	Isoaspartic acid (α-Amino-α-methylmalonic acid)........	250	......	...			....		....	......	....	....	....	Diamide, 200–1; Heat → ala-nine, 295 d.
73	DL-Threonine .	251	......	...		0.50	0.34	0.35			177–8	145....	....	Phenylhydan-toin, 164
74	DL-α-Amino-phenylacetic acid........	256 (subl.)	......	...			....		....	......	175, al.	....	....	Acetyl, 198.5; Formyl, 180
75	L-Cystine.....	260	−214.4 −70.0	24.4 18.5	c = 1.0 in 1.02 N-HCl c = 0.4 in 0.2 N-NaOH	......	....	0.1	204–5	160	181 (di)	180	....	Dicarboben-zyloxy, 123
76	DL-α-Amino-hydratropic acid (DL-α-Phenyl-alanine)......	260 (subl.)	......	...			....		....	......	....	....	....	N-Carbo-ethoxy, 191, al.

* Derivative data given in order: m.p., crystal color, solvent from which crystallized.

** Decomposition points of amino acids are only a first doubtful identification as they depend on velocity of heating and other conditions.

*** Aqueous phenol: 80% w/w; for basic amino acids 3 vol.—% of a conc. aq. NH₃ has to be present (in a separate vessel) in the chamber, otherwise low values are obtained; Collidine-lutidine mixture: 2,6-lutidine (100 ml.), 2,4,6-collidine (100 ml.), water (100 ml.), diethylamine (3 ml.); Butanol-acetic acid-water: 40 ml.: 10 ml.: 10 ml.

TABLE XVII. ORGANIC DERIVATIVES OF AMINO ACIDS
(Listed in order of increasing decomposition temperatures)* ** (Continued)

No.	Name	Decomp. temp., °C	Specific rotation			Rf values***			p-Toluene-sulfonyl	Phenyl urea	Benzoyl	3,5-Dinitro-benzoyl	Picrate	Miscellaneous
			[α]_D	T, °C	Conc. (C) and solvent	Aqueous phenol	Collidine-Lutidine	Butanol-Ac. acid						
77	Glycylglycine	260	......	...	....	0.39	....	0.22	178	176	208	210	....	Carbobenzyloxy, 178
78	DL-β-Phenylalanine	264	......	...	....	0.85	0.48	0.68	134–5	182	188	....	173	Carbobenzyloxy, 103
79	DL-Aspartic acid	270 (>300)	......	...	....	0.19	0.21	0.24	....	....	119 (hyd.); 176 (anh.)			Carbobenzyloxy, 116
80	DL-α-Aminooctanoic acid	270	......	...	....	0.89	0.55	....			128			....
81	L-Aspartic acid	270	24.6	24	c = 2.0 in 6 N-HCl	0.19	0.21	0.24	140	162	185			Carbobenzyloxy, 116
82	DL-α-Aminononanoic acid	273	......	...	....						128			
83	L-Hydroxyproline	274	−47.3 / −75.2	20 / 22.5	c = 1.31 in 1 N-HCl / c = 1.0 in water	0.63	0.28	......	153	175	100 (mono); 92 (di)			
84	DL-Tryptophane	275	......	...	....	0.75	0.50	0.50	176	....	240	....		N-Benzenesulfonyl, 185; Carbobenzyloxy, 169–70
85	α-Aminoisobutyric acid	280				0.74	0.32	......			198			1-Naphthylurea, 198
86	DL-α-Aminoheptanoic acid	281									135			
87	DL-Methionine	281				0.81	0.42	0.55	105	....	145	....	....	Acetyl, 114; Formyl, 100; Carbobenzyloxy, 112
88	5-Aminosalicylic acid	283									252			Monoacetyl, 218; Diacetyl, 184
89	DL-Lanthionine	283	......	...		0.26	0.11	......			195–8 (di)	....		
90	L-Methionine	283	−8.11	25	c = 0.8 in water	0.81	0.42	0.55	....	....	....	94–5 (hyd.); 150 (anh.)	....	Acetyl, 98–9; 1-Naphthylurea, 188
91	L-(+)-Isoleucine		40.6 / 11.29	20 / 20	c = 5.1 in 6.1 N-HCl / c = 3.1 in water	0.84	0.45	0.72	130–2	121	117	....	....	Formyl, 156
92	L-Phenylalanine	283; 320	−35.1	20	c = 1.94 in water	0.85	0.48	0.68	164	181	146	93	....	Carbobenzyloxy, 126–8
93	L-Hexahydrotyrosine	285	......	...	....									N-4-Nitrobenzoyl, 225
94	D-(−)-Isoleucine	285	−40.86	20	c = 4.53 in 6.1 N-HCl	0.84	0.45	0.72	130–2	121	117	....	....	Formyl, 156
95	L-Histidine	288; 253	13.0 / −39.0	22.7 / 25	c = 1.5 in 6 N-HCl / c = 1.13 in water	0.69	0.27	0.2	202–4	....	230 (mono)	189	86	Carbobenzyloxy, 209
96	L-Cysteic acid	289; 260	8.66	20	c = 1.85 g. in 25 ml water	......	......	......	....	....	....	....	....	Diphenylacyl ester, 203

*Derivative data given in order: m.p., crystal color, solvent from which crystallized.

**Decomposition points of amino acids are only a first doubtful identification as they depend on velocity of heating and other conditions.

***Aqueous phenol: 80% w/w; for basic amino acids 3 vol.—% of a conc. aq. NH₃ has to be present (in a separate vessel) in the chamber, otherwise low values are obtained; Collidine-lutidine mixture: 2,6-lutidine (100 ml.), 2,4,6-collidine (100 ml.), water (100 ml.), diethylamine (3 ml.); Butanol-acetic acid-water: 40 ml.: 10 ml.: 10 ml.

No.	Name	Decomp. temp., °C	$[\alpha]_D$	T, °C	Conc. (C) and solvent	Aqueous phenol	Collidine-Lutidine	Butanol-Ac. acid	p-Toluene-sulfonyl	Phenyl urea	Benzoyl	3,5-Dinitro-benzoyl	Picrate	Miscellaneous
							Rf values***							
97	L-Tryptophane	290; 252	−31.5 6.17	22.7 20	c = 1.0 in water c = 2.42 in 0.5 N-NaOH	0.75	0.50	0.5	176	166	183	233	....	Carboben-zyloxy, 126
98	DL-N-Methyl-α-alanine	292	......	...	......									Methylamide, 43; Hydro-chloride, 110
99	DL-Isoleucine .	292; 275 s.h.	......	...	......	0.84	0.45	0.72	141	120	118	......		Formyl, 121
100	L-(+)-α-Aminobutyric acid........	292; 303 s.h.	18.65	19	c = 4.8 in 6 N-HCl	0.71	0.31	0.45	......		121			Formyl, 126; 1-Naphthyl-urea, 195
101	DL-Leucine ...	293, s.h.; 332	......			0.84	0.45	0.73	......	165	137–41	187	......	......
102	DL-α-Amino-α-methyl-valeric acid (DL-α-Amino-α-methyl-pentanoic acid)	295, s.h.	......											1-Naphthyl-urea, 196
103	DL-Alanine ...	295	......			0.60	0.28	0.38	139	......	166	177	......	Carboben-zyloxy, 114–5 Formyl, 194–5
104	D-α-Amino-hydratropic acid	295 (subl.)	70.0	18	water	......								
105	L-Alanine.....	297	14.7 2.7	15 22	c = 5.8 in 0.97 N-HCl c = 10.3 in water	0.60	0.28	0.38	133		151	......	......	Carbobenzyl-oxy, 84; 1-Naphthyl-urea, 220–2
106	DL-Norleucine.	297; 327	......	...	......	0.84	0.45	0.74	124					Formyl, 114
107	DL-Valine	298, s.h.; 282	......			0.78	0.36	0.6	110	164	132	158	......	......
108	L-Djenkolic acid........	300–50	−60.5 −47.5	20.5 25	1% in 1N-HCl 2% in 1N-HCl	0.40	0.13	......			166 (mono); 88 (di)	......		
109	D-N-Methyl-α-alanine	300	5.6	20	water	......								Hydrochloride, 165–6
110	Taurine.......	300–5	......			0.42								N-Me., 241; N-Et., 147
111	L-(+)-Norleucine ...	301	21.3 6.26	20 20	c = 4.25 in 6 N-HCl c = 0.7 in water	0.84	0.45	0.74	......		53			Formyl, 115–6; 2-Naph-thalenesul-fonyl, 149
112	DL-Norvaline .	303, s.h.	......			0.80	0.39	0.65	......	117	......			Formyl, 132; Phenylhy-dantoin, 103
113	Creatine (α-Methylguan-idoacetic acid)	303	......										218–20	Diacetyl, 165
114	4-Aminocyclo-hexanecar-boxylic acid ..	303–4	......										......	Heat → lactam, 191–2

*Derivative data given in order: m.p., crystal color, solvent from which crystallized.
**Decomposition points of amino acids are only a first doubtful identification as they depend on velocity of heating and other conditions.
***Aqueous phenol: 80%, w/w; for basic amino acids 3 vol.—% of a conc aq. NH₃ has to be present (in a separate vessel) in the chamber, otherwise low
  values are obtained; Collidine-lutidine mixture: 2,6-lutidine (100 ml.), 2,4,6-collidine (100 ml.), water (100 ml.), diethylamine (3 ml.); Butanol-acetic
  acid-water: 40 ml.: 10 ml.: 10 ml.

No.	Name	Decomp. temp., °C	Specific rotation			Rf values***			p-Toluene-sulfonyl	Phenyl urea	Benzoyl	3,5-Dinitro-benzoyl	Picrate	Miscellaneous
			$[\alpha]_D$	T, °C	Conc. (C) and solvent	Aqueous phenol	Collidine-Lutidine	Butanol-Ac. acid						
115	DL-α-Amino-butyric acid	304	......	....	....	0.71	0.31	0.45	....	170	147	....	....	1-Naphthyl-urea, 194; Phthalyl, 96
116	meso-Lan-thionine	304	......	....	....	0.26	0.11	....	....		198–200	....	....	Dicarbo-benzyloxy, 139–40
117	Creatinine	305; 260	......									....	220	....
118	L-α-Amino-phenylacetic acid	305–10	−111.0; −157	20; 20	water dil. HCl	....								Acetyl, 191; Formyl, 190
119	meso-2,3-Di-aminosuccinic acid	306	......	?...								(di) 212 hyd.	....	Diacetyl, 235
120	L-(+)-Norva-line	307	23.0	20	c = 10 in 10% HCl	0.80	0.39	....			64	....	....	Acetyl, 137
121	L-Tyrosine	314–8 r.h. 290–5 s.h.	−8.64 −13.2	20 18	c = 4.4 in 6.3 N-HCl c = 0.91 in 3 N-NaOH	0.51	0.51	0.45	N-: 188	104	N-: 166-7; 211-2 (di)	....	....	N-Acetyl, 148; Diacetyl, 172; N-Carboben-zyloxy, 101
122	L-(+)-Valine	315	28.8	20	c = 3.4 in 6 N-HCl	0.78	0.36	0.60	147	......	127	157–8	....	Carboben-zyloxy, 64–5
123	L-Leucine	337	15.1 −10.8	25.9 24.7	c = 2.0 in 6 N-HCl c = 2.0 in water	0.84	0.45	0.73	124	115	118	187	....	....
124	DL-Tyrosine	340 r.h.; 295 s.h.	....	....		0.51	0.51	0.45	224–6	....	N-: 197	252–4 (di)	....	....
125	1-Aminocyclo-hexanecar-boxylic acid	350; 320 s.h.	....							....		209–10		Hydrochloride, 310
126	DL-2,3-Di-aminosuccinic acid	....									164 (di) hyd.	....		Diacetyl, 235
127	DL-Ornithine	....				0.79	0.11	0.15	188 (mono)	192	4-N-: 285–8; 188 (di)	....	208 (di)	....
128	L-(+)-Alloiso-leucine	....	38.1	20	c = 3.97 in 6 N-HCl	....	....	....	....	151			....	Formyl, 126; 1-Naphthylurea, 166; Benzene-sulfonyl, 147
129	DL-Lysine	....				0.81	0.11	0.14	....	196	249 (mono); 146 (di)	....	225 (mono)	Monohydro-chloride, 260–3; Dihydro-chloride, 187–9
130	L-Cysteine	....	......			0.57							....	S-Benzyl, 216; Oxid. → L-cystine, 260 d.; Hydrochloride, 175–8, $[\alpha]_D^{25}$: 9.5 (c = 2 in water)

*Derivative data given in order: m.p., crystal color, solvent from which crystallized.

**Decomposition points of amino acids are only a first doubtful identification as they depend on velocity of heating and other conditions.

***Aqueous phenol: 80% w/w; for basic amino acids 3 vol. — % of a conc. aq. NH₃ has to be present (in a separate vessel) in the chamber, otherwise low values are obtained; Collidine-lutidine mixture: 2,6-lutidine (100 ml.). 2,4,6-collidine (100 ml.), water (100 ml.), diethylamine (3 ml.); Butanol-acetic acid-water: 40 ml.: 10 ml.: 10 ml.

EXPLANATIONS AND REFERENCES TO TABLE XVIII

Acetamide (Acetyl derivative). *

$$RNH_2 + (CH_3CO)_2O \rightarrow CH_3CONHR + CH_3COOH$$

$$RR'NH + (CH_3CO)_2O \rightarrow CH_3CONRR' + CH_3COOH$$

Acetamide

For primary and secondary amines only.

From the amine with acetic anhydride without solvent.

For directions and examples see: Cheronis, pp. 591–593; Linstead, p. 60; Vogel, p. 652; Wild, p. 218; J. J. Sudborough, *J. Chem. Soc.*, **79**, 533 (1901); L. C. Raiford, R. Taft and H. P. Lankelma, *J. Amer. Chem. Soc.*, **46**, 2051 (1924).

From the amine with acetic anhydride in aqueous sodium hydroxide.

See: F. D. Chattaway, *J. Chem. Soc.*, 2495 (1931).

From the amine with acetic anhydride in pyridine.

See: Cheronis, pp. 590, 592–593.

From the amine hydrochloride with acetic anhydride in aqueous sodium acetate.

See: Linstead, p. 60; Vogel, p. 652.

From the amine with acetic anhydride in water.

See: Shriner, p. 226.

From the amine with acetic anhydride in acetic acid.

See: Wild, p. 218.

Benzamide (Benzoyl derivative). *

$$RNH_2 + C_6H_5COCl \rightarrow C_6H_5CONHR + HCl$$

$$RR'NH + C_6H_5COCl \rightarrow C_6H_5CONRR' + HCl$$

Benzamide

For primary and secondary amines only.

From the amine with benzoyl chloride in aqueous sodium hydroxide.

For directions and examples see: Cheronis, pp. 591, 593–594; Linstead, p. 60; Vogel, p. 652; Wild, p. 219.

From the amine with benzoyl chloride in a pyridine-benzene mixture.

See: Shriner, p. 226.

From the amine with benzoyl chloride in benzene.

See: Shriner, p. 227.

From the amine with benzoyl chloride in an aqueous sodium hydroxide-chloroform mixture.

See: Shriner, p. 226.

From the amine with benzoyl chloride.

See: Vogel, p. 653.

Benzenesulfonamide (Benzenesulfonyl chloride derivative). *

$$RNH_2 + C_6H_5SO_2Cl \rightarrow C_6H_5SO_2NHR + HCl$$

$$RR'NH + C_6H_5SO_2Cl \rightarrow C_6H_5SO_2NRR' + HCl$$

Benzene-
sulfonamide

For primary and secondary amines only.

From the amine with benzenesulfonyl chloride in aqueous sodium hydroxide.

For directions and examples see: Cheronis, pp. 595–596; Shriner, pp. 103–104; Vogel, p. 653; O. Hinsberg, *Chem. Ber.*, **23**, 2962 (1890); **38**, 906 (1905).

From the amine in aqueous sodium hydroxide with benzenesulfonyl chloride in methanol.

See: Cheronis, p. 596.

From the amine with benzenesulfonyl chloride in benzene.

See: Wild, p. 221.

From the amine in aqueous sodium hydroxide with benzenesulfonyl chloride in acetone.

See: Wild, p. 221.

From the amine with benzenesulfonyl chloride in aqueous pyridine.

See: Wild, p. 221.

From the amine with benzenesulfonyl chloride in pyridine.

See: Vogel, p. 653.

---

*Derivatives recommended for first trial.

WARNING: This is not an instruction manual. References should be consulted for the preparation of derivatives.

From the amine with benzenesulfonyl chloride in aqueous sodium hydroxide.
See: Wild, p. 221.

p-Toluenesulfonamide (p-Toluenesulfonyl chloride derivative).*

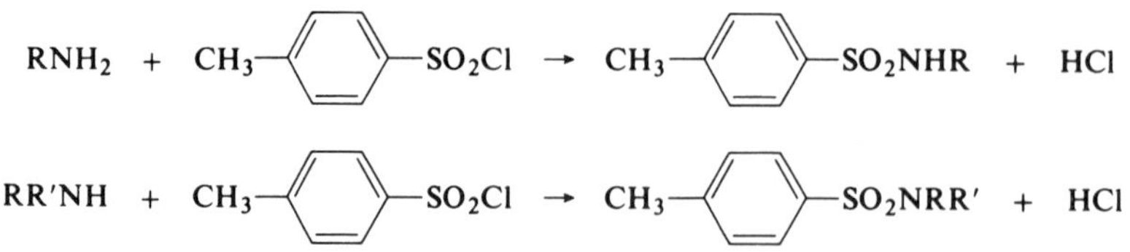

$$RNH_2 + CH_3-\text{C}_6\text{H}_4-SO_2Cl \rightarrow CH_3-\text{C}_6\text{H}_4-SO_2NHR + HCl$$

$$RR'NH + CH_3-\text{C}_6\text{H}_4-SO_2Cl \rightarrow CH_3-\text{C}_6\text{H}_4-SO_2NRR' + HCl$$

p-Toluenesulfonamide

For primary and secondary amines only.
From the amine with *p*-toluenesulfonyl chloride in aqueous sodium hydroxide.
For directions and examples see: Cheronis, p. 595; Linstead, p. 60; Shriner, pp. 103–104; Vogel, p. 653.
From the amine with *p*-toluenesulfonyl chloride in benzene.
See: Wild, p. 221.
From the amine with *p*-toluenesulfonyl chloride in acetone.
See: Wild, p. 221.
From the amine with *p*-toluenesulfonyl chloride in pyridine.
See: F. Bell, *J. Chem. Soc.*, 2787 (1929).
From the amine with *p*-toluenesulfonyl chloride in aqueous pyridine.
See: Wild, p. 221.

Phenylthiourea.*

$$RNH_2 + C_6H_5N{=}C{=}S \rightarrow C_6H_5NHCSNHR$$

$$RR'NH + C_6H_5N{=}C{=}S \rightarrow C_6H_5NHCSNRR'$$

Phenylthiourea

For primary and secondary amines only.
From the amine with phenylisothiocyanate in alcohol.
For directions and examples see: Cheronis, pp. 599–600; Shriner, p. 227; Vogel, p. 422; Wild, p. 227; T. Otterbacher and F. C. Whitmore, *J. Amer. Chem. Soc.*, **51**, 1909 (1929).
From the amine with phenylisothiocyanate without solvent.
See: Vogel, p. 422; Wild, p. 227; N. A. Lange, H. L. Ebert and L. K. Youse, *J. Amer. Chem. Soc.*, **51**, 1911 (1929).

1-Naphthylthiourea.*

$$RNH_2 + 1\text{-}C_{10}H_7N{=}C{=}S \rightarrow 1\text{-}C_{10}H_7NHCSNHR$$

$$RR'NH + 1\text{-}C_{10}H_7N{=}C{=}S \rightarrow 1\text{-}C_{10}H_7NHCSNRR'$$

1-Naphthylthiourea

For primary and secondary amines only.
From the amine with 1-naphthylisothiocyanate in ethanol.
For directions and examples see: Cheronis, pp. 600–601; Vogel, p. 422; Wild, p. 227; C. M. Suter and E. W. Moffet, *J. Amer. Chem. Soc.*, **55**, 2497 (1933).
From the amine with 1-naphthylisothiocyanate without solvent.
See: Vogel, p. 422; Wild, p. 227; C. M. Suter and E. W. Moffett, *J. Amer. Chem. Soc.*, **55**, 2497 (1933).

Phenylurea.

$$RNH_2 + C_6H_5N{=}C{=}O \rightarrow C_6H_5NHCONHR$$

$$RR'NH + C_6H_5N{=}C{=}O \rightarrow C_6H_5NHCONRR'$$

Phenylurea

For primary and secondary amines only.
From the amine with phenylisocyanate in petrol ether.

---

*Derivatives recommended for first trial.
WARNING: This is not an instruction manual. References should be consulted for the preparation of derivatives.

For directions and examples see: Linstead, p. 61; Wild, pp. 223–224.

From the amine with phenylisocyanate without solvent.

See: N. A. Lange, H. L. Ebert and L. K. Youse, *J. Amer. Chem. Soc.*, **51**, 1911 (1929).

1-Naphthylurea.*

$$RNH_2 \quad + \quad 1\text{-}C_{10}H_7N{=}C{=}O \quad \rightarrow \quad 1\text{-}C_{10}H_7NHCONHR$$

$$RR'NH \quad + \quad 1\text{-}C_{10}H_7N{=}C{=}O \quad \rightarrow \quad 1\text{-}C_{10}H_7NHCONR'R'$$

1-Naphthylurea

For primary and secondary amines only.

From the amine with 1-naphthylisocyanate without solvent.

For directions and examples see: Cheronis, p. 599; H. E. French and A. F. Wirtel, *J. Amer. Chem. Soc.*, **48**, 1736 (1926).

From the amine with 1-naphthylisocyanate in petrol ether.

See: Linstead, p. 61; Wild, pp. 223–224.

From the amine with 1-naphthylisocyanate with water.

See: Wild, p. 224.

Picrate.*

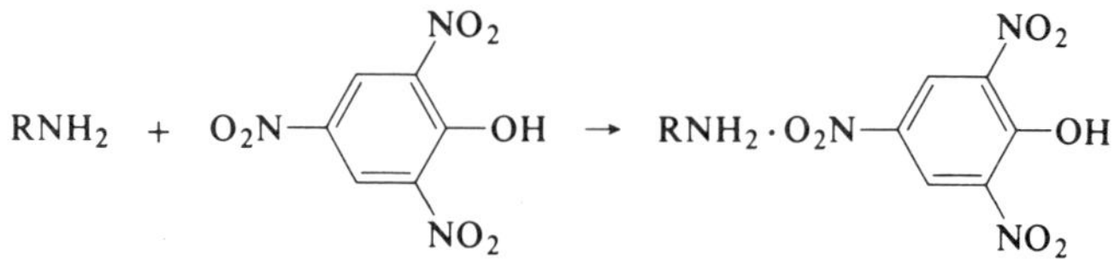

Picrate
(Molecular complex)

For primary, secondary and tertiary amines.

From the amine with picric acid in methanol or in ethanol.

For directions and examples see: Cheronis, pp. 603–604; Linstead, p. 50, 61; Shriner, p. 229; Vogel, pp. 422–423; Wild, p. 212.

From the amine with picric acid in water.

See: Vogel, p. 422.

From the amine with picric acid in acetone or benzene.

See: Wild, p. 212.

From the amine with picric acid.

See: Shriner, p. 229.

3,5-Dinitrobenzoic acid salt.*

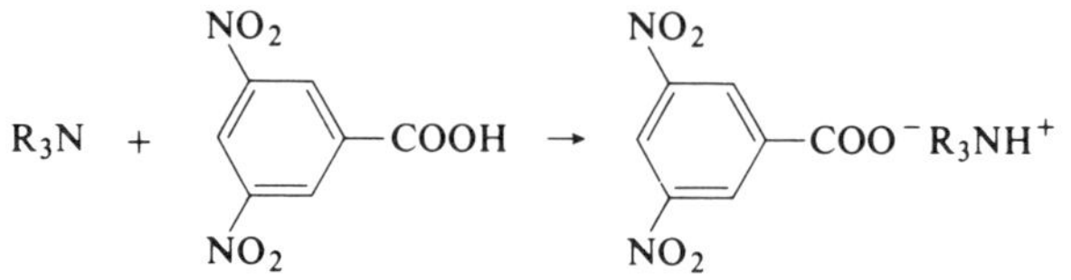

Trialkylammonium
3,5-dinitrobenzoate

Especially for tertiary amines.

From the amine with 3,5-dinitrobenzoic acid in methanol or ethanol.

For directions and examples see: Cheronis, pp. 602–603; Wild, p. 215; C. A. Buehler, E. J. Currier and R. Lawrence, *Ind. Eng. Chem., Anal. Ed.*, **5**, 277 (1933); C. A. Buehler and J. D. Calfree, *Ind. Eng. Chem., Anal. Ed.*, **6**, 351 (1934).

β-Resorcylic acid salt.

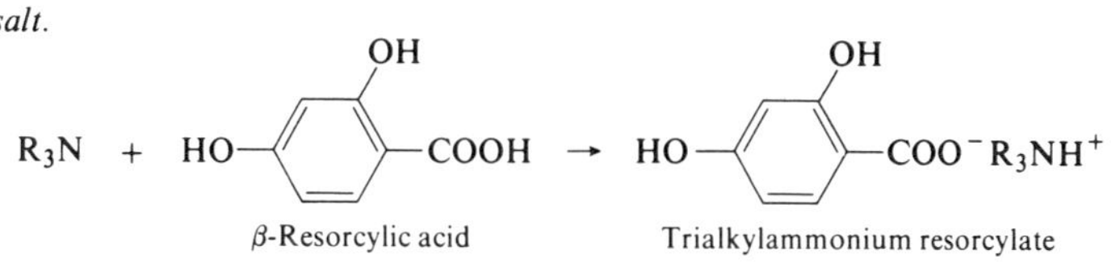

β-Resorcylic acid   Trialkylammonium resorcylate

*Derivatives recommended for first trial.

WARNING: This is not an instruction manual. References should be consulted for the preparation of derivatives.

Especially for tertiary amines.
From the amine with β-resorcylic acid in ether.
For directions and examples see: Cheronis, p. 603; K. W. Wilson, F. E. Anderson and R. W. Donohoe, *Anal. Chem.*, **23**, 1032 (1951).

*Chloroplatinic acid salt.**

$$R_3N \;+\; H_2PtCl_6 \;\rightarrow\; [R_3NH]_2{}^+PtCl_6{}^=$$

Chloroplatinate

Especially for tertiary amines.
From the amine in aqueous hydrochloric acid with aqueous chloroplatinic acid.
For directions and examples see: Shriner, p. 230; Wild, p. 213.

Hydrochloride.

$$RNH_2 \;+\; HCl \;\rightarrow\; [RNH_3{}^+]Cl^-$$

Hydrochloride

For primary, secondary and tertiary amines.
From the amine with gaseous hydrogen chloride in ether, benzene or chloroform.
For directions and examples see: Cheronis, p. 601; Shriner, p. 224; Wild, p. 211.
From the amine with dilute aqueous hydrochloric acid.
See: Wild, p. 211.

*Methiodide.**

$$R_3N \;+\; CH_3I \;\rightarrow\; [R_3NCH_3{}^+]I^-$$

Methiodide

Especially for tertiary amines.
From the amine with methyl iodide without solvent.
For directions and examples see: Linstead, p. 61; Shriner, p. 228; Vogel, p. 660; Wild, p. 232.
From the amine with methyl iodide in isopropyl ether.
See: Cheronis, p. 604.
From the amine with methyl iodide in ether or benzene.
See: Vogel, p. 660.

*Metho-p-toluenesulfonate (Methyl p-toluenesulfonate).**

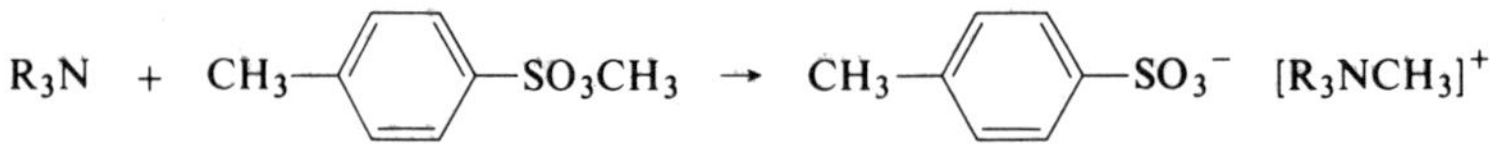

$$R_3N \;+\; CH_3-\!\!\left\langle\bigcirc\right\rangle\!\!-SO_3CH_3 \;\rightarrow\; CH_3-\!\!\left\langle\bigcirc\right\rangle\!\!-SO_3{}^- \; [R_3NCH_3]^+$$

Metho-*p*-toluenesulfonate

Especially for tertiary amines.
From the amine with methyl *p*-toluenesulfonate in isopropyl ether.
For directions and examples see: Cheronis, p. 604.
From the amine with methyl *p*-toluenesulfonate in benzene.
See: Linstead, p. 62; Shriner, p. 229; Vogel, p. 660; Wild, p. 233; C. S. Marvell, E. W. Scott and K. L. Amstutz, *J. Amer. Chem. Soc.*, **51**, 3638 (1929).

*Derivatives recommended for first trial.
WARNING: This is not an instruction manual. References should be consulted for the preparation of derivatives.

TABLE XVIII. ORGANIC DERIVATIVES OF AMINES
1. Primary and secondary amines a) Liquids 1) (Listed in order of increasing atmospheric b.p.)*

No.	Name	Boiling point, °C	Melting point, °C	n_D	Density g/ml	Acetamide	Benzamide	Benzene sulfonamide	p-Toluene sulfonamide	Phenyl thiourea	Picrate	Miscellaneous
1	Methylamine	−6	......	....	0.699_4^{-11}	28	80	30	75	113	207; 215	....
2	Dimethylamine	7	......	....	0.6804_4^0	....	41	47	79	135	158	....
3	Ethylamine	16.5; 19	......	....	0.7057_4^0	....	71	58	63	106; 135	165	....
4	Isopropylamine	33	.....	1.377^{15}	0.691_4^{18}	....	....		26	......	101	.....	1-Naphthylurea, 200; 1-Naphthylthiourea, 143
5	Ethyl methyl amine	36	......	....	....				......	......	196	Chloroplatinate, 207; Hydrochloride, 126–30
6	tert-Butylamine	46	.....	1.3794^{18}	0.7004^{15}	101–2	134	......	......	120	198	Hydrochloride, 270–80
7	n-Propylamine	49	.....	1.3901^{17}	0.714_4^{25}	....	84	36	52	63	135	1-Naphthylurea, 196
8	Isopropyl methyl amine	50	.....	....	0.7026_4^{19}					120	135	Phenylurea, 131
9	Cyclopropylamine	50	.....	1.421^{20}	0.824_4^{20}		99	120 (di)	......	......	149	Hydrochloride, 100
10	Ethyleneimine	56			0.832^{24}		....		52	......	142	Oxalate, 115
11	Diethylamine	56	.....	1.3873^{18}	0.7108_4^{18}	....	42	42	60	34	155	1-Naphthylthiourea, 108
12	Allylamine	58	.....	1.4194^{22}	0.7436_{20}^{20}			39	64	98	140	....
13	DL-sec-n-Butylamine (2-Aminobutane)	63	.....	1.395^{17}	0.718^{20}	....	76	70	55	101	139–40	....
14	unsym-Dimethylhydrazine	63		1.4075^{22}	0.7914^{22}							Hydrochloride, 81–2; Oxalate, 142; Sulfate, 105
15	Trimethyleneimine (Azetidine)	63	.....	1.4287^{24}	0.8436^{20}						166–7	Chloroplatinate, 203; Chloroaurate, 192
16	Isobutylamine	69	.....	1.3988^{17}	0.724_4^{25}		57	53	78	82	150	....
17	n-Butylamine	77	.....	1.401	0.7401_4^{20}					65	151	1-Naphthylurea, 149; 1-Naphthylthiourea, 108-9; Hydrochloride, 195
18	2-Amino-2-methylbutane	78	......	....	0.756_4^0						183	....
19	DL-sec-Butyl methyl amine	78–9			0.740^{15}						78	Chloroplatinate, 151
20	Ethyl propyl amine	80–1		1.3966	0.773^{24}							Hydrochloride, 225; Chloroplatinate, 198; Chloroaurate, 86
21	Sym-Dimethylhydrazine	81	.....	1.4209^{20}	0.8274_4^{20}						147–50	Oxalate, 119; Hydrochloride, 168
22	Cyclobutylamine	82		1.4363^{19}	0.8328_4^{20}							Chloroplatinate, 210–5
23	Di-isopropylamine	84	.....	....	0.722^{22}						140	N-Nitroso, 48; Chloroplatinate, 186–9; Hydrochloride, 216–7
24	Pyrrolidine	89	.....	1.4270^{15}	0.852^{22}				123	......	112, yel.; 163–4, red	....
25	n-Butyl methyl amine	90–1	.....	1.4018^{18}	0.7367_4^{15}						111	Hydrochloride, 170; Chloroplatinate, 205
26	5-Amino-1-pentene	91–4									.....	Chloroplatinate, 166; Chloroaurate, 195
27	DL-2-Amino-n-pentane (sec-n-Amylamine)	92	......	....	0.7384_0^{20}							Hydrochloride, 168; Oxalate, 226; 131 Chloroaurate, 82–3
28	Isoamylamine	96	.....	1.4096^{18}	0.751^{18}	....	....		......	102	138	1-Naphthylurea, 132

*Derivative data given in order: m.p., crystal color, solvent from which crystallized.

No.	Name	Boiling point, °C	Melting point, °C	n_D	Density g/ml	Acetamide	Benzamide	Benzene sulfonamide	p-Toluene sulfonamide	Phenyl thiourea	Picrate	Miscellaneous
29	D-2-Methyl-n-butylamine (active-Amyl amine)	96	.....	......	0.7505_4^{25}	......	......	......	......	......	......	$[\alpha]_D^{25}$: −5.86; Hydrochloride, 176; Chloroplatinate, 240
30	2-Methylpyrrolidine	97–8	.....	......	0.84_{20}^{20}	......	......	......	......	......	88.5–9.5	Oxalate, 178–9; Chloroplatinate, 172–3 (anh.); 206–7, rapid htng; Picrate of N-methyl deriv., 235
31	3-Methylpyrrolidine	103–5	.....	1.4480^{20}	0.8654_4^{0}	......	......	......	......	......	106	Chloroplatinate, 194
32	n-Amylamine	104	.....	......	0.7614_4^{20}	......	......	......	......	69	139	2-Naphthylthiourea, 114
33	2-(Methylamino)-n-pentane	105	.....	......	0.947^{20}	......	......	......	......	......	77–8	Chloroplatinate, 138
34	Piperidine	106	.....	1.4530^{20}	0.8606_4^{20}	......	48	93–4	96	101	152	......
35	2-Aminodiethylether	108–9	.....	1.4101^{20}	0.8512_4^{20}	......	......	......	......	......	122	Picrolonate, 204
36	Di-n-propylamine	109–10	.....	1.4046^{20}	0.7384_4^{20}	......	......	51	......	69	75	1-Naphthylurea, 93
37	2,5-Dimethylpyrrolidine	110–3	.....	1.4357^{15}	0.8185_4^{12}	......	......	......	......	......	117–8	Hydrochloride, 188–90; Chloroplatinate, 225
38	2,4-Dimethylpyrrolidine	115–7	.....	1.4325^{20}	0.8297_4^{20}	......	......	......	......	......	116–7	Chloroplatinate, 210
39	1,2-Ethylenediamine	116	8.5	1.454^{26}	0.898_4^{25}	172 (di)	244 (di)	168 (di)	360 (di)	102	233 (di)	......
40	L-2-Methylpiperidine	117	50–1	......	......	......	......	......	......	......	116–7	Hydrochloride, 190; Chloroplatinate, 194
41	DL-2-Methylpiperidine	118–9	.....	1.4464^{24}	0.8436_4^{24}	......	45	......	55	......	164	Hydrochloride, 207; Oxalate, 125
42	DL-1,2-Diaminopropane	119–20	.....	......	0.878^{15}	139 (di)	192 (di)	......	......	......	135 (di)	......
43	Isohexylamine	125	.....	......	0.758_4^{25}	......	......	......	......	......	123–5	Hydrochloride, 220; Oxalate, 166; Chloroplatinate, 200
44	DL-3-Methylpiperidine	126	.....	1.446^{24}	0.845_4^{24}	......	......	......	......	......	138 (di)	Hydrochloride, 172; N-2,4-Dinitrophenyl deriv., 67
45	2,6-Dimethylpiperidine	127–8	.....	1.4366^{25}	0.816_4^{25}	......	111	50	......	......	162–4	Chloroplatinate, 212
46	n-Hexylamine	130	−19	......	0.763_4^{25}	......	40	96	......	77	126	
47	3-Amino-n-hexane	130	.....	......	......	......	......	......	......	......	......	Hydrochloride, 227; Chloroplatinate, 190–200
48	Morpholine	130	.....	......	......	......	75	118	147	136	146	......
49	Cyclohexylamine	134	.....	1.4372^{20}	0.8191_4^{20}	101	149	89	......	148	......	
50	Trimethylenediamine (1,3-Diaminopropane; 1,3-Propylenediamine)	136	.....	......	0.884^{25}	1,3-di: 126; 107	1,3-di: 140; 147	96	148	......	250	Chloroplatinate, 240
51	2,2,6-Trimethylpiperidine	138–9	.....	......	......	......	......	......	......	......	195–6	Hydrochloride, 236; Chloroaurate, 128
52	Di-isobutylamine	139	−77	1.4093^{20}	0.745_4^{20}	86	......	55; 57	......	113	121	......
53	4-Amino-n-heptane	139–40	.....	......	0.767_4^{20}	......	......	......	......	......	......	Hydrochloride, 246–7; Chloroplatinate, 235
54	1,3-Diaminobutane	141–2	.....	......	......	......	......	......	......	......	240–5	Hydrochloride, 171–2
55	2-Amino-n-heptane	142	.....	1.4199^{19}	0.7665_4^{19}	......	......	......	......	......	......	Hydrochloride, 133; Oxalate, 204–5; Chloroaurate, 63–4
56	unsym-Diethylethylenediamine	145	.....	......	0.827_{19}^{19}	......	......	......	......	115 (mono); 211 (di)	......	Chloroplatinate, 211
57	Furfurylamine (α-Furylmethylamine)	145–6	.....	......	......	......	......	......	......	......	150	Oxalate, 145; With CO₂ from air → comp., 75; Hydrochloride, 110

* Derivative data given in order: m.p., crystal color, solvent from which crystallized.

No.	Name	Boiling point, °C	Melting point, °C	n_D	Density g/ml	Acetamide	Benzamide	Benzene sulfonamide	p-Toluene sulfonamide	Phenyl thiourea	Picrate	Miscellaneous
58	Cyclohexyl methyl amine	145–7	.....	.....	.....	.....	85–6	.....	.....	.....	170	Hydrochloride, 193
59	2-Ethylpiperidine (α-Ethylpiperidine)	146–7	.....	.....	0.8651_0^0	.....	.....	64–5	.....	.....	133	Hydrochloride, 181; Chloroplatinate, 202
60	2,2,4-Trimethyl-piperidine	148	.....	.....	0.832^{15}							Chloroplatinate, 215; Methiodide, 266
61	Sym-Diethylethylene-diamine	149–50	.....									Hydrochloride, 260; Chloroplatinate, 223; Chloroaurate, 220
62	4-Ethylpiperidine (γ-Ethylpiperidine)	151	.....	1.4503^{25}	0.876^0	.....	.....	74–5	.....	.....	.....	Chloroplatinate, 173; Chloroaurate, 105
63	3-Ethylpiperidine (β-Ethylpiperidine)	153	.....		0.871_4^{16}						63	Hydrochloride, 141; Chloroplatinate, 183
64	n-Heptylamine	155	−23	1.41954_α^{26}	0.777^{20}					75	121	1-Naphthylthiourea, 68–9
65	Di-n-butylamine	159								86	59	1-Naphthylthiourea, 123
66	Tetramethylenediamine (1,4-Diaminobutane; Putrescine)	159	27	.....	0.877_4^{25}	137 (di)	177 (di)	.....	224 (di)	.....	249–50 (di)	....
67	DL-2-Hydroxy-n-propylamine (Isopropanolamine)	163	.....		0.973^{18}						142	Chloroplatinate, 195; Hydrochloride, 73
68	Hexahydrobenzylamine	163.5	.....	1.4646^{18}	0.87_4^{20}		98; 107				184–6	Hydrochloride, 254
69	Cyclohexyl ethyl amine	164	.....		0.868_0^0						133	Hydrochloride, 184
70	2-Ethylcyclohexylamine	170–1	.....	1.4682^{20}	0.8744_4^{20}				121–2		190	Chloroplatinate, 239
71	2-Aminoethyl alcohol (Ethanolamine)	171	.....	1.4539^{20}	1.022_4^{20}						160	1-Naphthylurea, 186
72	3-Amino-2-hydroxy-pentane	172	.....		0.906^{18}						.....	N-Chloroacetyl deriv., 52–60; Monooxalate, 166; Dioxalate, 204
73	2-Aminopropyl alcohol	173–6	.....								.....	Hydrochloride, 86; Chloroplatinate, 198–9
74	2-Amino-3-hydroxy-pentane	174	.....	1.4458	0.9289^{24}							Chloroplatinate, 154; Picrolonate, 215
75	2-Fluoroaniline	176	−35; −29			80	113					Picrate of N,N-dimethyl deriv., 131
76	Pentamethylenediamine (1,5-Diaminopentane; Cadaverine)	178–80	.....		0.9174_4^0		135 (di)	119		148	237	....
77	n-Octylamine	180			0.777^{20}						112	1-Naphthylthiourea, 72
78	5-Methyl-2-pyrazoline	180					156				126	Phenylurea, 127
79	Benzyl methyl amine	181			0.945_{15}^{18}				95		117–8	Chloroplatinate, 197
80	Aniline	184		1.5863^{20}	1.022_4^{20}	114	160	112	103	54	180	....
81	Benzylamine	184–5	.....	1.5401	0.9826_4^{19}	65	105	88	116; 185	156	194	....
82	4-Fluoroaniline	186	−1	1.5195^{20}	1.1725_4^{20}	152	185				.....	N-4-Nitrobenzoyl deriv., 181
83	DL-α-Phenylethylamine (α-Aminoethyl-benzene)	187; 185	.....		0.9395^{15}	57	120				.....	Hydrochloride, 158
84	1,2-Diaminocyclohexane	187	.....			260 (di)	....				210–5 (di)	Hydrochloride, 280
85	3-Fluoroaniline	187–8, yel.			1.160^{16}	84						....
86	Di-isoamylamine	187–8	−44	1.4229^{21}	0.7672_4^{21}	....				72	94.5	1-Naphthylurea, 95; Methiodide, 221
87	3-Aminopropyl alcohol	188	.....	1.457^{26}	0.982_4^{26}	....					222	Chloroplatinate, 199

*Derivative data given in order: m.p., crystal color, solvent from which crystallized.

No.	Name	Boiling point, °C	Melting point, °C	n_D	Density g/ml	Acetamide	Benzamide	Benzene sulfonamide	p-Toluene sulfonamide	Phenyl thiourea	Picrate	Miscellaneous
88	1,2,3-Triaminopropane	190				200–2 (*tri*)	217–8 (*tri*)				>269	
89	4-Amino-2,6-dimethyl-piperidine	195									220	Chloroplatinate, >250
90	N-Methylaniline	196		1.573^{16}	0.989^{20}	102	63	79	94	87	145	
91	1-Phenylisopropylamine	196–7		1.5181^{25}	0.9424^{20}_0		159					Oxalate, 131; Hydrochloride, 236
92	β-Phenylethylamine (β-Aminoethylbenzene)	198			0.958^{24}_4	51	116	69		135	174; 167	
93	Benzyl ethyl amine	199			0.935^{17}_{15}				50		118	Hydrochloride, 184
94	2-Methylaniline (o-Toluidine)	200		1.5688^{20}	1.0053^{20}_{20}	110–1	146	124	185–6	136	213 ·	
95	n-Nonylamine	201				34–5	49				111	
96	3-Methylaniline (m-Toluidine)	203		1.5686^{20}	0.990^{25}_{25}	65	125	95	171–2		200	
97	Di-n-amylamine	205								72		2-Naphthylthiourea, 126; Hydrochloride, 275
98	DL-2-Phenylisopropylamine	205				64 initially; 93 on standing					143	Hydrochloride, 145–7
99	N-Ethylaniline	205		1.5559^{20}	0.9625^{20}_4	54	60		87	89	132; 138	
100	4-Methylpyrazole	207		1.4920^{20}_{He}	1.015^{20}_4						142	1-o-Nitrobenzoyl deriv., 107
101	3-Methylbenzylamine (m-Xylylamine)	207			0.9654^{20}_0	235–40	150				198; 156	Hydrochloride, 208; Chloroplatinate, 214
102	2-Chloroaniline	209; 207		1.5895^{20}	1.2125^{20}_4	87	99	129	193; 105	156	134	
103	N,2-Dimethylaniline (N-Methyl-o-toluidine)	208			0.973^{15}	56	66				90	
104	2-Methylbenzylamine (o-Xylylamine)	208	−20	1.5436^{19}	0.977^{19}_0	69	88				215	Chloroplatinate, 220–3
105	4-Methylbenzylamine (p-Xylylamine)	208	13	1.5364^{20}	0.952^{20}_0	107–8	137				204	
106	3-Methylpyrazole	208		1.497^{16}_{He}	1.020^{16}_4	29–30					144	N-o-Nitrobenzoyl deriv., 120
107	1-Phenylpropylamine	208		1.5173^{25}	0.9347^{25}_0		115–6	81				Hydrochloride, 190
108	2-Phenylpropylamine	210					85				182	Hydrochloride, 123–4
109	N,4-Dimethylaniline (N-Methyl-p-toluidine)	210				83		67			131	N-Nitroso deriv., 52; Hydrochloride, 119.5
110	2-Ethylaniline	210–11	46.6	1.5584^{22}	0.9810^{20}	111	147				194–5	
111	L-Menthylamine	212; 207				145	156			135	215	$[\alpha]_D^{19}$: −34.2
112	2,5-Dimethylaniline (p-2-Xylidine)	213–5, pa. yel.	14.2	1.5591^{21}	0.9735^{20}	139	140	138	232–3; 119	148	171	
113	1-Phenylisobutylamine	214		1.5123^{20}	0.920^{20}_0						166–8	Oxalate, 120–2; Hydrochloride, 275–7
114	3-Methylpyridazine	215			1.0486^{26}_{26}						143–4	
115	2,6-Dimethylaniline (m-2-Xylidine)	215; 218	11.2	1.5610^{20}	0.9842^{20}	177	168		212	204	180	
116	4-Ethylaniline	216; 214	−6	1.5550^{20}	0.9690^{20}	94	151		104			
117	2,4-Dimethylaniline (m-4-Xylidine)	217		1.561^{20}	0.9783^{20}_4	133; 130	192	130	181	152	209	
118	2-Chloro-N-methylaniline	218			1.1735^{11}						133	
119	2,4-Dimethylbenzylamine	218–9									223	Hydrochloride, 212; Chloroplatinate, 226

*Derivative data given in order: m.p., crystal color, solvent from which crystallized.

TABLE XVIII. ORGANIC DERIVATIVES OF AMINES

1. Primary and secondary amines a) Liquids 1) (Listed in order of increasing atmospheric b.p.)* (Continued)

No.	Name	Boiling point, °C	Melting point, °C	n_D	Density g/ml	Acetamide	Benzamide	Benzene sulfonamide	p-Toluene sulfonamide	Phenyl thiourea	Picrate	Miscellaneous
120	2-Amino-N,N-dimethylaniline	219	......	....	....	72	51	......	......	......	138–40	....
121	3,5-Dimethylaniline (m-5-Xylidine)	220	9.8	1.5581^{20}	0.9706^{20}	144; 140	144–5	......	......	153	200	N-Formyl deriv., 76
122	N-Ethyl-3-methylaniline (N-Ethyl-m-toluidine)	221; 215	......	....	....	......	72	......	......	......	......	Hydrochloride, 159; Chloroplatinate, 182
123	3,5-Dimethylbenzylamine	221	......	1.5305^{20}	0.950_0^{20}	....	....	......	......	......	225	Hydrochloride, 245; Chloroplatinate, 204
124	2,3-Dimethylaniline (o-3-Xylidine)	221–2	3.5	1.5684^{20}	0.9931^{20}	135	189	......	......	......	221	Hydrochloride, 254; N-Formyl deriv., 102
125	1-Aminoindane (1-Hydrindamine)	222	......	....	....	....	142–3	......	......	......	207	....
126	3-Phenylpropylamine	222	......	....	0.976^{25}	....	57–8	......	......	......	152–3	Hydrochloride, 218
127	2-Methyl-4,5,6,7-tetrahydroindole	222	......	....	0.987_4^{10}	....	....	86–91	......	......	141	Methiodide, 195; Chloroplatinate, 187
128	N-n-Propylaniline	222	......	....	0.949^{18}	47	....	54	......	104	......	....
129	2-n-Propylaniline	222–4	......	....	....	104–5	119	......	......	......	151	Hydrochloride, 173
130	2-Chloro-4-methylaniline	223	......	....	....	113	137	......	......	......	......	....
131	α-Amino-n-butylbenzene	223	......	....	0.9367_0^{20}	....	128	......	......	......	......	Chloroplatinate, 184; Hydrochloride, 288
132	trans-9-Aminodecalin	223	−25	1.492_{He}^{20}	0.939_4^{20}	183	148–9	......	......	......	......	N-Formyl deriv., 172
133	γ-Amino-n-butylbenzene	223	......	1.5152^{20}	0.9289_4^{15}	....	108, lgr.	......	......	......	......	Hydrochloride, 144; Chloroplatinate, 220
134	2-Methoxyaniline (o-Anisidine)	225	5–6	....	....	85; 88	60; 84	89	127	136	200	N-Formyl deriv., 84
135	4-Isopropylaniline (p-Cumidine)	225	......	....	0.953_4^{20}	102	162	......	......	......	......	....
136	4-n-Propylaniline	225	......	....	....	93–4	115	......	......	......	......	Hydrochloride, 203–4
137	N-Isobutylaniline	227	......	....	0.940_4^{18}	....	....	......	122–3	......	......	....
138	α-Methyl-α-phenylhydrazine	227	......	1.5824^{20}	....	92	153	132	......	......	......	....
139	4-tert-Butylaniline	228	17	....	....	173	140	......	179–80	......	......	N-Formyl deriv., 59; Hydrochloride, 270–4
140	cis-9-Aminodecalin	228	−13.5	1.498_{He}^{21}	0.951_4^{21}	127	147	......	......	......	......	N-Formyl deriv., 165–6
141	2-Ethoxyaniline (o-Phenetidine)	229	......	....	....	79	104	102	164	137	......	....
142	2,4,6-Trimethylaniline (Mesidine)	229; 232	......	....	....	216	204	137	167	193	189–91	....
143	2-Aminoindane (2-Hydrindamine)	230	......	....	....	127	155	......	......	......	239	Hydrochloride, 241
144	3-Chloroaniline	230; 236	......	1.5931^{20}	1.2225_{15}^{15}	72; 78	119–20	121	138; 210	124; 116	177	....
145	2,2'-Diaminodiethylsulfide	231–3	......	....	....	....	....	......	......	......	212	Dihydrochloride, 131
146	1,2,3,4-Tetrahydroisoquinoline	233	......	1.5798^{23}	1.064_4^{23}	46	129	154	......	......	200; 195	....
147	2-tert-Butylaniline	233–5	......	1.5453^{20}	0.977^{15}	159–61	....	......	......	......	......	....
148	3-Amino-4-(dimethylamino)toluene	234	......	....	....	....	........,.	......	......	......	151	Hydrochloride, 192–3
149	4-Isobutylaniline	235, pa. yel.	......	....	....	127	....	......	136–7	......	......	....
150	4-Aminoindane (4-Hydrindamine)	236	−3	....	....	126	136	......	......	......	......	....
151	2-Aminoundecane (2-Aminohendecane; sec-n-Undecylamine)	237	......	....	....	58	....	......	......	......	111	Hydrochloride, 84
152	unsym-Ethylphenylhydrazine	237	......	....	1.018^{15}	....	....	......	......	......	......	Hydrochloride, 137; Reduces warm Fehling

*Derivative data given in order: m.p., crystal color, solvent from which crystallized.

TABLE XVIII. ORGANIC DERIVATIVES OF AMINES
1. Primary and secondary amines a) Liquids 1) (Listed in order of increasing atmospheric b.p.)* (Continued)

No.	Name	Boiling point, °C	Melting point, °C	n_D	Density g/ml	Acetamide	Benzamide	Benzene sulfonamide	p-Toluene sulfonamide	Phenyl thiourea	Picrate	Miscellaneous
153	sym-Ethylphenyl-hydrazine	238–9	......	1.55^{15}	1.004^{15}_{15}	....	100	......	......	......	......	Hydrochloride, 164; Oxalate, 167
154	2-Bromo-4-methylaniline (3-Bromo-p-toluidine)	240	26	....	1.51^{20}	118	149				......	Hydrochloride, 221
155	1-Aminoundecane (1-Aminohendecane; n-Undecylamine; n-Hendecylamine)	240	15–6			48	60				......	Hydrochloride, 190
156	4-Chloro-N-methyl-aniline	240	......	....	$1.169^{11.5}$	92–4	....				153	Nitrosamine, 51
157	4-Chloro-2-methylaniline (5-Chloro-o-toluidine)	241	29			140					......	
158	2-Amino-p-cymene (p-Cymidine)	241		1.543^{19}	0.994^{20}	71	102				......	Hydrochloride, 207
159	N-Butylaniline	241	......	1.5381^{20}	0.9358^{20}_{4}	....	56	......	56	......		
160	Phenylhydrazine	243	19; 23	1.6081^{20}	1.0978^{20}_{4}	128; 107 (di)	168; 177 (di)	148	151	172		
161	α,α'-Diamino-m-xylene (m-Xylylenediamine)	245–8				di: 134–5, bz.	N,N'-di: 172				185–90	Dihydrobromide, 266
162	2-Chloro-6-methoxy-aniline (3-Chloro-o-anisidine)	246 sl. d.				123	135	......				
163	3-Ethoxyaniline (m-Phenetidine)	248	......			97	103	......	157	138	158	
164	4-Ethoxyaniline (p-Phenetidine)	248; 254	2–3	....	1.065^{16}_{4}	137	173	143	106	136	69	....
165	1,2,3,4-Tetrahydro-quinoline	250	20	1.593^{24}	1.054^{24}_{4}		75	67				
166	2-Aminoacetophenone	250–2d.	20			76–7	98	......	148	......	......	Semicarbazone, 290; Oxime, 109; Hydrochloride, 168 d.
167	3-Bromoaniline	251	18	1.626^{20}	1.579^{20}_{4}	87	120; 136	......		143	180	
168	3-Methoxyaniline (m-Anisidine)	251	......			81	....		68		169	Hydrochloride, 167–8
169	3-Bromo-2-methylaniline (6-Bromo-o-toluidine)	254				163	176–7					
170	4-Amino-1,2,3,5-tetra-methylbenzene (Iso-duridine)	255	23–4			215–7	....				200	
171	Dicyclohexylamine	255 sl. d.	abt. 20	1.488^{18}	0.925^{18}	103	153				173	
172	6-Methyl-1,2,3,4-tetra-hydroisoquinoline	256	......		1.0235^{8}_{4}						205	Hydrochloride, 195–7; Methiodide, 144–5; N-Nitroso deriv., 98
173	4-Amino-N,N-diethyl-aniline	261				104	172					
174	4-n-Butylaniline	261	......		0.945^{20}_{4}	105	126				......	Chloroplatinate, 200–2
175	1-Amino-5,6,7,8-tetra-hydronaphthalene	261–3	......	1.5896^{23}	1.0625^{16}	158				......	......	Hydrochloride, 259–61
176	7-Methyl-1,2,3,4-tetra-hydroquinoline	264					70–2				153–4	Hydrochloride, 175
177	4-Methylindole	267	5	....	1.062^{20}_{4}						194–5	....
178	2-Amino-4-chloro-N,N-dimethylaniline	267–8	......			90	....				191	
179	DL-3-Aminopropylene-glycol (2,3-Dihydroxy-propylamine)	268 part. d.	......	1.49^{10}	1.175^{20}_{4}	....	O,N-di: 109; O,O,N-tri: 113				......	Chloroplatinate, 185; Picrolonate, 220; O,N-di-4-Nitroben-zoyl deriv., 139

*Derivative data given in order: m.p., crystal color, solvent from which crystallized.

No.	Name	Boiling point, °C	Melting point, °C	n_D	Density g/ml	Acetamide	Benzamide	Benzene sulfon-amide	p-Toluene sulfon-amide	Phenyl thiourea	Picrate	Miscellaneous
180	**Diethanolamine** (Di-(2-hydroxyethyl)-amine)	270	28	1.4776^{20}	1.0966_4^{20}	....	....	......	......	......	110	Nitrate, 69; Chloroplatinate, 160
181	**3-(Dimethylamino) aniline**	272	......	....	0.995^{25}	87; 69 (*di*)	163–4	......	......	......	187	N-Chloroacetyl deriv., 102
182	**1-(N,N-Diethylamino) naphthalene**	290	......	1.5961^{20}	1.015_{20}^{20}	....	....	......	......	......	152–4	1,3,5-Trinitrobenzene add. comp., 95, scar.
183	**1-(Methylamino) naphthalene**	294	......	....	....	94–5	121	......	164	......	......	....
184	**Dibenzylamine**	300	......	1.5743^{22}	1.0256_4^{22}	....	112	68	159	......	......	Hydrochloride, 256
185	**α-Aminodiphenyl-methane** (Benzhydryl-amine)	303–4	......	$1.5963^{21.5}$	$1.0635_0^{21.5}$	146–7	172; 167	......	......	......	205–6	N-Formyl deriv., 132
186	**1,2-Diphenylethylamine** .	313	......	....	1.031^{15}	....	....	......	......	......	212–3	Oxalate, 158; Chloroplatinate, 188
187	**2,3-Diphenylpropyl-amine**	315–7	......	....	....	85 (*di*)	....	......	......	......	......	Hydrochloride, 188–90; Chloroaurate, 144–5
188	**2-(Methylamino) naphthalene**	317; 309	......	....	....	51	84	107	78	......	145	Hydrochloride, 182–3
189	**2-(N,N-Diethylamino) naphthalene**	320–2	......	....	....	....	....	......	......	......	......	1,3,5-Trinitrobenzene add. comp., 116, blk.; Hydrochloride, 177; Chloroplatinate, 95

*Derivative data given in order: m.p., crystal color, solvent from which crystallized.

TABLE XVIII. ORGANIC DERIVATIVES OF AMINES
1. Primary and secondary amines a) Liquids 2) (b.p. at reduced pressure only)
(Listed in order of increasing m.p. of the corresponding acetyl derivative)*

No.	Name	Boiling point, °C	Melting point, °C	n_D	Density g/ml	Acetamide	Benzamide	Benzene sulfon-amide	p-Toluene sulfon-amide	Phenyl thiourea	Picrate	Miscellaneous
1	**3-Aminostyrene**	112–5[12]	. . . . .	. . . .	1.0216$^{20}_{20}$	74–5	90, bz.-lgr.; 126, al.-w.	. . . . . .	. . . . .	. . . . .	. . . . .	Polymerizes readily
2	**2-Bromo-4-ethoxyaniline** (3-Bromo-p-phenet-idine).	160[23]	. . . . .	. . . .	. . . . . .	97	. . . .	. . . . . .	. . . . .	. . . . .	. . . . .	. . . .
3	**3-Aminothiophenol**	180–90[16]	. . . . .	. . . .	. . . . . .	N,S-*di*: 97 *di*)	. . . .	. . . . . .	. . . . .	. . . . .	. . . . .	Hydrochloride, 232
4	**2-n-Butylaniline**	122–5[12]	. . . . .	. . . .	0.953$^{20}_{4}$	100	116–7	. . . . . .	. . . . .	. . . . .	. . . . .	Hydrochloride, 137
5	**2-(2-Aminophenyl)ethyl** . . alcohol.	147–8[3.5]	. . . . .	1.5849[19]	. . . . . .	103.5	. . . .	. . . . . .	. . . . .	. . . . .	. . . . .	Hydrochloride, 126
6	**6-Amino-3,4′-dimethyl-biphenyl**.	165–7[4]	. . . . .	. . . .	. . . . . .	104	. . . .	. . . . . .	. . . . .	. . . . .	. . . . .	Hydrochloride, 216–26
7	**2,2-Diphenylpropylamine**	179–82[22]	. . . . .	. . . .	1.027[18]	106–7	82–3	. . . . . .	. . . . .	. . . . .	. . . . .	Hydrochloride, 261
8	**2-Chloro-4-methoxy-aniline** (3-Chloro-p-anisidine)	156[31]	. . . . .	. . . .	. . . . . .	114	. . . .	. . . . . .	. . . . .	. . . . .	. . . . .	Hydrochloride, 228
9	**2-Aminostyrene**	97–8[8]	. . . . .	1.6130[21]	1.015$^{21}_{21}$	129	. . . .	. . . . . .	. . . . .	. . . . .	. . . . .	Polymerizes readily
10	**2-Aminothiophene**	77–9[11]	. . . . .	. . . .	. . . . . .	161–2	172–3	. . . . . .	. . . . .	. . . . .	. . . . .	Oxidizes rapidly; N-2-toluenesulfonyl deriv., 183–4
11	**4,4′-Diamino-2,3′-dimethylbiphenyl**	244[12]	. . . . .	. . . . .	. . . . . .	N,N′-*di*: 253; *tetra*: 191	N,N′-*di*: 245	. . . . . .	. . . . .	. . . . .	. . . . .	. . . .

*Derivative data given in order: m.p., crystal color, solvent from which crystallized.

TABLE XVIII. ORGANIC DERIVATIVES OF AMINES
1. Primary and secondary amines c) Solids (Listed in order of increasing m.p.)*

No.	Name	Melting point, °C	Boiling point, °C	Acetamide	Benzamide	Benzene sulfonamide	p-Toluene sulfonamide	Phenyl thiourea	Picrate	Miscellaneous
1	**Di-*n*-heptylamine**	1	271	....	....	......	......	......	117–20	....
2	**4-Aminostyrene**................	23.5	98[4]	142	160–1	......	.....	......	.....	D_{21}^{21}: 1.012; $n_D^{21.5}$: 1.625
3	**3-Bromo-4-methylaniline** (2-Bromo-*p*-toluidine)	25–6	254–7	117–8	132	......				....
4	**2-Amino-3-methylpyridine** (2-Amino-β-picoline)	26	224	64	220	......			229	
5	**2-Aminothiophenol**	26	234	135 (N,S-*di*)	154 (N,S-*di*)	......				
6	**n-Dodecylamine**	27–8	247–9	....	....	......	73	......		Hydrochloride, 98; Chloroplatinate, 215
7	**DL-2,6-Dimethyl-1,2,3,4-tetra-hydroquinoline**	31–2	267	....	103–5	......				Hydrochloride, 180–3
8	**5-Bromo-2-methylaniline** (4-Bromo-*o*-toluidine)	32	253 part. d.	165	....					
9	**1-Amino-2-methylnaphthalene** (2-Methyl-1-naphthylamine)	32	....	188	180					
10	**2-Bromoaniline**	32	250	99	116	......		146; 161	129	....
11	**4,4'-Dimethyldibenzylamine** (*p*-Dixylylamine)	32.5	220[30] ...	....	....			......	153	Nitrosamine, 52; Hydrochloride, 272
12	**2-Aminodibenzyl**................	33	173–83[11]	117	166	......		......	167–8	Hydrochloride, 198
13	**3-Iodoaniline**	33; 27	145–6[15]	119	157	......	128			
14	*unsym.*-**Diphenylhydrazine**	34	220[40–50]	184	192					
15	α,α'-**Diamino-1,4-dimethylbenzene** (*p*-Xylylenediamine)	35	....	194 (*tetra*)	193 (N,N'-*di*)				232	
16	**3-Bromo-5-methylaniline** (5-Bromo-*m*-toluidine)	36	255–60	171–2	....					
17	**4-Amino-N-methylaniline**	36	258	63	165	......			206	
18	**Pentadecylamine**................	36; 33	300	72	....				.....	Hydrochloride, 199
19	**N-Benzylaniline**................	37	298	58	107	119	148–9	103	48	
20	**3-Iodo-4-methylaniline** (2-Iodo-*p*-toluidine)..................	37–8	....	130	....				.....	Oxalate, 103
21	**5-Aminoindane** (5-Hydrindamine) .	37–8	247–9[745]	106	137					
22	**2-Amino-5,6,7,8-tetrahydronaph-thalene** (5,6,7,8-Tetrahydro-2-naphthylamine)	38	275–7[713]	107	167				204	
23	**2-Amino-5-bromonaphthalene** (5-Bromo-2-napthylamine)	38	207–10[16]	165	109	......			216	N-Benzal, 63
24	**2,2-Diphenylethylamine**	38	180[33]	88	144–5				212–3	Phenylurethane, 191–2; Hydrochloride, 256–7
25	**2,3-Dimethyl-1,2,3,4-tetra-hydroquinoline**	38–9	....	....	92				178	....
26	**2-Iodo-4-methylaniline** (3-Iodo-*p*-toluidine)..................	40	....	133	161					Oxalate, 120; Hydrochloride, 188
27	**2-Chloro-4,6-dimethylaniline** (5-Chloro-*m*-4-xylidine)	40	....	205–6	148					2-Naphthylthiourea, 154
28	**2-Amino-6-methylpyridine** (6-Amino-α-picoline)	41	208–9	90	90	......			202	Hydrochloride, 155; Chloroplatinate, 218
29	**4-Amino-N,N-dimethylaniline**	41; 53	262	132–3	228				188	
30	**1,6-Diaminohexane** (Hexamethylenediamine)........	42	204–5	125–7 (*di*)	155 (*di*)	154 (*di*)			220	
31	**1,3-Diaminoisopropyl alcohol**	42	235	....	....				230	Hydrochloride, 185; Chloroplatinate, 240
32	**4-Amino-3-methylbiphenyl**	43	190[15]	165; 158	189					N-Benzal, 108
33	**2,4'-Diaminobiphenyl**	45	363	202 (*di*)	278 (*di*)					
34	**4-Methylaniline** (*p*-Toluidine).....	45	200	147	158	120	118	141	182	
35	**4-Aminothiophenol**	46	140–5[16]	154 (N-); 144 (132) (N,S-*di*)	180 (N-)	......			.....	Oxidized readily → 4,4'-diaminodiphenyl sulfide, 104–5

*Derivative data given in order: m.p., crystal color, solvent from which crystallized.

TABLE XVIII. ORGANIC DERIVATIVES OF AMINES

1. Primary and secondary amines c) Solids (Listed in order of increasing m.p.)* (Continued)

No.	Name	Melting point, °C	Boiling point, °C	Acetamide	Benzamide	Benzene sulfonamide	p-Toluene sulfonamide	Phenyl thiourea	Picrate	Miscellaneous
36	4-Aminobenzyl cyanide	46	....	97 (*mono*) 152–3 (*di*)	176–7	....	....	......	185	N-Formyl, 135
37	2-Aminopropiophenone	47	93[0.8]	71	130	....	....	......		Oxime, 88–9; Semicarba-zone, 190; N-Propionyl, 51
38	3-Bromo-4-ethoxyaniline (2-Bromo-*p*-phenetidine)	47	189[20]	114	....	....	....	......	178–9	....
39	4-Amino-2-thiocresol	47	....	95 (N-); 125 (N,S-*di*)	....	....	....	......		S-Me., 47
40	2-Iodo-5-methylaniline (4-Iodo-*m*-toluidine	48; 38	....	151; 146						N-Formyl, 129
41	1-Amino-4-fluoronaphthalene (4-Fluoro-1-naphthylamine)	48	162[16]	....	197					Hydrochloride, 280
42	4-Aminodibenzyl	48	....	....	170–1					Hydrochloride, 210; Chloroplatinate, 286–9
43	3,4-Dimethylaniline (*o*-4-Xylidine; 4-Amino-*o*-xylene)	49	224	99	....	118	....			N-Formyl, 52; Hydro-chloride, 256
44	2-Ethoxy-6-nitroaniline	49, yel.	....	64	....	....				N-Me., 59
45	Heptadecylamine	49	335–40	62	91					
46	2-Aminobiphenyl	49	299	121	102	....				N-Formyl, 75; N-Propionyl, 65
47	4-Amino-2-methyldiphenylamine	49–50	196[4]	139–40	....					Hydrochloride, 185–7
48	2-Bromo-4,6-dimethylaniline (5-Bromo-*m*-4-xylidine)	49–50	....	196–7	186				122	....
49	2,5-Dichloroaniline	50	251	132	120	....			86	Hydrochloride, 191–2
50	1-Aminooxindole	50	....	186–7	189	....				
51	1-Aminonaphthalene (*α*-naphthyl-amine)	50	....	159	160	167	157; 147	165	163; 181	
52	1-Amino-1,2,3-triazole	51	....		151				130	Hydrochloride, 114
53	2-Amino-1-methylnaphthalene (1-Methyl-2-naphthylamine)	51	....	188–9	222				..	
54	1-Amino-3-methylnaphthalene (3-Methyl-1-naphthylamine)	51–2	....	175–6	188–9					
55	1-Amino-4-methylnaphthalene (4-Methyl-1-naphthylamine)	51–2	176[12]	166–7	238–9	....				Hydrochloride, 233–4
56	4-Chloro-2-methoxyaniline (5-Chloro-*o*-anisidine)	52; 46	260	150	....	....			200	N-Formyl, 177–8; Hydro-chloride, 238
57	Indole	52	253	157–8	68	254				N-Nitroso, 171
58	2-Aminodiphenylmethane	52	190[22]	135	116	....				Hydrochloride, 137
59	2,2′-Ditolylamine (Di-*o*-tolylamine)	52–3	318		114–5	....				
60	4-Aminobiphenyl	53	302	171; 120 (*di*)	230	....	255; 160	......		N-Formyl, 172
61	1,4-Bis-(methylamino)benzene (*sym*-Dimethyl-*p*-phenylene-diamine)	53	150[17]						186	N,N′-Dinitroso, 148
62	Diphenylamine	53–4	....	101	180	124	141	152	182	....
63	DL-*α*-Aminobenzyl cyanide	55	....		159–60	....			160–1	....
64	4-Methoxy-3-nitroaniline (2-Nitro-*p*-anisidine)	57, or.	....	153	....					N-Chloroacetyl, 150; N,N-Di-Me., 46, red
65	5-Bromo-2-ethoxyaniline (4-Bromo-*o*-phenetidine)	57; 53	....	133	....				135–7	....
66	2-Amino-5-bromobiphenyl	57	....	130	162	....				
67	4-Methoxyaniline (*p*-Anisidine)	58	240	130; 127	154; 157	95	114	157; 171		
68	1-Amino-7-methylnaphthalene (7-Methyl-1-naphthylamine)	58–9	162[10]	182–3	204	....				
69	4-Bromo-2-methylaniline (5-Bromo-*o*-toluidine)	59	240	156–7	115	....				

*Derivative data given in order: m.p., crystal color, solvent from which crystallized.

TABLE XVIII. ORGANIC DERIVATIVES OF AMINES

1. Primary and secondary amines c) Solids (Listed in order of increasing m.p.)* (Continued)

No.	Name	Melting point, °C	Boiling point, °C	Acetamide	Benzamide	Benzene sulfon- amide	p- Toluene sulfon- amide	Phenyl thiourea	Picrate	Miscellaneous
70	2-Amino-1-chloronaphthalene (1-Chloro-2-naphthylamine)	59	....	147	98	131	....	....	....	N-Formyl, 136
71	2-Aminoazobenzene	59	....	126	122					
72	1-Amino-2-chloronaphthalene (2-Chloro-1-naphthylamine)	59–60	....	191 (mono); 88 (di)	....					
73	5-Methylindole	60	267	....	....				151	....
74	2-Aminopyridine	60; 58	204	71	165 (di)	....			216–7	....
75	3-(3-Indolyl)-propylamine	60–4	....	....					146–9; 156	Hydrochloride, 170
76	2-Methylindole	61	271–2	....	....				139	1,3,5-Trinitrobenzene add. comp., 152; N-Formyl, 75
77	2-Iodoaniline	61; 58	....	109	139				112	Hydrochloride, 153–4
78	1-Naphthyl phenyl amine (N-Phenyl-1-naphthylamine)	62	226²	115	152	....			....	
79	3-Chloro-4-methoxyaniline (2-Chloro-p-anisidine)	62	....	94	....				186	....
80	1-Amino-3-chloronaphthalene (3-Chloro-1-naphthylamine)	62	....	197	162					Hydrochloride, 219
81	2-Amino-4,4'-dimethylbiphenyl	62–3	....	118–9	95–6					
82	8-Amino-6-methylquinoline	62–4	....	91–2						1,3,5-Trinitrobenzene add. comp., 139
83	2-Amino-1-bromonaphthalene (1-Bromo-2-naphthylamine)	63	....	mono: 140; di: 105	....					N-Propionyl, 139; N-Benzal, 93–4; 1,3,5-Trinitrobenzene add. comp., 192
84	1,3-Diaminobenzene (m-Phenylene-diamine)	63	282–4	191 (di) 87–9 (mono)	240 (di) 125 (mono)	194	172	....	184	....
85	2,4-Dichloroaniline	63	245	145	117	128	126	......	106	....
86	2-Amino-5-methylnaphthalene (5-Methyl-2-naphthylamine)	63–4	....	123–4	155–6	....				
87	3-Bromo-4-methoxyaniline .... (2-Bromo-p-anisidine)	64	....	111	....					Hydrochloride, 255
88	2,5-Diaminotoluene.............	64	273–4	220 (di)	307	2-mono: 147	2-mono: 150			....
89	3-Aminopyridine	64	250–2	mono: 133; di: 88	119					
90	9-Aminofluorene	64	....	262	260–1	....				Hydrochloride, 255
91	4-Methylphenylhydrazine (p-Tolylhydrazine)	65	240–4d.	121	1-N-mono: 68–70; 2-N-mono: 146	....				
92	4-Aminobenzyl alcohol	65	....	188 (O,N-di)	4-mono: 150					Hydrochloride, 217
93	2-Bromo-6-methoxyaniline (3-Bromo-o-anisidine)	65	....	....	90					Hydrochloride, 225
94	1,3-Diamino-2,6-dimethylbenzene (2,4-Diamino-m-xylene)........	65–6	....	>260 (di)	232 (227) (di)	....				N,N'-Diformyl, 220
95	Aminoacetamide (Glycineamide) ..	65–7	....	....						Hydrochloride, 186–9; Chloroaurate, 197–8; Hot $H_2O \rightarrow$ glycine + NH_3
96	2-Aminocyclohexanol	66	219	....						Hydrochloride, 175; N-Phenyl, 150
97	2-Amino-5-methylbenzophenone ...	66, yel.	....	159	118	....	....	145	....
98	4-Bromoaniline	66	245	168	204	134		148	180	....
99	1,8-Diaminonaphthalene..........	66	....	311–2 (di)	....	207 (di)	....	....	....

*Derivative data given in order: m.p., crystal color, solvent from which crystallized.

TABLE XVIII. ORGANIC DERIVATIVES OF AMINES

TABLE XVIII. ORGANIC DERIVATIVES OF AMINES
1. Primary and secondary amines c) Solids (Listed in order of increasing m.p.)* (Continued)

No.	Name	Melting point, °C	Boiling point, °C	Acetamide	Benzamide	Benzene sulfon- amide	p- Toluene sulfon- amide	Phenyl thiourea	Picrate	Miscellaneous
100	3-Amino-5-bromopyridine	66–7	150[12]	76–8 (hyd.); 127 (anh.)	....	....	....	....	212–3	Chloroaurate, 185–7
101	1-Amino-8-methylnaphthalene (8-Methyl-1-naphthylamine)	67–8	....	183–4	195–6	....	....	....	....	
102	4-Iodoaniline	67–8	....	184	222	....	....	153	......	N-4-Nitrobenzoyl, 269; N-Benzal, 86
103	1-Amino-2,4,5-trimethylbenzene (Pseudocumidin)	68	....	162	167	136				
104	2,2′-Diaminodibenzyl	68	....	249 (di)	255 (di)				225–30	
105	2-Amino-4-methylnaphthalene ..... (4-Methyl-2-naphthylamine)	68	....	172–3	194–5	....	....	....	....	
106	3-Nitro-N-methylaniline	68	....	95	105	83				
107	1-Amino-3-bromonaphthalene (3-Bromo-1-naphthylamine)	70	....	174	166	......				Hydrochloride, 247
108	1-Amino-5-methyl-1,2,3-triazole ...	70			158, 138 (di)	....				N-Benzal, 67–8; Hydro- chloride, 138
109	8-Aminoquinoline	70; 65, yel.	....	103	98	....	154–6	....	....	Hydrochloride, 208–9
110	2-Nitroaniline	71, golden- yel.	....	92; 94	98; 110	104	142		73	....
111	3,4-Diaminotriphenylmethane	71–2	....	226 (di)	243 (di)	....				
112	4-Chloroaniline	72	....	179; 172	192	122	95; 119	152	......	
113	8-Amino-6-Chloroquinoline	73	....	....	....	....				Hydrochloride, 208; Chloroplatinate, 212; Methiodide, 178
114	4-Aminophenylurethane (N-carbethoxy-1,4- diaminobenzene)	73–4	....	202; 181	230	....				Hydrochloride, 242
115	4-Aminodiphenylamine	75 (anh.)	....	158	203	....				
116	3,5-Dimethylindole	75	278			....			180	
117	Duridine (3-Amino-1,2,4,5- tetramethylbenzene)	75	261	207	....					Hydrochloride, 260
118	1-Amino-3,4,5-trimethylbenzene....	75	240	163–4	....					N-Formyl, 98
119	2-Amino-1,4-dimethylnaphthalene (1,4-Dimethyl-2-naphthylamine)..	75	333	219–20	....					
120	4-Nitromesidine (2-Amino-4- nitromesitylene).............	75	....	191	169	163				
121	2-Methoxy-6-nitroaniline (3-Nitro-o-anisidine)...........	76, yel.	....	158–9						N-Me., 58, red
122	2-Bromo-1,4-diaminobenzene (2-Bromo-p-phenylenediamine)..	76	....	200(di)	235(di)					
123	4,6-Dimethyl-2-nitroaniline (5-Nitro-m-4-xylidine)	76; 70	....	176; 173	185					
124	1-Amino-5-methylnaphthalene (5-Methyl-1-naphthylamine)	77–8	....	194–5	173–4				210 d.	
125	2,4,6-Trichloroaniline	78	263	204; 206	174	152–4	....		83	
126	4-Methyl-3-nitroaniline (2-Nitro-p-toluidine)...........	78	....	148	172	160	164	171	......	
127	2,4-Dibromoaniline	79	....	146	134	......	134		124	
128	1-Naphthyl 4-tolyl amine........	79	....	124	140					
129	2-Aminodiphenylamine..........	79–80	....	121 (2-N-)	136 (2-N-)					
130	2,4-Diaminophenol (4-Hydroxy-m- phenylenediamine)	79–80	....	220–2 (2,4-N-) 180–2 (tri)	253 (di)	....			120	
131	4-Aminopyrazole................	80–2	....	....	173 (di)	....			193–4	

*Derivative data given in order: m.p., crystal color, solvent from which crystallized.

TABLE XVIII. ORGANIC DERIVATIVES OF AMINES

1. Primary and secondary amines c) Solids (Listed in order of increasing m.p.)* (Continued)

No.	Name	Melting point, °C	Boiling point, °C	Acetamide	Benzamide	Benzene sulfon-amide	p-Toluene sulfon-amide	Phenyl thiourea	Picrate	Miscellaneous
132	**4-Bromo-3-methylaniline** (6-Bromo-*m*-toluidine).........	81	240	103–4	......	......		.....	.....	N,N-Di-Me., 55
133	**2,2′-Diaminodibenzyl sulfide**.......	81	....	209 (*di*)	......	......			203–4	N,N′-Diformyl, 163
134	**2,2′-Diaminobiphenyl**............	81	162⁴	*mono*: 89; *di*: 161	159 (2-N-) 190 (*di*)	......				N,N′-Diformyl, 137
135	**3-Aminoacenaphthene**...........	81	....	192–3, al.	209, al.	......		.....	221	N-Formyl, 151; Alc, FeCl₃ → bl.-vlt. col.
136	**2-Aminobenzyl alcohol**..........	82	270–80 part. d.	N-*mono*: 114	O-: 198–9	......		.....	110	Hydrochloride, 108
137	**1-Amino-1,3,4-triazole**..........	82–3	....	....					194–5	Hydrochloride, 153; N-Formyl, 117; Chloro-platinate, 230
138	**4-Chloro-3-methylaniline** (6-Chloro-*m*-toluidine)........	83		91	119	......				2-Naphthylthiourea, 158
139	**2,6-Dibromoaniline**.............	83–4	262–4	210	....	......			123–4	....
140	**5-Chloro-2-methoxyaniline** (4-Chloro-*o*-anisidine).........	84	....	104	77–8	......			194	
141	**4-Aminotriphenylmethane**.......	84, bz.	248¹²	168	198	......				N,N-Di-Me., 132
142	**1-Amino-3-iodonaphthalene** (3-Iodo-1-naphthylamine)......	84		207	174	......				....
143	**4-Aminobutyrophenone**.........	84	....	142	....	......				Hydrochloride, 178
144	**4,4′-Diaminodiphenyl disulfide**.....	85, yel.; 106	....	205 (*di*)						N,N′-Dicarbethoxy, 136–7
145	**7-Methylindole**................	85	266	....	84				176	....
146	**2-Amino-4-bromobenzaldehyde**	85	....	....						Oxime, 194; Phenylhydra-zone, 215
147	**2,2′-Diaminodiphenyl sulfide**.......	85–6	....	160 (*di*)	162–3 (*di*)	......				....
148	**4-Aminoveratrol (3,4-Dimethoxy-aniline)**.....................	85–6	174–6	133	177	......				Chloroplatinate, 227
149	**2-Aminophenanthrene**...........	85, pa. yel.	....	225	216					
150	**4-Aminobenzonitrile**............	86	....	205	170	......			150	N-Formyl, 188–9; N-Propionyl, 169
151	**4-Iodo-2-methylaniline (5-Iodo-*o*-toluidine)**....................	87; 92	....	170; 162	184	......			189	N-Benzal, 55; Phenyl-urethane, 232
152	**4-Aminoacenaphthene**..........	87	....	175–6	196	......			190–200	
153	**3-Aminoacetanilide**............	87–9	....	191	....		241			
154	**3-Aminophenanthrene**...........	87.5	....	200–1	213					
155	**4-Amino-3-methyl-1-phenylpyrazole**	88	312	94–5 (hyd.); 120(anh.)	181				138	N-Formyl, 112 (anh.); 81 (hyd.); Chloroplatinate, 226
156	**2-Hydroxy-3-methylaniline** (3-Amino-*o*-cresol)............	89		N-*mono*: 78–9	....					N-Acetyl of Me. eth., 100
157	**3,4-Diaminotoluene**.............	89–90	265	210 (*di*); 95 (3-N); 131 (4-N)	263–4 (*di*)	178–9 (*di*)	4-*mono*: 140	......		....
158	**2-Nitrophenylhydrazine**	90, red	....	140–1; *di*: 57–8	166	......				N-Formyl, 177
159	**2,2′-Diaminodibenzyl disulfide** ...	90–1	....	202–5 (*di*)	....					N,N′-Dipropionyl, 190–1
160	**4-Chloro-1,3-diaminobenzene**......	91	....	242 (*di*)	178 (*di*)	160	215			
161	**1-Amino-2,6-dimethylnaphthalene** (2,6-Dimethyl-1-naphthylamine)..	91	....	211	219–20	......				
162	**1-Amino-4-mercaptonaphthalene** (4-Amino-1-thionaphthol)......	91–3	....	N-*mono*: 173	....					S-Me., 54
163	**2-Methyl-3-nitroaniline** (6-Nitro-*o*-toluidine)...........	92; 97	....	158	168					
164	**2-Methyl-6-nitroaniline** (3-Nitro-*o*-toluidine)...........	92	305d.	158	167	......		......		1-Naphthylthiourea, 171

*Derivative data given in order: m.p., crystal color, solvent from which crystallized.

TABLE XVIII. ORGANIC DERIVATIVES OF AMINES

1. Primary and secondary amines c) Solids (Listed in order of increasing m.p.)* (Continued)

No.	Name	Melting point, °C	Boiling point, °C	Acetamide	Benzamide	Benzene sulfon-amide	p-Toluene sulfon-amide	Phenyl thiourea	Picrate	Miscellaneous
165	3-Bromo-2-hydroxy-5-methylaniline (3-Amino-5-bromo-p-cresol)	93	....	N-mono: 129; di: 169	N-mono: 185; di: 166	N-mono: 157; di: 230	....	....	....	....
166	4-Chloro-2,6-dibromoaniline.......	93	....	226	194	....				....
167	2,2'-Diaminodiphenyl disulfide	93	....	156 (di)	....	....			141 (di)	....
168	1,18-Diaminooctadecane...........	93	....	....	150 (di)	....				Hydrochloride, >225
169	4,4'-Diaminodiphenylmethane	93	232⁹	236 (di); (228)	....	....				N,N'-Dibenzal, 130
170	3-Nitrophenylhydrazine	93, yel.	....	145; 150 (di)	151; 153 (di)	....				
171	7-Aminoquinoline	93–4 (anh.); 73 (hyd.)	....	167	189	....			....	Chloroplatinate, 225
172	2-Aminodibenzfuran	94	....	178; 83 (di)	201	....				
173	3-Aminoquinoline	94; 84	....	172; 167	....	....			210	....
174	7-Amino-2,4-dimethylquinoline	94–100	>300	212	....	....			215–7	
175	Skatole (3-Methylindole)	95	267	68	....	....			170–1	Hydrochloride, 167–8; N-Propionyl, 45
176	2-Chloro-4,6-dibromoaniline	95	....	227	192	....				
177	4-Hydroxybenzylamine	95	....			....				Hydrochloride, 195; N-Acetyl of Me. ether, 96
178	1-Amino-4,5-dimethyl-1,2,3-triazole.....................	95	....			....			124–5	Hydrochloride, 131; Chloroplatinate, 215
179	1-Amino-8-hydroxynaphthalene (8-Hydroxy-1-naphthylamine; 8-Amino-1-naphthol)	95–7	....	N-mono: 181; N,O-di: 118	N-mono: 193; N,O-di: 206	....	N-mono: 189	....	163–4	N-Formyl, 140–50
180	5-Amino-2-methylpyridine (5-Amino-α-picoline)...........	96	....	126	111	....			201	Dihydrochloride, 215–8
181	4,4'-Diamino-3,3'-dimethyl-diphenyl sulfide	96	....	di: 220	di: 233	....			186 (di)	Dihydrochloride, 248–9
182	6,6'-Diamino-3,3'-dimethyl-diphenylmethane	96	....	226 (di); 152 (tetra)	....	....			199	Dihydrochloride, 248–9
183	N-Ethyl-4-nitroaniline............	96	....	119	98	....	107			
184	2,4-Di-iodoaniline...............	96	....	141; 171	181	....				
185	1-Amino-8-nitronaphthalene (8-Nitro-1-naphthylamine).......	97, red	....	191	....	194				
186	3-Aminobenzyl alcohol	97	....	N-mono: 106–7	N-mono: 115; N,O-di: 113–4	....				
187	5-Bromo-2-methoxyaniline (4-Bromo-o-anisidine)...........	97–8	....	160	108	....				
188	2-Amino-4-methylpyridine (2-Amino-γ-picoline)..........	98	....	102–3	114; 182–3 (di)	....			227	
189	2-Aminophenacyl alcohol	98	....	N-mono: 141	N,O-di: 167	....				Phenylhydrazone, 198
190	1-Amino-4-chloronaphthalene (4-Chloro-1-naphthylamine)	98	....	186	....	....				
191	1,2-Diaminonaphthalene	98	....	234 (di)	291 (di)	1-mono: 215				
192	4-Amino-4'-methylbiphenyl.......	99	190¹⁸	221	....	....				Hydrochloride, 280–3
193	3-Aminoacetophenone............	99	....	128–9	....	....	130			Semicarbazone, 196
194	2,4-Diaminotoluene.............	99	....	N,N'-di: 224	224 (di)	2-mono: 138; 2,4-di: 192	4-mono: 160; 2,4-di: 192–3			....

*Derivative data given in order; m.p., crystal color, solvent from which crystallized.

No.	Name	Melting point, °C	Boiling point, °C	Acetamide	Benzamide	Benzene sulfonamide	p-Toluene sulfonamide	Phenyl thiourea	Picrate	Miscellaneous
195	4-Amino-3,2'-dimethylazobenzene . .	100, yel.	. . . .	185 (mono); 65 (75) (di), lgr.	. . . .	. . . .	. . . .	. . . . . .	. . . . . .	N-Chloroacetyl, 171–2
196	1,2-Diaminobenzene (o-Phenylene-diamine)	102	256–8	185 (di)	301 (di)	185	260 (di)	. . . . . .	208	. . . .
197	1-Amino-4-bromonaphthalene (4-Bromo-1-naphthylamine)	102; 95	. . . .	193	. . . .	. . . .	. . . .	. . . . . .	. . . . . .	N-Formyl, 172; 1,3,5-Tri-nitrobenzene add. comp., 196
198	2-Naphthyl 4-tolyl amine	103	. . . .	85	139	. . . .	. . . .	. . . . . .	. . . . . .	. . . .
199	3,4-Diaminobiphenyl . . . . . , ...	103	. . . .	3-mono: 211; 4-mono: 155; 3,4-di: 163	3-mono: 186; 4-mono: 221; 3,4-di: 248	. . . .	. . . .	. . . . . .	. . . . . .	. . . .
200	6,6'-Diamino-3,3'-dimethyl-diphenyl sulfide	103–4	. . . .	165 (di)	185 (di)	. . . .	. . . .	. . . . . .	179 (di)	. . . .
201	2-Amino-8-nitronaphthalene (8-Nitro-2-naphthylamine)	104, red	. . . .	196	162	. . . .	. . . .	. . . . . .	. . . . . .	. . . .
202	Piperazine.	104	140	mono: 52; di: 144	mono: 75; di: 196	282 (di)	173	. . . . . .	280	. . . .
203	4,4'-Diaminodibenzyl sulfide	104–5	. . . .	188 (di)	224 (di)	. . . .	. . . .	. . . . . .	. . . . . .	. . . .
204	3-Amino-4,4'-dimethylbiphenyl	104–5	. . . .	156–7	160–1	. . . .	. . . .	. . . . . .	. . . . . .	Hydrochloride, abt. 230
205	1,3-Diamino-4,6-dimethylbenzene (4,6-Diamino-m-xylene)	105	. . . .	1-mono: 165; di: 295	258–9 (di)	. . . .	221 (di)	. . . . . .	. . . . . .	N,N'-Diformyl, 182–3
206	2-Bromo-4-nitroaniline	105, yel.	. . . .	129	160	. . . .	. . . .	. . . . . .	. . . . . .	N-Me., 118
207	Triphenylmethylamine	105	. . . .	207–8	160–2	. . . .	. . . .	. . . . . .	. . . . . .	N-Benzyl, 110
208	4-Aminophenanthrene	105	. . . .	190	224	. . . .	. . . .	. . . . . .	216	. . . .
209	2-Aminobenzophenone	105–6, pa. yel.	. . . .	72; 89	80	. . . .	. . . .	. . . . . .	. . . . . .	Oxime (alkali-stable), 156; (acid stable), 127; N-Propionyl, 78
210	3-Amino-6-phenylpyridine	105–6	. . . .	148–9	201	. . . .	. . . .	. . . . . .	. . . . . .	. . . .
211	3-Amino-4-methylpyridine (3-Amino-γ-picoline)	106	260	84	81	. . . '. . .	. . . .	. . . . . .	179–80	Chloroplatinate, 227; Hydrochloride, 180
212	4-Bromophenylhydrazine	106	. . . .	. . . .	. . . .	. . . .	. . . .	. . . . . .	. . . . . .	Acetophenone deriv., 112
213	4-Aminoacetophenone.	106	294	167	205	128	203	. . . . . .	. . . . . .	Semicarbazone, 250; Oxime, 148
214	2,4-Diaminopyridine.	107	. . . .	. . . .	191–2 (di)	. . . .	. . . .	. . . . . .	. . . . . .	Chloroplatinate, 224
215	9-Phenanthrylmethylamine	107	. . . .	182–5	167	. . . .	. . . .	. . . . . .	241	N-Benzal, 104
216	2-Methyl-5-nitroaniline (4-Nitro-o-toluidine)	107	. . . .	151	. . . .	. . . .	172	. . . . . .	. . . . . .	N-Formyl, 178–9; N-4-Nitrobenzoyl, 214
217	2,5-Diaminopyridine	107–10	. . . .	290 (di)	230 (di)	. . . .	. . . .	. . . . . .	. . . . . .	. . . .
218	2-Naphthyl phenyl amine	108	. . . .	93	148; 136	. . . .	. . . .	. . . . . .	. . . . . .	. . . .
219	2-(4-Aminophenyl) ethyl alcohol	108	. . . .	105	O-mono: 59–60; N,O-di: 136	93	. . . .	. . . . . .	. . . . . .	Hydrochloride, 171
220	5-Aminoacenaphthene.	108	. . . .	238 (mono); 122 (di)	210; 199	. . . .	. . . .	. . . . . .	190–200	N-Formyl, 172; FeCl₃ → bl. col.
221	4,4'-Diamino-2,2'-dimethylbiphenyl (m-Tolidine)	108–9	. . . .	281 (275) (di)	. . . .	. . . .	. . . .	. . . . . .	225	N,N'-Dibenzal, 172–3
222	4-Aminoantipyrine (4-Amino-2,3-dimethyl-1-phenylpyrazolone-5). .	109, yel.	. . . .	199	. . . .	. . . .	. . . .	. . . . . .	144	. . . .
223	3-Amino-4-methylbenzophenone . . .	109	. . . .	108	. . . .	. . . .	. . . .	. . . . . .	. . . . . .	Hydrobromide, 130, dil. HBr
224	2-Aminobenzamide	109–11	. . . .	177	214–5	. . . .	. . . .	. . . . . .	. . . . . .	. . . .
225	1,4-Diamino-2-iodobenzene (2-Iodo-p-phenylenediamine).	110.5	. . . .	211	254	. . . .	. . . .	. . . . . .	. . . . . .	. . . .

*Derivative data given in order: m.p., crystal color, solvent from which crystallized.

TABLE XVIII. ORGANIC DERIVATIVES OF AMINES
1. Primary and secondary amines c) Solids (Listed in order of increasing m.p.)* (Continued)

No.	Name	Melting point, °C	Boiling point, °C	Acetamide	Benzamide	Benzene sulfon-amide	p-Toluene sulfon-amide	Phenyl thiourea	Picrate	Miscellaneous
226	5-Aminoquinoline...............	110	310	178	....	....	203–4	......	......	....
227	4-Amino-2-nitrostilbene...........	110–1, dk. red	....	192–3	....	....	....	......	......	Hydrochloride, 223
228	3-Aminocamphor................	110–5	....	121	141	....	....	......	191	Oxime, 145; N-Formyl, 87
229	4-Bromo-2-nitroaniline...........	111, or.	....	104	137–8	....	....	......	......	N-Me., 102; N-Et., 91
230	3'-Amino-4-methylbenzophenone...	111	....	139	....	....	....	......	......	Oxime, 146; Hydrochloride, 198
231	4-Amino-3-methylbenzophenone ...	112, pa. yel.	....	175	158	....	....	......	......	N-Propionyl, 128
232	2-Aminonaphthalene (β-Naphthylamine)	112	....	132	162	102	133	129	195	....
233	β-Aminopropiophenone (1-Amino-ethyl phenyl ketone)	112–4 (unst.)	....	90–1	104–5	....	....	......	164–5	Hydrochloride, 187; Chloroplatinate, 205
234	2-Hydroxybenzylaniline	113	....	93	....	....	....	......	......	Hydrochloride, 131; Chloroplatinate, 184
235	4-Ethoxy-2-nitroaniline (3-Nitro-p-phenetidine)	113; 108, red	....	104	....	72	94	......	......	....
236	5-Bromo-2-hydroxy-3-methyl-aniline.......................	113	....	N-mono: 119; di: 200	N-mono: 195	....	....	......	......	....
237	3-Nitroaniline	114	....	mono: 155; di: 76	155; 150 (di)	136	138	160	143	....
238	6-Aminoquinoline	114 (anh.)	....	mono: 138; di: 75	169	....	193	......	......	Methiodide, 199
239	cis-2,5-Dimethylpiperazine	114	162	....	152 (di)	....	146–7 (di)	......	......	N,N'-Dinitroso, 95
240	3-Amino-2-phenylquinoline	115–6	223³	mono: 124; di: 173	179–80	....	....	......	194–5	Methiodide, 238; Ethiodide, 202
241	5-Amino-3-methyl-1-phenylpyrazole	116	333	110	....	....	....	......	160–2	Hydrochloride, 199–200
242	4-Aminotriphenylcarbinol	116	....	176	....	....	....	......	......	N,N-Dimethyl, 92–3
243	5-Bromo-2-hydroxy-4-methyl-aniline.......................	116	....	N-mono: 199; di: 188	N-mono: 223	....	....	......	......	....
244	4-Chloro-2-nitroaniline	116–7, yel.	....	104	....	....	110	......	......	....
245	4-Methyl-2-nitroaniline (3-Nitro-p-toluidine)	117	....	99	148	102	146	......	......	Hydrochloride, 170–1
246	5-Amino-2-methylquinoline (5-Aminoquinaldine)	117–8 (anh.), grnsh.	....	205	....	....	....	......	......	N-Cinnamoyl, 257
247	trans-2,5-Dimethylpiperazine	118	162	....	228–9 (di)	....	225 (di)	......	......	N,N'-Dinitroso, 174
248	2,3,4,6-Tetrabromoaniline	118	....	228–9	....	....	....	......	......	1,3,5-Trinitrobenzene add. comp., 108
249	2-Methoxy-5-nitroaniline (4-Nitro-o-anisidine)	118, or.-red	....	175–6	160–1	....	128	......	......	N-Me., 87
250	4-Hydroxypyrazole.............	118	....	....	109 (di)	....	....	......	129	....
251	2-Amino-5,4'-dimethylazobenzene ..	118–9, or.-red	....	157	135	....	....	......	......	N-Carbethoxy, 94
252	1-Amino-5-nitronaphthalene (5-Nitro-1-naphthylamine).......	119, red	....	220	....	183	....	......	......	N-Formyl, 199
253	5-Hydroxy-2,4,6-tribromoaniline ...	119	....	O,N,N-tri: 136	....	....	146–7	......	......	....
254	1,4-Diaminonaphthalene..........	120	....	303 (di)	mono: 186; di: 280	....	mono: 187–8	......	......	....
255	1,9-Diaminofluorene	120	....	293 (di)	abt. 310 (di)	....	....	......	205	....
256	2-(ω-Aminoethyl)-indole (2-(2-Indolyl)-ethylamine).......	120	....	....	173–4	....	....	......	......	N-Benzal, 122
257	2,2'-Diamino-4,4'-dimethylbiphenyl	120	....	189 (di)	170 (di)	....	....	......	......	N,N'-Diformyl, 185

*Derivative data given in order: m.p., crystal color, solvent from which crystallized.

No.	Name	Melting point, °C	Boiling point, °C	Acetamide	Benzamide	Benzene sulfonamide	p-Toluene sulfonamide	Phenyl thiourea	Picrate	Miscellaneous
258	**2,6-Diaminopyridine**	121	. . . .	203 (*di*)	176 (*di*)	. . . .	. . . .	. . . .	240	. . . .
259	*cis*-**4,4′-Diaminostilbene**	121, pa. yel.	. . . .	172 (*di*)	253 (*di*)	. . . .	. . . .	. . . .	. . . . . .	. . . .
260	**4-Aminobenzhydrol**	121	. . . .	. . . .	145	. . . .	. . . .	. . . .	. . . . . .	Hydrochloride, 270–3
261	**3-Amino-6-hydroxyacetophenone** . . .	121; 110 yel.	. . . .	N-*mono*: 165; *di*: 174	. . . .	. . . .	. . . .	. . . .	. . . . . .	Oxime, 201; Et. eth., 60
262	**2-Aminotriphenylcarbinol**	121	. . . .	192	. . . .	. . . .	. . . .	. . . .	122–3	. . . .
263	**3-Hydroxyaniline** (3-Amino-phenol)	122	. . . .	*mono*: 148; *di*: 101	N-*mono*: 174 198; 204	. . . .	157	156	. . . . . .	. . . .
264	**2,4,6-Tribromoaniline**	122; 119	. . . .	232	. . . .	. . . .	. . . .	. . . .	. . . . . .	N-Formyl, 222
265	**4-Amino-2-hydroxyacetophenone** . . .	122–3	. . . .	N-*mono*: 91	. . . .	. . . .	. . . .	. . . .	. . . . . .	N,N-Di-Me., 120
266	**1-Aminoisoquinoline**	122–3	. . . .	. . . .	. . . .	. . . .	. . . .	. . . .	290–1	Hydrochloride, 233; Chloroplatinate, >300
267	**3,4,5-Tribromoaniline**	123	. . . .	255–6	210	. . . .	. . . .	. . . .	. . . . . .	. . . .
268	**4,4′-Diamino-2,2′-dimethyl-diphenylmethane**	123	. . . .	228 (*di*)	. . . .	. . . .	. . . .	. . . .	216	. . . .
269	*cis*-**2,2′-Diaminostilbene**	123; 107, red	. . . .	214–5 (*di*)	. . . .	. . . .	. . . .	. . . .	155–6	Hydrochloride, 230
270	**2,4-Dimethyl-5-nitroaniline**	123	. . . .	159	200	149	192	. . . .	. . . . . .	. . . .
271	**2-Amino-4-nitrobenzaldehyde**	124	. . . .	. . . .	. . . .	. . . .	. . . .	. . . .	. . . . . .	Oxime, 193; Semicarbazone, 390; Anil, 147, red
272	**4-Aminobenzophenone**	124	. . . .	153	152	. . . .	. . . .	. . . .	. . . . . .	N-Propionyl, 139
273	**7-Amino-8-hydroxyquinoline**	124, br.	. . . .	N-*mono*: 177	. . . .	. . . .	. . . .	. . . .	205	. . . .
274	**2-Amino-5-nitrobiphenyl**	125, yel.	. . . .	133	. . . .	. . . .	169	. . . .	. . . . . .	. . . .
275	**3-Hydroxy-4-methoxyaniline** (4-Aminoguaiacol)	125–7	. . . .	N-*mono*: 116–9	N,O-*di*: 162–4	. . . .	. . . .	. . . .	. . . . . .	. . . .
276	**2-Amino-1-nitronaphthalene** (1-Nitro-2-naphthylamine)	126, or.-yel.	. . . .	123	168	156	160	. . . .	. . . . . .	. . . .
277	**4-Aminoazobenzene**	126	. . . .	146	211	. . . .	. . . .	. . . .	. . . . . .	N-propionyl, 170
278	**Hydrazobenzene**	126–7	. . . .	*mono*: 159; *di*: 105	*mono*: 126, bz.; *di*: 162	. . . .	. . . .	. . . .	. . . . . .	. . . .
279	**5-Chloro-2-nitroaniline**	126.5, gold-yel.	. . . .	121	. . . .	. . . .	. . . .	. . . .	. . . . . .	N-Me., 107; N,N-Di-Me., 49
280	**Benzidine**	127	. . . .	317 (*di*); 199 (*mono*)	352 (*di*); 203–5 (*mono*)	232 (*di*)	243 (*di*)	. . . .	. . . . . .	. . . .
281	**2-Aminopyrimidine**	127–8	. . . .	. . . .	. . . .	. . . .	. . . .	. . . .	237–8	Chloroplatinate, 216; Hydrochloride, 196
282	**2-Amino-6-bromonaphthalene** (6-Bromo-2-naphthylamine)	128	. . . .	192	218	. . . .	. . . .	. . . .	. . . . . .	. . . .
283	**5-Bromo-2-hydroxyaniline** (2-Amino-4-bromophenol)	128; 88	. . . .	177–9	. . . .	. . . .	. . . .	. . . .	. . . . . .	Me. eth., 97–8
284	**5-Aminoisoquinoline**	128	. . . .	. . . .	. . . .	. . . .	. . . .	. . . .	>200	Methiodide, 228; Ethiodide, 216
285	**2-Aminovanillin** (2-Amino-4-hydroxy-3-methoxybenzalde-hyde)	128–9	. . . .	97	. . . .	. . . .	. . . .	. . . .	. . . . . .	Oxime, 151–2; Phenyl-hydrazone, 165
286	**2-Amino-3,7-dimethylnaphthalene** (3,7-Dimethyl-2-naphthylamine) . .	129; 134	. . . .	231	. . . .	. . . .	. . . .	. . . .	. . . . . .	Hydrochloride, 275
287	**4-Methoxy-2-nitroaniline** (3-Nitro-*p*-anisidine)	129; 123, dk. red	. . . .	117, yel.	140	. . . .	. . . .	. . . .	. . . . . .	N-4-Nitrobenzoyl, 204
288	**2-Aminotriphenylmethane**	129	. . . .	154–5	. . . .	. . . .	. . . .	. . . .	. . . . . .	N-Me., 130–2

*Derivative data given in order: m.p., crystal color, solvent from which crystallized.

No.	Name	Melting point, °C	Boiling point, °C	Acetamide	Benzamide	Benzene sulfon-amide	p-Toluene sulfon-amide	Phenyl thiourea	Picrate	Miscellaneous
289	2-Aminoquinoline	129	....	....	....	....	....	......	255–6	Methiodide, 247; Ethio-dide, 232; 1,3,5-Trinitro-benzene add. comp., 186, red.
290	4,4′-Diamino-3,3′-dimethyl-biphenyl (o-Tolidine)	129	....	mono: 103 (hyd.); di: 315; tetra: 211	198 (mono); 265 (di)	....				N,N′-Diformyl, 254; 1-Naphthylthiourea, 167; 3-Nitrophthalimide, 185
291	2,4-Diaminodiphenylamine........	130		188 (di)		2-mono: 213				
292	3-Aminocoumarin	130, yel.	....	201–2	173	....	....			
293	2-Methyl-4-nitroaniline (5-Nitro-o-toluidine)	130		202	....	158	174			1-Naphthylthiourea, 165
294	2-Amino-4-chloropyridine........	130–1	....	115–6	mono: 120; di: 165	....			243	....
295	4-Hydroxy-3-nitroaniline	131; 127, red	....	N-mono: 157–8						N-Me., 113; Et. eth., 40
296	4-Bromo-3-nitroaniline	131–2	....	146						N,N′-Di-Me., 72
297	2-Aminobenzothiazole...........	132; 129	....	186	186	....			256	
298	2-Amino-4-methylquinoline	133	320	....					abt. 250	N-Phenyl, 129; Chloro-platinate, 230
299	2,2′-Diaminobenzophenone	133, pa. yel.	....	168 (154) (di)					164	
300	2,2′-Diaminoazobenzene.........	134, red	....	271 (di)						
301	3,5-Dimethyl-2-hydroxyaniline	134–5	....	N-mono: 96	154 (O,N-di)	....	....			N-Formyl, 68
302	2-Hydroxy-5-methylaniline (4-Hydroxy-m-toluidine)........	135	....	N-mono: 160; N,O-di: 145	N-mono: 191; N,O-di: 190	....				N-Propionyl, 95–6; N,O-Dipropionyl, 91–2
303	3-Methyl-4-nitroaniline (6-Nitro-m-toluidine)	135		102	....	....				2-Naphthylthiourea, 159
304	2-Amino-3-methylnaphthalene (3-Methyl-2-naphthylamine).....	135	....	181–2	190	....				
305	2-Aminoacenaphthene...........	135		....	....				260, yel., eth.	Hydrochloride, 270
306	DL-2,2′-Diamino-6,6′-dimethyl-biphenyl	136	....	205 (di)	182 (di)	......	162–3 (di)	......		
307	1,4-Diamino-2-nitrobenzene (2-Nitro-p-phenylenediamine)	137, blk.	....	1-mono: 162; 4-mono: 189; di: 186	4-mono: 236	....				1,4-Di-4-nitrobenzoyl, >305
308	9-Aminophenanthrene	137–8; 104	....	207–8	199	....	....		190	
309	4,4′-Diamino-3,3′-dimethoxy-biphenyl (Dianisidine)	137–8	....	242 (di)	236 (di)	......	......		225 (di)	....
310	3,5-Dimethyl-4-hydroxyaniline (5-Amino-2-hydroxy-m-xylene) ..	137–8		160 (di)						Me. eth., 66
311	2,6-Dinitroaniline	138		197						
312	2-(4-Aminophenyl)-quinoline	138		mono: 189; di: 154	234					Methiodide, 220; N-Me., 82; N-Formyl, 160
313	2-Amino-3,6-dimethylnaphthalene (3,6-Dimethyl-2-naphthylamine) .	139	....	207	....					Hydrochloride, 283
314	2-Methoxy-4-nitroaniline (5-Nitro-o-anisidine)	139–40, pa. yel.	....	153–4	150	181	175; 170			
315	4-Aminopropiophenone..........	140		161	190	....	....			Oxime, 153
316	4-Amino-3-nitrobenzophenone	140; 135, yel.	....	....	154–5	......	......			N,N-Di-Me., 116; N-Et., 100

*Derivative data given in order: m.p., crystal color, solvent from which crystallized.

No.	Name	Melting point, °C	Boiling point, °C	Acetamide	Benzamide	Benzene sulfon- amide	p- Toluene sulfon- amide	Phenyl thiourea	Picrate	Miscellaneous
317	**2-Amino-4-methyldiphenylamine** . . .	140	. . . .	. . . .	161	. . . . . .	. . . . . .	. . . . . .	. . . . .	Hydrochloride, 200
318	**1,4-Diaminobenzene** (*p*-Phenylene- diamine)	140; 147	267	*mono*: 162–3; *di*: 304	*mono*: 128; *di*: 300	247 (*di*)	266 (*di*)	. . . . . .	. . . . .	3,5-Dinitrobenzoate, 178
319	**2-Hydroxy-5-nitroaniline**	142–3 (anh.); 80–90 (hyd.), or.	. . . .	 220	>200	. . . . . .	122 (O-)	. . . . . .	. . . . .	Me. eth., 118; Et. eth., 99
320	**2-Amino-4-nitrostilbene**	142–3, red	. . . . . .	N-*mono*: 220, yel., al.	. . . .	. . . . . .	. . . . . .	. . . . . .	. . . . .	Hydrochloride, 219
321	**5-Amino-8-hydroxyquinoline**	143	. . . . . .	N-*mono*: 221–2, al.; N,O- *di*: 206–7, al.	205 (O, N-*di*)	. . . . . .	. . . . . .	. . . . . .	. . . . .	Me. eth., 156, yel.
322	**1-Amino-2-nitronaphthalene** (2-Nitro-1-naphthylamine)	144, red- yel.	. . . . . .	199	175	. . . . . .	. . . . . .	. . . . . .	. . . . .	N-Et., 77, red
323	**2-Amino-5-nitronaphthalene** (5-Nitro-2-naphthylamine)	144, red	. . . . . .	186	182	. . . . . .	. . . . . .	. . . . . .	. . . . .	
324	**5-Hydroxy-2-methylaniline** (4-Hydroxy-*o*-toluidine)	144		N-*mono*: 178; N,O-*di*: 128	. . . .	183 (N-)	. . . . . .	. . . . . .	. . . . .	
325	**2,5-Dimethyl-4-nitroaniline** (5-Nitro-*p*-2-xylidine)	144–5	. . . . . .	168–9	. . . . . .	162	185	. . . . . .	. . . . .	
326	**4-Amino-4'-bromobiphenyl**	145		247	. . . . . .	. . . . . .	174	. . . . . .	. . . . .	
327	**1-Aminophenanthrene**	146		220	. . . . . .	. . . . . .	. . . . . .	. . . . . .	204	
328	**3,5-Dihydroxyaniline** (5-Amino- resorcinol)	146–52		119–21 (*tri*)	. . . . . .	. . . . . .	. . . . . .	. . . . . .	. . . . .	Di-Me. eth., 46; Picrate of Di-Me. eth., 167–70
329	**4-Amino-2-chlorobenzaldehyde**	147, yel.		152	. . . . . .	. . . . . .	. . . . . .	. . . . . .	. . . . .	N,N'-Di-Me., 82; N-Et., 101
330	**4-Nitroaniline**	147–8, yel.	. . . . . .	215	199, 203 (*di*)	139	191	. . . . . .	100	1-Naphthylthiourea, 187
331	**5-Amino-3-methyl-1,2,4-triazole**	148	. . . . . .	>270	285–90	. . . . . .	. . . . . .	. . . . . .	225	
332	**2,2'-Dihydroxyhydrazobenzene**	148	. . . .	. . . .	186 (*di*)	. . . . . .	. . . . . .	. . . . . .	. . . . .	Di-Me. eth., 102
333	**7-Amino-2-methylquinoline**	148 (anh.)	. . . . . .	. . . . . .	172–3	. . . . . .	. . . . . .	. . . . . .	213–4	. . . .
334	**4,4'-Diamino-2,2'-dimethyl azoxybenzene**	148, gold- yel.	. . . . . .	281 (*di*)	290	. . . . . .	. . . . . .	. . . . . .	. . . . .	
335	**4-Bromo-3-hydroxyaniline**	150		210–2	. . . .	. . . . . .	135–6 (O-)	. . . . . .	. . . . .	
336	**3-Amino-1-phenyl-1,2,4-triazole** . . .	150	. . . . . .	3-*mono*: 168; 3,3- *di*: 118	. . . . . .	. . . . . .	. . . . . .	. . . . . .	220	Hydrochloride, 187
337	**4-Aminochalcone** (4-Aminobenzal- acetophenone).	151, golden	. . . . . .	179	. . . . . .	. . . . . .	. . . . . .	. . . . . .	. . . . .	Oxime, 139
338	**4-Aminopyrimidine**	151–2	. . . . . .	202	. . . . . .	. . . . . .	. . . . . .	. . . . . .	226	N-Me., 74–5; N-Phenyl, 142–3
339	**Pentamethylaniline**	151–2	277–8	213	. . . . . .	. . . . . .	. . . . . .	. . . . . .	. . . . .	N-Formyl, 217; N-Me., 60; N,N-Di-Me., 53–4
340	**N-Methyl-4-nitroaniline**	152	. . . . . .	153	112	121	. . . . . .	. . . . . .	. . . . .	. . . .
341	**5-Bromo-2-nitroaniline**	152, red- yel.	. . . . . .	139	. . . . . .	. . . . . .	. . . . . .	. . . . . .	. . . . .	N-Me., 115; N-Et., 90
342	**3-Chloro-4-hydroxyaniline**	153	. . . . . .	N-*mono*: 144; *di*: 124	. . . . . .	. . . . . .	116–7 (O-)	. . . . . .	. . . . .	Me. eth., 62

*Derivative data given in order: m.p., crystal color, solvent from which crystallized.

No.	Name	Melting point, °C	Boiling point, °C	Acetamide	Benzamide	Benzene sulfon-amide	*p*-Toluene sulfon-amide	Phenyl thiourea	Picrate	Miscellaneous
343	**4-Chloro-2-hydroxyaniline**........	154	....	140 (*di*)	....	....	......	......	......	Hydrochloride, 226–7; Benzyl eth., 46–7; Me. eth., 52
344	**4-Aminoquinoline** (γ-Amino-quinoline)	154 (anh.)	....	178		....	......	......	274	Methiodide, 224; Ethio-dide, 232
345	**3-Aminobenzopyrazole**	154	....	177–8 (*di*)	182 (*di*)	....	......	......	......	....
346	**2,5-Dihydroxy-4-nitroaniline** (2-Amino-5-nitrohydroquinone)..	154, red	....	*mono*: 226; *di*: 183–4	....					Di-Me. eth., 158
347	**4-Hydroxy-2-nitroaniline**	154, red	....	N-*mono*: 218; N,O-*di*: 146						Me. eth., 129; 123
348	**3-Aminotriphenylcarbinol**	155	....	164		....	......	......	......	O,N,N-Trimethyl, 81
349	**L-2,2′-Diamino-6,6-dimethyl-biphenyl**	156	....	205 (*di*)	172 (*di*)					
350	**3,3′-Diaminoazobenzene**	156; 140, or.-yel.		272 (*di*)	286 (*di*)					
351	**5-Amino-1-phenyl-1,2,4-triazole** ...	157		....	....	....	......	......	175	Chloroplatinate, 197
352	**4-Nitrophenylhydrazine**	157, or.-red		205	193				119–20	....
353	**4-Aminopyridine** (γ-Amino-pyridine)	158	....	150 (anh.)	202				215–6	....
354	**4,4′-Diamino-3,3′-dimethyl-diphenylmethane**	158–9	....	224 (*di*); 119 (*tetra*)	215 (*di*)				192–3	....
355	**2-Amino-8-nitroquinoline**	159	....	211	166				257	....
356	**3-Amino-1,2,4-triazole**	159	....	....					231	Hydrochloride, 153
357	**2-Amino-4′-nitrobiphenyl**	159, or.-red		199	....		163			....
358	**3-Amino-2-methylquinoline**	159–60	270	165	161				235	N-Formyl, 163
359	**·1-Amino-4-hydroxy-3-nitro-naphthalene** (4-Hydroxy-3-nitro-1-naphthylamine)	160, ma-roon	....	250; 238	330					....
360	**2,4-Dihydroxy-5-nitroaniline**	160–1, red	....	N-*mono*: 261; *tri*: 176	....					Di-Me. eth., 136–7
361	**1,3-Diamino-4-nitrobenzene** (4-Nitro-*m*-phenylenediamine) ..	161; 157, yel.-red		1-*mono*: 200; 1,3-*di*: 246	222 (*di*)	....	169 (*di*)	......		N,N,N′,N′-Tetramethyl, 81
362	**3-Hydroxy-4-methylaniline** (2-Hydroxy-*p*-toluidine)	161	....	N-*mono*: 225; *di*: 132–3	....	....	111–2 (O-)	......		N-Chloroacetyl, 154–5
363	**2-Hydroxy-4-methylaniline** (3-Hydroxy-*p*-toluidine)	162		N-*mono*: 171	N-*mono*: 169; N,O-*di*: 162	....				....
364	**4-Aminoacetanilide**	162	....	304	....					
365	**3-Hydroxy-4-nitroaniline**	162; 158, or.-yel.		N-*mono*: 221; N,O-*di*: 149						Me. eth., 169; 161
366	**2,4-Dimethyl-6-hydroxyaniline**	163	....	*mono*: 186–7; *di*: 87–8	N-*mono*: 211; N,O-*di*: 148–9	....		......		Me. eth., 150
367	**2-Aminofluorenone**	163, vlt.-red	....	227	....					Hydrazone, 209; N-Car-bethoxy, 167–8
368	**1-(2-Aminoethyl)-4-hydroxybenzene** (4-(2-Aminoethyl)phenol; Tyramine)	164	....	N-*mono*: 162; *di*: 172					206	....

*Derivative data given in order: m.p., crystal color, solvent from which crystallized.

No.	Name	Melting point, °C	Boiling point, °C	Acetamide	Benzamide	Benzene sulfon- amide	p- Toluene sulfon- amide	Phenyl thiourea	Picrate	Miscellaneous
369	4-Aminophenacyl alcohol	165, yel.	. . . .	N-*mono*: 176–7; O-*mono*: 130; N,O-*di*: 162	188 (O-)	. . . .	. . . . . .	. . . . . .	. . . . . .	Phenylhydrazone, 199
370	3-Bromo-4-hydroxyaniline	165; 155, pa. br.	. . . .	N-*mono*: 157	N-*mono*: 184–5; *di*: 192	. . . .	. . . . . .	. . . . . .	. . . . . .	. . . .
371	2,7-Diaminonaphthalene.	166	. . . .	261 (*di*)	267 (*di*)	. . . .	. . . . . .	. . . . . .	210 (*di*)	. . . .
372	4-Amino-4'-iodobiphenyl	166–7; 159, yel.	. . . .	. . . .	. . . .	. . . .	. . . . . .	. . . . . .	. . . . . .	N-Benzal, 209; N-Pipero- nylidine, 150–1; Hydro- chloride, 295
373	4-Amino-3-nitrobiphenyl	167, red	. . . .	132	143	. . . .	. . . . . .	. . . . . .	. . . . . .	N-Me., 112
374	1,2-Diamino-4-hydroxybenzene (3,4-Diaminophenol)	167–8	. . . .	1,2-*di*: 205–7	1,2-*di*: 203; *tri*: 225	. . . .	. . . . . .	. . . . . .	. . . . . .	. . . .
375	4,4'-Diaminotriphenylcarbinol	168 s.h.; 175 r.h.	. . . .	4,4'-*di*: 267	. . . .	. . . .	. . . . . .	. . . . . .	. . . . . .	Me. eth., 162
376	4-Amino-2-phenylquinoline	168	. . . .	108, 117 (*di*)	182	. . . .	. . . . . .	. . . . . .	. . . . . .	Methiodide, 274; Ethio- dide, 244; N-Formyl, 275
377	2,6-Dinitro-4-methylaniline	168; 172	. . . .	195	186	. . . .	. . . . . .	. . . . . .	. . . . . .	. . . .
378	4-Amino-2-methylquinoline	168	333	. . . .	. . . .	. . . .	. . . . . .	. . . . . .	197–9	N-Phenyl, 150; Chloro- platinate, 223
379	6-Aminocoumarin	168–70, yel.	. . . .	216–7	173	159	. . . . . .	. . . . . .	. . . . . .	N-Formyl, 175–6
380	Picramic acid (3,5-Dinitro-2-hydroxyaniline)	169, red	. . . .	N-*mono*: 201; O-: 193	N-*mono*: 300; O-: 218	. . . .	191	. . . . . .	. . . . . .	. . . .
381	3,3'-Diaminobenzophenone	173, yel.	. . . .	226–7 (*di*)	. . . .	. . . .	. . . . . .	. . . . . .	. . . . . .	Oxime, 177–8
382	4,5-Dimethyl-2-hydroxyaniline	173–5	. . . .	N-*mono*: 191; N,O-*di*: 157	N-*mono*: 195–6; N,O-*di*: 152–3	. . . .	. . . . . .	. . . . . .	. . . . . .	. . . .
383	2-Hydroxyaniline	174	. . . .	*mono*: 209; 201; *di*: 124	N-*mono*: 165; O-: 185	141	146	. . . . . .	. . . . . .	. . . .
384	4-Hydroxy-3-methylaniline	175	. . . .	N-*mono*: 179	N,O-*di*: 194	. . . .	109–10 (O-)	. . . . . .	. . . . . .	. . . .
385	6-Amino-5,7-dimethylquinoline	175	>300	212	. . . .	. . . .	. . . . . .	. . . . . .	182	. . . .
386	4,4'-Diaminodiphenyl sulfone	175–6	. . . .	286 (*di*)	. . . .	. . . .	. . . . . .	. . . . . .	. . . . . .	N,N'-Di-Me., 179–80; N,N-Tetramethyl, 260
387	*trans*-2,2'-Diaminostilbene	176; 168, gold- yel.	. . . .	304 (*di*)	. . . .	. . . .	. . . . . .	. . . . . .	209	Hydrochloride, 267
388	6-Amino-5-nitroquinoline	178; 174, ycl.	. . . .	. . . .	. . . .	. . . .	168	. . . . . .	270	. . . .
389	6-Aminothymol	178–9	. . . .	N-*mono*: 74; *tri*: 91	N-*mono*: 178–9; N,O-*di*: 166–7	. . . .	. . . . . .	. . . . . .	. . . . . .	Oxid. → thymoquinone, 45.5
390	4-Hydroxy-2-methylaniline (5-Hydroxy-o-toluidine)	179	. . . .	N-*mono*: 130	92 (O-)	. . . .	. . . . . .	. . . . . .	. . . . . .	Hydrochloride, 215
391	2,4-Dinitroaniline	180; 188	. . . .	120	202; 220	. . . .	219	. . . . . .	. . . . . .	. . . .
392	1-Amino-4-chloroanthraquinone . . .	180, red	. . . .	203–4	. . . .	. . . .	. . . . . .	. . . . . .	. . . . . .	N,N-Di-Me., 172
393	2,6-Dimethyl-4-hydroxyaniline	181	. . . .	178–80	. . . .	. . . .	. . . . . .	. . . . . .	. . . . . .	N-Benzal, 104–5; N-Me., 43; N-Et., 161–2
394	4-Amino-2,6-dimethylpyrimidine . . .	183	. . . .	. . . .	. . . .	. . . .	. . . . . .	. . . . . .	214	N-Phenyl, 104
395	4-Aminobenzamide	183, yel.	. . . .	275	. . . .	. . . .	. . . . . .	. . . . . .	. . . . . .	N-Chloroacetyl, 241–3

*Derivative data given in order: m.p., crystal color, solvent from which crystallized.

No.	Name	Melting point, °C	Boiling point, °C	Acetamide	Benzamide	Benzene sulfon- amide	p- Toluene sulfon- amide	Phenyl thiourea	Picrate	Miscellaneous
396	4-Hydroxyaniline (4-Amino- phenol)	184; 186	. . . .	150 (di); 168 (mono)	N-mono: 216–7; N,O-di: 234	125	N-mono: 252–4; O-: 142	150	. . . . . .	3,5-Dinitrobenzoate, 178
397	1-Amino-3-hydroxynaphthalene (3-Hydroxy-1-naphthylamine) . . .	185	. . . .	N-mono: 179	309 (O,N- di)	. . . . . .	137 (O-)	. . . . . .	. . . .
398	5-Hydroxy-2-nitroaniline	185–6, or.	. . . .	N-mono: 266	. . . .					Me. eth., 131, br.; Et. eth., 105, yel.
399	6,6'-Diamino-3,3'-dimethyl triphenylmethane	185–6	430, part. d.	217 (di)	196 (di)					
400	4-Amino-2,6-dimethylpyridine	186	246	113	. . . .				194–5	Chloroplatinate, 250
401	4-Amino-4'-hydroxyazobenzene	186		N-mono: 203; di: 236–7						N,N-Di-Me., 203
402	4-Amino-4'-methylbenzophenone . . .	186–7	. . . .	155	. . . .					Phenylhydrazone, 163
403	6-Amino-2-methylquinoline	187–8	. . . .	168–9	. . . .					N-Cinnamoyl, 257
404	4-Amino-2,6-diethyl-5-methyl- pyrimidine (Cyanethine)	189	280 d.	59	. . . .					
405	2,4,6-Trinitroaniline (Picramide). .	190	. . . .	230	196	211				
406	1-Amino-6-hydroxynaphthalene (6-Hydroxy-1-naphthylamine) . . .	190; 185	. . . .	N-mono: 218; N,O-di: 187	N-mono: 152; N,O-di: 223	. . . . . .			170	
407	4,4'-Diaminoazoxybenzene	190, yel.	. . . .	275	. . . .					Sn + HCl → 1,4-Diamino- benzene, 147
408	4-Amino-3-nitrobenzaldehyde	191, yel.	. . . .	155	. . . .					Phenylhydrazone, 202; Oxime, 207; 4-Nitro- phenylhydrazone, 270–2
409	2-Amino-1,5-dinitronaphthalene (1,5-Dinitro-2-naphthylamine) . . .	191	. . . .	201	. . . .		182			
410	DL-2,2'-Diamino-1,1'-dinaphthyl . .	193	. . . .	235–6 (di)	235 (di)				185	
411	8-Amino-6-nitroquinoline	194, red	. . . .	224	. . . .					Chloroplatinate, 180; Methiodide, 176
412	1-Amino-4-nitronaphthalene (4- Nitro-1-naphthylamine)	195	. . . .	190	224	173; 158	185		. . . . . .	
413	2-Amino-4,6-dimethylpyrimidine . . .	197	. . . .	. . . .	. . . .				230	Hydrochloride, 181; Chloroplatinate, 225; N-Me., 98
414	4,6-Diamino-2-methylquinoline	197	. . . .	6-mono: 250	. . . .				. . . . . .	6-N-Cinnamoyl, 253–4; 4-N-Et., 195; 6-N-Et., 232
415	1,2-Diamino-4-nitrobenzene (4- Nitro-o-phenylenediamine)	198, red	. . . .	1-mono: 205; 2-mono: 195	235 (di)	. . . . . .			.	N,N'-Di-Me., 172
416	2,4-Dinitrophenylhydrazine	199–200	. . . .	197–8	206–7				. . . . . .	
417	2-Hydroxy-5-methyl-4-nitroaniline .	200, yel.	. . . .	N-mono: 242	. . . .					Me. eth., 132; N-Acetyl of Me. eth., 156
418	4-Amino-3-nitropyridine	200, yel.	. . . .						197–8	Hydrochloride, 258–9; Chloroplatinate, 256
419	4-Amino-4'-nitrobiphenyl	200, red	. . . .	264; 240, yel.	. . . .	174, yel.				
420	2-Amino-5-nitrobenzaldehyde	200, yel.	. . . .	160–1	. . . .		181–2			Oxime, 203; N,N-Di-Me. 105, yel.
421	2-Amino-7-hydroxynaphthalene (7-Hydroxy-2-naphthylamine) . . .	201	. . . .	N-mono: 232; N,O-di: 156	N-mono: 243–6; N,O-di: 181	. . . . . .				
422	2-Amino-1-bromo-3-methylanthra- quinone	202; 204	. . . .	. . . .	di: 243–4, pa. yel., al.					

*Derivative data given in order: m.p., crystal color, solvent from which crystallized.

No.	Name	Melting point, °C	Boiling point, °C	Acetamide	Benzamide	Benzene sulfonamide	p-Toluene sulfonamide	Phenyl thiourea	Picrate	Miscellaneous
423	4,4'-Diamino-1,1'-dinaphthyl......	202	....	363 (di)	320 (di)	....	....	....	147	....
424	4,4',4''-Triaminotriphenylmethane .	203	....	201 (tri)	....	....	....	....	....	1,3,5-Trinitrobenzene add. comp., 140, blk.
425	Isatin	204	....	141	....	....	....	....	....	Oxime, 201–2
426	3-Amino-5-phenylacridine	204	....	256	246	....	....	....	....	....
427	2-Amino-1,4-naphthoquinone......	204–5, or.-red	....	202	....	....	....	....	....	N-Phenyl, 191
428	1-Amino-2-methylanthraquinone ...	205, red	....	mono: 176–7; di: 203–6	....	....	218	....	....	....
429	4,4',4''-Triaminotriphenylcarbinol (Pararosaniline)	205	....	192 (tri)	....	....	....	....	....	Me. eth., 135
430	1-Amino-7-hydroxynaphthalene (7-Hydroxy-1-naphthylamine) ...	205–7	....	N-mono: 165	N-mono: 208–9; N,O-di: 208	....	....	....	....	....
431	4,6-Diaminoisophthaladehyde	208	....	270 (mono), 280 (di)	....	....	....	....	....	Dioxime, 220; Diphenyl-hydrazone, 337
432	N-4-Hydroxybenzylaniline........	208	....	....	....	....	....	....	....	Me. eth., 65; Et. eth., 65
433	6-Aminobenzopyrazole	210	....	248 (6-N-), 184–5 (di)	....	....	....	....	....	Dihydrochloride, 230
434	4,4'-Diamino-2,5,2',5'-tetra-methyltriphenylmethane	210	....	217 (di)	250 (di)	....	....	....	....	....
435	3-Indolylpyruvic acid	211, grey	....	....	....	....	....	....	....	4-Nitrophenylhydrazone, 153–4; Oxime, abt. 175
436	2-Amino-6-hydroxynaphthalene (6-Hydroxy-2-naphthylamine) ...	212–3	....	....	N,O-di: 228–30	....	....	....	....	Me. eth., 78; Et. eth., 91
437	5-Amino-1,4-dihydroxyanthra-quinone (5-Aminoquinizarin)	212–3, br.-red	....	....	....	....	....	....	....	N-Phenyl, 223; Di-Me. eth., 242–3
438	2-Amino-4,5-dimethylpyrimidine ...	214–5	....	....	....	....	....	....	250	Chloroplatinate, 227
439	5-Bromo-4-hydroxy-2-methyl-aniline	215; 205	....	171–2 (di)	229 (di)	....	....	....	....	....
440	4-Amino-4'-nitroazobenzene	216; 205	....	245	....	....	....	....	....	N-Me., 206–7, bl.
441	2-Hydroxy-6-nitroaniline	216, red	....	N-mono: 172	....	....	136 (O-)	....	....	Me. eth., 76
442	3,4-Diaminopyridine............	218–9	....	....	222–3 (di)	....	....	....	235–7	Chloroplatinate, 231
443	1-Amino-5-chloroanthraquinone ...	219, red	....	219	218	....	....	....	....	....
444	3,6-Dimethylcarbazole	219	....	129	....	....	....	....	192	N-Nitroso, 106
445	3-Aminothioxanthone	221–2, yel.-br.	....	236–7	....	....	....	....	....	Hydrochloride, 230
446	2-Amino-10-hydroxyphenanthrene .	221	....	182 (O, N-di)	225 (O, N-di)	....	....	....	....	....
447	5-Amino-4-nitroacenaphthene	222, red	....	252	233	....	....	....	....	N-Formyl, 227
448	5-Chloro-4-hydroxy-2-methyl-aniline	223–5; 204–5	....	162 (di)	220 (di)	....	....	....	....	....
449	2,6-Dimethylcarbazole	224	....	....	....	....	....	....	162	N-Nitroso, 113
450	2-Amino-1,8-dinitronaphthalene (1,8-Dinitro-2-naphthylamine) ...	226	....	238	....	....	221	....	....	....
451	trans-4,4'-Diaminostilbene	231, yel.	....	353 (di)	352 (di)	....	....	....	....	....
452	2-Amino-3-hydroxynaphthalene (3-Hydroxy-2-naphthylamine) ...	234	....	188 (O,N-di)	N-mono: 233–5	....	....	....	....	....
453	1-Amino-2,4-dinitronaphthalene (2,4-Dinitro-1-naphthylamine) ...	242	....	259	252	....	166	....	....	....
454	2,5-Dimethyl-4-hydroxyaniline	242	....	177–9	....	....	....	....	....	Et. eth., 69–70
455	1-Amino-3-bromoanthraquinone ...	243, red	....	214	....	....	227	....	....	....
456	4,4'-Diaminobenzophenone	244	....	237 (di)	....	....	....	....	....	Phenylhydrazone, 240
457	Carbazole	246	....	69	98	....	....	....	185	....
458	1-Amino-2-hydroxyanthraquinone ..	250, br.	....	N-mono: 170	....	....	....	....	....	Et. eth., 182, red

*Derivative data given in order: m.p., crystal color, solvent from which crystallized.

No.	Name	Melting point, °C	Boiling point, °C	Acetamide	Benzamide	Benzene sulfon-amide	p-Toluene sulfon-amide	Phenyl thiourea	Picrate	Miscellaneous
459	1-Aminoanthraquinone	252; 243	. . . .	218	255	. . . .	228–9	. . . . . .	. . . . . .	. . . .
460	3-Aminocarbazole	254	. . . .	3-*mono*: 217; *di*: 200; *tri*: 175	3-*mono*: 250	. . . .		. . . . . .	. . . . . .	. . . .
461	2,7-Diaminocarbazole	260	. . . .	320 (*di*)	. . . .	. . . .		. . . . . .	. . . . . .	N,N′-Dibenzal, 290
462	1,8-Diaminoanthraquinone	262, red	. . . .	284 (*di*)	324 (*di*)	. . . .		. . . . . .	. . . . . .	. . . .
463	1,4-Diaminoanthraquinone	268, vlt.	. . . .	271 (*di*)	284 (*di*), 280 (*mono*)			. . . . . .	. . . . . .	
464	2-Amino-3-nitrofluorenone	269, vlt.	. . . .	245–6	. . . .	. . . .			. . . . . .	N-Carbethoxy, 204
465	1,1′-Diamino-2,2′-dinaphthyl	281	. . . .	230 (*di*)	278 (*di*)	. . . .		. . . . . .	. . . . . .	. . . .
466	1,7-Diaminoanthraquinone	290, red	. . . .	283 (*di*)	325 (*di*)	. . . .		. . . . . .	. . . . . .	. . . .
467	2,7-Diaminofluorenone	290, vlt.	. . . .	222 (*di*)	. . . .	. . . .			230 (*di*)	Oxime, 255; Phenylhydra-zone, 230; 4-Nitrophenyl-hydrazone, 280
468	1,6-Diaminoanthraquinone	292, red	. . . .	295 (*di*)	275 (*di*)	. . . .		. . . . . .	. . . . . .	
469	1-Amino-5-nitroanthraquinone	293, red	. . . .	275	237	. . . .		. . . . . .	. . . . . .	N-Me., 250–2, vlt-.blk; N-Et., 238
470	1-Amino-4-nitroanthraquinone	296, yel.-red	. . . .	256–8	. . . .	. . . .		. . . . . .	. . . . . .	N-Me., 250
471	5,8-Diaminoquinizarin (1,4-Diamino-5,8-dihydroxyanthra-quinone)	>300, br.-vlt.	. . . .	5,8-*di*: 284	. . . .	5,8-*di*: 275			. . . . . .	
472	2-Aminoanthraquinone	305–8; 302	. . . .	*mono*: 262; *di*: 258	228	271	304		. . . . . .	
473	2-Amino-3-bromoanthraquinone . . .	307, or.-yel.	. . . .	259; 217	279	. . . .		. . . . . .	. . . . . .	N-Benzal, 174
474	2-Aminoquinizarin (2-Amino-1,4-dihydroxyanthraquinone)	313–4, grn.-yel.	. . . .	. . . .	. . . .	. . . .		. . . . . .	. . . . . .	N-Phenyl, 255–6; N-4-Tolyl, 220
475	1,5-Diaminoanthraquinone	319, red	. . . .	317 (*di*)	>350 (*di*)	. . . .		. . . . . .	. . . . . .	. . . .
476	2,7-Diaminoanthraquinone	>330, or.	. . . .	>350	300 (*di*)	. . . .		. . . . . .	. . . . . .	. . . .
477	2,5-Dianilino-1,4-benzoquinone	345, red-br.	. . . .	. . . .	. . . .	. . . .		. . . . . .	. . . . . .	Anil, 203; Dianil, 240, red
478	2,8-Diaminoacridone	>350	. . . .	>350 (*di*)	>250 (*di*)	. . . .		. . . . . .	. . . . . .	N,N′-Dibenzal, 370

*Derivative data given in order: m.p., crystal color, solvent from which crystallized.

TABLE XVIII. ORGANIC DERIVATIVES OF AMINES
2. Tertiary amines a) Liquids 1) (Listed in order of increasing atmospheric b.p.)*

No.	Name	Boiling point, °C	Melting point, °C	n_D	Density g/ml	Methyl p-toluene sulfonate	Methiodide	Picrate	Chloro-platinate	Miscellaneous
1	**Trimethylamine**	3	......	....	0.6709^0_4	....	230	216; 225	....	p-Toluenesulfonate salt, 162
2	**Dimethyl ethyl amine**	37.5	......	....				193	....	Hydrochloride, 221
3	**N-Methylpyrrolidine**	78–80	......	....				221	233	....
4	**Triethylamine**	89	.....	1.400^{20}	0.7255^{25}_4	....		173	....	2,4-Dinitrobenzoate salt, 81–3; β-Resorcylic acid salt, 120
5	**1,2-Dimethylpyrrolidine**	96		1.4252^{20}	0.7994^{20}_4			235	223	
6	**1,3-Dimethylpyrrolidine**	96–7			0.792^{15}_4			dimorphous, 181 or 110–5	58–9	HgCl₂ add. comp., 200
7	**Pyridine**	116		1.5092^{21}	0.978^{25}_4	139	117	167	241; 262–4	p-Toluenesulfonate salt, 160; Ethiodide, 91
8	**1,2,5-Trimethylpyrrolidine**	116		$1.4335^{9,2}_\alpha$	0.815^9_4	....	310	163		
9	**2-Dimethylaminodiethyl ether**	121		1.406^{20}	0.806^{20}		160–5	119–21		
10	**Dimethylaminoacetone**	123						176, s. h.		Oxime, 99
11	**1-Methylpyrazole**	127		1.4787^{11}_{He}	0.993^{14}_4		190	148	196–8	
12	**N-Ethylpiperidine**	128		1.4416^{20}_α	0.8237^{20}_4			167.5	202	
13	**2-Methylpyridine (α-Picoline)**	129		1.503^{17}	0.9497^{15}_4	150	230	169	216; 195	p-Toluenesulfonate salt, 161; Ethiodide, 123
14	**β-Dimethylaminoethyl alcohol** (2-Dimethylaminoethyl alcohol)	135		1.43^{20}	0.8866^{20}_4			96–7		
15	**1,3-Dimethylpyrazole**	136		1.467^{15}_α	0.9628^{15}_4		256	138		
16	**2-Methylpyrazine**	136–7			1.029^{20}_4		129–30	133		
17	**4-Methylpyrimidine**	141–2			1.031^{16}_{16}			131–4		HgCl₂ double salt, 198
18	**2,6-Dimethylpyridine (2,6-Lutidine)**	142–3					233	168	208	
19	**3-Methylpyridine (β-Picoline)**	143		1.504^{24}	0.9515^{25}_4			150	202	Styphnate, 154; Oxid. → nicotinic acid, 228
20	**4-Methylpyridine (γ-Picoline)**	143		1.506^{19}	0.957^{15}_4	....		167	231	β-Resorcylic acid salt, 125
21	**4-Chloropyridine**	147–8							202	....
22	**2-Ethylpyridine**	149			0.9371^{17}			187–9	165–7	....
23	**3-Chloropyridine**	149						135	168	
24	**Tri-n-propylamine**	156.5		1.4176^{20}	0.753^{20}_4		207–8	116	....	Ethiodide, 238
25	**2,4-Dimethylpyridine (2,4-Lutidine)**	157; 159		1.503^{14}	0.9273^{25}_4			183	216	β-Resorcylic acid salt, 143
26	**2,5-Dimethylpyridine (2,5-Lutidine)**	160						169	192–4	
27	**1,3,4-Trimethylpyrazole**	160		1.4866^{18}_{He}	0.956^{18}_4			164		
28	**3-Ethylpyridine**	162–4			0.954^0			128–30	208–9; 196	
29	**β-Diethylaminoethyl alcohol (2-Diethylaminoethyl alcohol)**	163		1.440^{25}	0.8601^{25}_{25}					4-Nitrophenylurethane, 60
30	**Tropidine (2-Tropene)**	163		1.4884^{19}_α	0.953^{20}_4		abt. 300	285	217	
31	**2,3-Dimethylpyridine (2,3-Lutidine)**	164						188	195	
32	**3,4-Dimethylpyridine (3,4-Lutidine)**	164						163	205	
33	**4-Ethylpyridine**	164–5			0.9417^{20}			168	213	
34	**2,4,5-Triethylpyridine (2,4,5-Collidine)**	165–8						128–31	205	
35	**1,4-Bis-dimethylaminobutane**	167						199		
36	**Tropane**	167			0.931^{20}_4		>300	281	230	
37	**1-Diethylaminoisopropyl alcohol**	167–72			0.8511^{20}_0			89	....	
38	**2-Chloropyridine**	170; 166			1.205^{15}	120				
39	**3-Bromopyridine**	170		1.5694^{20}	1.645^0_4	156	165		175	
40	**3,5-Dimethylpyridine (3,5-Lutidine)**	170–1						245	255	

*Derivative data given in order: m.p., crystal color, solvent from which crystallized.

No.	Name	Boiling point, °C	Melting point, °C	n_D	Density g/ml	Methyl p-toluene sulfonate	Methio-dide	Picrate	Chloro-platinate	Miscellaneous
41	**2,4,6-Trimethylpyridine** (2,4,6-Collidine)	172	. . . . .		0.917²⁰	. . . .	. . . .	156	223	. . . .
42	**1,4,5-Triethylpyrazole**	176–7	. . . . .	1.4848^{18}_{He}	0.9685^{18}_4	. . . .		175–6	. . . .	
43	**2,3,6-Trimethylpyridine** (2,3,6-Collidine)	176–8	. . . . .			. . . .		146	250–2	
44	**Benzyl dimethyl amine**	181						93	192	Picrolonate, 151
45	**2,3,5-Trimethylpyridine** (2,3,5-Collidine)	184	. . . . . .					183; 179	227–8	. . . .
46	**N,N,2-Trimethylaniline** (N,N-Dimethyl o-toluidine)	185	. . . . .	1.515²⁰	0.9286^{20}_4	. . . .		122; 116	. . . .	1,3,5-Trinitrobenzene add. comp., 113
47	**2,6-Dimethyl-4-ethylpyridine**	186			0.916^{14}_{14}			119–20	210	
48	**2,4-Diethylpyridine** . . . . : . .	187–8			0.9338⁰			98–100	170–1	
49	**3-Diethylaminopropyl alcohol**	190	. . . . .		. . . . .		175			
50	**Methyl 2-pyridyl ketone**	192					161	131	220	Oxime, 121; Phenylhy-drazone, 155; Ethio-dide, 205
51	**2,3,4-Trimethylpyridine** (2,3,4-Collidine)	192–3	. . . . .		0.912¹⁵			163–4	259	. . . .
52	**N,N-Dimethylaniline**	193	2–2.5	1.5582²⁰	0.9557^{20}_4	161	228; 220	163	173	p-Toluenesulfonate salt, 133; 3,5-Dinitroben-zoate salt, 115
53	**2-Bromopyridine**	194	. . . . .	1.657¹⁵		127				
54	**3-Ethyl-4-methylpyridine**	195–6			0.9656⁰			148–50	234; 205	
55	**3,5-Dimethyl-2-ethylpyridine**	198						152	189	
56	**N,N,2,6-Tetramethylaniline** (N,N-Dimethyl-m-2-xylidine; 2-Dimethylamino-m-xylene)	199–200	. . . . .	1.513²⁰	0.912^{20}_4					1,3,5-Trinitrobenzene add. comp., 108
57	**N-Ethyl-N-methylaniline**	201	. . . . .		0.919^{55}_4	. . . .	125	134–5	. . . .	Hydrochloride, 114
58	**N,N,2,5-Tetramethyl-aniline** (N,N-Dimethyl-p-2-xylidine; 2-Dimethylamino-p-xylene)	204	. . . . .					158	196	
59	**N,N,2,4-Tetramethyl-aniline** (N,N-Dimethyl-m-4-xylidine; 4-Dimethylamino-m-xylene)	205	. . . . .	1.5201²⁰	0.9164^{20}_4	. . . .		123–4	219	1,3,5-Trinitrobenzene add. comp., 114
60	**N,N-Diethyl-2-methylaniline** (N,N-Diethyl-o-toluidine)	206; 210					224	180	. . . .	
61	**2-Chloro-N,N-dimethylaniline**	207					152	132		
62	**N,N,4-Trimethylaniline** (N,N-Dimethyl-p-toluidine)	210	. . . . .	1.536²⁰	0.929^{20}_4	85	219	129		1,3,5-Trinitrobenzene add. comp., 124, vlt.
63	**3,4-Diethylpyridine**	211						139	221	. . . .
64	**Tri-n-butylamine**	211; 216			0.778^{20}_{20}		180	106	. . . .	β-Resorcylic acid salt, 121
65	**N,N,3-Trimethylaniline** (N,N-Dimethyl-m-toluidine)	212		1.5492²⁰	0.941^{20}_4		177			
66	**Methyl 4-pyridyl ketone**	212–4						130	205	Oxime, 142; Phenyl-hydrazone, 150; HgCl₂ double salt, 183–4
67	**N,N-Diethylaniline**	218; 216			0.9351^{20}_4	. . . .	102	142	. . . .	
68	**Methyl 3-pyridyl ketone**	220								Oxime, 133; Phenyl-hydrazone, 137; HgCl₂ double salt, 158
69	**N,N-Diethyl-4-methylaniline** (N,N-Diethyl-p-toluidine)	229			0.924¹⁶	. . . .	184	. . . .		
70	**2,3,4,5-Tetramethylpyridine**	232–4	. . . . .					170–2	210	. . . .
71	**Quinoline**	239	− 15.6	1.6268²⁰	1.0929^{20}_4	126	133	203	227; 218	p-Toluenesulfonate salt, 155; Ethiodide, 159; Styphnate, 207–8
72	**Isoquinoline**	243	26; 24	1.615²⁰; 1.622²⁵	1.0986^{20}_4	163	159	222	263	Ethiodide, 148

*Derivative data given in order: m.p., crystal color, solvent from which crystallized.

TABLE XVIII. ORGANIC DERIVATIVES OF AMINES
2. Tertiary amines a) Liquids 1) (Listed in order of increasing atmospheric b.p.)* (Continued)

No.	Name	Boiling point, °C	Melting point, °C	n_D	Density g/ml	Methyl p-toluene sulfonate	Methiodide	Picrate	Chloro-platinate	Miscellaneous
73	DL-Nicotine (DL-1-Methyl-2-(3-pyridyl)-pyrrolidine)	243	......	......	1.008_4^{20}	....	219	218	abt. 280	....
74	2-Dimethylaminobenzaldehyde	244, yel.	......	......	......	....	164	....	205–6	Oxime, 87; p-Nitrophenylhydrazone, 191
75	Tri-isoamylamine	245; 237	......	......	0.786_4^{20}	....	......	125	....	
76	N,N-Dipropylaniline	245	......	......	0.9104^{20}	....	156	261	....	
77	2-Ethylquinoline (α-Ethyl-quinoline)	245–6	......	1.598^{23}	1.050^{17}	....	180	148	188	
78	2-Methylquinoxaline	245–7	......	......	......	....	215	>250		
79	1-Methylindole	247; 239	......	......	1.0707^{0}	....	150			
80	2-Methylquinoline (Quinaldine)	247	......	1.6126^{20}	1.0585_4^{20}	161; 134	195	191; 195	228	β-Resorcylic acid salt, 145; Ethiodide, 233
81	8-Methylquinoline	248	......	1.616^{20}	1.072_4^{21}	....	200			
82	L-Nicotine (L-1-Methyl-2-(3-pyridyl)-pyrrolidine)	248	......	1.528^{20}	1.0097_4^{20}	....	218	275		$[\alpha]_D^{20}$: − 167–8
83	1-Ethylisoquinoline	250	......	......	......	....	207–10	200		....
84	2,4-Dimethyl-5,6,7,8-tetrahydro-quinoline	250	20	1.5415^{20}	1.0043_4^{20}	....	157	144	....	Hydrochloride, 195
86	N-Methyl-2-pyridone	255	......	......	......	....	145	141		Styphnate, 162
87	4,6-Dimethylquinoline	255–6; 280	......	......	......	....	236–7	238		....
88	3-Ethylisoquinoline	257	......	......	......	....	171–2	180		....
89	Tri-n-amylamine (Tri-n-pentyl-amine)	257; 245	......	......	......	80				
90	3-Methylquinoline (β-Methyl-quinoline)	257–9	16–7	1.6171^{20}	1.0673_4^{20}	....	221	187	249	Ethiodide, 220
91	6-Methylquinoline	258	......	1.6157^{20}	1.0654_4^{20}	154	219; 216	229		
92	3-Chloroquinoline (β-Chloro-quinoline)	258–60	......	......	......	....	276 subl.	182	>300	
93	3-Bromo-N,N-dimethylaniline	259	11	......	......	....	135			
94	5-Methylquinoline	260	......	......	......	....	105	210–3		
95	4-Methylquinoline (γ-Methyl-quinoline)	261–3	......	......	1.0862^{20}	....	173–4	210–1	226–30	Ethiodide, 141–3
96	2,4-Dimethylquinoline	264–5	......	......	1.061^{15}	....	263–5	193–4	229	Ethiodide, 214
97	2-Phenylpyridine	268–9	......	......	......	....	175	204		
98	6,8-Dimethylquinoline	269	......	......	1.066^{4}	....	288–9	235		
99	N,N-Di-n-butylaniline	271	......	......	......	180	125			
100	4-Ethylquinoline (γ-Ethyl-quinoline)	272–4	......	......	......	....	149	178–80	204	....
101	N,N-Dimethyl-1-aminonaphthalene (N,N-Dimethyl-α-naphthyl-amine)	273	......	1.624^{15}	1.0446_{15}^{15}	....		145		1,3,5-Trinitrobenzene add. comp., 105–7
102	5,8-Dimethylquinoline	273–5	4–5	......	1.07^{21}	....		198	234	
103	3-Bromoquinoline (β-Bromo-quinoline)	274–6	12	......	......	....		190		Oxalate, 107
104	3,5-Dimethyl-1-phenylpyrazole	275	......	......	......	....	190	103	186	....
105	6-Bromoquinoline	278	19; 24	......	......	....	278	217		....
106	2,4,7-Trimethylquinoline	280–1	......	1.5973^{24}	1.0337^{20}	....	322	232	272	....
107	4,7-Dimethylquinoline	283	......	......	......	....	224	227		....
108	3,4-Dimethyl-1-phenylpyrazole	285	......	1.5724^{20}	1.0574_4^{20}	....	122.5	180		....
109	8-Chloroquinoline	288	......	......	......	....	165	....	235	....
110	2,3'-Bipyridyl	289; 298	......	......	......	....		150; di: 165–8		
111	8-Bromoquinoline	302–4	......	......	......	....	281		230	
112	6-Methoxyquinoline	305d.	20; 28	......	......	....	236	305		
113	N-Benzyl-N-methylaniline	306	......	1.601^{30}	1.0422_{26}^{26}	....	164	127	....	

*Derivative data given in order: m.p., crystal color, solvent from which crystallized.

TABLE XVIII. ORGANIC DERIVATIVES OF AMINES

2. Tertiary amines a) Liquids (b.p. at reduced pressure only)
2) (Listed in order of increasing m.p. of the corresponding picrate derivative)*

No.	Name	Boiling point, °C	Melting point, °C	n_D	Density g/ml	Methyl p-toluene sulfonate	Methio-dide	Picrate	Chloro-platinate	Miscellaneous
1	N,N-Dimethyl-2-nitroaniline	151–3[30-3], or.-yel.	......	1.6102	....	....	......	102–3	....	Hydrochloride, 174; 1,3,5-Trinitrobenzene add. comp., 112
2	2,6-Diethylpyridine	71–3[17]	......	....	....	....	142	115	211–2	....
3	2-Iodopyridine (α-Iodopyridine)	93[13]	......	1.6366[20]	1.9735_0^{20}	....	207	120	210	....
4	1,3-Dimethyl-1,2,3,4-tetrahydroquinoline	130–2[17]	......	....	....	....	204	131	....	....
5	β,β-Diethylphenylhydrazine	110–2[14]	......	....	....	....	......	131	....	Reduces Fehling's and Tollen's reagent; Zn + AcOH → aniline, b.p. 184 + diethylamine, b.p. 56
6	3-Dimethylaminobenzaldehyde	138[9], yel.	......	....	....	....	185–6	147	168 r. h.	Oxime, 75–6; Semicarbazone, 229; p-Nitrophenyl-hydrazone, 188
7	4-Methyl-5,6,7,8-tetrahydroquinoline	122[11]	......	....	....	....	183	170	....	Hydrochloride, 203
8	3-Methyl-5,6,7,8-tetrahydroquinoline	126–7[17]	......	....	....	....	162	171	219	....
9	3-Ethylquinoline (β-Ethylquinoline)	135–8[12]	......	1.603[18]	1.0508_4^{20}	....	191	197	....	Hydrochloride, 173
10	4-Bromopyridine (γ-Bromopyridine)	27.5–30[0.3-0.5]	0–1	1.5679[20]	....	....	......	223	....	Decomposes to yel.-br. solid on standing

*Derivative data given in order: m.p., crystal color, solvent from which crystallized.

No.	Name	Melting point, °C	Boiling point, °C	Methyl p-toluene sulfonate	Methio-dide	Picrate	Chloro-platinate	Miscellaneous
1	Pyrimidine	21	123–4	....	....	156	....	Chloroaurate, 226
2	4,6-Dimethylpyrimidine	25	160	....	....	12–34	103–4	....
3	2,8-Dimethylquinoline	27	252	....	221	180	....	n_D: 1.6022; Ethiodide, 229
4	4-Bromoquinoline (γ-Bromoquinoline)	29–30; 25	270d.	....	265–70	....	....	D_4^{48}: 1.1334; n_D^{48}: 1.6231; Oxa-late, 169; Ethiodide, 146
5	Quinoxaline (Benzopyrazine)	30	230	....	176	....	....	
6	5-Methylpyrimidine	30.5	154	....	....	141	....	$HgCl_2$ double salt, 246; Chloro-aurate, 209
7	4-Chloroquinoline (γ-Chloroquinoline)	31	263	....	....	212	278	....
8	7-Chloroquinoline	31–2	267–8	....	250	....	253	....
9	8-Iodoquinoline	36	....	....	200	....	251	....
10	1,3,5-Trimethylpyrazole	37	170	....	....	147	187–91	n_{He}^{58}: 1.4589
11	2-Chloroquinoline (α-Chloroquinoline)	38	267	....	....	122	....	....
12	2,3-Dimethyl-5,6,7,8-tetrahydroquinoline	38	125¹⁴	....	117	169	....	....
13	7-Methylquinoline	39	252	....	....	237	223–4	....
14	4-Bromoisoquinoline	40	280–5	....	233	....	....	....
15	6-Chloroquinoline	41	262	143	248	....	....	Ethiodide, 168–9
16	4-(Diethylamino)benzaldehyde	41, yel.	....	....	....	....	....	Oxime, 93; Semicarbazone, 214; Phenylhydrazone, 103; Anil, 108–9
17	3-Nitropyridine	41	216	....	....	....	254	Hydrochloride, 154
18	2,4,8-Trimethylquinoline	42	270	....	229	193	....	....
19	4-Chloro-2-methylquinoline (4-Chloroquinaldine)	42–3	....	....	212	178	....	....
20	5-Chloroquinoline	45	256	....	231; 172	....	255	....
21	2,6,8-Trimethylquinoline	46	264–5	....	....	187–9	206–7	Hydrochloride, 207
22	2-(Dimethylamino)naphthalene (N,N-Dimethyl-β-naphthylamine)	47	305	....	206	....	....	....
23	2,4,5,8-Tetramethylquinoline	48, pa. yel.	168–72¹²	....	....	161	....	Hydrochloride, 254
24	5-Bromoquinoline	48; 52	280	....	205	....	....	Hydrochloride, 225
25	2-Bromoquinoline (α-Bromoquinoline)	49	....	....	210	....	....	....
26	8-Methoxyquinoline	50	283	....	160	143	....	....
27	7-Bromoquinoline	52; 34	290	....	240, yel.	....	....	Hydrochloride, 213
28	2-Iodoquinoline (α-Iodoquinoline)	52–3	....	....	211–2	....	....	Ethiodide, 220
29	3-Iodopyridine (β-Iodopyridine)	53; 50	....	....	....	....	211	Clinice cold CHCl₃ → chloride, 128–30, yel.
30	4,8-Dimethylquinoline	54–5	258–9	....	....	216–7	226	....
31	2,3,8-Trimethylquinoline	55–6	281	....	....	242–5	....	Hydrochloride, 260
32	2,6-Dimethylquinoline	60	266	175	236–7	186; 178	....	Styphnate, 200
33	N,N-Dimethyl-3-nitroaniline	60, red	....	....	205	119	....	....
34	3,4'-Bipyridyl	62	297	....	....	215	....	....
35	2,4,6-Trimethylquinoline	65.5 (anh.); 39.5 (hyd.)	281–2	....	245–7; 225	200–1	....	Hydrochloride, 268–72
36	3,3'-Bipyridyl (β,β-Bipyridyl)	68	291–2	....	....	232	....	....
37	2,3-Dimethylquinoline	68–9	263	....	218	230–1	230	....
38	2,2'-Bipyridyl (α,α'-Bipyridyl)	69	....	....	....	158	....	....
39	5-Nitroquinoline	72 (anh.)	....	....	215	....	....	Hydrochloride, 214
40	N,N-Dibenzylaniline	72; 70	....	....	135	131	....	....
41	2,2'-Bis-(dimethylamino)-biphenyl	72–3	....	....	190–2	....	....	Hydroiodide, 256–7
42	3,4-Dimethylquinoline	73–4; 65	293	....	191	215; 205	....	Hydrochloride, 290
43	8-Hydroxy-2-methylquinoline (8-Hydroxyquinaldine)	74	266	....	....	....	....	Me. eth., 125; b.p. 282
44	4-Dimethylaminobenzaldehyde	74	....	....	....	....	....	Semicarbazone, 222; p-Nitro-phenylhydrazone, 182; 2,4-Di-nitrophenylhydrazone, 325; Anil, 100, grn.-yel.
45	8-Hydroxyquinoline	75	....	....	143	204	....	Benzoate, 120; 1,3,5-Trinitro-benzene add. comp., 124
46	N,N-Dimethyl-4-aminophenol (N,N-Dimethyl-4-hydroxyaniline)	76	....	....	....	....	....	Acetate, 78; Me. eth., 49; p-Toluenesulfonyl, 130
47	8-Bromoisoquinoline	80.5	....	....	274	....	....	Nitrate, 193

*Derivative data given in order: m.p., crystal color, solvent from which crystallized.

No.	Name	Melting point, °C	Boiling point, °C	Methyl p-toluene sulfonate	Methio-dide	Picrate	Chloro-platinate	Miscellaneous
48	3,4'-Biquinolyl	83–4	....	....	....	244	....	Diethiodide, 198
49	2,2'-Dipyridylamine.................	84; 95 after resolidification	307–8	....	....	227–8	160	....
50	N,N-Dimethyl-4-nitrosoaniline (4-Nitroso-N,N-dimethylaniline)........	85	....	....	....	140	....	Hydrochloride, 177
51	N,N-Dimethyl-3-aminophenol (N,N-Dimethyl-3-hydroxyaniline)...........	85	....	....	....	....	....	Benzoate, 95; Me. urethane, 87
52	2,3,6-Trimethylquinoline	86–7	285	....	....	212	....	....
53	6,6'-Dimethyl-2,2'-bipyridyl	89–90	....	....	....	170–1	....	HgCl₂ add. comp., 238
54	4,4'-Bis-(dimethylamino)-diphenylmethane .	91	390	....	214 (di)	185 (mono), 178 (di)	....	1,3,5-Trinitrobenzene add. comp., 114, vlt.
55	6-Iodoquinoline	91	....	....	>300	....	265	Hydrochloride, 210
56	Tribenzylamine	91	....	....	184	190	....	Ethiodide, 190; β-Resorcylic acid salt, 141
57	2,3,4-Trimethylquinoline	92	285	....	260	216	215	Hydrochloride, 274
58	4-Dimethylaminobenzophenone	92	....	....	188–90	....	....	Anil, 151; Phenylhydrazone, 105
59	N-Methyl-4-pyridone	92–4 hyg.	....	....	....	....	176 (anh.)	HgCl₂ double salt, 177–80
60	1,5-Dimethylbenzimidazole	95	300	....	....	255	....	Hydrochloride, 215
61	1-Phenylisoquinoline	95–6	300	....	....	165	242	Hydrochloride, 235
62	6-Bromo-2-methylquinoline (6-Bromoquinaldine).................	96–7	....	....	237	....	....	Ethiodide, 218
63	4-Iodoquinoline (γ-Iodoquinoline)	97	....	....	251	....	185	....
64	4,4'-Bis-(dimethylamino)-benzhydrol	98; 102, grn.	....	....	195 (di)	....	....	Me. eth., 71–2; 1,3,5-Trinitrobenzene add. comp., 76
65	5-Iodoquinoline.....................	100	....	....	245	....	263	....
66	4,4'-Bis-(dimethylamino)-triphenylmethane (Leuco-malachite green)	102, bz.; 93, al.	....	....	231 (220) (di)	....	....	1,3,5-Trinitrobenzene add. comp., 89
67	2,2'-Biquinolylmethane	103	....	....	205	239, 210 (di)	....	....
68	2-Hydroxypyridine (α-Hydroxypyridine; α-Pyridone)	106–7	280–1	....	....	....	....	Benzoate, 42; HgCl₂ comp. with Me. eth., 200; HgCl₂ comp. with Et. eth., 141–2
69	Acridine............................	111	....	224	208	....	....	....
70	3,5-Dibromopyridine	112	222	219	274	....	....	....
71	1,2-Dimethylbenzimidazole	112 (anh.); 65(hyd.)	290	....	254	238	....	....
72	Antipyrine (2,3-Dimethyl-1-phenyl-5-pyrazolone)	113	319	....	....	188	....	Salicylate, 92
73	4,4'-Bipyridyl.....................	114 (anh.); 73 (hyd.)	....	....	....	257	....	Nitrate, 256
74	4-Dimethylaminoazobenzene	117, yel.	....	....	174, al.	....	....	Methochloride, 194
75	Triphenylamine	127	365	....	....	....	....	Hydrochloride, 214; Fuming HNO₃ in ac. a. → trinitro deriv., 280
76	3-Hydroxypyridine (β-Hydroxypyridine) ..	129	....	....	....	....	....	Oxalate, 177; Chloroplatinate of Et. eth., 192
77	Methyleneaminoacetonitrile	129	210	....	....	127	....	Acid hydrolysis → glycine
78	7-Nitroquinoline.....................	132–3	....	....	231–2	....	....	Ethiodide, 220
79	6,8'-Biquinolyl	148	....	....	126 (mono)	268	....	....
80	4-Hydroxypyridine (γ-Hydroxypyridine) ..	149 (anh.)	....	....	....	....	....	Acetate, 140–50; Benzoate, 81; Zn → pyridine, b.p. 116
81	6-Nitroquinoline.....................	154; 149	....	....	245	....	....	Styphnate, 190; Hydrobromide, 245
82	Quinuclidine......................	158 (sealed tube)	....	....	....	275–6	238–40	Ethiodide, 270–1
83	2,7'-Biquinolyl	160	....	....	263	240	....	....

*Derivative data given in order: m.p., crystal color, solvent from which crystallized.

TABLE XVIII. ORGANIC DERIVATIVES OF AMINES

2. Tertiary amines b) Solids (Listed in order of increasing m.p.)* (Continued)

No.	Name	Melting point, °C	Boiling point, °C	Methyl p-toluene sulfonate	Methiodide	Picrate	Chloro-platinate	Miscellaneous
84	2,2'-Biquinolyl ketone	164	. . . .	. . . .	. . . .	179	. . . .	Oxime, 201; Phenylhydrazone, 199
85	6-Hydroxypyrimidine	164–5	. . . .	. . . .	. . . .	190	. . . .	Acetyl, 180; 215–20 after re-solidification
86	7,7'-Biquinolyl	171–2	. . . .	. . . .	310 (mono)	300	. . . .	. . . .
87	4,4'-Bis-(dimethylamino) benzophenone (Michler's ketone)	174	. . . .	. . . .	105	156	. . . .	Oxime, 233
88	5,5'-Biquinolyl	175	. . . .	. . . .	272	>300	. . . .	Hydrochloride, 292
89	2,3'-Biquinolyl	176	. . . .	. . . .	286	. . . .	278	. . . .
90	6,6'-Biquinolyl	181	. . . .	. . . .	>290 (di)	. . . .	. . . .	Diethiodide, 270
91	6-Hydroxyquinoline	193	. . . .	. . . .	. . . .	236	. . . .	1,3,5-Trinitrobenzene add. comp., 193–5
92	2,2'-Biquinolyl (α,α'-Biquinolyl)	196	. . . .	. . . .	. . . .	210; 215	. . . .	. . . .
93	3-Hydroxyquinoline (β-Hydroxyquinoline)	198	. . . .	. . . .	. . . .	240–5	. . . .	. . . .
94	1,2-Di(2-pyrrolyl)ethanedione (2,2'-Bipyrroyl)	200, pa. yel.	. . . .	. . . .	. . . .	. . . .	. . . .	o-Phenylenediamine → di-pyrrylquinoxaline, 158; Monoxime, 147; Diphenyl-hydrazone, 146
95	4-Hydroxyquinoline (γ-Hydroxyquinoline)	201 (anh.)	. . . .	. . . .	. . . .	. . . .	. . . .	Hydrochloride, 187 (anh.); KMnO$_4$ → kynuric acid, 200 (anh.)
96	6-Hydroxy-2-methylquinoline (6-Hydroxyquinaldine)	213	. . . .	. . . .	. . . .	. . . .	. . . .	Et. eth., 71; Picrate of Et. eth., 192; Ethiodide of Et. eth., 182
97	5-Hydroxyquinoline	224	. . . .	. . . .	224	. . . .	230	Hydrochloride, 240
98	4-Hydroxy-2-methylquinoline (4-Hydroxyquinaldine)	232 (anh.)	. . . .	. . . .	201 (anh.)	200	215	Me. eth., 82
99	7-Hydroxyquinoline	235	. . . .	. . . .	251	244–5	. . . .	Benzoate, 88–9
100	5-Hydroxy-2-methylquinoline (5-Hydroxyquinaldine)	246; 232–4	. . . .	. . . .	. . . .	. . . .	. . . .	Picrate of Me. eth., 217; Picrate of Et. eth., 213; 206
101	4,4'-Dipyridylamine	273–5	. . . .	. . . .	. . . .	235; 174	>280	Hydrochloride, > 300
102	Hexamethylene tetramine	280	. . . .	205	190	179	. . . .	Dil. acid → formaldehyde, semicarbazone, 169

*Derivative data given in order: m.p., crystal color, solvent from which crystallized.

EXPLANATIONS AND REFERENCES TO TABLE XIX

*Substituted phenylhydrazones.**

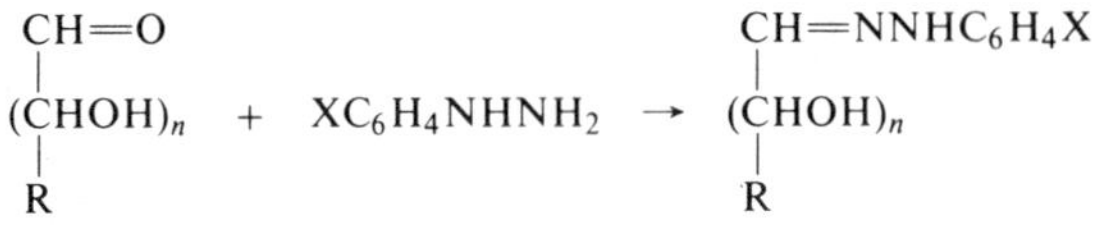

$$\begin{array}{c} CH{=}O \\ | \\ (CHOH)_n \\ | \\ R \end{array} + XC_6H_4NHNH_2 \rightarrow \begin{array}{c} CH{=}NNHC_6H_4X \\ | \\ (CHOH)_n \\ | \\ R \end{array}$$

Substituted
phenylhydrazone

From the carbohydrate and one equivalent of phenylhydrazine in aqueous acetic acid.
For directions and examples see: Cheronis, p. 520; Wild, p. 77.
From the carbohydrate, phenylhydrazine hydrochloride and sodium acetate in water.
See: Wild, p. 77.
From the carbohydrate with *p*-nitrophenylhydrazine hydrochloride and sodium acetate in methanol.
See: Cheronis, p. 523.
From the carbohydrate and *p*-nitrophenylhydrazine in alcohol.
See: Vogel, p. 456.
From the carbohydrate and benzylphenylhydrazine in aqueous alcohol.
See: Shriner, p. 77.

*Phenylosazone.**

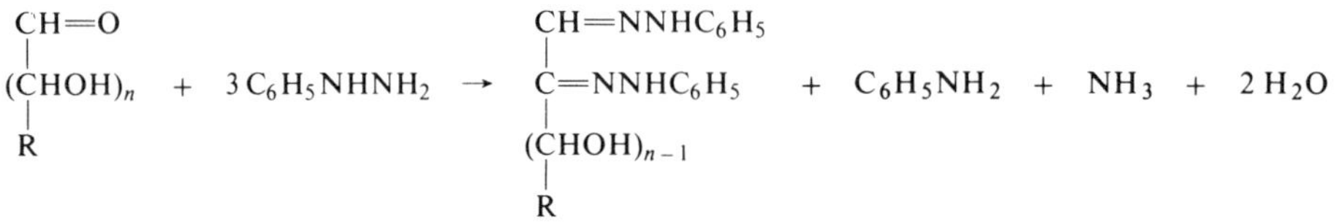

$$\begin{array}{c} CH{=}O \\ | \\ (CHOH)_n \\ | \\ R \end{array} + 3 C_6H_5NHNH_2 \rightarrow \begin{array}{c} CH{=}NNHC_6H_5 \\ | \\ C{=}NNHC_6H_5 \\ | \\ (CHOH)_{n-1} \\ | \\ R \end{array} + C_6H_5NH_2 + NH_3 + 2 H_2O$$

Phenylosazone

From the carbohydrate and excess of phenylhydrazine in glacial acetic acid.
For directions and examples see: Cheronis, pp. 523, 524.
From the carbohydrate, excess of phenylhydrazine hydrochloride and sodium acetate in aqueous acetic acid.
See: Cheronis, pp. 524, 525; Linstead, p. 38; Shriner, p. 132; Vogel, p. 455.
From the carbohydrate and excess of phenylhydrazine in methyl cellosolve-glacial acetic acid mixture.
See: W. T. Haskins, R. M. Hann and C. S. Hudson, *J. Amer. Chem. Soc.*, **68**, 1766 (1946).

Methylphenylosazone.

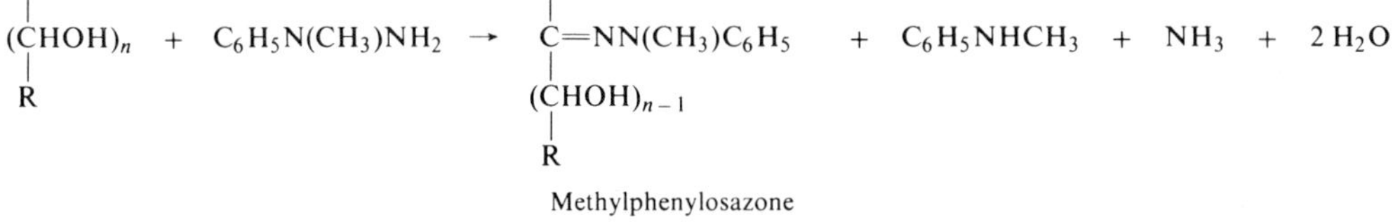

$$\begin{array}{c} CH{=}O \\ | \\ (CHOH)_n \\ | \\ R \end{array} + C_6H_5N(CH_3)NH_2 \rightarrow \begin{array}{c} CH{=}NN(CH_3)C_6H_5 \\ | \\ C{=}NN(CH_3)C_6H_5 \\ | \\ (CHOH)_{n-1} \\ | \\ R \end{array} + C_6H_5NHCH_3 + NH_3 + 2 H_2O$$

Methylphenylosazone

From the carbohydrate and *as*-methylphenylhydrazine in aqueous alcohol.
For directions and examples see: Vogel, p. 456.

*p-Phenylazobenzoate (azoate).**

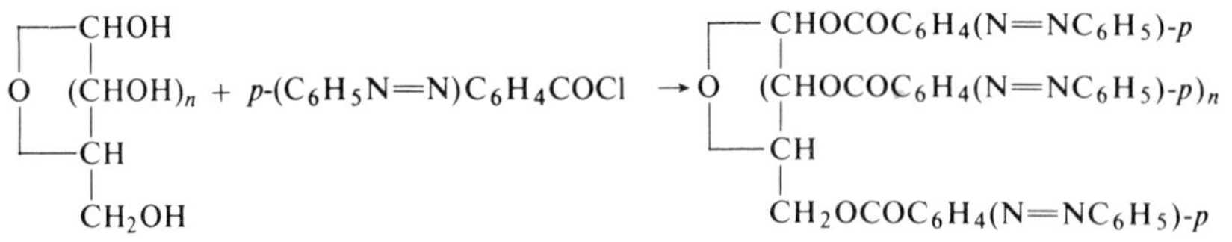

$$O\begin{array}{c} {-}CHOH \\ | \\ (CHOH)_n \\ | \\ {-}CH \\ | \\ CH_2OH \end{array} + p\text{-}(C_6H_5N{=}N)C_6H_4COCl \rightarrow O\begin{array}{c} {-}CHOCOC_6H_4(N{=}NC_6H_5)\text{-}p \\ | \\ (CHOCOC_6H_4(N{=}NC_6H_5)\text{-}p)_n \\ | \\ {-}CH \\ | \\ CH_2OCOC_6H_4(N{=}NC_6H_5)\text{-}p \end{array}$$

Azoyl chloride   Carbohydrate azoate

From the carbohydrate and azoyl chloride (*p*-phenylazobenzoyl chloride) in anhydrous pyridine.
For directions and examples see: Cheronis, p. 526; G. H. Coleman, A. G. Farnham and A. Miller, *J. Amer. Chem. Soc.*, **64**, 1501 (1942); G. H. Coleman and C. M. McClosky, *J. Amer. Chem. Soc.*, **65**, 1588 (1943).

*Derivatives recommended for first trial.
WARNING: This is not an instruction manual. References should be consulted for the preparation of derivatives.

Acetate.

$$\begin{matrix} & \text{—CHOH} & & & & & \text{—CHOCOCH}_3 \\ \text{O} & (\text{CHOH})_n & + & (\text{CH}_3\text{CO})_2\text{O} & \rightarrow & \text{O} & (\text{CHOCOCH}_3)_n \\ & \text{—CH} & & & & & \text{—CH} \\ & \text{CH}_2\text{OH} & & & & & \text{CH}_2\text{OCOCH}_3 \end{matrix}$$

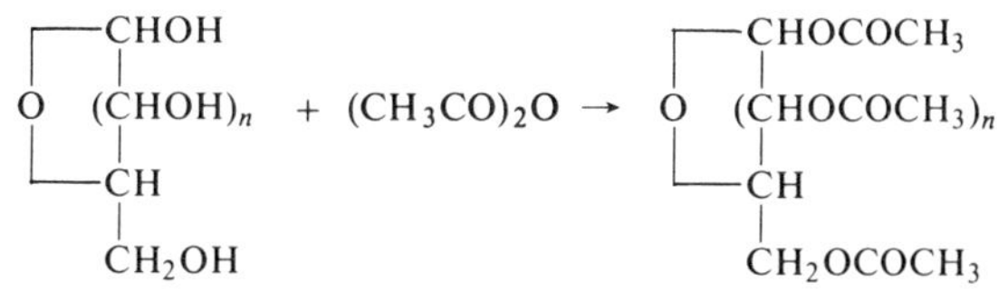

Carbohydrate
acetate

From the carbohydrate, acetic anhydride and sodium acetate.
For directions and examples see: Linstead, p. 39; Shriner, p. 212; Vogel, p. 451; Wild, p. 78.

Specific rotation.

Specific rotation can be used as means for identification.
For directions and examples see: Cheronis, p. 578; Wild, p. 78.

General references:

C. A. Browne and F. W. Zerban, *Physical and Chemical Methods of Sugar Analysis.*, 3rd edition, John Wiley and Sons, New York, 1941; J. Stanek, M. Carny, J. Kocourek and J. Pacak, *The Monosaccharides*, Academic Press, New York, 1963, pp. 865–955; G. R. Pigman in *The Carbohydrates*, (Ed. W. Pigman), Academic Press, New York, 1957, pp. 602–640.

*Derivatives recommended for first trial.
WARNING: This is not an instruction manual. References should be consulted for the preparation of derivatives.

TABLE XIX. ORGANIC DERIVATIVES OF CARBOHYDRATES

TABLE XIX. ORGANIC DERIVATIVES OF CARBOHYDRATES
a) Liquids (Listed in order of increasing m.p. of the corresponding phenylosazone derivatives)*

No.	Name	Melting point, °C	Specific rotation $[\alpha]_D$	T, °C	Conc.; Solvent	Rf-Values in n-butanol-acetic acid-water (4:1:5)	Phenylosazone M.P.	Phenylosazone $[\alpha]_D^T$; Solvent	Azoate (p-Phenylazobenzoate) M.P.	Azoate $[\alpha]_{6438}^{25}$, chl.	p-Nitrophenylhydrazone	p-Bromophenylhydrazone	Miscellaneous
1	DL-Methyltetrose.........	......	....	....	....	....	140–2	....	....	....	....	....	Phenylbenzylhydrazone, 99–100
2	Apiose..........	......	+3.8; +5.6	20 15	c = 3.4; water	....	156	....	....	....	....	....	p-Bromophenylosazone, 210–2
3	DL-Gulose	......	....	....	....	....	157–9	....	....	....	....	....	Phenylhydrazone, 143; p-Bromophenylosazone, 183
4	L-Erythrose	......	+11.5 → +15.2 → +30.5	24	c = 3; water	....	164	....	....	....	....	....	Benzylphenylhydrazone, 105, $[\alpha]_D^{20}$: +32.8, c = 5, 95% al.; Triacetyl, 134
5	D-Erythrose	......	−14.5	20	c = 11; water	....	164; 166	0.5, pyr.-al.	....	....	....	....	Benzylphenylhydrazone, 105–6, $[\alpha]_D^{20}$: +32.8, c = 5, 95% al.; p-Bromophenylosazone, 195; Phenylhydrazone, 116
6	DL-Erythrose.....	......	....	....	....	....	164; 166–8	....	....	....	....	....	Benzylphenylhydrazone, 83
7	DL-Erythrulose ...	......	....	....	....	....	164	....	....	....	....	....	Methylphenylosazone, 158–9
8	L-Erythrulose.....	......	+12	20	water	....	164	....	....	....	....	....	p-Bromophenylosazone, 195
9	L-Idose..........	......	+52.7	20	c = 6.2; water	....	168; 160	....	....	....	....	....	....
10	D-Gulose	......	−20.4 → +61.6	20	water	....	168; 160	+6, c = 0.4; me. al.	....	....	....	....	Phenylhydrazone, 143; p-Bromophenylosazone, 186; Benzylphenylhydrazone, 124, $[\alpha]_D$: −24, c = 0.5, me. al.
11	β-Methylglyceraldehyde	......	....	....	....	....	171	....	....	....	....	....	Benzylphenylhydrazone, 116
12	L-Methyltetrose...	......	−30.5 → −16.5	20	c = 9.47; 96% al.	....	172–3	....	....	....	....	....	Benzylphenylhydrazone, 96–7; Diethyl mercaptal, 109
13	D-Rhamnose (6-Desoxy-D-mannose)	......	−8.25	16.5	c = 10; water	....	185; 191	−95.2, pyr.	....	....	....	....	p-Bromophenylosazone, 225; 222–3
14	3-Amino-3-desoxy-D-glucose	......	−61 → −78	18	water	....	207	....	....	....	....	....	N-Benzoyl, 128–30
15	DL-Xylulose (DL-Xyloketose)	......	....	....	....	....	210–5	....	....	....	....	....	Methylphenylosazone, 173

*Derivative data given in order: m.p., crystal color, solvent from which crystallized.

TABLE XIX. ORGANIC DERIVATIVES OF CARBOHYDRATES
b) Solids (Listed in order of increasing m.p.)*

No.	Name	Melting point, °C	Specific rotation $[\alpha]_D$	T, °C	Conc.; Solvent	Rf-Values in n-butanol-acetic acid-water (4:1:5)	Phenylosazone M.P.	$[\alpha]_D^T$: Solvent	Azoate (p-Phenylazobenzoate) M.P.	$[\alpha]_{6438}^{25}$, chl.	p-Nitrophenylhydrazone	p-Bromophenylhydrazone	Miscellaneous
1	**1,3-Dihydroxy-acetone**	65–71 (monomer); 80 (dimer)	....	......	......	....	132	....	....	......	156; 160	....	Phenylhydrazone, 115; Me. phenylosazone, 127–130; Diacetate, 46–7; Dibenzoate, 120; Di-p-nitrobenzoate, 198; Oxime, 84
2	**β-Melibiose dihydrate** (6-[α-D-Galacto-sido]-D-glucose)	82–5	+111.7 → +129.5	20	c = 4; water	....	176–8	+43.2; pyr.	280	+172	....	....	p-Bromophenyl-osazone, 181–2; Phenylhydrazone, 145; 160; Oxime, 186; Octaacetate, 177.5, $[\alpha]_D^{20}$: +102.5
3	**D-Ribose**	87; 95	−21.5; −23.7	20	c = 4; water	0.31	164; 160	....	....	....	....	170, ($[\alpha]_D^{20}$: −5.7, al.)	p-Bromophenyl-osazone, 180–5; β-Me. glucoside, 83–4, $[\alpha]_D^{20}$: −113.6
4	**L-Ribose**	87	+20.3 → +20.7	20	c = 4; water	....	166	....	....	....	....	164–5	Phenylhydrazone, 154–5
5	**2-Desoxy-D-ribose**	90	+2.88 → +2.13	23	water	....	....	....	....	....	....	....	Benzylphenylhydra-zone, 127–9
6	**Glycollic alde-hyde** (Glyco-aldehyde)	95–7	....	......	......	....	179	....	....	....	....	....	p-Nitrophenylosazone, 311; Diphenyl-osazone, 207; Benzyl-phenylosazone, 198; Monoacetate, 157–8; Phenylhydrazone, 162
7	**D-Fructose**	102–4	−132.2 → −92.4	20	c = 4; water	0.23	210	....	125	−440	176, ($[\alpha]_D$: +16, pyr.-al.)	....	o-Nitrophenylhydra-zone, 156–7; α-Me. phenylosazone, 161–2; Pentaacetate: α-form, 70, $[\alpha]_D^{20}$: +34.7, chl.; β-form, 108–9, $[\alpha]_D^{20}$: −120.5, chl.
8	**Lactic aldehyde** (Lactaldehyde)	105	....	......	......	....	154; 145	....	....	....	128–9	....	Phenylhydrazone, 93
9	**α-L-Rhamnose** (6-Desoxy-L-mannose)	105; 93–4 (hyd.)	−8.6 → +8.2	20	c = 4; water	0.37	222; 182	+94, pyr.	....	....	186; 191	....	p-Nitrophenylosa-zone, 208; 2-Naph-thylhydrazone, 170, $[\alpha]_D$: +8.4, me. al.; Semicarbazone, 183, $[\alpha]_D^{20}$: +75 → +57, w.
10	**L-Altrose**	105; 107–9	−32.3	20	water	....	165; 178	....	....	....	....	....	Benzylphenylhydra-zone, 148
11	**D-Altrose**	105	+32.6	20	c = 7.6; water	....	178	....	....	....	....	....	Benzylphenylhydra-zone, 148–50
12	**2-Amino-2-desoxy-D-glu-cose** (Glucosa-mine)	105–10	+48; +44	.....	water	....	210	....	....	....	....	....	Phenylurea, 210; N-Acetyl, 190; Oxime, 127; Semicarbazone, 165
13	**α-D-Lyxose**	106–7; 101	+5.5 → −14.0	.....	c = 8; water	....	164	....	....	....	172	162; 156–7	Benzylphenylhydra-zone, 116; 128; $[\alpha]_D^{20}$: +26.4, c = 4.9, abs. al.

*Derivative data given in order: m.p., crystal color, solvent from which crystallized.

TABLE XIX. ORGANIC DERIVATIVES OF CARBOHYDRATES
b) Solids (Listed in order of increasing m.p.)* (Continued)

No.	Name	Melting point, °C	Specific rotation			Rf-Values in n-butanol-acetic acid-water (4:1:5)	Phenylosazone		Azoate (p-Phenylazobenzoate)		p-Nitrophenylhydrazone	p-Bromophenylhydrazone	Miscellaneous
			$[\alpha]_D$	T, °C	Conc.; Solvent		M.P.	$[\alpha]_D^T$: Solvent	M.P.	$[\alpha]_{6438}^{25}$, chl.			
14	**Raffinose** (2-[6-(α-D-Galactosido)-α-D-glucoside]-β-D-fructose) . . .	118–9, (anh.); 80 (hyd.)	+123; +105.2	20	water; c = 4; water	0.05	. . . . . .	. . . . . .	145	+146	. . . . . .	. . . . . .	Trityl, 130; α-Methylphenylhydrazone, 190; Emulsin → sucrose + galactose.
15	**β-L-Rhamnose** .	122–6	+9.1	20	water	. . . . . .	222; 185	+94; pyr.	. . . . . .	. . . . . .	190–1, ($[\alpha]_D^{20}$: +21.4)	. . . . . .	α-Methylphenylhydrazone, 124; p-Bromophenylosazone, 222
16	**D-Tagatose**	124	+1.0	22	c = 1; water	. . . . . .	196–7; 201	. . . . . .	. . . . . .	. . . . . .	. . . . . .	. . . . . .	Diacetone deriv., 65–6, $[\alpha]_D^{20}$: +71.8, w.
17	**D-Threose**	126–32	+29 → +19.6	22	water	. . . . . .	164	. . . . . .	. . . . . .	. . . . . .	. . . . . .	. . . . . .	Benzylphenylhydrazone, 194, bz.; Acetone deriv., 84; Triacetate, 113–4, $[\alpha]_D^{20}$: +35.5, chl.
18	**D-1-Amino-fructose**	127–8	. . . . . .				210	. . . . . .	. . . . . .	. . . . . .	. . . . . .	. . . . . .	. . . . . .
19	**β-D-Allose**	128	+0.58 → +14.41	20	c = 5; water	. . . . . .	178; 174	. . . . . .	. . . . . .	. . . . . .	. . . . . .	145, ($[\alpha]_D^{20}$: −6.7, al.)	. . . .
20	**β-L-Allose**	128–9	−1.9	20	water	. . . . . .	165	. . . . . .	. . . . . .	. . . . . .	. . . . . .	141–5, ($[\alpha]_D^{20}$: +6.4, al.)	. . . .
21	**D-Talose**	128–30	+30 → +20.6	21	water	. . . . . .	201; 197	. . . . . .	. . . . . .	. . . . . .	205		Phenylhydrazone, 178; Benzylphenylhydrazone, 199
22	**DL-Xylose**	129–31	. . . . .	. . . . .	. . . . . .	. . . . . .	210–5	. . . . . .	. . . . . .	. . . . . .	. . . . . .		
23	**α-D-Mannose** . .	133	+29.3 → +14.2	20	c = 4; water	0.20	210	. . . . . .	194–5, ($[\alpha]_D^{20}$: +56, pyr.-al. (1:1))	. . . . . .	208–10		Phenylhydrazone, 199–200, $[\alpha]_D^{20}$: +26.3 → +33.8, pyr.; α-Methylphenylhydrazone, 178, $[\alpha]_D$: +8.6, c = 0.5, me. al.; Benzylphenylhydrazone, 165
24	**β-D-Mannose** . .	132	−17.0 → +14.2	20	c = 4; water	. . . . . .	210	. . . . . .	194–5	208–10			Phenylhydrazone, 199–200; α-Methylphenylhydrazone, 178; CaCl₂ add. comp., 101–2
25	**L-Mannose**	132	+14.0 → −14.0	. . . . .	water	. . . . . .	208	. . . . . .	. . . . . .	. . . . . .	. . . . . .		Phenylhydrazone, 195, $[\alpha]_D$: +1.2, HCl
26	**DL-Mannose** . .	132–3	. . . . .	. . . . .	. . . . . .	. . . . . .	217–9	. . . . . .	. . . . . .	. . . . . .	. . . . . .		Phenylhydrazone, 195
27	**α-D-Manno-heptose**	134–5	+85.05 → +68.64	20	c = 11; water	. . . . . .	200	. . . . . .	. . . . . .	. . . . . .	207–8		Phenylhydrazone, 197; Hexaacetate, 106, 50% al.; 139–40, eth.
28	**DL-Glyceraldehyde** (*dimer*) . .	139; 142	. . . . . .	. . . . .	. . . . . .	. . . . . .	132	. . . . . .	. . . . . .	. . . . . .	. . . . . .		p-Bromophenylosazone, 168; Dibenzoate, 231; Di-p-nitrobenzoate, 247; Semicarbazone, 160; 2,4-Dinitrophenylhydrazone, 166–7
29	**D-Isorhamnose** (6-Desoxy-D-glucose)	139–40	+72.3 → 29.7	20	c = 10; water	. . . . . .	185; 187–9	. . . . . .	. . . . . .	. . . . . .	. . . . . .	. . . . . .	. . . .

*Derivative data given in order: m.p., crystal color, solvent from which crystallized.

TABLE XIX. ORGANIC DERIVATIVES OF CARBOHYDRATES
b) Solids (Listed in order of increasing m.p.)* (Continued)

No.	Name	Melting point, °C	Specific rotation			Rf-Values in n-butanol-acetic acid-water (4:1:5)	Phenylosazone		Azoate (p-Phenyl-azobenzoate)		p-Nitro-phenyl-hydrazone	.p-Bromo-phenyl-hydrazone	Miscellaneous
			$[\alpha]_D$	T, °C	Conc.; Solvent		M.P.	$[\alpha]_D^T$: Solvent	M.P.	$[\alpha]_{5438}^{25}$, chl.			
30	α-L-Glucose	141–3	−95.5 → −51.4	20	c = 4; water	....	208	....	....	....	....	....	Diphenylhydrazone, 162
31	L-Xylose	144; 141–3	−79.3 → −18.6	20	c = 9.94; water	....	159–61	....	....	....	....	....	Tetraacetate, 126 (β-form)
32	α-D-Xylose	145; 143	+93.6 → +18.8	20	c = 4; water	0.28	164; 155	−40.9, al.	157	+244	155	128	Me. phenylhydrazone, 108; Benzylphenylhydrazone, 95, $[\alpha]_D$: −33, c = 0.57, al.; 2-Naphthylhydrazone, 124, $[\alpha]_D$: +18.6, me. al.
33	D-Fucose (6-Desoxy-D-galactose; D-Rhodeose)	145	+89.3 → +75.7	22	water	....	177	....	....	....	....	....	Methylphenylosazone, 181; Oxime, 188–9, $[\alpha]_D$: +13.2, w.
34	L-Fucose (6-Desoxy-L-galactose; L-Rhodeose)	145	−152.6 → −75.9	20	c = 4; water	0.27	178	....	....	210–1	181–4		Phenylhydrazone, 170; α-Methylphenylhydrazone, 174, $[\alpha]_D^{19}$: −17.0, pyr.; Oxime, 188–9; α-Me. glucoside, 158, $[\alpha]_D^{20}$: −197.5, w.; β-Me. glucoside, 119, $[\alpha]_D^{20}$: +16.04, w.
35	α-D-Glucose	146 (anh.); 83 (hyd.)	+112.2 → +52.7	20	c = 4; water	0.18	210	−1.5, c = 2, pyr.-al. (1:1)	266	+223	88; 196 ($[\alpha]_D$: +21.5, me. al.)	164–6, ($[\alpha]_D$: −43.6 → +18.9; c = 4, pyr.)	2-Naphthylhydrazone, 178; p-Nitrophenylosazone, 257; 2,4-Dinitrophenylosazone, 256–7; α-Pentaacetate, 112
36	2-Desoxy-D-glucose	148	+46.6	18	water	....	....	....	....	....	....	....	Benzylphenylhydrazone, 158–9
37	β-D-Glucose	148–50	+18.7 → +52.7	20	c = 4; water	....	210	....	....	....	....	....	p-Nitrophenylosazone, 257; 2,4-Dinitrophenylosazone, 256–7; β-Pentaacetate, 132
38	Melezitose (2-[3-(α-D-Glucosido)-D-fructosido]-α-D-glucose)	153–4 (+2 H₂O)	+88.2	20	c = 4; water	....	....	....	130 (sinteres)	+188	....	....	....
39	Turanose (3-[α-D-Glucosido]-D-fructose)	157 (anh.); 60–5 (hyd.)	+27.3 → +75.8	20	c = 4; water	....	215–20	....	....	....	....	....	Heptaacetate, 140–1, eth., $[\alpha]_D^{20}$: +37, chl.
40	β-D-Arabinose	158–9	−175 → −105	.....	c = 9.45; water	0.21	162–3; 160	....	....	....	....	....	Oxime, 136; Benzyl-phenylhydrazone, 173
41	β-L-Arabinose	160	+190.6 → +104.5	20	water	....	166	....	262	+755	186	155	Benzylphenylhydrazone, 174; Me. phenylhydrazone, 165; Oxime, 139; Tetraacetate, α-form: 94–6, eth., β-form: 86, w.; Tetrabenzoate, 160–1; 173; Semicarbazone, 190; 163

*Derivative data given in order: m.p., crystal color, solvent from which crystallized.

No.	Name	Melting point, °C	Specific rotation			Rf-Values in n-butanol-acetic acid-water (4:1:5)	Phenylosazone		Azoate (p-Phenyl-azobenzoate)		p-Nitro-phenyl-hydrazone	p-Bromo-phenyl-hydrazone	Miscellaneous
			$[\alpha]_D$	T, °C	Conc.; Solvent		M.P.	$[\alpha]_D^T$: Solvent	M.P.	$[\alpha]_{5438}^{25}$, chl.			
42	β-D-Galac-turonic acid...	160	(+55.3)	20	water	....	....	....	....	....	....	151 ($[\alpha]_D$ +11.5, me. al.)	Phenylhydrazone, 140; Brucine salt, 180
43	β-Maltose (4-[α-D-Glucosido]-β-D-glucose)...	160–5; 102–3 (+1 H$_2$O)	+111.7 → +130.4	20	c = 4; water	0.11	205–6	....	275	+2	....	....	Phenylhydrazone, 130; p-Nitrophenyl-osazone, 261; p-Bro-mophenylosazone, 198; 2-Naphthyl-hydrazone, 176; Octa-acetate, 160–1, $[\alpha]_D^{20}$: +62.59, chl.
44	DL-Fucose (6-Desoxy-DL-galactose; DL-Rhodeose)	161	....	......	......	......	187	....	......	......	....	....	Diacetone deriv., 41
45	DL-Sorbose...	162–3	....	......	......	0.20	169–70	....	......	......	....	....	....
46	L-Galactose...	162–3	−120 → −73.6 →	......	c = 10; water		192–5	....	......	......	....	....	Phenylhydrazone, 158–60, $[\alpha]_D$: +21.6, w.
47	DL-Galactose..	163; 144	....	......	......		206	....	......	......	....	....	Phenylhydrazone, 158–60; α-Methyl-phenylhydrazone, 183
48	β-D-Glucuronic acid........	163	+36.3	20	water		....	....	......	......	225	....	Semicarbazone, 188; Cinchonine salt, 204, $[\alpha]_D^{20}$: +139.9, w.
49	DL-Arabinose.	164	....	......	......		169	....	......	......	....	160	Diphenylhydrazone, 204; p-Bromophenyl-osazone, 200–2
50	L-Sorbose.....	165; 159–61	−43.7 → −43.4	20	c = 12; water	0.20	156; **168**	−6, me. al.	......	......	....	....	p-Bromophenylosa-zone, 181; o-Nitro-phenylosazone, 211–2; β-Me. glucoside, 120–2, $[\alpha]_D^{20}$: −88.5, w.; Pentaacetate, 97, $[\alpha]_D$: +2.9, chl.
51	D-Sorbose	165	+42.9	20	c = 1; water	....	168; 160	....	......	......	....	....	β-Me. glucoside, 119, $[\alpha]_D$: +88.5, w.
52	3-(β-D-Galac-tosido)-D-arabinose	166–8	−50.3 → +63.1	19	water		242	....	......	......	....	....	Benzylphenylhydra-zone, 223–5
53	α-D-Galactose.	167	+150.7 → +80.2	20	c = 5; water	0.16	196; 201	....	276	+436	154; 197	168	α-Methylphenylhydra-zone, 190–1; Benzyl-phenylhydrazone, 157; Diphenylhydra-zone, 157; α-Penta-acetate, 95
54	Stachyose (α-Galactosyl <u>1—6'</u> α-galactosyl <u>1'—4</u> α-glucosyl <u>1—2'</u> β-fructo-side)	167–70	+148	20	water		....	....	......	......	....	....	Tetradecaacetate, 95–6, $[\alpha]_D^{22}$: +120, al.; Tetradeca-p-nitro-benzoate, 166
55	Sucrose (2-[α-D-Glucosido]-β-D-fructose).	169–70, me. al., 185, w.-al.	+66.53	20	c = 26; water	0.14	......	....	125	+35	....	....	Nonreducing; Octa-acetate, 72; 69, $[\alpha]_D^{20}$: +59.6, chl.; Tritrityl, 128

*Derivative data given in order: m.p., crystal color, solvent from which crystallized.

No.	Name	Melting point, °C	Specific rotation $[\alpha]_D$	T, °C	Conc.; Solvent	Rf-Values in n-butanol-acetic acid-water (4:1:5)	Phenylosazone M.P.	$[\alpha]_D^T$: Solvent	Azoate (p-Phenylazobenzoate) M.P.	$[\alpha]_{5438}^{25}$, chl.	p-Nitrophenyl-hydrazone	p-Bromophenyl-hydrazone	Miscellaneous
56	D-Glucoheptulose	171	+67.4	20	water	....	209–10	....	......	......	....	....	Hexaacetate, 112, $[\alpha]_D^{20}$: +87.0; α-Me. glucoside, 138–40, $[\alpha]_D^{22}$: +108.5, w.
57	4-β-D-Glucosido-β-D-mannose	176 (anh.); 139–40 (hyd.)	+15.1 → +10.7	16	water	....	198	....	......	......	....	....	....
58	α-L-Rhamnohexose	180–1	−80 → −61.4	20	c = 9.67; water	....	200	....	......	......	....	....	Benzylphenylhydrazone, 183–4
59	L-Ascorbic acid	190; 187	+49	18	me. al.	0.38	......	....	262 (di)	......	....	170 (di)	Diphenylhydrazone, 187; Di-2,4-dinitrophenylhydrazone, 282
60	Gentiobiose (6-[β-D-Glucosido]-D-glucose)	190–5 (anh.); 86 (hyd.)	+21.4 → +8.7	20	c = 5; water	....	163–4; 170; 179.	−42.9[20], 95% al.	......	......	....	....	Octaacetate (α): 188–9, $[\alpha]_D^{20}$: +52.3, chl.; (β): 192–3, $[\alpha]_D^{20}$: −5.3, chl.
61	α-D-Glucoheptose	193	−20	20	water	....	194–5	....	......	......	....	....	β-Me. glucoheptoside, 169, $[\alpha]_D$: −75, w.; Hexaacetate, 164 (α-form), 135 (β-form)
62	α,α-Trehalose (1-[α-D-Glucosido]-α-D-glucose)	210; 203 (anh.); 97 (+2 H₂O)	+178.3	20	c = 7; water	....	......	....	134–5	+210	....	....	Nonreducing; Octanitrate, 124; Octaacetate, 100–2, $[\alpha]_D^{20}$: +162, chl.; Hexaacetate, 93–6, $[\alpha]_D^{19}$: +158.3, chl.
63	Primeverose (6-[β-D-Xylosido]-D-glucose)	210; 208	+24.1 → −3.3	.....	c = 2.5; water	....	220	....	......	......	....	....	β-Heptaacetate, 216, $[\alpha]_D^{20}$: −23.5, chl.
64	Lactose (4-[β-D-Galactosido]-D-glucose)	α-form, 223 (anh.); 201 (hyd.); β-form, 252 (anh.)	+90 → +55.3 (+52.3) +35 → +55.3 (+52.3)	20 / 20	c = 4; water / c = 4; water	0.09	200; 210–2	....	......	......	....	....	p-Nitrophenylosazone, 258; Octaacetate, 100; Benzylphenylhydrazone, 128; 2-Naphthylhydrazone, 203
65	β-Cellobiose (4-[α-D-Glucosido]-β-D-glucose)	225	+14.2 → +34.6	20	c = 8; water	....	208–10; 198	−6.5[20], pyr.-al. (1:1)	273	+105	....	....	Phenylhydrazone, 90; Octaacetate, (α) 229–30, $[\alpha]_D^{20}$: +42, chl.; Semicarbazone, 183–5; Octaacetate (β), 192; 202, $[\alpha]_D^{20}$: −14.5, chl.; Oxime, 123–5
66	6-[β-Cellobiosido]-α-D-glucose	247–52 (anh.); 200 (hyd.)	+15.0 → +8.4	.....	water	....	224	....	......	......	....	....	
67	6-[-β-Lactosido]-α-D-glucose	257	+34.7 → +22.6	24	water	....	233	....	......	......	....	....	

*Derivative data given in order: m.p., crystal color, solvent from which crystallized.

EXPLANATIONS AND REFERENCES TO TABLE XX

*Formation of amine by reduction.**

$$RNO_2 + 6[H] \rightarrow RNH_2 + 2H_2O$$
$$\text{Amine}$$

From the nitro compound and tin in hydrochloric acid.

For directions and examples see: Cheronis, p. 625; Linstead, p. 69; Shriner, p. 262; Vogel, p. 529; Wild, p. 247.

From catalytic hydrogenation (Raney nickel, platinum oxide and palladium on charcoal) of the nitro compound in ethanol, methanol or dioxane.

See: Cheronis, p. 626; Linstead, p. 70; N. D. Cheronis and M. Koeck, *J. Chem. Ed.*, **20**, 488 (1943); K. Johnson and E. F. Degering, *J. Amer. Chem. Soc.*, **61**, 3194 (1939); S. V. Voris and P. E. Spoerri, *J. Amer. Chem. Soc.*, **60**, 935 (1938); E. R. Blout and D. C. Silverman, *J. Amer. Chem. Soc.*, **66**, 1442 (1944).

From the nitro compound and lithium aluminum hydride in ethers.

See: N. G. Gaylord, *Reduction with Complex Metal Hydrides*, Interscience, New York, 1956, pp. 762–773.

For partial reduction of polynitro compounds with sodium or ammonium polysulfide *see:* Linstead, p. 71; Vogel, p. 551.

NOTE: For directions and examples for the preparation of the derivatives of the amine formed on reduction of the nitro compounds see explanations and references to Table XVIII, p. 291, 292, 293, 294.

*Polynitro derivative.**

$$ArNO_2 \xrightarrow{HNO_3} Ar(NO_2)_n \qquad n > 1$$

From the aromatic nitro compound with concentrated or fuming nitric acid and sulfuric acid.

For directions and examples see: Cheronis, pp. 580, 627; Shriner, p. 249; Vogel, pp. 526, 527.

From fuming nitric acid in acetic acid or acetic anhydride.

See: Wild, pp. 24, 247, 248; J. Reilly and W. J. Hickinbottom, *J. Chem. Soc.*, **117**, 135 (1920); O. L. Brady and W. H. Gibson, *J. Chem. Soc.*, **119**, 102 (1921).

Molecular compounds of aromatic polynitro compounds with aromatic hydrocarbons.

$$Ar(NO_2)_n + Ar'H \rightarrow Ar(NO_2)_n \cdot Ar'H \qquad n > 1$$
$$\text{Molecular}$$
$$\text{compound}$$

Molecular addition compounds are formed from the aromatic polynitro compound and aromatic hydrocarbons.

For directions and examples see: Table IV, p. 32, 33, 34. Wild, p. 248; T. Asahina and C. Shinomiya, *J. Chem. Soc. Japan*, **59**, 341 (1938); O. C. Dermer and R. B. Smith, *J. Amer. Chem. Soc.*, **61**, 748 (1939).

Nitroaromatic acids from side-chain oxidation.

$$Ar(NO_2)R \rightarrow Ar(NO_2)COOH$$
$$\text{Nitroaromatic}$$
$$\text{acid}$$

From the alkylaromatic nitro compound and basic aqueous potassium permanganate.

For directions and examples see: Cheronis, p. 627; Vogel, p. 629.

From the alkylaromatic nitro compound and sodium bichromate and sulfuric acid in water.

See: Cheronis, p. 628; Vogel, p. 629.

---

*Derivatives recommended for first trial.

WARNING: This is not an instruction manual. References should be consulted for the preparation of derivatives.

TABLE XX. ORGANIC DERIVATIVES OF NITRO COMPOUNDS
a) Liquids (Listed in order of increasing atmospheric b.p.)*

No.	Name	Boiling point, °C	Melting point, °C	n_D	Density g./ml.	Amine Boiling point, °C	Amine Melting point, °C	Acet-amide	Benz-amide	Benzene sulfon-amide	Picrate	Nitration Melting point, °C	Position of nitro groups	Miscellaneous
1	Nitroethylene	98–9	.....	.....	1.073^{14}	16.5	.....	.....	71	58	165	.....	.....	Polymerizes readily on contact with base
2	Nitromethane	101	−17	1.3797^{25}	1.1297_4^{25}	−6	.....	28	80	30	207; 215	.....	.....	
3	Nitroethane	114	.....	1.392^{20}	1.0497_4^{20}	16.5	.....	.....	71	58	165	.....	.....	
4	2-Nitropropane	120	.....	1.394	1.024^0	33	.....	.....	26	.....	.....	.....	.....	Phenylthiourea deriv. of amine, 101; 1-Naphthylurea deriv. of amine, 200
5	3-Nitropropylene (3-Nitropropene)	125–30	.....	.....	1.051^{21}	58	.....	.....	.....	39	140	.....	.....	
6	1-Nitropropane	132	.....	1.4002^{24}	1.008_4^{24}	49	.....	.....	84	36	135	.....	.....	
7	DL-2-Nitrobutane	140	.....	1.4013	0.9877^0	63	.....	.....	76	70	139–40	.....	.....	
8	2-Methyl-1-nitropropane	140–1	.....	.....	$0.9877^{7.5}$	69	.....	.....	57	53	150	.....	.....	p-Toluenesulfonamide deriv. of amine, 78
9	2-Methyl-2-nitrobutane	150	.....	.....	.....	78	.....	.....	.....	.....	183	.....	.....	
10	DL-2-Nitropentane	152–4	.....	.....	.....	92	.....	.....	.....	.....	.....	.....	.....	Hydrochloride of amine, 168; Oxalate, 226; 131; Chloroaurate, 82–3
11	1-Nitrobutane	153	.....	1.4103^{20}	0.9710_4^{20}	77	.....	.....	.....	.....	151	.....	.....	Phenylthiourea deriv. of amine, 65; 1-Naphthylurea deriv. of amine, 149
12	1-Nitroisobutylene (1-Nitroisobutene)	154–8	.....	.....	1.052_0^0	69	.....	.....	57	53	150	.....	.....	
13	3-Methyl-1-nitrobutane	164	.....	.....	.....	96	.....	.....	.....	.....	138	.....	.....	Phenylthiourea deriv. of amine, 102; 1-Naphthylurea deriv. of amine, 132
14	1-Nitropentane	173	.....	1.4175	0.9525_4^{20}	104	.....	.....	.....	.....	139	.....	.....	Phenylthiourea deriv. of amine, 69; 2-Naphthylthiourea deriv. of amine, 114
15	2-Nitrohexane	176	.....	.....	0.9357_0^{20}	116–8	.....	.....	.....	.....	.....	.....	.....	
16	1-Nitrohexane	193	.....	1.4234	0.9396_4^{20}	130	.....	.....	40	96	126	.....	.....	
17	1-Nitroheptane	193–5	.....	.....	0.9476^{17}	155	.....	.....	.....	.....	121	.....	.....	Phenylthiourea deriv. of amine, 75
18	2-Nitroheptane	194–8	.....	.....	0.9466^0	142	.....	.....	.....	.....	.....	.....	.....	Hydrochloride of amine, 133; Oxalate, 204–5; Chloroaurate, 63–4
19	Nitrocyclohexane	205–6	−34	1.4612^{19}	1.068_4^{19}	134	.....	104	147	.....	.....	.....	.....	SnCl$_2$ + HCl → Cyclohexanone oxime, 89–90
20	1-Nitrooctane	206–10 part. d.	.....	.....	0.9346^{20}	180	.....	.....	.....	.....	112	.....	.....	1-Naphthylthiourea deriv. of amine, 72
21	Nitrobenzene	210–1	.....	1.553^{20}	1.2031^{20}	184	.....	114	160	112	.....	90	1,3	....
22	2-Nitrotoluene	222	.....	1.5474^{20}	1.1622_{15}^{19}	200	.....	110–11	146; 143	124	213	70–1	2,4	....

*Derivative data given in order: m.p., crystal color, solvent from which crystallized.

No.	Name	Boiling point, °C	Melting point, °C	n_D	Density g./ml.	Data for the corresponding amine obtained on reduction of *all* nitro groups						Nitration product		Miscellaneous
						Amine		Acet-amide	Benz-amide	Benzene sulfon-amide	Picrate	Melting point, °C	Position of nitro groups	
						Boiling point, °C	Melting point, °C							
23	1-Ethyl-2-nitroben-zene	224	......	1.5407^{19}	1.126^{24}	210–11; 214	......	111–2	147	......	194–5	......	......	
24	1,3-Dimethyl-2-nitrobenzene (2-Nitro-*m*-xylene) ..	226	13	......	1.112^{15}	215; 218	......	177	168	......	180	182	1,3,5	*p*-Toluenesulfon-amide deriv. of amine, 212
25	Phenylnitromethane	226d.	......	1.5323^{20}	1.1598^{20}_{0}	184–5	......	60	105	88	194	......	......	
26	3-Nitrotoluene	233	16	1.5470^{21}	1.1571^{20}_{4}	203	......	65	125	95	200	......	......	Oxid. → 3-nitroben-zoic acid, 140
27	1,4-Dimethyl-2-nitrobenzene (2-Nitro-*p*-xylene) ...	241–2	......	......	1.132^{15}	213–5	......	139	140	138	171	139	1,2,4	....
28	1-Ethyl-4-nitro-benzene.........	241	......	1.5458^{19}	1.124^{25}	216; 214	......	94	151	......	......	37	2,4,6	*p*-Toluenesulfon-amide deriv. of amine, 104
29	1,3-Dimethyl-4-nitrobenzene (4-Nitro-*m*-xylene) ..	246	2	......	$1.126^{17.5}$	217	......	133; 130	192	129–30	209	182	1,3,5	....
30	1,2-Dimethyl-3-nitrobenzene (3-Nitro-*o*-xylene) ...	250	15	......	......	221–2	......	135	189	......	221	82	1,2	....
31	2-Nitro-*p*-cymene ..	264	......	1.5309^{20}	1.0744^{20}_{4}	241	......	71	102	......	......	54	2,6	....
32	2-Nitroanisole	265	10	1.5620^{20}	1.2540^{20}_{4}	225	5–6	85; 88	60; 84	89	200	68	2,4,6	....
33	1-*tert*-Butyl-4-nitrobenzene......	267	......	......	......	230	17	169–70	134–6	......	......	......	......	Dil. HNO₃ → 4-nitrobenzoic acid, 240
34	2-Nitrophenetole ...	268	5–6	1.5425^{20}	1.1903^{15}	229	......	79	104	102	......	86	2,4	....

*Derivative data given in order: m.p., crystal color, solvent from which crystallized.

No.	Name	Melting point, °C	Boiling point, °C	Amine Boiling point, °C	Amine Melting point, °C	Acet-amide	Benz-amide	Benzene sulfon-amide	Picrate	Nitration product Melting point, °C	Nitration product Position of nitro groups	Miscellaneous
1	2-Methyl-2-nitropropane (*tert*-Nitrobutane)	25–6	127	46	. . . . . .	. . . . . .	134	. . . . .	198	. . . . . .	. . . . . .	Phenylthiourea deriv. of amine, 120
2	4-Fluoro-1-nitrobenzene	25–7	. . . . . .	184–6	. . . . . .	152	185	. . . . . .	. . . . .	. . . . . .	. . . . . .	N-*p*-Nitrobenzamide deriv. of amine, 181
3	1-Nitro-2,3,6-trimethyl-benzene	30	. . . . . .	235	. . . . . .	186						
4	3,4-Dimethyl-1-nitro-benzene (4-Nitro-*o*-xylene)	30	. . . . . .	226	51; 47–8	99					82	1,2	N-Formyl deriv. of amine, 52; N-Chloroacetyl, 109
5	2-Chloro-1-nitrobenzene	32	. . . . . .	209	. . . . . .	87	99	129	134	50; 52	2,4	. . . .
6	2,4-Dichloro-1-nitro-benzene	33	258	. . . . .	63	143–6	115	128	106	. . . . . .	. . . . . .	N-Formyl deriv. of amine, 154
7	4-Bromo-3-nitrotoluene	33	136[16]	. . . . . .	121; 114							
8	3-Nitrophenetole (3-Ethoxy-1-nitro-benzene)	34	. . . . . .	248	. . . . . .	97	103	. . . . .	158			*p*-Toluenesulfonamide deriv. of amine, 157
9	2-Nitrobiphenyl	37; 33	. . . . . .	. . . . . .	49–50	121	102	. . . . . .	. . . . . .			N-Formyl deriv. of amine, 75
10	6-Chloro-2-nitrotoluene	37	238	. . . . .	245	157–9; 136	173	. . . . . .				Oxid. → 6-chloro-2-nitro-benzoic acid, 161
11	3-Iodo-1-nitrobenzene . .	38; 35	. . . . . .	. . . . .	33; 27	119	157	. . . . . .				*p*-Toluenesulfonamide deriv. of amine, 128
12	3-Nitroanisole (3-Methoxy-1-nitro-benzene)	38	258	251	. . . . . .	81	. . . . . .		169	106	3,5	*p*-Toluenesulfonamide deriv. of amine, 68
13	4-Chloro-2-nitrotoluene	38	240	. . . . .	21–2	139–40; 131	. . . . . .					Oxid. → 4-chloro-2-nitro-benzoic acid, 142
14	5-Nitroindane	40, yel.	152[14]	250	37–8	106	137	. . . . . .				. . . .
15	2-Bromo-1-nitrobenzene	43	. . . . . .	250	32	99	116	. . . . . .	129	72	1,3	. . . .
16	4-Nitroindane	44	139[10]	236	–3	126	136	. . . . . .				. . . .
17	Nitromesitylene	44	. . . . . .	232–3	. . . . . .	216–7	204	. . . . .	189–91	86	*di*	*p*-Toluenesulfonamide deriv. of amine, 167
18	3-Chloro-1-nitro-benzene	45	. . . . . .	230	. . . . . .	72; 78	119–20	121	177			. . . .
19	2-Nitroazoxybenzene . . .	49, yel.	. . . . . .	. . . . . .	98	156	. . . . . .					. . . .
20	2-Iodo-1-nitrobenzene . .	49	. . . . . .	. . . . . .	61; 58	109	139	. . . . .	112			. . . .
21	4-Nitrotoluene	52	234	200	45	147	158	120	182	70	2,4	. . . .
22	4-Chloro-1,3-dinitro-benzene (1-Chloro-2,4-dinitrobenzene)	52	. . . . . .	. . . . .	91	142 (*di*)	178 (*di*)	. . . . . .		183	2,4,6	NaOH → 2,4-Dinitrophenol, 114; Hydrazine → 2,4-di-nitrophenylhydrazine, 199
23	4-Nitroanisole (4-Methoxy-1-nitro-benzene).	53	. . . . . .	240	58	130; 127	154	95	89	2,4		. . . .
24	2,5-Dichloro-1-nitro-benzene	54	. . . . . .	. . . . .	50, lgr.	132	120	. . . . . .		104	1,3	. . . .
25	4-Iodo-3-nitrotoluene . . .	55	. . . . . .	. . . . . .	48; 38	151; 136	. . . . . .					N-Formyl deriv. of amine, 129; NaOH → 3-Nitro-*p*-cresol, 36–7
26	3-Bromo-1-nitrobenzene	56	. . . . .	251	18	87	120; 136	. . . . . .	180	59	1,2	. . . .
27	1-Nitronaphthalene	57; 60	. . . . . .	. . . . . .	50	159	160	167	163; 181			. . . .
28	β-Nitrostyrene	58, yel.	250–60d.	. . . . . .	. . . . .	. . . . . .	. . . . . .					Irradiation → dimer, 180–7
29	1-Methyl-2-nitro-naphthalene	58–9, yel.	. . . . . .	. . . . . .	51	188–9	222	. . . . . .				. . . .

*Derivative data given in order: m.p., crystal color, solvent from which crystallized.

TABLE XX. ORGANIC DERIVATIVES OF NITRO COMPOUNDS
b) Solids (Listed in order of increasing m.p.)* (Continued)

No.	Name	Melting point, °C	Boiling point, °C	Amine Boiling point, °C	Amine Melting point, °C	Acetamide	Benzamide	Benzene sulfonamide	Picrate	Nitration Melting point, °C	Nitration Position of nitro groups	Miscellaneous
				Data for the corresponding amine obtained on reduction of *all* nitro groups						Nitration product		
30	4-Nitrophenetole (1-Ethoxy-4-nitrobenzene).	60; 58	.....	248; 254	3–4	137	173	143	69	86	2,4	.....
31	3,4-Dinitrotoluene	61	.....	265	89–90	4-*mono*: 131–2; *di*: 210	3-*mono*: 193–4; *di*: 263–4	178–9 (*di*)	.....	.....	.....	Oxid. → 3,4-dinitrobenzoic acid, 165; 161
32	3-Nitrobiphenyl	61; 59	.....	.....	30	148						.....
33	2,3-Dinitrotoluene	63	.....	255	63–4	.....						(NH$_4$)$_2$ S → 2-Nitro-*m*-toluidine, 108, red; HNO$_3$ → 2,3-Dinitrobenzoic acid, 201
34	1-Methyl-8-nitronaphthalene	63–4			67–8	183–4	195–6					.....
35	2,6-Dinitrotoluene	66			105	202–3				80; 82	2,4,6	Oxid. → 2,6-Dinitrobenzoic acid, 202–3
36	2,4,6-Trinitroanisole (1-Methoxy-2,4,6-trinitrobenzene).	68										Naphthalene adduct, 69–70; NH$_3$ in al. → picramide, 188
37	2,4-Dinitrotoluene	70; 72		292	99	224 (*di*)	224 (*di*)	2-*mono*: 138; *di*: 191	.....	80; 82	2,4,6	Naphthalene adduct, 60; Oxid. → 2,4-dinitrobenzoic acid, 182–3; SnCl$_2$ + HCl → 4-Nitro-*o*-toluidine, 107, yel.
38	2-Nitroazobenzene	71, or.-red			59	126	122					.....
39	1-Methyl-4-nitronaphthalene	71–2, pa. yel.			51–2	166–7	238–9					Dil. HNO$_3$ → 4-nitro-1-naphthoic acid, 220–1
40	4-Bromo-1,3-dinitrobenzene (1-Bromo-2,4-dinitrobenzene).	75; 72										NaOH → 2,4-Dinitrophenol, 114; Al. NH$_3$ → 2,4-dinitroaniline, 180; 188, yel.; Sn + HCl → 1,3-Diaminobenzene, 63; Hydrazine → 2,4-dinitrophenylhydrazine, 199
41	3,5-Dimethyl-1-nitrobenzene	75	273	220–1		144; 140						N-Formyl deriv. of amine, 76–7
42	4,5-Dimethyl-1,3-dinitrobenzene	76										(NH$_4$)$_2$ S → 1-Amino-3,4-dimethyl-5-nitrobenzene, 75; Acetyl deriv. of this, 209–10; Benzoyl deriv. of this, 223–4
43	5-Methyl-2-nitronaphthalene	76–7			63–4	123–4	155–6					.....
44	2-Nitronaphthalene	78			112	132	162	102	195			.....
45	2,4,6-Trinitrophenetole (1-Ethoxy-2,4,6-trinitrobenzene)	78										Naphthalene adduct, 39; NH$_3$ in al. → picramide, 188
46	2,4,6-Trinitrotoluene (T. N. T.)	80; 82										Naphthalene adduct, 97; CrO$_3$/conc. H$_2$SO$_4$ → 2,4,6-trinitrobenzoic acid, 220
47	2-Methyl-1-nitronaphthalene	81, yel.			32, pet. eth.	188	180					.....
48	4-Nitrophenanthrene	81			105	190	224					.....
49	3,4-Dimethyl-1,2-dinitrobenzene	82										Reduct. → 1-amino-3,4-dimethyl-2-nitrobenzene, 66, red.; Acetyl deriv. of this, 115–6; Benzoyl deriv. of this, 199–200

*Derivative data given in order: m.p., crystal color, solvent from which crystallized.

No.	Name	Melting point, °C	Boiling point, °C	Amine Boiling point, °C	Amine Melting point, °C	Acet-amide	Benz-amide	Benzene sulfon-amide	Picrate	Nitration product Melting point, °C	Position of nitro groups	Miscellaneous
50	5-Methyl-1-nitro-naphthalene	82–3	. . . . . .	. . . . . .	77–8	194–5	173–4	. . . . . .	. . . . . .	. . . . . .	. . . . . .	. . . .
51	Picryl chloride	83	. . . . . .	. . . . . .	. . . .	208 (*tri*)	. . . .	211	. . . . . .	. . . . . .	. . . . . .	NaOH → Picric acid, 122; NH₃ → 2,4,6-Trinitroaniline, 188; 192–5
52	4-Chloro-1-nitrobenzene	84	. . . . . .	. . . . . .	72	179; 172	192	122	. . . . . .	. . . . . .	. . . . . .	NaOH → 4-Nitrophenol, 114
53	2,5-Dibromo-1,4-dinitro-benzene	127	. . . . . .	. . . . . .	. . . .	. . . .	. . . .	. . . . . .	. . . . . .	. . . . . .	. . . . . .	2,5-Dibromo-*p*-nitroaniline, 175, yel.
54	2,4-Dimethyl-1,3-dinitrobenzene	84; 82	. . . . . .	. . . . . .	65–6, lgr.	>260 (*di*)	232 (227) (*di*)	. . . . . .	. . . . . .	. . . . . .	. . . . . .	Reduct. → 1-amino-2,4-dimethyl-3-nitrobenzene, 84; N,N′-Diformyl, 219–20
55	2,4-Dinitromesitylene . .	85	. . . . . .	. . . . . .	. . . .	. . . .	. . . .	. . . . . .	. . . . . .	232	2,4,6	Reduct. → 2-amino-4-nitro-mesitylene, 75; Acetyl deriv. of this, 191; Benzoyl deriv. of this, 169; Benzenesulfonyl deriv. of this, 163
56	2,5-Dibromo-1-nitro-benzene	85	. . . . . .	. . . . . .	51–2	171–2	. . . .	. . . . . .	. . . . . .	. . . . . .	. . . . . .	. . . .
57	4-Bromo-1-nitro-naphthalene	85	. . . . . .	. . . . . .	102	193	. . . .	. . . . . .	. . . . . .	. . . . . .	. . . . . .	N-Formyl deriv. of amine, 172
58	2,4-Dinitrophenetole 1,3-Dinitro-4-ethoxybenzene	86	. . . . . .	. . . . . .	67–8	193 (*di*)	. . . .	. . . . . .	. . . . . .	78	2,4,6	Reduct. → 2-nitro-*p*-pheneti-dine, 40
59	4-Chloro-1-nitro-naphthalene	87; 85	. . . . . .	. . . . . .	98	186	. . . .	. . . . . .	. . . . . .	. . . . . .	. . . . . .	
60	1,3-Dinitrobenzene	90	. . . . . .	. . . . . .	63	191 (*di*), 87–9 (*mono*)	240 (*di*), 125 (*mono*)	194	184	. . . . . .	. . . . . .	(NH₄)₂S → 3-Nitroaniline, 114; Naphthalene adduct, 52
61	2,3-Dimethyl-1,4-dinitrobenzene	90	. . . . . .	. . . . . .	116	275–6 (*di*)	. . . .	. . . . . .	. . . . . .	. . . . . .	. . . . . .	1-amino-2,3-dimethyl-4-nitrobenzene, 114
62	3,5-Dinitrotoluene	92	. . . . . .	283–5	. . . .	235–6 (*di*)	. . . .	. . . . . .	. . . . . .	. . . . . .	. . . . . .	Oxid. → 3,5-dinitro-benzoic acid, 204–5; (NH₄)₂ S → 5-Nitro-*m*-toluidine, 98
63	3,6-Dimethyl-1,2-dinitrobenzene	93	. . . . . .	. . . . . .	75	. . . .	. . . .	. . . . . .	. . . . . .	. . . . . .	. . . . . .	Oxid. → 2,3-dinitro-*p*-toluic acid, 249
64	4,6-Dimethyl-1,3-dinitrobenzene	93	. . . . . .	. . . . . .	105	1-*mono*: 165; *di*: 295	258–9 (*di*)	. . . . . .	. . . . . .	125	4,5,6	N,N′-Diformyl deriv. of amine, 182–3
65	2,4′-Dinitrobiphenyl	93	. . . . . .	363	45	202 (*di*)	276–8 (*di*)	. . . . . .	. . . . . .	. . . . . .	. . . . . .	
66	8-Chloro-1-nitro-naphthalene	94	. . . . . .	. . . . . .	88–9; 96	137	. . . .	. . . . . .	. . . . . .	. . . . . .	. . . . . .	
67	2,4-Dinitroanisole 1,3-Dinitro-4-methoxybenzene	95	. . . . . .	. . . . . .	. . . .	. . . .	. . . .	. . . . . .	. . . . . .	. . . . . .	. . . . . .	2,4-Dinitrophenol, 114; Naph-thalene adduct, 50; Reduct. → 2-amino-4-nitroanisole, 118, or.-red; Acetyl deriv. of this, 175–6
68	3-Nitroazobenzene	96, or.	. . . . . .	. . . . . .	56–7	130–1	. . . .	. . . . . .	. . . . . .	. . . . . .	. . . . . .	
69	4-Chloro-2-nitroanisole (5-Chloro-2-methoxy-1-nitrobenzene)	98	. . . . . .	. . . . . .	84	104	77–8	. . . . . .	194	. . . . . .	. . . . . .	
70	2-Nitrophenanthrene . . .	99, pa. yel.	. . . . . .	. . . . . .	85, pa. yel.	225	216	. . . . . .	. . . . . .	. . . . . .	. . . . . .	CrO₃ → 2-Nitrophenanthra-quinone, 260, golden yel.
71	8-Bromo-1-nitro-naphthalene	99–100	. . . . . .	. . . . . .	90	138–9	. . . .	. . . . . .	. . . . . .	. . . . . .	. . . . . .	

*Derivative data given in order: m.p., crystal color, solvent from which crystallized.

TABLE XX. ORGANIC DERIVATIVES OF NITRO COMPOUNDS
b) Solids (Listed in order of increasing m.p.)* (Continued)

No.	Name	Melting point, °C	Boiling point, °C	Amine Boiling point, °C	Amine Melting point, °C	Acetamide	Benzamide	Benzene sulfonamide	Picrate	Nitration product Melting point, °C	Position of nitro groups	Miscellaneous
72	3,5-Dimethyl-1,4-dinitrobenzene	101	. . . . . .	. . . . . .	104	. . . .						Reduct. → 1-amino-2,6-dimethyl-4-nitrobenzene, 158
73	1,2-Dinitronaphthalene	102–3, br.	. . . . . .	. . . . .	98	234 (di)	291 (di)	1-mono: 215	. . . . . .			. . . .
74	5-Nitroacenaphthene . . .	106; 101, yel.	. . . . . .	. . . . .	108	238	210; 199	. . . . . .	190–200			. . . .
75	2,β-Dinitrostyrene	106–7, yel.	. . . . . .	. . . . .	. . . .	. . . .						Alk. KMnO₄ → 2-nitrobenzoic acid, 146–8
76	5-Chloro-1-nitronaphthalene	111	. . . . . .	. . . . .	85	128	. . . .					. . . .
77	3-Nitrodurene (3-Nitro-1,2,4,5-tetramethyl-benzene)	112–3	. . . . .	261–2	75	207						
78	4-Nitrobiphenyl	114	. . . . . .	302	53	171	230	. . . . . .				N-Formyl deriv. of amine, 172
79	9-Nitrophenanthrene . . .	116–7	. . . . . .	. . . . .	137–8; 104	207–8	199	. . . . .	190			Picrate, 78–9
80	1,2-Dinitrobenzene	118	. . . . . .	. . . . .	102	185 (di)	301 (di)	185	. . . . . .			(NH₄)S → 2-Nitroaniline, 71; Hot aq. NaOH → 2-nitrophenol, 45
81	2,4′-Dinitrodiphenyl-methane	118, yel.	. . . . . .	. . . . .	88–9	224–5 (210) (di)						Oxid. → 2,4′-dinitrobenzophenone, 197
82	4,5-Dimethyl-1,2-dinitrobenzene	118; 115	. . . . . .	. . . . .	126	227–8 (di)						Reduct. → 1-amino-4,5-dimethyl-2-nitrobenzene, 140
84	3-Methyl-2-nitro-1,4-naphthoquinone	121–2; 125, yel.										Dil. KMnO₄ → phthalic acid, 200–6; Na₂SO₃ Reduct. or Fe + ac. a. → 2-amino-3-methyl-1,4-naphthoquinone, 167, red
85	1,3,5-Trinitrobenzene . . .	122	. . . .						. . . . . .			Anthracene adduct, 164; Naphthalene adduct, 156; Fluorene adduct, 105
86	5-Bromo-1-nitronaphthalene	122	. . . . . .	. . . . .	69; 63–4	215	. . . .					. . . .
87	Picric acid	122										Naphthalene adduct, 149; Fluorene adduct, 84; Anthracene adduct, 138; n-Butylammonium picrate, 151
88	2,5-Dimethyl-1,3-dinitrobenzene	123–4	. . . . . .	. . . . .	102–3							Reduct. → 1-amino-2,5-dimethyl-3-nitrobenzene, 98
89	1-Nitro-2,4,6-tribromobenzene	125	. . . . . .	. . . . .	122	232	198					Formyl deriv. of amine, 222
90	4-Bromo-1-nitrobenzene	126	. . . . . .	. . . . .	66	168	204	134	180			NaOH → 4-Nitrophenol, 114
91	2,2′-Dinitrobiphenyl	124; 128	. . . . . .	. . . . .	81	mono: 89–90; di: 161	mono: 158–60; di: 190–1	. . . . . .				N,N′-Diformyl deriv. of amine, 137
92	1,4-Dinitronaphthalene .	131–2, yel.	. . . . . .	. . . . .	120, yel.	303–4 (di)	280 (di)	. . . . . .				. . . .
93	3,5-Dimethyl-1,2-dinitrobenzene	132	. . . . . .	. . . . .	78	. . . .						Reduct. → 1-amino-2,4-dimethyl-6-nitrobenzene, 76
94	4-Nitroazobenzene	135, or.	. . . . . .	>360	126	144–6	211; 205					

*Derivative data given in order: m.p., crystal color, solvent from which crystallized.

No.	Name	Melting point, °C	Boiling point, °C	Amine Boiling point, °C	Amine Melting point, °C	Acet-amide	Benz-amide	Benzene sulfon-amide	Picrate	Nitration product Melting point, °C	Nitration product Position of nitro groups	Miscellaneous
95	4-Chloro-1,5-dinitro-naphthalene	138										NaOH → 4,8-Dinitro-1-naphthol, 235; Sn + HCl → 1,5-Diaminonaphthalene, 190; PCl₅ → 1,4,5-Trichloronaphthalene, 131
96	2-Nitroindene	141										Zn + Ac. a. → 2-indanone oxime, 155
97	4-Bromo-1,5-dinitro-naphthalene	143										NaOH → 4,8-Dinitro-1-naphthol, 235; HNO₃ At 180 → 3-nitrophthalic acid, 218
98	2,4-Dinitrostilbene	143–5, yel.			119–20, pa. yel.							
99	1,3-Dinitronaphthalene	144–5, yel.			96	263–5 (di)						
100	9-Nitroanthracene	146, yel.			145–50	273–4						CrO₃ Oxid. of amine → anthraquinone, 273; 286, yel.
101	4-Chloro-1,3-dinitro-naphthalene	146–7										Warm dil. NaOH → 2,4-dinitro-1-naphthol, 140
102	2,5-Dimethyl-1,4-dinitrobenzene	147; 142			150							Reduct. → 1-amino-2,5-dimethyl-4-nitrobenzene, 144–5
103	3-Nitroacenaphthene	151–2, yel.			81–2	192–3	209–10		221			
104	4-Nitroazoxybènzene	153, pa. yel.			138	151; 172						
105	3,8-Dinitroacenaphthene	155–6, br.-yel.			167–8, yel.							
106	2-Nitrofluorene	156; 154			129	191						
107	3-Nitro-1,2-naphtho-quinone	156, red										SnCl₂ + HCl → 3-Amino-1,2-naphthohydroquinone, 164; Dil. HNO₃ → phthalic acid, 200–6
108	2,2'-Dinitrodiphenyl-methane	159			160							Oxid. → 2,2'-dinitrobenzophenone, 188–9
109	1,6-Dinitronaphthalene	161–2; 166, pa. yel.			85–6; 77	257 (263) (di)	265 (di)					
110	1,8-Dinitronaphthalene	170; 173			66		311–2 (di)			218	1,3,8	
111	4-Bromo-1,8-dinitro-naphthalene	170, yel.										NaOH → 4,5-Dinitro-1-naphthol, 235; HNO₃ At 180 → 3-nitrophthalic acid, 218; Al. NH₃ → 4-amino-1,8-dinitronaphthalene, 246, red; Acetyl deriv. of this, 245
112	3-Nitrophenanthrene	170–1			87–8	200–1	213					
113	4-Iodo-1-nitrobenzene	173			67–8	184	222					
114	1,4-Dinitrobenzene	173; 171			140; 147	304 (di), 162–3 (mono)	300 (di), 128 (mono)	247 (di)				Aq. NaOH → 4-nitrophenol, 114
115	3,3'-Dinitrodiphenyl-methane	175			53–4	193 (di)						Oxid. → 3,3'-dinitrobenzophenone, 155

*Derivative data given in order: m.p., crystal color, solvent from which crystallized.

TABLE XX. ORGANIC DERIVATIVES OF NITRO COMPOUNDS
b) Solids (Listed in order of increasing m.p.)* (Continued)

No.	Name	Melting point, °C	Boiling point, °C	Amine Boiling point, °C	Amine Melting point, °C	Acet-amide	Benz-amide	Benzene sulfon-amide	Picrate	Melting point, °C	Position of nitro groups	Miscellaneous
										Nitration product		
116	4-Nitrophenanthrene-quinone	179–80, pa. yel.	......	......	......	......	......	......	......	......	......	$CrO_3 \rightarrow$ 6-Nitrodiphenic acid, 248–50; o-Phenylene di-amine $\rightarrow$ quinoxaline deriv., 217–8; Monoxime, 169–70; Dioxime, 210; Monosemicar-bazone, 210–11
117	4-Chloro-1,8-dinitro-naphthalene	180, pa. yel.	......	......	......	......	......	......	......	......	......	NaOH $\rightarrow$ 4,5-Dinitro-1-naph-thol, 235; $PCl_5 \rightarrow$ 1,4,5-Tri-chloronaphthalene, 131
118	9-Nitrofluorene	181–2	......	......	64; 47	262	260–1	......	......	......	......	
119	4,4'-Dinitrodiphenyl-, methane	183	......	......	93	236–7 (di)	......	......	......	......	......	Oxid. $\rightarrow$ 4,4'-dinitrobenzo-phenone, 189
120	4-Chloro-3-nitro-1,2-naphthoquinone	184, red	......	......	......	......	......	......	......	......	......	Aniline $\rightarrow$ 2-anilino-3-nitro-1,4-naphthoquinone-4-anil, 250
121	2-Nitroanthraquinone	185	......	......	303–6	262	227–8	......	......	......	......	
122	2,2'-Dinitrostilbene	196, yel.	......	......	176, golden yel.	304 (di)	......	......	209	......	......	
123	4,β-Dinitrostyrene	199, yel.	......	......	......	......	......	......	......	......	......	Acid $K_2Cr_2O_7 \rightarrow$ 4-nitro-benzoic acid, 240
124	3,3'-Dinitrobiphenyl	200, yel.	......	......	94	257–8 (di)	......	......	......	......	......	
125	2,5-Dinitrofluorene	207, yel.	......	......	175	289 (di)	......	......	......	......	......	
126	2,2'-Dinitroazobenzene	209–10; 194–5, yel.	......	......	134, red	271 (di), or.	......	......	......	......	......	
127	1,5-Dinitronaphthalene	214; 217	......	......	190	360 (di)	......	......	......	154	1,4,5	......
128	4,4'-Dinitroazobenzene	222–3; 216, or.-red	......	......	250–1	212 (mono)	......	......	......	......	......	
129	2,5-Dinitrophenan-threnequinone	228, yel.-red	......	......	......	......	......	......	......	......	......	Monoxime, 190–1; o-Phenyl-enediamine $\rightarrow$ quinoxaline deriv., 262–4
130	1-Nitroanthraquinone	230	......	......	252; 243	218	255	......	......	......	......	
131	2,7-Dinitronaphthalene	234, yel.	......	......	166; 159	261 (di)	267 (di)	......	210 (di)	......	......	
132	4,4'-Dinitrobiphenyl	237; 240	......	......	128	317 (di), 199 (mono)	352 (di), 203–5 (mono)	......	......	......	......	
133	1,3-Dinitroanthra-quinone	240, yel.	......	......	290	......	>300	......	......	......	......	
134	1,6-Dinitroanthra-quinone	255–7, yel.	......	......	262, red	295 (di)	275 (di)	......	......	......	......	
135	2-Nitrophenanthrene-quinone	258–60, yel.	......	......	205–10, dk. vlt.	......	......	......	......	......	......	$CrO_3 \rightarrow$ 4-Nitrodiphenic acid, 217; Monoxime, 213; Mono-thiosemicarbazone, 234–5
136	3-Nitrophenanthrene-quinone	279–80, or.	......	......	......	......	......	......	......	......	......	$CrO_3 \rightarrow$ 5-Nitrodiphenic acid, 268; Monoxime, 240; Dioxime, 200; Monosemi-carbazone, 254, red
137	2,7-Dinitroanthra-quinone (Fritzsche's reagent)	280; 262, pa. yel.	......	......	>330	>350 (di)	300 (di)	......	......	......	......	......

*Derivative data given in order: m.p., crystal color, solvent from which crystallized.

No.	Name	Melting point, °C	Boiling point, °C	Data for the corresponding amine obtained on reduction of *all* nitro groups						Nitration product		Miscellaneous
				Amine		Acet-amide	Benz-amide	Benzene sulfon-amide	Picrate	Melting point, °C	Position of nitro groups	
				Boiling point, °C	Melting point, °C							
138	*trans*-4,4'-Dinitro-stilbene............	288, yel.	......	......	231, yel.	353 (*di*)	352 (*di*)	......	......	......	......	....
139	**9,10-Dinitroanthracene** .	294; 263, yel.	......	......	....	....	....	......	......	......	......	Oxid. → anthraquinone, 273; 286, yel.
140	**1,7-Dinitroanthra-quinone**	295	......	......	290, red	283 (*di*)	325 (*di*)	......	......	......	......	....
141	**2,7-Dinitrophenanthrene-quinone**	301–3, pa. yel.	......	......	>360, dk. vlt.	....	....	......	......	......	......	CrO₃ → 4,4'-Dinitrodiphenic acid, 257–8; Monoxime, 246–8; *o*-Phenylenediamine → quinoxaline deriv., 356; Fluorene adduct, 270, red.-yel.
142	**1,8-Dinitroanthra-quinone**	311–2	......	......	262, red	284 (*di*)	324 (*di*)	......	......	......	......	....
143	**1,5-Dinitroanthra-quinone**	384–5, pa. yel.	......	......	319, red	317 (*di*)	>350 (*di*)	......	......	......	......	Monoxime, 253

*Derivative data given in order: m.p., crystal color, solvent from which crystallized.

*Hydrolysis to the corresponding acid.**

$$RCN \ + \ 2\,H_2O \ \xrightarrow{H_2SO_4} \ RCOOH \ + \ NH_4HSO_4$$
$$\text{Acid}$$

$$RCN \ + \ H_2O \ \xrightarrow{NaOH} \ RCOONa \ + \ NH_3$$
$$\text{Sodium salt}$$
$$\text{of the acid}$$

From the nitrile and 75% sulfuric acid, or 4:1 phosphoric acid-sulfuric acid.

For directions and examples see: Cheronis, pp. 618, 619; Linstead, p. 65; Shriner, p. 258; Vogel, p. 410; Wild, p. 250.

From the nitrile and potassium hydroxide in aqueous methanol, ethanol or benzyl alcohol.

See: Linstead, p. 65; Vogel, pp. 410, 805; Wild, p. 250; L. Palfray, S. Sabetai and S. Rovira, *Compt. Rend.,* **209,** 483 (1939).

From the nitrile and potassium hydroxide in ethylene glycol or glycerol.

See: Cheronis, pp. 618, 620; S. Rovira and L. Palfray, *Compt. Rend.,* **211,** 396 (1940).

NOTE: For the directions and examples for the preparation of the derivatives of the carboxylic acid formed on hydrolysis see the explanations and references to Tables XII, XIII and XIV, pp. 186, 187, 188, 189.

*Partial Hydrolysis to the corresponding amide.**

$$RCN \ + \ H_2O \ \xrightarrow{H_2SO_4} \ RCONH_2$$
$$\text{Amide}$$

From the nitrile with sulfuric acid.

For directions and examples see: Cheronis, pp. 619, 620; Vogel, p. 411.

*Reduction to the corresponding amine.**

$$RCN \ + \ 4[H] \ \rightarrow \ RCH_2NH_2$$
$$\text{Amine}$$

From the nitrile and sodium in absolute ethanol.

For directions and examples see: Cheronis, p. 621; Shriner, p. 259; Vogel, p. 411; Wild, p. 254; H. B. Cutter and M. Taras, *Ind. Eng. Chem., Anal. Ed.,* **13,** 830 (1941).

From the nitrile and lithium aluminum hydride in ether.

See: W. G. Brown in *Organic Reactions,* Vol. 6 (Ed. R. Adams), John Wiley and Sons, New York, 1951, p. 469; N. G. Gaylord, *Reduction with Complex Metal Hydrides,* Interscience, New York, 1956, pp. 731–750.

For summary of reduction methods see: V. Migrdichian, *Organic Cyanogen Compounds,* Reinhold Publishing Corp., New York, 1947, pp. 151–172.

NOTE: For directions and examples for the preparation of the derivatives of the amine formed on reduction of the nitrile see explanations and references to Table XVIII, pp. 291, 292, 293, 294.

---

*Derivatives recommended for first trial.
WARNING: This is not an instruction manual. References should be consulted for the preparation of derivatives.

TABLE XXI. ORGANIC DERIVATIVES OF NITRILES
a) Liquids 1) (Listed in order of increasing atmospheric b.p.)*

No.	Name	Boiling point, °C	Melting point, °C	n_D	Density g/ml	Acid B.P., °C	Acid M.P., °C	Amide	Anilide	S-Benzyl thiuronium chloride	Amine B.P., °C	Benzamide	Benzene sulfonamide	Phenyl thiourea	Picrate	Miscellaneous
1	Cyanoacetylene.	42.5	5	1.38699[17]	0.8159[17]	144d.; 83–4[50]	18	61–2	87	. . . . . .	. . . . . .	. . . .	. . . .	. . . .	. . . .	HgNO₃ → Wh. precipitate; Dimer, 64.5–5.0
2	Cyanoacetaldehyde	71–2	. . . . . .	. . . . . .	0.881[15]	. . . . .	. . . . .	. . . .	. . . .	. . . . .	45–6[15]	. . . .	. . . .	. . . .	. . . .	HNO₃ → Cyanoacetic acid, 66; 2,4-Dinitrophenylhydrazone, 170–1, aq. al.; *p*-Nitrophenylhydrazone, 153–4
3	Acrylonitrile . . .	77–8	. . . . . .	1.393[20]	0.797₄[20]	140	13	85	105	. . . . .	. . . . .	. . . .	. . . .	. . . .	. . . .	Gives solid polymer on addition of conc. NaOMe sol.
4	Fluoroacetonitrile.	80	. . . . .	. . . .	. . . .	165	33	77	. . . .	. . . . .	. . . . .	. . . .	. . . .	. . . .	. . . .	
5	Acetonitrile (Cyanomethane)	81–2	. . . . .	1.3442[20]	0.7828₄[20]	118	. . . .	82	114	135	16.5	71	58	106; 135	165	. . . .
6	Trichloroacetonitrile.	86; 83–4	. . . . .	. . . . . .	1.439[12]	196–7	58	141	95–7	. . . . .	. . . . .	. . . .	. . . .	. . . .	. . . .	
7	Methacrylonitrile (α-Methylacrylonitrile)	90–1	. . . . .	1.399[25]	0.7991[18]	160	15–6	102–6	. . . .	. . . . .	. . . . .	. . . .	. . . .	. . . .	. . . .	Gives solid polymer on heating with benzoyl peroxide
8	Propionitrile (Cyanoethane)	97; 103.5	. . . . .	1.3659[25]	0.777₄[25]	141	. . . .	79	106	151	49	84	36	63	135	. . . .
9	Isobutyronitrile.	104; 107–8	. . . . .	. . . . . .	0.773	154.3	–47	129	109–10	143	69	57	53	82	150	
10	Trimethylacetonitrile (*tert*-Butylcyanide) .	106	15–6	1.3792	. . . .	. . . .	35	153–4	127–9	. . . . .	. . . . .	. . . .	. . . .	. . . .	. . . .	
11	2-Ethylacrylonitrile.	111	. . . . .	1.4132	. . . .	180	. . . .	84, bz.	. . . .	. . . . .	. . . . .	. . . .	. . . .	. . . .	. . . .	
12	Dichloroacetonitrile.	113	. . . . .	1.374[11.5]	. . . .	194	5–6	98	. . . .	. . . . .	. . . . .	. . . .	. . . .	. . . .	. . . .	Me. ester of acid, 143–4
13	α-Chloroisobutyronitrile . .	116	. . . . .	1.4045[25]; 1.435[14]	1.064¹⁴[14]	. . . .	31	. . . .	69–70	. . . . .	. . . . .	. . . .	. . . .	. . . .	. . . .	
14	*n*-Butyronitrile (1-Cyanopropane)	117	. . . . .	1.3812[24]	0.796[15]	162	. . . .	116	96	146	77	. . . .	. . . .	65	151	. . . .

*Derivative data given in order: m.p., crystal color, solvent from which crystallized.

TABLE XXI. ORGANIC DERIVATIVES OF NITRILES

a) Liquids 1) (Listed in order of increasing atmospheric b.p.)* (Continued)

No.	Name	Boiling point, °C	Melting point, °C	n_D	Density g/ml	Derivatives of the corresponding acid RCN → RCOOH					Derivatives of the corresponding amine RCN → RCH₂NH₂					Miscellaneous
						Acid		Amide	Anilide	S-Benzyl thiuronium chloride	Amine	Benzamide	Benzene sulfonamide	Phenyl thiourea	Picrate	
						B.P., °C	M.P., °C				B.P., °C					
15	*trans*-Crotononitrile........	119	......	1.4217	....	189	72	158	115	......	83–4	.....	.....	109.5–10.5	131.5–2.5	n_D^{20} of amine: 1.4263; 1-Naphthylthiourea of amine, 129–30
16	Allylcyanide ...	119	......	1.4060^{20}	0.835^{15}	169; 163	.....	73	58	75–7	......	......	.....	123–7; 56–7	136.8–7.4	n_D^{20} of amine: 1.4191; Al. KOH → crotonic ac., 72; 1-Naphthylthiourea of amine, 109–10
17	Methoxyacetonitrile........	120	......	1.380^{28}	0.9373_4^{28}	203–4	.....	96	58	....	......					....
18	2-Hydroxyisobutyronitrile (Acetone cyanohydrin) .	120d.	−19	1.3996^{20}	0.93_4^{20}	.....	79	98	136							
19	3-Hydroxy-4-methoxybenzonitrile........	124; 131.5–2.0		....	....	.....	255–7									Acetate, 116; Acetate of acid, 206–7; Me. ester of acid, 83–4; 66–7
20	2-Methylbutyronitrile........	125–6	......	1.380^{25}	0.8061_4^0	177	.....	112	110	......	95.5–6.0	.....	.....			HCl salt of amine, 176; H_2PtCl_6 salt of amine, 240
21	Chloroacetonitrile........	127	......	....	1.193^{20}	189	63	120	137	......	......	.....	.....		142–3	Addition comp. with $AlCl_3$, 38, HCl salt of amine, 144
22	Isovaleronitrile .	130	......	....	0.7884_0^{20}	176	.....	136	113; 109–10	153	96	.....	.....	102	138	3-Nitrohydrogen phthalate of amine, 108
23	2,4-Pentadienonitrile........	135–8	......	1.4880	0.8444	.....	72	124	.....							Me. ester of acid, 50–2²⁰

*Derivative data given in order: m.p., crystal color, solvent from which crystallized.

TABLE XXI. ORGANIC DERIVATIVES OF NITRILES
a) Liquids 1) (Listed in order of increasing atmospheric b.p.)* (Continued)

No.	Name	Boiling point, °C	Melting point, °C	n_D	Density g/ml	Acid B.P., °C	Acid M.P., °C	Amide	Anilide	S-Benzyl thiuronium chloride	Amine B.P., °C	Benzamide	Benzene sulfonamide	Phenyl thiourea	Picrate	Miscellaneous
24	2-Chlorocrotononitrile	136	......	....	....	212; 85–95[10]	99	212	.....	......	128–31	,....	.....	......	191	Me. ester of acid, 161; HCl salt of amine, 220
25	Ethoxyacetonitrile........	136–7[753]	.....	....	....	156–7[16]	.....	80–2	.....	......	108[750]	.....	.....	......,	121–3	n_D^{25} of amine: 1.4108; Et. ester of acid, b.p. 152
26	2-Methylcrotononitrile	138	......	1.4319	0.8313	198.5	64	75–6	77	......	......	.....	.....	......	.....	p-Toluidide of acid, 70.5–1.5
27	2-Bromoisobutyronitrile ..	139–40	......	1.445[25]	....	.....	48–9	148	83	......	......	.....	.....	......	.....	....
28	4-Pentenonitrile	140	.....	1.4213[14]	0.848[14][15]	188–9	.....	94	.....	91–4; 98	......	.....	.....	......	.....	H_2PtCl_6 salt of amine, 166; Thiourea deriv. of amine, 43.5–4.0
29	Thiophene-2,3-dicarbonitrile (2,3-Dicyanothiophene)....	140	.....	....	....	.....	272–4	di: 228	.....	......	......	.....	.....	......	.....	Di-Me. ester of acid, 32–3
30	3,3-Dimethylacrylonitrile ..	140–2	......	....	0.8292[14]	199	70	107–8; 65–6	126–7	......	105–8	.....	.....	105.0–5.5	139–40d.	HCl salt of amine, 193–4
31	Valeronitrile (1-Cyanobutane).	141	......	1.3991[15]	0.8035[15][4]	186	.....	106	63	......	104	.....	.....	69	139	....
32	2-Chlorobutyronitrile........	143		....	....	189[627]	.....	75.5–6.0	74–5	......	......	.....	.....	......	142; 124	....
33	Diethylacetonitrile........	145		....	....	190	.....	107	.....	......	71.5	.....	.....	......	168–9	....
34	2-Furanecarbonitrile (α-Furonitrile; 2-Cyanofuran)..	147	......	1.4798[20]	1.0822[20][4]	.....	133–4	142	124	211	145–6	.....	.....	......	150	....
35	2-Methylacetoacetonitrile ...	147; 145–6	.....	1.4239[20]	0.9794[20][4]	224[34]	73	138–40	.....	......	......	.....	.....	......	.....	Semicarbazone, 153; p-Nitrophenylhydrazone, 147
36	Cyclobutanecarbonitrile (Cyanocyclobutane)	150	......	....	....	195	.....	152–3; 155	112.5–3.0	......	110[753]	.....	.....	......	.....	HCl salt of amine, 235.5

*Derivative data given in order: m.p., crystal color, solvent from which crystallized.

TABLE XXI. ORGANIC DERIVATIVES OF NITRILES
a) Liquids 1) (Listed in order of increasing atmospheric b.p.)* (Continued)

No.	Name	Boiling point, °C	Melting point, °C	n_D	Density g/ml	Derivatives of the corresponding acid RCN → RCOOH					Derivatives of the corresponding amine RCN → RCH₂NH₂					Miscellaneous
						Acid		Amide	Anilide	S-Benzyl thiuronium chloride	Amine	Benzamide	Benzene sulfonamide	Phenyl thiourea	Picrate	
						B.P., °C	M.P., °C				B.P., °C					
37	2-Chloro-3-methylbutyronitrile.......	154–5	......	....	0.9922[12]	210–2; 126[32]	37–9	......	.....	....	......	.....	.....	......	137–8; 160	Et. ester of acid, b.p. 178–9; HCl salt of amine, 190d.; H₂PtCl₆ salt of amine, 193–5
38	Isocapronitrile (4-Methylpentanonitrile)......	155	......	1.4085[14]	0.807[14]₄	199.4	–33	119; 121	111–2	......	125	.....	.....	......	123–5	....
39	2,2-Dimethylacetoacetonitrile.......	163–4	......		1.008[13]	103[1]	.....	121			.....					Oxime, 99–100
40	2-Methylhexanonitrile..	165	......	1.4070	0.7985	210	.....	72	98	......	45–54[15]	.....	.....	......		....
41	3-Methoxypropionitrile..	165	......	1.4032	0.9367[25]₄	107[10]	.....	50	.....	.....	120					
42	n-Capronitrile (n-Hexanonitrile)......	165	–80.31	1.4115[20]	0.8093[20]₂₀	205		100	95	.....	130	40	96	77	126	HCl salt of amine, 219
43	(Ethylamino)acetonitrile (N-Ethylglycinonitrile)......	166–7; 81–3[29]	......	......					180–2	.....	126–9	di: 117–8	.....	.....	di: 194–5	HCl salt, 141–2
44	d,l-3-Methylhexanonitrile..	171–2[749]	......	1.4143	0.8109	212–3[755]		99–100	.....		148–9[756]	......	.....	......		p-Toluidide of acid, 73–4; n_D^{20} of amine, 0.7787
45	Chlorofumaronitrile.......	172; 64[10]	......	1.49571[20]	1.2499[20]				191–2	di: 186						Di-Me. ester of acid, b.p. 113–4[17]
46	2-Acetoxypropionitrile (O-Acetyl lactonitrile)...	172–3	......			167–70[78]	57–60	......								H₂PtCl₆ salt of amine, 207–9
47	3-Ethoxypropionitrile.......	173	......	1.4068	0.9189[25]₄	119[19]	.....	50	.....		138					n_D^{20} of amine, 1.4242; D_4^{20} of amine, 0.8697
48	3-Chlorobutyronitrile.......	176	......		1.0772[9]	101[13]	43–4.5		89–90	....					147	H₂PtCl₆ salt of amine, 212
49	3-Chloropropionitrile.....	178	......		1.1443[18.5]	204	41	......	119, w.	....					.....	p-Toluidide of acid, 121; HCl salt of amine, 146–8

*Derivative data given in order: m.p., crystal color, solvent from which crystallized.

TABLE XXI. ORGANIC DERIVATIVES OF NITRILES

a) Liquids 1) (Listed in order of increasing atmospheric b.p.)* (Continued)

| No. | Name | Boiling point, °C | Melting point, °C | n_D | Density g/ml | Derivatives of the corresponding acid RCN → RCOOH | | | | | Derivatives of the corresponding amine RCN → RCH₂NH₂ | | | | | | Miscellaneous |
						Acid B.P., °C	Acid M.P., °C	Amide	Anilide	S-Benzyl thiuronium chloride	Amine B.P., °C	Benzamide	Benzene sulfonamide	Phenyl thiourea	Picrate	
50	Indole-3-carbonitrile (3-Cyanoindole) .	178, rose	.....	.....	.....	208–10	.....	.....	.....	.....	.....	.....	.....	.....	.....	N-Acetyl deriv., 202; Et. ester of acid, 82; M.p. of amine, 84
51	5-Methyl-hexanonitrile . .	178–80	.....	.....	.....	216	.....	104	75	149.5	.....	.....	.....	.....	.....	Me. ester of acid, b.p. 166–7
52	Thiophene-3-carbonitrile (3-Cyanothiophene)	179; 203–5	.....	1.5565[21]	1.1956[20 20]	.....	138	180	.....	.....	.....	.....	.....	.....	.....	. . . .
53	d,l-4-Methyl-hexanonitrile . .	180	.....	1.4144	0.8141	217–8	.....	98	.....	.....	152–3[750]	.....	.....	.....	.....	n_D^{20} of amine, 1.4238; D_4^{20} of amine, 0.7802
54	d,l-Lactonitrile (Acetaldehyde cyanohydrin) .	182–4	.....	1.4058[18]	0.9877[20 4]	122[15]	18	79; 75–6	59	153	161–2	.....	.....	.....	142	. . . .
55	Glycolonitrile (Formaldehyde cyanohydrin) .	183 sl.d.	.....	.....	.....	.....	80	120	97	141; 146–7	171	.....	.....	.....	160	Benzoyl deriv., 195–6
56	Heptanonitrile .	183; 187	.....	.....	0.8107[20 0]	223	.....	95	71	.....	155	.....	.....	75	121	
57	4-Cyanoheptane	183–4	.....	.....	.....	221–2	.....	123–4	.....	.....	167	.....	.....	.....	.....	Et. ester of acid, b.p. 183; H₂PtCl₆ salt of amine, 211 d.
58	Benzonitrile	190	−13	1.5289[20]	1.0102[15 15]	.....	122	129	162	167	184–5	105	88	156	194	. . . .
59	Thiophene-2-carbonitrile (2-Cyanothiophene)	192	.....	1.5641[15]	1.1800[15 4]	.....	129–30; 192	180	140	.....	58[5]	.....	.....	.....	181–2	HCl salt of amine, 193–4
60	2-Octynonitrile .	194–6	.....	.....	.....	148–9[19]	f.p. 2–5	91	44	.....	.....	.....	.....	.....	.....	
61	4-Chlorobutyro-nitrile	196–7	.....	.....	1.162[10]	196[22]	16	88–9	60–70, bz.-pet. eth.							

*Derivative data given in order: m.p., crystal color, solvent from which crystallized.

TABLE XXI. ORGANIC DERIVATIVES OF NITRILES
a) Liquids 1) (Listed in order of increasing atmospheric b.p.)* (Continued)

No.	Name	Boiling point, °C	Melting point, °C	n_D	Density g/ml	Acid B.P., °C	Acid M.P., °C	Amide	Anilide	S-Benzyl thiuronium chloride	Amine B.P., °C	Benzamide	Benzene sulfonamide	Phenyl thiourea	Picrate	Miscellaneous
62	Methyl cyanoacetate	200; 115[36]	−22.5	1.4170[25]	1.0962[25]	.....	.....	......	.....	......	58[15]	.....	......	......	.....	Hydrolysis → malonic acid, 135; HCl salt of amine, 102.5; H_2PtCl_6 salt of amine, 192; NH_3 → Cyanoacetamide, 118
63	Dibenzyl acetonitrile	200–15	......	......	....	.....	89	128–9	155	......	......	.....	......	......	.....	....
64	2-Tolunitrile (2-Methylbenzonitrile)	205	−13	1.5272[25]	0.9912[25]	.....	104	140	125	146	208	88	.....	......	215	Acetyl deriv. of amine, 69
65	2,3,3-Trimethyl-1-cyclopentene-1-carbonitrile (β-Campholytonitrile)	205; 225	......	....	0.9127[15]	255–6	135	130, al.	104, aq. al.	......	205.5–6.5	.....	......	......	178	Et. ester of acid, 222–5; HCl salt of amine, 175–6
66	Caprylonitrile (Octanonitrile)	206; 199	......	1.4224[15]He	0.8172[15]	239	16	110	57	......	180	.....	......	......	112	....
67	1,1-Dicyanopropane (Ethyl malononitrile)	206[756]; 90–1[20]	......	....	0.9515[11]	.....	111.5	di: 216	.....	......	......	.....	......	......	.....	Dihydrazide of acid, 168, al.
68	Ethyl cyanoacetate	207	......	1.4179[20]	1.056[25]	.....	.....	......	198–9	......	......	.....	......	......	.....	NH_3 → Cyanoacetamide, 118
69	1,1-Dicyanobutane (Propyl malononitrile)	210[750]	......	....	0.9224[18]	.....	96	di: 184	di: 198	......	......	.....	......	......	.....	....
70	3-Tolunitrile (3-Methylbenzonitrile)	212	−23	....	1.0316[20]	.....	113; 110	95	126	140	207	.....	......	......	198; 156	Acetyl deriv. of amine, 150
71	Cyclohexylacetonitrile	215	......	1.457[18]	0.913[18]	244.6	33	171–2	.....	......	188–9	79–81	......	......	155–6	HCl salt of amine, 252–3; n_D^{25} of amine, 1.4625
72	4,4-Dicyano-1-butene (Allyl malononitrile)	217–8	f.p. −12	....	....	.....	105, eth.	......	.....	......	......	.....	......	......	.....	Di-Et. ester of acid, b.p. 222–3; p-Nitrobenzyl ester of acid, 46, al.

*Derivative data given in order: m.p., crystal color, solvent from which crystallized.

TABLE XXI. ORGANIC DERIVATIVES OF NITRILES

a) Liquids 1) (Listed in order of increasing atmospheric b.p.)* (Continued)

No.	Name	Boiling point, °C	Melting point, °C	n_D	Density g/ml	Acid B.P. °C	Acid M.P. °C	Amide	Anilide	S-Benzyl thiuronium chloride	Amine B.P., °C	Benz-amide	Benzene sulfon-amide	Phenyl thiourea	Picrate	Miscellaneous
						Derivatives of the corresponding acid RCN → RCOOH					Derivatives of the corresponding amine RCN → RCH₂NH₂					
73	3-Isopropyli-dene-1-methyl-cyclopentane-1-carbonitrile (β-Fencholeno-nitrile)	217–9	......	......	$0.9203^{15,6}$	259	72–3	86.5–7.5	......						......	Me. ester of acid, 97–9
74	3-Hydroxy-propionitrile	220	......		1.059^0	d	syrup	......			188				222	Sodium salt of acid, 143; $P_2O_5 \rightarrow$ acrylo-nitrile, b.p. 77
75	1,1-Dicyano-3-methylbutane (Isobutyl malononitrile)	222	......	......		.....	108, bz.	di: 195–6, al.							......	
76	Nonanonitrile	224	−34.2	1.42522	0.8221^{15}_4	255	15	99	57	......	201	49	......	......	111	Acetyl deriv. of amine, 34.5
77	2-Phenylcro-tononitrile	$224–6^{751}$	......	1.5555	1.013	.....	136	98–9								....
78	Ethylenecyano-hydrin	229.7; 220	......	......	1.059^0						$107–8^{756}$				130; 222	Me. ester of acid, b.p. 177–84; H_2PtCl_6 salt of amine, 199
79	2-Phenylpropio-nitrile	232	......	......		265–8	.....	97.5	.....	210	......	.....	......		182	Me. ester of acid, 221; M.p. of amine, 85; HCl salt of amine, 123–4; H_2PtCl_6 salt of amine, 229d.
80	Phenylaceto-nitrile (Benzyl cyanide)	234	......	1.5211^{25}	1.0214^{15}_{15}	.....	76–7	157	118	163	198	116	69	135	174; 167	....
81	Phenoxyaceto-nitrile	239–40	......	......	$1.09^{17.5}$	285	98–9	101.5	.....		$228–9^{755}$				167–8	HCl salt of amine, 215; HBr salt of amine, 192–3

*Derivative data given in order: m.p., crystal color, solvent from which crystallized.

TABLE XXI. ORGANIC DERIVATIVES OF NITRILES
a) Liquids 1) (Listed in order of increasing atmospheric b.p.)* (Continued)

No.	Name	Boiling point, °C	Melting point, °C	n_D	Density g/ml	Acid B.P. °C	Acid M.P. °C	Amide	Anilide	S-Benzyl thiuronium chloride	Amine B.P., °C	Benzamide	Benzene sulfonamide	Phenyl thiourea	Picrate	Miscellaneous
82	4-Hydroxy-butyronitrile	240	.....	....	1.029[8]	204	.....	.....	.....	.....	205–6	.....	.....	.....	.....	Acid forms readily butyro-lactone, b.p. 204; CrO_3 + butyro-lactone → succinic acid, 186
83	(3-Tolyl)aceto-nitrile (m-Xylylcyanide)	240–1	.....	....	1.0022[22]	120–3[26]	61	141	.....	.....	214–5[744]	.....	.....	.....	176	Et. ester of acid, b.p. 237–8; HCl salt of amine, 159
84	(4-Tolyl)aceto-nitrile (p-Xylylcyanide)	242–3	18	1.5153[25]	0.9922[22]	265–7	94	185	.....	.....	214.5	95–6	.....	.....	155	Et. ester of acid, b.p. 240; HCl salt of amine, 216–7
85	4-Isopropyl-benzonitrile	243–4[734]	.....	....	....	.....	117–8, al.	153; 133	.....	.....	227[724]	.....	.....	.....	.....	Et. ester of acid, b.p. 263–4; HCl salt of amine, 239–40
86	(2-Tolyl)aceto-nitrile (o-Xylyl cyanide)	244	.....	....	1.0156[22]	.....	88–9	161	.....	.....	215.5–7.0	.....	.....	.....	177	HCl salt of amine, 227–8
87	Decanonitrile	245	.....	1.4320[15]He	0.8294[15]	269	31	100; 108	70	.....	.....	.....	.....	.....	.....	....
88	3-Methyl-2-phenylbutyro-nitrile	245–9[745]	.....	1.5038[25]	0.967[15.5]	159–60[14]	61–2	111–2	132–3	.....	155–6[24]	.....	.....	.....	.....	HCl salt of amine, 128
89	1,2-Dicyano-propane (Methyl suc-cinonitrile)	252–4	12	....	....	.....	115	di: 225	di: 200	.....	172–3	154	.....	.....	.....	HCl salt of diamine, 144–5
90	1-Undecano-nitrile (1-Hendecano-nitrile)	253–4	.....	....	....	164[15]	28.2–.6	98.0–.7	71	.....	.....	.....	.....	.....	.....	Hydrazide of acid, 101–2; Phenyl-hydra-zide of acid, 110
91	2-Phenylvalero-nitrile	254–5[750]	.....	1.5000	0.960[15]	280	58	83–5	.....	.....	90[3]	.....	.....	.....	.....	....
92	10-Undeceno-nitrile (10-Hendeceno-nitrile)	257; 129–30[14]	.....	1.4442[20]	0.8443[20]	274	24.5	87	.....	.....	.....	.....	.....	.....	.....	

*Derivative data given in order: m.p., crystal color, solvent from which crystallized.

No.	Name	Boiling point, °C	Melting point, °C	n_D	Density g/ml	Derivatives of the corresponding acid RCN → RCOOH					Derivatives of the corresponding amine RCN → RCH₂NH₂					Miscellaneous
						Acid B.P. °C	Acid M.P. °C	Amide	Anilide	S-Benzyl thiuronium chloride	Amine B.P., °C	Benz-amide	Benzene sulfon-amide	Phenyl thiourea	Picrate	
93	3-Phenylpropio-nitrile	261	.....	....	1.0014[18]	280[754]	48.5	105	98	.....	221.5[755]	57–8	.....	......	152–3	HCl salt of amine, 218; H₂PtCl₆ salt of amine, 233
94	2-Cyanobenzal chloride (α,α-Dichloro-o-tolunitrile)	261	.....	....		.....	155, bz.	117	.....	.....						
95	N-Methylani-linonitrile (N-Cyano-N-methylaniline)	266	13	....		.....	95–100	163								Picrate, 195
96	3-(2-Chloro-phenyl)propio-nitrile	267–8	.....	1.5390	1.1390[20]	.....	96.5, w.	119, bz.								Me. ester of acid, 255; HCl salt of amine, 167
97	1,3-Dicyano-2-methylpropane (2-Methyl-glutaro-nitrile)	269–71	.....			205–8[12]	79	di: 175–6	.....	.....	78[11]				.....	Di-p-tolui-dide of acid, 174–5; n_D^{25} of amine, 1.4585
98	O-Benzoyl lacto-nitrile (Lacto-nitrile ben-zoate)	269–70	.....			.....		112	124	.....				.		Di-p-nitro-benzyl ester of acid, 119.5
99	3-Cyanobenzal chloride (α,α-Dichloro-m-tolunitrile)	272–5	.....			.....		132	.....						.....	......
100	4-Cyanobenzal chloride (α,α-Dichloro-p-tolunitrile)	273–6[770]						151–8							.....	Et. ester of acid, 45–6
101	Dodecanonitrile (Lauronitrile)	276.7	4	1.43595	0.8273[15]	225	44	110; 102, aq. al.	78	141	247–9	.....	.....	......	.....	M.p. of amine, 28.3; Acetyl deriv. of amine, 68.5–9.5, bz.; p-Toluene-sulfonyl deriv. of amine, 73
102	1,3-Dicyano-propane (Glutaro-nitrile)	286	.....	1.4365[23]	0.995$_4^{15}$	.....	97	175	224	.....	178–80	di: 135	119	148	237	....

*Derivative data given in order: m.p., crystal color, solvent from which crystallized.

TABLE XXI. ORGANIC DERIVATIVES OF NITRILES
a) Liquids 1) (Listed in order of increasing atmospheric b.p.)* (Continued)

| No. | Name | Boiling point, °C | Melting point, °C | n_D | Density g/ml | Derivatives of the corresponding acid RCN → RCOOH | | | | | Derivatives of the corresponding amine RCN → RCH$_2$NH$_2$ | | | | | Miscellaneous |
| | | | | | | Acid | | Amide | Anilide | S-Benzyl thiuronium chloride | Amine | Benzamide | Benzene sulfonamide | Phenyl thiourea | Picrate | |
						B.P., °C	M.P., °C				B.P., °C					
103	**4-Methoxyhydrocinnamonitrile** (3-(4-Methoxyphenyl)-propionitrile).	290–300	. . . . .	. . . .	. . . .	. . . . .	104–5	125	. . . . .	. . . . . .	118–20[2]	. . . . .	. . . . .	. . . . . .	. . . . .	Me. ester of acid, 38; M.p. of amine, 65.7–6.3; HCl salt of amine, 220–5
104	**1,4-Dicyanobutane** (Adiponitrile)	295	0–1	1.4597[20]	0.951$^{19}_{19}$	. . . . .	153; 150	220	239	. . . . . .	204–5	*di*: 155	*di*: 154	. . . . . .	220	M.p. of amine, 42

*Derivative data given in order: m.p., crystal color, solvent from which crystallized.

TABLE XXI. ORGANIC DERIVATIVES OF NITRILES

TABLE XXI. ORGANIC DERIVATIVES OF NITRILES
a) Liquids 2) (b.p. at reduced pressure only) (Listed in order of increasing m.p. of the corresponding acid)*

No.	Name	Boiling point, °C	Melting point, °C	n_D	Density g/ml	Acid B.P., °C	Acid M.P., °C	Amide	Anilide	S-Benzyl thiuronium chloride	Amine B.P., °C	Benzamide	Benzene sulfonamide	Phenylthiourea	Picrate	Miscellaneous
1	1,2,2,3-Tetramethyl-3-cyclopentene-1-acetonitrile (5-Methyl-α-campholenonitrile) ...	$115-9^{18}$	.....	1.47221^{18}	0.9217^{18}_{4}	$150-1.5^{12}$	35.6-7.0	99-100, lgr.	......	......	......	......	......	......	......	....
2	1-Cyanocyclohexene	81^{12}	.....	1.4818^{25}	0.954^{25}	$238-40^{638}$	38	127-8	......	......	$55-7^{12}$	......	......	......	181	....
3	2-Hydroxybutyronitrile (Propanal cyanohydrin)	$102-3^{23}$	.....	1.4150	0.9621	225-60d.	43-4	......	89-90	......	172^{755}	112.1-3.1	......	......	......	N,O-Di-p-nitrobenzoyl deriv. of amine, 119.2; Acetate, 43, CS₂
4	Hydnocarponitrile .	$155-6^{2-3}$	.....	1.4559^{25}	0.8580^{25}	......	59-60	108.5d.	......	......	......	......	......	......	......	......
5	α-Chloro-α-phenylacetonitrile	$131-5^{13}$	.....	......	......	......	60-1	116	......	......	......	......	......	......	......	......
6	Butyl cyanoacetate ...	115^{15}	.....	1.4243^{25}	0.998^{25}	......	66	119-20	198-9	......	......	......	......	......	......	......
7	3-Bromopropionitrile	69^{7}	.....	1.4789^{25}	......	......	62	......	......	......	......	......	......	......	154, yel.	Nitrile + alkali → acrylic acid, p-toluidide of which, 141
8	2,4-Diphenylbutyronitrile	$152-6^{1}$	.....	......	......	190^{1}	72-3; 76	96	......	......	......	......	......	......	......	......
9	Thiophene-2-acetonitrile	$115-20^{22}$	.....	1.5399^{25}	1.153^{25}_{4}	......	76; 63-4	146-7	......	......	$72-4^{3}$	61, bz.-lgr.	......	109.5-10	......	HCl salt of amine, 202-4; N-Acetyl deriv. of amine, 45.5-6.5
10	trans-4-Chlorocrotononitrile	$61-1.4^{11}$	.....	1.4705	1.1207	$117-8^{13}$	83	130-2	......	......	......	......	......	......	......	......
11	2-Cyanopentanoic acid	$125-30^{92}$	.....	......	......	......	96	di: 184	di: 198	......	......	......	......	......	......	Amide of nitrile, 124-5; Anilide of nitrile, 88-9
12	Azelaonitrile (1,7-Dicyanoheptane)..	183^{11}; 160^{3}	.....	1.4426^{25}	......	......	106	di: 175	di: 186-7	......	258-9	......	......	......	......	M.p. of amine, 37
13	3-Chloro-2-hydroxy-2-methylpropionitrile (Chloroacetone cyanohydrin)	110^{22}	.....	1.4520	1.2027^{15}	230-5	110	......	......	......	......	......	......	......	......	....
14	1,11-Dicyanoundecane (1,11-Dicyanohendecane) .	$189-90^{7}$	.....	......	......	......	111-2	di: 175-6	mono: 112.5-3.0; di 160-1	......	......	......	......	......	......	M.p. of amine, 58; HCl salt of amine, 254-5, al.

*Derivative data given in order: m.p., crystal color, solvent from which crystallized.

TABLE XXI. ORGANIC DERIVATIVES OF NITRILES

a) Liquids 2) (b.p. at reduced pressure only) (Listed in order of increasing m.p. of the corresponding acid)* (Continued)

No.	Name	Boiling point, °C	Melting point, °C	n_D	Density g/ml	Acid B.P., °C	Acid M.P., °C	Amide	Anilide	S-Benzyl thiuronium chloride	Amine B.P., °C	Benzamide	Benzene sulfonamide	Phenylthiourea	Picrate	Miscellaneous
						Derivatives of the corresponding acid RCN → RCOOH					**Derivatives of the corresponding amine RCN → RCH$_2$NH$_2$**					
15	**2-Cyanobutyric acid**	153[15]	.....	.....	.....	.....	111.5	212–4	.....	.....					.....	Hydrazide of acid, 95–6; Amide, 113
16	**2-Cyanobiphenyl**...	172[15]	.....	.....	.....	.....	114	177		.....					.....	Acid + conc. H$_2$SO$_4$ → fluorenone, 83
17	**1,12-Dicyanododecane** (α,ω-Dodecane dicyanide)...	225–8[17]	.....	.....	.....	.....	129, w.	di: 189	di: 191; 170–1	.....					.....	Di-p-toluidide of acid, 165; M.p. of amine, 61.5; HCl salt of diamine, 309–10
18	**1-Cyano-4-isopropenylcyclohexene** .	116–8[11]	.....	1.4978	0.9439	164–5[10]	132–3	164–5	.....						.....	.....
19	**Sebaconitrile** (1,8-Dicyanooctane) ..	201–3[16]	.....	.....	.....	.....	134	di: 210	di: 198						.....	M.p. of amine, 60
20	**Suberonitrile** (1,6-Dicyanohexane) ..	180[12]	.....	1.4448[22]	.....	.....	141	di: 216–7	di: 186–7	.....	240–1; ·225–6	di: 121–2	.....	.....	di: 180	M.p. of amine, 52
21	**3-Cyanoindene** (Indene-3-carbonitrile).......	140–2[13]	.....	.....	.....	.....	161; 156–7	180	158	.....					.....	Hydrazide of acid, 186
22	**Aminoacetonitrile** (Glycinonitrile) ..	58[15], part d.	.....	.....	.....	.....	262 d.	65–6	62 (+2 H$_2$O)	.....	116.5	di: 244	di: 168	.....	di: 233–5	HCl salt, 165.5–6.5; M.p. of amine, 8.5

*Derivative data given in order: m.p., crystal color, solvent from which crystallized.

TABLE XXI. ORGANIC DERIVATIVES OF NITRILES
b) Solids (Listed in order of increasing m.p.)*

No.	Name	Melting point, °C	Boiling point, °C	Acid B.P., °C	Acid M.P., °C	Amide	Anilide	S-Benzyl thiuronium chloride	Amine B.P., °C	Benzamide	Benzene sulfonamide	Picrate	Miscellaneous
				Derivatives of the corresponding acid RCN → RCOOH					Derivatives of the corresponding amine RCN → RCH₂NH₂				
1	2-Cyanodiphenylmethane	19	313–4	.....	117	163	......	......	......	......	......	......	......
2	N-Piperidinoacetonitrile	19	210	....	215–7	......	......	......	182–3; 58–61⁹	......	....	di: 225; 220–1	Methiodide, 192–3; HCl salt of acid, 215–6; Phenylthiourea deriv. of amine, 92–3
3	3-Chloro-2-tolunitrile	19	107^{28}	....	159; 154	......							......
4	Tetradecanonitrile	19–20	......	....	54	103	82	......				......	M.p. of amine, 37
5	Cinnamonitrile	20	255–6	....	133	153; 109	147	175; 179				181, yel., aq. al.	HCl salt of amine, 235
6	Trichloroacrylonitrile	20	......	....	76	97–8; 87	98	......				......	$n_D^{20.5}$: 1.5100
7	DL-Mandelonitrile (Benzaldehyde cyanohydrin)	22	......	....	118–9	133–4	151–2; 146	......	116–7²	148–9	....	153–4, al.	M.p. of amine, 56.5–8.0; O-Benzoyl deriv., 63–4; 3-Nitrobenzoyl deriv., 83–4; p-Toluidide of acid, 174; HCl salt of amine, 208–19, acet.
8	Pentadecanonitrile	23	322	....	52	102	78	......	299–301				M.p. of amine, 34.0–6.5; HCl salt of amine, 199; N-Acetyl deriv. of amine, 72
9	2-Methoxybenzonitrile	24–5	255–6	....	100–1	129	131	......	226–8				H₂PtCl₆ salt of amine, 187
10	(2-Chlorophenyl)acetonitrile (2-Chlorobenzyl cyanide)	25	251	....	95	175, w.	138–9		105–8¹²			187, bz.	....
11	1,1-Dicyanoethane (Methylmalononitrile)	26	......	....	135; 138 d.	di: 217	di: 182					di: 252 d.	Di-p-toluidide of acid, 227–8; Di-HCl salt of amine, 201
12	2-Cyanopyridine (2-Pyridinecarbonitrile; Picolinonitrile)	26	212–5	....	136–7	106–7	76	......	95–8²⁰			159–60 d.	HAuCl₄ salt, 190; N-Acetyl deriv. of amine, 59–60, bz.-pet. eth.; Oxalate salt of amine, 166–7 d.
13	4-Tolunitrile (4-Methylbenzonitrile)	27; 29	217	....	179–80	155; 165	147–8	......	208	137	....	205–15 d.	D_{30}^{30}: 0.9805; M.p. of amine, 13; N-Acetyl deriv. of amine, 107–8
14	D-Mandelonitrile	28–9	170 d.	....	133	123							$[\alpha]_{5461}^{25}$: +46.9 in bz.
15	d,l-(2-Bromophenyl)acetonitrile (2-Bromobenzyl cyanide)	29	242 d.	....	84	143–4; 144–8						150–1	Et. ester of acid, b.p., 150–2¹³; M.p. of amine, 163–4; HBr salt of amine, 163–4
16	(4-Chlorophenyl)acetonitrile (4-Chlorobenzyl cyanide)	30	265–7	....	105	175	164–5		114–6¹⁵			212	HCl salt of amine, 218.0–8.5; p-Toluenesulfonate deriv. of amine, 235
17	Malononitrile (Methylene cyanide)	30	218–9	....	135	170			136	140	96	250	n_D^{34}: 1.4146; N-Acetyl deriv. of amine, 126
18	Hexadecanonitrile	31	......	....	63	106–7	90	......	......			di:	D_4^{31}: 0.8224
19	Maleonitrile (cis-1,2-Dicyanoethylene)	31	......	....	130	181	187	163; 173	163–70	di: 178.5–9.5	di: 155, al.	di: 250 d.	....
20	2,2-Dicyanopropane (Dimethylmalononitrile)	31–2	169.5, subl.	....	192–3, subl.; part. d. >130	di: 269	203–4	159–60	153	di: 152	....	......	Di-Me. ester of acid, b.p. 177⁷⁵³; HCl salt of amine, 256–7

*Derivative data given in order: m.p., crystal color, solvent from which crystallized.

TABLE XXI. ORGANIC DERIVATIVES OF NITRILES

b) Solids (Listed in order of increasing m.p.)* (Continued)

No.	Name	Melting point, °C	Boiling point, °C	Derivatives of the corresponding acid RCN → RCOOH					Derivatives of the corresponding amine RCN → RCH$_2$NH$_2$				Miscellaneous
				Acid		Amide	Anilide	S-Benzyl thiuronium chloride	Amine	Benz-amide	Benzene sulfon-amide	Picrate	
				B.P., °C	M.P., °C				B.P., °C				
21	*tert*-Butylacetonitrile (Neopentyl cyanide) ..	32–3	138	186–8	....	132	131	......	......	......	......	......	HCl salt of amine, 158–60, subl.
22	1-Naphthylacetonitrile .	33	....		131	154; 180	......	......	......	......	......	......	....
23	4,4-Dicyanoheptane (Dipropylmalono-nitrile)............	33–4 (*anh.*); 49–50 (*hyd.*)	223–4; 135–40$^{0.2}$	.....	161	*di*: 214	*di*: 168.0–.5, me. al.	......	132^{25}	*di*: 154	......	......	
24	Heptadecanonitrile	34	....	.....	61	106	......	......	335–40	91	......	......	M.p. of amine, 49; N-Acetyl deriv. of amine, 62
25	1-Naphthonitrile (1-Cyanonaphthalene)...	34; 37	299	.....	162	202	......	......	155^{12}		148	223	N-Acetyl deriv. of amine, 134, lgr.; Methiodide deriv. of amine, 213, al.
26	2-Cyanopropionic acid..	35	142–5^{11}	.....	135; 120	*di*: 206	*di*: 182; 214	......	......	......	......	......	Amide, 105; 81; Mono-*p*-toluidide of acid, 145 d.; Di-*p*-toluidide of acid, 227–8; 245
27	4-Fluorobenzonitrile ...	35	189–90	.....	183	154–5	......	......	183		......	203	....
28	Coumarilonitrile (Coumarin-2-carbonitrile)..	36	....	310–5, sl.d.	192–3, w.	159	159	......	......	......	......	......	Et. ester of acid, 27; Ph. ester of acid, 101
29	Indole-3-acetonitrile ...	36.0–.5	157$^{0.2}$	.....	164–5; 199	150–1	149.5–50	......	......	137–8	......	247 d.	Me. ester of acid, 135; M.p. of amine, 116–7; 146; HCl salt of amine, 248–9; N-Acetyl deriv. of amine, 77, pet. eth.
30	3-Bromobenzonitrile ...	38	225	.....	155	155	......	......	244–5	135–6	......	205	....
31	2-(N-Anilino)-butyro-nitrile	39	....	.....	141	123, w.	92, al.	......	......	......	......	......	Et. ester of acid, 26; b.p. 278
32	*trans-o*-Chlorocinnamo-nitrile	40	....	.....	212, yel., al.	168	176	......	......	......	......	......	Me. ester of acid, b.p. 278–9
33	Octadecanonitrile	41; 43	....	.....	70	109	95; 88	......	......	......	......	......	
34	3-Chlorobenzonitrile ...	41	....	.....	158; 155	134	122–5	......	110–2^{17}	214	......	203	....
35	2-Chlorobenzonitrile ...	43	232	.....	141	142	118	......	103–4^{11}	116–7	......	217	N-Acetyl deriv. of amine, 79–80
36	4-Chloromandelonitrile .	43	....	.....	119–22; 112–3	122–3	......	......	......	......	......	......	O-Benzoyl deriv., 57–8; Me. ester of acid, 85–6, bz.-pet. eth.
37	Nonadecanonitrile	43	....	.....	69	109.5–.8	95.5–6.5	......	......	......	......	......	Me. ester of acid, 39.5–40
38	2-Bromo-4-tolunitrile ..	44	....	.....	204	....	......	......	......	......	......	......	
39	3,3-Dicyanopentane (Diethylmalononitrile)	44–5	195; 92^{24}	.....	125, w.	*mono*: 146; *di*: 224	......	......	......	......	......	......	
40	4-Cyanobutyric acid ...	45	....	.....	97–8	182–3	*di*: 221–2	......	......	105	......	......	Amide, 69–70: Et. ester of acid, b.p. 245; M.p. of amine, 157–8; HCl salt of amine, 92–4; HAuCl$_4$ salt of amine, 86–7; 106
41	5-Chloro-2-tolunitrile ..	45–6	....	.....	169	....	......	......	......	......	......	......	Me. ester of acid, 30–1
42	(4-Aminophenyl)aceto-nitrile (4-Aminobenzyl cyanide)	46	312	.....	199	161–2	......	......	......	......	......	......	N-Benzoyl deriv., 176–7; Picrate, 185
43	*meso*-2,3-Dimethyl-succinonitrile	46	....	.....	209; 198 d.	*di*: 310–3	*di*: 235	......	......	......	......	......	Di-Me. ester of acid, b.p. 198–9

*Derivative data given in order: m.p., crystal color, solvent from which crystallized.

TABLE XXI. ORGANIC DERIVATIVES OF NITRILES
b) Solids (Listed in order of increasing m.p.)* (Continued)

Derivatives of the corresponding acid: RCN → RCOOH (Acid B.P./M.P., Amide, Anilide, S-Benzyl thiuronium chloride). Derivatives of the corresponding amine: RCN → RCH$_2$NH$_2$ (Amine B.P., Benzamide, Benzene sulfonamide, Picrate).

No.	Name	Melting point, °C	Boiling point, °C	Acid B.P., °C	Acid M.P., °C	Amide	Anilide	S-Benzyl thiuronium chloride	Amine B.P., °C	Benzamide	Benzene sulfonamide	Picrate	Miscellaneous
44	3-Bromo-4-tolunitrile	47			140	137							
45	(4-Bromophenyl)acetonitrile (4-Bromobenzyl cyanide)	47			114, subl.	192–4							Et. ester of acid, 30; HCl salt of amine, 240–3
46	N-Anilinoacetonitrile	48, lgr.			127–8	136	113						
47	3-Cyanopropionic acid	48–50			235	185	mono: 157; di: 269 d.	mono: 148.5; di: 230		79–80			Amide, 97; Me. ester of acid, b.p. 215; Di-p-toluidide of acid, 256; M.p. of amine, 193; 203 d.; HCl salt of amine, 135–6; 95–6
48	3-Chloro-4-tolunitrile	48–50			200–2								Me. ester of acid, 28
49	3,3-Diphenylacrylonitrile (β-Phenyl cinnamonitrile)	49			162; 167		130–1						
50	3-Bromo-2-hydroxybenzonitrile	49–50			184	165							
51	4,4-Dicyanoheptane (Dipropylmalononitrile)	49–50 (hyd.); 33–4 (anh.)			161	di: 214	di: 168.0–.5, me. al.		132[25]	di: 154			
52	trans-2,3-Diphenylacrylonitrile	49–51	213–4[23]		172	127, acet.	141, al.						
53	Eicosanonitrile	49.5			77; 75.2	108.9	92		196.2[4.0]				M.p. of amine, 57.8; n_D^{70} of amine, 1.4341
54	3-Cyanopyridine (Nicotinonitrile)	50	240–5		232	122	85, w.; 132, bz.-lgr.		88–90[2]	132		tri: 206–8	HAuCl$_4$ salt of amine, 196–8; Di-HCl salt of amine, 224
55	(4-Iodophenyl)acetonitrile (4-Iodobenzyl cyanide)	50–1			135								HCl salt of amine, 294–6 d.
56	4-Cyanodiphenylmethane	51			157–8								Acid $\xrightarrow{CrO_3}$ 4-Benzoylbenzoic acid, 197–200, al.
57	2-(N-Anilino)-valeronitrile	51, pet. eth.			147–8, al.	99, eth.-pet. eth.							
58	2-Aminobenzonitrile (Anthranilonitrile)	51, yel., CS$_2$	267–8[777]		147	109–11	130–1			167			Et. ester of acid, b.p. 266–8; p-Toluide of acid, 151
59	2-Bromobenzonitrile	53	253		150	155–6			118[9]				HCl salt of amine, 241; 208
60	5-Cyanothiazole	53			218	186							Me. ester of acid, 68–9; N-Acetyl deriv. of amine, 159–60
61	3-Aminobenzonitrile	53–4, aq. al.	288–90		174	78–9	114						N-Acetyl deriv., 248; Me. ester of acid, 36–8; Et. ester of acid, b.p. 294; Fe/AcOH → Benzonitrile, b.p. 190 + NH$_3$
62	2-Quinolinoacetonitrile	53–4	140[1]		274–5				138–40[7]			di: 202	Picrate, 176–7 d.; Me. ester of acid, 72, lgr.
63	2-Iodobenzonitrile	55			162	184				154			HCl salt of amine, 248–50; N-Acetyl deriv. of amine, 134–5

*Derivative data given in order: m.p., crystal color, solvent from which crystallized.

TABLE XXI. ORGANIC DERIVATIVES OF NITRILES
b) Solids (Listed in order of increasing m.p.)* (Continued)

No.	Name	Melting point, °C	Boiling point, °C	Acid B.P. °C	Acid M.P. °C	Amide	Anilide	S-Benzyl thiuronium chloride	Amine B.P. °C	Benz-amide	Benzene sulfonamide	Picrate	Miscellaneous
64	**2,4,6-Trimethylbenzo-nitrile**	55, bz.	225–30	. . . . .	155, lgr.	187–8	. . . . . .	. . . . . .	98.5–100[6]	153–4	. . . . .	. . . . .	Me. ester of acid, b.p. 241–2[718]
65	**α-Aminobenzyl cyanide** .	55	. . . . . .	. . . .	256	130–2, al.	. . . . . .	. . . . . .	135[19]	*di:* 223–5	. . . . .	. . . . .	N-Acetyl deriv., 130–8, et. ac.-pet. eth.; N-Benzoyl deriv., 151; Picrate, 160–1, yel.
66	**Cyanoform** (Tricyano-methane)	55–6, pet. eth.	. . . . . .	. . . .	. . . .	. . . . .	. . . . . .	. . . . . .					NH₄ salt, 183
67	**Succinonitrile**	56.6	265–7	. . . .	186–8	260	230	149	159	177	. . . . .	250–5	M.p. of amine, 27; N-Acetyl deriv. of amine, 137
68	**2-Iodo-4-tolunitrile** (2-Iodo-4-methylbenzo-nitrile)	57–8	. . . . . .	. . . .	205–6	167						. . . .
69	**2,6-Dinitrobenzonitrile** .	58 (145)	. . . . . .	. . . .	202–3	. . . . .	. . . . . .	. . . . . .				. . . . .	Me. ester of acid, 147; M.p. of amine, 88; HCl salt of amine, 185; H₂PtCl₆ salt of amine, 193
70	**d,l-2,3-Dimethyl-succinonitrile**	58–9	. . . . . .	. . . .	135	*mono:* 148–9; *di:* 244	*di:* 222	. . . . . .					Di-Me. ester of acid, b.p. 200
71	**2-Chloro-4-tolunitrile** . .	61–2	. . . . . .	. . . .	155–6	182	. . . . . .	. . . . . .				. . . .
72	**4-Methoxybenzonitrile** .	61–2	256–7	. . . .	184–6	162–3	169	177; 184–5	236–7	. . . . . .	. . . .	. . . . .	N-Acetyl deriv. of amine, 96; H₂PtCl₆ salt of amine, 210
73	**2,4-Dichlorobenzonitrile**	61–2	. . . . . .	. . . .	164; 160	194	. . . . . .	. . . . . .	140[122]	. . . . . .	. . . .	. . . . .	Me. ester of acid, b.p. 132[15]; n_D^{25} of amine: 1.5738; HCl salt of amine, 281.2–4.3
74	**4-Methoxycinnamo-nitrile**	64	. . . . . .	. . . .	170	186	. . . . . .	. . . . . .					Me. ester of acid, 90; Et. ester of acid, 49–50
75	**3,5-Dichlorobenzo-nitrile**	65, subl.	. . . . . .	. . . .	188	. . . . .	. . . . . .	. . . . . .	254[6]			241	Me. ester of acid, 58; n_D^{26} of amine: 1.5690; HCl salt of amine, 300
76	**cis-1,4-Dicyanocyclo-hexane**	65	. . . . . .	. . . .	168–9								Acid + conc. HCl at 180 → *trans* isomer, 300
77	**Bromomalononitrile**	65–6	. . . . . .	. . . .	113d.	181	. . . . . .	. . . . . .					Di-p-toluidide of acid, 217
78	**2-Naphthonitrile** (2-Cyanonaphthalene) . . .	66; 62	305	. . . .	184	192; 195	. . . . . .	. . . . . .				226	M.p. of amine, 60; N-Acetyl deriv. of amine, 126; Methiodide deriv. of amine, 168, al.
79	**Cyanoacetic acid**	66	. . . . . .	. . . .	135–6	170	226–7	. . . . . .		120, w.	. . . .	. . . . .	Amide, 119–20; Anilide, 198–9; Warming with benzaldehyde → α-cyanocinnamic ac., 180; M.p. of amine, 200; HCl salt of amine, 123
80	**2-Cyano-2-ethylbutyric acid** (Diethylcyano-acetic acid)	66; 57	240–5; 164[8]	. . . .	125, w.	*mono:* 146; *di:* 224	. . . . . .	. . . . . .					NH₃ → Diethylcyano-acetamide, 121

*Derivative data given in order: m.p., crystal color, solvent from which crystallized.

360

No.	Name	Melting point, °C	Boiling point, °C	Acid B.P., °C	Acid M.P., °C	Amide	Anilide	S-Benzyl thiuronium chloride	Amine B.P., °C	Benz-amide	Benzene sulfon-amide	Picrate	Miscellaneous
81	2,4-Diphenylglutaro-nitrile	66; 70–1	220–7[5]	.....	2 forms: (a) 164–5, w.; (b) 185–6, chl.-pet. eth.	....	....	....	....	....	....	....	Di-HCl salt of amine, 319–20, iso-PrOH
82	α-Chloro-3-tolunitrile	67, al.	258–60	.....	132, w.	124	....	....	....	....	....	173	HCl salt of amine, 169; H_2PtCl_6 salt of amine, 219
83	4-Chloro-2-tolunitrile	67	....	.....	172	183	....	....	....	....	....	....	....
84	1-Cyanoacenaphthene (Acenaphthene-1-carbonitrile)	68	....	.....	161	....	....	....	....	....	....	....	....
85	Phenylmalononitrile (α-Cyanobenzyl cyanide)	69	....	.....	152–3	233	....	....	....	....	....	....	....
86	6-Nitro-2-tolunitrile	69–70	....	.....	184	163	....	....	....	....	....	....	Me. ester of acid, 66
87	(4-Hydroxyphenyl) acetonitrile (4-Hy-droxybenzyl cyanide)	69–70, w.	330	.....	148–50	175	....	....	....	....	....	200	Acetate, 49–50; M.p. of amine, 160–1
88	5-Bromo-2-tolunitrile	70	....	.....	187	180	....	....	....	....	....	....	....
89	α-Bromo-2-tolunitrile (2-Cyanobenzyl bromide)	71–2	124[4]	.....	147	....	....	....	....	....	....	....	Me. ester of acid, 32.0–.5
90	2,2-Diphenylglutaro-nitrile	71–2.5	....	.....	195–7; 183	1-mono: 142–4	....	....	....	....	....	....	Anhydride of acid, 134; Imide of acid, 158–9
91	(2-Aminophenyl)aceto-nitrile (2-Aminobenzyl cyanide)	72	....	.....	119	93	....	....	....	....	....	....	N-Acetyl deriv., 120; Benzamide, 175–9; N-Acetyl deriv. of acid, 158
92	3,4-Dichlorobenzo-nitrile	72	....	.....	208–9	133	....	....	139–40[17]	....	....	228	Me. ester of acid, 46.5–7.5; HCl salt of amine, 240–2
93	1,2,2,3-Tetramethyl-cyclopentene-1-carbo-nitrile (Campholic nitrile)	73	217–9	255	106	80	91, al.	....	210	98	....	....	....
94	Dicyanodimethyl amine (Bis(cyanomethyl) amine)	75; 77	....	.....	247.5; 225d.	di: 143	di: 140.5	....	208	tri: 166, chl.	....	tri: 212d.	N-Nitroso deriv., 43; N-Benzoyl deriv., 131–2; Tri-HCl salt of amine, 233
95	Diphenylacetonitrile (α-Phenylbenzyl cyanide)	75	....	.....	148	168	180	145	134[2]	144–5	....	211–2 d.	M.p. of amine, 42–3.5; HBr salt of amine, 205–7
96	4-Cyano-N,N-dimethyl-aniline	75.6	318	.....	242.5–3.5	206	182–3	....	....	....	....	....	Me. ester of acid, 102; HCl salt of amine, 212
97	1-Cyanoisoquinoline	78; 93	....	.....	161	....	....	....	....	....	....	....	....
98	4-Cyanopyridine	78; 83	....	.....	315	155–6	....	....	120–5[12]	....	....	179–80, al.	HCl salt, 199; $HAuCl_4$ salt, 208–10
99	α-Chloro-4-tolunitrile (4-Cyanobenzyl chloride)	78–80, al.	263	.....	203	173	....	....	....	....	....	185	H_2PtCl_6 salt of amine, 226
100	2,5-Diphenylvaleronitrile	79	....	.....	80–1, lgr.	....	....	....	....	....	....	....	....
101	3-Cyanobenzaldehyde (3-Formylbenzo-nitrile)	79–81	....	.....	175, w.	190d.	....	....	....	....	....	....	Oxime, 99–101, w.; Semi-carbazone of acid, 265; Phenylhydrazone of acid, 164

*Derivative data given in order: m.p., crystal color, solvent from which crystallized.

No.	Name	Melting point, °C	Boiling point, °C	Acid B.P., °C	Acid M.P., °C	Amide	Anilide	S-Benzyl thiuronium chloride	Amine B.P., °C	Benz-amide	Benzene sulfonamide	Picrate	Miscellaneous
				Derivatives of the corresponding acid RCN → RCOOH					Derivatives of the corresponding amine RCN → RCH₂NH₂				
102	6-Nitro-3-tolunitrile....	80	....	.....	219	151	......	......	......	......	......	......	Me. ester of acid, 81–2; Et. ester of acid, 55, al.
103	Benzoylacetonitrile	81	....	.....	103–4d.	113	108	......	......	......	......	155d.	Carbazone of acid, 125; HCl salt of amine, 128
104	6-Chloro-2-tolunitrile ..	82–3	....	.....	102	167	......	......	......	......	......	......	Me. ester of acid, 104
105	8-Cyanoquinoline......	84, 50% al.	....	.....	187	171–3, w.	......	......	......	......	......	......	Et. ester of acid, 38; b.p. 175–7⁷
106	2-Nitro-3-tolunitrile....	84	....	.....	223	192	......	......	......	......	......	......	Me. ester of acid, 74, me. al.
107	2,3,4,5-Tetrachloro-benzonitrile.........	84	....	.....	194–5	207–8, acet.-al.	197, al.	......	......	......	......	......	M.p. of amine, 90–1
108	4-Cyanobiphenyl	85–6	....	.....	228	223	......	......	195–200¹⁵	......	......	......	Me. ester of acid, 117–8; M.p. of amine, 128; HCl salt of amine, 308–10; 282
109	2-Naphthylacetonitrile .	86; 81	....	.....	142	200	......	......	......	......	......	......	....
110	cis-2,3-Diphenylacrylo-nitrile	86	228–30²³	.....	137–8	167–8, chl.-lgr.	179, chl.-pet. eth.	......	......	......	......	......	....
111	4-Aminobenzonitrile (4-Cyanoaniline)	86	....	.....	188	182.9	......	......	268–70	......	......	......	N-Acetyl deriv., 205; N-Benzoyl deriv., 170; Picrate, 150
112	1-Cyano-2-phenylacrylo-nitrile (Benzalmalono-nitrile).............	87	....	.....	195–6d.	di: 189–90	......	......	......	......	......	......	Di-Me. ester of acid, 44; Di-Et. ester of acid, 32
113	5-Bromo-2,4-dimethyl-benzonitrile.........	88–90	....	.....	180–1	197.5–8.5	......	......	......	......	......	......	....
114	2-Cyanotriphenyl-methane	89	270–85²⁰⁻³⁰	.....	162	......	......	......	......	......	......	......	Me. ester of acid, 98, me. al.
115	5-Cyanoquinoline......	89 (anh.); 70 (+1.5 H₂O)	....	.....	342	......	......	......	......	......	......	......	Picrate, 241; Styphnate, 241d., yel.; HCl salt, 248, yel.; Me. ester of acid, b.p. 128–32⁰·²
116	2,6-Dimethylbenzo-nitrile	90–1	....	.....	116	138.5–9.0; 120–5	......	......	96–8	......	......	......	Me. ester of acid, b.p. 94⁹
117	Phenylcyanoacetic acid .	92	....	.....	......	......	......	......	......	......	......	......	Amide, 147; Anilide, 136
118	2-(N-Anilino)-propio-nitrile	92, al.	....	.....	162, w.	144	127, al.	......	......	......	......	......	Et. ester of acid, b.p. 272
119	2,4-Dibromobenzonitrile	92	....	.....	174	198	......	......	......	......	......	......	Me. ester of acid, 33
120	β-(2-Nitrophenyl)-acrylonitrile.........	92, w.	194–6⁷⁻⁸	.....	cis: 146–7, yel.; trans: 240	185	......	......	......	......	......	......	Et. ester of acid, 60
121	5-Chloro-2-nitro-4-tolunitrile	93	....	.....	180–1	......	......	......	......	......	......	......	....
122	α-Bromo-3-tolunitrile (3-Cyanobenzyl bromide)...........	93, al.	....	.....	155–6	......	......	......	......	......	......	......	....
123	4-Nitro-3-tolunitrile....	93–4	....	.....	134	176–7	......	......	......	......	......	......	Me. ester of acid, 78–9, me. al.
124	2-(N-Anilino)-isobutyro-nitrile	93–4, al.	....	.....	184–5, w.	136	155, al.	......	......	......	......	......	....
125	2-Cyanoquinoline......	94	....	.....	157	133; 123	......	......	......	......	......	......	....

*Derivative data given in order: m.p., crystal color, solvent from which crystallized.

TABLE XXI. ORGANIC DERIVATIVES OF NITRILES

b) Solids (Listed in order of increasing m.p.)* (Continued)

No.	Name	Melting point, °C	Boiling point, °C	Derivatives of the corresponding acid RCN → RCOOH					Derivatives of the corresponding amine RCN → RCH₂NH₂				Miscellaneous
				Acid		Amide	Anilide	S-Benzyl thiuronium chloride	Amine	Benz-amide	Benzene sulfon-amide	Picrate	
				B.P., °C	M.P., °C				B.P., °C				
126	**4-Cyanovaleric acid (2-Methylglutaromono-nitrile)**.	95.6, w.	. . . .	205–8¹²	79	*di:* 175–6	. . . . . .	. . . . .	. . . . .	. . . .	. . . .	. . . .	Di-*p*-toluidide of acid, 74–5; H₂PtCl₆ salt of amine, 202–3
127	**Fumaronitrile**.	96	. . . .	. . . .	295; 300	266	313–4	178; 182	. . . . .	. . . .	. . . .	. . . .	. . . .
128	**4-Chlorobenzonitrile** : . . .	96; 94–6	223; 95⁵	. . . .	240	179; 170	194	. . . . .	217	140	. . . .	210	. . . .
129	**9-Phenanthrylaceto-nitrile**	96.5–7.0	. . . .	. . . .	224.5	250–2	. . . . .	. . . . .	. . . .	. . . .	. . . .	. . . .	. . . .
130	**3,5-Dibromobenzonitrile**	97, subl.	. . . .	. . . .	219–20	187	. . . . .	. . . . .	. . . .	. . . .	. . . .	. . . .	Me. ester of acid, 63
131	**2-Chloro-3-nitrobenzo-nitrile**	97–101, pa. yel.	. . . .	. . . .	185	. . . . .	. . . . .	. . . . .	. . . .	. . . .	. . . .	. . . .	Me. ester of acid, 70; Et. ester of acid, b.p. 314d.
132	**2-Hydroxybenzonitrile (2-Cyanophenol)**	98	. . . .	211²⁰	159	133	135	. . . . .	. . . .	. . . .	. . . .	. . . .	D₄^{99.6}: 1.1052; n_α^{99.6}: 1.53716; O-Benzoyl deriv., 106, pet. eth.; M.p. of amine, 125; 129; H₂PtCl₆ salt of amine, 197d.; HI salt of amine, 184
133	**4-Chloro-2-nitrobenzo-nitrile**	98	. . . .	. . . .	142	172	. . . . .	. . . . .	. . . .	. . . .	. . . .	. . . .	Me. ester of acid, 42–3
134	**4-Cyanotriphenyl-methane**	100, me. al.	. . . .	. . . .	165, ac. a.	. . . . .	196, ac. a.	. . . . .	. . . .	. . . .	. . . .	. . . .	. . . .
135	**4-Chloro-3-nitrobenzo-nitrile**	100–1	. . . .	. . . .	181–2	156	131	. . . . .	. . . .	. . . .	. . . .	210d.	Me. ester of acid, 83; HCl salt of amine, 227–8
136	**3-Nitro-4-tolunitrile**. . . .	101	. . . .	. . . .	164–5	153	. . . . .	. . . . .	. . . .	. . . .	. . . .	. . . .	. . . .
137	**2-Cyano-3-phenyl-propionic acid**.	101–2; 75	. . . .	. . . .	120–1	225	. . . . .	. . . . .	. . . .	. . . .	. . . .	. . . .	Amide, 130; Di-Me. ester of acid, 35–6
138	**3-Cyanophenanthrene** . .	102	. . . .	. . . .	269	233–4; 227–8	216–7	. . . . .	. . . .	. . . .	. . . .	. . . .	. . . .
139	**2,3,3-Triphenylpropio-nitrile**	102, me. al.	. . . .	. . . .	222–3, al.	213	. . . . .	. . . . .	. . . .	. . . .	. . . .	. . . .	Me. ester of acid, 162; HCl salt of amine, 269–72
140	**4-Cyanoquinoline**.	102	. . . .	. . . .	253–4	181	. . . . .	. . . . .	. . . .	. . . .	. . . .	. . . .	Methiodide, 216; HAuCl₄ salt, 232; Di-HCl salt of amine, 255d.
141	**4-Bromo-1-naphtho-nitrile (1-Bromo-4-cyanonaphthalene)** . . .	102–3	. . . .	. . . .	212; 220	. . . . .	. . . . .	. . . . .	. . . .	. . . .	. . . .	. . . .	Me. ester of acid, 42
142	**4-Bromo-2,5-dimethyl-benzonitrile**.	103–4	. . . .	. . . .	171.5–2.5	209–10	. . . . .	. . . . .	. . . .	. . . .	. . . .	. . . .	. . . .
143	**5-Nitro-3-tolunitrile**. . . .	104–5	. . . .	. . . .	174	164–5	. . . . .	. . . . .	. . . .	. . . .	. . . .	. . . .	Me. ester of acid, 84–5
144	**2,4-Dinitrobenzonitrile**	104–5, al.	. . . .	. . . .	182–3	203–4	. . . . .	. . . . .	. . . .	. . . .	. . . .	. . . .	Me. ester of acid, 70; Hydrazide of acid, 231–3
145	**4-Nitro-2-tolunitrile**. . . .	105	. . . .	. . . .	179	173–4	. . . . .	. . . . .	. . . .	. . . .	. . . .	. . . .	Me. ester of acid, 69
146	**6-Chloro-3-nitrobenzo-nitrile**	105–6	. . . .	. . . .	165	178	. . . . .	. . . . .	. . . .	. . . .	. . . .	. . . .	Me. ester of acid, 73 ·
147	**5-Bromo-3-nitro-2-tolunitrile**	106–7	. . . .	. . . .	226	235	. . . . .	. . . . .	. . . .	. . . .	. . . .	. . . .	. . . .
148	**2-Nitro-4-tolunitrile**. . . .	107, pa. yel.	. . . .	. . . .	190	166	. . . . .	. . . . .	. . . .	. . . .	. . . .	. . . .	. . . .
149	**9-Cyanophenanthrene**	107; 111.0–.3	. . . .	. . . .	256.5–7.0	232–3; 226	218	. . . . .	. . . .	167	. . . .	241	M.p. of amine, 108.5; HCl salt of amine, 294; N-Acetyl deriv. of amine, 182–3
150	**3-Cyanoquinoline**.	108	. . . .	. . . .	275	198–9; 195	. . . . .	. . . . .	. . . .	. . . .	. . . .	. . . .	Picrate of acid, 217–8

*Derivative data given in order: m.p., crystal color, solvent from which crystallized.

No.	Name	Melting point, °C	Boiling point, °C	Acid B.P., °C	Acid M.P., °C	Amide	Anilide	S-Benzyl thiuronium chloride	Amine B.P., °C	Benzamide	Benzene sulfonamide	Picrate	Miscellaneous
151	**2-Cyanophenanthrene** ..	109	......	....	259–60	242–3	217–8	......	......	....	.....	....	......
152	**3-Nitro-2-tolunitrile**....	109–10	......	....	151–2, pa. yel.	158	......	......	......	....	.....	....	Me. ester of acid, 50
153	**2-Nitrobenzonitrile**	110	......	....	146	174–6	155	......	......	....	.....	....	HCl salt of amine, 248–50
154	**4-Chloro-1-naphtho-nitrile** (1-Chloro-4-cyanonaphthalene) ...	110	......	....	223–4; 210	235–6	......	......	......	....	.....	....	......
155	**5-Cyanoacenaphthene** (Acenaphthene-5-carbonitrile)........	110–1	......	....	219, bz.	198	......	......	......	182–4	148–9	....	......
156	**4-Bromobenzonitrile** ...	112	235–7	....	251	189–90	......	......	250	143	.....	221	M.p. of amine, 20; N-Acetyl deriv. of amine, 113
157	**2,4,5-Trimethoxybenzo-nitrile**	112–4, al.	......	*ca.* 300	144, bz.-pet. eth.	184.5	154.5	......	......	....	.....	....	Me. ester of acid, 97.5; Et. ester of acid, 72
158	**4-Hydroxybenzonitrile** (4-Cyanophenol)	113	......	....	213–4	162 (+1 H_2O)	196–7	......	......	....	.....	....	M.p. of amine, 109 (anh.); 95 (+1H_2O); HCl salt of amine, 195; HI salt of amine, 198–200
159	**2,3-Diphenylvaleronitrile** (2 forms)...........	(a) 115, al.	(a) 235–40[20] (b) 210–2[20]	....	(a) 152–3 (b) 178, lgr.								....
160	**α-Bromo-4-tolunitrile** (4-Cyanobenzyl bromide)...........	115–6, al.	......	....	229–30								Me. ester of acid, 54; Et. ester of acid, 35–6
161	**(4-Nitrophenyl)aceto-nitrile** (4-Nitrobenzyl cyanide)	116	......	....	153	197–8; 191	198	......	......	....	.....	....	......
162	**6-Bromo-3-nitrobenzo-nitrile**	117	......	....	180	197–8	166	......	......	....	.....	....	......
163	**(2-Hydroxyphenyl) acetonitrile** (2-Hy-droxybenzyl cyanide) .	117–9	......	240–3	147–9	116–8, al.	......	163	......	....	.....	....	O-Benzoyl deriv., 50, lgr.; HCl salt of amine, 155
164	**3-Nitrobenzonitrile**	118	......	....	140	141–3	153–4	......	......	....	.....	....	HCl salt of amine, 224
165	**4-Bromo-3-nitrobenzo-nitrile**	120	......	....	203–4	156	......	......	......	....	.....	....	......
166	**4-Cyanoazobenzene**	120–1, br., bz.	......	....	241, red, al.	224–5, red	......	......	......	....	.....	....	Me. ester of acid, 123–4, or., me. al.; Et. ester of acid, 86–7, red, al.
167	**Dipicolinonitrile** (2,6-Dicyanopyridine)	123; 113	......	....	252d.; 228	*di:* 302	......	......	......	....	.....	....	Di-Me. ester of acid, 124–5; Di-Et. ester of acid, 41–2
168	**2-Cyanohexanoic acid** ..	123–6.5	......	....	101	*di:* 200	*di:* 193	......	......	....	.....	....	......
169	**Dibromomalononitrile** (Bromodicyano-methane)	124	......	....	147d.; 136–7d.	*di:* 200; 206d.	......	......	......	....	.....	....	Di-Me. ester, 67
170	**1-Cyanoanthracéne**	126	......	....	245, yel., al.	260	......	......	......	....	.....	....	Me. ester of acid, 108, yel., ac. a.
171	**2,2,3-Triphenylpropio-nitrile**	126	......	....	162; 132	111, al.	......	......	......	....	.....	....	Me. ester of acid, 127
172	**1-Cyanophenanthrene** ..	128	......	....	232–3	284	245	......	......	....	.....	....	......

*Derivative data given in order: m.p., crystal color, solvent from which crystallized.

No.	Name	Melting point, °C	Boiling point, °C	Acid B.P. °C	Acid M.P. °C	Amide	Anilide	S-Benzyl thiuronium chloride	Amine B.P. °C	Benz-amide	Benzene sulfon-amide	Picrate	Miscellaneous
173	2,3-Diphenylbutyro-nitrile (2 forms)	(a) 129–30	210–2[16]	.....	133–4	173–4	......	......	......				....
			(b) 188–92[13]		186	193							Et. ester of acid, 91–2
174	5-Bromo-3-nitro-4-tolunitrile	130	....	.....	206	171	......						....
175	2,5-Dichlorobenzonitrile	130	....	301	154	155	......		135[9]			230	HCl salt of amine, 151–2; n_D^{23} of amine: 1.5885
176	2,5-Dibromobenzonitrile	132			157	......							Me. ester of acid, 40–1; *p*-Nitrophenyl ester of acid, 183–4
177	5-Bromo-2-nitro-4-tolunitrile	132		.....	203; 200	191							Et. ester of acid, 61
178	2-Hydroxy-3-nitro-benzonitrile (2-Cyano-6-nitrophenol)	132–3			148	155; 145–6	......						Me. ester of acid, 132 (94), al.
179	4-Nitro-1-naphthonitrile (1-Cyano-4-nitro-naphthalene)	133			220–1	218							Me. ester of acid, 107–8
180	4-Acetamidobenzo-nitrile	133, w.	....		185, ac. a.	177, al.	167–8, al.	......					N-Methylamide of acid, 172, al.
181	6-Cyanoquinoline	135, bz.-lgr.			291–2	174, bz.-al.	......		158–9[2]				Me. ester of acid, 90; HCl salt of amine, 239; n_D^{20} of amine: 1.6390
182	Apiolonitrile (2,5-Di-methoxy-3,4-methyl-enedioxybenzonitrile)	135.5, al.	....		175, w.	......							Me. ester of acid, 71–2, al.
183	1-Nitro-2-naphthonitrile (2-Cyano-1-nitro-naphthalene)	138	....		239	......	......						Hot aq. Ba(OH)₂ → 1-hydroxy-2-naphthoic acid, 191–2, al.
184	3,5-Dichloro-2-hydroxy benzonitrile	139			219.5; 223	209							Me. ester of acid, 147
185	*trans*-1,4-Dicyanocyclo-hexane	140			300	......							Di-Me. ester of acid, 71
186	3,3,3-Triphenylpro-pionitrile	140, al.	....		177	198	......						Me. ester of acid, 120–1.5
187	4-Cyano-2-phenyl-quinoline (2-Phenyl-4-quinolinonitrile)	140, al.	ca. 365	.....	218	196	198						M.p. of amine, >287; HCl salt of amine, 232–5
188	Phthalonitrile (*o*-Di-cyanobenzene)	141		.....	200–6	*di*: 219	*di*: 253	*di*: 151; 157	......	*di*: 184	.....	170	N,N'-Diacetyl deriv. of diamine, 146
189	8-Nitro-2-naphthonitrile (2-Cyano-8-nitro-naphthalene)	143	....		295; 288	218	......						Et. ester of acid, 121, lgr.
190	5-Chloro-2-naphtho-nitrile (5-Chloro-2-cyanonaphthalene)	144	....		270	186–7	202						Me. ester of acid, 81; Et. ester of acid, 45
191	5-Chloro-1-naphtho-nitrile (5-Chloro-1-cyanonaphthalene)	145	....		245; 241–2	239	......						Et. ester of acid, 42
192	3,5-Dichloro-4-hydroxy-benzonitrile	146			269; 265	......							Acetate, 93; Me. ester of acid, 122
193	4-Nitrobenzonitrile	147; 149			241	200	211; 204	......			....	184–5	HCl salt of amine, 235–40
194	5-Bromo-1-naphtho-nitrile (1-Bromo-5-cyanonaphthalene)	147	....		261; 256	241	......						Et. ester of acid, 48–9

*Derivative data given in order: m.p., crystal color, solvent from which crystallized.

No.	Name	Melting point, °C	Boiling point, °C	Acid B.P. °C	Acid M.P. °C	Amide	Anilide	S-Benzyl thiuronium chloride	Amine B.P. °C	Benz-amide	Benzene sulfonamide	Picrate	Miscellaneous
				Derivatives of the corresponding acid RCN → RCOOH					Derivatives of the corresponding amine RCN → RCH₂NH₂				
195	**5-Iodo-2-naphthonitrile** (2-Cyano-5-iodo-naphthalene)	148.5	. . . . . .	. . . .	264, al.	196	203	. . . . . .	. . . . . .	. . . . . .	. . . . . .	. . . . . .	M.p. of amine, 120; HCl salt of amine, 251–3; N-Acetyl deriv. amine, 135–6
196	**3-Cyano-3-phenylpro-pionic acid**	150	$215-8^{10}$	. . . .	166–7	. . . . . .	. . . . . .	. . . . . .	. . . . . .	. . . . . .	. . . . . .	. . . . . .	Di-Me. ester of acid, 55, al.; Imide of acid, 88–90; M.p. of amine, 209; HCl salt of amine, 203; N-Acetyl deriv. of amine, 65
197	**2-Cyano-2-propylvaler-amide** (Dipropyl-cyanoacetamide)	153	. . . . . .	. . . .	161	*di*: 214	*di*: 168–8.5, me. al.	. . . . . .	. . . . . .	. . . . . .	. . . . . .	. . . . . .	. . . .
198	**2,6-Dibromobenzonitrile**	155, subl.	308–9	. . . .	157	208.5	. . . . . .	. . . . . .	. . . . . .	. . . . . .	. . . . . .	. . . . . .	Me. ester of acid, 83; Hydrazide of acid, 204
199	**3-Chloro-4-hydroxy-benzonitrile**	155	. . . . . .	. . . .	169–70, w.; 164–5	180–2	. . . . . .	. . . . . .	. . . . . .	. . . . . .	. . . . . .	. . . . . .	Me. ester of acid, 106–7; Et. ester of acid, 77–8
200	**5-Chloro-2,4-dinitro-benzonitrile**	156	. . . . . .	. . . .	182–3	212	226	. . . . . .	. . . . . .	. . . . . .	. . . . . .	. . . . . .	. . . .
201	**4-Benzamidobenzonitrile** (N-Benzoylanthra-nilonitrile)	156	. . . . . .	. . . .	181	218–9	279	. . . . . .	. . . . . .	. . . . . .	. . . . . .	. . . . . .	Me. ester of acid, 100; Et. ester of acid, 98
202	**5-Bromo-2-hydroxy-benzonitrile**	158–9	. . . . . .	. . . .	165	232	222	. . . . . .	. . . . . .	. . . . . .	. . . . . .	. . . . . .	O-Acetyl deriv. of acid, 60
203	*d,l*-**2,3-Diphenyl-succinonitrile**	160	. . . . . .	. . . .	183 (+1 H₂O)	. . . . . .	*mono*: 173–5, al.	. . . . . .	. . . . . .	. . . . . .	. . . . . .	. . . . . .	. . . .
204	**Isophthalonitrile** (*m*-Dicyanobenzene) . .	161.5–2.0	. . . . . .	. . . .	345–7	*di*: 280	. . . . . .	. . . . . .	. . . . . .	. . . . . .	. . . . . .	. . . . . .	. . . .
205	**2-Hydroxy-4-nitrobenzo-nitrile** (2-Cyano-5-nitrophenol)	160–1, yel.	. . . . . .	. . . .	235; 226, w.	192–4	. . . . . .	. . . . . .	. . . . . .	. . . . . .	. . . . . .	. . . . . .	Benzoate, 122, yel., al.; Et. ester of acid, 84–5
206	*d,l*-**4-Cyano-3,4-di-phenylbutyric acid** (*d,l*-2,3-Diphenyl-glutaromononitrile) . .	162–3, bz.	. . . . . .	. . . .	208–10 (cor.), aq. ac. a.	*mono*: 200–5 d., al.	*mono*: 201–2, 50% al.	. . . . . .	. . . . . .	. . . . . .	. . . . . .	. . . . . .	Et. ester, 99–100, al.; Imide of acid, 225–9, aq. al.
207	*d*-**3-Carboxy-2,2,3-tri-methylcyclopentyl-acetonitrile**	164	. . . . . .	. . . .	. . . . . .	233, PhNO₂	. . . . . .	. . . . . .	. . . . . .	. . . . . .	. . . . . .	. . . . . .	$[\alpha]_D$: +64.41; Me. ester, 77; Et. ester, 58
208	**5-Chloro-2-hydroxy-benzonitrile** (4-Chloro-2-cyanophenol)	165–7	. . . . . .	. . . .	172; 167.5	226	. . . . . .	. . . . . .	. . . . . .	. . . . . .	. . . . . .	. . . . . .	Me. ester of acid, 84
209	**2,3-Diphenylcinnamo-nitrile** (Cyanotri-phenylethylene)	166–7; 162–3	. . . . . .	. . . .	213	223	. . . . . .	. . . . . .	. . . . . .	. . . . . .	. . . . . .	. . . . . .	. . . .
210	**1,7-Dicyanonaphthalene**	167, al.	. . . . . .	. . . .	294–6	. . . . . .	. . . . . .	. . . . . .	. . . . . .	. . . . . .	. . . . . .	. . . . . .	. . . .
211	**4,4′-Dicyanodiphenyl-methane**	169	. . . . . .	. . . .	334; 290	. . . . . .	. . . . . .	. . . . . .	. . . . . .	. . . . . .	. . . . . .	. . . . . .	Di-Me. ester of acid, 81–2
212	**2,2′-Diphenic acid mono-nitrile** (2-Carboxy-2′-cyanobiphenyl)	170–2, bz.	. . . . . .	. . . .	233.5	*mono*: 193; *di*: 212	*mono*: 181–3	. . . . . .	. . . . . .	. . . . . .	. . . . . .	. . . . . .	Di-Me. ester of acid, 74; Me. ester, 110; Et. ester, 91–2
213	**5-Nitro-2-naphthonitrile** (2-Cyano-5-nitro-naphthalene)	172–3	. . . . . .	. . . .	295, yel.	261–3, br.-yel.	. . . . . .	. . . . . .	. . . . . .	. . . . . .	. . . . . .	. . . . . .	Me. ester of acid, 112, yel.

* Derivative data given in order: m.p., crystal color, solvent from which crystallized.

TABLE XXI. ORGANIC DERIVATIVES OF NITRILES

b) Solids (Listed in order of increasing m.p.)* (Continued)

No.	Name	Melting point, °C	Boiling point, °C	Derivatives of the corresponding acid RCN → RCOOH					Derivatives of the corresponding amine RCN → RCH$_2$NH$_2$				Miscellaneous
				Acid B.P. °C	Acid M.P. °C	Amide	Anilide	S-Benzyl thiuronium chloride	Amine B.P. °C	Benzamide	Benzene sulfonamide	Picrate	
214	**9-Cyanoanthracene (9-Anthracenecarbonitrile)**	175; 170–2	. . . . . .	. . . .	207, pa. yel.	. . . . . .	. . . . . .	. . . . . .	. . . . .	. . . .	. . . .	. . . . .	Me. ester of acid, 111; M.p. of amine, 90
215	**2,3-Dicyanopyridine** . . .	175–6	. . . . . .	. . . .	228–9	2-*mono*: 168.5 d; *di*: 165	. . . . . .	. . . . . .	. . . . .	. . . .	. . . .	. . . . .	. . . .
216	**1,3-Dicyanonaphthalene**	179, ac. a.	. . . . . .	. . . .	267–8	. . . . . .	. . . . . .	. . . . . .	. . . . .	. . . .	. . . .	. . . . .	. . . .
217	**3-Cyanocoumarin**	182	. . . . . .	. . . .	187 d.	236	250	. . . . . .	. . . . .	. . . .	. . . .	. . . . .	Me. ester of acid, 116–7; Et. ester of acid, 64
218	**2-Cyanocinnamic acid** . .	183, al.	. . . . . .	. . . .	195–6 d.	*di*: 189–90	. . . . . .	. . . . . .	. . . . .	. . . .	. . . .	. . . . .	NH$_3$ → 2-Cyanocinnamamide, 123; Me. ester of nitrile, 89; Di-Me. ester of acid, 44–5
219	**2-Cyanobenzoic acid** . . .	187; 192	. . . . . .	. . . .	200–6	*di*: 219	*di*: 253	*di*: 151; 157	. . . . .	*di*: 184	. . . .	170	NH$_3$ → 2-Cyanobenzamide, 173; Me. ester 51; Et. ester, 70; 65
220	**1,2-Dicyanonaphthalene**	190, bz.	. . . . . .	. . . .	175	*di*: 265	. . . . . .	. . . . . .	. . . . .	. . . .	. . . .	. . . . .	
221	**2-Hydroxy-5-nitrobenzonitrile (2-Cyano-4-nitrophenol)**	194–6, yel., w.	. . . . . .	. . . .	229–30; 227	225, al.	. . . . . .	. . . . . .	. . . . .	. . . .	. . . .	. . . . .	*p*-Nitrobenzoyl ester of acid, 115
222	**Tetracyanoethylene**	198–200, subl.	223	. . . .	. . . . .	. . . . . .	. . . . . .	. . . . . .	. . . . .	. . . .	. . . .	. . . . .	n_D^{25}: 1.560; D^{25}: 1.348; N,N-Dimethylaniline → N,N-dimethyl 4-tricyanovinylaniline, 173–5, ac. a.; Anthracene → adduct, 268–70, acet.
223	**5-Nitro-1-naphthonitrile (1-Cyano-5-nitronaphthalene)**	205	. . . . . .	. . . .	241–2; 239	235–6	. . . . . .	. . . . . .	. . . . .	. . . .	. . . .	. . . . .	Me. ester of acid, 109–10; Et. ester of acid, 93
224	**1,4-Dicyanonaphthalene**	208, ac. a.	. . . . . .	. . . .	309; 288	. . . . . .	. . . . . .	. . . . . .	. . . . .	. . . .	. . . .	. . . . .	Di-Me. ester of acid, 67; Di-Et. ester of acid, 64
225	**1,6-Dicyanonaphthalene**	208–10	. . . . . .	. . . .	310	. . . . . .	. . . . . .	. . . . . .	. . . . .	. . . .	. . . .	. . . . .	Di-Me. ester of acid, 99
226	**1,5-Dicyanonaphthalene**	211; 266–7	. . . . . .	. . . .	310, ac. a.	. . . . . .	. . . . . .	. . . . . .	. . . . .	. . . .	. . . .	. . . . .	Di-Me. ester of acid, 114–5; Di-Et. ester of acid, 123–4
227	**3-Cyanobenzoic acid** . . .	217	. . . . . .	. . . .	345	280	. . . . . .	. . . . . .	. . . . .	. . . .	. . . .	. . . . .	NH$_3$ → 3-Cyanobenzamide, >300; Me. ester, 65; Et. ester, 56
228	**4-Cyanobenzoic acid** . . .	219	. . . . . .	. . . .	ca. 300, subl.	*di*: >250	*di*: 334–7	. . . . . .	. . . . .	. . . .	. . . .	232 d.	NH$_3$ → 4-Cyanobenzamide, 223; Me. ester, 62; Et. ester, 54
229	**Terephthalonitrile (*p*-Dicyanobenzene)**	222	. . . . . .	. . . .	ca. 300, subl.	*di*: >250	*di*: 334–7	. . . . . .	. . . . .	. . . .	. . . .	232 d.	N,N'-Diacetyl deriv. of diamine, 225
230	**1,8-Dicyanonaphthalene**	232	. . . . . .	. . . .	260	*di*: 250–82 d.	. . . . . .	. . . . . .	. . . . .	. . . .	. . . .	. . . . .	Di-Me. ester of acid, 102–3; Di-Et. ester of acid, 58–60
231	**4,4'-Dicyanobiphenyl** . . .	233–4	. . . . . .	. . . .	. . . . .	. . . . . .	. . . . . .	. . . . . .	. . . . .	. . . .	. . . .	. . . . .	Di-Me. ester of acid, 214; 224; Di-Et. ester of acid, 112; Heating acid with lime → biphenyl, 71
232	**/-2,3-Diphenylsuccinonitrile**	239–40	. . . . . .	. . . .	176–7; 190, w.	. . . . . .	. . . . . .	. . . . . .	. . . . .	. . . .	. . . .	. . . . .	Imide of acid, 196–8, ac. a.

*Derivative data given in order: m.p., crystal color, solvent from which crystallized.

| No. | Name | Melting point, °C | Boiling point, °C | Derivatives of the corresponding acid RCN → RCOOH | | | | | Derivatives of the corresponding amine RCN → RCH$_2$NH$_2$ | | | | Miscellaneous |
| | | | | Acid | | Amide | Anilide | S-Benzyl thiuronium chloride | Amine | Benz-amide | Benzene sulfon-amide | Picrate | |
				B.P., °C	M.P., °C				B.P., °C				
233	1-Cyano-9,10-anthra-quinone	247, yel., ac. a.	. . . . . .	. . . . .	293–4, pa. yel., ac. a.	280, pa. yel., al.	288–9, pa. yel., PhNO$_2$	. . . . . .	. . . . .	. . . . . .	. . . . .	. . . . . .	Me. ester of acid, 189, yel.; Et. ester of acid, 169, yel.
234	2,3-Dicyanonaphthalene	251, al.	. . . . . .	. . . . .	239–41	. . . . . .	. . . . . .	. . . . . .	. . . . .	. . . . . .	. . . . .	. . . . . .	Imide of diacid, 275
235	2,7-Dicyanonaphthalene	267–8, ac. a.	. . . . . .	. . . . .	>320	di: 297–8	. . . . . .	. . . . . .	. . . . .	. . . . . .	. . . . .	. . . . . .	Di-Me. ester of acid, 135–6
236	2,6-Dicyanonaphthalene	293, al.	. . . . . .	. . . . .	>300 d.	di: >320	. . . . . .	. . . . . .	. . . . .	. . . . . .	. . . . .	. . . . . .	Di-Me. ester of acid, 191

*Derivative data given in order: m.p., crystal color, solvent from which crystallized.

EXPLANATIONS AND REFERENCES TO TABLES XXII AND XXIII

The main derivatives of the sulfonic acids are obtained by converting them to the corresponding sulfonyl chlorides. Hence sulfonic acids and sulfonyl chlorides are often identified through the same derivatives.

Sulfonyl chloride.

$$RSO_3Na \ + \ PCl_5 \ \rightarrow \ RSO_2Cl \ + \ POCl_3 \ + \ NaCl$$

$$\underset{\substack{\text{Sulfonyl}\\\text{chloride}}}{}$$

From the sulfonic acid or its sodium or potassium salt with phosphorus pentachloride without solvent.

For directions and examples see: Cheronis, p. 638; Linstead, p. 89; Shriner, pp. 268, 270; Vogel, p. 553; Wild, p. 161.

Sulfonamide. *

$$RSO_3Na \ \rightarrow \ RSO_2Cl \ \xrightarrow{\ NH_3\ } \ RSO_2NH_2$$

Sulfonyl · chloride   Sulfon- amide

From the sulfonyl chloride (prepared from the acid or its salt) and concentrated aqueous ammonia solution.

For directions and examples see: Linstead, p. 49; Shriner, pp. 268, 270; Vogel, p. 553; Wild, p. 161.

From the sulfonyl chloride, aqueous ammonia and ammonium carbonate.

See: Cheronis, p. 639.

Sulfonanilide. *

$$RSO_3Na \ \rightarrow \ RSO_2Cl \ \xrightarrow[\text{NaOH}]{C_6H_5NH_2} \ RSO_2NHC_6H_5 \ + \ NaCl$$

Sulfonyl chloride   Sulfonanilide

From the sulfonyl chloride (prepared from the acid), aniline, and sodium hydroxide.

For directions and examples see: Linstead, p. 89; Wild, p. 161.

From the sulfonyl chloride and aniline.

See: Vogel, p. 553.

Sulfon-p-toluidide. *

$$RSO_3Na \ \rightarrow \ RSO_2Cl \ \xrightarrow[\text{NaOH}]{p\text{-}CH_3C_6H_4NH_2} \ RSO_2NHC_6H_4CH_3\text{-}p \ + \ NaCl$$

Sulfonyl chloride   Sulfon-*p*-toluidide

From the sulfonyl chloride, *p*-toluidine and aqueous sodium hydroxide.

For directions and examples see: Vogel, p. 553.

Sulfon-1-naphthylamide. *

$$RSO_3Na \ \rightarrow \ RSO_2Cl \ \xrightarrow{\ 1\text{-}C_{10}H_7NH_2\ } \ RSO_2NHC_{10}H_7\text{-}1 \ + \ NaCl$$

Sulfonyl chloride   Sulfon-1- naphthylamide

From the sulfonyl chloride (prepared from the acid) and 1-naphthylamine in benzene.

For directions and examples see: Cheronis, p. 639.

S-Benzylthiuronium salt. *

$$RSO_3Na \ + \ [C_6H_5CH_2SC(NH_2)_2]^+ Cl^- \ \rightarrow \ [C_6H_5CH_2SC(NH_2)_2]^+ RSO_3^- \ + \ NaCl$$

S-Benzylthiuronium chloride   S-Benzylthiuronium sulfonate

From the sodium, potassium or ammonium salt of the sulfonic acid and S-benzylthiuronium chloride in water.

For directions and examples see: Cheronis, pp. 635, 636; Linstead, pp. 15, 89; Shriner, p. 269; Wild, pp. 149, 159; E. Chambers and G. W. Watt, *J. Org. Chem.,* **6,** 376 (1941); E. Campaigne and C. M. Suter, *J. Amer. Chem. Soc.,* **64,** 3040 (1942); S. Veibel, *J. Amer. Chem. Soc.,* **67,** 1867 (1945).

---

*Derivatives recommended for first trial.

WARNING: This is not an instruction manual. References should be consulted for the preparation of derivatives.

From sodium or potassium sulfonate and S-benzylthiuronium chloride in alcohol.
See: J. J. Donleavy, *J. Amer. Chem. Soc.*, **58**, 1004 (1936).

*Anilinium salt.**

$$RSO_3Na \ + \ C_6H_5NH_2 \ + \ HCl \ \rightarrow \ [C_6H_5NH_3]^+RSO_3^- \ + \ NaCl$$
Anilinium sulfonate

From the sodium or potassium salt of the acid, aniline and hydrochloric acid in water.
For directions and examples see: Cheronis, p. 637; O. C. Dermer and V. H. Dermer, *J. Org. Chem.*, **7**, 581 (1942).

*p-Toluidinium salt.**

$$RSO_3Na \ + \ p\text{-}CH_3C_6H_4NH_2 \ + \ HCl \ \rightarrow \ [p\text{-}CH_3C_6H_4NH_3]^+RSO_3^- \ + \ NaCl$$
p-Toluidinium sulfonate

From the sulfonic acid and *p*-toluidine.
For directions and examples see: Shriner, p. 269.
From the sodium, potassium or ammonium salt with *p*-toluidine or *p*-toluidine hydrochloride in water.
See: Shriner, p. 269; Vogel, p. 555; O. C. Dermer and V. H. Dermer, *J. Org. Chem.*, 7, 581 (1942); A. D. Barton and L. Young, *J. Amer. Chem. Soc.*, **65**, 294 (1943).
From the sodium, potassium, ferric or barium salt (after boiling with sulfuric acid) with *p*-toluidine and hydrochloric acid.
See: Cheronis, p. 637; Fieser, *J. Amer. Chem. Soc.*, **51**, 2460 (1929).

*o-Toluidinium salt.**

$$RSO_3Na \ + \ o\text{-}CH_3C_6H_4NH_2 \ + \ HCl \ \rightarrow \ [o\text{-}CH_3C_6H_4NH_3]^+RSO_3^- \ + \ NaCl$$
o-Toluidinium sulfonate

From the sodium or the potassium salt of the sulfonic acid with *o*-toluidine and hydrochloric acid in water.
For directions and examples see: Cheronis, p. 637; O. C. Dermer and V. H. Dermer, *J. Org. Chem.*, **7**, 581 (1942).

*Phenylhydrazinium salt.**

$$RSO_3H \ + \ C_6H_5NHNH_2 \ \rightarrow \ [C_6H_5NHNH_3]^+RSO_3^-$$
Phenylhydrazinium
sulfonate

From the sulfonic acid with phenylhydrazine in water-alcohol.
For directions and examples see: Wild, p. 159; P. H. Latimer and R. W. Bost, *J. Amer. Chem. Soc.*, **59**, 2500 (1937).

Phenols by KOH fusion.

$$ArSO_3Na \ + \ NaOH \ \rightarrow \ ArOH \ + \ Na_2SO_3$$
Phenol

By fusion of the sodium arylsulfonate and sodium hydroxide in a nickel crucible.
For directions and examples see: Vogel, p. 552.
By fusion of the sodium arylsulfonate, potassium hydroxide and zinc dust.
See: Linstead, p. 89.

---

*Derivatives recommended for first trial.
WARNING: This is not an instruction manual. References should be consulted for the preparation of derivatives.

TABLE XXII. ORGANIC DERIVATIVES OF SULFONIC ACIDS

a) Listed in order of increasing m.p. of the corresponding sulfonamide*

No.	Name	Melting point, °C	S-Benzyl thiuronium salt	p-Toluidinium salt	Anilinium salt	o-Toluidinium salt	Sulfonyl chloride	Sulfonamide	Sulfonanilide	Sulfon-1-naphthylamide	Miscellaneous
1	Propane-1-sulfonic acid			67–8			b.p. 180	52, eth.		84	Phenylhydrazine salt, 204–5
2	Ethane sulfonic acid		115				b.p. 171	60, eth.		66	Phenylhydrazine salt, 182.8
3	Propane-2-sulfonic acid	− 37					b.p. 79[18]	60, eth.-pet. eth.		134	B.p. 159[1,4]; $D_4^{25} = 1.1877$; $n_D^{20} = 1.4332$; m-T ui-dide, 109
4	Heptane-1-sulfonic acid						16	75			Phenylhydrazine salt, 100–0.5
5	2,4,5-Trimethoxybenzene sulfonic acid						130	76	170		
6	Methane sulfonic acid	20					b.p. 60[21]	90	100	125–6	Phenylhydrazine salt, 193.5–4d.
7	Hexadecane-1-sulfonic acid (Cetyl sulfonic acid)	54					54	97			
8	10-Bromocamphor-3-sulfonic acid						97	100.2			
9	Benzyl sulfonic acid			113, al.	102	83	92–3, eth., bz.	105, w., al.	102, al.	166 (146), yel., al.	Diethylamide, 29; Ethylamide, 65–6; Hydrazide, 131–2; Methylamide, 109–10; Phenylhydrazine salt, 173
10	3-Toluene sulfonic acid (3-Methylbenzene sulfonic acid)	oil		106		108	12	108, al.	96, al.		
11	3-Hydroxynaphthalene-2-sulfonic acid				241–2		112	110			
12	Pyridine-3-sulfonic acid	357					Hydrochloride, 141–4 d.	110–1	145		Diethylamide, 49–50; Hydrazide, 94, me. al.
13	2,6-Dimethylbenzene sulfonic acid	98					39	113 (96)			
14	2-(N-Methylamino)benzene sulfonic acid	182 d.						114.5–5.5			N-4-Toluene sulfonyl, 193
15	Indane-4-sulfonic acid						53–3.5	118–9, w.			
16	2-Phenylethane-1-sulfonic acid	91					33	122	77		
17	4-Formylbenzene sulfonic acid (Benzaldehyde-4-sulfonic acid)							122–4			Amide oxime, 185; Dimethylamide, 134–7; Di-O-acetate, 86–7.5; Chloride diacetate, 111–3
18	2-Methylnaphthalene-1-sulfonic acid						83–5	124			
19	4-Fluorobenzene sulfonic acid						36 (30)	125 (123), w.			
20	4-Chloro-3-methylbenzene sulfonic acid						65	128	92		Sulfonyl bromide, 67.5
21	3-Chloro-4-methoxybenzene sulfonic acid						82	131			
22	3-Ethoxybenzene sulfonic acid						38	131			
23	D-Camphor-10-sulfonic acid	193					67	132	121		
24	2-Fluoronaphthalene-6-sulfonic acid	105					97, chl.	133	129		
25	DL-Camphor-8-sulfonic acid	56–8					106	133–5, w.			
26	3-Methyl-4-nitrobenzene sulfonic acid						50	133.5			
27	3-Chloro-4-methylbenzene sulfonic acid						38	134	96		
28	3,5-Dimethylbenzene sulfonic acid			121–2, al.			94 (90), bz.	135, al.	119, al.		

*Derivative data given in order: m.p., crystal color, solvent from which crystallized.

No.	Name	Melting point, °C	S-Benzyl thiuronium salt	p-Tolui-dinium salt	Ani-linium salt	o-Tolui-dinium salt	Sulfonyl chloride	Sulfon-amide	Sulfon-anilide	Sulfon-1-naph-thylamide	Miscellaneous
29	Indane-5-sulfonic acid	92	......	....	...	......	46–7, eth.	135.5–6, al.	129, al.	....	....
30	D-Camphor-8-sulfonic acid		....				138, ($[\alpha]_D^{14}$: +128.7 in chl.)	137, ($[\alpha]_D^{13}$: +93.6 in al.)	....		
31	4-Toluene sulfonic acid (4-Methylbenzene sulfonic acid) ...	104–5 (92)	181–2	198	238	190	71, eth.	*anh.*: 138.5–9; *dihyd.*: 105	103, eth.-al.	157, al.	Phenylhydrazide, 155, al.; *o*-Tolui-dide, 110, aq. ac. a.; Triethylam-monium salt, 65
32	2,4-Dimethylbenzene sulfonic acid.	62 (*hyd.*)	146	....	...	......	34	139 (137)	110	....	
33	4-Vinylbenzene sulfonic acid (4-Styrene sulfonic acid)		......	182–3			....	139–40	....		Dimethylamide, 62–3
34	3,4-Dichlorobenzene sulfonic acid .		....				22.4 (19)	140 (135)			
35	2-Bromonaphthalene-1-sulfonic acid		....				97	140			
36	2,4,6-Trimethylbenzene sulfonic acid	77	....				56	142	109		
37	3-Aminobenzene sulfonic acid (Metanilic acid)		148					142			
38	D-Camphor-2-sulfonic acid		....	196–7			88	143	124		Me. ester, 77, ($[\alpha]_D$: +98.6 in chl.)
39	4-Methylnaphthalene-2-sulfonic acid		....				124–5, eth.	143–4, al.	....		
40	3,4-Dimethylbenzene sulfonic acid	64	208	....	......	......	52	144	....		
41	4-Chlorobenzene sulfonic acid	93	175	208–10	222–3	163–4	53	144	104	190	
42	4-Methyl-3-nitrobenzene sulfonic acid	92, hyg.	......	130	109	128	36	144.5	....	153	
43	3-Bromocamphor-8-sulfonic acid..	195–6, (*anh.*)					136–7	145			
44	5-Chloro-2-methylbenzene sulfonic acid						24 (21)	145, aq. al.			
45	4-Bromo-3-methylbenzene sulfonic acid	....					50	146			
46	4-Methoxy-3-nitrobenzene sulfonic acid	....					66	146.3			
47	3-Chlorobenzene sulfonic acid		......	199–200	206–7			148			
48	2,5-Dimethylbenzene sulfonic acid	......	184	....		237	24–6	148	....		
49	Naphthalene-1-sulfonic acid......	90	137	181	183	237	68 (66)	150	112 (152)		
50	4-Ethoxybenzene sulfonic acid....						39	150			
51	4,6-Dichloro-2,5-dimethylbenzene sulfonic acid	....					81	150	175		
52	3-Bromo-4-methylbenzene sulfonic acid	....					60	151			
53	Benzene sulfonic acid	66	148	205	240	176	14.5	153 (156)	112 (110)	170–1	N-Xanthylsulfon-amide, 200
54	2-Aminobenzene sulfonic acid (Orthanilic acid).............	....	132	....				153	....		N-Benzoyl deriv. of amide, 198; Hydro-chloride, 201
55	2-Iodonaphthalene-1-sulfonic acid	....					110	154	....		
56	2,6-Dichloro-4-methylbenzene sulfonic acid						56	154–5	....		
57	2-Chloro-5-methylbenzene sulfonic acid						56	156	229–30.5		
58	2-Toluene sulfonic acid (2-Methylbenzene sulfonic acid) ...	57	170	203–4	218	......	10	156.3	136, aq. al.	....	Sulfonyl bromide, b.p. 138[10]; N-Xanthylsulfon-amide, 182–3.5

*Derivative data given in order: m.p., crystal color, solvent from which crystallized.

No.	Name	Melting point, °C	S-Benzyl thiuronium salt	p-Tolui-dinium salt	Ani-linium salt	o-Tolui-dinium salt	Sulfonyl chloride	Sulfon-amide	Sulfon-anilide	Sulfon-1-naph-thylamide	Miscellaneous
59	3-Bromocamphor-10-sulfonic acid	47.5	......	....	....	....	65	156.5	....	....	....
60	2,4-Dinitrobenzene sulfonic acid	106–8 (hyd.)	......	....	....	....	102	157 (154)	....	....	Hydrazide, 110
61	2-Methyl-4-nitrobenzene sulfonic acid	130 (anh.)	......	....	....	177	106	157	....	....	
62	Benzophenone-3,3'-disulfonic acid	....	......	....	....	....	di: 137–8	di: 157	di: 177–8	....	Methylamide, 106–7; Dimethylamide, 118–9
63	3-Nitrobenzyl sulfonic acid	74	......	....	....	....	100, bz.	159, w.	....	....	
64	4,6-Dimethyl-2-hydroxy-1,3-benzene disulfonic acid	......	......	....	....	....	di: 89–91	di: 160–1	....	....	
65	2-Nitrodiphenylamine-4-sulfonic acid	220 d.	......	....	....	....	157	162	....	....	
66	2-Ethoxybenzene sulfonic acid	......	......	....	....	....	65–6	163	158	....	Phenylhydrazide, 132–3
67	3-Methyl-2-nitrobenzene sulfonic acid	......	......	....	....	....	58.5	163.5	....	....	
68	3-Amino-6-methylbenzene sulfonic acid	......	......	....	....	....	....	164	146–7	....	Chloride of N-acetyl deriv., 124; Chloride of N-chloro-acetyl deriv., 87; Amide of N-acetyl deriv., 242
69	4-Chloro-2-nitrobenzene sulfonic acid	......	......	....	....	....	75	164	138	....	Anhydride, 114–5; Phenylhydrazide, 151; Ph. ester, 82
70	4-Aminobenzene sulfonic acid (Sulfanilic acid)	......	185	109	......	132	....	165	200	196	N-Acetyl, 214; Me. ester, 92
71	3,6-Dichloro-2,5-dimethylbenzene sulfonic acid	......	......	....	....	....	71	165	171	....	
72	6-Aminonaphthalene-1-sulfonic acid	......	172–4	....	....	....	....	165	....	....	Benzoylguanidine salt, 210–11
73	4-Bromobenzene sulfonic acid	102–3 (88–9)	170	215–6	237–8	182–3	76, eth.	166 (161)	119	183–4	....
74	5-Bromo-2-methylbenzene sulfonic acid	......	......	....	....	....	33–5	167	....	....	
75	2,3-Dimethylbenzene sulfonic acid	......	......	....	....	....	47	167	....	....	
76	5-Chloro-2-methyl-3-nitrobenzene sulfonic acid	......	......	....	....	....	60	167	....	....	
77	3-Nitrobenzene sulfonic acid	48	146	222	222	193	64	167	126	166–7	
79	4,6-Dichloro-2-methylbenzene sulfonic acid	......	......	....	....	....	43	168	....	....	
80	4-Chloronaphthalene-2-sulfonic acid	......	......	....	....	....	106	168	....	....	Et. ester, 76–9
81	4-Bromo-2-methylbenzene sulfonic acid	......	......	....	....	....	50	168	....	....	
82	Propane-1,3-disulfonic acid	92, d. without melting	......	....	....	....	di: 45	di: 169, w.	di: 129	....	B.p. 157[1,4]; Di-m-toluide, 222; Di-hydrazide, 105
83	Propane-1,1-disulfonic acid	......	......	....	....	....	....	di: 169–70	151–2, al.	....	Di-(N-ethyl)anilide, 128–9, al.
84	3-Carboxybenzene sulfonic acid (3-Sulfobenzoic acid)	98 (hyd.)	163	....	224–6	....	di: 20	di: 170	....	....	
85	4-Methyl-2-nitrobenzene sulfonic acid	141 (anh.)	......	....	....	....	98–9	170	....	....	o-Anisidide, 135
86	2,4-Dimethyl-3-nitrobenzene sulfonic acid	144 (anh.)	......	....	....	....	96	172	....	....	

*Derivative data given in order: m.p., crystal color, solvent from which crystallized.

TABLE XXII. ORGANIC DERIVATIVES OF SULFONIC ACIDS

No.	Name	Melting point, °C	S-Benzyl thiuronium salt	p-Tolui-dinium salt	Ani-linium salt	o-Tolui-dinium salt	Sulfonyl chloride	Sulfon-amide	Sulfon-anilide	Sulfon-1-naph-thylamide	Miscellaneous
87	2,5-Dimethyl-3-nitrobenzene sulfonic acid	128	......	135–6	......	126.5–7.5	60–1	172–3	143–4	....	
88	4-Nitrodiphenylamine-2-sulfonic acid	......					102–4	173	164	....	
90	3,4-Dibromobenzene sulfonic acid	66.5–7.5 (anh.)					34	175	....		
91	4-Chloro-3-nitrobenzene sulfonic acid	......					40–1	175–6, yel., al.	....		
92	3-Amino-4-methylbenzene sulfonic acid	......					....	176	....		N-Acetyl of chloride, 144; N-Benzoyl of Chloride, 196; N-Benzoyl, 203
93	7-Chloronaphthalene-2-sulfonic acid	118 (anh.); 68 (tetra-hyd.)	......				86.5	176	....		Me. ester, 89; Et. ester, 65
94	4-Bromo-3-nitrobenzene sulfonic acid	....					55–7	176–7	....		
95	4-Hydroxybenzene sulfonic acid	....	169	202	170	192	....	176–7	141	....	
96	5-Methylnaphthalene-1-sulfonic acid	115	......					176–8	....		
97	4-Methylnaphthalene-1-sulfonic acid	....					81	177	158		
98	4-Nitrobenzene sulfonic acid	95 (109-11), hyg.	......	179–80	......		80, lgr.	180, 50% al.	136 (171), al.		
99	3-Chloro-2-methylbenzene sulfonic acid	60–72; 72 (anh.)	......				72, pet. eth.	180, w.	......		
100	2,5-Dichlorobenzene sulfonic acid	93–7 (>100)	170	247–8	262–3	250–1	38	181 (186)	160	160	
101	2,4,5-Trimethylbenzene sulfonic acid	112					61–2	181			
102	8-Aminonaphthalene-2-sulfonic acid	....					....	181	146–7	....	N-Acetyl deriv. of amide, 213; Benzoylguanidine salt, 214–6
103	5-Chloro-4-methyl-2-nitrobenzene sulfonic acid	128	....				99	181			
104	2,4-Dichlorobenzene sulfonic acid	86	......	204–6	......	170–2	55	182	....		
105	4-Iodobenzene sulfonic acid	....					85	183	143		
106	Quinoline-8-sulfonic acid	312					124	183–4	....		Picrate of Na salt, 226–7; Me. ester, 96; Et. ester, 73
107	6-Chloronaphthalene-2-sulfonic acid	....					110.5	183–4	....		Me. ester, 89; Et. ester, 79; Sulfonyl bromide, 124
108	5-Nitronaphthalene-2-sulfonic acid	118–9, yel.	......	......	260	......	125	184, yel.	....		
109	4-Chloro-2-methylbenzene sulfonic acid	....					54	185	....		
110	4-Chloro-2,5-dimethylbenzene sulfonic acid	100					50	185	155		

*Derivative data given in order: m.p., crystal color, solvent from which crystallized.

No.	Name	Melting point, °C	S-Benzyl thiuronium salt	p-Tolui-dinium salt	Ani-linium salt	o-Tolui-dinium salt	Sulfonyl chloride	Sulfon-amide	Sulfon-anilide	Sulfon-1-naph-thylamide	Miscellaneous
111	2-Carboxy-5-methylbenzene sulfonic acid	190 (158), (anh.)	......	......	......	......	di: 59	185	......	......	Nitrile of the sulfonyl chloride, 67, lgr.; NH$_4$ salt of 2-amide, 186 (mono-hyd.)
112	8-Chloronaphthalene-2-sulfonic acid		......	......	......	......	94	185–6	......	......	Et. ester, 92
113	2-Chloro-5-nitrobenzene sulfonic acid	168–9 d. (hyd.)					89–90, w.	185–6, w.			
114	2-Bromobenzene sulfonic acid						51, eth.	186, w.			
115	2,3-Dichloro-6-methylbenzene sulfonic acid						49	186			
116	2-Methyl-5-nitrobenzene sulfonic acid	133.5 (di-hyd.)	......	256–7	......	256–8	46–7	186	148	......	
117	2-Chloro-4-methylbenzene sulfonic acid		......				46 (52)	186			
118	3,5-Dichloro-2-methylbenzene sulfonic acid						54	186			
119	6-Chloro-3-nitrobenzene sulfonic acid	168–9					90, eth.	186, w.			
120	2,4-Dimethyl-5-nitrobenzene sulfonic acid	132 (122), dil. HNO$_3$					98	187 (179)	......		Sulfonyl fluoride, 109–10
121	2-Methyl-5-nitrobenzene sulfonic acid	131	......				46–7 (44), eth.-pet. eth.	187	148		
122	4-Chloronaphthalene-1-sulfonic acid	130–3 d.	......		145–6	151	95	187	145–6	162	Me. ester, 83; Et. ester, 104
123	8-Iodonaphthalene-1-sulfonic acid		......				115	187	140	......	
124	2,4-Diaminobenzene-1,5-disulfonic acid		......				275	187	236	......	
125	2,6-Dichloro-3-methylbenzene sulfonic acid		......				19.5	188			
126	4-Nitronaphthalene-1-sulfonic acid		......				99	188			
127	2-Chlorobenzene sulfonic acid		......				28.5, eth.	188	......		
128	5-Methylnaphthalene-2-sulfonic acid		......				120–2	188–9	248–50		
129	Phenanthrene-3-sulfonic acid	175–6 (anh.); 120–1 (mono-hyd.); 88–9 (di-hyd.)	......	222	......		110–1 (108)	190	......		Me. ester, 119–20, al.; Et. ester, 107–8
130	2,4-Dibromobenzene sulfonic acid	110 (anh.)					79, eth.	190	......		
131	8-Nitronaphthalene-1-sulfonic acid	115 (tri-hyd.)	......				165 d.	190.5–1.5	178–8.5	......	
132	4-Methylbenzene-2,4-disulfonic acid	oil	......	277 d.	di: 189	170–1	54 (56), eth.	di: 190.5–1	189	......	
133	3,5-Dichloro-4-methylbenzene sulfonic acid		......				69	191			
134	2,5-Dimethyl-6-nitrobenzene sulfonic acid	145 (anh.)	......	158.5–9, al.	......	143–5, 50% al.	110, eth.-pet.-eth.	192, 50% al.	182, bl., al.	......	

*Derivative data given in order: m.p., crystal color, solvent from which crystallized.

No.	Name	Melting point, °C	S-Benzyl thiuro-nium salt	p-Tolui-dinium salt	Ani-linium salt	o-Tolui-dinium salt	Sulfonyl chloride	Sulfon-amide	Sulfon-anilide	Sulfon-1-naph-thylamide	Miscellaneous
135	Quinoline-6-sulfonic acid	> 260	. . . . . .	. . . . . .	. . . . . .	. . . . . .	91	192	. . . . . .	. . . . . .	
136	3,4-Dicarboxybenzene sulfonic acid (4-sulfophthalic acid)	138–40 (mono-hyd.)	. . . . . .	. . . . . .	. . . . . .	. . . . . .	167–70 d., eth.	192– 200 d., w.	. . . . . .	. . . . . .	
137	2-Nitrobenzene sulfonic acid	70 (85)	. . . . . .	. . . . . .	. . . . . .	. . . . . .	69	193	115	. . . . . .	
138	Phenanthrene-9-sulfonic acid	174 (anh.); 134 (hyd.)	. . . . . .	235			127	193–4, al.	. . . . . .	. . . . . .	Me. ester, 106, me. al.; Et. ester, 108, al.
139	2-Carboxybenzene sulfonic acid (2-Sulfobenzoic acid)	68–9 (hyd.); 134 (anh.)	206	197 (200)	165	127–8	79, pet. eth.; 40, eth.	C: 193–4 (anh.); S: 153–4, sl. htng	194–5	. . . . . .	
140	4-Bromonaphthalene-1-sulfonic acid	. . . . . .	. . . . . .	. . . . . .	. . . . . .	. . . . . .	87	195	. . . . . .	. . . . . .	
141	2,5-Dibromobenzene sulfonic acid	128 (anh.)					71, pet. eth.-eth.	195, al.			
142	7-Methylnaphthalene-1-sulfonic acid	. . . . . .					96	195–6	162–4	. . . . . .	
143	5-Fluoronaphthalene-1-sulfonic acid	105–6					122–3	196–7	. . . . . .	. . . . . .	Me. ester, 118, eth.
144	Acenaphthene-3-sulfonic acid	. . . . . .	. . . . . .	. . . . . .	284–6	. . . . . .	113–4	196–9	. . . . . .	. . . . . .	Me. ester, 122–3; Et. ester, 137–9, lgr.
145	2,5-Dimethyl-4-nitrobenzene sulfonic acid	140	. . . . . .	143.5–4.5		143.5–4.5	75	197–8	131	. . . . . .	. . . .
146	8-Chloronaphthalene-1-sulfonic acid	. . . . . .					101 (96–8)	197.6	. . . . . .	. . . . . .	Me. ester, 70; Et. ester, 67–8
147	4-Chloro-3-methyl-5-nitrobenzene sulfonic acid	. . . . . .					52	201			
148	5-Amino-2-hydroxybenzene sulfonic acid (4-Aminophenol-2-sulfonic acid)	100 (anh.)						202	159		Pyridine salt of O,N-diacetyl deriv., 143–4
149	4-Nitrobenzyl sulfonic acid	71	. . . . . .	. . . . . .	. . . . . .	. . . . . .	90	204	220	. . . . . .	
150	Anthracene-1-sulfonic acid	. . . . . .					90	205	. . . . . .	. . . . . .	
151	6-Methylnaphthalene-2-sulfonic acid	. . . . . .					97–8	205–6	. . . . . .	. . . . . .	
152	4-Iodonaphthalene-1-sulfonic acid	. . . . . .					124 (121)	206 (204)	136	. . . . . .	
153	4-Fluoronaphthalene-1-sulfonic acid	100	. . . . . .	. . . . . .			86, chl.	206	144	. . . . . .	Et. ester, 93
154	4-Aminonaphthalene-1-sulfonic acid (Naphthionic acid)	. . . . . .	195					206	. . . . . .	. . . . . .	N-Acetyl deriv. of amide, 241; N-Acetyl deriv. of anilide, 231
155	4-Amino-2-nitrobenzene sulfonic acid	. . . . . .					59–60	206–7			
156	Retene-6-sulfonic acid	121–3					146–7.5	206–7.5	. . . . . .	. . . . . .	Me. ester, 117–9; Et. ester, 114–5
157	2,6-Dimethyl-4-hydroxybenzene-1,3-disulfonic acid	. . . . . .					119	208	207	. . . . . .	. . . .
158	4-(N-methylamino)benzene sulfonic acid	244–5 d.						210–1			N-4-Toluenesulfonyl, benzidine salt, 255
159	6-Chloronaphthalene-1-sulfonic acid	. . . . . .					70	214	. . . . . .	. . . . . .	Et. ester, 114–5
160	1-Nitronaphthalene-2-sulfonic acid	105, grn.	. . . . . .	. . . . . .	(202)	. . . . . .	120–1, pink, bz.-pet. eth.	214, 50% al.	202	. . . . . .	. . . .
161	2,5-Dichlorobenzene-1,3-disulfonic acid	. . . . . .					114	215–7	. . . . . .	. . . . . .	

*Derivative data given in order: m.p., crystal color, solvent from which crystallized.

TABLE XXII. ORGANIC DERIVATIVES OF SULFONIC ACIDS
a) Listed in order of increasing m.p. of the corresponding sulfonamide* (Continued)

No.	Name	Melting point, °C	S-Benzyl thiuronium salt	p-Toluidinium salt	Anilinium salt	o-Toluidinium salt	Sulfonyl chloride	Sulfonamide	Sulfonanilide	Sulfon-1-naphthylamide	Miscellaneous
162	5-Methylbenzene-1,3-disulfonic acid	......	......	......	......	......	94, eth.	216, w.	153, al.	......	
163	Naphthalene-2-sulfonic acid	91, hyg.	190–1	221	269	213	76 (79)	217 (213)	132		
164	4-Acetamidobenzene-1-sulfonic acid	......	......	......	......	......		218	......	215	
165	5-Aminonaphthalene-2-sulfonic acid	......	191	......	......	......	......	218–9 d.	127–8	......	N-Acetyl, 238–9
166	8-Nitronaphthalene-2-sulfonic acid	135–6 (hyd.)	......				169	223; 228	172–3		
167	5-Chlorobenzene-1,3-disulfonic acid	......					106	224	......		
168	2-Methylbenzene-1,4-disulfonic acid	......					98, bz.-pet. eth.	di: 224	di: 178		
169	4-Carboxy-3-nitrobenzene sulfonic acid	111 (+2½-H$_2$O)	......				di: 160	di: 226; mono-S: 192	......		
170	5-Chloronaphthalene-1-sulfonic acid	......					95	226	138		Me. ester, 89; Et. ester, 46; Sulfonyl bromide, 110
171	3,4-Di-iodobenzene sulfonic acid	122–5, after drying at 100					82, bz.-pet. eth.	227, aq. al.	......		Me. ester, 93, al.; Et. ester, 82.5, al.
172	2,4,6-Tribromobenzene sulfonic acid	64	......	......			64	228	220–2		
173	4'-Nitrobiphenyl-4-sulfonic acid	......					178	228	......		
174	3,4-Dichloro-2-methylbenzene sulfonic acid	......					52	228			
175	Benzene-1,3-disulfonic acid	......	214	......			63	229	148–50	245	Alkali fusion → resorcinol, 110
176	Biphenyl-4-sulfonic acid	......					115	230	125		
177	2,4-Di-iodobenzene sulfonic acid	162 (anh.)	......				77–8	230	......		Me. ester, 78, al.; Et. ester, 57, al.
178	1-Ethoxybenzene-2,5-disulfonic acid	......					di: 106–8	di: 233	......		
179	Methane disulfonic acid (Methionic acid)	......					8; b.p. 133^{10}	di: 233	di: 192–3	......	B.p. 220–70$^{10-15}$ d.
180	3,5-Dinitrobenzene sulfonic acid	......					99, chl.-lgr.	235, w., al.	......		
181	4-Aminobenzene-1,3-disulfonic acid (Aniline-2,4-disulfonic acid)	120 d.	......					di: 235	......		
182	5-Iodonaphthalene-1-sulfonic acid	......					114	236 (239)			
183	5-Nitronaphthalene-1-sulfonic acid				265		113	236	123		Me. ester, 117–8, chl.
184	4-Carboxybenzene sulfonic acid (4-Sulfobenzoic acid)	94 (hyd.), 260 (anh.)	213	......				di: 57	di: 236	di: 252	
185	2,3-Dichloro-4-methylbenzene sulfonic acid						41	237			
186	6-Hydroxynaphthalene-2-sulfonic acid	167 (anh.); 129 (hyd.)	217 (207)	248	264	208	....	237	161		
188	4-Methylbenzene-1,2-disulfonic acid	......					109–11, bz.-pet. eth.	237–9	190, al.		

*Derivative data given in order: m.p., crystal color, solvent from which crystallized.

No.	Name	Melting point, °C	S-Benzyl thiuronium salt	o-Toluidinium salt	Anilinium salt	p-Toluidinium salt	Sulfonyl chloride	Sulfonamide	Sulfonanilide	Sulfon-1-naphthylamide	Miscellaneous
189	4,5-Dimethylbenzene-1,3-disulfonic acid						79, yel., al.	239	200, al.		
190	4-Hydroxybenzene-1,3-disulfonic acid (Phenol-2,4-disulfonic acid)	>100 d.					di: 89	di: 239	di: 205		
191	4-Methoxybenzene-1,3-disulfonic acid						86	240	209		
192	4-Acetamidonaphthalene-1-sulfonic acid (Acetylnaphthionic acid)			232–3	231–2			241	231		
193	Naphthalene-2,7-disulfonic acid		212	299	251–2	238	158 (162), bz.	242			
194	5-Nitrobenzene-1,3-disulfonic acid						di: 97–8	di: 242			
195	2,4,6-Trimethylbenzene-1,3-disulfonic acid (Mesitylene disulfonic acid)						di: 125	di: 244	di: 150–1		
196	2,3,4,6-Tetrabromobenzene sulfonic acid						96.5	ca. 245 d.			
197	4,6-Dimethylbenzene-1,3-disulfonic acid						130, pet. eth.	249, w.	196, 50% al.		
198	1-Chloronaphthalene-2-sulfonic acid	130–3 d. (anh.)					84–5	250	171–2		Et. ester, 104
199	Azobenzene-4,4'-disulfonic acid	169 d. (anh.)					di: 222 (170)	di: 250 d.			
200	Phenanthrene-2-sulfonic acid	150		291			156, ac. a.	253–4, al.	157–8		Me. ester, 101–2 (96–8); Et. ester, 89, yel.-br., al.
201	Benzene-1,2-disulfonic acid		206				143	254	241		Imide, 186
202	2-Amino-5-methylbenzene-1,4-disulfonic acid	d. at 290					di: 156, chl.	di: 257, w.	di: 196–7, aq. al.		
203	5-Aminonaphthalene-1-sulfonic acid (Laurent's acid)		179					259–60	171		N-Acetyl deriv. of aniline salt, 344
204	2-Methylbenzene-1,3-disulfonic acid						88, bz.	>260	162, al.		
205	Anthracene-2-sulfonic acid						122, yel., tol.	261	201		Me. ester, 157, yel.; Et. ester, 160; Phenylhydrazide, 210
206	Anthraquinone-2-sulfonic acid		211	308	309		197, pa. yel., bz.	261, yel., ac. a.	193, yel.-br.		Me. ester, 123; Et. ester, 125
207	7-Nitronaphthalene-1-sulfonic acid						169–70	261–2			
208	Azoxybenzene-3,3'-disulfonic acid	126					138	273			
209	Naphthalene-1,4-disulfonic acid						160 (166)	273, w., al.	179		
210	4,6-Dichlorobenzene-1,3-disulfonic acid						123	276			
211	Benzidine-2,2'-disulfonic acid						Hydrochloride, 205	278			
212	9,10-Dichloroanthracene-2-sulfonic acid						221	279	248		
213	4-Nitronaphthalene-2,7-disulfonic acid						di: 140–1	di: 286–7			
214	Benzene-1,4-disulfonic acid						131 (139)	288	249		
215	Azobenzene-3,4'-disulfonic acid						di: 123–5	di: 288			
216	Naphthalene-1,3-disulfonic acid						di: 137.5	di: 292–3			
217	2,5-Dimethylbenzene-1,3-disulfonic acid						81, lgr.	295, al.	174, al.		
218	Naphthalene-1,6-disulfonic acid	125 (anh.)	81	314–5	298–9	323–4	129, bz.	297–8			

*Derivative data given in order: m.p., crystal color, solvent from which crystallized.

No.	Name	Melting point, °C	S-Benzyl thiuronium salt	p-Tolui-dinium salt	Ani-linium salt	o-Tolui-dinium salt	Sulfonyl chloride	Sulfon-amide	Sulfon-anilide	Sulfon-1-naph-thylamide	Miscellaneous
219	Naphthalene-1,7-disulfonic acid ..	......	......	....	......	....	di: 123	di: 298–300	......	....	....
220	Biphenyl-4,4'-disulfonic acid	72	171	330	......	....	203	300	......	....	....
221	Naphthalene-2,6-disulfonic acid ..	......	256	......	......	....	225, bz.	305	......	....	....
222	Azobenzene-3,3'-disulfonic acid...	......	......	......	......	....	166	305	......	....	....
223	Naphthalene-1,5-disulfonic acid ..	240–5 (anh.)	257 (251)	......	......	....	di: 183	di: 310 (>340)	di: 249	....	Di-Me. ester, 205, chl.
224	Benzene-1,3,5-trisulfonic acid	>100	......	......	......	....	tri: 187	tri: 310–5	tri: 237	....	Tri-Et. ester, 147, bz.
225	Anthracene-1,5-disulfonic acid ...	......	......	......	......	....	di: 249, pa. yel.	di: >330, yel.	di: 293	....	....
226	Anthracene-1,8-disulfonic acid ...	......	......	......	......	....	225, yel., bz.	333	224	....	....
227	Anthraquinone-1,8-disulfonic acid	293–4	......	......	......	....	222–3, yel., PhNO$_2$	>340	237–8, yel., PhNO$_2$	....	....
228	Anthraquinone-1,5-disulfonic acid	310–1 (hyd.), yel.	......	......	......	....	265–70, yel., PhNO$_2$	>350	269–70, red-yel., PhNO$_2$		

*Derivative data given in order: m.p., crystal color, solvent from which crystallized.

TABLE XXII. ORGANIC DERIVATIVES OF SULFONIC ACIDS

b) M.p. of the amide deriv. not available; listed in order of increasing m.p. of the corresponding anilide deriv.*

No.	Name	Melting point, °C	S-Benzyl thiuron-ium salt	p-Tolui-dinium salt	Ani-linium salt	o-Tolui-dinium salt	Sulfonyl chloride	Sulfon-amide	Sulfon-anilide	Sulfon-1-naph-thylamide	Miscellaneous
1	Ethane-1,2-disulfonic acid	104	201–2	270 d.	270, w.	......	di: 95	......	69	....	m-Toluidide, 230; Di-Et. ester, 77, eth.
2	Vinylsulfonic acid (Ethylene-sulfonic acid)	....	145–6, w.	....	....	......	b.p. 118–20^{250}		71; b.p. 174^1	....	B.p. 135^2; n_D^{25}: 1.4505
3	Phenol-O-sulfonic acid	145 (hyd.)	....	124–5	165	......			126.5–7.5	....	
4	8-Aminonaphthalene-1-sulfonic acid (Peri acid)	....	300						139–40	......	Anilinium salt of N-acetyl deriv., 273
5	3,5-Dimethyl-2-hydroxybenzene sulfonic acid	121–5 d.	......						142–3	......	Chloride of O-acetyl deriv., 62, pet. eth.; Methylanilide, 111–2
6	Benzophenone-2-sulfonic acid	....					96–7	......	143–5	......	
7	7-Hydroxynaphthalene-1,3,6-trisulfonic acid	....					196		152–5	......	
8	1-Hydroxynaphthalene-2-sulfonic acid	>250	169	....	....	......	O-acetyl deriv., 157–8	......			O-acetyl deriv. of p-toluidide, 135–6
9	2-Hydroxynaphthalene-1,6-disulfonic acid	....					di: 111		di: 191	....	
10	Anthraquinone-2,7-disulfonic acid	....					di: 186, chl. eth.		di: 192		
12	7-Hydroxynaphthalene-1,3-disulfonic acid (G-Acid)	....	228	294	......	271	161–2		195		
13	7-Hydroxynaphthalene-1-sulfonic acid (Bayer Acid)	....	218	232	240	242	....		195		
14	4-Hydroxynaphthalene-1-sulfonic acid (NW-Acid)	170, r. h.	103	196	186–7	203–4			199–200	....	2-Naphthylamide, 204
15	5-Hydroxynaphthalene-1-sulfonic acid	110–2 d.	....						201		Chloride of O-acetyl deriv., 129
16	2-Hydroxynaphthalene-3,6-disulfonic acid (R-Acid)	....	233	250	254	257	....		202	......	
17	Anthraquinone-1-sulfonic acid	218	191	....	284	......	216–8, yel., $PhNO_2$	......	214, gold-yel.	....	$NH_3 \rightarrow$ 1-Aminoanthraquinone, 252 (243)
18	Anthraquinone-1,6-disulfonic acid	215–7, gold, ac. a.	....				197–8, yel., $PhNO_2$	......	227–8, yel., cl.-bz.		
19	2-Hydroxynaphthalene-1,5-disulfonic acid	....				......	di: 177	......	di: 231	....	
20	2-Hydroxynaphthalene-1,7-disulfonic acid	....	219		....		169		233		
21	Anthraquinone-1,7-disulfonic acid	120 (hyd.)	....			......	231–2, br.-yel., $PhNO_2$	......	237–8, yel., cl.-bz.		
22	Anthraquinone-2,6-disulfonic acid	....				......	di: 250, yel., cl.-bz.	......	di: 321		

*Derivative data given in order: m.p., crystal color, solvent from which crystallized.

TABLE XXIII. ORGANIC DERIVATIVES OF SULFONYL CHLORIDES
(Listed in order of increasing m.p.)*

No.	Name	Melting point, °C	Sulfonic acid	Amide	Anilide	1-Naphthyl amide	Salts of the corresponding acid				Miscellaneous
							S-Benzyl thiuronium	p-Toluidine	Aniline	o-Toluidine	
1	Methanedisulfonyl chloride	8	b.p.: 220–70$^{15-20}$ d.	233	192–3	. . . . . .	. . . . . .	. . . . . .	. . . . . .	. . . . . .	B.p. 133^{10}
2	2-Ethylbenzenesulfonyl chloride . .	11.7	. . . .	100	. . . . . .	. . . . . .	. . . . . .	. . . . . .	. . . . . .	. . . . . .	
3	3-Methylbenzenesulfonyl chloride (Toluene-3-sulfonyl chloride) . . .	12	. . . .	108, al.	96						
4	4-Ethylbenzenesulfonyl chloride . .	12	. . . .	110	. . . . . .	. . . . . .	. . . . . .	. . . . . .	. . . . . .	. . . . . .	N-Xanthylsulfonamide, 196
5	Benzenesulfonyl chloride	14.5	43–4 (mono-hyd.); 66 (anh.)	156; 153	. . . . . .	170–1	148	205	240	176	N-Xanthylsulfonamide, 200
6	Heptane-1-sulfonyl chloride	16	. . . .	75	. . . . . .	. . . . . .					
7	2,6-Dichloro-3-methylbenzenesulfonyl chloride	19.5	. . . .	188	. . . . . .						
8	3-Carboxybenzenesulfonyl chloride	20	98 (hyd); 148 (anh.)	di: 170	. . . . . .	. . . . . .	163	224–6			The m.p. is that of the 1,3-dichloride.
9	3,4-Dichlorobenzenesulfonyl chloride	22.4;19	. . . .	140; 135							
10	5-Chloro-2-methylbenzenesulfonyl chloride	24	. . . .	145, aq. al.							
11	2,5-Dimethylbenzenesulfonyl chloride	24–6	48 (anh.); 86 (hyd.)	148	. . . . . .	. . . . . .	184	. . . . . .	. . . . . .	. . . . . .	N-Xanthylsulfonamide, 176
12	2-Chlorobenzenesulfonyl chloride .	28.5	. . . .	188							
13	2-Phenylethane-1-sulfonyl chloride	33	91	122	77	. . . . . .	. . . . . .	. . . . . .	. . . . . .	. . . . . .	
14	5-Bromo-2-methylbenzenesulfonyl chloride	33–5	. . . .	166–7							
15	2,4-Dimethylbenzenesulfonyl chloride	34	62 (hyd.)	110							
16	3,4-Dibromobenzenesulfonyl chloride	34	66.5–7.5 (anh.)	175	. . . . . .	. . . . . .	. . . . . .	. . . . . .	. . . . . .	. . . . . .	
17	2,4,6-Trichlorobenzenesulfonyl chloride	35–40	. . . .	210–2d.	. . . . . .						
18	4-Methyl-3-nitrobenzenesulfonyl chloride	36	92, hyg.	144.5	109	153	. . . . . .	130–1		28	. . . . . .
19	4-Fluorobenzenesulfonyl chloride .	36; 30	. . . .	125	. . . . . .	. . . . . .	. . . . . .	. . . . . .	. . . . . .	. . . . . .	
20	3-Ethoxybenzenesulfonyl chloride .	38	. . . .	131	. . . . . .	. . . . . .	. . . . . .	. . . . . .	. . . . . .	. . . . . .	
21	3-Chloro-4-methylbenzenesulfonyl chloride	38	. . . .	134	96	. . . . . .					
22	2,5-Dichlorobenzenesulfonyl chloride	38	93–7	181	160	160	170	247–8	262–3	250–1	
23	2,6-Dimethylbenzenesulfonyl chloride	39	98	113; 96	. . . . . .	. . . . . .	. . . . . .	. . . . . .	. . . . . .	. . . . . .	
24	4-Ethoxybenzenesulfonyl chloride .	39	. . . .	150							
25	4-Chloro-3-nitrobenzenesulfonyl chloride	40–1; 60–2	. . . .	175–6, yel., al.							
26	2,3-Dichloro-4-methylbenzenesulfonyl chloride	41	. . . .	237							
27	4,6-Dichloro-2-methylbenzenesulfonyl chloride	43	. . . .	168							
28	3,3-Dimethylbutane-1-sulfonyl chloride	43–4	. . . .	96–7	. . . . . .						
29	Propane-1,3-disulfonyl chloride . . .	45	92d.	169, w.	di: 125	. . . . . .	. . . . . .	. . . . . .	. . . . . .	. . . . . .	Di-m-toluidide 222
30	2-Chloro-4-methylbenzenesulfonyl chloride	46; 52	. . . .	186	. . . . . .						
31	Indane-5-sulfonyl chloride	46–7, eth.	92	135.5–6, al.	129, al.						
32	2-Methyl-5-nitrobenzenesulfonyl chloride	46–7'	133.5 (+2H$_2$O)	186	148	. . . . . .	. . . . . .	256–7	. . . . . .	256–8	B.p. 183–5^{10}
33	2,3-Dimethylbenzenesulfonyl chloride	47	. . . .	167	. . . . . .						

*Derivative data given in order: m.p., crystal color, solvent from which crystallized.

No.	Name	Melting point, °C	Sulfonic acid	Amide	Anilide	1-Naph-thyl amide	Salts of the corresponding acid				Miscellaneous
							S-Benzyl thiu-ronium	p-Tolui-dine	Aniline	o-Tolui-dine	
34	4-Bromo-3-methylbenzenesulfonyl chloride	50	. . . .	146	. . . .	. . . . . .	. . . . . .	. . . . .	. . . . .	. . . . .	. . . .
35	3-Methyl-4-nitrobenzenesulfonyl chloride	50	. . . .	133.5	. . . .	. . . . . .	. . . . . .	. . . . .	. . . . .	. . . . .	. . . .
36	4-Bromo-2-methylbenzenesulfonyl chloride	50	. . . .	168	. . . .	. . . . . .	. . . . . .	. . . . .	. . . . .	. . . . .	. . . .
37	4-Chloro-2,5-dimethylbenzene-sulfonyl chloride	50	100	185	155						
38	2-Bromobenzenesulfonyl chloride	51, eth.	. . . .	186, w.	. . . .	. . . . . .	. . . . . .	. . . . .	. . . . .	. . . . .	. . . .
39	3,4-Dichloro-2-methylbenzene-sulfonyl chloride	51–2	. . . .	228							
40	3,4-Dimethylbenzenesulfonyl chloride	52	64; 55	144	. . . .		208				
41	4-Chloro-3-methyl-5-nitrobenzene-sulfonyl chloride	52		201							
42	4-Chlorobenzenesulfonyl chloride .	53	69; 93	144	104	190	175	208–10	222–3	163–4	. . . .
43	Indane-4-sulfonyl chloride	53–3.5	. . . .	118–9, w.	. . . .	. . . . . .	. . . . . .	. . . . .	. . . . .	. . . . .	B.p. 140–1
44	4-Methylbenzene-1,3-disulfonyl chloride (Toluene-2,4-disulfonyl chloride)	54; 46	. . . .	di: 186–7; 191	189	. . . . . .	. . . . . .	. . . . .	. . . . .	. . . . .	
45	4-Chloro-2-methylbenzenesulfonyl chloride	54		185	. . . .						
46	3,5-Dichloro-2-methylbenzene-sulfonyl chloride	54		186							
47	Hexadecane-1-sulfonyl chloride . .	54	54	97	. . . .	. . . . . .					
48	2,4-Dichlorobenzenesulfonyl chloride	55	86	182	. . . .			204–6		170–2	. . . .
49	4-Bromo-3-nitrobenzenesulfonyl chloride	55–7	. . . .	176–7	. . . .						
50	2,4,6-Trimethylbenzenesulfonyl chloride	56	78	142	109						
51	2-Chloro-5-methylbenzenesulfonyl chloride	56	. . . .	156	229–30.5						
52	2,6-Dichloro-4-methylbenzene-sulfonyl chloride	56	. . . .	154–5							
53	4-Carboxybenzenesulfonyl chloride	57	94 (hyd.); 260 (anh.)	di: 236	di: 252	. . . . . .	. . . . . .				The m.p. is that of the 1,4-dichloride
54	Tetralin-6-sulfonyl chloride	58	. . . .	135	155–6						
55	3-Methyl-2-nitrobenzenesulfonyl chloride	58.5	. . . .	163.5	. . . .						
56	5-Carboxy-2-methylbenzenesul-fonyl chloride (4-Toluic acid-2-sulfonyl chloride)	59	190; 158 (anh.)	185							The m.p. is that of the 1,5-dichloride
57	4-Amino-3-nitrobenzenesulfonyl chloride (2-Nitroaniline-4-sulfonyl chloride)	59–60	. . . .	206–7							
58	5-Chloro-2-methyl-3-nitrobenzene-sulfonyl chloride	60	. . . .	167	. . . .						
59	3-Bromo-4-methylbenzenesulfonyl chloride	60	. . . .	151	. . . .						
60	2,5-Dimethyl-3-nitrobenzene-sulfonyl chloride	61	128; 200	173	143–4	. . . . . .		136			
61	2,4,5-Trimethylbenzenesulfonyl chloride	61	112	181	. . . .						
62	Benzene-1,3-disulfonyl chloride . . .	63	. . . .	229	148–50	245	214	. . . . . .			N-Xanthylsulfon-amide, 170; Alk. fusion → resor-cinol, 110
63	4-Chloro-3-methylbenzenesulfonyl chloride	63	. . . .	128	92	. . . . . .					. . . .

*Derivative data given in order: m.p., crystal color, solvent from which crystallized.

TABLE XXIII. ORGANIC DERIVATIVES OF SULFONYL CHLORIDES
(Listed in order of increasing m.p.)* (Continued)

No.	Name	Melting point, °C	Sulfonic acid	Amide	Anilide	1-Naphthyl amide	Salts of the corresponding acid				Miscellaneous
							S-Benzyl thiuronium	p-Toluidine	Aniline	o-Toluidine	
64	7-Methylnaphthalene-2-sulfonyl chloride	63–4	. . . .	163–4	. . . .	. . . . . .	. . . . . .	. . . . . .	. . . . . .	. . . . . .	
65	2,4,6-Tribromobenzenesulfonyl chloride	64	64	228	220–2d.	. . . . .					
66	3-Nitrobenzenesulfonyl chloride . .	64	48	167	126	166.5	146	222	126.5–7.5	193	. . . .
67	2,3,4-Trichlorobenzenesulfonyl chloride	64–5	. . . .	227–30	. . . .						
68	3-Bromocamphor-10-sulfonyl chloride	65	47.5	156	. . . .						
70	2-Ethoxybenzenesulfonyl chloride .	65–6	. . . .	163	158	. . . . . .					
71	4-Methoxy-3-nitrobenzenesulfonyl chloride	66	. . . .	146.3	. . . .						
72	D-Camphor-10-sulfonyl chloride . .	67	193	132	121; 88						
73	2-Methylbenzenesulfonyl chloride (Toluene-2-sulfonyl chloride) . . .	68	57	156.3	136	. . . . . .	170	203–4	218	. . . . . .	N-Xanthylsulfon-amide, 182–3.5
74	Naphthalene-1-sulfonyl chloride . .	68; 66	90	150	112; 152	. . . . . .	137	181	183	237	. . . .
75	4-Methylbenzenesulfonyl chloride (Toluene-4-sulfonyl chloride) . . .	69	104–5	138.5–9 (anh.); 105 (+2H₂O)	103	157	181–2	198	238	190	. . . .
76	2-Nitrobenzenesulfonyl chloride . .	69	70; 85	193	115	. . . . . .					
77	3,5-Dichloro-4-methylbenzene-sulfonyl chloride	69	. . . .	191	. . . .						
78	2,4-Dimethoxybenzenesulfonyl chloride	70	. . . .	167	. . . .						
79	6-Chloronaphthalene-1-sulfonyl chloride	70	. . . .	214	. . . .						
80	3,4-Dimethyl-5-nitrobenzenesul-fonyl chloride	70	. . . .	180	. . . .						
81	2,5-Dibromobenzenesulfonyl chloride	71	128 (anh.)	195	. . . .						
82	3,6-Dichloro-2,5-dimethylbenzene-sulfonyl chloride	71	. . . .	165	171						
83	3-Chloro-2-methylbenzenesulfonyl chloride	72, pet. eth.	60–72	180, w.	. . . .						
84	4-Methoxynaphthalene-2-sulfonyl chloride	75	. . . .	157	145						
85	2-Chloronaphthalene-1-sulfonyl chloride	75	. . . .	153	. . . .						
86	4-Chloro-2-nitrobenzenesulfonyl chloride	75	82	164; 237	138	. . . . . .	. . . . . .	. . . . . .	. . . . . .	. . . . . .	Phenylhydrazide 151; Ph. ester, 82
87	2,5-Dimethyl-4-nitrobenzene-sulfonyl chloride	75	140	197–8	131	. . . . . .		143.5–4.5	. . . . . .	143.5–4.5	
88	4-Bromobenzenesulfonyl chloride . .	76, eth.	88–90	166; 161	119	183.5	170	215–6	237–8	182–3	
89	Naphthalene-2-sulfonyl chloride . .	76; 79	91, hyg.; 122	217; 213	132	. . . . .	190–1	221	269	213	
90	6-Bromonaphthalene-1-sulfonyl chloride	77	. . . .	217	. . . .						
91	2,4-Di-iodobenzenesulfonyl chloride	77–8	167 (anh.)	230	. . . .				. . . . . .	Me. ester, 78, al.; Et. ester, 57, al.
92	2-Carboxybenzenesulfonyl chloride	79, pet. eth.	68–9 (hyd.); 134 (anh.)	. . . .	194–5	. . . . .	206	196; 200	165	127–8	The m.p. is that of the 1,2-dichloride
93	2,4-Dibromobenzenesulfonyl chloride	79, eth.	110 (anh.)	190	. . . .						. . . .
94	4,5-Dimethylbenzene-1,3-disul-fonyl chloride	79, yel.	. . . .	239	200, al.	. . . . .					

*Derivative data given in order: m.p., crystal color, solvent from which crystallized.

No.	Name	Melting point, °C	Sulfonic acid	Amide	Anilide	1-Naph-thyl amide	Salts of the corresponding acid				Miscellaneous
							S-Benzyl thiu-ronium	p-Tolui-dine	Aniline	o-Tolui-dine	
95	4-Nitrobenzenesulfonyl chloride ..	80, lgr.	109–11; 95 hyg.	180, 50% al.	171; 136 d.	......	......	179–80	......	83	
96	6-Methoxynaphthalene-1-sulfonyl chloride	80.5	....	149.5	177.5						
97	2,5-Dimethylbenzene-1,3-disul-fonyl chloride	81, lgr.	....	295, al.	174, al.						
98	4,6-Dichloro-2,5-dimethylbenzene-sulfonyl chloride	81	....	150	175						
99	4-Methylnaphthalene-1-sulfonyl chloride	81, eth.	....	174; 177 al.	158						
100	3,4-Di-iodobenzenesulfonyl chloride	82, bz.-pet. eth.	122–5	227, aq. al.	....						
101	3-Chloro-4-methoxybenzenesul-fonyl chloride	82	....	131							
102	7-Methoxynaphthalene-2-sulfonyl chloride	83	....	220	121						
103	2-Methylnaphthalene-1-sulfonyl chloride	83–5	....	124							
104	1-Chloronaphthalene-2-sulfonyl chloride	84–5	130–3d. (anh.)	250	171–2						
105	4-Iodobenzenesulfonyl chloride	85	....	183	143						
106	4-Ethoxynaphthalene-2-sulfonyl chloride	85	....	183	143.5						
107	4,5-Dichloro-3-methylbenzene-sulfonyl chloride	85–8		183–5	....						
108	4-Methoxybenzene-1,3-disulfonyl chloride	86	....	240	209						
109	4-Fluoronaphthalene-1-sulfonyl chloride	86	100 (hyd.)	206	144						Et. ester, 93
110	7-Chloronaphthalene-2-sulfonyl chloride	87	68 (tetra-hyd.); 118 (anh.)	76	....						Me. ester, 89; Et. ester, 65
111	4-Bromonaphthalene-1-sulfonyl chloride	87	....	195	....						
112	D-Camphor-3-sulfonyl chloride ...	88	77	143	124	......		196–7	......		Me. ester, 77
113	2-Methylbenzene-1,3-disulfonyl chloride	88	....	260	162						
114	8-Methylnaphthalene-2-sulfonyl chloride	88	....	116							
115	4-Hydroxybenzene-1,3-disulfonyl chloride (Phenol-2,4-disulfonyl chloride)	89	>100d.	239	....						
116	3,5-Dimethyl-2-hydroxybenzene-1,3-disulfonyl chloride	89–91	....	160–1							
117	Anthracene-1-sulfonyl chloride ...	90	....	205							
118	2-Chloro-5-nitrobenzenesulfonyl chloride	90, w.	168–9d. (hyd.)	185–6	....						
119	Quinoline-6-sulfonyl chloride.....	91	>260	192	....						
120	Benzylsulfonyl chloride	92–3, eth., lgr.	....	105, w., al.	102	166; 146	......	113, al.	102	83	Hydrazide, 131–2, Phenylhydrazide, 173
121	6-Iodonaphthalene-1-sulfonyl chloride	92.5	....	213	....						....
122	6-Methoxynaphthalene-2-sulfonyl chloride	93	....	189	120						
123	5-Chloro-2-nitrobenzenesulfonyl chloride	93	....	159	....						
124	1-Bromonaphthalene-2-sulfonyl chloride	93	....	271	....						

*Derivative data given in order: m.p., crystal color, solvent from which crystallized.

TABLE XXIII. ORGANIC DERIVATIVES OF SULFONYL CHLORIDES
(Listed in order of increasing m.p.)* (Continued)

No.	Name	Melting point, °C	Sulfonic acid	Amide	Anilide	1-Naphthyl amide	Salts of the corresponding acid				Miscellaneous
							S-Benzyl thiuronium	p-Toluidine	Aniline	o-Toluidine	
125	5-Methylbenzene-1,3-disulfonyl chloride	94, eth.	....	216, w.	153, al.	......	......	......	......	......	
126	3,5-Dimethylbenzenesulfonyl chloride	94; 90, bz.	....	135, al.	129, al.			121–2, al.			
127	8-Chloronaphthalene-2-sulfonyl chloride	94		185	....						
128	1-Iodonaphthalene-2-sulfonyl chloride	94		247	....						
129	4-Chloronaphthalene-1-sulfonyl chloride	94–5	130–3d.	187	....	162				151	o-Toluidide, 145–6; Me. ester, 83; Et. ester, 104
130	Ethane-1,2-disulfonyl chloride	95	....	69	....	......	201–2	270d.	270, w.	......	Di-Et ester, 77, eth.; m-Toluidide, 230
131	5-Bromonaphthalene-1-sulfonyl chloride	95	....	232–3							
132	5-Chloronaphthalene-1-sulfonyl chloride	95	....	226	138						Sulfonyl bromide, 110; Me. ester, 89; Et. ester, 46
133	7-Methylnaphthalene-1-sulfonyl chloride	96	....	195–6	162–4						
134	2,4-Dimethyl-3-nitrobenzene-sulfonyl chloride	96	144 (anh.)	172							
135	5-Bromonaphthalene-2-sulfonyl chloride	96	....	220							
136	2-Benzoylbenzenesulfonyl chloride (Benzophenone-2-sulfonyl chloride)	96–7	....	....	143–5						
137	2,3,4,6-Tetrabromobenzenesulfonyl chloride	96.5	....	245d.							
138	10-Bromocamphor-3-sulfonyl chloride	97	....	100–2							
139	6-Fluoronaphthalene-2-sulfonyl chloride	97, chl.	105 (hyd.)	133	129	......	190–1	221	269	213	
140	2-Bromonaphthalene-1-sulfonyl chloride	97	....	140							
141	6-Methylnaphthalene-2-sulfonyl chloride	97–8	....	205–6							
142	5-Nitrobenzene-1,3-disulfonyl chloride	97–8	....	242							
143	2,4-Dimethyl-5-nitrobenzene-sulfonyl chloride	98	132; 122, dil. HNO₃	187; 179	....						Sulfonyl fluoride, 109–10
144	2-Methylbenzene-1,4-disulfonyl chloride	98	....	224	di: 178						
145	4-Methyl-3-nitrobenzenesulfonyl chloride	98–9		170	....					......	o-Anisidide, 135
146	4-Methoxynaphthalene-1-sulfonyl chloride	98.5	....	226	147.5						
147	5-Chloro-4-methyl-2-nitro-benzenesulfonyl chloride	99	128	181							
148	3,5-Dinitrobenzenesulfonyl chloride	99, chl., lgr.		235							
149	4-Nitronaphthalene-1-sulfonyl chloride	99	....	188							
150	7-Iodonaphthalene-2-sulfonyl chloride	100	....	210							
151	7-Bromonaphthalene-2-sulfonyl chloride	100	....	218							

*Derivative data given in order: m.p., crystal color, solvent from which crystallized.

TABLE XXIII. ORGANIC DERIVATIVES OF SULFONYL CHLORIDES
(Listed in order of increasing m.p.)* (Continued)

No.	Name	Melting point, °C	Sulfonic acid	Amide	Anilide	1-Naphthyl amide	Salts of the corresponding acid				Miscellaneous
							S-Benzyl thiuronium	p-Toluidine	Aniline	o-Toluidine	
152	3-Nitrobenzylsulfonyl chloride....	100, bz.	74 (hyd.)	159 d., w.	....	......	......	......	......	.....	Me. amide, 106–7; Dimethylamide, 118–9
153	8-Chloronaphthalene-1-sulfonyl chloride..................	101	....	197	....	......	......	......	......	.....	...
154	2,4-Dinitrobenzenesulfonyl chloride..................	102	106–8 (hyd.); 130 (anh.)	157; 154	....	......	......	......	......	.....	Hydrazide, 110
155	4-Nitrodiphenylamine-2-sulfonyl chloride..................	102–4	....	173	164	......	......	......	......	.....	...
156	4-Ethoxynaphthalene-1-sulfonyl chloride..................	103	....	170	180	......	......	......	......	.....	...
157	7-Ethoxynaphthalene-2-sulfonyl chloride..................	103	....	142	153	......	......	......	......	.....	...
158	3,7-Diethylnaphthalene-1-sulfonyl chloride..................	105–7	....	207	....	......	......	......	......	.....	...
159	5,6-Dichloronaphthalene-1-sulfonyl chloride.........	106	....	223	....	......	......	......	......	.....	...
160	4-Chloronaphthalene-2-sulfonyl chloride..................	106	....	168	....	......	......	......	......	.....	Et. ester, 76–9
161	2-Methyl-4-nitrobenzene-sulfonyl chloride............	106	....	157	....	......	......	......	......	.....	...
162	DL-Camphor-8-sulfonyl chloride..	106	56–8	133–5, w.	....	......	......	......	......	.....	...
163	5-Chlorobenzene-1,3-disulfonyl chloride..................	106	....	224	....	......	......	......	......	.....	...
164	3-Ethoxybenzene-1,4-disulfonyl chloride..................	106–8	....	di: 233	....	......	......	......	......	.....	...
165	6-Ethoxynaphthalene-2-sulfonyl chloride..................	107.5	....	183	153	......	......	......	......	.....	...
166	4-Methylbenzene-1,2-disulfonyl chloride..................	109–11	....	237–9	190	......	......	......	......	.....	...
167	2,5-Dimethyl-6-nitrobenzene-sulfonyl chloride............	110	145 (anh.)	192	182	......	......	158.5–9	......	143–5, 50% al.	...
168	2-Iodonaphthalene-1-sulfonyl chloride..................	110	....	154	....	......	......	......	......	.....	...
169	Phenanthrene-3-sulfonyl chloride .	110–1	175–6 (anh.); 120–1 (+1 H₂O); 88d. (+2H₂O)	190	....	......	222	......	......	.....	Me. ester, 119–20, al.; Et. ester, 107–8
170	6-Chloronaphthalene-2-sulfonyl chloride..................	110.5	....	184	....	......	......	......	......	.....	...
171	2-Hydroxynaphthalene-1,6-disulfonyl chloride...........	111	....	....	di: 191	......	......	......	......	.....	...
172	Acenaphthene-5-sulfonyl chloride..................	111	....	223	178	......	......	......	......	.....	...
173	3-Hydroxynaphthalene-2-sulfonyl chloride..................	112	....	110	....	......	......	......	241–2	.....	...
174	5-Nitronaphthalene-1-sulfonyl chloride..................	113	....	236	123	......	......	......	......	.....	...
175	Acenaphthene-3-sulfonyl chloride..................	113–4	87–9	199	284–6	......	......	......	......	.....	Me. ester, 122–3; Et. ester, 137–9, lgr.
176	2,5-Dichlorobenzene-1,3-disulfonyl chloride...........	114	....	215–7	....	......	......	......	......	.....	...
177	5-Chloronaphthalene-2-sulfonyl chloride..................	115	....	216	....	......	......	......	......	.....	...
178	Biphenyl-4-sulfonyl chloride (4-Phenylbenzenesulfonyl chloride .	115	....	230	125	......	......	......	......	.....	...

*Derivative data given in order: m.p., crystal color, solvent from which crystallized.

TABLE XXIII. ORGANIC DERIVATIVES OF SULFONYL CHLORIDES
(Listed in order of increasing m.p.)* (Continued)

No.	Name	Melting point, °C	Sulfonic acid	Amide	Anilide	1-Naphthyl amide	Salts of the corresponding acid				Miscellaneous
							S-Benzyl thiuronium	p-Tolui-dine	Aniline	o-Tolui-dine	
179	2-Ethoxynaphthalene-1-sulfonyl chloride	116	....	158	187	......					
180	4,5-Dichloronaphthalene-1-sulfonyl chloride	117	....	229	....						
181	2,6-Dimethyl-4-hydroxybenzene-1,3-disulfonyl chloride	117–8	....	206–8	205–7	......					
182	6-Ethoxynaphthalene-1-sulfonyl chloride	118	....	154	194.5						
183	4,6-Dichloronaphthalene-1-sulfonyl chloride	119	....	226	....						
184	5-Methoxynaphthalene-1-sulfonyl chloride	119.5	....	194.5	157						
185	5-Methylnaphthalene-2-sulfonyl chloride	120–2	....	188–9	248–50; 133–4	......					
186	8-Bromonaphthalene-2-sulfonyl chloride	121	....	187	....						
187	5-Ethoxynaphthalene-1-sulfonyl chloride	121	....	182.5	130						
188	2-Methoxynaphthalene-1-sulfonyl chloride	121	....	159	196.5						
189	1-Nitronaphthalene-2-sulfonyl chloride	121, pink, bz.-pet. eth.	105, lgr.	214	202						
190	6,8-Dichloronaphthalene-2-sulfonyl chloride	121	....	228	....						
191	2-Chloro-5-methyl-6-nitro-benzene sulfonyl chloride	122	....	177							
192	Anthracene-2-sulfonyl chloride	122	....	261	201						Me. ester, 157; Et. ester, 160
193	5-Fluoronaphthalene-1-sulfonyl chloride	122–3	105 (hyd.)	196–7							Me. ester, 118, eth.
194	4,6-Dichlorobenzene-1,3-disulfonyl chloride	123	....	276							
195	Azobenzene-3,4′-disulfonyl chloride	123–5		di: 288							
196	7,8-Dichloronaphthalene-2-sulfonyl chloride	124	....	227							
197	4-Iodonaphthalene-1-sulfonyl chloride	124; 121	....	206; 204	136						
198	6-Bromonaphthalene-2-sulfonyl chloride	124	....	127	....						
199	Quinoline-8-sulfonyl chloride	124	312	183–4	....						Me. ester, 96; Et. ester, 73
200	4-Methylnaphthalene-2-sulfonyl chloride	124–5	....	143–4							
201	1,5-Dichloronaphthalene-1-sulfonyl chloride	125	....	282	....						
202	2,4,6-Trimethylbenzene-1,3-disulfonyl chloride	125	....	di: 244	di: 150–1						
203	5-Nitronaphthalene-2-sulfonyl chloride	125	118–9, yel.	184							
204	6-Nitronaphthalene-1-sulfonyl chloride	127	....	223–4							
205	Phenanthrene-9-sulfonyl chloride	127	174 (anh.)	193–4	....	......		235			Me. ester, 106, me. al.; Et. ester, 108 al.
206	Naphthalene-1,6-disulfonyl chloride	129	125 (anh.)	298	....	......	81; 235	314–5	298–9	323–4	....
207	7-Chloronaphthalene-1-sulfonyl chloride	129	....	235	....	......					

*Derivative data given in order: m.p., crystal color, solvent from which crystallized.

No.	Name	Melting point, °C	Sulfonic acid	Amide	Anilide	1-Naphthyl amide	Salts of the corresponding acid				Miscellaneous
							S-Benzyl thiuronium	p-Toluidine	Aniline	o-Toluidine	
208	4,6-Dichloronaphthalene-2-sulfonyl chloride	130	....	218	....	....	....	....	....	....	....
209	2,4,5-Trimethoxybenzenesulfonyl chloride	130	....	76	170						
210	4,6-Dimethylbenzene-1,3-disulfonyl chloride	130, pet. eth.	....	249, w.	196, 50% al.						
211	5,6,7-Trichloronaphthalene-1-sulfonyl chloride	131	....	249	....						
212	Benzene-1,4-disulfonyl chloride	131; 139		288	249						
213	5,8-Dichloronaphthalene-2-sulfonyl chloride	134	....	244							
214	3,7-Dichloronaphthalene-1-sulfonyl chloride	136	....	269	....						
215	3-Bromocamphor-8-sulfonyl chloride	136–7	....	....							
216	8-Chloro-7-methoxynaphthalene-1-sulfonyl chloride	137	....	153	196						
217	Benzophenone-3,3'-disulfonyl chloride	137–8	....	di: 157	di: 177–8	....					N-Xanthylsulfonamide, 197
218	Naphthalene-1,3-disulfonyl chloride	137.5	....	di: 292–3							
219	7,8-Dichloronaphthalene-1-sulfonyl chloride	138	....	221	....						
220	Azoxybenzene-3,3'-disulfonyl chloride	138	126	di: 273	....						
221	D-Camphor-8-sulfonyl chloride	138		137	....						
222	3-Methoxynaphthalene-2-sulfonyl chloride	138	....	113	174						
223	8-Cyanonaphthalene-1-sulfonyl chloride	139	....	333.4							
224	4-Nitronaphthalene-2-sulfonyl chloride	139.5	....	225							
225	6-Iodonaphthalene-2-sulfonyl chloride	140	....	222							
226	8-Iodonaphthalene-1-sulfonyl chloride	140	115	187							
227	4-Nitronaphthalene-2,7-disulfonyl chloride	140–1	....	286–7							
228	4-Hydroxybenzenesulfonyl chloride	141	....	176–7	....	....	169	202	170	192	
229	4,8-Dichloronaphthalene-2-sulfonyl chloride	141	....	205							
230	5-Iodonaphthalene-1-sulfonyl chloride	141	....	239							
231	Pyridine-3-sulfonyl chloride	Hydrochloride, 141–4	357	110–1	145	....				......	Hydrazide, 94
232	6,7-Dichloronaphthalene-1-sulfonyl chloride	142	....	268	....						
233	Benzene-1,2-disulfonyl chloride	143	....	254	241						
234	6-Ethoxy-1-nitronaphthalene-2-sulfonyl chloride	146	....	218							
235	Retene-6-sulfonyl chloride	146–7.5, yel.-br.	121–3	206–7.5	....						
236	7-Bromonaphthalene-1-sulfonyl chloride	147	....	209	....						
237	4-Acetamidobenzenesulfonyl chloride	149	....	219	214	215					
238	5,7-Dichloronaphthalene-1-sulfonyl chloride	149	....	272	....						

*Derivative data given in order: m.p., crystal color, solvent from which crystallized.

No.	Name	Melting point, °C	Sulfonic acid	Amide	Anilide	1-Naphthyl amide	Salts of the corresponding acid				Miscellaneous
							S-Benzyl thiuronium	p-Toluidine	Aniline	o-Toluidine	
239	4,5-Dibenzylnaphthalene-1-sulfonyl chloride	151	. . . .	168	. . . .	. . . . . .	. . . . . .	. . . . . .	. . . . . .	. . . . . .	. . . .
240	4,7-Dichloronaphthalene-1-sulfonyl chloride	151	. . . .	217	. . . .	. . . . . .	. . . . . .	. . . . . .	. . . . . .	. . . . . .	. . . .
241	7-Ethoxy-8-nitronaphthalene-1-sulfonyl chloride	155	. . . .	173.4	. . . .	. . . . . .	. . . . . .	. . . . . .	. . . . . .	. . . . . .	. . . .
242	2-Amino-5-methylbenzene-1,3-disulfonyl chloride	156, chl.	. . . .	di: 257, w.	di: 196–7, aq. al.	. . . . . .	. . . . . .	. . . . . .	. . . . . .	. . . . . .	. . . .
243	Phenanthrene-2-sulfonyl chloride	156	150	253–4	157–8	. . . . . .	. . . . . .	291	. . . . . .	. . . . . .	Me. ester, 101–2; Et. ester, 89, yel.-br.
244	4,7-Dichloronaphthalene-2-sulfonyl chloride	156	. . . .	196	. . . .	. . . . . .	. . . . . .	. . . . . .	. . . . . .	. . . . . .	. . . .
245	6,7,8-Trichloronaphthalene-2-sulfonyl chloride	157	. . . .	245	. . . .	. . . . . .	. . . . . .	. . . . . .	. . . . . .	. . . . . .	. . . .
246	4,5-Dichloronaphthalene-2-sulfonyl chloride	158	. . . .	197	. . . .	. . . . . .	. . . . . .	. . . . . .	. . . . . .	. . . . . .	. . . .
247	5,6,8-Trichloronaphthalene-2-sulfonyl chloride	158	. . . .	235	. . . .	. . . . . .	. . . . . .	. . . . . .	. . . . . .	. . . . . .	. . . .
248	Naphthalene-2,7-disulfonyl chloride	158; 162	. . . .	242	. . . .	. . . . . .	212	299	251–2	238	. . . .
249	Naphthalene-1,4-disulfonyl chloride	160; 166	. . . .	273, w., or al.	179	. . . . . .	. . . . . .	. . . . . .	. . . . . .	. . . . . .	. . . .
250	4-Carboxy-3-nitrobenzene-sulfonyl chloride	di: 160	111 (+2½ H₂O)	192	. . . .	. . . . . .	. . . . . .	. . . . . .	. . . . . .	. . . . . .	The m.p. is that of the 1,4-dichloride; Diamide, 226
251	7-Hydroxynaphthalene-1,3-disulfonyl chloride	161–2	. . . .	. . . .	195	. . . . . .	228	294	. . . . . .	271	. . . .
252	Fluorene-2-sulfonyl chloride	164	155 (hyd.)	213d.	. . . .	. . . . . .	. . . . . .	. . . . . .	. . . . . .	. . . . . .	. . . .
253	2,5-Dimethylbenzene-1,4-disulfonyl chloride	164	. . . .	310	223	. . . . . .	. . . . . .	. . . . . .	. . . . . .	. . . . . .	. . . .
254	8-Nitronaphthalene-1-sulfonyl chloride	165 d.	115 d. (+3H₂O)	191	178–8.5	. . . . . .	. . . . . .	. . . . . .	. . . . . .	. . . . . .	. . . .
255	7-Iodonaphthalene-1-sulfonyl chloride	165	. . . .	240	. . . .	. . . . . .	. . . . . .	. . . . . .	. . . . . .	. . . . . .	. . . .
256	Azobenzene-3,3′-disulfonyl chloride	166	. . . .	di: 305	. . . .	. . . . . .	. . . . . .	. . . . . .	. . . . . .	. . . . . .	. . . .
257	3,6-Dichloronaphthalene-2-sulfonyl chloride	166	. . . .	218	. . . .	. . . . . .	. . . . . .	. . . . . .	. . . . . .	. . . . . .	. . . .
258	5,6-Dichloronaphthalene-2-sulfonyl chloride	167	. . . .	192	. . . .	. . . . . .	. . . . . .	. . . . . .	. . . . . .	. . . . . .	. . . .
259	Phthalic acid-4-sulfonyl chloride (3,4-Dicarboxybenzenesulfonyl chloride)	167–70, d. eth.	138–40 (+1H₂O)	192–200 d., w.	. . . .	. . . . . .	. . . . . .	. . . . . .	. . . . . .	. . . . . .	. . . .
260	8-Nitronaphthalene-2-sulfonyl chloride	169	135–6 (+1½ H₂O)	223	172–3	. . . . . .	. . . . . .	. . . . . .	. . . . . .	. . . . . .	. . . .
261	4-Amino-2-hydroxybenzene-sulfonyl chloride	169	. . . .	155	. . . .	. . . . . .	. . . . . .	. . . . . .	. . . . . .	. . . . . .	. . . .
262	2-Hydroxynaphthalene-1,7-disulfonyl chloride	169	. . . .	233	. . . .	. . . . . .	. . . . . .	. . . . . .	. . . . . .	. . . . . .	. . . .
263	7-Nitronaphthalene-1-sulfonyl chloride	169–70	. . . .	261–2	. . . .	. . . . . .	. . . . . .	. . . . . .	. . . . . .	. . . . . .	. . . .
264	4,6,7,8-Tetrachloronaphthalene-2-sulfonyl chloride	176	. . . .	235	. . . .	. . . . . .	. . . . . .	. . . . . .	. . . . . .	. . . . . .	. . . .
265	4′-Nitrobiphenyl-4-sulfonyl chloride	178	. . . .	228	. . . .	. . . . . .	. . . . . .	. . . . . .	. . . . . .	. . . . . .	. . . .
266	Naphthalene-1,5-disulfonyl chloride	183	245 (anh.)	310; 340	249	. . . . . .	257; 251 d.	332	. . . . . .	. . . . . .	Di-Me. ester, 205, chl.
267	Anthraquinone-2,7-disulfonyl chloride	186, chl.	. . . .	. . . .	di: 192	. . . . . .	. . . . . .	. . . . . .	. . . . . .	. . . . . .	. . . .

*Derivative data given in order: m.p., crystal color, solvent from which crystallized.

| No. | Name | Melting point, °C | Sulfonic acid | Amide | Anilide | 1-Naphthyl amide | Salts of the corresponding acid | | | | Miscellaneous |
							S-Benzyl thiuronium	p-Toluidine	Aniline	o-Toluidine	
268	Benzene-1,3,5-trisulfonyl chloride	187	....	*tri*: 310–5	*tri*: 237	......	......	......	......	......	Tri-Et. ester, 147, bz.
269	7-Hydroxynaphthalene-1,3,6-trisulfonyl chloride	196	....	....	152–5	......					....
270	Anthraquinone-2-sulfonyl chloride	197	....	261	193	......	211	308	309		Me. ester, 123; Et. ester, 125
271	Anthraquinone-1,6-disulfonyl chloride	197–8,yel., PhNO₂	215–7, gold	....	227–8, yel.	......					
272	Biphenyl-4,4'-disulfonyl chloride	203	....	300	....	......	171	330 d.			
273	Benzidine-2,2'-disulfonyl chloride	Hydro-chloride, 205	....	*di*: 278	....				...		
274	Anthraquinone-1-sulfonyl chloride	216–8, yel., PhNO₂	218	....	214	......	191	......	284	......	NH₃ → 1-Amino-anthraquinone, 252; 243
275	9,10-Dichloroanthracene-2-sulfonyl chloride	221	....	279	248	......					....
276	Azobenzene-4,4'-disulfonyl chloride	222	169d. (anh.)	250 d.	....					......	Et. ester, 104
277	Anthraquinone-1,8-disulfonyl chloride	222–3, yel, PhNO₂	293–4	>340	237–8, yel., PhNO₂	......					
278	Anthracene-1,8-disulfonyl chloride	225	....	333	224	......					
279	Naphthalene-2,6-disulfonyl chloride	225	....	305	....	......	256		360		
280	2-Hydroxynaphthalene-1,5-disulfonyl chloride	231	....	....	231						
281	Anthracene-1,5-disulfonyl chloride	240	....	*di*: 330	*di*: 293	......					
282	Anthraquinone-2,6-disulfonyl chloride	250, yel. cl. bz.	....	....	*di*: 321						
283	Anthraquinone-1,3-disulfonyl chloride	265–70, yel.	310–1 (hyd.)	>350	269–70, yel.-red						
284	2,4-Diaminobenzene-1,5-disulfonyl chloride	275	....	187	236	......					
285	Anthraquinone-1,7-disulfonyl chloride	301–2, br.-yel, PhNO₂	120 (hyd.)	....	237–8, yel. cl. bz.	......					

*Derivative data given in order: m.p., crystal color, solvent from which crystallized.

Formation of sulfonic acid by hydrolysis. *

$$RSO_2NH_2 \ + \ H_2O \ \xrightarrow{HCl} \ RSO_3H \ + \ NH_4Cl$$

Sulfonic
acid

From hydrolysis of the sulfonamide by 25% hydrochloric acid.

For directions and examples see: Cheronis, p. 631; Shriner, pp. 104, 267; R. S. Schreiber and R. L. Shriner, *J. Amer. Chem. Soc.*, **56**, 1618 (1934).

From hydrolysis of the sulfonamide in a mixture of concentrated sulfuric acid and 85% phosphoric acid.

See: Cheronis, p. 633.

Formation of the amine by hydrolysis.

$$2\,ArSO_2NHR \ + \ 5\,HBr \ + \ 5\,C_6H_5OH \ \rightarrow \ ArSSAr \ + \ 2\,RNH_2 \ + \ 5\,p\text{-}BrC_6H_4OH \ + \ 4\,H_2O$$

Amine

From hydrolysis of the sulfonamide in 48% hydrobromic acid and phenol.

For directions and examples see: Shriner, pp. 105, 267; H. R. Snyder and R. E. Heckert, *J. Amer. Chem. Soc.*, **74**, 2006 (1952); H. R. Snyder and H. C. Geller, *J. Amer. Chem. Soc.*, **74**, 4864 (1952).

NOTE: For directions and explanations for the preparation of derivatives of the sulfonic acid formed by the hydrolysis of the sulfonamide see explanations and references to Table XXII, pp. 369, 370.

For directions and explanations for the preparation of the amine formed by the hydrolysis of the sulfonamide see explanations and references to Table XVIII, pp. 291, 292, 293.

N-Xanthylsulfonamide. *

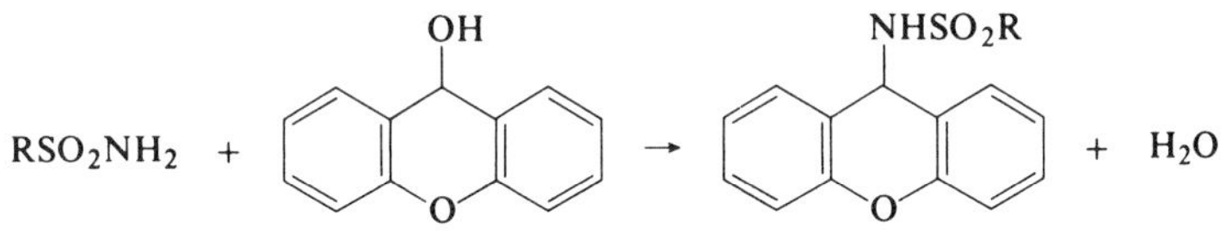

Xanthydrol   N-Xanthylsulfonamide

From the sulfonamide and xanthydrol in glacial acetic acid.

For directions and examples see: Cheronis, p. 634; Linstead, p. 95; Shriner, p. 267; R. F. Phillips and V. S. Frank, *J. Org. Chem.*, **9**, 9 (1944).

N-Acetylsulfonamide.

$$RSO_2NH_2 \ + \ (CH_3CO)_2O \ \rightarrow \ RSO_2NHCOCH_3 \ + \ CH_3COOH$$

$$RSO_2NHR' \ + \ CH_3COCl \ \rightarrow \ RSO_2NR'COCH_3 \ + \ HCl$$

N-Acetyl-
sulfonamide

From the sulfonamide and acetic anhydride.

For directions and examples see: Cheronis, p. 634.

From the sulfonamide and acetyl chloride in acetic acid.

See: Linstead, p. 95; Vogel, p. 555.

*Derivatives recommended for first trial.

WARNING: This is not an instruction manual. References should be consulted for the preparation of derivatives.

TABLE XXIV. ORGANIC DERIVATIVES OF SULFONAMIDES AND SULFONANILIDES
(Listed in order of increasing m.p.)*

No.	Name	Melting point, °C	Sulfonic acid	Derivatives of the corresponding acid				Salts of the corresponding acid				Miscellaneous derivatives of the acid
				Chloride	Amide	Anilide	1-Naphthyl-amide	S-Benzyl-thiu-ronium	p-Tolui-dinium	Ani-linium	o-Tolui-dinium	
1	2-Methylpropane-1-sulfonamide..........	14–6	....	b.p. 80[13]	....	38	107	......	....	......	......	
2	N,N-Diethylbenzylsul-fonamide.............	29	....	92	105, w., al.	102	166 (146)	......	113, al.	102	83	
3	2-Methylpropane-1-sulfonanilide.........	38	....	b.p. 80[13]	14–6	....	107	......	....	......	......	
4	3-Methylbutane-1-sulfonanilide.........	42	....	b.p. 98[13]	3	....	90–1	......	....	......	......	
5	Butane-1-sulfonamide ...	45	–15	b.p. 75[10]	....	10–5	60.5	......	....	......	......	Phenylhydrazi-nium salt, 114–5
6	Propane-1-sulfonamide ..	52, eth.	7.5	b.p. 78[15]	....	10	84	......	67–8	......	......	Phenylhydrazi-nium salt, 204.5d.
7	Ethane sulfonamide	58, eth.	–17	b.p. 178	....	58	66	115	....	......	......	Phenylhydrazi-nium salt, 182.8
8	Ethane sulfonanilide.....	58	–17	b.p. 178	58	....	66	115	....	......	......	Phenylhydrazi-nium salt, 182.8
9	N,N-Diethyltoluene-4-sulfonamide..........	60	104–5	69	105 (dihyd.); 138.5–9 (anh.)	103	157	181–2	198	238	190	m-Toluidide, 109
10	Propane-2-sulfonamide ..	60, eth.-pet. eth.	–37	b.p. 61[9]	....	84	134	......	....	......	......	
11	N-Ethyltoluene-4-sulfonamide..........	64	104–5	69	105 (dihyd.); 138.5–9 (anh.)	103	157	181–2	198	238	190	
12	N-Ethylbenzyl sulfon-amide...............	65–6, eth., lgr.	....	92	105, w., al.	102	166 (146)	......	113, al.	102	83	
13	N-(1-Naphthyl)ethane sulfonamide..........	66	–17	b.p. 178	58	58	......	115	....	......	......	
14	Ethane-1,2-disulfon-anilide..............	69	....	di: 95, eth.	....	....	......	201–2	d. at 270	270, w.	......	Di-Et. ester, 77, eth.; m-Tolui-dide, 230
15	N-Methyltoluene-2-sul-fonamide.............	74–5	57	68	....	136	......	170	203–4	218	......	
16	Heptane-1-sulfonamide ..	75	....	16	....	....	......	......	....	......	......	
17	2,4,5-Trimethoxybenzene sulfonamide..........	76	....	130	....	170	......	......	....	......	......	
18	2-Phenylethane-1-sulfon-anilide..............	77	91	33	122	....	......	......	....	......	......	
19	N-Methyltoluene-4-sulfonamide..........	78–9	104–5	69	105 (dihyd.); 138.5–9 (anh.)	103	157	181–2	198	238	190	
20	Propane-2-sulfonanilide..	84	....	b.p. 61[9]	60	....	134	......	....	......	......	
21	N-(1-Naphthyl)propane-1-sulfonamide..........	84	7.5	b.p. 78[15]	52	10	......	......	67–8	......	......	
22	N,N-Dimethyltoluene-4-sulfonamide..........	86–7	104–5	69	105 (dihyd.); 138.5–9 (anh.)	103	157	181–2	198	238	190	
23	Methane sulfonamide....	90	20	b.p. 60[21]	....	100.5	125.5	......	....	......	......	Phenylhydrazi-nium salt, 193.5–4d.
24	N-(1-Naphthyl)-3-methyl-butane-1-sulfonamide...	90–1	....	b.p. 98[13]	3	42	......	......	....	......	......	
25	4-Chloro-3-methylbenzene sulfonanilide.........	92	....	63	128	....	......	......	....	......	......	
26	Toluene-3-sulfonanilide ..	96	....	12	108	....	......	......	106	......	......	

*Derivative data given in order: m.p., crystal color, solvent from which crystallized.

TABLE XXIV. ORGANIC DERIVATIVES OF SULFONAMIDES AND SULFONANILIDES

TABLE XXIV. ORGANIC DERIVATIVES OF SULFONAMIDES AND SULFONANILIDES
(Listed in order of increasing m.p.)* (Continued)

No.	Name	Melting point, °C	Sulfonic acid	Derivatives of the corresponding acid				Salts of the corresponding acid				Miscellaneous derivatives of the acid
				Chloride	Amide	Anilide	1-Naphthylamide	S-Benzyl thiuronium	p-Toluidinium	Anilinium	o-Toluidinium	
27	3-Chloro-4-methylbenzene sulfonanilide	96	....	38	134	....						
28	3,3-Dimethylbutane sulfonamide	96–7		43–4								
29	Hexadecane-1-sulfonamide	97	54	54		....						
30	2-Ethylbenzene sulfonamide	100	....	11.7								
31	10-Bromocamphor-3-sulfonamide	100–2	....	97								
32	Methane sulfonanilide	100.5	20	b.p. 60^{21}	90	....	125.5	......	......	......	......	Phenylhydrazinium salt, 193.5–4d.
33	N,N-Dimethylbenzyl sulfonamide	101	....	92–3, eth., lgr.	105, w., al.	102, al.	166 (146)	......	113, al.	102	83	Hydrazide, 131–2; Phenylhydrazide, 173
34	Benzyl sulfonanilide (Toluene-α-sulfonanilide)	102, al.	....	92	105, w., al.	....	166 (146)	......	113, al.	102	83	Hydrazide, 131–2; Phenylhydrazide, 173
35	Toluene-4-sulfonanilide	103	92 (104–5)	69	137	....	......	181–2	198	238	190	N-Xanthylsulfonamide, 197
36	4-Chlorobenzene sulfonanilide	104	69 (93)	53	144	....	190	175	208–10	222–3	163–4	....
37	Benzyl sulfonamide (Toluene-α-sulfonamide)	105, w., al.	....	92–3, eth., lgr.	....	102, al.	166 (146)	......	113, al.	102	83	Hydrazide, 131–2; Phenylhydrazide, 173
38	N-(1-Naphthyl)-2-methylpropane sulfonamide	107	....	b.p. 80^{13}	14–6	38	......					....
39	Toluene-3-sulfonamide	108, al.	....	12	....	96	......		106	......	108	
40	2,4-Dimethyl-6-nitrobenzene sulfonamide	108	97	....								
41	2,4,6-Trimethylbenzene sulfonanilide	109	78	56	142	....						N-Xanthylsulfonamide, 203
42	N-Methylbenzyl sulfonamide	109–10	....	92–3, eth., bz.	105, w., al.	102, al.	166 (146)	......	113, al.	102	83	N-Xanthylsulfonamide, 188; Hydrazide, 131–2; Phenylhydrazide, 173
43	2,4-Dimethylbenzene sulfonanilide	110	62 (hyd.)	34								
44	4-Ethylbenzene sulfonamide	110	....	12								N-Xanthylsulfonamide, 196
45	3-Hydroxynaphthalene-2-sulfonamide	110	....	112						241–2		....
46	Pyridine-3-sulfonamide	110–1	357	Hydrochloride, 141–4 d.	....	145				......		Hydrazide, 94
47	Naphthalene-1-sulfonanilide	112 (152)	90	68; 66	150	....	......	137	181	183	237	....
48	Benzene sulfonanilide	112	66 (anh.)	14.5	156	....	170–1	148	205	240	176	N-Xanthylsulfonamide, 200
49	3-Methoxynaphthalene-2-sulfonamide	113	....	138	....	174						....
50	2,6-Dimethylbenzene sulfonamide	113 (96)	98	39	....							
51	2-(N-Methylamino)benzene sulfonamide	114.5–5.5	182 d.	....						......		2-N-p-Toluenesulfonyl deriv. of sulfonamide, 193

*Derivative data given in order: m.p., crystal color, solvent from which crystallized.

TABLE XXIV. ORGANIC DERIVATIVES OF SULFONAMIDES AND SULFONANILIDES
(Listed in order of increasing m.p.)* (Continued)

No.	Name	Melting point, °C	Sulfonic acid	Derivatives of the corresponding acid				Salts of the corresponding acid				Miscellaneous derivatives of the acid
				Chloride	Amide	Anilide	1-Naphthylamide	S-Benzylthiuronium	p-Toluidinium	Anilinium	o-Toluidinium	
52	2-Nitrobenzene sulfonanilide	115	70 (85)	69	193	....	......	......	......	......	......	....
53	N-Benzyltoluene-4-sulfonamide	115–6	92	69	137	....	......	181–2	198	238	190	N-Xanthylsulfonamide, 197
54	8-Methylnaphthalene-2-sulfonamide	116	....	88	....	....	......	......	......	......	......	....
55	Indane-4-sulfonamide	118–9, w.	....	53–3.5; b.p. 140–1³	....	....	......	......	......	......	......	....
56	4-Bromobenzene sulfonanilide	119	88–90	76, eth.	166; 161	....	183.5	170	215–6	237–8	182–3	....
57	3,5-Dimethylbenzene sulfonanilide	119	....	94; 90	135	....	......	......	121–2 d.	......	......	....
58	6-Methoxynaphthalene-2-sulfonanilide	120	....	93	189	....	......	......	......	......	......	....
59	D-Camphor-10-sulfonanilide	121	193	67	132	....	......	......	......	......	......	....
60	7-Methoxynaphthalene-2-sulfonanilide	121	....	83	220	....	......	......	......	......	......	....
61	2-Phenylethane-1-sulfonamide	122	91	33	....	77	......	......	......	......	......	....
62	4-Formylbenzene sulfonamide	122–4	....	....	....	....	......	......	......	......	......	Oxime, 158; O,O-Diacetate of sulfonamide, 86–7.5
63	5-Nitronaphthalene-1-sulfonanilide	123	....	113	236	....	......	......	......	......	......	Me. ester, 117–8, chl.
64	2-Methylnaphthalene-1-sulfonamide	124	....	83–5	....	....	......	......	......	......	......	....
65	D-Camphor-3-sulfonanilide	124	77	88	143	....	......	......	196–7	......	......	Me. ester, 77, $[\alpha]_D$ +98.6 in chl.
66	Biphenyl-4-sulfonanilide	125	....	115	230	....	......	......	......	......	......	....
67	4-Fluorobenzene sulfonamide	125	....	36; 30	....	....	......	......	......	......	......	....
68	N-(1-Naphthyl)methane sulfonamide	125.5	20	b.p. 60²¹	90	100.5	......	......	......	......	......	....
69	3-Nitrobenzene sulfonanilide	126	48	64	167	....	166.5	146	222	222	193	....
70	Phenol-O-sulfonanilide	126.5–7.5	145 (mono-hyd.)	....	....	....	......	......	124–5	126.5–7.5	......	....
71	5-Aminonaphthalene-2-sulfonanilide	127–8	....	....	219	....	......	191	......	......	......	5-N-Acetyl deriv. of sulfonamide, 247
73	4-Chloro-3-methylbenzene sulfonamide	128	....	63	....	92	......	......	......	......	......	Sulfonyl bromide, 67.5
74	6-Fluoronaphthalene-2-sulfonanilide	129	105 (hyd.)	97	133	....	......	......	......	......	......	....
75	5-Ethoxynaphthalene-1-sulfonanilide	130	....	121	182.5	....	......	......	......	......	......	....
76	3-Chloro-4-methoxybenzene sulfonamide	131	....	82	....	....	......	......	......	......	......	....
77	4-Aminonaphthalene-2-sulfonamide	131 (hyd.)	....	....	....	....	......	......	......	......	......	4-N-Acetyl deriv. of sulfonamide, 220
78	2,5-Dimethyl-4-nitrobenzene sulfonanilide	131	140	75	197–8	....	......	......	143.5–4.5	......	143.5–4.5	....

*Derivative data given in order: m.p., crystal color, solvent from which crystallized.

No.	Name	Melting point, °C	Sulfonic acid	Derivatives of the corresponding acid				Salts of the corresponding acid				Miscellaneous derivatives of the acid
				Chloride	Amide	Anilide	1-Naphthyl-amide	S-Benzyl-thiuronium	p-Tolui-dinium	Ani-linium	o-Tolui-dinium	
79	3-Ethoxybenzene sulfonamide	131	.....	38	.....	.....	.....	.....	.....	.....	.....	.....
80	D-Camphor-10-sulfonamide	132	193	67	.....	121 (88)	.....	.....	.....	.....	.....	.....
81	Naphthalene-2-sulfonanilide	132	91 (hyg.)	76; 79	217; 213	.....	.....	.....	.....	.....	.....	.....
82	6-Fluoronaphthalene-2-sulfonamide	133	105 (hyd.)	97, chl.	.....	129	.....	190–1	221	269	213	.....
83	DL-Camphor-8-sulfonamide	133–5, w.	56–8	106	.....	.....	.....	.....	.....	.....	.....	.....
84	3-Methyl-4-nitrobenzene sulfonamide	133.5	.....	50	.....	.....	.....	.....	.....	.....	.....	.....
85	3-Chloro-4-methylbenzene sulfonamide	134	.....	38	.....	96	.....	.....	.....	.....	.....	.....
86	N-(1-Naphthyl)propane-2-sulfonamide	134	−37	b.p. 61[9]	60	84	.....	.....	.....	.....	.....	m-Toluidide, 109
87	3,5-Dimethylbenzene sulfonamide	135, al.	.....	94; 90, bz.	.....	129, al.	.....	.....	121–2, al.	.....	.....	.....
88	Tetraline-6-sulfonamide	135	.....	58	.....	155–6	.....	.....	.....	.....	.....	.....
89	Indane-5-sulfonamide	135.5–6, al.	92	46–7, eth.; b.p. 148–9[4]	.....	129, al.	.....	.....	.....	.....	.....	.....
90	Toluene-2-sulfonanilide	136	57	68	156	.....	.....	170	203–4	218	.....	N-Xanthylsulfonamide, 183
91	4-Iodonaphthalene-1-sulfonanilide	136	.....	124; 121	206; 204	.....	.....	.....	.....	.....	.....	.....
92	D-Camphor-8-sulfonamide	137	.....	138	.....	.....	.....	.....	.....	.....	.....	$[\alpha]_D^{13}$: +93.6, in al.
93	4-Chloro-2-nitrobenzene sulfonanilide	138	82	75	237	.....	.....	.....	.....	.....	.....	.....
94	2,4-Dimethylbenzene sulfonamide	138	62 (hyd.)	34	.....	110	.....	146	.....	.....	.....	N-Xanthylsulfonamide, 188
95	Toluene-4-sulfonamide	138.5–9.0 (anh.); 105 (dihyd.)	104–5	69	.....	103	157	181–2	198	238	190	N-Xanthylsulfonamide, 197
96	8-Aminonaphthalene-1-sulfonanilide	139–40	.....	.....	.....	.....	.....	300	.....	.....	.....	.....
97	4-Vinylbenzene sulfonamide	139–40	.....	.....	.....	.....	.....	.....	182–3	.....	.....	Dimethylamide, 62–3
98	2-Bromonaphthalene-1-sulfonamide	140	.....	97	.....	.....	.....	.....	.....	.....	.....	.....
99	3,4-Dichlorobenzene sulfonamide	140; 135	.....	22.4; 19	.....	.....	.....	.....	.....	.....	.....	.....
100	2,4,6-Trimethylbenzene sulfonamide	142	78	56	.....	109	.....	.....	.....	.....	.....	N-Xanthylsulfonamide, 203
101	7-Ethoxynaphthalene-2-sulfonamide	142	.....	103	.....	153	.....	.....	.....	.....	.....	.....
102	3-Aminobenzene sulfonamide	142	.....	.....	.....	.....	.....	148	.....	.....	.....	.....
103	3,5-Dimethyl-2-hydroxybenzene sulfonanilide	142–3	121–5	.....	.....	.....	.....	.....	.....	.....	.....	2-O-Acetyl deriv of sulfonyl chloride, 62, pet. eth.
104	D-Camphor-3-sulfonamide	143	77	88	.....	124	.....	.....	196–7	.....	.....	N-Methylanilide, 111–2; Me. ester, 77, $[\alpha]_D$: +98.6 in chl.
105	5-Chloro-2-methylbenzene sulfonamide	143	21; 24	.....	.....	.....	.....	.....	.....	.....	.....	.....

*Derivative data given in order: m.p., crystal color, solvent from which crystallized.

No.	Name	Melting point, °C	Sulfonic acid	Derivatives of the corresponding acid				Salts of the corresponding acid				Miscellaneous derivatives of the acid
				Chloride	Amide	Anilide	1-Naph-thyl-amide	S-Benzyl-thiu-ronium	p-Tolui-dinium	Ani-linium	o-Tolui-dinium	
106	4-Iodobenzene sulfonanilide	143	....	85	183	....		....		......		....
107	2,5-Dimethyl-3-nitro-benzene sulfonanilide ...	143–4	128 (200)	61	173	....			135–6	......	126.5–7.5	
108	4-Methylnaphthalene-2-sulfonamide	143–4	....	124–5								
109	Benzophenone-2-sulfonanilide	143–5	....	96–7	....							
110	4-Ethoxynaphthalene-2-sulfonamide	143.5	....	85	183							
111	3,4-Dimethylbenzene sulfonamide..........	144	64 (55)	52				208				
112	4-Fluoronaphthalene-1-sulfonanilide	144	100 (hyd.)	86	206	....		....		......		Et. ester, 93
113	4-Chlorobenzene sulfonamide..........	144	69 (93)	53	....	104	190	175	208–10	222–3	163–4	....
114	4-Methyl-3-nitrobenzene sulfonamide..........	144.5	92 (hyg.)	36	....	109	153	....	130–1	......	28	
115	3-Chloro-6-methylbenzene sulfonamide	145, aq. al.	....	24								....
116	Pyridine-3-sulfonanilide..	145	....	....	110–1							
117	3-Bromocamphor-8-sulfonamide..........	145	195–6 (anh.)	136–7	....							
118	4-Chloronaphthalene-1-sulfonanilide	145–6	130–3	94–5	187	....	162			145–6	151	Me. ester, 83; Et. ester, 104
119	4-Bromo-3-methylbenzene sulfonamide	146	....	50								
120	4-Methoxy-3-nitroben-zene sulfonamide	146.3	....	66								
121	1-Aminonaphthalene-7-sulfonanilide	147	....	....	181 (hyd.)							Benzoylguanidine salt, 214–6
122	4-Methoxynaphthalene-2-sulfonanilide	147.5	....	98.5	226							
123	3-Chlorobenzene sulfon-amide.............	148		....					199–200	206–7	......	
124	2-Methyl-5-nitrobenzene sulfonanilide	148	133.5	46–7	186	....			256–7	......	256–8	....
125	2,5-Dimethylbenzene sulfonamide..........	148	48 (anhyd.); 86 (hyd.)	24–6	....			184				N-Xanthylsulfon-amide, 176
126	Benzene-1,3-disulfon-anilide	148–50	....	63	229	....	245	214				N-Xanthylsulfon-amide, 170
127	6-Methoxynaphthalene-1-sulfonamide..........	149.5	....	80.5	....	177.5						
128	Naphthalene-1-sulfon-amide.............	150	90	68; 66	....	112 (152)	......	137	181	183	237	
129	4-Ethoxybenzene sulfon-amide.............	150	....	39	....							
130	4,6-Dichloro-2,5-dimethylbenzene sulfon-amide.............	150		81	....	175						
131	3-Bromo-4-methylben-zene sulfonamide	151	....	60	....							
132	2-Hydroxynaphthalene-3,6,8-trisulfonanilide ...	152–5	....	tri: 196								
133	7-Ethoxynaphthalene-2-sulfonanilide	153	....	103	142							
134	2-Chloronaphthalene-1-sulfonamide..........	153	....	75	....							

* Derivative data given in order: m.p., crystal color, solvent from which crystallized.

No.	Name	Melting point, °C	Sulfonic acid	Derivatives of the corresponding acid				Salts of the corresponding acid				Miscellaneous derivatives of the acid
				Chloride	Amide	Anilide	1-Naphthylamide	S-Benzylthiuronium	p-Toluidinium	Anilinium	o-Toluidinium	
135	8-Chloro-7-methoxynaphthalene-1-sulfonamide	153	....	137	....	196	......	......	......	......	......	....
136	2-Aminobenzene sulfonamide	153	....	....	....	....	......	132	......	......	......	2-N-Benzoyl deriv. of sulfonamide, 198; Hydrochloride, 201
137	5-Methylbenzene-1,3-disulfonanilide	153, al.	....	94, eth.	216, w.	....	......	......	......	......	......	....
138	6-Ethoxynaphthalene-2-sulfonanilide	153	....	107.5	183	....	......	......	......	......	......	....
139	2-Iodonaphthalene-1-sulfonamide	154	....	110	....	....	......	......	......	......	......	....
140	6-Ethoxynaphthalene-1-sulfonamide	154	....	118	....	194.5	......	......	......	......	......	....
141	2,6-Dichloro-4-methylbenzene sulfonamide	154–5		56	....	....	......	......	......	......	......	....
142	4-Chloro-2,5-dimethylbenzene sulfonanilide	155	100	50	185	....	......	......	......	......	......	....
143	4-Amino-2-hydroxybenzene sulfonamide	155	....	169	....	....	......	......	......	......	......	....
144	Tetraline-6-sulfonanilide	155–6	....	58	135	....	......	......	......	......	......	....
145	Benzene sulfonamide	156 (153)	43–4 (monohyd); 66 (anh.)	14.5	....	....	170–1	148	205	240	176	N-Xanthylsulfonamide, 200
146	2-Chloro-5-methylbenzene sulfonamide	156	....	56	....	229–30.5	......	......	......	......	......	....
147	D-3-Bromocamphor-10-sulfonamide	156	47.5	65	....	....	......	......	......	......	......	....
148	Toluene-2-sulfonamide	156.3	57	68	....	136	......	170	203–4	218	......	N-Xanthylsulfonamide, 182–3,5
149	4-Methoxynaphthalene-2-sulfonamide	157	....	75.5	145	....	......	......	......	......	......	....
150	5-Methoxynaphthalene-1-sulfonanilide	157	....	119.5	194.5	....	......	......	......	......	......	....
151	N-(1-Naphthyl)toluene-4-sulfonamide	157	104–5	69	105 (dihyd.); 138.5–9 (anh.)	103	......	181–2	198	238	190	....
152	Benzophenone-3,3'-disulfonamide	157	....	di: 137–8	....	di: 177–8	......	......	......	......	......	N-Xanthylsulfonamide, 197
153	2,4-Dinitrobenzene sulfonamide	157; 154	106–8 (hyd.); 130 (anh.)	102	....	....	......	......	......	......	......	Hydrazide, 110
154	2-Methyl-4-nitrobenzene sulfonamide	157	....	106	....	....	......	......	......	......	......	....
155	2-Nitrodiphenylamine-4-sulfonanilide	157	220d.	....	162	....	......	......	......	......	......	....
156	Phenanthrene-2-sulfonanilide	157–8	150	156	253–4	....	......	......	291	......	......	Me. ester, 101–2; Et. ester, 89, yel.-br.
157	4-Methylnaphthalene-1-sulfonanilide	158	....	81	174; 177	....	......	......	......	......	......	....
158	2-Ethoxynaphthalene-1-sulfonamide	158	....	116	....	187	......	......	......	......	......	....
159	4-Methoxynaphthalene-1-sulfonanilide	158	....	81	177	....	......	......	......	......	......	....

*Derivative data given in order: m.p., crystal color, solvent from which crystallized.

No.	Name	Melting point, °C	Sulfonic acid	Derivatives of the corresponding acid				Salts of the corresponding acid				Miscellaneous derivatives of the acid
				Chloride	Amide	Anilide	1-Naph-thyl-amide	S-Benzyl thiu-ronium	p-Tolui-dinium	Ani-linium	o-Tolui-dinium	
160	2-Ethoxybenzene sulfon-anilide	158	. . . .	65–6	163	. . . .	. . . .				. . . . . .	Phenylhydrazide, 132–3
161	2-Methoxynaphthalene-1-sulfonamide.	159	. . . .	121	. . . .	196.5						
162	3-Nitrobenzylsulfonamide (3-Nitrotoluene-α-sul-fonamide)	159d., w.	74 (hyd.)	100, bz.	. . . .							Me. amide, 106–7; Dimethyl-amide, 118–9
163	5-Amino-2-hydroxyben-zene sulfonanilide	159 (98)	100 (anh.)	. . . .	202 d.							. . . .
164	5-Chloro-2-nitrobenzene sulfonamide.	159	. . . .	93								
165	2,5-Dichlorobenzene sul-fonanilide	160	93–7	38	181	. . . .		170				
166	3,5-Dimethyl-2-hydroxy-benzene-1,4-disulfon-amide.	160–1	. . . .	di: 89–91	. . . .							
167	6-Hydroxynaphthalene-2-sulfonanilide	161	129 (hyd.); 167 (anhyd.)	. . . .	238	. . . .		217 (207)	247	264	208	. . . .
168	2-Methylbenzene-1,3-disulfonanilide	162	. . . .	88	260							
169	N-(1-Naphthyl)-4-chloro-naphthalene-1-sulfon-amide.	162	130–3	94–5	187	145–6				145–6	151	Me. ester, 83; Et. ester, 104
170	2-Nitrodiphenylamine-4-sulfonamide.	162	220 d.	. . . .	. . . .	157						. . . .
171	7-Methylnaphthalene-1-sulfonanilide	162–4	. . . .	96	197	. . . .						
172	2-Ethoxybenzene sulfon-amide.	163	. . . .	65–6	. . . .	158						Phenylhydrazide, 132–3
173	7-Methylnaphthalene-2-sulfonamide.	163–4	. . . .	63–4	. . . .							. . . .
174	3-Methyl-2-nitrobenzene sulfonamide.	163.5	. . . .	58.5	. . . .							
175	5-Amino-2-methylbenzene sulfonamide.	164	. . . .	. . . .	. . . .	146–7		. . . . . :			. . . . . .	5-N-Acetyl deriv. of sulfonamide, 242
176	4-Chloro-2-nitrobenzene sulfonamide.	164	. . . .	75	. . . .	138						Phenylhydrazide, 151; Ph. ester, 82
177	4-Nitrodiphenylamine-2-sulfonanilide	164	. . . .	102–4	174							
178	4-Aminobenzene sulfon-amide.	165	. . . .	. . . .	. . . .	200	196	185	. . . . . .			
179	3,6-Dichloro-2,5-di-methylbenzene sulfon-amide.	165	. . . .	71	. . . .	171						
180	6-Aminonaphthalene-1-sulfonamide.	165	. . . .	. . . .	. . . .	. . . .		172–4	. . . . . .	. . . . . .		Benzoylguanidine salt, 210–1
181	N-(1-Naphthyl)benzyl sulfonamide.	166 (146)	. . . .	92–3, eth., bz.	105, w., al.	102, al.	. . . . .		113, al.	102	83	Hydrazide, 131–2; Phenyl-hydrazide, 173
182	4-Bromobenzene sulfon-amide.	166; 161	88–90	76, eth.	. . . .	119	183.5	170	215–6	237–8	182–3	. . . .
183	5-Bromo-2-methylbenzene sulfonamide.	166–7	. . . .	33–5	. . . .							
184	N-(1-Naphthyl)-3-nitro-benzene sulfonamide. . . .	166.5	48	64.	167	126	. . . . .	146	222	126.5–7.5	193	. . . .
185	3-Nitrobenzene sulfon-amide.	167	48	64	. . . .	126	166.5	146	222	126.5–7.5	193	

*Derivative data given in order: m.p., crystal color, solvent from which crystallized.

No.	Name	Melting point, °C	Sulfonic acid	Derivatives of the corresponding acid				Salts of the corresponding acid				Miscellaneous derivatives of the acid
				Chloride	Amide	Anilide	1-Naphthylamide	S-Benzylthiuronium	p-Toluidinium	Anilinium	o-Toluidinium	
186	2,4-Dimethoxybenzene sulfonamide	167	....	70	....	....	....	....	....	....	....	....
187	5-Chloro-2-methyl-3-nitrobenzene sulfonamide	167	....	60	....	....	....	....	....	....	....	....
188	4-Hydroxynaphthalene-1-sulfonamide	167	....	....	....	199–200	....	....	....	....	....	....
189	2,3-Dimethylbenzene sulfonamide	167	....	47	....	....	....	....	....	....	....	....
190	4,6-Dichloro-2-methylbenzene sulfonamide	168	....	43	....	....	....	....	....	....	....	....
191	4-Chloronaphthalene-2-sulfonamide	168	....	106	....	....	....	....	....	....	....	Et. ester, 76-9
192	4,5-Dibenzylnaphthalene-1-sulfonamide	168	....	151	....	....	....	....	....	....	....	....
193	4-Bromo-2-methylbenzene sulfonamide	168	....	50	....	....	....	....	....	....	....	....
194	Propane-1,3-disulfonamide	169, w.	92 d.	di: 45	....	di: 125	....	....	....	....	....	Di-m-toluidide, 222; Di-hydrazide, 105
195	Propane-1,1-disulfonamide	169–70	....	....	....	151–2, al.	....	....	....	....	....	....
196	2,4,5-Trimethoxybenzene sulfonanilide	170	....	130	76	....	....	....	....	....	....	....
197	4-Acetamidonaphthalene-1-sulfonanilide	170	....	241	....	....	....	....	....	....	....	....
198	4-Ethoxynaphthalene-1-sulfonamide	170	....	103	....	180	....	....	....	....	....	....
199	3-Carboxybenzene sulfonamide	di: 170	98 (hyd.); 148 (anh.)	di: 20	....	....	....	163	224–6	....	....	....
200	4-Methyl-2-nitrobenzene sulfonamide	170	....	98–9	....	....	....	....	....	....	....	o-Anisidide, 135
201	N-(1-Naphthyl)benzene sulfonamide	170–1	43–4 (mono-hyd.); 66 (anh.)	14.5	156	112	....	148	205	240	176	Me. ester, b.p. 150[15]; N-Xanthylsulfonamide, 200
202	3,6-Dichloro-2,5-dimethylbenzene sulfonanilide	171	....	71	165	....	....	....	....	....	....	....
203	5-Aminonaphthalene-1-sulfonanilide	171	....	....	260	....	....	179	....	....	....	....
204	4-Nitrobenzene sulfonanilide	171 (136)	109–11 (95)	80, lgr.	180	....	....	....	179–80	....	....	....
205	2,4-Dimethyl-3-nitrobenzene sulfonamide	172	144 (anh.)	96	....	....	....	....	....	....	....	....
206	8-Nitronaphthalene-2-sulfonanilide	172–3	135.6 (hyd.)	169	223	....	....	....	....	....	....	....
207	2,5-Dimethyl-3-nitrobenzene sulfonamide	173	128 (200)	61	....	143–4	....	....	136	....	....	....
208	4-Nitrodiphenylamine-2-sulfonamide	173	....	102–4	....	164	....	....	....	....	....	....
209	7-Ethoxy-8-nitronaphthalene-1-sulfonamide	173.4	....	155	....	....	....	....	....	....	....	....
210	2,5-Dimethylbenzene-1,3-disulfonanilide	174, al.	....	81, lgr.	295, al.	....	....	....	....	....	....	....
211	3-Methoxynaphthalene-2-sulfonanilide	174	....	138	113	....	....	....	....	....	....	....
212	3,4-Dibromobenzene sulfonamide	175	66.5–7.5 (anhyd.)	34	....	....	....	....	....	....	....	....

*Derivative data given in order: m.p., crystal color, solvent from which crystallized.

TABLE XXIV. ORGANIC DERIVATIVES OF SULFONAMIDES AND SULFONANILIDES
(Listed in order of increasing m.p.)* (Continued)

No.	Name	Melting point, °C	Sulfonic acid	Chloride	Amide	Anilide	1-Naphthylamide	S-Benzylthiuronium	p-Toluidinium	Anilinium	o-Toluidinium	Miscellaneous derivatives of the acid
				Derivatives of the corresponding acid				Salts of the corresponding acid				
213	**4,6-Dichloro-2,5-dimethylbenzene sulfonanilide**	175	....	81	150	....	....	....	....	....	....	....
214	**4-Chloro-3-nitrobenzene sulfonamide**	175–6, yel., al.	....	40–1 (60–2)	....							
215	**7-Chloronaphthalene-2-sulfonamide**	176	68 (tetra-hyd.); 118 (anhyd.)	87	....							Me. ester, 89; Et. ester, 65
216	**3-Amino-4-methylbenzene sulfonamide**	176	....									3-N-Benzoyl deriv. of sulfonamide, 203; 3-N-Acetyl deriv. of sulfonyl chloride, 144; 3-N-Benzoyl deriv. of sulfonyl chloride, 196
217	**4-Bromo-3-nitrobenzene sulfonamide**	176–7	....	55–7	....	....	....	....	....	....	....	....
218	**4-Hydroxybenzene sulfonamide**	176–7	....	141	....	....		169	202	170	192	....
219	**5-Methylnaphthalene-1-sulfonamide**	176–8	115	....								
220	**4-Methylnaphthalene-1-sulfonamide**	177 d.; 174	....	81, lgr.	....	158						
221	**2-Chloro-5-methyl-6-nitrobenzene sulfonamide**	177	....	122								
222	**Benzophenone-3,3′-disulfonanilide**	177–8	....	di: 137–8	di: 157							
223	**6-Methoxynaphthalene-1-sulfonanilide**	177.5	....	80.5	149.5							
224	**Acenaphthene-5-sulfonanilide**	178	....	111	223							
225	**2-Methylbenzene-1,4-disulfonanilide**	di: 178	....	98	224							
226	**8-Nitronaphthalene-1-sulfonanilide**	178–8.5	115 (trihyd.)	165 d.	190.5–1.5	....						
227	**Naphthalene-1,4-disulfonanilide**	179	....	160 (166)	273, w., al.	....						
228	**4-Nitrobenzene sulfonamide**	180, 50% al.	109–11 (95) (hyg.)	80, lgr.	....	171 (136) d.			179–80			
229	**4-Ethoxynaphthalene-1-sulfonanilide**	180	....	103	170							
230	**3,4-Dimethyl-5-nitrobenzene sulfonamide**	180	....	70								
231	**3-Chloro-2-methylbenzene sulfonamide**	180, w.	60–72	72, pet. eth.	....							
232	**2-Aminonaphthalene-8-sulfonamide**	181 (hyd.)	....	....	147							1-N-Acetyl deriv. of sulfonamide, 213; Benzoylguanidine salt, 214–6
233	**2,5-Dichlorobenzene sulfonamide**	181	93–7 (>1.00)	38	....	160	160	170	247–8	262–3	250–1	....
234	**2,4,5-Trimethylbenzene sulfonamide**	181	112	61	....							

*Derivative data given in order: m.p., crystal color, solvent from which crystallized.

TABLE XXIV. ORGANIC DERIVATIVES OF SULFONAMIDES AND SULFONANILIDES
(Listed in order of increasing m.p.)* (Continued)

No.	Name	Melting point, °C	Sulfonic acid	Derivatives of the corresponding acid				Salts of the corresponding acid				Miscellaneous derivatives of the acid
				Chloride	Amide	Anilide	1-Naph-thyl-amide	S-Benzyl thiu-ronium	p-Tolui-dinium	Ani-linium	o-Tolui-dinium	
235	5-Chloro-4-methyl-2-nitrobenzene sulfonamide	181	128	99	....	....	......	......	....	......	....	....
236	2,4-Dichlorobenzene sulfonamide	182	86	55	....	....	......	......	204–6	......	170–2	....
237	2,5-Dimethyl-6-nitrobenzene sulfonanilide	182	145 (anh.)	110	192	....	......	......	158.5–9, al.	......	143–5, 50% al.	....
238	5-Ethoxynaphthalene-1-sulfonamide	182.5	....	121	....	130						
239	6-Ethoxynaphthalene-2-sulfonamide	183	....	107.5	....	153						
240	4-Iodobenzene sulfonamide	183	....	85	....	143						
241	4-Ethoxynaphthalene-2-sulfonamide	183	....	85	....	143.5						
242	Quinoline-8-sulfonamide	183–4	312	124	....	......	......	......	......	......	......	Me. ester, 96; Et. ester, 73; Picrate of Na salt, 226–7
243	4,5-Dichloro-3-methylbenzene sulfonamide	183–5	....	85–8								
244	N-(1-Naphthyl)-4-bromo-benzene sulfonamide	183.5	88–90	76, eth.	166; 161	119	......	170	215–6	237–8	182–3	....
245	6-Chloronaphthalene-2-sulfonamide	184	....	110.5								
246	5-Nitronaphthalene-2-sulfonamide	184	118–9, yel.	125	....	......	......	......	......	260 d.	......	....
247	8-Chloronaphthalene-2-sulfonamide	185	....	94								
248	4-Chloro-2-methylbenzene sulfonamide	185	....	54								
249	4-Chloro-2,5-dimethylbenzene sulfonamide	185	100	50	....	155						
250	2-Carboxy-5-methylbenzene sulfonamide (4-Toluic acid-2-sulfon-amide)	185	190 (158) (anh.)	di: 59								
251	2-Chloro-5-nitrobenzene sulfonamide	185–6	168–9 d. (hyd.)	90, w.	....							
252	2-Bromobenzene sulfonamide	186, w.	....	51, eth.								
253	3,5-Dichloro-2-methylbenzene sulfonamide	186	....	54								
254	2-Methyl-5-nitrobenzene sulfonamide	186	133.5 (dihyd.)	46–7; b.p. 183–5[10]	....	148	......	......	256–7	......	256–8	
255	2-Chloro-4-methylbenzene sulfonamide	186	....	46; 52	....							
256	4-Methylbenzene-1,3-di-sulfonamide (Toluene-2,4-disulfonamide)	186–7 (191)	....	54; 46	....	189	......	......	277 d.	di: 189	di: 170–1	Di-m-toluidide, 138
257	2-Ethoxynaphthalene-1-sulfonanilide	187	....	116	158	....						
258	4-Chloronaphthalene-1-sulfonamide	187	130–3 d.	94–5	....	145–6	162	......	......	145–6	151	Me. ester, 83; Et. ester, 104
259	8-Iodonaphthalene-1-sulfonamide	187	115	140	....	......	......	......	......	......	......	....

*Derivative data given in order: m.p., crystal color, solvent from which crystallized.

No.	Name	Melting point, °C	Sulfonic acid	Derivatives of the corresponding acid				Salts of the corresponding acid				Miscellaneous derivatives of the acid
				Chloride	Amide	Anilide	1-Naph-thyl-amide	S-Benzyl thiu-ronium	p-Tolui-dinium	Ani-linium	o-Tolui-dinium	
260	**2,4-Dimethyl-5-nitro-benzene sulfonamide....**	187 (179)	132 (122) dil. HNO₃	98	....	....						Sulfonyl chloride, 109–10
261	**2,4-Diaminobenzene-1,5-disulfonamide**	187	....	275	....	236						
262	**8-Bromonaphthalene-2-sulfonamide.**..........	187	....	121								
263	**2-Chlorobenzene sulfon-amide.**..............	188	....	28.5								
264	**4-Nitronaphthalene-1-sulfonamide.**..........	188	....	99								
265	**2,6-Dichloro-3-methyl-benzene sulfonamide....**	188	....	19.5								
266	**5-Methylnaphthalene-2-sulfonamide.**..........	188–9		120–2		248–50 (133–4)	......					
267	**4-Methylbenzene-1,3-disulfonanilide**	189	....	54; 46	186–7	......						
268	**6-Methoxynaphthalene-2-sulfonamide.**..........	189	....	93	....	120						
269	**Sulfanilylguanidine** (Sulfaguanidine)	189–90 (anh.); 143 (hyd.)	....	....								4-N-Acetyl deriv. of sulfonamide, 262–6 (248–51); Hydrochloride, 205–6
270	**N-(1-Naphthyl)-4-chloro-benzene sulfonamide....**	190	69 (93)	53	144	104	.....	175	208˙–10	222–3	163–4	....
271	**2,4-Dibromobenzene sulfonamide.**..........	190	110 (anh.)	79, eth.	....	....						
272	**4-Methylbenzene-1,2-disulfonanilide** (Toluene-3,4-disulfonanilide)....	190	....	109–11	237–9	....						
273	**Phenanthrene-3-sulfon-amide.**..............	190	175–6 (anh.); 120–1 (mono-hyd.); 88 d. (dihyd.)	110–1	....	....		222			......	Me. ester, 119–20, al.; Et. ester, 107–8
274	**4-Aminonaphthalene-1-sulfonanilide**	190	....	....							......	4-N-Acetyl deriv. of sulfonamide, 247
275	**8-Nitronaphthalene-1-sulfonamide.**..........	191	115 d. (trihyd.)	165 d.	....	178–8.5	.....					....
276	**2-Hydroxynaphthalene-1,6-disulfonanilide**	191	....	*di:* 111								
277	**3,5-Dichloro-4-methyl-benzene sulfonamide....**	191	....	69								
278	**Sulfapyridine**	191–2	....	....								4-N-Acetyl deriv. of sulfonamide, 226–7, acet.
279	**Anthraquinone-2,7-disul-fonanilide**	192		*di:* 186, chl.								....
280	**4-Carboxy-3-nitrobenzene sulfonamide** (2-Nitro-benzoic acid-4-sulfon-amide)..............	192	111 (+2½ H₂O)	*di:* 160	....	......						Diamide, 226
281	**Quinoline-6-sulfonamide** .	192	>260	91	....	....						....
282	**5,6-Dichloronaphthalene-2-sulfonamide**	192	....	167								

*Derivative data given in order: m.p., crystal color, solvent from which crystallized.

No.	Name	Melting point, °C	Sulfonic acid	Derivatives of the corresponding acid				Salts of the corresponding acid				Miscellaneous derivatives of the acid
				Chloride	Amide	Anilide	1-Naphthylamide	S-Benzylthiuronium	p-Toluidinium	Anilinium	o-Toluidinium	
283	Anthraquinone-2,7-disulfonamide	192	....	186	....	....	....	....	....	....	....	....
284	2,5-Dimethyl-6-nitrobenzene sulfonamide	192	145 (anh.)	110	....	182	....	....	158.5-9	....	143-5, 50% al.	....
285	2-Amino-5-methylbenzene-1,3-disulfonanilide	192	....	156	257	....	....					
286	Methane disulfonanilide	192-3	220-7^{15} d.	8; b.p. 133^{10}	di: 233	....						
287	3,4-Dicarboxybenzene sulfonamide (Phthalic acid-4-sulfonamide)	192-200 d., w.	138-40 (mono-hyd.)	167-70 d., eth.	....							
288	2-Nitrobenzene sulfonamide	193	70 (85)	69	....	115						
289	Anthraquinone-2-sulfonanilide	193	....	197	261	....	....	211	308	309	......	Me. ester, 123; Et. ester, 125
290	Phenanthrene-9-sulfonamide	193-4	174 (anh.)	127	....	....	....	....	235			Me. ester, 106, me. al.; Et. ester, 108, al.
291	2-Carboxybenzene sulfonanilide	194-5	68-9 (hyd.); 134 (anh.)	79, pet. eth.	....	....	....	206	196 (200)	165	127-8	....
292	5-Methoxynaphthalene-1-sulfonamide	194.5	....	119.5	....	157						
293	6-Ethoxynaphthalene-1-sulfonanilide	194.5	....	118	154							
294	7-Hydroxynaphthalene-1,3-disulfonanilide	195	....	161-2	....	....	....	228	294	......	271	
295	4-Bromonaphthalene-1-sulfonamide	195	....	87	....							
296	7-Hydroxynaphthalene-1-sulfonanilide	195	....	....	....	....	....	218	232	240	242	
297	2,5-Dibromobenzene sulfonamide	195	128 (anh.)	71	....							
298	7-Methylnaphthalene-1-sulfonamide	195-6	....	96	....	162-4						
299	4,6-Dimethylbenzene-1,3-disulfonanilide	196, 50% al.	....	130, pet. eth.	249, w.	....						
300	4,7-Dichloronaphthalene-2-sulfonamide	196	....	156	....							
301	N-(1-Naphthyl)-4-aminobenzene sulfonamide	196	....	....	165	200	....	185				
302	8-Chloro-7-methoxynaphthalene-1-sulfonanilide	196	....	137	153	....						
303	5-Fluoronaphthalene-1-sulfonamide	196-7	105 (hyd.)	122-3	....	....						Me. ester, 118, eth.
304	2-Methoxynaphthalene-1-sulfonanilide	196.5	....	121	159	....						
305	8-Chloronaphthalene-1-sulfonamide	197	....	101	....							
306	4,5-Dichloronaphthalene-2-sulfonamide	197	....	158	....							
307	2,5-Dimethyl-4-nitrobenzene sulfonamide	197-8	140	75	....	131	....	....	143.5-4.5	......	143.5-4.5	....

*Derivative data given in order: m.p., crystal color, solvent from which crystallized.

403

No.	Name	Melting point, °C	Sulfonic acid	Derivatives of the corresponding acid				Salts of the corresponding acid				Miscellaneous derivatives of the acid
				Chloride	Amide	Anilide	1-Naphthyl-amide	S-Benzyl thiuronium	p-Toluidinium	Anilinium	o-Toluidinium	
308	**Sulfamethazine (Sulfadimethylpyrimidine)**.....	198–9 $(+\frac{1}{2}$ H$_2$O), pa. yel.	....	....	....	....	....	....	....	....	....	4-N-Acetyl deriv. of sulfonamide, 249–50
309	Acenaphthene-3-sulfonamide.............	199	87–9	113–4	....	284–6						Me. ester, 122–3; Et. ester, 137–9, lgr.
310	4-Hydroxynaphthalene-1-sulfonanilide.........	199–200	170	....	167	....	....	103	196	186–7	203–4	2-Naphthyl sulfonamide, 204
311	4-Aminobenzene sulfonanilide.............	200	....	....	165	....	196	185	109	....	132	4-N-Acetyl deriv. of sulfonanilide, 214; Me. ester, 92
312	4,5-Dimethylbenzene-1,3-disulfonanilide........	200, al.	....	79, yel.	239	....						....
313	4-Chloro-3-methyl-5-nitrobenzene sulfonamide......	201	....	52	....							....
314	Anthracene-2-sulfonanilide.............	201	....	122	261	....					....	Phenylhydrazide, 210; Me. ester, 157; Et. ester, 160
315	5-Hydroxynaphthalene-1-sulfonanilide.........	201	110–2 d.	....							....	O-Acetyl deriv. of sulfonyl chloride, 129
316	2-Hydroxynaphthalene-3,6-disulfonanilide.....	202	....	....			....	233	250	254	257	....
317	5-Amino-2-hydroxybenzene sulfonamide......	202 d.	100 (anh.)	....	....	159 (98)						....
318	1-Nitronaphthalene-2-sulfonanilide.........	202	105, grn.	121, bz.-pet. eth.	214	....						....
319	Sulfathiazole..........	202.5	....	....							....	4-N-Acetyl deriv. of sulfonamide, 256–7
320	**4-Nitrobenzyl sulfonamide** (4-Nitrotoluene-α-sulfonamide)........	204	71	90	220 d.	....						....
321	Anthracene-1-sulfonamide.............	205	....	90								....
322	4,8-Dichloronaphthalene-2-sulfonamide........	205	....	141								....
323	3-Amino-4-hydroxybenzene sulfonamide......	205 (170)	155–6 d.	....								....
324	4-Hydroxybenzene-1,3-disulfonanilide (Phenol-2,4-disulfonanilide)....	205	>100 d.	89	239	....						....
325	6-Methylnaphthalene-2-sulfonamide..........	205–6	....	97–8								....
326	2,6-Dimethyl-4-hydroxybenzene-1,3-disulfonanilide.............	205–7	....	117–8	206–8	....						....
327	4-Iodonaphthalene-1-sulfonamide...........	206; 204	....	124; 121	....	136						....
328	4-Fluoronaphthalene-1-sulfonamide..........	206	100 (hyd.)	86	....	144	....	....	....	....	....	Et. ester, 93
330	4-Amino-3-nitrobenzene sulfonamide..........	206-7	....	59–60								....

* Derivative data given in order: m.p., crystal color, solvent from which crystallized.

No.	Name	Melting point, °C	Sulfonic acid	Derivatives of the corresponding acid				Salts of the corresponding acid				Miscellaneous derivatives of the acid
				Chloride	Amide	Anilide	1-Naphthylamide	S-Benzylthiuronium	p-Toluidinium	Anilinium	o-Toluidinium	
331	Retene-6-sulfonamide	206–7.5	121–3	146–7.5, yel.-br.	....	....						Me. ester, 117–9; Et. ester, 114–5
332	2,6-Dimethyl-4-hydroxy-benzene-1,3-disulfonamide	206–8	....	117–8	....	205–7						....
333	3,7-Diethylnaphthalene-1-sulfonamide	207	....	105–7								
334	6-Bromonaphthalene-2-sulfonamide	207	....	124								
335	7-Bromonaphthalene-1-sulfonamide	209	....	147								
336	4-Methoxybenzene-1,3-disulfonanilide	209	....	86	240	..						
337	7-Iodonaphthalene-2-sulfonamide	210	....	100								
338	4-(N-Methylamino)benzene sulfonamide	210–11	244–5 d.	....								p-Toluenesulfonate, benzidine salt, 255
339	2,4,6-Trichlorobenzene sulfonamide	210–2 d.	....	35–40								
340	4-Aminonaphthalene-1-sulfonamide	212	....	....		190						
341	6-Iodonaphthalene-1-sulfonamide	213	....	92.5	....							
342	Fluorene-2-sulfonamide	213 d.	155 (hyd.)	164								
343	Anthraquinone-1-sulfonanilide	214	218	216–8, yel., PhNO₂	....			191	......	284	......	NH₃ → 1-Aminoanthraquinone, 252 (243)
344	1-Nitronaphthalene-2-sulfonamide	214	105, grn.	121, pink, bz.-pet. eth.	....	202						....
345	4-Acetamidobenzene sulfonanilide	214	....	149	219	....	215					
346	6-Chloronaphthalene-1-sulfonamide	214	....	70	....							Et. ester, 114–5
347	N-(1-Naphthyl)-4-acetamidobenzene sulfonamide	215	....	149	219	214						
348	2,5-Dichlorobenzene-1,3-disulfonamide	215–7	....	114								
349	5-Methylbenzene-1,3-disulfonamide	216, w.	....	94, eth.	....	153, al.						
350	5-Chloronaphthalene-2-sulfonamide	216	....	115								
351	Naphthalene-2-sulfonamide	217; 213	91 (hyg.); (122)	76; 79	....	132	......	190–1	221	269	213	....
352	4,7-Dichloronaphthalene-1-sulfonamide	217	....	151								
353	6-Bromonaphthalene-1-sulfonamide	217	....	77								
354	4,6-Dichloronaphthalene-2-sulfonamide	218	....	136								
355	7-Bromonaphthalene-2-sulfonamide	218	....	100								
356	3,6-Dichloronaphthalene-2-sulfonamide	218	....	166	....							

* Derivative data given in order: m.p., crystal color, solvent from which crystallized.

No.	Name	Melting point, °C	Sulfonic acid	Derivatives of the corresponding acid				Salts of the corresponding acid				Miscellaneous derivatives of the acid
				Chloride	Amide	Anilide	1-Naphthylamide	S-Benzylthiuronium	p-Toluidinium	Anilinium	o-Toluidinium	
357	**6-Ethoxy-1-nitro-naphthalene-2-sulfonamide**	218	....	146	....	....	......	......	......	......	......	
358	**5-Aminonaphthalene-2-sulfonamide**	218–9 d.				127–8						1-N-Acetyl deriv. of sulfonamide, 238–9
359	**4-Acetamidobenzene sulfonamide**	219	....	149	....	214	215					....
360	**5-Bromonaphthalene-2-sulfonamide**	220	....	96								
361	**4-Nitrobenzyl sulfonanilide (4-Nitrotoluene-α-sulfonanilide)**	220 d.	71	90	204	....						
362	**7-Methoxynaphthalene-2-sulfonamide**	220	....	83	....	121						
363	**2,4,6-Tribromobenzene sulfonanilide**	220–2 d.	64	64	228							
364	**7,8-Dichloronaphthalene-1-sulfonamide**	221	....	138		....						
365	**8-Hydroxynaphthalene-1-sulfonamide**	222 d.	107 (hyg.)	....								
366	**6-Iodonaphthalene-2-sulfonamide**	222	....	140								
367	**2,5-Dimethylbenzene-1,4-disulfonanilide**	223	....	164	310	....						
368	**5,6-Dichloronaphthalene-1-sulfonamide**	223	....	106								
369	**Acenaphthene-5-sulfonamide**	223	....	111	....	178		......				
370	**6-Nitronaphthalene-1-sulfonamide**	223–4		127								
371	**2-Methylbenzene-1,4-disulfonamide**	224	....	98	....	*di*: 178						
372	**5-Chlorobenzene-1,3-disulfonamide**	224	....	106								
373	**Anthracene-1,8-disulfonanilide**	224	....	225	333	....						
374	**4-Nitronaphthalene-2-sulfonamide**	225	....	139.5								
375	**4,6-Dichloronaphthalene-1-sulfonamide**	226	....	119								
376	**4-Carboxamido-3-nitrobenzene sulfonamide (2-Nitrobenzamide-4-sulfonamide)**	226	111 (+2.5 H$_2$O)	*di*: 160	192	....					'	
377	**5-Chloronaphthalene-1-sulfonamide**	226	....	95	....	138	......	......	......	......	......	Sulfonyl bromide, 110; Me. ester, 89; Et. ester, 46
378	**4-Methoxynaphthalene-1-sulfonamide**	226	....	98.5	....	147.5						....
379	**3,4-Di-iodobenzene sulfonamide**	227, aq. al.	122–5	82, bz.-pet. eth.	....							
380	**7,8-Dichloronaphthalene-2-sulfonamide**	227	....	124								
381	**Anthraquinone-1,6-disulfonanilide**	227–8, yel.	215–7, gold	197–8, yel., PhNO$_2$								
382	**2,3,4-Trichlorobenzene sulfonamide**	227–30	....	64–5								

*Derivative data given in order: m.p., crystal color, solvent from which crystallized.

No.	Name	Melting point, °C	Sulfonic acid	Chloride	Amide	Anilide	1-Naphthylamide	S-Benzylthiuronium	p-Toluidinium	Anilinium	o-Toluidinium	Miscellaneous derivatives of the acid
383	3,4-Dichloro-2-methylbenzene sulfonamide	228	. . . .	51–2	. . . .	. . . .	. . . .	. . . . .	. . . .	. . . .	. . . .	. . . .
384	4′-Nitrobiphenyl-4-sulfonamide.	228		178								
385	2,4,6-Tribromobenzene sulfonamide.	228	64	64	. . . .	220–2 d.						
386	8-Nitronaphthalene-2-sulfonamide.	228; 223	135–6 (+1.5 H$_2$O)	169	. . . .	172–3						
387	6,8-Dichloronaphthalene-2-sulfonamide	228		121								
388	Benzene-1,3-disulfonamide.	229		63	. . . .	148–50	245	214			. . . . .	N-Xanthylsulfonamide, 170; Alk. fusion → resorcinol, 110.
389	4,5-Dichloronaphthalene-1-sulfonamide	229		117								. . . .
390	Biphenyl-4-sulfonamide . .	230		115		125						
391	2,4-Di-iodobenzene sulfonanilide	230	167 (anh.)	77–8							. . . . .	Me. ester, 78, al; Et. ester, 52, al.
392	2-Hydroxynaphthalene-1,5-disulfonanilide	231		di: 231								
393	5-Bromonaphthalene-1-sulfonamide.	232–3		95								
394	2-Hydroxynaphthalene-1,7-disulfonanilide	233		169								
395	Methane disulfonamide . .	233	b.p. 220–70$^{15-20}$ d.	di: 8; b.p. 133^{10}	. . . .	di: 192–3						
396	2-Ethoxybenzene-1,4-disulfonamide	233		di: 106–8								
397	3,5-Dinitrobenzene sulfonamide.	235		99, chl., lgr.								
398	4-Aminobenzene-1,3-disulfonamide (Aniline-2,4-disulfonamide).	235, w.	120 d.	. . . .							
399	7-Chloronaphthalene-1-sulfonamide.	235		129								
400	5,6,8-Trichloronaphthalene-2-sulfonamide . .	235		158								
401	4,6,7,8-Tetrachloronaphthalene-2-sulfonamide . .	235		176								
402	5-Nitronaphthalene-1-sulfonamide.	236		113	. . . .	123						
403	4-Carboxamidobenzene sulfonamide.	236	94 (hyd.); 260 (anh.)	di: 57	. . . .	di: 252						
404	2,4-Diaminobenzene-1,5-disulfonanilide	236		275	187							
405	2,3-Dichloro-4-methylbenzene sulfonamide	237		41								. . . .
406	Benzene-1,3,5-trisulfonanilide	tri: 237	>100	tri: 187	tri: 310–5	. . . .					. . . . .	Tri-Et. ester, 147, bz.
408	Anthraquinone-1,7-disulfonanilide	237–8, yel., cl. bz.	120 (hyd.)	321–2, br.-yel., PhNO$_2$	. . . .							
409	Anthraquinone-1,8-disulfonanilide	237–8, yel., PhNO$_2$	293–4	222–3	>340	. . . .						
410	4-Methylbenzene-1,2-disulfonamide.	237–9	. . . .	109–11	. . . .	190						

*Derivative data given in order: m.p., crystal color, solvent from which crystallized.

TABLE XXIV. ORGANIC DERIVATIVES OF SULFONAMIDES AND SULFONANILIDES
(Listed in order of increasing m.p.)* (Continued)

No.	Name	Melting point, °C	Sulfonic acid	Derivatives of the corresponding acid				Salts of the corresponding acid				Miscellaneous derivatives of the acid
				Chloride	Amide	Anilide	1-Naph-thyl-amide	S-Benzyl thiu-ronium	p-Tolui-dinium	Ani-linium	o-Tolui-dinium	
411	6-Hydroxynaphthalene-2-sulfonamide.........	238	129 (hyd.); 167 (anh.)	....	....	161	......	217 (207)	248	264	208	.....
412	4-Hydroxybenzene-1,3-disulfonamide (Phenol-2,4-disulfonamide).....	239	>100 d.	89	....	205	......					
413	5-Iodonaphthalene-1-sulfonamide...........	239	....	141								
414	4,5-Dimethylbenzene-1,3-disulfonamide........	239	....	79, yel.	....	200, al.						
415	7-Iodonaphthalene-1-sulfonamide..........	240	....	165								
416	4-Methoxybenzene-1,3-disulfonamide........	240	....	86		209						
417	4-Acetamidonaphthalene-1-sulfonamide........	241	....			170						
418	Benzene-1,2-disulfonanilide.............	241	....	143	254	....		206				
419	5-Nitrobenzene-1,3-disulfonamide..........	242	....	di: 97–8								
420	Naphthalene-2,7-disulfonamide...........	242	....	158; 162		....		212	299	251–2	238	.....
421	2,4,6-Trimethylbenzene-1,3-disulfonamide.....	244	....	di: 125	....	di: 150–1						
422	5,8-Dichloronaphthalene-2-sulfonamide........	244	....	134								
423	2,3,4,6-Tetrabromobenzene sulfonamide	245 d.	....	96.5								
424	6,7,8-Trichloronaphthalene-2-sulfonamide..	245	....	157	....							
425	N,N'-Di(1-naphthyl)benzene-1,3-disulfonamide.	245	....	63	229	148–50		214	......	......		Alk. fusion → resorcinol, 110; N-Xanthylsulfonamide, 170
426	Anthraquinone-1,5-disulfonamide..........	246 (350)	310 d.	265–70	....	270 d.						.....
427	1-Iodonaphthalene-2-sulfonamide..........	247	....	94								
428	9,10-Dichloroanthracene-2-sulfonanilide........	248	....	221	279							
430	5-Methylnaphthalene-2-sulfonanilide.........	248–50	....	120–2	188–9							
431	4,6-Dimethylbenzene-1,3-disulfonamide........	249, w.	....	130, pet. eth.	....	196, 50% al.						
432	Benzene-1,4-disulfonanilide.............	249	....	131 (139)	288							
433	5,6,7-Trichloronaphthalene-1-sulfonamide..	249	....	131								
434	Naphthalene-1,5-disulfonanilide.............	249	245 (anh.)	di: 183	310 (340)	....	......	257; 251d.	332	......	......	Di-Me. ester, 205, chl.
435	1-Chloronaphthalene-2-sulfonamide...........	250	130–3d. (anh.)	84–5	....	171–2						
436	Azobenzene-4,4'-disulfonamide........	250 d.	169d. (anh.)	di: 222	....							Et. ester, 104
437	4-Carboxanilidobenzene sulfonanilide.........	252	94 (hyd.); 260 (anh.)	di: 57	di: 236							....

* Derivative data given in order: m.p., crystal color, solvent from which crystallized.

No.	Name	Melting point, °C	Sulfonic acid	Derivatives of the corresponding acid				Salts of the corresponding acid				Miscellaneous derivatives of the acid
				Chloride	Amide	Anilide	1-Naphthylamide	S-Benzyl thiuronium	p-Toluidinium	Anilinium	o-Toluidinium	
438	Phenanthrene-2-sulfonamide	253–4	150	156	....	157–8	.....	......	291	.....	.....	Me. ester, 101–2; Et. ester, 89, yel.-br.
439	Benzene-1,2-disulfonamide	254	....	143	....	241	.....	206				....
440	2-Amino-5-methylbenzene-1,3-disulfonamide	257	....	156		192						
441	2-Amino-5-methylbenzene-1,4-disulfonamide	257, w.	290	di: 156, chl.		di: 196–7, aq. al.	.....					
442	5-Aminonaphthalene-1-sulfonamide	260	....	....		171	.....	179			.....	5-N-Acetyl deriv. of sulfonamide, 231–2
443	2-Methylbenzene-1,3-disulfonamide	260	....	88	....	162						....
444	Anthracene-2-sulfonamide	261		122		201						Me. ester, 157; Et. ester, 160
445	Anthraquinone-2-sulfonamide	261	....	197		193	.....	211	308	309	.....	Me. ester, 123; Et. ester, 125
446	7-Nitronaphthalene-1-sulfonamide	261–2	....	169–70								
447	6,7-Dichloronaphthalene-1-sulfonamide	268	....	142								
448	3,7-Dichloronaphthalene-1-sulfonamide	269	....	136								
449	Anthraquinone-2,6-disulfonanilide	269–70	310–11 (hyd.)	265–70, yel.	>350	....						
450	Anthraquinone-1,5-disulfonanilide	270 d.	310 d.	265–70	246 (350)	....						
451	1-Bromonaphthalene-2-sulfonamide	271	....	93								
452	5,7-Dichloronaphthalene-1-sulfonamide	272	....	149								
453	Naphthalene-1,4-disulfonamide	273, w., al.		160 (166)	....	179						
454	Azoxybenzene-3,3'-disulfonamide	273	126	di: 138								
455	4,6-Dichlorobenzene-1,3-disulfonamide	276	....	123								
456	Benzidine-2,2'-disulfonamide	278	....	Hydro-chloride, 205								
457	9,10-Dichloroanthracene-2-sulfonamide	279	....	221	....	248						
458	1,5-Dichloronaphthalene-2-sulfonamide	282	....	125								
459	4-Nitronaphthalene-2,7-disulfonamide	286–7	....	140–1								
460	Azobenzene-3,4'-disulfonamide	288	....	123–5								
461	Benzene-1,4-disulfonamide	288	....	131 (139)	....	249						
462	Naphthalene-1,3-disulfonamide	292–3	....	di: 137.5	....							
463	Anthracene-1,5-disulfonanilide	293		di: 240	di: >330							
464	2,5-Dimethylbenzene-1,3-disulfonamide	295, al.	....	81, lgr.	....	174, al.						

*Derivative data given in order: m.p., crystal color, solvent from which crystallized.

No.	Name	Melting point, °C	Sulfonic acid	Derivatives of the corresponding acid				Salts of the corresponding acid				Miscellaneous derivatives of the acid
				Chloride	Amide	Anilide	1-Naph-thyl-amide	S-Benzyl thiu-ronium	p-Tolui-dinium	Ani-linium	o-Tolui-dinium	
465	**Naphthalene-1,6-disulfon-amide**	298	125 (anh.)	129	. . . .	. . . .	. . . . . .	81 (235)	314–5	298–9	323–4	. . . .
466	**Naphthalene-1,7-disulfon-amide**	298–300	123		. . . .	. . . .	. . . . . .		. . . . . .	. . . . . .	. . . . . .	. . . .
467	**Biphenyl-4,4'-disulfon-amide**	300	72	203	. . . .	. . . .	. . . . . .	171	330 d.	. . . . . .	. . . . . .	. . . .
468	**Naphthalene-2,6-disulfon-amide**	305	. . . .	225	. . . .	. . . .	. . . . . .	256	. . . . . .	360	. . . . . .	. . . .
469	**Azobenzene-3,3'-disulfon-amide**	305	. . . .	*di*: 166	. . . .	. . . .	. . . . . .					. . . .
470	**2,5-Dimethylbenzene-1,4-disulfonamide**	310	. . . .	164		223		. . . . . .				
471	**Naphthalene-1,5-disulfon-amide**	310 (340)	245 (anh.)	183	. . . .	249	. . . . . .	257; 251 d.	332	. . . . . .	. . . . . .	Di-Me. ester, 205, chl.
472	**Benzene-1,3,5-trisulfon-amide**	310–5	>100	*tri*: 187	. . . .	*tri*: 237	. . . . . .					Tri-Et. ester, 147, bz.
473	**Anthraquinone-2,6-disul-fonanilide**	321	. . . .	*di*: 250, yel., cl. bz.	. . . .							. . . .
474	**Anthracene-1,5-disulfon-amide**	330	. . . .	*di*: 240	. . . .	*di*: 293	. . . . . .					
475	**Anthracene-1,8-disul-fonamide**	333	. . . .	225	. . . .	224						
476	**8-Cyanonaphthalene-1-sulfonamide**	333–4	. . . .	139								
477	**Anthraquinone-1,8-disul-fonamide**	>340	293–4	222–3, yel., PhNO₂	. . . .	237–8, yel., PhNO₂						
478	**Anthraquinone-1,3-disul-fonamide**	>350	310–11 (hyd.)	265–70, yel.	. . . .	269–70, red-yel.	. . . . . .					

*Derivative data given in order: m.p., crystal color, solvent from which crystallized.

EXPLANATIONS AND REFERENCES TO TABLE XXV

*2,4-Dinitrophenyl thioether (2,4-Dinitrophenyl sulfide).**

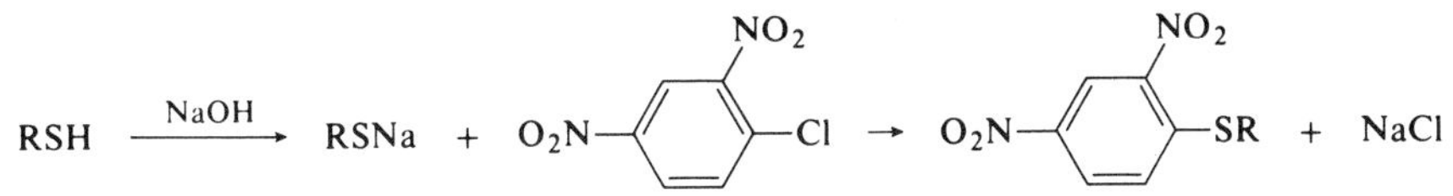

$$RSH \xrightarrow{NaOH} RSNa + O_2N\text{—}\underset{NO_2}{\overset{}{\bigcirc}}\text{—}Cl \rightarrow O_2N\text{—}\underset{NO_2}{\overset{}{\bigcirc}}\text{—}SR + NaCl$$

2,4-Dinitrophenyl
thioether

From the sodium thiolate (prepared from the thiol and sodium hydroxide) and 2,4-dinitrochlorobenzene in methanol.

For directions and examples see: Cheronis, p. 642.

From the sodium thiolate and 2,4-dinitrochlorobenzene in aqueous or absolute alcohol.

See: Linstead, p. 86; Shriner, p. 255; Vogel, p. 500; Wild, p. 91; R. W. Bost, J. O. Turner and R. D. Norton, *J. Amer. Chem. Soc.*, **54**, 1985 (1932); R. W. Bost, J. O. Turner and M. W. Conn, *J. Amer. Chem. Soc.*, **55**, 4956 (1933).

*2,4-Dinitrophenyl sulfone.**

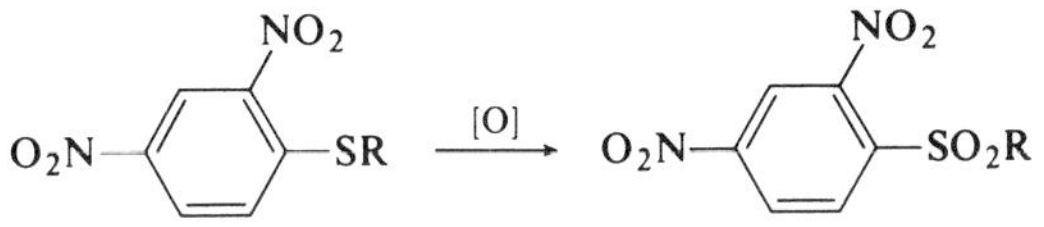

$$O_2N\text{—}\underset{NO_2}{\overset{}{\bigcirc}}\text{—}SR \xrightarrow{[O]} O_2N\text{—}\underset{NO_2}{\overset{}{\bigcirc}}\text{—}SO_2R$$

2,4-Dinitrophenyl
sulfone

From the thioether (prepared from the thiol and 2,4-dinitrochlorobenzene) and potassium permanganate in aqueous or glacial acetic acid.

For directions and examples see: Cheronis, p. 641; Linstead, p. 87; Vogel, p. 501; Wild, pp. 91–2.

From the thioether with hydrogen peroxide, ammonium molybdate and perchloric acid in water.

See: Cheronis, p. 642.

Hg salt.

$$2\,RSH + Hg(CN)_2 \rightarrow (RS)_2Hg + 2\,HCN$$

Mercuric
thiolate

From the thiol and aqueous mercuric cyanide in ethanol.

For directions and examples see: Linstead, p. 86; Wild, pp. 90–91; E. Wertheim, *J. Amer. Chem. Soc.*, **51**, 3661 (1929).

*3,5-Dinitrothiobenzoate.**

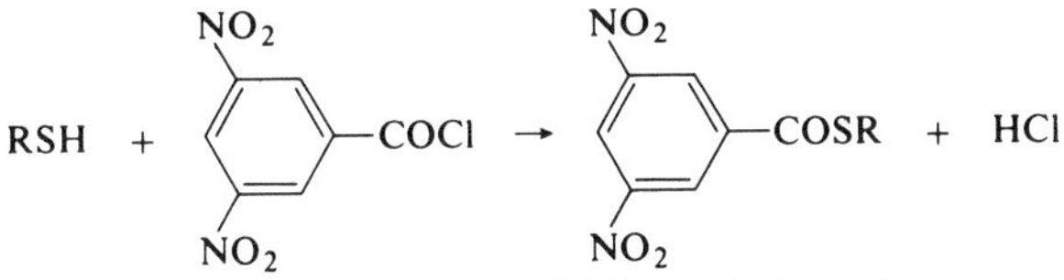

$$RSH + \underset{NO_2}{\overset{NO_2}{\bigcirc}}\text{—}COCl \rightarrow \underset{NO_2}{\overset{NO_2}{\bigcirc}}\text{—}COSR + HCl$$

3,5-Dinitrothiobenzoate

From the thiol, 3,5-dinitrobenzoyl chloride and pyridine.

For directions and examples see: Cheronis, p. 643; Shriner, p. 255; Vogel, p. 501; Wild, p. 92; E. Wertheim, *J. Amer. Chem. Soc.*, **51**, 3661 (1929).

*3-Nitrothiophthalate.**

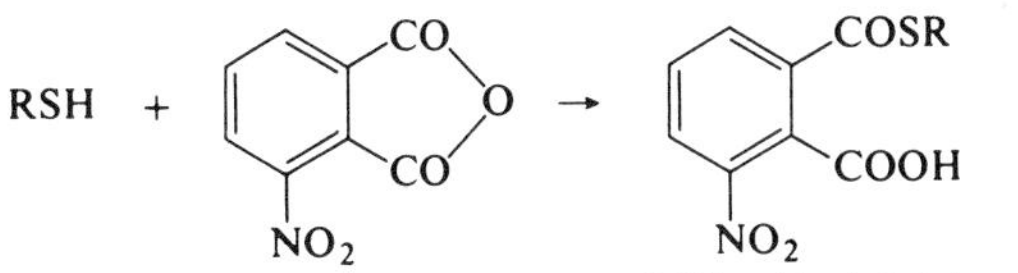

$$RSH + \underset{NO_2}{\overset{CO}{\bigcirc}}\diagdown O \rightarrow \underset{NO_2}{\overset{COSR}{\bigcirc}}\diagdown COOH$$

3-Nitrothiophthalate

From 3-Nitrophthalic anhydride and the thiol.

For directions and examples see: Wild, p. 93; E. Wertheim, *J. Amer. Chem. Soc.*, **51**, 3661 (1929).

*Derivatives recommended for first trial.
WARNING: This is not an instruction manual. References should be consulted for the preparation of derivatives.

411

EXPLANATIONS AND REFERENCES TO TABLE XXV (Continued)

*S-Alkylmercaptosuccinic acid (Alkylthiosuccinic acid).**

$$RSH + \begin{matrix} CHCOONa \\ \| \\ CHCOONa \end{matrix} \xrightarrow{H^+} \begin{matrix} RSCHCOOH \\ | \\ CH_2COOH \end{matrix}$$

S-Alkylmercaptosuccinic acid

From the thiol and disodium maleate in ethanol.

For directions and examples see: J. G. Hendrickson and L. F. Hatch, *J. Org. Chem.*, **25**, 1747 (1960).

1-Anthraquinonyl thioether.

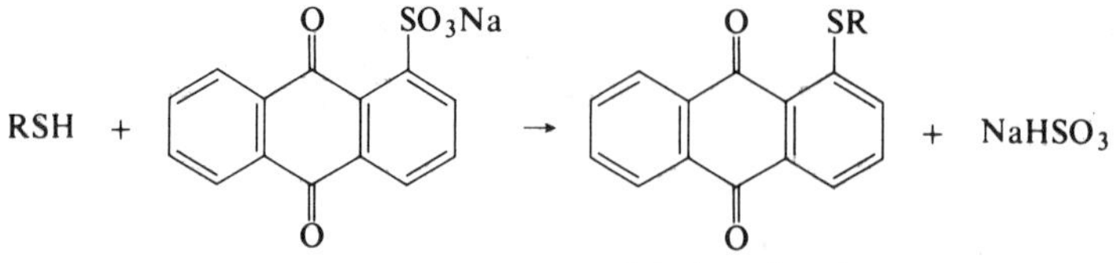

1-Anthraquinonyl thioether

From the thioether with sodium anthraquinone-1-sulfonate and sodium hydroxide in water.

For directions and examples see: E. E. Reid, C. M. MacKall and G. E. Miller, *J. Amer. Chem. Soc.*, **43**, 2104 (1921); W. S. Hoffman and E. E. Reid, *J. Amer. Chem. Soc.*, **45**, 1831 (1923); L. M. Ellis and E. E. Reid, *J. Amer. Chem. Soc.*, **54**, 1674 (1932).

Acetate.

$$RSH + CH_3COCl \rightarrow CH_3COSR + HCl$$

$$RSH + (CH_3CO)_2O \rightarrow CH_3COSR + CH_3COOH$$

$$RSH + CH_2{=}C{=}O \rightarrow CH_3COSR$$

Acetate

From the thiol with acetyl chloride, or from the thiol with acetic anhydride and aqueous sodium hydroxide, or from the thiol with ketene.

For directions and examples see: A. Schöberl and A. Wagner in *Methoden der Organischen Chemie (Houben-Weyl)*, Vol. 9 (Ed. E. Muller), Georg Thieme Verlag, Stuttgart, 1955, pp. 753–756.

Methyl thioether.

$$RSNa + CH_3I \rightarrow RSCH_3 + NaI$$

Methyl thioether

From the sodium thiolate with alkyl halide.

For directions and examples see: E. E. Reid, *The Chemistry of Bivalent Sulfur*, Vol. 2, Chemical Publishing Co., New York, 1960, p. 25.

Disulfide.

$$2\,RSH \xrightarrow{[O]} RSSR + H_2O$$

Disulfide

From the thiol (or thiophenol) with ferric chloride in aqueous acetic acid.

For directions and examples see: Linstead, p. 87; Wild, p. 95; T. Zincke and W. Frohneberg, *Chem. Ber.*, **43**, 840 (1910).

From the thiol with chlorine, bromine or iodine in hydrocarbon solvent.

See: E. E. Reid, *The Chemistry of Bivalent Sulfur*, Vol. 1, Chemical Publishing Co., New York, 1958, p. 124.

*Derivatives recommended for first trial.

WARNING: This is not an instruction manual. References should be consulted for the preparation of derivatives.

TABLE XXV. ORGANIC DERIVATIVES OF THIOLS (MERCAPTANS)
a) Liquids (Listed in order of increasing atmospheric b.p.)*

No.	Name	Boiling point, °C	Melting point, °C	n_D^{20}	D_4^{20}	2,4-Dinitrophenyl thio-ether	2,4-Dinitrophenyl sulfone	3,5-Dinitrothiobenzoate	3-Nitrothiophthalate	1-Anthraquinonyl thio-ether	Mercury salt	S-Alkyl mercapto-succinic acid	Disulfide	Miscellaneous
1	Methanethiol (Methyl mercaptan)	5.96	−123	......	0.8599^{25}	127–8	189.5	......	......	221	176	133	−84.72; b.p. 116–8	....
2	Ethanethiol (Ethyl mercaptan)	36	−144.4	1.4318	0.83147^{25}	114–5	160	62	149	184	85	119.5	−101.4; b.p. 153.5	Acetyl, b.p. 114
3	2-Propanethiol (sec-Propyl mercaptan)	56	−130.7	1.4256	0.8142	93.5–5.0	140.5	84	145	134	63	......	−69; b.p. 176	....
4	2-Methyl-2-propanethiol (tert-Butyl mercaptan)	64.2	1.26	1.4230	0.7999	109–11	......	......	......	......	164		b.p. 200–1	Benzoyl, b.p. 110[28]
5	1-Propanethiol (n-Propyl mercaptan)	67.5	−113.8	1.4348	0.8047	85–6.5	127.5	52	137	151	72	118–9	−85.59; b.p. 195–6	....
6	2-Butanethiol (sec-Butyl mercaptan)	84–5	−165.0	1.4367	0.8294	65.6–6.0	120	......			189	135	b.p. 95–7[14]	Benzoyl, b.p. 150[20]
7	2-Methyl-1-propanethiol (Isobutyl mercaptan)	88.72	....	1.4386	0.8357	74.5–5.0	105.5	63–4	136	144	95	120.9–1.4	b.p. 220	....
8	2-Propene-1-thiol (Allyl mercaptan)	90; 67–9	....	1.4680	0.93044	72	105	52					b.p. 174d.	
9	1-Butanethiol (n-Butyl mercaptan)	98–100	−119 to −115	1.44402	0.8337	66	92	49	144	112.5	86	103.7–4; 144.5	b.p. 226	Benzoyl, b.p. 160[23]
10	2-Pentanethiol (sec-Amyl mercaptan)	112.9	−169	1.4386^{25}	0.82815^{25}	......							b.p. 122–3[10]	
11	2-Methoxyethanethiol	113		1.4488^{23}	....	90							......	Acetyl, b.p. 110[110]
12	D,L-3-Methylbutanethiol (Isoamyl mercaptan)	117; 118–20	....	1.44118	0.83475							115.6–6.0	b.p. 250	
13	1-Phenylethane-1-thiol	119–20	....	1.557	1.022		161						58	Acetyl, b.p. 123–5[13]
14	D-2-Methyl-1-butanethiol	119–21		....	0.8403^{25}	78–9					60	122.3–.6	b.p. 122–3	$[\alpha]_D^{23}$: +3.21
15	2-Chloropropanethiol	125	....	1.4844	1.1062	76–7							b.p. 113–20[20]	Acetyl, b.p. 70–1[9]
16	2-Chloroethanethiol	125–6		1.5289	1.203	95–7							b.p. 170–80	Acetyl, b.p. 51[4]
17	2-Ethoxyethanethiol	125–6		1.5795	0.9462	66							b.p. 150–2[15]	
18	1-Pentanethiol (n-Amyl mercaptan)	126.64	−75.83	1.44366	0.8390	79.5–80.5	83	40	132	114	75	107–8	b.p. 140–5[17]	PdCl$_2$ deriv., 41
19	2-Hexanethiol (sec-Hexyl mercaptan)	142; 138–9	−147.0	1.4426^{25}	0.83050^{25}	......							......	....
20	1,2-Ethanedithiol (Ethylene dithioglycol)	147; 46–7[16]	−41.0	1.5550	1.1185^{25}	248								Di-Me. eth., b.p. 183
21	1-Hexanethiol (n-Hexyl mercaptan)	151–2	−81.03	1.4490	0.8526	73.5–5.0	97	......	......	129	58	96.0–.5	......	......
22	2-Hydroxyethanethiol	158; 54[12]	....	1.4443	1.1143	100–2	......	......			123	......	28	Diacetyl, b.p. 98–9; Dibenzoyl, 39; S-Phenyl-urethane, 59–60, bz.

*Derivative data given in order: m.p., crystal color, solvent from which crystallized.

TABLE XXV. ORGANIC DERIVATIVES OF THIOLS (MERCAPTANS)
a)Liquids (Listed in order of increasing m.p.)* (Continued)

No.	Name	Boiling point, °C	Melting point, °C	n_D^{20}	D_4^{20}	2,4-Dinitrophenyl thioether	2,4-Dinitrophenyl sulfone	3,5-Dinitrothiobenzoate	3-Nitrothiophthalate	1-Anthraquinonyl thioether	Mercury salt	S-Alkyl mercaptosuccinic acid	Disulfide	Miscellaneous
23	Cyclohexanethiol (Cyclohexyl mercaptan)...........	158–60	....	1.4933	0.9782	148	172	......	......	......	78	150.5–1.5	b.p. 288	....
24	cis-3-Methyl-1-cyclohexanethiol	165	....	1.4647^{25}	0.916^{25}	....	......	......	......	......	......	......	......	$[\alpha]_{546}$: −2.24
25	Thiophenol (Mercaptobenzene)..	169.5; 172.5	−14.9	1.5888	1.0780	121	161	149	131	......	......	......;	66.5; 61	4-Nitrothiobenzoyl, 115.7–.8; Phenylurethane, 128
26	trans-3-Methyl-1-cyclohexanethiol	171	....	1.4663^{25}	0.914^{25}	....	......	......	......	......	......	......	......	$[\alpha]_{546}$: +5.50
27	2-Thiophenethiol	171.1; 166	....	1.6021	$1.168^{19.5}$	119	143	......	......	......	......	......	56	Acetyl, b.p. 230–2
28	1,3-Propanedithiol....	172.9	−79.0	1.5371^{25}	1.0775^{25}	194	......	......	......	......	......	......	b.p. 198^{20}	Dibenzoyl, 56.3
29	1-Heptanethiol (n-Heptyl mercaptan) ..	176–7	−43.4	1.4498^{25}	0.83891^{25}	81–2	101	53	96	132	77	105.8–6.2	b.p. 164^{6}	....
30	2-Octanethiol (sec-Octyl mercaptan) ...	186.4	−79.0	1.4481^{25}	0.83293^{25}	....	......	......	......	......	......	......	b.p. 161–71^{6}	....
31	2-Thiocresol (2-Toluenethiol)	194.3	15	....	....	101; 98–9.5	155	......	......	......	170.3	......	......	S-4-Nitrobenzoyl, 90–1
32	Phenylmethanethiol (Benzyl mercaptan)..	194–5	....	......	1.058	130; 128.5–9.5	182.5	120	137	......	......	189–90; 192	74; 70	Ph. eth., 42
33	3-Thiocresol (3-Toluenethiol)	195.4	....	....	....	100–1.5; 91	145	......	......	......	......	......	......	S-4-Nitrobenzoyl, 95–6; Ag. deriv., 126–7
34	1,4-Butanedithiol	195.6	−53.9	1.5265^{25}	1.0395^{25}	....	......	......	......	......	......	......	......	Dibenzoyl, 49.5
35	2-Phenylethanethiol...	199	....	1.5643^{19}	1.0318^{18}	93–4.5	133	......	......	......	......	......	b.p. 168–$80^{1.5}$	Acetyl, b.p. 134–5^{13}
36	1-Octanethiol (n-Octyl mercaptan) ...	199.1	−49.2	1.4519^{25}	0.83956^{25}	78; 76–7.5	98	......	......	95	71	96.1–.6	b.p. 178–83^{5}	....
37	2-Chlorothiophenol ...	205	....	....	$1.2752^{19.5}$	138	......	......	......	......	......	......	90	....
38	2,5-Dimethylthiophenol (p-Xylene-2-thiol)...	211–2	......	....	....	......	......	......	......	......	......	......	......	S-Ph. eth., b.p. 172.5^{11}; S-4-Tolyl, eth., b.p. 188^{11}
39	2,4-Dimethylthiophenol (m-Xylene-4-thiol) ..	214	....	....	....	......	......	......	......	......	......	......	......	S-Ph. eth., b.p. 171^{11}; S-Benzyl eth., 35

*Derivative data given in order: m.p., crystal color, solvent from which crystallized.

No.	Name	Boiling point, °C	Melting point, °C	n_D^{20}	D_4^{20}	2,4-Dinitrophenyl thioether	2,4-Dinitrophenyl sulfone	3,5-Dinitrothiobenzoate	3-Nitrothiophthalate	1-Anthraquinonyl thioether	Mercury salt	S-Alkyl mercaptosuccinic acid	Disulfide	Miscellaneous
40	2-Hydroxythiophenol (Thiocatechol)	216–7[751]; 88–90[8]	5–6	....	1.2373[0]	....	......	......	......	....	......	....	....	O-Me. eth., b.p. 218–9; Di-Me. eth., b.p. 237
41	Bis(2-mercaptoethyl) ether	217	−80	1.5339	1.1648[25]	....	......	......	......	....	......	....	....	4-Nitrobenzoyl, 106.5
42	1,5-Pentanedithiol	217.3; 110[16]	−72.5	....	....	....	......	......	......	....	......	....	....	Dibenzoyl, 45
43	1-Nonanethiol (n-Nonyl mercaptan)	220.2	−20.1	1.45197	0.83714	86; 84–5	92	......	......	117.5	......	105–6	b.p. 211–2[6]	....
44	2-Isopropyl-5-methyl-benzenethiol (Thiothymol)	230–1	....	....	....	....	......	......	......	78, al.	......	....	....	....
45	5-Isopropyl-2-methyl-benzenethiol (Thiocarvacrol)	235–6	....	....	0.9975[17.5]	....	......	......	......	....	109	....	....	S-Me. eth., b.p. 244
46	1,6-Hexanedithiol	237.1	−21.0	1.5077[25]	0.9886[25]	....	......	......	......	....	......	....	....	Dibenzoyl, 57
47	1-Naphthalenethiol (α-Mercapto naphthalene)	285; 114.8[10.5]	....	1.6802	1.1607	....	......	......	......	....	......	....	....	Benzyl eth., 78–80; 4-Nitrobenzoyl, 121–30; Acetyl, b.p., 200–3[25]

*Derivative data given in order: m.p., crystal color, solvent from which crystallized.

415

TABLE XXV. ORGANIC DERIVATIVES OF THIOLS (MERCAPTANS)
b) Solids (Listed in order of increasing m.p.)*

No.	Name	Melting point, °C	Boiling point, °C	2,4-Dinitrophenyl thioether	2,4-Dinitrophenyl sulfone	Acetate	Benzoate	S-Alkyl mercaptosuccinic acid	Disulfide	Methyl thioether	Miscellaneous
1	3-Hydroxythiophenol (Thio-resorcinol).	17	168^{35}	......	......	......	di: 78	......	95	15; b.p. 224 sl. d.	Di-Me. eth., b.p. 224–5
2	Hexadecanethiol (Cetyl mercaptan)	19	$123–8^{0.5}$	91; 96	105	......	......	105–6.5	55.5	......	......
3	1,10-Decanedithiol	20; 17.8	297.1	......	......	......	di: 57; 55	......	......	......	D_4^{25}: 0.9432; n_D^{25}: 1.4940
4	Benzoylmethanethiol (2-Mercapto-acetophenone)	23–4	$116–22^{4}$	......	......	......	......	......	81	......	D_4^{20}: 1.1753; Oxime, 70; Phenylhydrazone, 90–1
5	2-Aminothiophenol	26	234; $125–7^{6}$	152	......	di: 135	......	......	93	b.p. 234 sl. d.	......
6	3-Phenylenedithiol (Dithio-resorcinol).	27.1	245; 123^{17}	......	......	......	......	......	......	......	Trinitrobenzene add. comp., 76–7
7	4-Dimethylaminothiophenol	28.5	259–60	176	......	......	......	......	118	......	......
8	2-Phenylenedithiol (Dithiocatechol)	29	238–9	......	......	di: 88.5	di: 74–5; 94–5	......	......	......	......
9	4-Hydroxybenzenethiol (Thio-hydroquinone)	30	$144–6^{20}$	......	......	S-: 85–6, bz.-lgr.; di: 66	75; di: 161	......	......	84–5	S-Et. eth., 39–41
10	threo-Dithiothreitol (threo-2,3-Dihydroxy-1,4-dithiobutane)	42–3	$123–5^{2}$	......	......	tetra: 73, me. al.	......	......	......	......	Oxid. → trans-4,5-dihydroxy-o-dithiane, 132; Di-isopropylidene deriv., 78, me. al.
11	4-Thiocresol (4-Toluenethiol)	43–4	195	102.5–4	189.5	di: 66	di: 161	......	......	......	S-4-Tolyl deriv., 57; S-4-Nitrobenzoyl 114–5; S-Chloroacetyl, 40
12	4-Chloro-1-naphthalenethiol	43–4, al.	......	......	......	......	......	......	122	......	......
13	4-Aminothiophenol	46	$140–5^{16}$	......	......	N-mono: 154; 163, yel.	......	......	82	b.p. 272–3	......
14	1,4-(Dimethylthio)-benzene (p-Xylylene dimercaptan)	46–7	156^{12}	......	......	......	di: 135	......	......	......	......
15	5-Amino-2-methylthiophenol	47, bz.-pet. eth.	......	......	......	di: 125, yel., bz.-pet. eth.	......	......	......	147, lgr.	Tri-Me. eth., b.p. 159^{17}
16	4-Chlorothiophenol	54	123	......	......	......	......	163–4	73	......	......
17	2-Hydroxy-1-naphthalenethiol	55, pet. eth.	......	......	......	O-: 120, CCl₄; di: 57	......	......	......	......	......
18	1,3,5-Benzenetrithiol	57–60	......	......	......	tri: 73–4, al.	......	......	......	tri: 66–8, al.	......
19	2-Nitrothiophenol	58–61	......	131–3	......	......	......	......	199	64–5	......
20	1-Amino-2-propanethiol	63–5	......	......	......	......	......	......	Dihydrochloride, 214	......	Hydrochloride, 87–8, al.; Picrate, 143–4 d.
21	4-Bromothiophenol	75	231	142	190	51–2, me. al.	......	......	94.5	38, al.	Benzenesulfonate, 75
22	3-Nitrothiophenol	77	......	......	......	......	......	......	84	......	......
23	4-Nitrothiophenol	77	......	160	......	......	123–7, 50% ac. a.	......	184	72	......
24	4-Nitro-1-naphthalenethiol	77–9	......	193	......	......	......	......	189	......	......
25	2-Naphthalenethiol (2-Mercapto-naphthalene).	81	286	145	228	53.5	......	......	139	......	4-Nitrobenzoyl, 183–4; 2-Tolyl eth., b.p. 229.5^{11}

*Derivative data given in order: m.p., crystal color, solvent from which crystallized.

No.	Name	Melting point, °C	Boiling point, °C	2,4-Dinitrophenyl thioether	2,4-Dinitrophenyl sulfone	Acetate	Benzoate	S-Alkyl mercaptosuccinic acid	Disulfide	Methyl thioether	Miscellaneous
26	DL-*erythro*-Dithiothreitol (*erythro*-2,3-Dihydroxy-1,4-dithiobutane).	82–3, lt. pet. eth.	....	....	......	*tetra*: 126, bz.	....	....	....	......	Oxid. → *cis*-4,5-dihydroxy-*o*-dithiane, 132; Di-isopropylidene deriv., 145, pet. eth.
27	4-Iodothiophenol.............	85–6, al.	....	140.5	......	....	....	....	124	45; 38	CrO$_3$/AcOH → sulfone, 83
28	4-Amino-1-naphthalenethiol	91–3				N-*mono*: 173	....		168	......	
29	2-(3-Aminopropionamido)ethanethiol (Aletheine).............	93–6; subl. 140$^{10^{-5}}$	....			*di*: 139–40, et. ac.			....		Hydrochloride, 214–7, 95% al.; Oxalate, 121–2, al.
30	Bis(4-mercaptophenyl)ether	98				*di*: 68					
31	4-Phenylenedithiol (1,4-Dimercaptobenzene)...............	98, aq. al.				*di*: 126, pet. eth.				*di*: 85, me. al.	Di-Et. eth., 81.5, al.
32	2-Aminoethanethiol	98–100	130	94.5	......	*di*: 30	....		Dihydrochloride, 216	......	Hydrochloride, 70–2, al.; Picrate, 126; S-Acetyl hydrochloride, 137
33	Triphenylmethanethiol	107	....	190	......	139–41	185		ca. 155	....	....
34	4-Bromo-2-nitrothiophenol	110	142			....	....		....		....
35	4-Biphenylthiol	111–2, al.		146	170				150	107–8, al.	....
36	3-Amino-1-propanethiol	112–3							Dihydrochloride, 219	......	Hydrochloride, 69, dil. al.
37	1,8-Naphthalenedithiol	113–4, al.							....	*di*: 84	
38	4-Hydroxy-1-naphthalenethiol	114	....			*di*: 77					
39	Bis(4-thiophenyl)sulfide	114				*di*: 65			190	......	
40	2,4,6-Trinitrothiophenol	114		217							
41	1,5-Naphthalenedithiol	118–21, yel.				*di*: 187–9	*di*: 232		....	*di*: 250	....
42	4-Chloro-2-nitrothiophenol	120–2	141								
43	2,4-Dinitrothiophenol	131–2	193–7	240–1		107	113		280	....	....
44	6-Hydroxy-2-naphthalenethiol	137, al.	....	......		*di*: 110; 107, al.	....		221		
45	2-Benzothiazolthiol.............	177–9, aq. me. al.	....			....				52, aq. al.	Et. eth., 26, al.
46	2,7-Naphthalenedithiol	181; 174, al.				*di*: 110	*di*: 152–3				
47	1-Anthraquinonethiol	187, yel., ac. a.	....			....			>350	218, yel., al.	Et. eth., 183, yel., al.; Benzyl eth., 241, yel., ac. a.
48	2-Anthraquinonethiol	206, yel., ac. a.							257	162, yel., ac. a.	Et. eth., 138, yel., al.; Benzyl eth., 138, yel., al.
49	2-Benzimidazolthiol.............	298; 296–7, dil. al.								......	Benzyl eth., 186–7; 1-N-Me. eth., 190–2

*Derivative data given in order: m.p., crystal color, solvent from which crystallized.

EXPLANATIONS AND REFERENCES TO TABLE XXVI

*Sulfone.**

$$RSR' \xrightarrow{[O]} RSO_2R'$$
$$\text{Sulfone}$$

From the thioether in glacial acetic acid with dilute aqueous potassium permanganate.

For directions and examples see: Cheronis, p. 641; Linstead, p. 87; G. W. Fenton and C. K. Ingold, *J. Chem. Soc.*, 2338 (1929); H. Rheinboldt and E. Giesbrecht, *J. Amer. Chem. Soc.*, **68**, 973 (1946).

From the thioether with aqueous hydrogen peroxide in acetone or in acetic acid.

See: O. Hinsberg, *J. prakt. Chem.*, **90**, 350 (1914); H. Rheinboldt and E. Giesbrecht, *J. Amer. Chem. Soc.*, **68**, 973 (1946); C. G. Overberger, S. P. Lighthelm and E. A. Swire, *J. Amer. Chem. Soc.*, **72**, 2856 (1950).

From the thioether with hydrogen peroxide and ammonium molybdate in aqueous perchloric acid.

See: Cheronis, p. 641.

From the thioether with potassium bichromate and sulfuric acid in water.

See: G. Raiziss, L. W. Clemence, M. Severac and J. C. Moetsch, *J. Amer. Chem. Soc.*, **61**, 2763 (1939).

From the thioether with chromic anhydride in glacial acetic acid.

See: C. G. Overberger, S. P. Lightelm and E. A. Swire, *J. Amer. Chem. Soc.*, **72**, 2856 (1950).

For extensive lists of references for the oxidation of thioethers to the corresponding sulfones *see:* A. Schöberl and A. Wagner in *Methoden der Organischen Chemie (Houben-Weyl)*, Vol. 9, (Ed. E. Miller), Georg Thieme Verlag, Stuttgart, 1955, pp. 227–231; E. E. Reid, *Organic Chemistry of Bivalent Sulfur*, Vol. 2, Chemical Publishing Co., New York, 1960, pp. 64–65.

Sulfoxide.

$$RSR' \xrightarrow{[O]} RSOR'$$
$$\text{Sulfoxide}$$

From the thioether with hydrogen peroxide in acetic acid, in acetone or in alcohol-acetic acid mixture.

For directions and examples see: O. Hinsberg, *Chem. Ber.*, **43**, 289 (1910); R. L. Shriner, H. C. Struck and W. V. Jorison, *J. Amer. Chem. Soc.*, **52**, 2060 (1930); P. Karrer, N. J. Antia and R. Schwyzer, *Helv. chim. Acta*, **34**, 1392 (1951).

From the thioether with perphthalic acid in ether.

See: H. Böhme, *Chem. Ber.*, **70**, 378 (1937).

From the thioether with chromic anhydride in aqueous acetic acid.

See: R. Knoll, *J. prakt. Chem.*, **113**, 40 (1926).

For additional references for the oxidation of thioethers to the corresponding sulfoxides *see:* A. Schöberl and A. Wagner in *Modern Methoden der Organischen Chemie (Houben-Weyl)*, Georg Thieme Verlag, Stuttgart, 1955, pp. 211–215.

Mercuric halide addition compound.

$$R_2S + HgX_2 \rightarrow R_2S \cdot HgX_2$$
$$\text{Mercuric halide}$$
$$\text{addition compound}$$

From the thioether with mercuric chloride, bromide or iodide in ethanol, acetone or aqueous solution.

For directions and examples see: W. F. Faragher, J. C. Morrell and S. Comay, *J. Amer. Chem. Soc.*, **51**, 2774 (1929); E. E. Reid, *Organic Chemistry of Bivalent Sulfur*, Vol. 2, Chemical Publishing Co., New York, 1960.

Mercuric halide or mercuric acetate derivative.

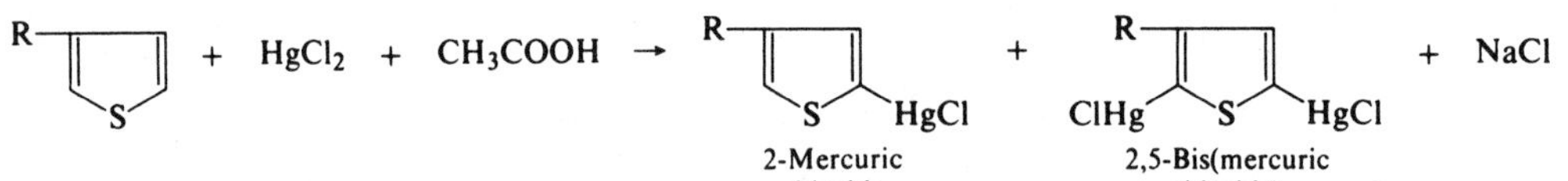

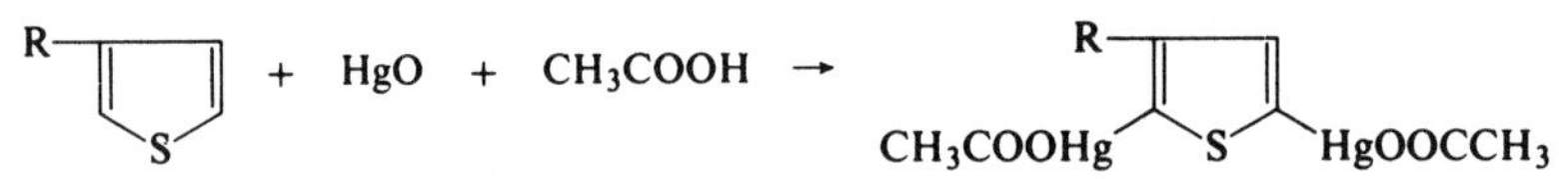

*Derivatives recommended for first trial.

WARNING: This is not an instruction manual. References should be consulted for the preparation of derivatives.

These derivatives are for substituted thiophenes only.

From the substituted thiophene with the mercuric salt (with or without sodium acetate) in ethanol or in acetic acid.

For directions and examples see: H. D. Hartough, *Thiophene and its Derivatives*, (*The Chemistry of Heterocyclic Compounds*, Vol. 3), Interscience, London, 1952, pp. 444–453.

For various additional compounds of thioethers with metal salts *see*: E. E. Reid, *Organic Chemistry of Bivalent Sulfur*, Vol. 2, Chemical Publishing Co., New York, 1960, pp. 52–60.

*Derivatives recommended for first trial.

WARNING: This is not an instruction manual. References should be consulted for the preparation of derivatives.

TABLE XXVI. ORGANIC DERIVATIVES OF THIOETHERS (SULFIDES)
a) Liquids 1) Noncyclic (Listed in order of increasing b.p.)*

No.	Name	Boiling point, °C	Melting point, °C	n_D^{20}	D_4^{20}	Sulfone	Sulfoxide	Disulfide	Miscellaneous
1	Dimethyl sulfide (Methyl sulfide)	37.3	−98.27	1.4356	0.8458[21]	109; b.p. 238	18.45; b.p. 189	109.7	Tri-HgCl$_2$ add. comp., 158; 150–1, rapid htng.; HgI$_2$ add. comp., 75; SnBr$_4$ add. comp., 85–7; PtCl$_2$ add. comp., 159; PtBr$_2$ add. comp., 159; PdCl$_2$ add. comp., 130; PdBr$_2$ add. comp., 125; AgNO$_3$ add. comp., 126
2	Ethyl methyl sulfide	66.9	−104.8	1.4353	0.8483	36, eth.	. . . .	130	HgCl$_2$ add. comp., 128; HgI$_2$ add. comp., 59; PdCl$_2$ add. comp., 67
3	Methyl vinyl sulfide	67.3	. . . . . .	1.4845	0.9026	. . . .	. . . .	. . . .	. . . .
4	Divinyl sulfide (Vinyl sulfide) . . .	84	. . . . . .	. . . .	0.9174	. . . .	. . . .!	. . . .	. . . .
5	Allyl methyl sulfide	91–3	. . . . . .	1.4712	0.8767	. . . .	. . . .	. . . .	. . . .
6	Diethyl sulfide (Ethyl sulfide) . . .	92	−102.05	1.44233	0.8368	73–4; b.p. 248	4–6; 15; b.p. 88–9[15]	152.6; 154	Disulfoxide, 123–4[11]; Mono-HgCl$_2$ add. comp., 90; Di-HgCl$_2$ add. comp., 119.5; HgI$_2$ add. comp., 110; AgNO$_3$ add. comp., 122; SnCl$_4$ add. comp., 102; SnBr$_4$ add. comp., 84; PtCl$_2$ add. comp., 106; PtBr$_2$ add. comp., 118; PtI$_2$ add. comp., 136; PdCl$_2$ add. comp., 83; PdBr$_2$ add. comp., 100
7	Ethyl vinyl sulfide	92	. . . . . .	1.4756	0.8756	. . . .	. . . .	. . . .	. . . .
8	Isopropyl methyl sulfide	93.5; 85	−101.48	1.4392	0.8291	. . . .	. . . .	. . . .	. . . .
9	Methyl n-propyl sulfide	95.5	−112.98	1.4442	0.8438	. . . .	. . . .	. . . .	. . . .
10	tert-Butyl methyl sulfide	99	. . . . . .	1.4402	0.8257	. . . .	. . . .	. . . .	. . . .
11	Chloromethyl methyl sulfide	107.1	. . . . . .	1.4967	. . . .	. . . .	. . . .	. . . .	. . . .
12	Ethyl isopropyl sulfide	107.3	−122.19	1.4407	0.8246	. . . .	. . . .	. . . .	. . . .
13	Isobutyl methyl sulfide	112.5	. . . . . .	1.4433	0.8335	. . . .	. . . .	. . . .	. . . .
14	Methyl 2-methylallyl sulfide	113.0–.2	. . . . . .	1.4712	. . . .	. . . .	. . . .	. . . .	. . . .
15	Allyl ethyl sulfide	115–6	. . . . . .	. . . .	0.8676	. . . .	. . . .	. . . .	. . . .
16	Ethyl n-propyl sulfide	118.5; 110–2	−117.04	1.4461	0.84448	25; b.p. 142[23]	. . . .	173.7	. . . .
17	Di-isopropyl sulfide (Isopropyl sulfide)	120.7	−78.08	1.4381	0.8135	36	68.5	176	PtCl$_2$ add. comp., 163; PtBr$_2$ add. comp., 174; PtI$_2$ add. comp., 176; PtI$_4$ add. comp., 139
18	n-Butyl methyl sulfide	122.5	. . . . . .	1.4477	0.8427	. . . .	. . . .	. . . .	HgCl$_2$ add comp., 116.5
19	Chloromethyl ethyl sulfide	128	. . . . . .	. . . .	. . . .	33	. . . .	b.p. 78–80[16]	. . . .
20	Isopropyl propyl sulfide	132	. . . . . .	1.4440	0.8269	. . . .	. . . .	. . . .	. . . .
21	sec-Butyl ethyl sulfide	133.6	. . . . . .	1.4477	0.8353	. . . .	. . . .	. . . .	. . . .
22	Ethyl isobutyl sulfide	134.2	. . . . . .	1.4452	0.8306	. . . .	. . . .	. . . .	HgCl$_2$ add. comp., 108
23	Diallyl sulfide (Allyl sulfide)	139[75N]; 35[5–7]	−83	1.4877[27]	0.88765[27]	b.p. 109[3]	b.p. 107–9[7–8]	b.p. 78–80[16]	. . . .
24	Methyl 2-methylbutyl sulfide . . .	139–40	. . . . . .	. . . .	0.8410[19]	. . . .	. . . .	. . . .	. . . .
25	2-Chloroethyl methyl sulfide	140; 44[20]	. . . . . .	1.4908	1.1155	. . . .	. . . .	. . . .	. . . .
26	Di-n-propyl sulfide (n-Propyl sulfide)	141–2	−101.9	1.4481	0.8358	30	14.5–5.0; b.p. 82[15]	194	Mono-HgCl$_2$ add. comp., 88–9; Di-HgCl$_2$ add. comp., 122; 127.5; Chloroamine-T → sulfilimide, 110–1.5
27	n-Butyl ethyl sulfide	144.2	−95.13	1.4491	0.8376	50	. . . .	193	. . . .
28	Methyl pentyl sulfide (Amyl methyl sulfide)	144.5–5.5	. . . . . .	1.448	0.843	. . . .	. . . .	. . . .	HgCl$_2$ add. comp., 127
29	Di-tert-butyl sulfide (tert-Butyl sulfide)	150	. . . . . .	1.4505	. . . .	. . . .	. . . .	201; b.p. 88[21]	. . . .
30	Diacetyl sulfide (Thioacetic anhydride)	155–8d.; 63[20]	. . . . . .	1.4810[21]	1.124	. . . .	. . . .	. . . .	Reduction → acetaldehyde, b.p. 20.2, 2,4-dinitrophenylhydrazone, 168
31	Dichloromethyl sulfide (Chloro-methyl sulfide)	156.5	−54; −37	1.5313	1.4065	70.5–2.0	. . . .	. . . .	. . . .
32	2-Chloroethyl ethyl sulfide	157; 63–5[47]	. . . . . .	1.06644	1.4878	. . . .	. . . .	. . . .	. . . .

*Derivative data given in order: m.p., crystal color, solvent from which crystallized.

No.	Name	Boiling point, °C	Melting point, °C	n_D^{20}	D_4^{20}	Sulfone	Sulfoxide	Disulfide	Miscellaneous
33	2-Aminoisopropyl methyl sulfide	158	......	....	....	b.p. 140[4]	....	....	....
34	Ethyl 3-methylbutyl sulfide	160	......	1.4495	0.8349	13.5	....	....	$HgCl_2$ add. comp., 87
35	4-Chlorophenyl methyl sulfide	170	......	1.6023[25]	1.1224[25]	57–8	....	....	....
36	3-Aminopropyl methyl sulfide	170	......	....	....	44; b.p. 165–8[6]	197	....	Hydrochloride, 136; Picrate, 127; Oxalate, 207d.
37	Di-isobutyl sulfide (Isobutyl sulfide)	172–3	......	1.4463	0.8262	17; b.p. 265	68.5	215	Mono-$HgCl_2$ add. comp., 116; Di-$HgCl_2$ add. comp., 131; $PtCl_2$ add. comp., (i) 83; (ii) 139; $PtBr_2$ add. comp., 143–4; PtI_2 add. comp., 187; $PtCl_4$ add. comp., 162; $AuCl_3$ add. comp., 87; $PdCl_2$ add. comp., 95; $PdBr_2$ add. comp., 140; PdI_2 add. comp., 145
38	Di-2-methylallyl sulfide (2-Methylallyl sulfide)	173	......	....	....	....	....	....	....
39	Chloromethyl dichloromethyl sulfide	177.2[753]	......	1.5395	1.5258	....	....	....	....
40	Dicrotyl sulfide (Crotyl sulfide)	186.5; 88.9[20]	......	1.495[25]	0.9032[0]	....	....	....	....
41	Di-n-butyl sulfide (n-Butyl sulfide)	188.0; 182; 109–15[15]	−79.7	1.45405	0.8386	44, resolidifies at 32.5	33	231	Di-$HgCl_2$ add. comp., 113; 110.5; $PtBr_2$ add. comp., 65; PtI_2 add. comp., 67; $PdCl_2$ add. comp., 32; $Pd(NO_3)_2$ add. comp., 166; $AgNO_3$ add. comp., 98
42	4-Aminobutyl methyl sulfide	188–90	......	....	....	42; b.p. 165[4]	....	....	Hydrochloride, 153–4, acet.; Picrate, 116–8
43	Di-dichloromethyl sulfide (Dichloromethyl sulfide)	189; 62–4[10]	......	1.5464	1.6273	....	....	....	....
44	Methyl phenyl sulfide	194–6; 78–9[13]	......	1.5870	1.0533[25]	88, w.	....	....	....
45	2-Chloroethyl chloromethyl sulfide	194.5; 77[10]	......	1.5311	1.338	....	....	....	....
46	Benzyl methyl sulfide	195–8	......	1.5550[25]	....	127, w.	....	....	....
47	Ethyl phenyl sulfide	205; 200–2	......	1.5701[15]	1.024[15]	42; b.p. 160[12]	....	....	$PdCl_2$ add. comp., 140
48	Isopropyl phenyl sulfide	208	......	1.5468	0.9855	....	....	....	$PdCl_2$ add. comp., 162
49	Methyl 4-tolyl sulfide	211–2; 104–5[20]	......	1.57537[16]	1.0302[16]	89, bz.-pet. eth.	50–4	....	....
50	Di-(3-methylbutyl)sulfide (Isoamyl sulfide)	215.3	......	1.4471	0.8285	31; b.p. 295	....	250	$PdCl_2$ add. comp., 95; $PdBr_2$ add. comp., 133; PdI_2 add. comp., 143; $SnCl_4$ add. comp., 64; $SnBr_4$ add. comp., 45–6
51	Allyl phenyl sulfide	215–8; 104–6[25]	......	1.5760	1.0275	....	....	....	....
52	Di-2-chloroethyl sulfide (2-Chloroethyl sulfide; Mustard gas; Yperite)	217	14.4	1.53125	1.2741	56; b.p. 183[20]	109–11	....	....
53	Phenyl propyl sulfide	219–20	......	1.5571	0.9995	44	....	....	$PdCl_2$ add. comp., 91
54	Ethyl 4-tolyl sulfide	220–1	......	1.5568	1.0016[17.5]	55–6	....	....	....
55	Benzyl ethyl sulfide	222–3; 98–9[13]	......	....	....	84	....	....	Mono-$HgCl_2$ add. comp., 84; Di-$HgCl_2$ add. comp., 142
56	3-Methylbutyl phenyl sulfide	240–2	......	1.5380	0.9681	36	....	....	$PdCl_2$ add. comp., 97
57	2-Chloroethyl phenyl sulfide	245; 121[15]	......	1.5838	1.1799	45	....	....	....
58	2-Chloroethyl 4-tolyl sulfide	255–7; 150–2[20]	......	....	....	78	....	....	....
59	2-Hydroxyethyl 4-tolyl sulfide	282–3; 119–20[1]	......	....	....	55	....	....	....
60	Di-(3-tolyl)sulfide (m-Tolyl sulfide)	290; 174[12]	......	....	....	94	b.p. 215[15]	b.p. 150 d.	....

Derivative data given in order: m.p., crystal color, solvent from which crystallized.

No.	Name	Boiling point, °C	Melting point, °C	n_D^{20}	D_4^{20}	Sulfone	Sulfoxide	Disulfide	Miscellaneous
61	**Diphenyl sulfide** (Phenyl sulfide)	296; 157–8[16.5]	−21.5	1.6312	1.1160	128–9; b.p. 379	70.5	61	Disulfone of the disulfide, 193–4
62	**Di-*n*-heptyl sulfide** (*n*-Heptyl sulfide)	298	. . . . . .	. . . . . .	. . . .	80	. . . .	. . . .	. . . .
63	**4-Chlorophenyl phenyl sulfide**. . .	305–15d.; 167–8[10]	. . . . . .	. . . . . .	. . . .	34; 90	. . . .	. . . .	. . . .
64	**Phenyl 3-tolyl sulfide**	309.5; 164.5[11]	−6.5	. . . . . .	1.0937[16]	. . . .	. . . .	. . . .	. . . .
65	**Phenyl 2-tolyl sulfide**	309.9; 300.5; 160.5[11]	. . . . . .	. . . . . .	1.1012[15]	81, al.	. . . .	. . . .	. . . .
66	**Phenyl 4-tolyl sulfide**	311.5; 167.5[11]	15.7	. . . . . .	1.0900[15.7]	127–8, al.	. . . .	. . . .	. . . .

*Derivative data given in order: m.p., crystal color, solvent from which crystallized.

422

TABLE XXVI. ORGANIC DERIVATIVES OF THIOETHERS (SULFIDES)
a) Liquids 2) Cyclic (Listed in order of increasing b.p.)*

No.	Name	Boiling point, °C	Melting point, °C	n_D^{20}	D_4^{20}	Sulfone	HgCl$_2$ addition compound	Miscellaneous
1	Ethylene sulfide (Thiirane; Thiacyclopropane) .	55–6	....	1.4914	1.0046	....	....	Polymerizes rapidly
2	2-Methylethylene sulfide (2-Methylthiirane) ...	76	....	1.4731[19]	0.946[18]	....	....	
3	Thiophene.............................	84.12	−38.30	1.5287	1.0644	....	....	2-HgCl deriv., 182–3; 2-HgBr deriv., 169–70; 2-HgI deriv., 116–7
4	2,2-Dimethylethylene sulfide (2,2-Dimethyl-thiirane)...............................	87; 84–6	....	1.4641	....	....	....	
5	Trimethylene sulfide (Thietane; Thiacyclo-butane)................................	95	−73.25	1.506[23]	1.0200	76, w.	93–5 d.	Methiodide, 98.5–9.0
6	2-Ethylethylene sulfide (2-Ethylthiirane)......	104	....	1.475[19]	0.930[18]	....	....	
7	2-Methyltrimethylene sulfide (2-Methyl-thietane)...............................	106	....	1.4831	0.9571	b.p. 251.5–3.5	....	
8	2-Methylthiophene......................	112.4	....	1.52042	1.02183	....	....	5-HgCl deriv., 204; 5-HgBr deriv., 179–80; 5-HgI deriv., 111–2
9	2,4-Dimethyltrimethylene sulfide (2,4-Di-methylthietane)........................	113–4	....	1.4502[18]	0.8710[18]	b.p. 255.0–5.5	....	
10	3-Methylthiophene......................	115.4	....	1.52042	1.02183	....	....	2-HgCl deriv., 128–9; 2,5-Di-HgOOCCH$_3$ deriv., >240d.
11	2,2-Dimethyltrimethylenesulfide (2,2-Di-methylthietane).......................	120	....	1.4739[18]	....	55	118	
12	Tetramethylene sulfide (Thiolane; Thiophane; Thiacyclopentane).....................	121.2; 120.2–.5	−96.17	1.5047	0.99869	28.36	128	Sulfoxide, 105–7[12]
13	2-Methyltetramethylene sulfide (2-Methyl-thiolane).............................	132.5[750]	−100.71	1.4922	0.9555	b.p. 279–80[758]	di: 162	
14	2-Ethylthiophene.......................	132.5–4.0	....	1.5127	0.990[24]	....	....	5-HgCl deriv., 147–8; 5-HgI deriv., 96-7
15	3-Ethylthiophene	135–6	....	1.5146	0.9980	....	....	2-HgCl deriv., 67–8; 2,5-Di-HgCl deriv., 295–7d.
16	2,5-Dimethylthiophene	135.5–6.0	−62.57	1.5126	0.98587	....	....	3-HgCl deriv., 156–7; 3-HgI deriv., 175
17	2,4-Dimethylthiophene	137–8; 140	....	1.5130	0.9956	....	....	5-HgCl deriv., 138–9; 5-HgI deriv., 137–9
18	3-Methyltetramethylene sulfide (3-Methyl-thiolane).............................	138.2	−81.10	1.4924	0.9634	1; 0.5	83	....
19	2,3-Dimethylthiophene	140.2–1.2	−49.1 to −48.9	1.5188	1.0021	....	....	5-HgCl deriv., 218.5–9.5; 5-HgI deriv., 184.0–4.5; 4,5-Di-HgOOCCH$_3$, 237–40
20	trans-2,5-Dimethyltetramethylene sulfide (trans-2,5-Dimethylthiolane).............	142	−76.35	1.4766	0.9188	3; b.p. 278	111	....
21	cis-2,5-Dimethyltetramethylene sulfide (cis-2,5-Dimethylthiolane)......................	142.3	....	1.4799	0.9222	4; b.p. 278	di: 180	
22	3,4-Dimethylthiophene	144–6	....	1.5212	1.008_{21}^{23}	....	....	2-HgCl deriv., 139–40.5; 2-HgBr deriv., 152; 2-HgI deriv., 142
23	1,4-Thioxane	148.9	−17	1.5070	1.1177	130; 105.5	171	Sulfoxide, 25; 45
24	2-Methylpentamethylene sulfide (2-Methyl-thiane)...............................	151	−58.14	1.4905	0.9428	68.5	102	
25	2-Isopropylthiophene	152	....	1.5037	0.9673	....	....	
26	3-Isopropylthiophene	155.7; 157	....	1.5052	0.9733	....	....	5-HgCl deriv., 137
27	3-Methylpentamethylene sulfide (3-Methyl-thiane)...............................	157–8	−60.17	1.4922	0.9473	83	136	....
28	2-Ethyltetramethylene sulfide (2-Ethylthiolane)	157–8	....	1.4896	0.9451	....	mono: 100; di: 146–8	
29	2-Propylthiophene	157.5–9.5	....	1.5048	0.9683	....	....	5-HgCl deriv., 155; 5-HgSCN deriv., 169.0–9.5
30	4-Methylpentamethylene sulfide (4-Methyl-thiane)...............................	158.6	−28.11	1.5049	0.9687	121.5	136	
31	2-Ethyl-5-methylthiophene	159.8–60.4	−68.6	1.5073	0.9663	....	....	

*Derivative data given in order: m.p., crystal color, solvent from which crystallized.

No.	Name	Boiling point, °C	Melting point, °C	n_D^{20}	D_4^{20}	Sulfone	HgCl₂ addition compound	Miscellaneous
32	2-Ethyl-3-methylthiophene	160.0–1.5	. . . .	1.5092[22.5]	0.9792[22.5]	. . . .	. . . .	5-HgCl deriv., 172–3; 5-HgI deriv., 156–7
33	2,6-Dimethyl-1,4-thioxane	160–1	. . . .	1.4733	. . . .	105.5	. . . .	. . . .
34	3-Propylthiophene	160–2		1.5057	0.9716	. . . .	. . . .	. . . .
35	2-Allylthiophene.	161; 158.5–9.0		1.5281[20.5]	1.0175[20.5]	. . . .	. . . .	. . . .
36	3,5-Dimethyl-1,4-thioxane	162	. . . .	. . . .	. . . .	102	. . . .	. . . .
37	3-Ethyl-5-methylthiophene	162–4	− 60 to − 59	1.5098	0.9742	. . . .	. . . .	. . . .
38	2,3,5-Trimethylthiophene	163–5; 164.5[746]	. . . .	1.5131	0.9753	. . . .	. . . .	x-HgCl deriv., 160–1
39	2-*tert*-Butylthiophene	163.9	− 59.2	1.49788	0.9514	. . . .	. . . .	. . . .
40	3-*tert*-Butylthiophene	168.9	− 54.8	1.50149	0.9574	. . . .	. . . .	. . . .
41	Hexamethylene sulfide (Thiepane; Thiacyclo-heptane)	170; 173–4	. . . .	1.5125	0.9883	71	149	Methiodide, 141.5–2.0
42	2,3,4-Trimethylthiophene	172.7; 160–3		1.5208	0.995	. . . .	. . . .	. . . .
43	1,3-Dithiolane(1,3-Dithiacyclopentane)	175	. . . .	1.5975[15]	1.259[17]	*di*: 205	117; 126	Methiodide, 96; Disulf-oxide, 134
44	2-Methyl-5-propylthiophene	179.5–80.5	. . . .	1.5026	. . . .	. . . .	. . . .	. . . .
45	Cyclohexene sulfide (7-Thiabicycloheptane) . . .	180; 71.5–3.5[21]	. . . .	1.5309	0.9274	. . . .	. . . .	. . . .
46	2-*n*-Butylthiophene.	181–2[740]	. . . .	1.50896	0.9537	. . . .	. . . .	. . . .
47	2,5-Diethylthiophene	181–2; 63–6[14]	. . . .	1.5036	0.962[14]	. . . .	. . . .	. . . .
48	3-*n*-Butylthiophene	181–3		1.51005	0.9570	. . . .	. . . .	. . . .
49	2,3,4,5-Tetramethylthiophene	182–4; 187–9		1.5196	0.9442[21/21]	. . . .	. . . .	. . . .
50	3,4-Diethylthiophene	185–7	. . . .	1.5157[17]	. . . .	. . . .	. . . .	2-HgCl deriv., 118
51	2-Ethyl-1,3-dithiolane	191–2	. . . .	. . . .	. . . .	124	. . . .	. . . .
52	2,4-Dimethyltetramethylene sulfide (2,4-Dimethylthiolane).	197–8[742]	. . . .	1.4818	0.9265	b.p. 123.3[5]	89	. . . .
53	3-Ethyl-2,4,5-trimethylthiophene	204–6[748]	. . . .	1.5132	0.9609	. . . .	. . . .	. . . .
54	2-*n*-Octylthiophene	257–9; 106–8[1]	. . . .	1.4824	0.920	. . . .	. . . .	. . . .

*Derivative data given in order: m.p., crystal color, solvent from which crystallized.

TABLE XXVI. ORGANIC DERIVATIVES OF THIOETHERS (SULFIDES)
b) Solids (Listed in order of increasing m.p.)*

No.	Name	Melting point, °C	Boiling point, °C	Sulfone	Sulfoxide	Disulfide	Miscellaneous
1	**Ethyl 2-naphthyl sulfide**	16	170.5[15]	43–5	. . . .		
2	**Ethyl hexadecyl sulfide**	19	. . . .	88	. . . .		
3	**Thiane** (Pentamethylene sulfide; Thiacyclo- hexane)	19.07; 13	142	98.5–9.0	. . . .		D_4^{20}: 0.9849; n_D^{20}: 1.5067; $HgCl_2$ add. comp., 137.5, al.; Meth-iodide, 192 subl.
4	**2-Methyl-1,4-dithiane**	20	. . . .	di: 304			
5	**Didecyl sulfide** (Decyl sulfide).	27	217–8[8]	206–7	. . . .		
6	**3-Tolyl 4-tolyl sulfide**	27.8, al.	179[11]	116, ac. a.	72		
7	**Diundecyl sulfide** (Undecyl sulfide; n-Hendecyl sulfide)	34.8	. . . .				
8	**Di-(2-bromoethyl) sulfide** (Bromoethyl sulfide) .	35		111–2			
9	**4-Iodophenyl phenyl sulfide** (4-Iododiphenyl sulfide)	35	. . . .	141			
10	**2-Aminophenyl phenyl sulfide** (2-Amino-diphenyl sulfide).	35–6, al.	212[25]	122, dil. al.	. . . .		N-Benzenesulfonyl, 225–6
11	**4-Bromophenyl methyl sulfide**	37.5	. . . .	56–7			
12	**Didodecyl sulfide** (n-Dodecyl sulfide)	40.5	. . . .		. . . .	34.5	
13	**Benzyl phenyl sulfide**	41; 44.5, al.	197[27]	146–6.5; 148, al.	123		
14	**Di-(4-chlorobenzyl)sulfide** (4-Chlorobenzyl sulfide)	41				59	
15	**1-Naphthyl phenyl sulfide**	41.8, aq. al.	220–5[11]	99.5–100.5, al.			
16	**3-Nitrophenyl phenyl sulfide** (3-Nitrodiphenyl sulfide)	42.5		80.5–81			
17	**Ethyl 4-nitrophenyl sulfide**	44		138.5			
18	**Isopropyl 4-nitrophenyl sulfide**	44.5		115.3			
19	**Di-(4-methoxyphenyl)sulfide** (4-Methoxyphenyl sulfide)	46	. . . .	130	96	45	Disulfone, 221, r.h.; 210–2, s.h.
20	**Dibenzoyl sulfide** (Thiobenzoic anhydride; Benzoyl sulfide)	48, al.			. . . .	133; 128	
21	**Dibenzyl sulfide** (Benzyl sulfide)	50, chl.		151.7, al.-bz.	134.8	73	D_{50}^{50}: 1.0712; $HgCl_2$ add. comp., 131; HgI_2 add. comp., 37–8; $FeCl_3$ add. comp., 94; $PtCl_2$ add. comp., 159; $PtCl_4$ add. comp., 172d.; $PtBr_2$ add. comp., 139; PtI_2 add. comp., 129
22	**2,5-Dichlorophenyl methyl sulfide**	51	. . . .	88			
23	**Methyl 2-naphthyl sulfide**	51.8; 64	226[11]	115–6, al.	67.5		Disulfone, 166
24	**Bis(phenylthio)methane**	52		di: 120–1			
25	**Ditetradecyl sulfide** (n-Tetradecyl sulfide)	53.8	. . . .			46	
26	**Di-(2-diphenoxyethyl)sulfide**	54, al.	. . . .	108, pink, al.	97		
27	**1,3-Dithiane**	54		di: 330; 308			
28	**Bis(benzylthio)methane**	55		di: 216			
29	**4-Nitrophenyl phenyl sulfide** (4-Nitrodiphenyl sulfide)	55, yel., lgr.	240[25]	142, aq. al.			
30	**Di-n-octyl sulfide** (n-Octyl sulfide)	57	. . . .	76		b.p. 178–83[5]	
31	**Di-(4-tolyl)sulfide** (4-Tolyl sulfide)	57.3	179[11]	158, bz.	95, pet. eth.	48, al.	
32	**2-Aminophenyl 4-aminophenyl sulfide** (2,4'-Diaminodiphenyl sulfide)	61; 62.5, aq. al.	. . . .	124–6			Diacetyl, 208
33	**Dihexadecyl sulfide** (n-Hexadecyl sulfide).	61.3	. . . .	103.4	99.8		
34	**2-Chloroethyl 4-nitrophenyl sulfide**	62	. . . .	128	. . . .		
35	**Di-(2-tolyl)sulfide** (2-Tolyl sulfide)	64, al.	285; 174[15]	134–5, al.	121, pet. eth.	38–9, al.	. . . .
36	**Methyl 2-nitrophenyl sulfide**	64.5, yel., al.		106	. . . .		$D_4^{78.2}$: 1.2626; $n_D^{78.2}$: 1.62458; $AgNO_3$ add. comp., 122, yel., al.
37	**Benzyl 4-bromophenyl sulfide**	65	. . . .	159	. . . .		

*Derivative data given in order: m.p., crystal color, solvent from which crystallized.

No.	Name	Melting point, °C	Boiling point, °C	Sulfone	Sulfoxide	Disulfide	Miscellaneous
38	**1,2-Bis(phenylthio)ethane**	69–70	. . . .	*di*: 180	. . . .	. . . .	. . . .
39	**Dioctadecyl sulfide (Octadecyl sulfide)**	71; 64.5	. . . .	. . . .	. . . .	62.5	. . . .
40	**2-Phenyl-1,3-dithiane.**	71–2	. . . .	*di*: 265	. . . .	. . . .	. . . .
41	**Methyl 4-nitrophenyl sulfide**	72	. . . .	141	. . . .	. . . .	$D_4^{80.1}$: 1.2391; $n_D^{80.1}$: 1.64008
42	**Di-(3-phenylpropyl)sulfide (3-Phenylpropyl sulfide)**	73	. . . .	117	. . . .	b.p. 165–6[0.03]	. . . .
43	**Di-(2-methoxyphenyl)sulfide (2-Anisyl sulfide)** .	73, al.	252–3[10]	157–8, bz.	. . . .	120	. . . .
44	**Di-(4-methylbenzyl)sulfide (4-Methylbenzyl sulfide)**	76	. . . .	197	. . . .	. . . .	. . . .
45	**Cinnamyl phenyl sulfide**	78	. . . .	111–2	90–1	. . . .	. . . .
46	**4-(Methylthio)benzaldehyde**	78, yel., lgr.	273; 153[17]	. . . .	. . . .	. . . .	Phenylhydrazone, 138; Thiosemi-carbazone, 177–9, yel.
47	**4-Nitrobenzyl phenyl sulfide**	79	. . . .	209.5	. . . .	. . . .	. . . .
48	**1,2-Bis(tolylthio)ethane**	80–1	. . . .	*di*: 200–1	. . . .	. . . .	. . . .
49	**2-Nitrophenyl phenyl sulfide (2-Nitrodiphenyl sulfide)**	80.2; 77, yel.	210[15]	147.5, al.	. . . .	. . . .	. . . .
50	**Di-(2-aminobenzyl) sulfide**	81	. . . .	. . . .	. . . .	90–1, lgr.-et. ac.	N,N′-Diformyl, 163; N,N′-Diacetyl, 209; Picrate, 203–4d.
51	**4-Nitrophenyl 4-tolyl sulfide**	81.5, yel.	. . . .	170–1, yel.	. . . .	. . . .	. . . .
52	**Di-(2-aminophenyl) sulfide**	87	. . . .	146–7	. . . .	93, al.	N,N′-Diacetyl, 164–5; N,N′-Dibenzoyl, 162–3
53	**Di-(2-phenylethyl) sulfide (2-Phenylethyl sulfide)**	92.5; 90	. . . .	100.6	69	b.p. 172–5[0.8]	. . . .
54	**4-Aminophenyl phenyl sulfide (4-Amino-diphenyl sulfide)**	96, lgr.	243[29]	176, al.	152, w.	. . . .	Hydrochloride, 197–8d.; N-4-Toluenesulfonyl, 73
55	**Di-(4-amino-3-methylphenyl) sulfide**	96, 25% al.	. . . .	. . . .	. . . .	. . . .	Dihydrochloride, 248–9, dil. HCl; N,N′-Diacetyl, 22, al.; N,N′-Dibenzoyl, 233, me. al.; Dipicrate, 186, w.
56	**Di-(4-chlorophenyl) sulfide (4-Chlorophenyl sulfide)**	98; 88–90	212[18]	148–9, subl.	143	73	. . . .
57	**3-Aminophenyl 4-nitrophenyl sulfide (3-Amino-4′-nitrodiphenyl sulfide)**	99–100	. . . .	. . . .	. . . .	. . . .	N-Acetyl, 115–6; N,N-Dimethyl, 83–4
58	**Di-(2-amino-5-methylphenyl) sulfide**	103–4, al.	. . . .	. . . .	. . . .	98	Dihydrochloride, 100d., al.; N,N′-Diacetyl, 165, al.; N,N′-Dibenzoyl, 185–6, al.; Diurethane, 113, bz.-pet. eth.; Dipicrate, 179, bz.
59	**Di-(4-aminobenzyl) sulfide**	104–5	. . . .	. . . .	. . . .	96–8, al.	N,N′-Diacetyl, 188; N,N′-Dibenzoyl, 224
60	**Di-(4-aminophenyl) sulfide**	108–9, w.	. . . .	178, me. al.	175d., al.	85; 106, al.	N,N′-Diacetyl, 220–1; N,N′-Dibenzoyl, 234
61	**Di-(1-naphthyl) sulfide**	110, al.	290[15]	187, al.	166, al.	91	. . . .
62	**1,4-Dithiane**	111–2	199–200	*mono*: 200; *di*: >330	. . . .	. . . .	Methiodide, 73–4; Sulfoxide-sulfone, 279
63	**Di-(4-bromophenyl) sulfide (4-Bromophenyl sulfide)**	112, al.	243[20]	172	153, al.	94.5	. . . .
64	**2,4-Dinitrophenyl phenyl sulfide (2,4-Dinitro-diphenyl sulfide)**	121; 117, bz.	. . . .	161	. . . .	. . . .	. . . .
65	**Di-(2-nitrophenyl) sulfide (2-Nitrophenyl sulfide)**	122–3, yel., al.-ac. a.	. . . .	164	. . . .	198–9, ac. a. or bz.	. . . .
66	**Benzyl 4-nitrophenyl sulfide**	123	. . . .	172	. . . .	. . . .	. . . .
67	**Di-(3-hydroxyphenyl) sulfide (3-Hydroxyphenyl sulfide)**	130	. . . .	190–1; 186–7	94–5, pet. eth.	95	Acetyl, 87
68	**1,3-Bis(2-nitrophenylthio)propane**	140	. . . .	*di*: 156–7	. . . .	. . . .	. . . .
69	**Di-(2-hydroxyphenyl) sulfide (2-Hydroxyphenyl sulfide)**	142, bz.	. . . .	179; 164–5, bz.	. . . .	b.p. >200 d.	Diacetyl, 95–6, al. Di-Me. eth., 73
70	**1-Naphthyl 2-naphthyl sulfide (1,2′-Dinaphthyl sulfide)**	151	291–2[15]	123	. . . .	. . . .	. . . .
71	**Di-(2-naphthyl) sulfide (2-Naphthyl sulfide)** . . .	151	296[15]	177, al.	137.5–8.5	139	. . . .

*Derivative data given in order: m.p., crystal color, solvent from which crystallized.

No.	Name	Melting point, °C	Boiling point, °C	Sulfone	Sulfoxide	Disulfide	Miscellaneous
72	**Di-(4-hydroxyphenyl) sulfide** (4-Hydroxyphenyl sulfide)	151, al.	. . . .	240–1, w.	195, acet.	150–1	Diacetyl, 94; 55; Di-Me. eth., 46; Di-Et. eth. 55
73	**Di-(4-nitrobenzyl) sulfide** (4-Nitrobenzyl sulfide)	158–9	. . . .	260.5	212	126.5	. . . .
74	**Di-(4-nitrophenyl) sulfide** (4-Nitrophenyl sulfide)	174–5; 156–7, or., or pa. yel.	. . . .	282; 245; 225	. . . .	182, ac. a.	. . . .
75	**Di-(3-nitrophenyl) sulfide** (3-Nitrophenyl sulfide)	193	. . . .	201	. . . .	84, al.	. . . .
76	**Di-(2,4-dinitrophenyl) sulfide** (2,4-Dinitrophenyl sulfide)	193–7; 193–4, yel., ac. a.	. . . .	240–1	. . . .	280	. . . .
77	**Di-(2,4,6-trinitrophenyl) sulfide** (Dipicryl sulfide)	230–1; 226, yel.	. . . .	307	. . . .	. . . .	. . . .

*Derivative data given in order: m.p., crystal color, solvent from which crystallized.

427

EXPLANATIONS AND REFERENCES TO TABLES XXVII, XXVIII AND XXIX

The dissociation of an organic carboxylic acid, phenol or the conjugate acid of an amine in aqueous solution is expressed by the equation

$$HA_{aq}^{\pm n} + H_2O \rightleftharpoons A_{aq}^{\pm n-1} + H_3O_{aq}^+$$

and the corresponding equilibrium constant K_e is given by

$$K_e = \frac{(a_{A_{aq}^{\pm n-1}})(a_{H_3O^+})}{(a_{HA_{aq}^{\pm n}})(a_{H_2O})}$$

where the a's are the activities of the species. At low electrolyte concentrations a_{H_2O} is virtually constant, and a second constant, K_a, the thermodynamic dissociation constant, is defined as

$$K_a = K_e(a_{H_2O}) = \frac{(a_{A_{aq}^{\pm n-1}})(a_{H_3O^+})}{(a_{HA_{aq}^{\pm n}})} = \frac{(c_{A_{aq}^{\pm n-1}})(c_{H_3O^+})}{(c_{HA_{aq}^{\pm n}})} \cdot \frac{f_{\pm}^2}{f_{HA_{aq}^{\pm n}}}$$

where the c's are the concentrations and the f's are the activity coefficients of the species.

The dissociation constants in the Tables are given in the more convenient pK_a notation, where

$$pKa = -\log K_a$$

For Table XXVII, $HA^{\pm n}$ = RCOOH, and $A^{\pm n-1}$ = RCOO⁻.

For Table XXVIII, $HA^{\pm n}$ = ArOH, and $A^{\pm n-1}$ = ArO⁻.

For Table XXIX, $HA^{\pm n}$ = RR′R″NH⁺ and $A^{\pm n-1}$ = RR′R″N(R, R′ and R″ may be alkyl or aryl groups or a hydrogen atom).

For monobasic acids $pK_a = pK_1$.

For dicarboxylic acids both pK_1 and pK_2 are given; pK_1 is defined above, and pK_2 is the analogous dissociation constant of the monoanion, $A^{\pm n-1}$, obtained on the first dissociation. For other dibasic acids such as the conjugate acids of amino acids, or diamines, pK_1 is as defined above, and pK_2 is the dissociation constant for the species obtained after the first protonation.

For a comprehensive compilation of the dissociation constants of organic acids (including phenols) in aqueous solution, as well as summary of the methods for pK determinations, see: G. Kortüm, W. Vogel and K. Andrussow, in *Pure and Applied Chemistry*, Vol. 1, Butterworths, London, 1961, pp. 190–536.

For a comprehensive compilation of the dissociation constants of organic bases (especially amines) in aqueous solution see: D. D. Perrin, *Dissociation Constants of Organic Bases in Aqueous Solution*, Butterworths, London, 1965.

For general references including methods of determination of pK, and data for both acids and bases see: J. F. King, in *Elucidation of Structures by Physical and Chemical Methods*, Vol 1 (Ed. K. W. Bently) (*Technique of Organic Chemistry*, Vol. 9), Interscience, New York, 1963, Chapter 6, pp. 318–401; H. C. Brown, D. H. McDaniel and O. Hafliger in *Determination of Organic Structures by Physical Methods*, Vol. 1 (Ed. E. A. Braude and F. C. Nachod), Academic Press, New York, 1955, Chapter 14, p. 567.

---

*Derivatives recommended for first trial.

WARNING: This is not an instruction manual. References should be consulted for the preparation of derivatives.

TABLE XXVII. ACID DISSOCIATION CONSTANTS OF ORGANIC ACIDS IN AQUEOUS SOLUTION
(Listed in order of increasing pKa)

No.	Name	T,°C	pK_1	pK_2
1	Heptafluoro-*n*-butyric acid	25	0.17	....
2	Trifluoroacetic acid	25	0.23	....
3	Trichloroacetic acid	25	0.63	....
4	2,4,6-Trinitrobenzoic acid	25	0.65	
5	Tribromoacetic acid	25	0.66	
6	3-Chlorophenylglycine	25	1.05	3.93
7	2,6-Dinitrobenzoic acid	25	1.14	....
8	Trichloroacrylic acid	25	1.15	
9	Difluoroacetic acid	25	1.24	
10	Oxalic acid	25	1.27	4.28
11	Dichloroacetic acid	25	1.29	....
12	2-Chloro-6-nitrobenzoic acid	25	1.34	
13	2-Bromo-6-nitrobenzoic acid	25	1.37	
14	Benzenehexacarboxylic acid	25	1.40	2.19; $pK_3 = 3.31$; $pK_4 = 4.78$; $pK_5 = 5.89$; $pK_6 = 6.96$
15	*d,l*-2,3-Dibromosuccinic acid	20	1.42	3.24
16	2,4-Dinitrobenzoic acid	25	1.42	....
17	*erythro*-2-Bromo-3-chlorosuccinic acid	19	1.43	2.60
18	*d,l*-2,3-Dichlorosuccinic acid	20	1.46	2.86
19	*threo*-2-Bromo-3-chlorosuccinic acid	20	1.46	2.77
20	*meso*-2,3-Dibromosuccinic acid	20	1.51	2.71
21	*meso*-2,3-Dichlorosuccinic acid	20	1.52	2.94
22	4,4,4-Trifluorovaline	25	1.537	8.098
23	4,4,4-Trifluorothreonine	25	1.554	7.822
24	2-Amino-4,4,4-trifluoro-*n*-butyric acid	25	1.600	8.169
25	2,5-Dinitrobenzoic acid	25	1.62	....
26	Nitroacetic acid	25	1.68	....
27	Trifluoroacrylic acid	25	1.79	....
28	Benzenepentacarboxylic acid	25	1.80	2.73; $pK_3 = 3.97$; $pK_4 = 5.25$; $pK_5 = 6.46$
29	Cyclopropane-1,1-dicarboxylic acid	25	1.82	5.43
30	Hydroxyproline	25	1.82	9.66
31	DL-Histidine	25	1.82	6.04; $pK_3 = 9.12$
32	2,3-Dinitrobenzoic acid	25	1.85	....
33	2-Methyl-4-nitrobenzoic acid	25	1.86	
34	1,2,4,5-Benzenetetracarboxylic acid	25	1.92	2.87; $pK_3 = 4.49$; $pK_4 = 5.63$
35	*trans*-Ethylene oxide-1,2-dicarboxylic acid	19	1.93	3.25
36	*cis*-Ethylene oxide-1,2-dicarboxylic acid	18	1.94	3.92
37	Maleic acid	25	1.94	6.23
38	Ornithine	25	1.94	8.65
39	2-Chloro-4-nitrobenzoic acid	25	1.96	....
40	4-Aminosalicylic acid (4-Amino-2-hydroxybenzoic acid)	25	1.99	3.92
41	2-Chloro-3-nitrobenzoic acid	25	2.02	....
42	Asparagine	25	2.05	3.87
43	Anthranilic acid	25	2.05	4.95
44	5,5,5-Trifluoroleucine	25	2.05	8.92
45	S-Ethylcysteine	25	2.05	8.60
46	1,2,3,4-Benzenetetracarboxylic acid	25	2.06	3.25; $pK_3 = 4.73$; $pK_4 = 6.21$
47	Di-*n*-propylmalonic acid	25	2.07	7.51
48	3-(4-Chlorophenyl)alanine	25	2.08	8.96
49	3-(3-Fluorophenyl)alanine	24	2.10	8.98
50	Arginine	25	2.10	9.07
51	1,3,5-Benzenetricarboxylic acid	25	2.12	3.89; $pK_3 = 4.70$
52	D,L-3,5-Di-iodotyrosine	25	2.12	6.48
53	3-(2-Fluorophenyl)alanine	24	2.12	9.01
54	3-(4-Fluorophenyl)alanine	24	2.13	9.05
55	D,L-β-Phenylalanine	25	2.16	9.15
56	*l*-Lysine	25	2.16	9.18; $pK_3 = 10.79$
57	*d*-Lysine	25	2.16	9.16; $pK_3 = 10.81$
58	Glutamic acid	20	2.16	4.324; $pK_3 = 9.96$
59	6,6,6-Trifluoronorleucine	25	2.164	9.463
60	3-(3-Chlorophenyl)alanine	25	2.17	8.91
61	2-Chloro-5-nitrobenzoic acid	25	2.17	....
62	D,L-Serine	25	2.21	4.15
63	Diethylmalonic acid	25	2.21	7.29
64	N-Propylalanine	25	2.21	10.19
65	N-Ethylalanine	25	2.22	10.22
66	D,L-N-Methylalanine	25	2.22	10.19
67	2-Nitrobenzoic acid	25	2.22	....
68	3-(2-Chlorophenyl)alanine	25	2.23	8.94
69	6-Bromo-2-methylolbenzoic acid	20	2.25	
70	6-Chloro-2-methylolbenzoic acid	20	2.26	....
71	*d,l*-Valine	25	2.286	9.744
72	*d,l*-2-Aminobutyric acid	25	2.29	9.83
73	2-Benzyl-2-cyanopropionic acid	25	2.29	
74	2-Amino-*n*-pentanoic acid	25	2.318	9.808
75	(3,4-Dihydroxyphenyl)alanine	25	2.32	8.68; $pK_3 = 9.88$
76	2-Chloro-3-hydroxysuccinic acid	25	2.32	....
77	3-Hydroxyglutaric acid	25	2.32	4.24; $pK_3 = 9.56$
78	*d,l*-Leucine	25	2.32	9.74
79	*d,l*-Norleucine	25	2.335	9.83
80	*d,l*-Alanine	25	2.34	9.87
81	*cis*-Caronic acid (*cis*-1,1-Dimethyl-2,3-cyclopropanedicarboxylic acid)	25	2.34	8.31
82	N-Ethylglycine	25	2.34	10.23
83	Glycine	25	2.35	9.78
84	N-Methylglycine	25	2.35	10.18
85	N-Propylglycine	25	2.35	10.19
86	N-*n*-Butylglycine	25	2.35	10.25
87	N-Isobutylglycine	25	2.35	10.12
88	2-Aminoisobutyric acid	25	2.36	10.25
89	(Methylsulfonyl)acetic acid	25	2.36	....
90	2-Cyano-2-cyclohexylacetic acid	25	2.37	
91	2-Cyanopropionic acid	25	2.37	....
92	D,L-Tryptophane	25	2.38	9.39
93	1,2,3,5-Benzenetetracarboxylic acid	25	2.38	3.51; $pK_2 = 4.44$; $pK_3 = 5.81$
94	4-Aminobenzoic acid	25	2.38	....
95	2-Cyanoisobutyric acid	25	2.42	
96	Cyanoacetic acid	25	2.46	
97	Pyruvic acid	25	2.49	
98	O-Acetylcitric acid	25	2.49	
99	3-Pentenoic acid	25	2.51	
100	1,2,4-Benzenetricarboxylic acid	25	2.52	3.84; $pK_3 = 5.20$
101	(2-Chlorovinyl)acetic acid	25	2.54	....
102	Oxaloacetic acid	25	2.55	4.37
103	Fluoroacetic acid	25	2.58	....

No.	Name	T,°C	pK₁	pK₂	No.	Name	T,°C	pK₁	pK₂
104	Phenylmalonic acid	25	2.58	5.03	162	(2,4-Dichloro-6-methylphenoxy)acetic acid	20	3.13	....
105	2-Chloro-3-hydroxybutyric acid	25	2.58	....	163	2-Cyanobenzoic acid	25	3.14	....
106	2-Fluoroacrylic acid	25	2.58	....	164	(3-Methoxyphenoxy)acetic acid	25	3.14	....
107	2,4-Dioxo-n-pentanoic acid	25	2.58	....	165	Ethyl-n-propylmalonic acid	25	3.15	7.43
108	2-Chloro-3-hydroxy-3-phenyl propionic acid	25	2.61	....	166	4,4,4-Trifluorocrotonic acid	25	3.15	
109	2-Chloro-6-hydroxybenzoic acid	25	2.63	....	167	(4-Iodophenoxy)acetic acid	25	3.16	
110	2-Butynoic acid (Tetrolic acid)	25	2.65	....	168	(2-Iodophenoxy)acetic acid	25	3.17	
111	1-Aminocyclohexanecarboxylic acid	25	2.66		169	3,3-Difluoroacrylic acid	25	3.17	
112	Bromosuccinic acid	50	2.69	4.69	170	Dimethylmalonic acid	25	3.17	6.06
113	3-Hydroxy-2-naphthoic acid	25	2.71	....	171	Phenoxyacetic acid	25	3.17	
114	5-Aminosalicylic acid (5-Amino-2-hydroxybenzoic acid	25	2.74	5.84	172	Iodoacetic acid	25	3.18	
115	Triethylsuccinic acid	25	2.74		173	3-Iodo-2-methylolbenzoic acid	20	3.18	
116	Salicylic acid (2-Hydroxybenzoic acid)	30	2.75; (3.00)	12.38	174	2-Hydroxy-3-chloroisobutyric acid	25	3.20	
117	2,4-Dichlorobenzoic acid	25	2.76	....	175	(4-Methoxyphenoxy)acetic acid	25	3.21	
118	1,2,3-Benzenetricarboxylic acid	25	2.80	4.20 pK₃ = 5.87	176	(4-Methylphenoxy)acetic acid	25	3.22	
					177	meso-Tartaric acid	25	3.22	4.82
119	3,4-Dinitrobenzoic acid	25	2.82	....	178	2-Chlorocrotonic acid	25	3.22	
120	3,5-Dinitrobenzoic acid	25	2.82	....	179	2,4-Dihydroxybenzoic acid	30	3.22	
121	Guanidinoacetic acid	25	2.82	....	180	(2-Methoxyphenoxy)acetic acid	25	3.23	
122	2-Bromobenzoic acid	25	2.85		181	(2-Methylphenoxy)acetic acid	25	3.23	
123	Malonic acid	25	2.86	5.65	182	Cyclopentane-1,1-dicarboxylic acid	25	3.23	4.08
124	Chloroacetic acid	25	2.86	....	183	3-Bromomandelic acid	25	3.23	
125	Ethylmethylmalonic acid	25	2.86	6.43	184	3-Chloromandelic acid	25	3.24	
126	2-Iodobenzoic acid	25	2.86		185	2,6-Dimethylbenzoic acid	25	3.25	
127	2-Chloropropionic acid	18	2.88		186	3-Iodomandelic acid	25	3.26	
128	(4-Nitrophenoxy)acetic acid	25	2.89		187	2-Fluorobenzoic acid	25	3.27	
129	Bromoacetic acid	25	2.90		188	3-Chloro-2-methylbenzoic acid	25	3.27	
130	2-Chlorobenzoic acid	25	2.92		189	(4-Chloro-2-methylphenoxy)acetic acid	25	3.28	
131	(4-Cyanophenoxy)acetic acid	25	2.93		190	3-Bromo-2-methylbenzoic acid	20	3.28	
132	Isopropylmalonic acid	25	2.94	5.38	191	cis-3-Chloroacrylic acid	18	3.32	
133	(3-Nitrophenoxy)acetic acid	25	2.95		192	cis-Cyclopropane-1,2-dicarboxylic acid	24	3.33	6.47
134	Phthalic acid	25	2.95	5.41	193	(2,6-Dimethylphenoxy)acetic acid	25	3.36	
135	2-Chloroisobutyric acid	18	2.97	....	194	Anthraquinone-1-carboxylic acid	20	3.37	
136	3,5-Dinitro-4-methylbenzoic acid	25	2.97		195	3-Hydroxy-3-phenylpropionic acid	18	3.40	
137	(2-Cyanophenoxy)acetic acid	25	2.97		196	d,l-Mandelic acid	25	3.41	
138	2-Bromopropionic acid	18	2.97	....	197	Anthraquinone-2-carboxylic acid	20	3.42	
139	Ethylmalonic acid	25	2.99	5.83	198	N-Formylglycine	19	3.43	
140	n-Propylmalonic acid	25	2.996	5.84	199	2,4,6-Trimethylbenzoic acid	25	3.44	
141	d-Tartaric acid	25	3.00	4.34	200	3-Nitrobenzoic acid	25	3.44	
142	Fumaric acid	25	3.02	4.38	201	Cyclohexane-1,1-diacetic acid	25	3.45	7.08
143	(3-Cyanophenoxy)acetic acid	25	3.03		202	2-Phenylbenzoic acid (Biphenyl-2-carboxylic acid)	25	3.46	
144	Benzilic acid	18	3.05	....	203	meso-2,3-Diphenylsuccinic acid	25	3.48	
					204	(2,4-Dinitrophenyl)acetic acid	25	3.50	
146	Methylmalonic acid	25	3.05	5.76	205	Tetramethylsuccinic acid	25	3.50	7.28
147	(2-Chlorophenoxy)acetic acid	25	3.05		206	d,l-2,3-Diethylsuccinic acid	25	3.51	6.60
148	3,3,3-Trifluoropropionic acid	25	3.06		207	2-Phenoxybenzoic acid	20	3.53	
149	3-Aminobenzoic acid	25	3.07	4.73	208	2-Hydroxy-2-phenylpropionic acid	18	3.53	
150	(3-Chlorophenoxy)acetic acid	25	3.07						
151	2-Hydroxy-3-chlorobutyric acid	25	3.08		210	Terephthalic acid	25	3.54	4.46
152	(3-Fluorophenoxy)acetic acid	25	3.09		211	2-tert-Butylbenzoic acid	25	3.54	
153	(2-Fluorophenoxy)acetic acid	25	3.09		212	3-Aminopropionic acid	25	3.55	
154	(4-Chlorophenoxy)acetic acid	25	3.10		213	4-Cyanobenzoic acid	25	3.55	
155	(3-Bromophenoxy)acetic acid	25	3.10		214	3-(Methylamino)benzoic acid	25	3.55	
156	α-Iodopropionic acid	18	3.11		215	3-Methoxy-2-methylbenzoic acid	20	3.58	
157	(2-Bromophenoxy)acetic acid	25	3.12		216	d,l-2,3-Diphenylsuccinic acid	25	3.58	
158	3-Chlorolactic acid	25	3.12		217	2-Aminocyclohexanecarboxylic acid	25	3.59	10.21
159	(4-Bromophenoxy)acetic acid	25	3.13		218	3-Cyanobenzoic acid	25	3.60	
160	(3-Iodophenoxy)acetic acid	25	3.13		219	3-Ethoxy-2-methylolbenzoic acid	20	3.62	
161	(4-Fluorophenoxy)acetic acid	25	3.13		220	Isophthalic acid	25	3.62	4.60
					221	3-Ethyl-3-methylglutaric acid	25	3.62	6.70

No.	Name	T,°C	pK₁	pK₂	No.	Name	T,°C	pK₁	pK₂
222	3,3-Diethylglutaric acid	25	3.62	7.12	279	*cis*-Tetrahydronaphthalene-2,3-	20	3.98	6.47
223	*meso*-2,3-Diethylsuccinic acid	25	3.63	6.46		dicarboxylic acid			
224	(2,4-Dichlorophenoxy)acetic acid	20	3.64	. . . .	280	4-Chlorobenzoic acid	25	3.98	. . . .
225	Malonamic acid (Malonic acid mono-	25	3.64	. . . .	281	2,5-Dimethylbenzoic acid	25	3.98	. . . .
	amide)				282	3-Bromopropionic acid	18	3.99	. . . .
226	2-Isopropylbenzoic acid	25	3.64	. . . .	283	2-Hydroxy-2-methylbutyric acid	18	3.99	
227	Decahydronaphthyloxyacetic acid	25	3.64	. . . .	284	3-Cyanopropionic acid	25	3.99	
228	2-Cyclohexyloxypropionic acid	25	3.64		285	3-Chloropropionic acid	25	3.996	
229	*trans*-3-Chloroacrylic acid	18	3.65	. . . .	286	*trans*-Tetrahydronaphthalene-2,3-	20	4.00	5.70
230	9-Anthracenecarboxylic acid	20	3.65	. . . .		dicarboxylic acid			
231	Ethoxyacetic acid	18	3.65	. . . .	287	(2-Nitrophenyl)acetic acid	25	4.004	. . . .
232	*trans*-Cyclopropane-1,2-dicarboxylic	24	3.65	5.13	288	3-Aminopentanoic acid	25	4.02	10.40
	acid				289	4-Aminobutyric acid	25	4.03	. . . .
233	N-Acetylglycine	25	3.67		290	*cis*-Cyclobutane-1,3-dicarboxylic acid . . .	25	4.03	5.31
234	1-Anthracenecarboxylic acid	20	3.68	. . . .	291	2-Hydroxyisobutyric acid	18	4.04	
235	2-Benzyl-2-phenylsuccinic acid	20	3.69	6.49	292	(2-Iodophenyl)acetic acid	25	4.04	
236	3,3-Di-*n*-propylglutaric acid	25	3.69	7.31	293	*trans*-4-Nitrocinnamic acid	25	4.05	
237	Cyclopentyloxyacetic acid	25	3.70		294	(2-Bromophenyl)acetic acid	25	4.05	
238	3,3-Dimethylglutaric acid	25	3.70	6.29	295	(2-Chlorophenyl)acetic acid	25	4.07	
239	*cis*-3-Aminocyclohexanecarboxylic acid . .	15	3.70	. . . .	296	2-Methoxybenzoic acid	20	4.08	:
240	*d,l*-N-Acetylalanine	25	3.72		297	3-Methoxybenzoic acid	25	4.09	. . . .
241	N-Propionylglycine	25	3.72		298	3-Iodopropionic acid	18	4.09	. . . .
242	2,3-Dimethylbenzoic acid	25	3.74		299	*cis*-Cyclohexane-1,3-dicarboxylic acid . . .	16	4.10	5.46
243	Formic acid	25	3.74		300	Ethylsuccinic acid	25	4.00	. . . . . , ...
244	Phthalamic acid (Phthalic acid mono-	25	3.75		301	Iminodipropionic acid	30	4.11	9.61
	amide)				302	Benzylsuccinic acid	20	4.11	5.65
245	Glutaconic acid	25	3.77	5.08	303	*trans*-3-Nitrocinnamic acid	25	4.12	. . . .
246	*meso*-2,3-Dimethylsuccinic acid	25	3.77	5.94	304	4-Fluorobenzoic acid	25	4.14	. . . .
247	2-Ethylbenzoic acid	25	3.79	. . . .	305	(3-Chlorophenyl)acetic acid	25	4.14	. . . .
248	3-Methylcyclopentyl-1,1-diacetic acid . . .	25	3.79	6.74	306	4,4,4-Trifluorobutyric acid	25	4.15	. . . .
249	*trans*-Cyclobutane-1,2-dicarboxylic acid . .	20	3.79	5.61	307	*trans*-2-Nitrocinnamic acid	25	4.15	. . . .
250	Cyclohexyloxyacetic acid	25	3.80	. . . .	308	3-Isopropoxybenzoic acid	20	4.15	. . . .
251	2-Hydroxybutyric acid	18	3.80	. . . .	309	2-Naphthoic acid	25	4.16	. . . .
252	Cyclopentyl-1,1-diacetic acid	25	3.80	6.77	310	Succinic acid	25	4.16	5.61
253	3-Bromobenzoic acid	25	3.81	. . . .	311	(3-Iodophenyl)acetic acid	25	4.16	. . . .
254	3-Chlorobenzoic acid	25	3.82	. . . .	312	3-Ethoxybenzoic acid	20	4.17	. . . .
255	*trans*-Caronic acid (*trans*-1,1-Dimethyl-	25	3.82	5.32	313	2,2-Diphenyladipic acid	20	4.17	5.80
	2,3-cyclopropanedicarboxylic acid)				314	(4-Iodophenyl)acetic acid	25	4.18	. . . .
256	2,2-Diethylsuccinic acid	25	3.84	. . . .	315	2-Anthracenecarboxylic acid	20	4.18	. . . .
257	*trans*-3-Aminocyclohexanecarboxylic acid	15	3.85	. . . .	316	*trans*-Cyclohexane-1,4-dicarboxylic acid .	16	4.18	. . . .
258	3-Iodobenzoic acid	25	3.85	. . . .	317	4,4,5,5,6,6,6-Heptafluorohexanoic acid . . .	25	4.18	. . . .
259	(4-Nitrophenyl)acetic acid	25	3.85	. . . .	318	2,4-Dimethylbenzoic acid	25	4.18	. . . .
260	*cis*-3-Methylcyclohexyloxyacetic acid	25	3.85	. . . .	319	*trans*-Cyclohexane-1,2-dicarboxylic acid .	19	4.18	5.93
261	Lactic acid	25	3.86	. . . .	320	(4-Bromophenyl)acetic acid	25	4.19	. . . .
262	*cis*-Cinnamic acid	25	3.88	. . . .	321	(4-Chlorophenyl)acetic acid	25	4.19	. . . .
263	Hydroxyacetic acid	25	3.89	. . . .	322	Mesaconic acid	18	4.20	. . . .
264	1,2,3-Cyclohexanetricarboxylic acid	23	3.89	4.85	323	Benzoic acid	25	4.20	. . . .
				pK₃ = 8.83	324	3-Propoxybenzoic acid	20	4.20	. . . .
265	*cis*-Cyclobutane-1,2-dicarboxylic acid	19	3.90	5.89	325	2-Ethoxybenzoic acid	20	4.21	. . . .
266	2-Methylcyclohexyloxyacetic acid	25	3.90	. . . .	326	3,4-Diphenyladipic acid	25	4.22	5.19
267	3-Fluorobenzoic acid	25	3.90	. . . .	327	*trans*-2-Chlorocinnamic acid	25	4.23	. . . .
268	3-Hydroxybenzoic acid	30	3.90	9.78	328	3-Fluoromandelic acid	25	4.24	. . . .
269	2-Methylbenzoic acid	25	3.91	. . . .	329	(1-Naphthyl)acetic acid	25	4.24	. . . .
270	2,2-Diphenylglutaric acid	20	3.91	5.38	330	(2-Isopropoxy)benzoic acid	20	4.24	. . . .
271	3-Phenoxybenzoic acid	20	3.91	. . . .	331	2-Propoxybenzoic acid	20	4.24	. . . .
272	2-(Bromomethyl)butyric acid	18	3.92	. . . .	332	3-Butoxybenzoic acid	20	4.25	. . . .
273	Diphenylacetic acid	25	3.94	. . . .	333	(4-Fluorophenyl)acetic acid	25	4.25	. . . .
274	2,2-Dibenzylsuccinic acid	20	3.96	6.66	334	Acrylic acid	25	4.25	. . . .
275	Triphenylacetic acid	25	3.96	. . . .	335	3-Methylglutaric acid	25	4.25	5.41
276	*trans*-Cyclopentane-1,2-dicarboxylic acid .	25	3.96	5.85	336	(2-Naphthyl)acetic acid	25	4.26	. . . .
277	4-Bromobenzoic acid	25	3.97	. . . .	337	*cis*-Cyclopentane-1,3-dicarboxylic acid . . .	25	4.26	5.51
278	(3-Nitrophenyl)acetic acid	25	3.97	. . . .	338	5-Aminopentanoic acid	25	4.27	

No.	Name	T, °C	pK₁	pK₂	No.	Name	T, °C	pK₁	pK₂
339	3-Methylbenzoic acid	25	4.27	....	401	3-(2-Chlorophenyl)propionic acid	25	4.58	
340	2,2-Diphenylpimelic acid	25	4.28	5.39	402	3-(3-Chlorophenyl)propionic acid	25	4.58	
341	3-Ethylglutaric acid	25	4.29	5.33	403	4-Methyl-3-pentenoic acid	25	4.60	
342	Angelic acid	18	4.29		404	cis-3-Hydroxycyclohexanecarboxylic acid	25	4.60	
343	trans-3-Chlorocinnamic acid	25	4.29		405	2-Hydroxycinnamic acid	25	4.61	
344	3,5-Dimethylbenzoic acid	25	4.30		406	4-Hydroxybenzoic acid	27.8	4.61	9.31
345	3-Isopropylglutaric acid	25	4.30	5.51	407	Levulinic acid	18	4.64	
346	3-n-Propylglutaric acid	25	4.31	5.31	408	2-Methyl-3-hydroxybutyric acid	18	4.65	
347	Phenylacetic acid	25	4.31		409	3-(3-Methoxyphenyl)propionic acid	25	4.65	
348	trans-Cyclohexane-1,3-dicarboxylic acid	19	4.31	5.73	410	4-Acetylbutyric acid	18	4.66	
349	2,2-Diphenylsuberic acid	20	4.31	5.39	411	2-Methylacrylic acid	18	4.66	
350	trans-Cyclopentane-1,3-dicarboxylic acid	25	4.32	5.42	412	3-Phenylpropionic acid	25	4.66	
351	2,2-Diphenylazelaic acid	20	4.33	5.38	413	3-(2-Methylphenyl)propionic acid	25	4.66	
352	(3,4-Dimethoxyphenyl)acetic acid	25	4.33		414	4-Pentenoic acid	25	4.67	
353	3,4,5-Trihydroxybenzoic acid	30	4.33		415	4-Ureidobutyric acid	25	4.68	
354	cis-Cyclohexane-1,2-dicarboxylic acid	20	4.34	6.77	416	3-(3-Methylphenyl)propionic acid	25	4.68	
355	4-Isopropylbenzoic acid	25	4.35		417	3-(4-Methylphenyl)propionic acid	25	4.68	
356	Vinylacetic acid	25	4.35		418	(4-Isopropoxy)benzoic acid	20	4.68	
357	Glutaric acid	25	4.35	5.42	419	trans-2-Hydroxycyclohexanecarboxylic acid	25	4.68	
358	4-Ethylbenzoic acid	25	4.35						
359	(4-Methoxyphenyl)acetic acid	25	4.36		420	trans-4-Hydroxycyclohexanecarboxylic acid	25	4.68	
360	4-Methylbenzoic acid	25	4.37						
361	(4-Methylphenyl)acetic acid	25	4.37		421	3-(4-Methoxyphenyl)propionic acid	25	4.69	
362	(4-Ethylphenyl)acetic acid	25	4.37		422	2-Pentenoic acid	25	4.69	
363	4-Methoxycinnamic acid	25	4.38		423	trans-Crotonic acid	25	4.69	
364	trans-Cyclohexane-1,2-diacetic acid	20	4.38	5.42	424	4-Hydroxypentanoic acid	18	4.69	
365	(4-Isopropylphenyl)acetic acid	25	4.39		425	2-Hexenoic acid	25	4.70	
366	trans-4-Aminocyclohexanecarboxylic acid	25	4.39	10.55	426	4-Hexenoic acid	25	4.72	
367	3-Hydroxycinnamic acid	25	4.40		427	5-Hexenoic acid	25	4.72	
368	4-tert-Butylbenzoic acid	25	4.40		428	2-Ethylpentanoic acid	18	4.72	
369	cis-Crotonic acid	18	4.41		429	2-Ethylbutyric acid	25	4.75	
370	3,4-Dimethylbenzoic acid	25	4.41		430	4-Phenylbutyric acid	25	4.76	
371	trans-2-Bromocinnamic acid	25	4.41		431	Acetic acid	25	4.76	
372	cis-Cyclohexane-1,2-diacetic acid	20	4.42	5.45	432	Isovaleric acid	25	4.78	
373	cis-Cyclopentane-1,2-diacetic acid	20	4.42	5.42	433	4-Propoxybenzoic acid	20	4.78	
374	(4-tert-Butylphenyl)acetic acid	25	4.42		434	4,4-Dimethylpentanoic acid	18	4.79	
375	trans-Cyclopentane-1,2-diacetic acid	20	4.43	5.43	435	Cyclobutanecarboxylic acid	25	4.79	
376	trans-4-Chlorocinnamic acid	25	4.43		436	d,l-2-Methylpentanoic acid	18	4.79	
377	Adipic acid	25	4.43	5.42	437	5-Methyl-4-hexenoic acid	25	4.80	
378	4-Cyanobutyric acid	25	4.44		438	4-Methyl-2-pentenoic acid	25	4.80	
379	trans-Cinnamic acid	25	4.44		439	3-(2-Methoxyphenyl)propionic acid	25	4.80	
380	trans-3-Methylcinnamic acid	25	4.44		440	2-Methylbutyric acid	18	4.81	
381	3-(Acetylamino)propionic acid	25	4.45		441	n-Butyric acid (n-Butanoic acid)	25	4.82	
382	2-Ureidoisobutyric acid	25	4.46		442	trans-3-Hydroxycyclohexanecarboxylic acid	25	4.82	
383	4-Methoxybenzoic acid	25	4.47						
384	3-(4-Nitrophenyl)propionic acid	25	4.47		443	Nicotinic acid	25	4.82	11.98
385	Pimelic acid	25	4.48	5.42	444	Cyclopropanecarboxylic acid	25	4.83	
386	3-(1-Naphthoyl)propionic acid	20	4.48		445	cis-4-Aminocyclohexanecarboxylic acid	25	4.83	10.62
387	3-Methylcyclohexyl-1,1-diacetic acid	25	4.49	6.08	446	d,l-3-Methylpentanoic acid	18	4.84	
388	4-Methylcyclohexyl-1,1-diacetic acid	25	4.49	6.10	447	Isonicotinic acid	20	4.84	12.23
389	5,5,5-Trifluoropentanoic acid	25	4.49		448	cis-4-Hydroxycyclohexanecarboxylic acid	25	4.84	
390	3-Ureidopropionic acid	25	4.49		449	Isocaproic acid	18	4.84	
391	3-(2-Nitrophenyl)propionic acid	25	4.50		450	n-Pentanoic acid (n-Valeric acid)	25	4.84	
392	trans-2-Methylcinnamic acid	25	4.50		451	Isobutyric acid	25	4.86	
393	2-Methoxycinnamic acid	25	4.50		452	Propionic acid (Propanoic acid)	25	4.87	
394	3-Hexenoic acid	25	4.52		453	4-Hydroxyisocaproic acid	18	4.87	
395	Suberic acid	25	4.52	5.40	454	n-Hexanoic acid (n-Caproic acid)	25	4.88	
396	Azelaic acid	25	4.53	5.40	455	n-Heptanoic acid	25	4.89	
					456	n-Octanoic acid (n-Caprylic acid)	25	4.89	
398	Succinamic acid (Succinic acid mono-amide)	25	4.54		457	Cyclohexylpropionic acid	25	4.91	
					458	d,l-2,3-Dimethylsuccinic acid	25	4.94	6.20
399	trans-4-Methylcinnamic acid	20	4.56		459	n-Nonanoic acid (Pelargonic acid)	25	4.94	
400	O-Acetylsalicylic acid (Aspirin)	17	4.57	....	460	Cyclohexylbutyric acid	25	4.95	....

No.	Name	T.°C	pK$_1$	pK$_2$	No.	Name	T.°C	pK$_1$	pK$_2$
461	Tiglic acid	18	4.96	....	468	*cis*-3-Methyl-2-pentenoic acid	25	5.15	....
462	3-(2-Naphthoyl)propionic acid	20	4.96	....	469	Itaconic acid	18	5.54	....
463	Cyclopentanecarboxylic acid	25	4.99	....	470	Citraconic acid	18	6.17	....
464	2,2-Dimethylbutyric acid	18	5.03	....	471	Ethylenediamine-N,N,N′,N′-tetra-acetic acid	25	6.27	10.95
465	Trimethylacetic acid	25	5.05	....	472	Ethylenediamine-N,N′-diacetic acid	30	6.42	9.46
466	3,3-Dimethylacrylic acid (3-Methyl-crotonic acid)	25	5.12	....	473	Ethylenediamine-N,N′-dipropionic acid	30	6.87	9.60
467	*trans*-3-Methyl-2-pentenoic acid	25	5.13	....					

TABLE XXVIII. ACID DISSOCIATION CONSTANTS OF PHENOLS IN AQUEOUS SOLUTION
(Listed in order of increasing pKa)

No.	Name	T,°C	pK_1	pK_2	No.	Name	T,°C	pK_1	pK_2
1	Picric acid (2,4,6-Trinitrophenol)	25	0.29; (0.71)	....	51	2-Hydroxy-3-methoxybenzylamine	25	8.70	10.52
2	4-Hydroxypyrimidine	20	1.85	8.59	52	3-Hydroxypyridine	20	8.72	....
3	2-Hydroxypyrimidine	20	2.24	9.17	53	2-Fluorophenol	25	8.82	....
4	4-Chloro-2,6-dinitrophenol	25	2.97	....	54	Isovanillin (5-Formyl-2-methoxyphenol; 3-Hydroxy-4-methoxybenzaldehyde)	25	8.889	....
5	2,6-Dinitrophenol	25	3.71	....	55	3-Hydroxy-2-methoxybenzylamine	25	8.89	10.52
6	2,4-Dinitrophenol	25	4.09	....	56	4-Hydroxy-3-methoxybenzylamine	25	8.94	10.42
7	2,6-Dinitrohydroquinone	21	4.42	9.14	57	3-Nitro-2,4,6-trimethylphenol	25	8.98	....
8	8-Hydroxyquinoline	20	5.017	9.813	58	Sodium 4-hydroxybenzenesulfonate	25	9.01	....
9	2,5-Dinitrophenol	25	5.04	....	59	Pyrogallol (1,2,3-Trihydroxybenzene)	25	9.01	11.64
10	3,4-Dinitrophenol	25	5.42	....	60	2-Methylhydroquinone (Toluhydroquinone)	25	9.05	11.62
11	8-Hydroxyquinaldine	25	5.55	10.31	61	3-Chlorophenol	25	9.08; (9.02)	....
12	4-Methyl-8-hydroxyquinoline	25	5.58	10.00					
13	3,4-Dimethyl-8-hydroxyquinoline	25	5.80	10.05	62	3-Bromophenol	25	9.11	....
14	5-Formyl-2-nitrophenol (3-Hydroxy-4-nitrobenzaldehyde)	25	6.00	....	63	3-Iodophenol	25	9.17	....
					64	3-Acetylphenol	25	9.19	....
15	5-Chloro-2-nitrophenol	25	6.05	....	65	4-Iodophenol	25	9.20	....
16	5-Carboethoxy-2-nitrophenol (Ethyl 3-hydroxy-4-nitrobenzoate)	25	6.11	....	66	Sodium 3-hydroxybenzenesulfonate	25	9.29	....
17	5-Carbomethoxy-2-nitrophenol (Methyl 3-hydroxy-4-nitrobenzoate)	25	6.15	....	67	1-Naphthol	20.5	9.30; (9.85)	....
18	2,4-Dimethyl-8-hydroxyquinoline	25	6.20	10.60	68	3-(Methylsulfonyl)phenol	25	9.33	....
19	3-Nitrocatechol	25	6.68	....	69	4-Bromophenol	25	9.34	....
20	2-Nitro-5-phenylphenol (3-Hydroxy-4-nitrobiphenyl)	25	6.74	....	70	3-Fluorophenol	25	9.36; (9.28)	....
21	2-Formylphenol (Salicylaldehyde)	25	6.79		71	1,4-Naphthohydroquinone (1,4-Dihydroxynaphthalene)	26.5	9.37	10.93
22	5-Methoxy-2-nitrophenol	25	7.09	....	72	4-Chlorophenol	25	9.38; (9.42)	....
23	4-Nitrophenol	25	7.16	....					
24	2-Nitrophenol	25	7.21	....	73	Sodium 4-hydroxybenzoate	20	9.39	....
25	2,6-Dimethyl-4-nitrophenol	25	7.22	....	74	Resorcinol (1,3-Dihydroxybenzene)	30	9.44	11.32
26	5-Methyl-2-nitrophenol	25	7.25	....	75	Catechol (1,2-Dihydroxybenzene)	30	9.48	12.08
27	2,6-Dichlorohydroquinone	25	7.30	9.99	76	4-Phenylphenol (4-Hydroxybiphenyl)	22.5	9.51	....
28	Vanillin (4-Formyl-2-methoxyphenol; 4-Hydroxy-3-methoxybenzaldehyde)	25	7.396	....	77	3-(Methylthio)phenol	25	9.53	....
					78	4-(Methylthio)phenol	25	9.53	....
29	2-Nitrohydroquinone	21	7.63	10.06	79	2,4,6-Trimethylolphenol	25	9.56	....
30	4-Formylphenol (4-Hydroxybenzaldehyde)	25	7.66	....	80	2-Naphthol	19.5	9.57; (9.93)	....
31	4-(Methylsulfonyl)phenol	25	7.83	....	81	3-Phenylphenol (3-Hydroxybiphenyl)	22.5	9.64	....
33	o-Vanillin (2-Formyl-6-methoxyphenol; 2-Hydroxy-3-methoxybenzaldehyde)	25	7.91	....	82	3-Methoxyphenol	25	9.65	....
					83	2,6-Dimethylolphenol	25	9.66	....
34	4-Cyanophenol (4-Hydroxybenzonitrile)	25	7.95	....	84	2-Aminophenol (2-Hydroxyaniline)	28	9.71	....
35	3-Formylphenol (3-Hydroxybenzaldehyde)	25	8.00	....	85	2,4-Dimethylphenol	25	9.77	....
36	4-Acetylphenol	25	8.05	....	86	4-Methylolphenol	25	9.82	....
37	3,5-Dimethyl-4-(methylsulfonyl)phenol	25	8.13	....	87	3-Methylolphenol	25	9.83	....
38	4-Cyano-3,5-dimethylphenol (2,6-Dimethyl-4-hydroxybenzonitrile)	25	8.21	....	88	3-Aminophenol (3-Hydroxyaniline)	21.5	9.87	9.92
39	3,5-Dimethyl-4-nitrophenol	25	8.25	....	89	Sodium 4-hydroxybenzenephosphonate	25	9.90	....
40	4-Cyano-2,6-dimethylphenol (3,5-Dimethyl-4-hydroxybenzonitrile)	25	8.27	....	90	3-Ethylphenol	28	9.90	....
					91	2,6-Dimethylol-4-methylphenol	25	9.92	....
41	2-Carboxamidophenol (Salicylamide)	20	8.37	....	92	2-Methylphenol	25	9.92	....
42	3-Nitrophenol	25	8.38	....	93	4-Fluorophenol	25	9.92	....
43	4-Carbobenzyloxyphenol (Benzyl 4-hydroxybenzoate)	25	8.41	....	94	Sodium 3-hydroxybenzoate	20	9.94	....
					95	2-Methoxyphenol	25	9.98	....
44	2-Bromophenol	25	8.42	....	96	Phenol	25	9.99; (9.95)	....
45	Phloroglucinol (1,3,5-Trihydroxybenzene)	25	8.45 (7.0)	8.88					
					97	Eugenol (4-Allyl-2-methoxyphenol)	25	10.00	....
46	2-Iodophenol	25	8.46	....	98	2-Phenylphenol (2-Hydroxybiphenyl)	22.5	10.01	....
47	4-Carbobutoxyphenol (n-Butyl 4-hydroxybenzoate)	25	8.47	....	99	4-Ethylphenol	28	10.01	....
48	4-Carbomethoxyphenol (Methyl 4-hydroxybenzoate)	25	8.47	....	100	3-Methylphenol (m-Cresol)	25	10.09	....
					101	3-Ethyl-5-methylphenol	28	10.10	....
49	2-Chlorophenol	25	8.48	....	102	3,5-Dimethylphenol	25	10.15	....
50	4-Carboethoxyphenol (Ethyl 4-hydroxybenzoate)	25	8.50	....	103	4-Methyl-2-methylolphenol	25	10.15	....
					104	4-Methoxyphenol	25	10.20	....
					105	Sodium 3-hydroxybenzenephosphonate	25	10.2	....

TABLE XXVIII. ACID DISSOCIATION CONSTANTS OF PHENOLS IN AQUEOUS SOLUTION
(Listed in order of increasing pKa)

No.	Name	T, °C	pK_1	pK_2	No	Name	T, °C	pK_1	pK_2
106	2-Ethylphenol	28	10.2	.....	115	2,6-Dimethylphenol	25	10.59	.....
107	2,5-Dimethylphenol	24	10.22	.....	116	2,4,6-Trimethylphenol	25	10.88;	.....
108	4-Methylphenol (p-Cresol)	25	10.26	.....				(10.99)	
109	2-Methylphenol (o-Cresol)	25	10.28	.....	117	Hydroquinone (1,4-Dihydroxybenzene)	25	10.85;	11.39
110	4-Indanol	25	10.32	.....				(9.96)	
111	3,4-Dimethylphenol	25	10.32	.....	118	4-Hydroxypyridine	20	11.09	.....
112	2,4,5-Trimethylphenol	25	10.45	.....	119	Tetramethylhydroquinone (Durohydro-	25	11.51	.....
113	2,4-Dimethylphenol	25	10.45	.....		quinone)			
114	2,3-Dimethylphenol	25	10.50	.....	120	2-Hydroxypyridine	20	11.62	.....

TABLE XXIX. DISSOCIATION CONSTANTS OF
ORGANIC BASES IN AQUEOUS SOLUTION
(Listed in order of increasing pKa)
(The data relates to the acid dissociation constant (Ka) of the conjugate acid (BH⁺) of the listed base (B))

No.	Name	T,°C	pK_1	pK_2	No.	Name	T,°C	pK_1	pK_2
1	2,4,6-Trinitroaniline	25	−9.41	......	59	2-Amino-6-nitronaphthalene	25	2.62	
2	2,4-Dinitroaniline	25	−4.53	......	60	N,N-Dimethyl-3-nitroaniline	25	2.63	
3	2,6-Dinitro-4-methylaniline	25	−3.96		61	2-Chloroaniline	25	2.65	
4	2,4-Dichloro-6-nitroaniline	25	−3.61		62	2-Amino-4-cyanonaphthalene	25	2.66	
5	2,6-Dichloro-4-nitroaniline	20	−2.55		63	1-Amino-3-bromonaphthalene	25	2.67	
6	N-Cyanodiethylamine	25	−2.0		64	3-Bromoquinoline	25	2.69	
7	1-Amino-2-nitronaphthalene	25	−1.74		65	1-Amino-3-chloronaphthalene	25	2.69	......
8	4-Chloro-2-nitroaniline	25	−1.02		66	5-Nitroquinoline	20	2.69	
9	Dicyanomethyl ethyl amine	25	−0.6		67	6-Nitroquinoline	20	2.72	
10	2-Fluoropyridine	25	−0.44		68	1-Amino-5-nitronaphthalene	25	2.73	
11	Pyrrole	25	−0.27; (−3.8)		69	2-Amino-8-nitronaphthalene	25	2.73	
12	2-Nitroaniline	25	−0.26		70	3-Cyanoaniline	25	2.748	
13	Bis (cyanomethyl) amine	25	0.2		71	1-Amino-8-nitronaphthalene	23	2.79	
14	2-Chloropyridine	25	0.49; (0.72)		72	1-Amino-3-iodonaphthalene	25	2.82	
15	1-Amino-4-nitronaphthalene	20	0.54	......	73	3-Bromopyridine	25	2.84	
16	Quinoxaline	20	0.56	......	74	3-Chloropyridine	25	2.84	
17	N,N-Dimethyl-4-nitroaniline	25	0.607		75	1-Amino-6-nitronaphthalene	25	2.89	
18	Pyrazine	27	0.65	−5.78	76	4-Methyl-3-nitroaniline	25	2.96	
19	Diphenylamine	25	0.79		77	3-Cyano-N,N-dimethylaniline	25	2.969	
20	3-Nitropyridine	25	0.81		78	3-Fluoropyridine	25	2.97	
21	2-Bromopyridine	25	0.90		79	2-Amino-5-nitronaphthalene	25	3.01	......
22	2-Cyanoaniline	25	0.95		80	2-Methoxypyridine	25	3.06	
23	2,6-Dimethyl-4-nitroaniline	22	0.98		81	2-Amino-7-nitronaphthalene	25	3.10	
24	4-Nitroaniline	25	1.00		82	1,3-Dimethylpyrazole	25	3.11	
25	N-Chlorodiethylamine	25	1.02		83	2-Methoxyquinoline	20	3.16	
26	2-Methyl-4-nitroaniline	24.5	1.04		84	3-Acetylpyridine	25	3.18	
27	2-Bromoquinoline	25	1.05		85	4-Hydroxypyridine	20	3.20	11.12
28	Tris (2-cyanoethyl) amine	25	1.1		86	2-Fluoroaniline	25	3.20	......
29	Pyrimidine	20	1.23; (1.31)	......	87	1-Amino-4-bromonaphthalene	25	3.21	......
30	2-Amino-3-nitronaphthalene	25	1.48		88	3-Iodopyridine	25	3.25	
31	3-Methyl-4-nitroaniline	25	1.50		89	1-Amino-3-methoxynaphthalene	25	3.26	
32	2,5-Dichloroaniline	22	1.57		90	1-Amino-3-hydroxynaphthalene	25	3.30	
33	4-Cyanoaniline	25	1.74		91	1-Amino-5-chloronaphthalene	25	3.34	
34	4-Cyano-N,N-dimethyl aniline	25	1.78		92	2-Amino-4-chloronaphthalene	25	3.38	
35	2-Iodopyridine	25	1.82		93	4-Aminofluorene	25	3.39	
36	2,3-Dimethyl-4-nitroaniline	25	1.96		94	2-Amino-4-bromonaphthalene	25	3.40	
37	2,4-Dichloroaniline	25	2.00		95	2-Amino-4-iodonaphthalene	25	3.41	
38	1-Amino-3-nitronaphthalene	25	2.07	......	96	1-Amino-7-nitronaphthalene	25	3.48	
39	3-Methoxy-5-nitroaniline	25	2.11		97	1-Amino-6-chloronaphthalene	25	3.48	
40	4-Aminobenzophenone (4-Benzoylaniline)	25	2.17		98	Quinazoline	20	3.49	
41	4-Aminoacetophenone (4-Acetylaniline)	25	2.19; (2.75)		99	3-Chloroaniline	25	3.52	
42	2-Aminoacetophenone (2-Acetylaniline)	25	2.22		100	4-Bromo-2,6-dimethylaniline	25	3.54	
43	Pyridazine	20	2.24		101	3-Methylpyrazole	25	3.56	
44	1-Amino-3-cyanonaphthalene	25	2.26		102	3-Aminoacetophenone (3-Acetylaniline)	25	3.56	
45	Cinnoline	20	2.27		103	3-Fluoroaniline	25	3.57	
46	1,2,4-Triazole	25	2.30		104	4-Bromo-2-methylaniline	25	3.58	
47	2,4-Dibromoaniline	15	2.3		105	3-Bromoaniline	25	3.58	
48	2,6-Dibromoaniline	25	2.34		106	2-(Methylthio)pyridine	20	3.59	
49	7-Nitroquinoline	20	2.40		107	3-Iodoaniline	25	3.61	
50	2-Amino-4-nitronaphthalene	25	2.43		108	5-Bromoquinoline	25	3.62	
51	Thiazole	20	2.44		109	1-(Methylamino)naphthalene	27	3.67	
52	3-Nitroaniline	25	2.466		110	2-Amino-7-chloronaphthalene	23	3.71	
53	Pyrazole	25	2.48		111	4-Bromopyridine	20	3.78	
54	2-Bromoaniline	25	2.53		112	4-Iodoaniline	25	3.78	
55	1-Amino-7-nitronaphthalene	25	2.55		113	2-Aminobiphenyl	22	3.82	
56	8-Nitroquinoline	20	2.55		114	3,5-Dimethoxyaniline	25	3.82	
57	3,5-Dimethyl-4-nitroaniline	25	2.59		115	4-Chloropyridine	20	3.84	
58	2-Iodoaniline	25	2.60	......	116	4-Bromoaniline	25	3.86	
					117	1-Aminofluorene	25	3.87	
					118	1-Amino-6-methoxynaphthalene	25	3.90	
					119	1-Aminonaphthalene	25	3.92	
					120	2,6-Dimethylaniline	25	3.95	......

TABLE XXIX. DISSOCIATION CONSTANTS OF ORGANIC BASES IN AQUEOUS SOLUTION

(Listed in order of increasing pKa) (Continued)

(The data relates to the acid dissociation constant (Ka) of the conjugate acid (BH⁺) of the listed base (B))

No.	Name	T,°C	pK₁	pK₂	No.	Name	T,°C	pK₁	pK₂
121	8-Aminoquinoline	20	3.95	......	183	8-Methylquinoline	25	4.91	......
122	1-Amino-5-hydroxynaphthalene	25	3.96	......	184	3,5-Dimethylaniline	25	4.91	
123	1-Amino-3-methylnaphthalene	25	3.96		185	3-Aminoquinoline	20	4.91	
124	1-Amino-6-hydroxynaphthalene	25	3.97		186	3-Methoxypyridine	25	4.91	
125	4-Chloroaniline	25	4.00		187	4-*tert*-Butylaniline	25	4.95	
126	3-(Methylthio)aniline	25	4.00		188	3,5-Di-*tert*-butylaniline	25	4.97	
127	4-Iodopyridine	20	4.02		189	2-Vinylpyridine	25	4.98	
128	2-Amino-4-methoxynaphthalene	25	4.05		190	1,3-Diaminobenzene	25	4.98	2.41
129	2-Amino-5-hydroxynaphthalene	25	4.07			(*m*-Phenylenediamine)			
130	1-Amino-7-methoxynaphthalene	25	4.07		191	N,3-Dimethylaniline	21	5.00	
131	3-Bromo-4-methoxyaniline	23	4.08		192	2-*tert*-Butylaniline	25	5.03	
132	1-Aminoanthracene	25	4.1		193	6-Methoxyquinoline	20	5.03	
133	2-Aminonaphthalene	25	4.16		194	N,N-Dimethylaniline	25	5.068	
134	N-Allylaniline	25	4.17		195	4-Methylaniline	25	5.08	
135	3-Ethoxyaniline	25	4.17		196	3-Hydroxypyridine	25	5.10	8.60
136	1-(Ethylamino)naphthalene	25	4.18		197	N-Ethylaniline	24	5.12	
137	2-Amino-7-methoxynaphthalene	25	4.19		198	N-*n*-Butylaniline	25	5.12	
138	1-Amino-7-hydroxynaphthalene	25	4.20		199	3,5,6-Trimethylaniline	20.5	5.12	
139	3-Methoxyaniline	25	4.20		200	2-Benzylpyridine	25	5.13	
140	4-Aminobiphenyl	29	4.22		201	6-Methylquinoline	25	5.15	
141	4-Bromo-N,N-dimethylaniline	25	4.232		202	2-Amino-5,6,7,8-tetrahydronaphthalene	17	5.17	
142	3-Aminobiphenyl	17	4.25		203	3,4-Dimethylaniline	25	5.17	
143	2-Amino-7-hydroxynaphthalene	25	4.25		204	4-Ethoxyaniline	28	5.20	
144	2,3,5,6-Tetramethylaniline	25	4.30		205	4-Methylquinoline	25	5.20;	
145	2-Bromo-N,N-dimethylaniline	25	4.31	......				(5.59)	
146	4-(Methylthio)aniline	25	4.35		206	Pyridine	25	5.25	
147	2-*n*-Propyl.aniline	25	4.36		207	Bis(2-cyanoethyl)amine	25	5.26	
148	Tris(2-chloroethyl)amine	25	4.37		208	7-Methylquinoline	25	5.29	
149	2-Ethylaniline	25	4.37		209	N-Cyclopentylaniline	25	5.30	
150	2,4,6-Trimethylaniline	25	4.37		210	5-Aminoindane	16	5.31	
151	3,5-Dimethylpyrazole	25	4.38		211	4-Methoxyaniline	25	5.31	
152	3-(Methylthio)pyridine	20	4.42		212	Aminoacetonitrile	25	5.34	
153	2-Isopropylaniline	25	4.42		213	N,N,3-Trimethylaniline	25	5.344	
154	N-Isobutylaniline	25	4.43		214	N,4-Dimethylaniline	23	5.36	
155	2-Ethoxyaniline	28	4.43		215	Isoquinoline	20	5.42	
156	2-Methylaniline	25	4.44		216	N-*n*-Hexylaniline	19	5.42	
157	1-Amino-5,6,7,8-tetrahydronaphthalene	16	4.47		217	5-Aminoquinoline	20	5.42	
158	Phenanthridine	20	4.48		218	2,2,2-Trichloroethylamine	20	5.47	
159	2-Methoxyaniline	25	4.52		219	Benzimidazole	25	5.53	
160	2,5-Dimethylaniline	25	4.53		220	1-Methylbenzimidazole	25	5.54	
161	1-(Cyanomethyl)pyridine	25	4.55		221	3-Ethylpyridine	25	5.56	
162	(Cyanomethyl) diethyl amine	25	4.55		222	1-Ethylbenzimidazole	25	5.59	
163	Bis(2-Cyanoethyl) ethyl amine	25	4.55		223	6-Aminoquinoline	20	5.59	
164	2-(Dimethylamino)naphthalene	25	4.566		224	N-Cyclohexylaniline	25	5.60	
165	Aniline	25	4.603		225	4-Vinylpyridine	25	5.62	
166	5-Methylquinoline	25	4.62		226	N,N,4-Trimethylaniline	25	5.627	
167	N,2-Dimethylaniline	23	4.62		227	3-Methylpyridine	25	5.63	
168	2-Aminofluorene	25	4.64		228	4-Methylbenzimidazole	25	5.65	
169	2-Amino-6-methoxynaphthalene	25	4.64		229	N,N-Di-*n*-propylaniline	23	5.68	
170	4-Fluoroaniline	25	4.65		230	2-Methylquinoline	25	5.69	
171	3-*tert*-Butylaniline	25	4.66		231	1-Isopropylbenzimidazole	25	5.71	
172	3-Isopropylaniline	25	4.67		232	3-Isopropylpyridine	25	5.72	
173	2,3-Dimethylaniline	25	4.70		233	2-*tert*-Butylpyridine	25	5.76	
174	3-Methylaniline	25	4.70		234	N-Isopropylaniline	25	5.77	
175	3-Ethylaniline	25	4.70		235	5-Methylbenzimidazole	25	5.78	
176	1,2-Diaminobenzene (*o*-Phenylenediamine)	25	4.74	0.6	236	3-*tert*-Butylpyridine	25	5.82	
177	N-*n*-Propylaniline	25	4.79		237	2-Isopropylpyridine	25	5.83	
178	Quinoline	25	4.81		238	4-Ethylpyridine	25	5.87	
179	3-Aminofluorene	25	4.82		239	2-Ethylpyridine	25	5.89	
180	1-(Dimethylamino)naphthalene	28	4.83		240	2-Methylpyridine	25	5.94	
181	N-Methylaniline	25	4.848	......	241	4-(Methylthio)pyridine	20	5.94	
182	2,4-Dimethylaniline	25	4.89	......	242	2-Hexylpyridine	25	5.95	......

TABLE XXIX. DISSOCIATION CONSTANTS OF
ORGANIC BASES IN AQUEOUS SOLUTION
(Listed in order of increasing pKa) (Continued)
(The data relates to the acid dissociation constant (Ka) of the conjugate acid (BH$^+$) of the listed base (B))

No.	Name	T.°C	pK$_1$	pK$_2$	No.	Name	T.°C	pK$_1$	pK$_2$
243	2-*n*-Propylpyridine	25	5.97	. . . . . .	305	Bis(2-hydroxyethyl)amine	25	8.88	. . . . . .
244	4-*tert*-Butylpyridine	25	5.99	. . . . . .	306	N,N-Dimethylbenzylamine	25	8.91	. . . . . .
245	2-Pentylpyridine	25	6.00	. . . . . .	307	3-Bromopropylamine	21	8.93	. . . . . .
246	4-Isopropylpyridine	25	6.02	. . . . . .	308	1,2-Bis(dimethylamino)ethane	30	8.97	5.85
247	4-Methylpyridine	25	6.03	. . . . . .	309	1-(Aminoethyl)benzene	25	9.08	. . . . . .
248	3-Aminopyridine	25	6.03	. . . . . .	310	2-Acetoxyethylamine	25	9.1	. . . . . .
249	N,N,2-Trimethylaniline	25	6.11	. . . . . .	311	4-Aminopyridine	25	9.114	
250	N,2,6-Trimethylaniline	25	6.12	. . . . . .	312	4-Aminoquinoline	20	9.13	
					313	(3-Cyanopropyl) diethyl amine	25	9.13	
252	2-Methylbenzimidazole	25	6.19	. . . . . .	314	3-Methoxybenzylamine	25	9.15	
253	1,4-Diaminobenzene (*p*-Phenylenediamine)	25	6.2	2.67	315	2-Methylbenzylamine	25	9.19	
254	2-Isopropylbenzimidazole	25	6.21	. . . . . .	316	1-Aminoindane	22.5	9.21	
255	2-Ethylbenzimidazole	25	6.27	. . . . . .	317	*trans*-1-Amino-2-hydroxycyclopentane	25	9.28	
256	N,N-Di-*n*-butylaniline	19	6.30	. . . . . .	318	Diallylamine	25	9.29	
257	2,5-Dimethylpyridine	25	6.40	. . . . . .	319	Dimethyl (2-hydroxyethyl) amine	20	9.31	
258	2-Phenylimidazole	25	6.40	. . . . . .	320	3-Methylbenzylamine	25	9.33	
259	Bis(2-chloroethyl)methyl amine	25	6.43	. . . . . .	321	Benzylamine	25	9.35;	
260	4-Methoxyquinoline	30	6.45	. . . . . .				(9.62)	
261	3,4-Dimethylpyridine	25	6.46	. . . . . .	322	4-Methylbenzylamine	25	9.36	
262	4-Methoxypyridine	25	6.47	. . . . . .	323	3,4-Dimethoxybenzylamine	25	9.39	
263	Bis(2-chloroethyl) ethyl amine	25	6.55	. . . . . .	324	2,3-Dimethoxybenzylamine	25	9.41	
264	1,2-Dimethylbenzimidazole	25	6.55	. . . . . .	325	2-(Phenethylamino)ethylamine	25	9.44	6.59
265	2,3-Dimethylpyridine	25	6.57	. . . . . .	326	N,N-Diethylbenzylamine	25	9.44	
266	2,6-Dimethylpyridine	25	6.60	. . . . . .	327	4-Methoxybenzylamine	25	9.47	
267	7-Aminoquinoline	20	6.61	. . . . . .	328	2-(Methylthio)ethylamine	20	9.49	
268	N,N-Diethylaniline	22	6.61	. . . . . .	329	2-Hydroxyethylamine	25	9.498	
269	4-Ethoxypyridine	20	6.67	. . . . . .	330	2-(Dimethylamino)ethylamine	25	9.53	6.63
270	2-Aminopyridine	25	6.71	. . . . . .	331	N-Methylbenzylamine	25	9.54	
271	2,4-Dimethylpyridine	25	6.77	. . . . . .	332	1,2-Bis(diethylamino)ethane	25	9.55	6.18
272	Imidazole	25	6.95	. . . . . .	333	2-Aminoindane	21.5	9.57	. . . . . .
273	N-*tert*-Butylaniline	25	7.00	. . . . .	334	N-Propylbenzylamine	25	9.58	. . . . . .
274	(2-Cyanoethyl) dimethyl amine	29	7.0	. . . . . .	335	1,2,3-Triaminopropane	20	9.59	7.95;
275	2-Benzyl-2-pyrroline	25	7.06	. . . . .					pK$_3$ =
276	2-Aminoquinoline	20	7.30	. . . . . .					3.72
277	N,N-Di-isopropylaniline	25	7.37	. . . . . .	336	2-Methoxyethylamine	20	9.61	. . . . . .
278	N-Methylmorpholine	25	7.38	. . . . . .	337	5-Bromo-*n*-pentylamine	21	9.62	. . . . . .
279	2,4,6-Trimethylpyridine	25	7.43	. . . . . .	338	*trans*-1-Amino-2-hydroxycyclohexane	25	9.63	. . . . . .
280	4-Methylimidazole	25	7.518	. . . . . .	339	1-Amino-1,2,3,4-tetrahydronaphthalene	20	9.63	. . . . . .
281	1,3-Triazine	25	7.6	. . . . . .	340	N-Ethylbenzylamine	25	9.64	. . . . . .
282	N-Ethylmorpholine	25	7.67	. . . . . .	341	3,3,3-Trichloro-*n*-propylamine	20	9.65	. . . . . .
283	2-Cyanoethylamine	29	7.7	. . . . . .	342	1-Allylpiperidine	25	9.65	. . . . . .
284	Tris(2-hydroxyethyl)amine	25	7.762	. . . . . .	343	2-Methoxybenzylamine	25	9.70	. . . . . .
285	2-Methylimidazole	25	7.85	. . . . . .	344	*cis*-1-Amino-2-hydroxycyclopentane	25	9.70	. . . . . .
286	N-Methylaziridine	25	7.86	. . . . . .	345	2-(Furfurylamino)ethylamine	20	9.72	6.20
287	N-*n*-Butylaziridine	25	7.86	. . . . . .	346	*cis*-1-Amino-2-hydroxycyclohexane	25	9.72	. . . . . .
288	2-Ethyl-2-pyrroline	25	7.87	. . . . . .	347	Piperazine	25	9.81	5.55
289	2,3,5,6-Tetramethylpyridine	20	7.90	. . . . . .	348	Trimethylamine	25	9.81	. . . . . .
290	2-Cyclohexyl-2-pyrroline	25	7.91	. . . . . .	349	Phenethylamine ((2-Aminoethyl)benzene)	25	9.84	. . . . . .
291	N-Ethylaziridine	24	7.93	. . . . . .	350	Diethyl 2-hydroxyethyl amine	20	9.87	. . . . . .
292	Aziridine	25	8.01	. . . . . .	351	1-Methyl-3-pyrroline	25	9.88	. . . . . .
293	N,2-Diethylaziridine	25	8.18	. . . . . .	352	1,2-Diaminoethane (1,2-Ethylenediamine)	25	9.928	6.848
294	2-Ethylaziridine	25	8.29	. . . . . .	353	*cis*-1,2-Diaminocyclohexane	20	9.93	6.13
295	Triallylamine	25	8.31	. . . . . .	354	2-Amino-1,2,3,4-tetrahydronaphthalene	17	9.93	. . . . . .
296	Morpholine	25	8.33	. . . . . .	355	Tri-*n*-butylamine	25	9.93	. . . . . .
297	2,4-Dimethylimidazole	25	8.36	. . . . . .	356	4,4,4-Trichloro-*n*-butylamine	20	9.93	. . . . . .
298	2-Bromoethylamine	24	8.49	. . . . . .	357	*trans*-1,2-Diaminocyclohexane	20	9.94	6.47
299	Bis(2-hydroxyethyl) methyl amine	25	8.52	. . . . . .	358	3-Hydroxypropylamine	25	9.96	. . . . . .
300	1,2-Bis(furfurylamino)ethane	20	8.61	5.74	359	*meso*-2,3-Diaminobutane	25	9.97	6.92
301	2,2-Dimethylaziridine	25	8.64	. . . . . .	360	*d,l*-2,3-Diaminobutane	25	10.00	6.91
302	*trans*-2,3-Dimethylaziridine	24	8.69	. . . . . .	361	1,2-Diaminopropane	25	10.00	7.13
303	*cis*-2,3-Dimethylaziridine	23	8.72	. . . . . .		(1,2-Propylenediamine)			
304	(2-Chloroethyl) diethyl amine	25	8.80	. . . . . .	362	*cis*-Neobornylamine	25	10.01	. . . . . .

TABLE XXIX. DISSOCIATION CONSTANTS OF
ORGANIC BASES IN AQUEOUS SOLUTION
(Listed in order of increasing pKa) (Continued)
(The data relates to the acid dissociation constant (Ka) of the conjugate acid (BH$^+$) of the listed base (B))

No.	Name	T,°C	pK$_1$	pK$_2$	No.	Name	T,°C	pK$_1$	pK$_2$
363	2-(Diethylamino)ethylamine	25	10.02	7.07	417	n-Pentylamine	25	10.63	......
364	1-Methylpiperidine	25	10.08		418	n-Undecylamine (n-Hendecylamine)	25	10.63	
365	Dimethyl isobutyl amine	20	10.08	......	419	n-Nonylamine	25	10.64	
366	5,5,5-Trichloro-n-pentylamine	20	10.12	......	420	Acridine	25	10.65	
367	2-(Methylamino)ethylamine	20	10.15	6.86	421	n-Octylamine	25	10.65	
368	cis-1,2,6-Trimethylpiperidine	30	10.15	......	422	Methylamine	25	10.657	
369	2,2-Dimethyl-n-propylamine	25	10.15		423	1-Ethyl-2-methylpiperidine	25	10.66	
370	1,2-Bis(methylamino)ethane	25	10.16	7.40	424	n-Heptylamine	25	10.66	
371	Dimethyl propyl amine	20	10.16		425	2-Aminoheptane	25	10.67	
372	Dimethyl ethyl amine	20	10.16		426	Cyclohexylamine	25	10.68	
373	trans-Bornylamine	25	10.17		427	tert-Butylamine	25	10.68	
374	1,2,2,4-Tetramethylpiperidine	30	10.18		428	tert-Butyl dimethyl amine	20	10.69	
375	n-Butyl dimethyl amine	25	10.19		429	n-Propylamine	25	10.69	
376	1,2-Dimethylpyrrolidine	26	10.20		430	1,2,2,6-Tetramethylpiperidine	30	10.70	
377	1,2-Dimethylpiperidine	25	10.22	......	431	Ethylamine	25	10.70	
378	1,5-Diaminopentane	25	10.25	9.13	432	Isobutylamine	25	10.72	
379	Tri-n-propylamine	25	10.26	......	433	3-(Trimethylsilyl)-n-propylamine	25	10.73	
380	1,2-Bis(propylamino)ethane	25	10.27	7.53	434	Dimethylamine	25	10.73	
381	2-(Butylamino)ethylamine	25	10.30	7.53	435	Triethylamine	25	10.75	
382	1,3-Diaminopropane	25	10.30	8.29	436	2-Cyclohexylpyrrolidine	25	10.76	
	(1,3-Propylenediamine)				437	1,4-Diaminobutane	20	10.80	9.35
383	2-Benzylpyrrolidine	25	10.31	......	438	Di-isobutylamine	21	10.91	
384	Tri-isobutylamine	25	10.32		439	1,6-Diaminohexane	25	10.93	9.83
385	N-Methylpyrrolidine	25	10.32		440	Di-isoamylamine	27.8	10.94	......
386	2-(propylamino)ethylamine	25	10.34	7.54	441	Quinuclidine	25	10.95	
387	4-Hydroxy-n-butylamine	20	10.35		442	2-Methylpiperidine	25	10.95	
388	1,2-Bis(isopropylamino)ethane	25	10.40	7.59	443	2-(Trimethylsilyl)ethylamine	25	10.97	
389	1-n-Propylpiperidine	26.5	10.41		444	Di-n-tridecylamine	25	11.00	
390	3-Aminopentane	25	10.42		445	Di-n-octadecylamine	25	11.00	......
391	3-Aminocyclohexene	25	10.42		446	1,8-Diaminooctane	20	11.00	10.1
392	1-n-Butylpiperidine	26	10.43		447	Di-n-propylamine	25	11.00	
393	1-Ethylpiperidine	23	10.45		448	Di-n-dodecylamine	25	11.00	
394	1,2-Bis(ethylamino)ethane	25	10.46	7.70	449	Di-n-pentadecylamine	25	11.00	
395	Diethyl methyl amine	20	10.46		450	Di-n-hexylamine	25	11.01	
396	5-Hydroxy-1-pentylamine	23	10.46		451	Di-n-octylamine	25	11.01	
397	Dimethyl isopropyl amine	20	10.47		452	2,2,4-Trimethylpiperidine	30	11.04	
398	trans-1-Amino-4-methylcyclohexane	25	10.48		453	Cyclohexyl methyl amine	25	11.04	
399	(Aminomethyl)cyclohexane	25	10.49		454	Diethylamine	25	11.04	
400	cis-1-Amino-2-methylcyclohexane	25	10.49		455	2,2,6-Tetramethylpiperidine	25	11.07	
401	2-Aminooctane	25	10.49		456	Azepine	25	11.07	
402	trans-1-Amino-2-methylcyclohexane	25	10.51		457	cis-2,6-Dimethylpiperidine	25	11.07	
403	cis-1-Amino-3-methylcyclohexane	25	10.56		458	3-Methylpiperidine	25	11.07	
404	2-(Ethylamino)ethylamine	25	10.56	7.63	459	Piperidine	25	11.123	
405	Dimethyl sec-butyl amine	20	10.57		460	Di-isopropylamine	21	11.13	
406	6-Hydroxy-n-hexylamine	21	10.60		461	Di-n-pentylamine	26	11.16	
407	6-Bromo-n-hexylamine	21	10.60		462	2,2,6-Trimethylpiperidine	30	11.21	
408	1-Aminoheptadecane	25	10.60		463	(tert-Butylamino)cyclohexane	25	11.23	
409	1-Aminodocosane	25	10.60		464	Di-n-butylamine	25	11.25	
410	1-Aminooctadecane	25	10.60		465	1,2,2,4,4-Pentamethylpiperidine	25	11.25	
411	1-Aminopentadecane	25	10.61		466	Pyrrolidine	25	11.27	
412	n-Butylamine	25	10.61		467	Azetidine	25	11.29	
413	1-Aminohexadecane	25	10.61		468	Isopropylamine	25	11.54;	
414	trans-1-Amino-3-methylcyclohexane	25	10.61	......				(10.63)	
415	1-Aminotetradecane	25	10.62		469	1,2-Dimethyl-2-pyrroline	25	11.90	
416	2-(Isopropylamino)ethylamine	25	10.62	7.70	470	Acetamidine (Methylamidine)	25	12.40	......

Review aminis

(ch. 19)

P. 517-542
777-800
800-833
897-918
976-1079

Nomenclature

p. 835

p. 74

practice IR + NMR

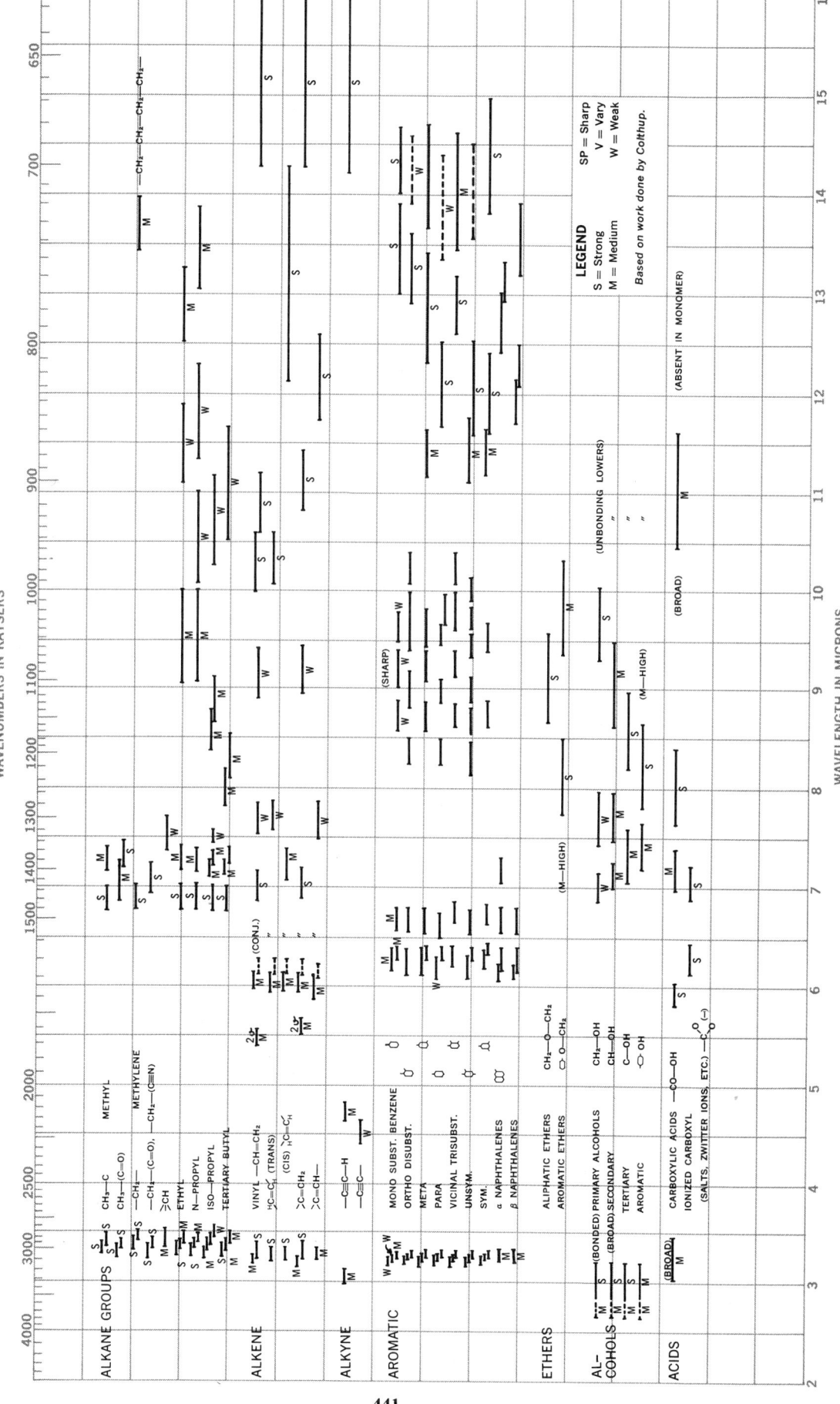

INFRARED CORRELATION CHART No. 1

Prepared from information supplied by Beckman Instruments

WAVENUMBERS IN KAYSERS

WAVELENGTH IN MICRONS

LEGEND

S = Strong   SP = Sharp

M = Medium   V = Vary

W = Weak

Based on work done by Colthup.

441

INFRARED CORRELATION CHART No. 1 (Con't.)

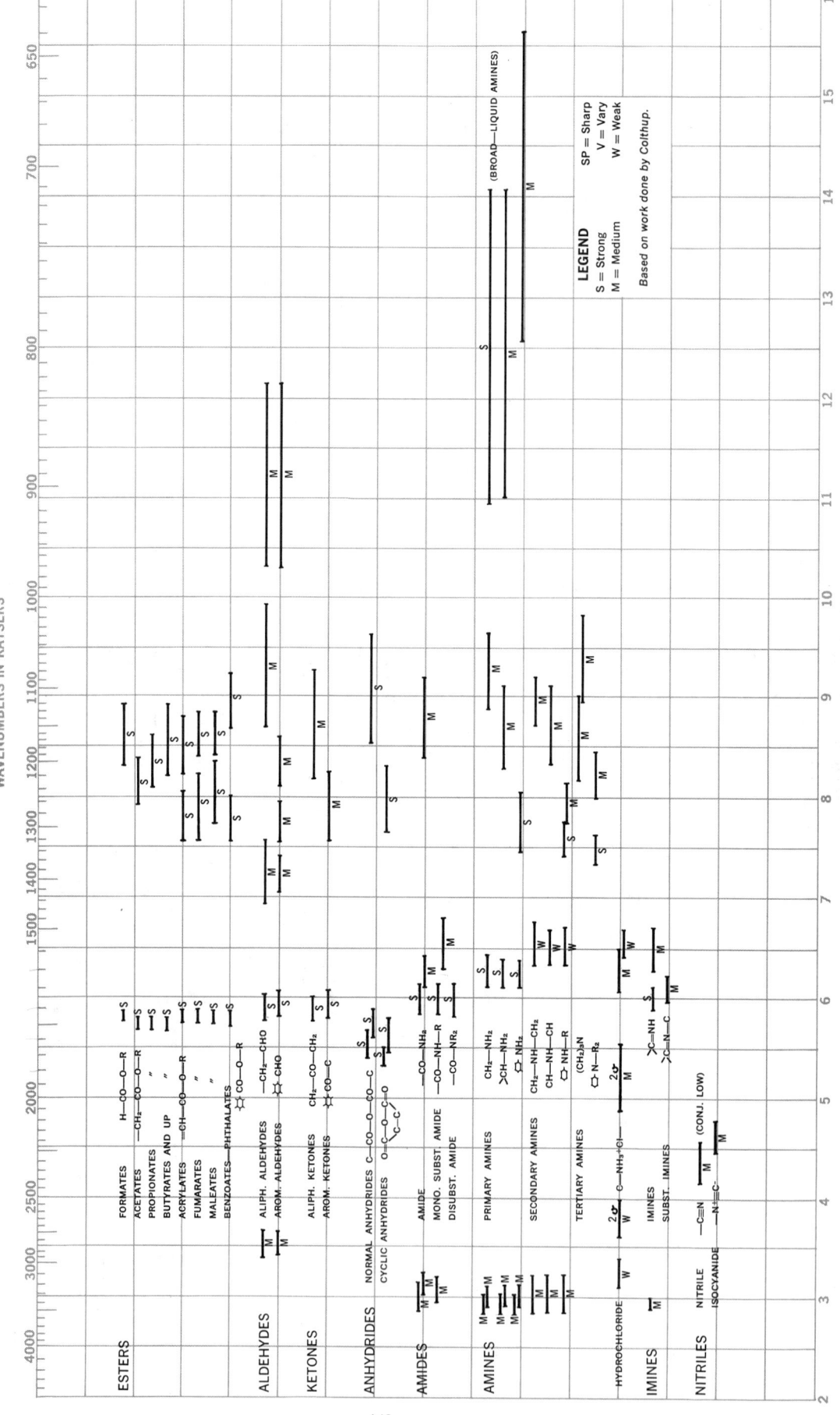

WAVENUMBERS IN KAYSERS

WAVELENGTH IN MICRONS

LEGEND

S = Strong   SP = Sharp

M = Medium   V = Vary

W = Weak

Based on work done by Colthup.

442

INFRARED CORRELATION CHART No. 1 (Con't.)

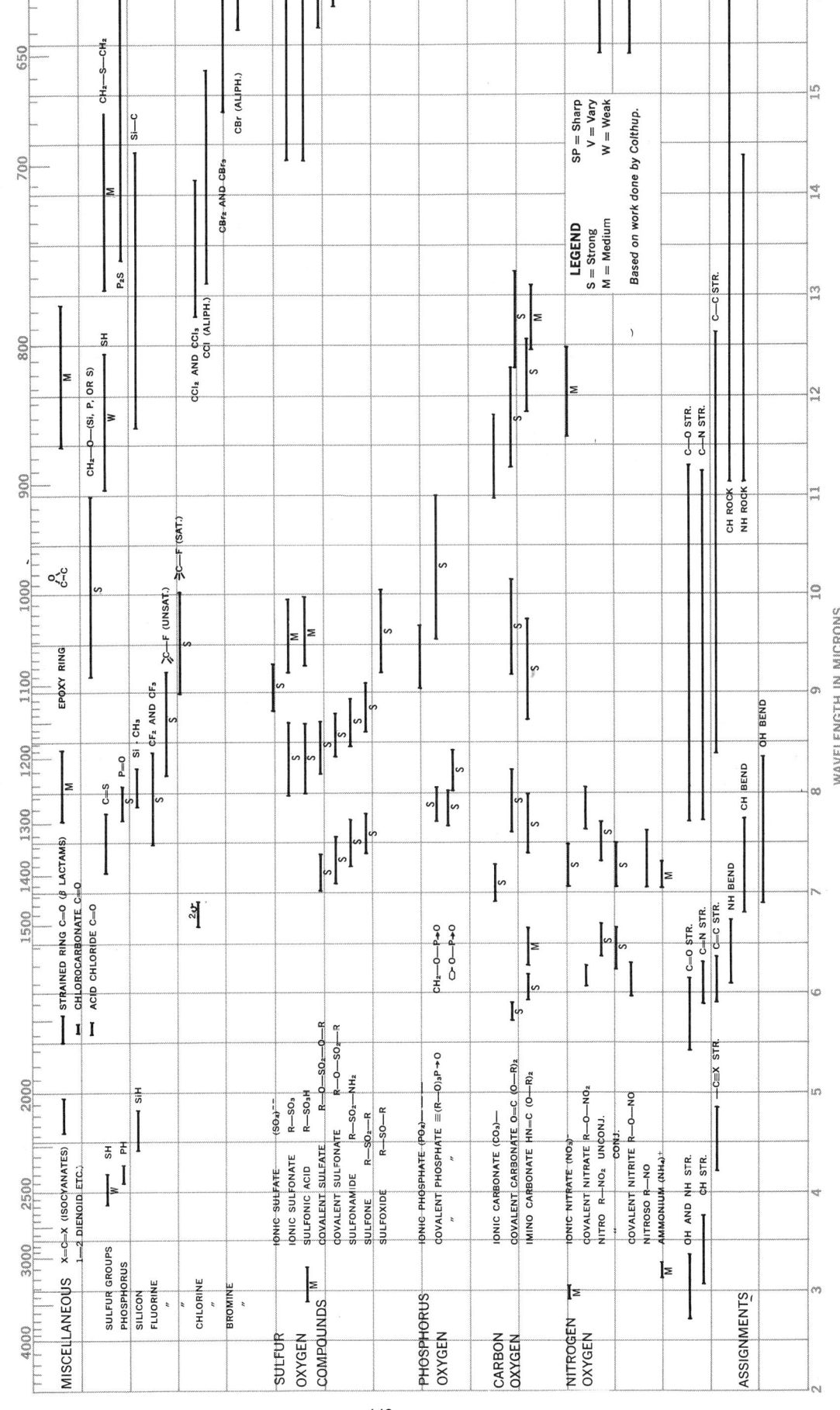

443

INFRARED CORRELATION CHART No. 2

Prepared from information supplied by Beckman Instruments

This chart presents some information regarding structure, double-bond vibrations, hydrogen stretching and triple-bond vibrations.

HYDROGEN STRETCHING AND TRIPLE-BOND VIBRATIONS, 3750-2000 CM.$^{-1}$ DOUBLE-BOND VIBRATIONS, ETC. 2000-1500 CM.$^{-1}$

WAVENUMBERS IN KAYSERS

WAVELENGTH IN MICRONS

LEGEND
S = Strong   SP = Sharp
M = Medium   V = Vary
W = Weak

Based on work done by Bellamy.

444

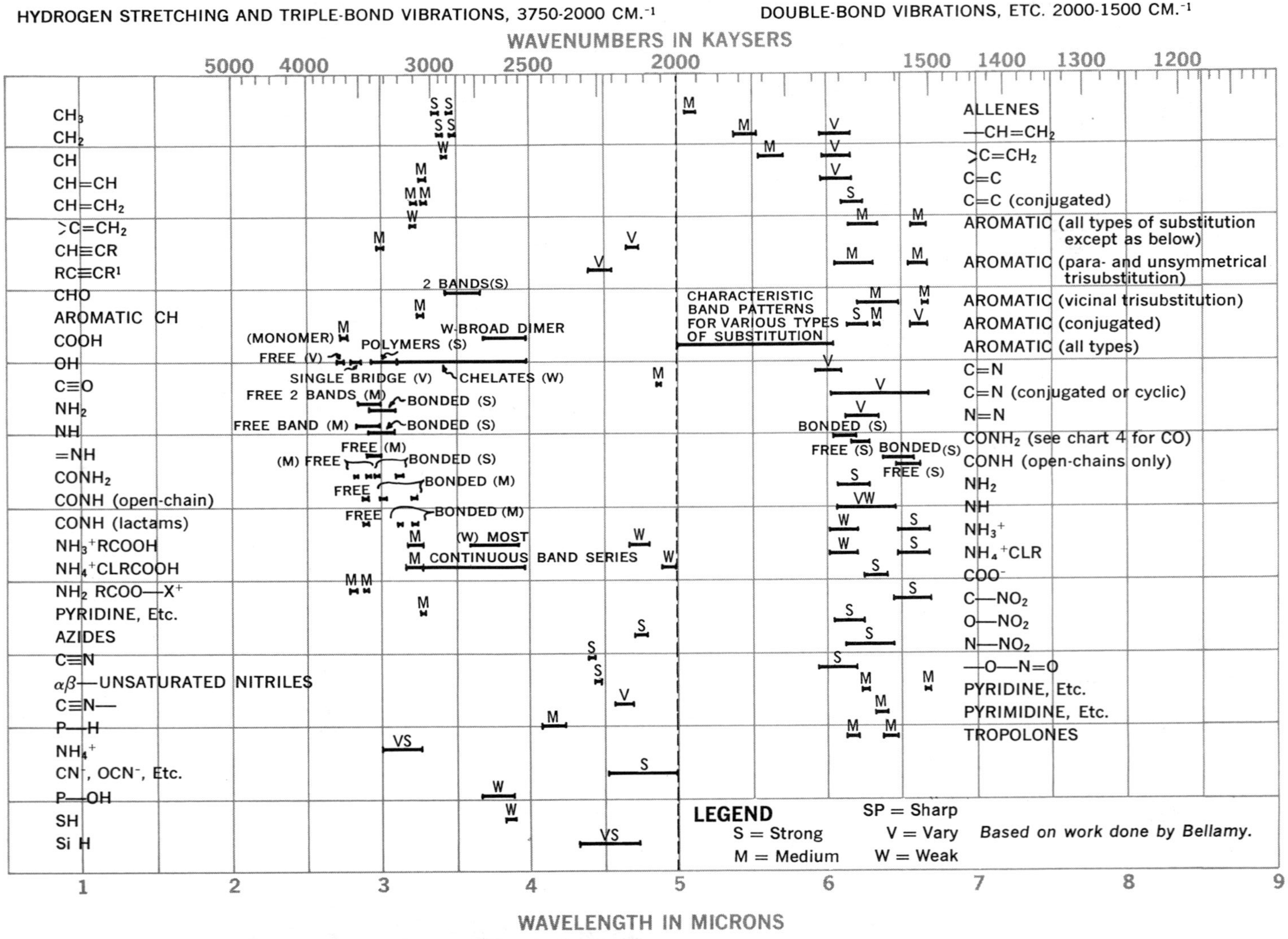

INFRARED CORRELATION CHART No. 3

Prepared from information supplied by Beckman Instruments

This chart presents some correlations between structure and the carbonyl vibrations of some classes of organic compounds. In all cases the absorption bands are strong and fall within the range of 1900-1500 cm^{-1}.

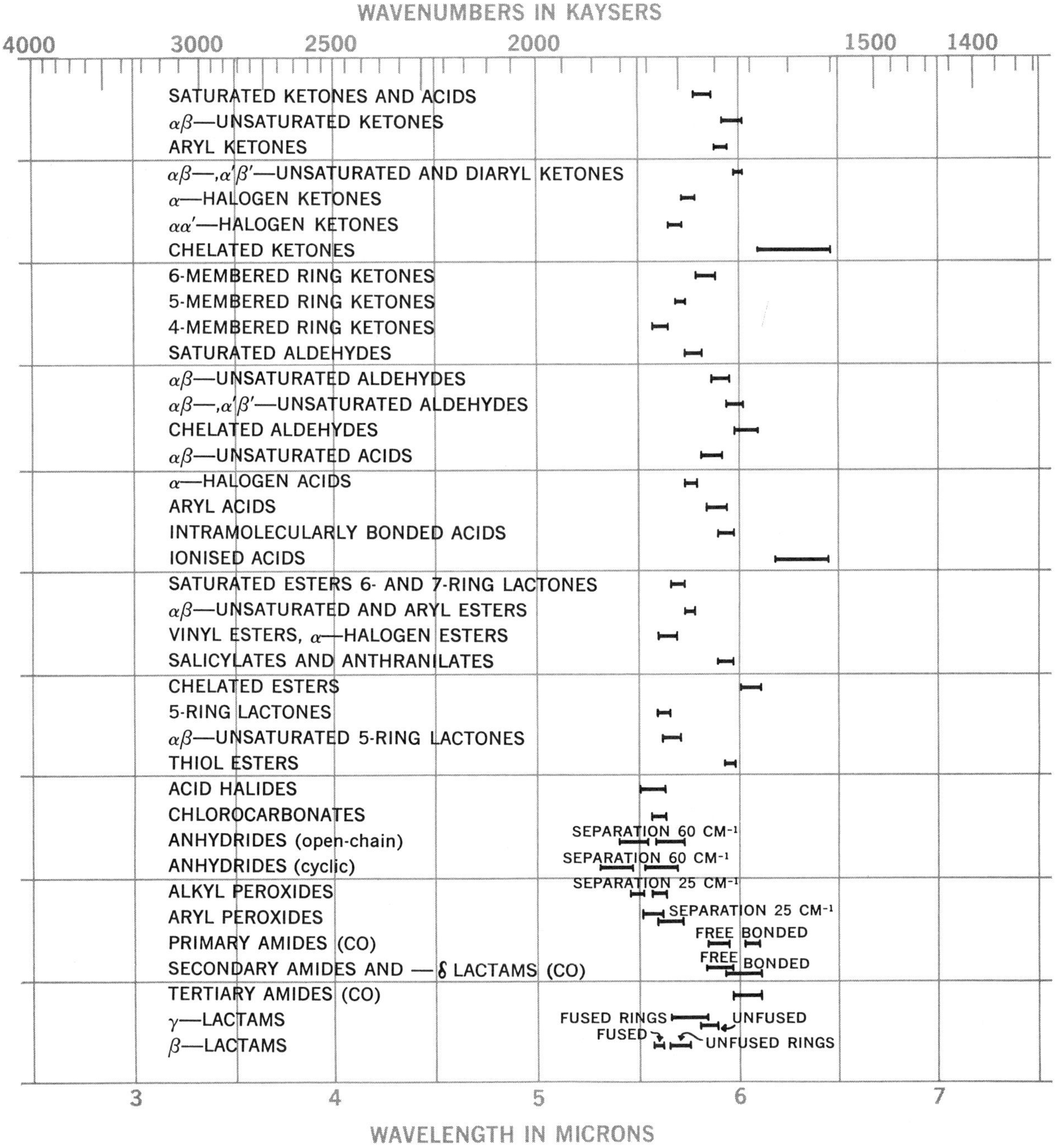

WAVENUMBERS IN KAYSERS

4000 3000 2500 2000 1500 1400

SATURATED KETONES AND ACIDS
$\alpha\beta$—UNSATURATED KETONES
ARYL KETONES
$\alpha\beta$—,$\alpha'\beta'$—UNSATURATED AND DIARYL KETONES
α—HALOGEN KETONES
$\alpha\alpha'$—HALOGEN KETONES
CHELATED KETONES
6-MEMBERED RING KETONES
5-MEMBERED RING KETONES
4-MEMBERED RING KETONES
SATURATED ALDEHYDES
$\alpha\beta$—UNSATURATED ALDEHYDES
$\alpha\beta$—,$\alpha'\beta'$—UNSATURATED ALDEHYDES
CHELATED ALDEHYDES
$\alpha\beta$—UNSATURATED ACIDS
α—HALOGEN ACIDS
ARYL ACIDS
INTRAMOLECULARLY BONDED ACIDS
IONISED ACIDS
SATURATED ESTERS 6- AND 7-RING LACTONES
$\alpha\beta$—UNSATURATED AND ARYL ESTERS
VINYL ESTERS, α—HALOGEN ESTERS
SALICYLATES AND ANTHRANILATES
CHELATED ESTERS
5-RING LACTONES
$\alpha\beta$—UNSATURATED 5-RING LACTONES
THIOL ESTERS
ACID HALIDES
CHLOROCARBONATES
ANHYDRIDES (open-chain)   SEPARATION 60 CM^{-1}
ANHYDRIDES (cyclic)   SEPARATION 60 CM^{-1}
ALKYL PEROXIDES   SEPARATION 25 CM^{-1}
ARYL PEROXIDES   SEPARATION 25 CM^{-1}
PRIMARY AMIDES (CO)   FREE BONDED
SECONDARY AMIDES AND —δ LACTAMS (CO)   FREE BONDED
TERTIARY AMIDES (CO)
γ—LACTAMS   FUSED RINGS   UNFUSED
β—LACTAMS   FUSED   UNFUSED RINGS

3   4   5   6   7

WAVELENGTH IN MICRONS

INFRARED CORRELATION CHART No. 4

Prepared from information supplied by Beckman Instruments

This chart presents some correlations between structure and single-bond vibrations for a number of classes of compounds having absorption between 1500-650 cm⁻¹.

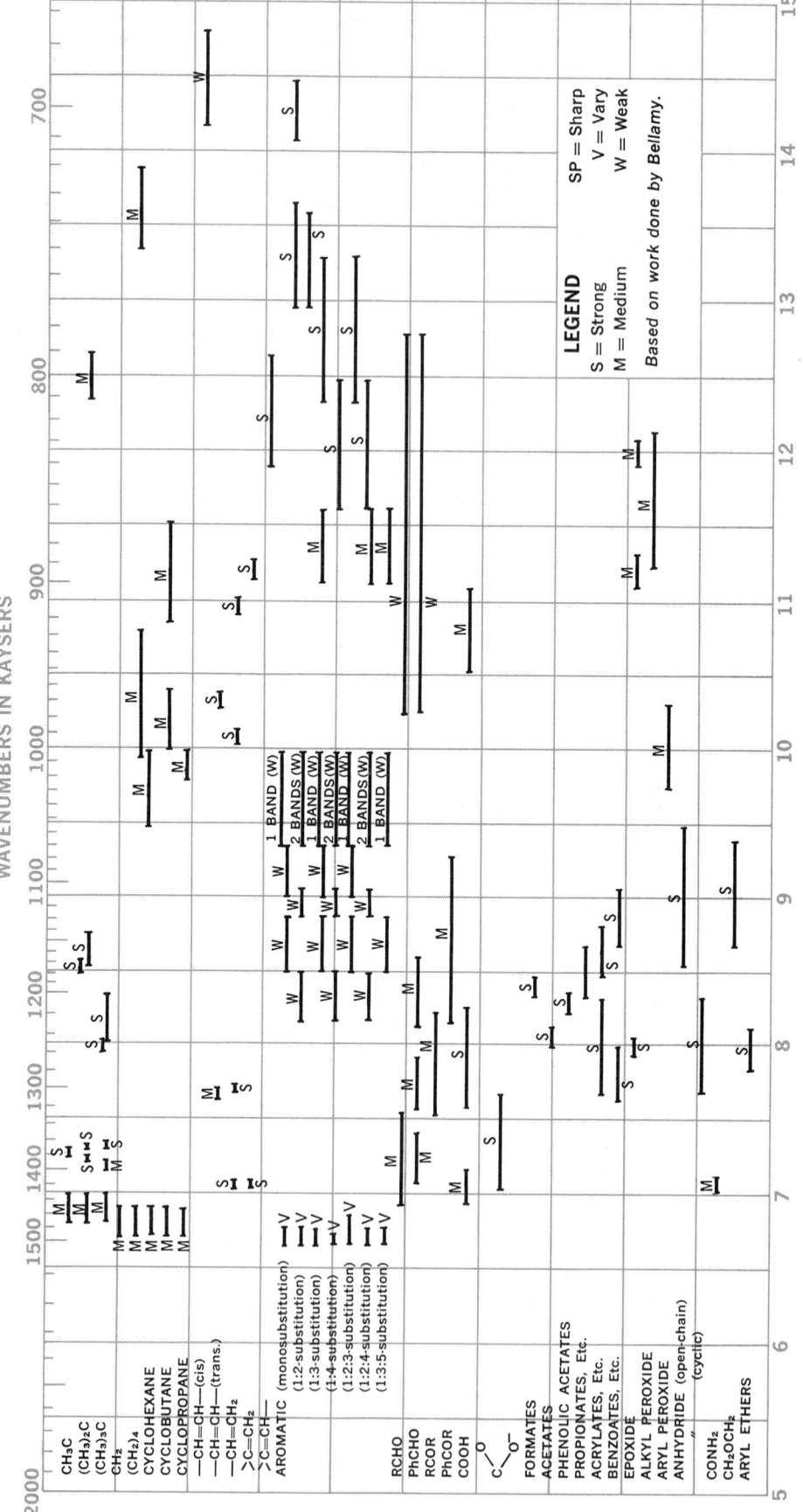

INFRARED CORRELATION CHART No. 4 (Con't.)

Prepared from information supplied by Beckman Instruments

This chart presents some correlations between structure and single-bond vibrations for a number of classes of compounds having absorption between 1500-650 cm⁻¹.

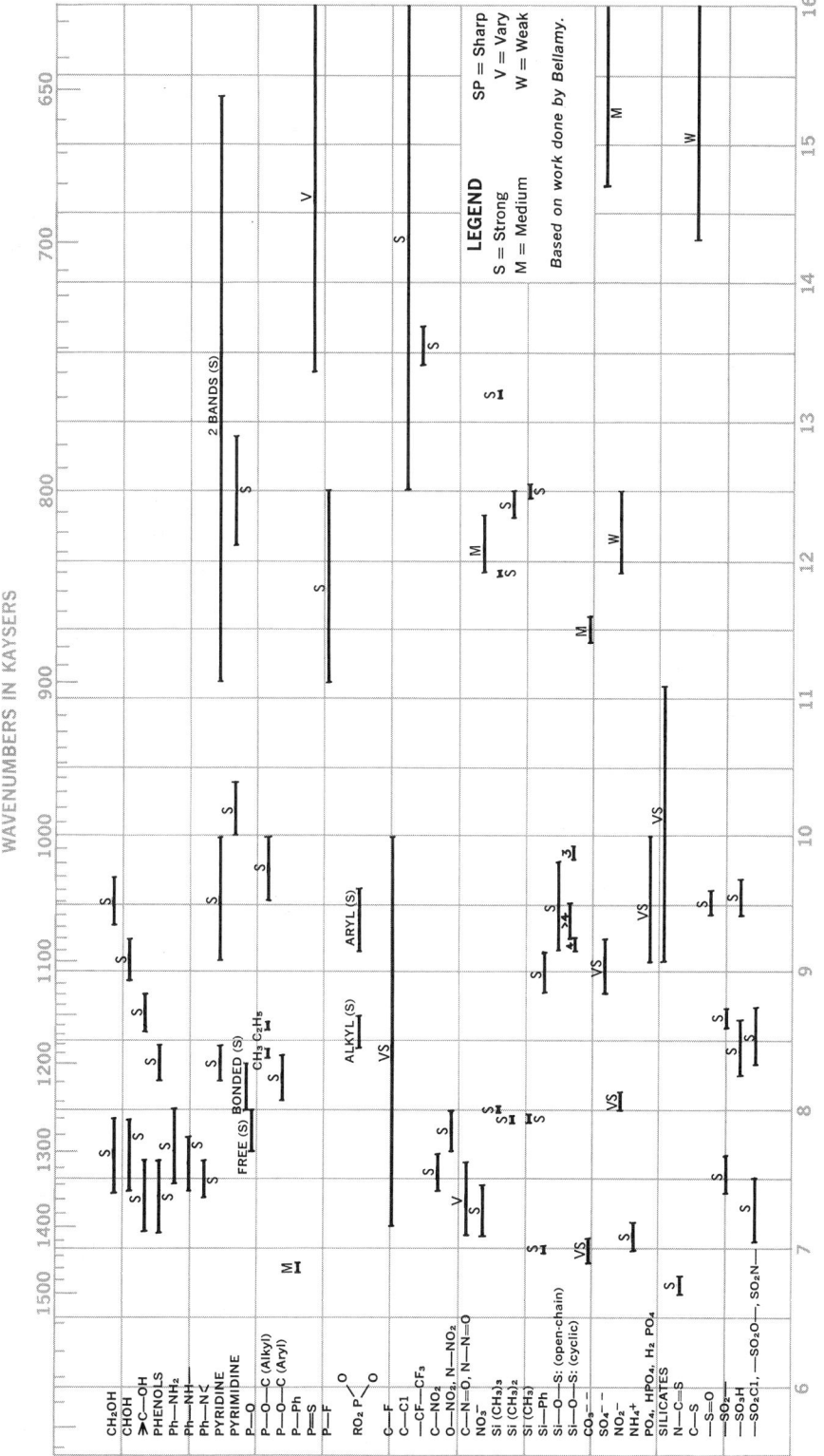

WAVENUMBERS IN KAYSERS

WAVELENGTH IN MICRONS

LEGEND

S = Strong   SP = Sharp

M = Medium   V = Vary

              W = Weak

Based on work done by Bellamy.

447

FAR INFRARED VIBRATIONAL FREQUENCY CORRELATION CHART

Based on evidence compiled by James E. Stewart of Beckman Instruments.
This chart shows the vibrational frequency correlation in the far infrared region.
Because research is continuing in the far infrared region, this chart is not
all-inclusive.

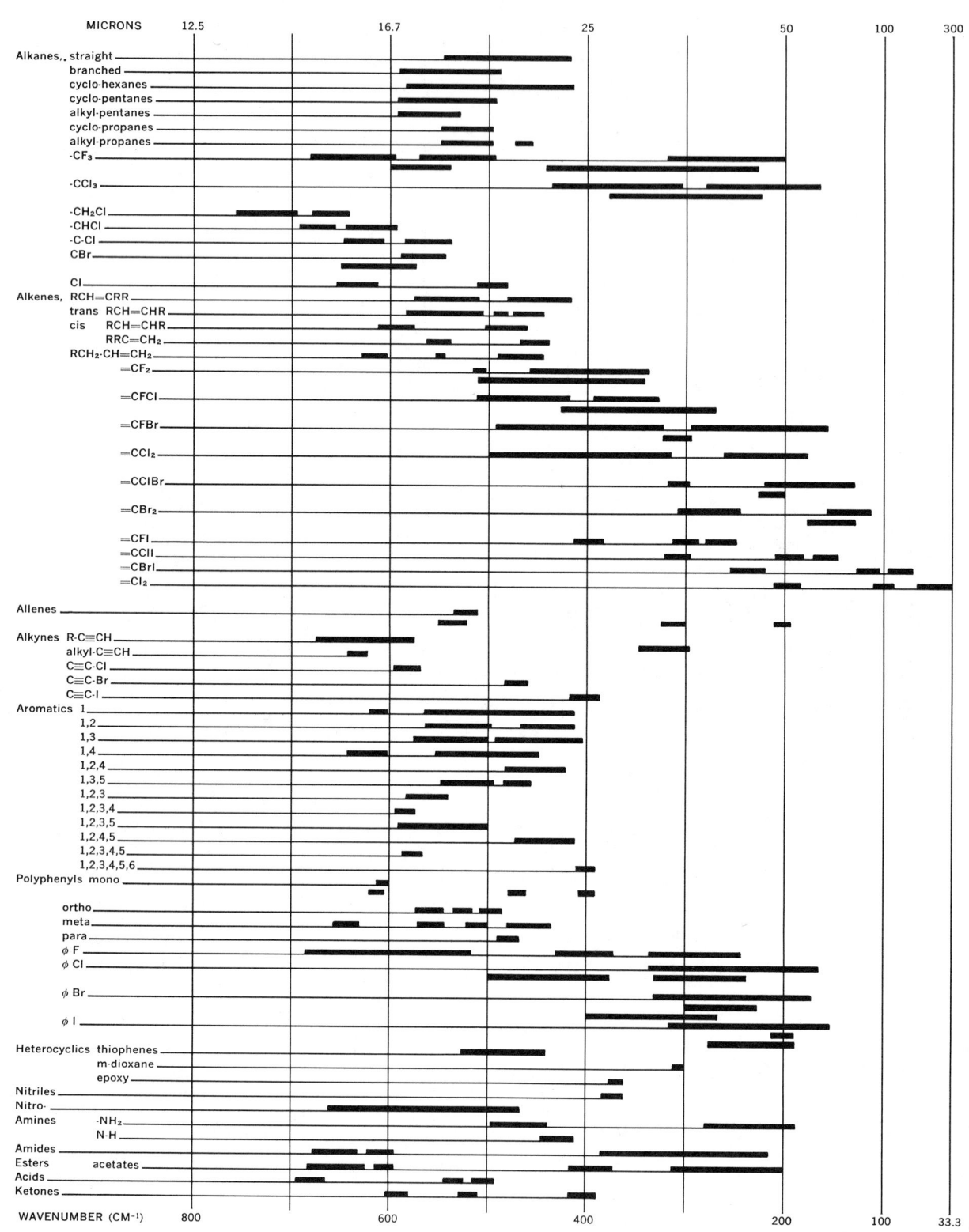

FAR INFRARED VIBRATIONAL FREQUENCY CORRELATION CHART (Con't.)

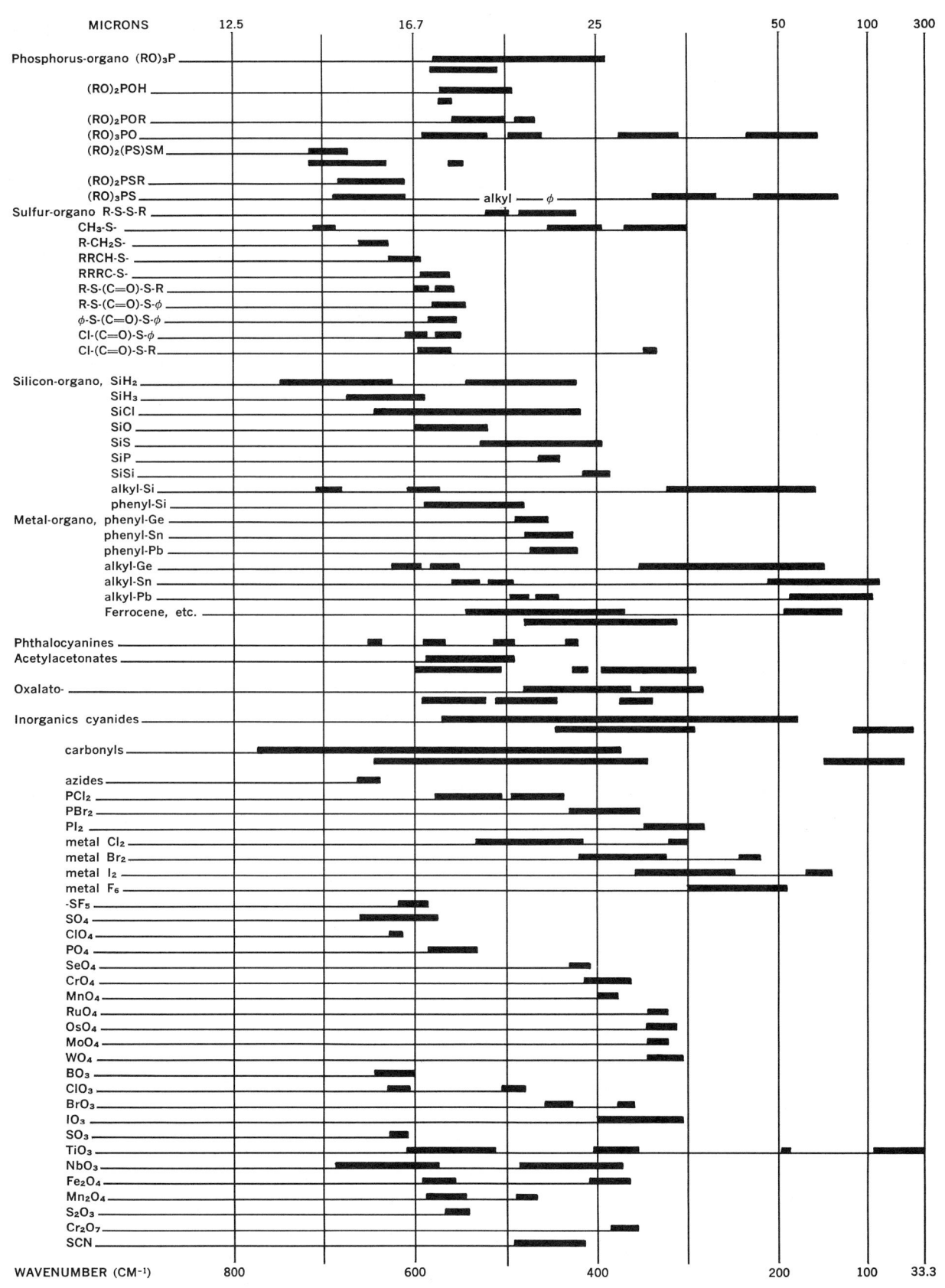

CHARACTERISTIC NMR SPECTRAL POSITIONS
FOR HYDROGEN IN ORGANIC STRUCTURES

By permission from Erno Mohacsi, J. of Chemical Education, 41, 38 (1964)

This table is useful for quick qualitative determination of proton spectrum lines by providing a tabulation of line positions obtained using tetramethylsilane as an internal reference. The listing has been kept as simple as possible for this purpose. The proton spectrum lines are arranged according to the chemical shift relative to tetramethylsilane and are given in values of τ and σ. The purpose of this table is to supplement tables available in standard references and to summarize information available in the literature.

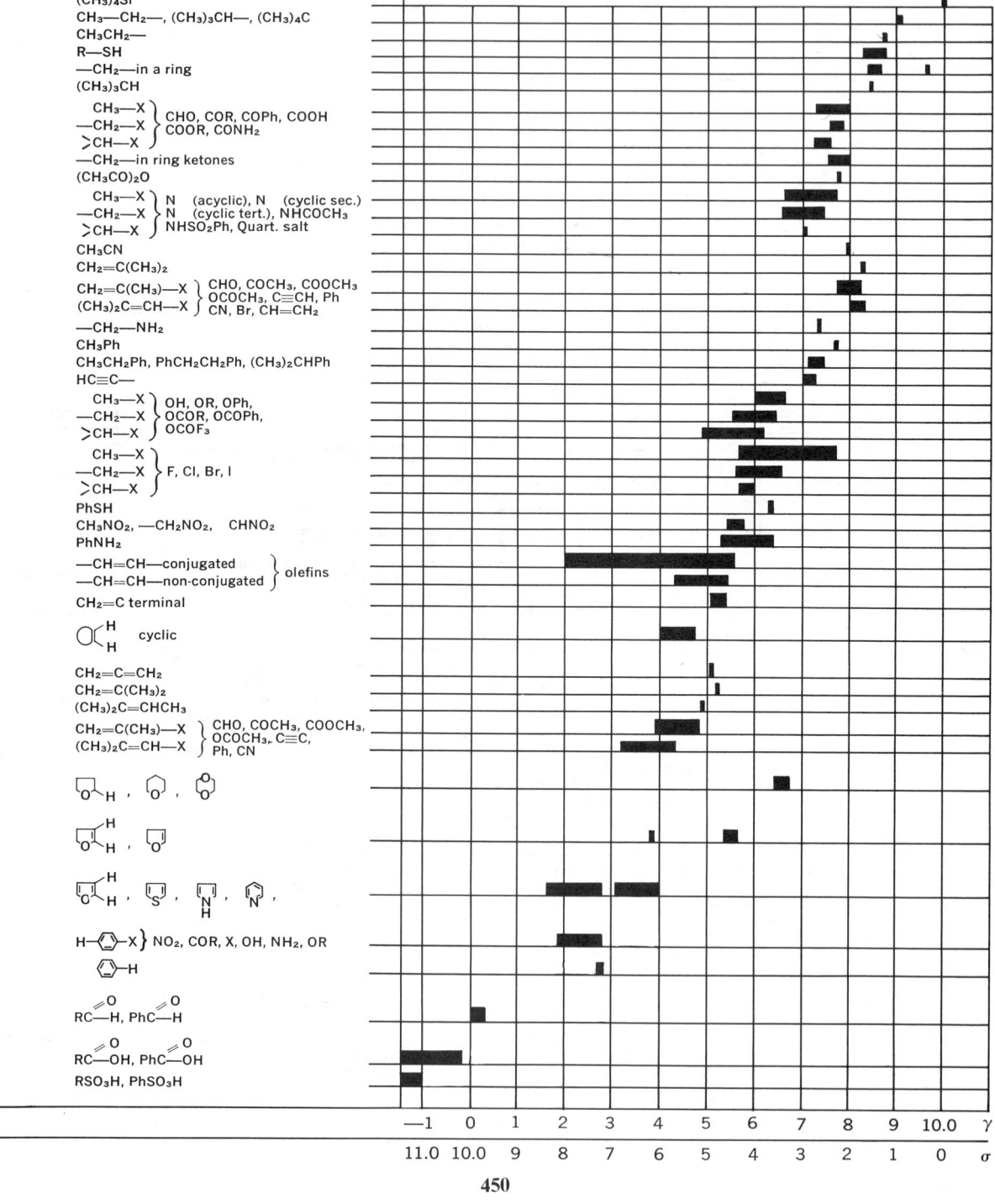

MISCIBILITY OF ORGANIC SOLVENT PAIRS

Table   A

Doctor J. S. Drury

Industrial and Engineering Chemistry   Vol. 44, No. 11, Nov. 1952

(Reprinted by permission)

The classifications were made by shaking together 5 ml. of each of the solvents listed in a test tube for 1 minute, then allowing the mixture to settle. If no interfacial meniscus was observed, the solvent pair was considered miscible. If such a meniscus was present, the solvent pair was regarded as immiscible. The classification of immiscible is a qualitative one since solvent pairs may exhibit some degree of partial miscibility while existing as separate phases. Solvent pairs possessing a pronounced degree of partial miscibility are designated by the symbol Is.

#	Compounds	Acetone	Acetyl acetone	2-Amino-2-methyl-1-propanol	Aniline	Benzaldehyde	Benzene	Benzin	Benzyl alcohol	Butyl acetate	Butyl alcohol	n-Butyl ether	Capryl alcohol	Carbon tetrachloride	Diacetone alcohol	Diethanolamine	Diethyl cellosolve	Diethyl ether	Dimethylaniline	Ethyl alcohol	Ethyl benzoate	Ethylene glycol	2-Ethylhexanol	Formamide	Furfuryl alcohol	Glycerol	Hydroxyethyl-ethylenediamine	Isoamyl alcohol	Methyl isobutyl ketone	Nitromethane	Dibutoxytetra-ethylene glycol	Pyridine	Triethanolamine	Trimethylene glycol
1	Acetone	..	M	M	..	M	M	M	M	M	M	M	M	M	M	M	M	M	M	M	M	M	M	M	M	I	M	M	M	M	M	M	..	M
2	Acetyl acetone	M	..	R	..	M	M	M	M	M	M	M	M	M	M	R	M	M	M	M	M	M	M	M	M	I	R	M	M	M	M	M	..	M
3	Adiponitrile	M	M	M	M	..	M	..	M	M	M	I	..	I	M	..	M	I	M	M	M	M	I	I	M	M	I	M	I	M	..	M	M	M
4	2-Amino-2-methyl-1-propanol	M	R	..	..	M	M	I	M	M	M	Is	M	M	R	M	M	M	M	M	M	M	M	M	M	M	M	M	M	M	M	M	..	M
5	Benzaldehyde	M	M	M	..	..	M	M	M	M	M	M	M	M	M	I	M	M	M	M	M	M	Is	M	M	M	Is	R	M	M	M	M	M	..	M
6	Benzene	M	M	M	..	M	..	M	M	M	M	M	M	M	M	Is	I	M	M	M	M	M	M	I	M	I	I	M	M	M	I	M	M	..	I
7	Benzin	M	M	I	..	M	M	..	I	M	M	M	M	M	I	I	M	M	M	M	M	M	I	M	I	I	Is	M	M	M	I	M	M	..	I
8	Benzonitrile	M	M	M	M	..	M	..	M	M	M	M	M	M	M	..	M	M	M	M	M	M	M	I	M	I	M	M	M	M	M	M	M	I
9	Benzothiazole	M	M	M	M	..	M	..	M	M	M	M	M	M	M	..	M	M	M	M	M	M	M	M	I	M	I	M	M	M	M	M	M	M
10	Benzyl alcohol	M	M	M	..	M	M	I	..	M	M	M	M	M	M	M	M	M	M	M	M	M	M	M	M	M	I	M	M	M	M	M	..	M
11	Benzyl mercaptan	M	M	I	M	..	M	..	M	M	M	M	M	M	M	..	M	M	M	M	M	M	M	M	I	M	I	M	M	M	M	M	R	M
12	Butyl acetate	M	M	M	..	M	M	M	M	..	M	M	M	M	M	M	I	M	M	M	M	M	M	Is	M	I	M	I	M	M	I	M	M	..	Is
13	Butyl alcohol	M	M	M	..	M	M	M	M	M	..	M	M	M	M	M	M	M	M	M	M	M	M	M	I	M	M	M	M	M	M	M	..	Is
14	n-Butyl ether	M	M	Is	..	M	M	M	M	M	..	M	M	M	M	I	M	M	M	M	M	M	I	M	I	I	M	M	M	I	M	M	..	I
15	Capryl alcohol	M	M	M	..	M	M	M	M	M	M	..	M	M	M	M	M	M	M	M	M	I	M	I	I	M	M	M	I	M	M	M	..	M
16	Carbon tetrachloride	M	M	M	..	M	M	M	M	M	M	M	..	Is	I	M	M	M	M	M	M	I	M	I	I	M	M	M	Is	M	M	M	..	M
17	Diacetone alcohol	M	M	R	..	M	Is	I	M	M	M	M	M	Is	..	M	M	M	M	M	M	M	M	M	M	M	I	R	M	M	M	M	M	..	M
18	Diethanolamine	M	R	M	..	I	I	I	M	I	M	I	M	I	M	..	I	I	Is	M	M	M	M	M	M	M	M	M	I	I	I	M	..	M
19	Diethyl Cellosolve	M	M	M	..	M	M	M	M	M	M	M	M	M	M	I	M	..	M	M	M	M	M	M	M	M	M	I	M	M	M	M	..	M
20	Diethyl ether	M	M	M	..	M	M	M	M	M	M	M	M	M	M	I	M	M	..	M	M	M	I	M	I	M	M	M	M	M	M	M	..	I
21	Dimethylaniline	M	M	M	..	M	M	M	M	M	M	M	M	M	M	Is	M	M	M	..	M	I	M	I	M	I	M	M	M	M	M	M	..	I
22	Di-N-propylaniline	M	M	I	M	..	M	..	M	M	I	M	M	M	M	M	M	M	M	..	M	I	M	I	M	I	M	M	M	M	I	I	I	I
23	Ethyl alcohol	M	M	M	..	M	M	M	M	M	M	M	M	M	M	M	M	M	M	M	..	M	M	M	M	M	M	M	M	M	M	M	..	M
24	Ethyl benzoate	M	M	M	..	M	M	M	M	M	M	M	M	M	M	..	M	M	M	M	..	I	M	I	M	I	M	M	M	M	M	M	..	Is
25	Ethyl isothiocyanate	M	M	R	M	..	M	..	M	M	M	M	M	M	M	..	M	M	M	M	M	M	I	M	I	R	M	M	M	M	M	M	M	M
26	Ethyl thiocyanate	M	M	M	..	M	M	M	M	M	M	M	M	..	M	M	M	M	M	M	M	I	M	I	M	M	M	M	M	M	M	M	M	I
27	Ethylene glycol	M	M	M	..	Is	I	M	M	M	Is	M	I	M	I	M	I	I	M	I	M	..	M	M	M	M	M	M	M	M	M	M	..	M
28	2-Ethylhexanol	M	M	M	..	M	M	M	M	M	M	M	M	M	M	M	M	M	M	M	M	I	..	I	M	M	M	I	M	M	M	M	..	M
29	Formamide	M	M	M	..	M	I	I	M	I	M	I	I	I	M	M	M	I	I	M	I	M	I	..	M	M	Is	M	M	M	..	M	..	M
30	Furfuryl alcohol	M	M	M	..	M	M	I	M	M	M	M	M	M	M	M	M	M	M	M	M	M	M	..	M	M	M	M	M	M	M	M	..	M
31	Glycerol	I	I	M	..	I	I	I	M	I	M	I	I	I	I	M	I	I	I	M	I	M	I	M	I	M	..	I	I	I	I	M	..	M
32	Hydroxyethyl-ethylenediamine	M	R	M	..	R	I	Is	M	I	M	I	M	I	R	M	I	I	I	M	M	M	M	M	M	M	..	M	M	M	M	M	..	M
33	Isoamyl alcohol	M	M	M	..	M	M	M	M	M	M	M	M	M	M	M	M	M	M	M	M	M	M	M	I	M	..	M	M	M	M	M	..	M
34	Isoamyl sulfide	M	M	I	M	..	M	..	M	M	M	M	M	..	M	M	M	M	M	I	I	I	I	M	I	M	M	M	..	M	M	I	R
35	Isobutyl mercaptan	M	M	M	..	M	..	M	M	M	M	M	M	M	M	M	M	M	M	I	M	I	M	I	M	M	M	M	..	M	M	R	R
36	Methyl disulfide	M	M	M	M	..	M	..	M	M	M	M	M	M	M	M	M	M	I	M	I	M	I	M	M	M	M	I	M	M	..	M	I	R
37	Methyl isobutyl ketone	M	M	M	..	M	M	M	M	M	M	M	M	M	M	I	M	M	M	M	M	I	M	Is	M	I	M	M	M	..	M	M	M	I
38	Nitromethane	M	M	M	..	M	I	M	M	M	M	I	Is	M	M	I	M	M	M	M	M	M	I	I	M	M	I	M	M	..	M	M	..	I
39	Dibutoxytetra-ethylene glycol	M	M	M	..	M	M	M	M	M	M	M	M	M	M	I	M	M	M	M	M	M	M	M	M	M	M	..	M	..	M	M	..	M
40	Pyridine	M	M	M	..	M	M	M	M	M	M	M	M	M	M	M	M	M	M	M	M	M	M	M	M	M	M	M	M	..	M	..	..	M
41	Tri-n-butylamine	M	M	I	I	..	M	..	M	M	M	M	..	M	I	..	M	M	M	M	I	M	I	M	I	M	M	..	M	I	I	M	I	I
42	Trimethylene glycol	M	M	M	..	M	I	I	M	Is	M	I	M	I	M	M	M	I	I	M	Is	M	M	M	M	M	M	M	I	I	M	M	..	..

MISCIBILITY OF ORGANIC SOLVENT PAIRS (Continued)

Tables B and C

W. M. Jackson and J. S. Drury

Reprinted from Vol. 51 pp. 1491 to 1493, December 1959.
Copyright 1959 by the American Chemical Society and reprinted by permission of the copyright owner.

The classifications were made at 20°C in the following manner. One-milliliter portions of each solvent comprising a pair were shaken together for approximately a minute. If no interfacial meniscus was observed after the contents of the tube were allowed to settle, the solvent pair was considered to be miscible, M. If a meniscus was observed without apparent change in the volume of either solvent, the pair was regarded as immiscible, I. This classification is a qualitative one, since solvent pairs may exhibit various degrees of partial miscibility while existing as separate phases. If an obvious change occurred in the volume of each solvent, but a meniscus was present, the pair was classified as partially miscible, S. The designation R indicates that the two solvents reacted.

Table B

Compound number	Compounds	Acetone	Isoamyl acetate	n-Amyl cyanide	Benzene	Benzyl ether	2-Bromoethyl acetate	Chloroform	Cinnamaldehyde	Di-n-amylamine	Di-n-butyl carbonate	Diethylacetic acid	Diethylenetriamine	Diethyl formamide	Diisobutyl ketone	Diisopropylamine	Di-n-propylaniline	Di-n-propyl aniline	Ethyl alcohol	Ethyl benzoate	Ethyl ether	Ethyl phenylacetate	Heptadecanol[a]	3-Heptanol	n-Heptyl acetate	n-Hexyl ether	Methyl isopropyl ketone	4-Methyl-n-valeric acid	o-Phenetidine	Sulfuric acid (concd.)	Tetradecanol[a]	Tri-n-butyl phosphate	Triethylene glycol	Triethylenetetramine	2,6,8-Trimethyl 4-nonanone	Compound number
1	Acetone	..	M	M	M	M	M	M	M	M	M	M	M	M	M	M	M	M	M	M	M	M	M	M	M	M	M	M	R	M	M	M	I	M	M	1
2	Isoamyl acetate	M	..	M	M	M	M	M	M	M	M	M	M	M	M	M	M	M	M	M	M	M	M	M	M	M	M	R	M	M	I	M	M	M		2
3	n-Amyl cyanide	M	M	..	M	M	M	M	M	M	M	M	M	M	M	M	M	M	M	M	M	M	M	M	M	M	M	R	M	M	M	I	M			3
4	Benzene	M	M	M	..	M	S	M	M	M	M	M	M	M	M	M	M	M	M	M	M	M	M	M	M	M	M	I	M	M	S	I	M	M		4
5	Benzyl ether	M	M	M	M	..	M	S	M	M	M	M	M	M	M	M	M	M	M	M	M	M	M	M	M	M	M	I	M	M	M	M	M			5
6	2-Bromoethyl acetate	M	M	M	S	M	..	M	M	M	R	M	M	R	M	M	R	M	M	M	M	M	M	S	M	M	M	R	M	M	M	R	M			6
7	Chloroform	M	M	M	M	M	M	..	M	M	M	M	R	M	M	M	M	M	M	M	M	M	M	M	M	M	M	R	M	M	M	I	M			7
8	Cinnamaldehyde	M	M	M	M	M	M	M	..	M	M	R	I	M	R	M	M	M	M	M	M	M	M	M	M	M	R	R	M	M	S	I	M			8
9	Di-n-amylamine	M	M	M	M	M	M	R	M	..	M	R	I	M	R	M	M	M	M	M	M	M	M	M	R	M	R	M	M	I	M	M	M			9
10	Di-n-butyl carbonate	M	M	M	M	M	R	M	M	M	..	M	M	M	M	M	M	M	M	M	M	M	M	M	M	M	R	M	M	I	I	M	M			10
11	Diethylacetic acid	M	M	M	M	M	M	M	R	R	M	..	R	M	R	R	M	M	M	M	M	M	M	M	M	M	R	M	M	M	M	R	M	I		11
12	Diethylenetriamine	M	M	M	M	M	R	M	R	I	M	R	..	M	R	R	M	M	M	M	M	M	M	R	I	R	R	R	R	M	M	R	M			12
13	Diethyl formamide	M	M	M	M	M	R	M	M	M	M	M	M	..	M	M	M	M	M	M	M	M	M	R	I	R	R	M	R	M	I	M	R	M		13
14	Diisobutyl ketone	M	M	M	M	M	M	M	R	R	M	R	R	M	..	M	M	M	M	M	M	M	M	M	M	M	R	M	M	I	M	M	M			14
15	Diisopropylamine	M	M	M	M	M	R	M	M	M	M	R	R	M	M	..	M	M	M	M	M	M	M	M	M	M	R	M	M	I	M	M	M			15
16	Di-n-propylaniline	M	M	M	M	M	M	M	M	M	M	M	M	M	M	M	..	M	M	M	M	M	M	M	M	M	R	M	M	I	M	M	M			16
17	Ethyl alcohol	M	M	M	M	M	M	M	M	M	M	M	M	M	M	M	M	..	M	M	M	M	M	M	M	M	M	M	R	M	M	M	M	M		17
18	Ethyl benzoate	M	M	M	M	M	M	M	M	M	M	M	M	M	M	M	M	M	..	M	M	M	M	M	M	M	M	M	R	M	M	M	I	M	M	18
19	Ethyl ether	M	M	M	M	M	M	M	M	M	M	M	M	M	M	M	M	M	M	..	M	M	M	M	M	M	M	M	R	M	M	I	M	M		19
20	Ethyl phenylacetate	M	M	M	M	M	M	M	M	M	M	M	M	M	M	M	M	M	M	M	..	M	M	M	M	M	M	M	R	M	M	I	M	M		20
21	Heptadecanol[a]	M	M	M	M	M	M	M	M	M	M	M	M	M	M	M	M	M	M	M	M	..	M	M	M	M	M	M	R	M	M	I	M	M		21
22	3-Heptanol	M	M	M	M	M	M	M	M	M	M	M	M	M	M	M	M	M	M	M	M	M	..	M	M	M	M	M	R	M	M	I	M	M		22
23	n-Heptyl acetate	M	M	M	M	M	M	M	M	M	M	M	R	M	M	M	M	M	M	M	M	M	M	..	M	M	M	M	R	M	M	I	R	M		23
24	n-Hexyl ether	M	M	M	M	M	S	M	M	M	M	M	I	I	M	M	M	M	M	M	M	M	M	M	..	M	M	M	R	M	M	I	R	M		24
25	Methyl isopropyl ketone	M	M	M	M	M	M	M	M	M	M	M	M	M	M	M	M	M	M	M	M	M	M	M	M	..	M	M	R	M	M	M	I	M		25
26	4-Methyl-n-valeric acid	M	M	M	M	M	M	M	M	M	R	M	R	R	M	M	R	M	M	M	M	M	M	M	M	M	..	M	R	M	R	R	R	M		26
27	o-Phenetidine	M	M	M	M	M	M	M	M	M	M	M	M	M	M	M	M	M	M	M	M	M	M	M	M	M	M	..	R	M	M	M	M	M		27
28	Sulfuric acid (concd.)	R	R	R	I	R	R	I	R	R	R	R	R	R	R	R	R	R	M	M	M	R	R	R	R	R	R	R	..	R	R	R	R	R		28
29	Tetradecanol[a]	M	M	M	M	M	M	M	M	M	M	M	M	M	M	M	M	M	M	M	M	M	M	M	M	M	M	M	R	..	M	M	M	M		29
30	Tri-n-butyl phosphate	M	M	M	M	M	M	M	M	M	M	M	M	M	M	M	M	M	M	M	M	M	M	M	M	M	R	M	R	M	..	I	M	M		30
31	Triethylene glycol	M	I	M	S	I	M	M	M	S	I	M	M	M	I	I	M	I	M	I	M	I	M	M	I	I	M	M	R	I	M	..	M	I		31
32	Triethylenetetramine	M	M	M	M	M	R	M	R	I	I	R	M	R	I	I	M	M	M	M	M	M	M	R	I	M	R	R	M	M	I	..	I		32
33	2,6,8-Trimethyl 4-nonanone	M	M	M	M	M	M	M	M	M	M	I	M	M	M	I	M	M	M	M	M	M	M	M	M	M	M	M	R	M	M	I	I	..		33

[a] Union Carbide name.

Compound number	Compounds	Acetone	Isoamyl acetate	n-Amyl cyanide	Anisaldehyde	Benzene	Benzyl ether	Chloroform	o-Cresol	Diisobutyl ketone	Diethylacetic acid	Diethyl formamide	Di-n-propyl aniline	Ethyl alcohol	Ethyl ether	3-Heptanol	n-Heptyl acetate	n-Hexyl ether	α-Methylbenzylamine	α-Methylbenzyldiethanolamine	α-Methylbenzyldimethylamine	α-Methylbenzylethanolamine	2-Methyl-5-ethylpyridine	Methyl isopropyl ketone	4-Methyl-n-valeric acid	o-Phenetidine	2-Phenylethylamine	Isopropanolamine	Pyridine	Salicylaldehyde	Tetradecanol	Tri-n-butyl phosphate	Triethylenetetramine	2,6,8-Trimethyl 4-nonanone
1	1,3-Butylene glycol	M	I	M	I	I	I	M	M	I	M	M	I	M	S	M	I	I	M	M	M	M	M	M	M	M	M	M	M	M	M	M	M	I
2	2,3-Butylene glycol	M	M	M	M	S	I	M	M	M	M	M	I	M	M	M	M	I	M	M	M	R	M	M	M	R	M	M	R	R	M	M	M	M
3	2-Chloroethanol	M	M	M	M	S	M	M	M	M	M	M	M	M	M	M	M	R	M	M	M	R	M	M	M	R	R	M	M	M	M	M	M	M
4	3-Chloro-1,2-propanediol	M	M	M	M	I	M	M	M	M	M	M	M	M	M	M	M	I	R	M	M	M	M	M	M	M	R	R	M	M	S	M	R	S
5	Dibutyl hydrogen phosphite	M	M	M	M	M	M	M	M	M	M	M	M	M	M	M	M	M	M	M	M	M	M	M	M	M	M	M	M	M	M	M	M	M
6	Diethylene glycol dibutyl ether	M	M	M	M	M	M	M	M	M	M	M	M	M	M	M	M	R	M	S	M	M	M	M	M	R	R	M	M	M	M	M	R	M
7	Diethylene glycol diethyl ether	M	M	M	M	M	M	M	M	M	M	M	M	M	M	M	M	M	M	M	M	M	M	M	M	M	M	M	M	M	M	M	M	M
8	Diethylene glycol monobutyl ether	M	M	M	M	M	M	M	M	M	M	M	M	M	M	M	M	M	M	M	M	M	M	M	M	M	M	M	M	M	M	M	M	M
9	Diethylene glycol monoethyl ether	M	M	M	M	M	M	M	M	M	M	M	M	M	M	M	M	I	M	M	M	M	M	M	M	M	M	M	M	M	M	M	M	M
10	Diethylene glycol monomethyl ether	M	M	M	M	M	M	M	M	M	M	M	M	M	M	M	M	M	M	M	M	M	M	M	M	M	M	M	M	M	M	M	M	M
11	Dipropylene glycol	M	M	M	M	M	M	M	M	M	M	M	M	M	M	M	M	I	M	M	M	M	M	M	M	M	M	M	M	M	M	M	M	M
12	Ethylene diacetate	M	M	M	M	M	M	M	M	M	M	M	M	M	I	M	I	I	M	M	M	M	M	I	M	M	M	M	M	I	I	S	M	I
13	Ethylene glycol	M	I	I	I	I	I	S	M	I	M	M	I	M	I	M	I	I	M	M	M	M	I	M	M	M	M	M	I	M	M	M	I	I
14	Ethyl glycol ethylbutyl ether	M	M	M	M	M	M	M	M	M	M	M	M	M	M	M	M	M	M	M	M	M	M	M	M	M	M	M	M	M	M	M	M	M
15	Ethylene glycol monobutyl ether	M	M	M	M	M	M	M	M	M	M	M	M	M	M	M	M	M	M	M	M	M	M	M	M	M	M	M	M	M	M	M	M	M
16	Ethylene glycol monoethyl ether	M	M	M	M	M	M	M	M	M	M	M	M	M	M	M	M	M	M	M	M	M	M	M	M	M	M	M	M	M	M	M	M	M
17	Ethylene glycol monomethyl ether	M	M	M	M	M	M	M	M	M	M	M	M	M	M	M	M	M	M	M	M	M	M	M	M	M	M	M	M	M	M	M	M	M
18	Ethylene glycol monophenyl ether	M	M	M	M	M	M	M	M	M	M	M	M	M	I	I	I	I	M	M	I	M	M	I	I	I	M	M	M	M	I	I	I	M
19	Glycerol	I	I	I	I	I	I	I	M	I	M	M	I	M	I	I	I	I	M	M	I	M	M	I	I	I	M	M	M	I	M	M	I	I
20	1,2-Propanediol	M	M	M	M	M	I	I	M	M	I	M	I	M	S	M	I	I	M	M	M	M	M	M	M	M	M	M	M	I	S	M	M	M
21	1,3-Propanediol	M	I	I	I	I	I	I	M	M	I	M	I	M	S	M	I	I	M	M	M	M	M	M	M	M	M	M	M	I	M	M	I	M
22	Triethylene glycol	M	I	M	M	S	I	M	M	I	M	M	I	M	I	M	I	I	M	M	M	M	M	M	M	M	M	M	M	M	M	I	I	M
23	Triethyl phosphate	M	M	M	M	M	M	M	M	M	M	M	M	M	M	M	M	M	M	M	M	M	M	M	M	M	M	M	M	M	M	M	M	M
24	Trimethylene chlorohydrin	M	M	M	M	M	M	M	M	M	M	M	M	M	M	M	M	R	M	M	M	R	M	M	M	R	R	M	M	M	M	M	R	M

ᵃ Union Carbide name.

EMERGENT STEM CORRECTION FOR
LIQUID-IN-GLASS THERMOMETERS

Accurate thermometers are calibrated with the entire stem immersed in the bath which determines the temperature of the thermometer bulb. However, for reasons of convenience it is common practice when using a thermometer to permit its stem to extend out of the apparatus. Under these conditions both the stem and the mercury in the exposed stem are at a temperature different from that of the bulb. This introduces an error into the observed temperature. Since the coefficient of thermal expansion of glass is less than that of mercury, the observed temperature will be less than the true temperature if the bulb is hotter than the stem and greater than the true temperature, providing the thermal gradient is reversed. For exact work the magnitude of this error can only be determined by experiment. However, for most purposes it is sufficiently accurate to apply the following equation which takes into account the difference of the thermal expansion of glass and mercury:

$$T_c = T_o + F \times L(T_o - T_m)$$

Where
T_c = corrected temperature

T_o = observed temperature

T_m = mean temperature of exposed stem. The mean temperature of the exposed stem may be determined by fastening the bulb of a second thermometer against the midpoint of the exposed liquid column.

L = the length of the exposed column in degrees above the surface of the substance whose temperature is being determined.

F = correction factor. For approximate work and when the liquid in the thermometer is mercury a value for F of 0.00016 is generally used. For more accurate work with mercury filled thermometers values as given in the following table are used. For thermometers filled with organic liquids it is customary to use 0.001 for the value of F.

Values of F for various glasses

$T_m°C.$	Corning 0041	Corning 8800	Corning 8810	Jena 16 III	Jena 59 III
50	0.000157	0.000166	0.000156	0.000158	0.000164
150	0.000159	0.000167	0.000157	0.000158	0.000165
250	0.000163	0.000168	0.000161	0.000161	0.000170
350	0.000168	0.000173	0.000166	. . . .	0.000177

CORRECTION OF BOILING POINTS TO STANDARD PRESSURE

By H. B. Hass and R. F. Newton

This correction may be made by using the equation:

$$\Delta t = \frac{(273.1 + t)(2.8808 - \log p)}{\phi + .15(2.8808 - \log p)} \tag{1}$$

where Δt = degrees C to be added to the observed boiling point.

t = the observed boiling point.

$\log p$ = the logarithm of the observed pressure in millimeters of mercury.

ϕ = the entropy of vaporization at 760 mm.

The value of ϕ may be estimated from the graph and the table. Substances not included in the table may be classified by grouping them with compounds which bear a close physical or structural resemblance to them.

Example 1. Benzene boils at 20°C. at 75 mm pressure. What is its normal boiling point? We do not find benzene in the table but we find hydrocarbons in group 2, and a group 2 compound with a boiling point of 20° has a ϕ of 4.6.

Substituting in the equation

$$\Delta t = \frac{(273.1 + 20)(2.8808 - 1.8751)}{4.60 + .15(2.8808 - 1.8751)} = 62°$$

Adding this to 20° gives 82° as a first approximation.

The graph shows that the ϕ for a compound of group 2 boiling at 82° is 4.72 instead of 4.60 which we originally used. Since ϕ is in the denominator, this increase will lower our Δt by the ratio, 4.60/4.72, or the corrected Δt is 62 × 4.60/4.72 = 60.4. Adding Δt to t, gives 80.4° as a second approximation.

The formula can best be used in a slightly different form when the reverse calculation is desired, i.e., when one calculates the vapor pressure at a given temperature, lower than the normal boiling point.

$$2.8808 - \log p = \frac{\phi \Delta t}{273.1 + t - .15 \Delta t} \tag{2}$$

Example 2. Alcohol boils at 78.4°C. What is its vapor pressure at 20°C.? Substituting in equation 2:

$$2.8808 - \log p = \frac{6.06 \times 58.4}{293.1 - (.15 \times 58.4)} = 1.245$$

$$\log p = 2.8808 - 1.245 = 1.6358$$

$$p = 43.2 \text{ mm.}$$

Here no second approximation is necessary, since the correct value of ϕ was taken immediately, the normal boiling point having been known.

Compound	Group	Compound	Group
Acetaldehyde	3	Benzyl alcohol	5
Acetic acid	4	Butylethylene	1
Acetic anhydride...........	6	Butyric acid	7
Acetone	3	Camphor....................	2
Acetophenone	4	Carbon monoxide	1
Amines......................	3	Carbon oxysulfide	2
n-Amyl alcohol	8	Carbon suboxide	2
Anthracene	1	Carbon sulfoselenide	2
Anthraquinone	1	m.p. Chloroanilines.........	3
Benzaldehyde	2	Chlorinated derivatives......	Same group as though Cl was H
Benzoic acid	5		
Benzonitrile.................	2	o.m.p. Cresols...............	4
Benzophenone	2	Cyanogen	4

CORRECTION OF BOILING POINTS (Continued)

Compound	Group	Compound	Group
Cyanogen chloride.............	3	Methyl benzoate.............	3
Dibenzyl ketone	2	Methyl ether	3
Dimethyl amine	4	Methyl ethyl ether	3
Dimethyl oxalate	4	Methyl ethyl ketone	2
Dimethyl silicane	2	Methyl fluoride	3
Esters	3	Methyl formate	4
Ethanol	8	Methyl salicylate	2
Ethers	2	Methyl silicane	1
Ethylamine	4	α,β Naphthols	3
Ethylene glycol	7	Nitrobenzene	3
Ethylene oxide	3	Nitromethane...............	3
Formic acid.................	3	o.m.p. Nitrotoluenes........	2
Glycol diacetate	4	o.m.p. Nitrotoluidines.......	2
Halogen derivatives	Same group as though halogen were hydrogen.	Phenanthrene	1
		Phenol	5
		Phosgene...................	2
Heptylic acid................	7	Phthalic anhydride	2
Hydrocarbons	2	Propionic acid	5
Hydrogen cyanide	3	n-Propyl alcohol............	8
Isoamyl alcohol..............	7	Quinoline	2
Isobutyl alcohol	8	Sulfides....................	2
Isobutyric acid...............	6	Tetranitromethane	3
Isocaproic acid	7	Trichloroethylene...........	1
Methane	1	Valeric acid	7
Methanol	7	Water	6
Methyl amine...............	5		

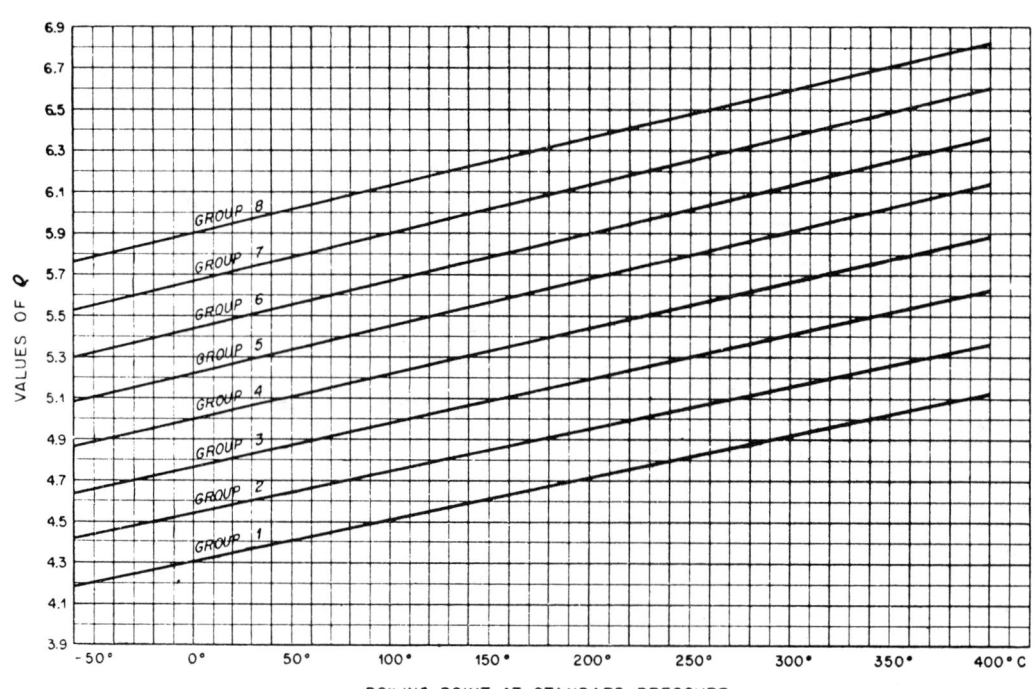

456

MOLECULAR ELEVATION OF THE BOILING POINT

(Most values from Hoyt, C.S. and Fink, C.K., Journal of Physical Chemistry, Vol. 41, No. 3., March, 1937.)
Molecular elevation of the boiling point showing the elevation of the boiling point in degrees C due to the addition of one gram molecular weight of the dissolved substance to 1000 grams of any one of the solvents below. The correction in the last column gives the number of degrees to be subtracted for each mm. of difference between the barometric reading and 760 mm.

Solvent	K_B	Barometric Correction per mm.
Acetic acid	3.07	0.0008
Acetone	1.71	0.0004
Aniline	3.52	0.0009
Benzene	2.53	0.0007
Bromobenzene	6.26	0.0016
Carbon bisulfide	2.34	0.0006
Carbon tetrachloride	5.03	0.0013
Chloroform	3.63	0.0009
Cyclohexane	2.79	0.0007
Ethanol (ethyl alcohol)	1.22	0.0003
Ethyl acetate	2.77	0.0007
Ethyl ether	2.02	0.0005
n-Hexane	2.75	0.0007
Methanol (methyl alcohol)	0.83	0.0002
Methyl acetate	2.15	0.0005
Nitrobenzene	5.24	0.0013
n-Octane	4.02	0.0010
Phenol	3.56	0.0009
Toluene	3.33	0.0008
Water	0.512	0.0001

MOLECULAR DEPRESSION OF THE FREEZING POINT

Showing the depression of the freezing point due to the addition of one gram molecular weight of solute, for various solvents.

Solvent	Depression for one gram molecular weight dissolved in 1000 grams, °C	Solvent	Depression for one gram molecular weight dissolved in 1000 grams, °C
Acetic acid	3.90	Diphenyamine	8.60
Acetophenone	5.65	Diphenyl ether	8.00
Aniline	5.87	Ethylene dibromide	11.80
Anthracene	14.65	Ethyl ether	11.79
Anthraquinone	14.80	Formic acid	2.77–2.80
Benzene	4.90–5.23	Hexachlorobenzene	20.75
Benzoic acid	7.85–8.79	Menthol	12.4
Benzophenone	9.88	Naphthalene	6.90–7.10
d-Bromocamphor	11.87	β-Naphthol	11.25
Bromoform	14.25	Nitrobenzene	6.89–7.10
$tert$-Butyl alcohol	12.80	Phenenthrene	12.0
Camphor	49.80	Phenol	7.20–7.50
Carbazole	12.30	Phenylhydrazine	5.86
Carbon disulfide	3.83	Pyridine	4.97
Carbon tetrachloride	29.8–34.8	Stearic acid	4.50
Chloroform	4.67–4.90	Triphenylmethane	12.45
Cyclohexane	20.0–20.30	Urethane	5.00–5.14
Dicyclohexyl	14.50	Water	1.85–1.87
m-Dinitrobenzene	10.60	p-Xylene	4.30
Diphenyl	8.00–8.35		

CARBOHYDRATES

These data for carbohydrates were compiled originally for the Biology Data Book by M. L. Wolfram, G. G. Maher and R. G. Pagnucco (1964). Data are reproduced here by permission of the copyright owners of the above publication, the Federation of American Societies for Experimental Biology, Washington, D.C. pp. 351–359.

All data are for crystalline substances, unless otherwise specified. Selection of substances was restricted to natural carbohydrates found free (or in chemical combination and released on hydrolysis) and to biological oxidation products of the natural carbohydrates. The nomenclature conforms with that of the British-American report as published in the *Journal of Organic Chemistry*, 28:281 (1963). Substances have been arranged alphabetically under the name of the parent sugar within groups formulated according to increasing carbon content (excluding carbon in substituents), with synonymous common names in parentheses. **Melting Point:** b.p. = boiling point; d. = decomposes; s. = sinters. **Specific Rotation** was determined in water at concentrations of 1–5 g per 100 ml. of solution and at 20°–25°C, unless otherwise specified; other temperatures or wavelengths are shown in brackets; c = grams solute per 100 ml of solution.

Part I. NATURAL MONOSACCHARIDES: ALDOSES AND KETOSES

	Substance (Synonym)	Chemical Formula	Melting Point °C	Specific Rotation $[\alpha]_D$
	(A)	(B)	(C)	(D)
		Aldoses		
1	D-Glyceraldehyde	$C_3H_6O_3$	....	+13.5 ± 0.5 (syrup)
2	D-Glyceraldehyde, 3-deoxy-3,3-*C*-bis-(hydroxymethyl)- (Cordycepose)	$C_5H_{10}O_4$	....	−26 (c 0.6, C_2H_5OH
3	D-Glyceraldehyde, 3,3-bis(*C*-hydroxymethyl)- (Apiose)	$C_5H_{10}O_5$	....	+5.6 (c 10) [15°] syrup
4	β-D-Arabinose	$C_5H_{10}O_5$	155	−175 → −103
5	D-Arabinose, 2-*O*-methyl-	$C_6H_{12}O_5$	Syrup	−102
6	α-L-Arabinose	$C_5H_{10}O_5$	158 amorphous	+55.4 → +105
7	β-L-Arabinose	$C_5H_{10}O_5$	160	+190.6 → +104.5
8	DL-Arabinose	$C_5H_{10}O_5$	163.5–164.5	None
9	α-L-Lyxose	$C_5H_{10}O_5$	105	+5.8 → +13.5
10	L-Lyxose, 5-deoxy-3-*C*-formyl- (Streptose)	$C_6H_{10}O_5$	....	....
11	L-Lyxose, 3-*C*-formyl- (Hydroxy-streptose)	$C_6H_{10}O_6$	....	....
12	Pentose, 4,5-anhydro-5-deoxy-D-*erythro*-	$C_5H_8O_3$	....	....
13	Pentose, 2-deoxy-D-*erythro*-	$C_5H_{10}O_4$	96–98	−91 → −58
14	D-Ribose	$C_5H_{10}O_5$	87	−23.1 → −23.7
15	D-Ribose, 2-*C*-hydroxymethyl- (Hamamelose)	$C_6H_{12}O_6$	....	−7.1 [λ578]
16	α-D-Xylose	$C_5H_{10}O_5$	145	+93.6 → +18.8
17	D-Xylose, 5-deoxy-	$C_5H_{10}O_4$	....	+16
18	β-D-Xylose, 2-*O*-methyl-	$C_6H_{12}O_5$	137–138	−21 → +34
19	α-D-Xylose, 3-*O*-methyl-	$C_6H_{12}O_5$	95	+45 → +19
20	D-Allose, 6-deoxy-	$C_6H_{12}O_5$	140–143 / 146–148	+1.6 [18°] (c 0.6) / −4.7 → 0
21	D-Allose, 6-deoxy-2,3-di-*O*-methyl- (Mycinose)	$C_8H_{16}O_5$	102–106	−46 → −29
22	Amicetose (a trideoxy hexose)	$C_6H_{12}O_3$	Oil, b.p. 65–70	+28.6 ($CHCl_3$)
23	Antiarose	$C_6H_{12}O_5$	....	Levo
24	α-D-Galactose	$C_6H_{12}O_6$	167	+150.7 → +80.2
25	β-D-Galactose	$C_6H_{12}O_6$	143–145	+52.8 → +80.2
26	D-Galactose, 3,6-anhydro-	$C_6H_{10}O_5$	....	+21.3 [10°]
27	α-D-Galactose, 6-deoxy- (D-Fucose; Rhodeose)	$C_6H_{12}O_5$	140–145	+127 → +76.3 (c 10)
28	D-Galactose, 6-deoxy-3-*O*-methyl- (Digitalose)	$C_7H_{14}O_5$	106[1], 119[2]	+106

	Substance (Synonym)	Chemical Formula	Melting Point °C	Specific Rotation $[\alpha]_D$
	(A)	(B)	(C)	(D)
	Aldoses (Con't)			
29	D-Galactose, 6-deoxy-4-O-methyl-	$C_7H_{14}O_5$	131–132	+82
30	D-Galactose, 6-deoxy-2,3-di-O-methyl-	$C_8H_{16}O_5$	....	+73
31	α-D-Galactose, 3-O-methyl-	$C_7H_{14}O_6$	144–147	+150.6 → +108.6
32	α-D-Galactose, 6-O-methyl-	$C_7H_{14}O_6$	122–123	+117 → +77.3
33	L-Galactose	$C_6H_{12}O_6$	....	*See* D-Galactose
34	α-L-Galactose, 3,6-anhydro-	$C_6H_{10}O_5$	....	−39.4 → −25.2
35	α-L-Galactose, 6-deoxy- (L-Fucose)	$C_6H_{12}O_5$	145	−124.1 → −76.4
36	L-Galactose, 6-deoxy-2-O-methyl-	$C_7H_{14}O_5$	149–150	−75 ± 4 (c 0.5)
37	L-Galactose, 6-sulfate	$C_6H_{12}O_9S$	....	−47 (c 0.2) (Na salt)
38	DL-Galactose	$C_6H_{12}O_6$	143–144, 163	None (racemic)
39	α-D-Glucose	$C_6H_{12}O_6$	146, 83 (H_2O)	+112 → +52.7
40	β-D-Glucose	$C_6H_{12}O_6$	148–150	+18.7 → +52.7
41	D-Glucose, 6-acetate	$C_7H_{14}O_7$	135	+48
42	D-Glucose, 2,3-di-O-methyl-	$C_8H_{16}O_6$	85–86, 121	+50
43	D-Glucose, 6-O-benzoyl- (Vaccinin)	$C_{13}H_{16}O_7$	Amorphous	+48 (C_2H_5OH)
44	α-D-Glucose, 6-deoxy- (Chinovose; Epirhamnose; Glucomethylose; Isorhamnose; Isorhodeose; Quinovose)	$C_6H_{12}O_5$	139–140	+73.3 → +29.7 (c 8)
45	α-D-Glucose, 6-deoxy-3-O-methyl- (D-Thevetose)	$C_7H_{14}O_5$	116	+84 → +33
46	D-Glucose, 6-sulfonic acid, 6-deoxy- (6-Sulfoquinovose)	$C_6H_{12}O_8S$	173–174	+87[3]
47	D-Glucose, 3-O-methyl-	$C_7H_{14}O_6$	162–167	+98 → +59.5
48	α-L-Glucose	$C_6H_{12}O_6$	141–143	−95.5 → −51.4
49	L-Glucose, 6-deoxy-3-O-methyl- (L-Thevetose)	$C_7H_{14}O_5$	126–129	−36.9 ± 2
50	D-Gulose, 6-deoxy-	$C_6H_{12}O_5$	....	....
51	Hexose, 2-deoxy-D-*arabino*-[4]	$C_6H_{12}O_5$	148	+46.6 [18°]
52	Hexose, 2,6-dideoxy-3-O-methyl-D-*arabino*- (D-Oleandrose)	$C_7H_{14}O_4$	....	−11
53	Hexose, 3,6-dideoxy-D-*arabino*- (Tyvelose)	$C_6H_{12}O_4$	....	+24 ± 2
54	Hexose, 2,6-dideoxy-3-O-methyl-L-*arabino*- (L-Oleandrose)	$C_7H_{14}O_4$	62–63	+11.9 ± 2.5
55	Hexose, 3,6-dideoxy-L-*arabino*- (Ascarylose)	$C_6H_{12}O_4$	....	−24 ± 2
56	Hexose, 2,6-dideoxy-3-O-methyl-D-*lyxo*- (Diginose)	$C_7H_{14}O_4$	90–92	+56 ± 4
57	Hexose, 2,6-dideoxy-L-*lyxo*- (L-Fucose, 2-deoxy-)	$C_6H_{12}O_4$	103–106	−61.6
58	Hexose, 2,6-dideoxy-3-O-methyl-L-*lyxo*-	$C_7H_{14}O_4$	78–85	−65
59	Hexose, 2,6-dideoxy-D-*ribo*- (Digitoxose; D-Altrose, 2,6-dideoxy-)	$C_6H_{12}O_4$	110	+46.4
60	Hexose, 2,6-dideoxy-3-O-methyl-D-*ribo*- (Cymarose)	$C_7H_{14}O_4$	93	+52
61	Hexose, 3,6-dideoxy-D-*ribo*- (Paratose)	$C_6H_{12}O_4$	....	+10 ± 2 (c 0.9)
62	Hexose, 4,6-dideoxy-3-O-methyl-D-*ribo*- (D-Gulose, 4,6-dideoxy-3-O-methyl-; Chalcose)	$C_7H_{14}O_4$	96–99	+120 → +76
63	Hexose, 2,6-dideoxy-D-*xylo*- (Boivinose)	$C_6H_{12}O_4$	96–98	−3.9 → +3.9

	Substance (Synonym)	Chemical Formula	Melting Point °C	Specific Rotation $[\alpha]_D$
	(A)	(B)	(C)	(D)

	Aldoses (Con't)			
64	Hexose, 2,6-dideoxy-3-O-methyl-D-xylo- (Sarmentose)	$C_7H_{14}O_4$	78–79	$+12 \to +15.8$
65	Hexose, 3,6-dideoxy-D-xylo- (Abequose)	$C_6H_{12}O_4$	....	-3.2 ± 0.6
66	Hexose, 2,6-dideoxy-3-C-methyl-L-xylo- (Mycarose)	$C_7H_{14}O_4$	129–129	-31.1
67	Hexose, 2,6-dideoxy-3-C-methyl-3-O-methyl-L-xylo-(Cladinose)	$C_8H_{16}O_4$	oil, b.p. 120–132 (0.25 mm)	-23.1
68	Hexose, 3,6-dideoxy-L-xylo- (Colitose)	$C_6H_{12}O_4$	....	$+4 (H_2O); -51 \pm 2$ (CH_3OH)
69	D-Idose[5]	$C_6H_{12}O_6$	....	....
70	L-Idose, 1,6-anhydro-	$C_6H_{10}O_5$	....	....
71	α-D-Mannose	$C_6H_{12}O_6$	133	$+29.3 \to +14.5$
72	β-D-Mannose	$C_6H_{12}O_6$	132	$-16.3 \to +14.5$
73	D-Mannose, 6-deoxy- (D-Rhamnose)	$C_6H_{12}O_5$	86–90	-7.0
74	α-L-Mannose, 6-deoxy-monohydrate (L-Rhamnose)	$C_6H_{14}O_6$	93–94	$-8.6 \to +8.2$
75	β-L-Mannose, 6-deoxy-	$C_6H_{12}O_5$	123–125	$+38.4 \to +8.9$
76	L-Mannose, 6-deoxy-2-O-methyl-	$C_7H_{14}O_5$	....	....
77	L-Mannose, 6-deoxy-3-O-methyl- (L-Acofriose)	$C_7H_{14}O_5$	114–115	$+30 [18°]$
78	L-Mannose, 6-deoxy-2,4-di-O-methyl-	$C_8H_{16}O_5$	82	$-19 [16°]$
79	L-Mannose, 6-deoxy-5-C-methyl-4-O-methyl-(Noviose)	$C_8H_{16}O_5$	128–130	$+19.9 (50\% C_2H_5OH)$
80	Rhodinose (a 2,3,6-trideoxyhexose)	$C_6H_{12}O_3$	....	-11 ± 1.6
81	D-Talose	$C_6H_{12}O_6$	128–132	$+16.9$
82	D-Talose, 6-deoxy- (D-Talomethylose)	$C_6H_{12}O_5$	129–131	$+20.6$
83	L-Talose, 6-deoxy- (L-Talomethylose)	$C_6H_{12}O_5$	116–118	$-19.5 \pm 2 [18°]$
84	L-Talose, 6-deoxy-2-O-methyl- (L-Acovenose)	$C_7H_{14}O_5$	....	-19.4
85	Heptose, D-glycero-D-galacto-	$C_7H_{14}O_7$	139–140	$+47 \to +64 (c\ 0.5)$
86	Heptose, D-glycero-D-manno-	$C_7H_{14}O_7$	....	....
87	Heptose, D-glycero-L-manno-	$C_7H_{14}O_7$	....	....

	Ketoses			
88	Dihydroxyacetone	$C_3H_6O_3$	80 (dimer)	None
89	Tetrulose, L-glycero-[8] (L-Erythrulose; Ketoerythritol; L-Threulose)	$C_4H_8O_4$	Syrup	$+12$
90	Pentulose, D-erythro- (Adonose; D-Ribulose)	$C_5H_{10}O_5$	Syrup	$+16.6 [27°]$
91	Pentulose, L-erythro- (L-Ribulose)	$C_5H_{10}O_5$	....	-16.6
92	Pentulose, D-threo- (D-Xylulose)	$C_5H_{10}O_5$	....	-33
93	Pentulose, 5-deoxy-D-threo-	$C_5H_{10}O_4$	....	$-5 \pm 1 (CH_3OH)$
94	Pentulose, L-threo- (L-Xylulose; L-Lyxulose; Xyloketose)	$C_5H_{10}O_5$	Syrup	$+33.1$
95	Hexulose, β-D-arabino-(β-D-Fructose; Levulose)	$C_6H_{12}O_6$	102–104[7]	$-133.5 \to -92$
96	Hexulose, 6-deoxy-D-arabino- (D-Rhamnulose)	$C_6H_{12}O_5$	....	-13 ± 2
97	Hexulose, D-lyxo- (D-Tagatose)	$C_6H_{12}O_6$	131–132	$+2.7 \to -4, -5$
98	5-Hexulose, D-lyxo	$C_6H_{12}O_6$	158	-86.6
99	Hexulose, 6-deoxy-L-lyxo- (L-Fuculose)	$C_6H_{12}O_5$	....	....

	Substance (Synonym)	Chemical Formula	Melting Point °C	Specific Rotation $[\alpha]_D$
	(A)	(B)	(C)	(D)

	Ketoses (Con't)			
100	Hexulose, D-*ribo*- (D-Psicose)	$C_6H_{12}O_6$	Amorphous	+4.7
101	Hexulose, L-*xylo*- (L-Sorbose)	$C_6H_{12}O_6$	159–161	−43.1
102	Hexulose, 6-deoxy-L-*xylo*-	$C_6H_{12}O_5$	88	−25 ± 2 (c 0.7)
103	Heptulose, D-*altro*- (Sedoheptulose; Sedoheptose)	$C_7H_{14}O_7$	Amorphous	+2.5 (c 10)
104	Heptulose·hemihydrate, L-*galacto*- (Perseulose)	$C_7H_{14}O_7 \cdot \frac{1}{2}H_2O$	110–115	−90 → −80
105	Heptulose, L-*gulo*-	$C_7H_{14}O_7$	....	−28
106	Heptulose, D-*ido*-	$C_7H_{14}O_7$	172	−34 ± 8 (c 0.3)
107	Heptulose, D-*manno*- (Mannoketoheptose; D-Mannotagatoheptose)	$C_7H_{14}O_7$	152	+29.4
108	Heptulose, D-*talo*-	$C_7H_{14}O_7$	....	....
109	Octulose, D-*glycero*-L-*galacto*-	$C_8H_{16}O_8$	....	−57, −43.4 → −13.4
110	Octulose, D-*glycero*-D-*manno*-	$C_8H_{16}O_8$	....	+20 (CH_3OH)

[1] Original melting point. [2] Melting point after four-months' storage. [3] As a methyl glycoside cyclohexylamine salt. [4] Included because of speculations concerning it in biological processes. [5] Either D-idose or L-altrose is in the polysaccharide varianose. [6] Early literature refers to this as D-erythrose. [7] The $\cdot\frac{1}{2}H_2O$ and $\cdot 2H_2O$ forms also exist.

Part II. NATURAL MONOSACCHARIDES: AMINO SUGARS

	Substance (Synonym)	Chemical Formula	Melting Point °C	Specific Rotation $[\alpha]_D$
	(A)	(B)	(C)	(D)

	Aldosamines			
1	D-Ribose, 3-amino-3-deoxy-	$C_5H_{11}NO_4$	158–158.5 d.	−24.6 (hydrochloride)
2	D-Galactose, 2-amino-2-deoxy- (Galactosamine; Chondrosamine)	$C_6H_{13}NO_5$	185	+121 → +80 (hydrochloride)
3	α-L-Galactose, 2-amino-2,6-dideoxy- (L-Fucosamine)	$C_6H_{13}NO_4$	192–193 d.	−119 → −92 [27°] (hydrochloride)
4	α-D-Glucose, 2-amino-2-deoxy- (Glucosamine; Chitosamine)	$C_6H_{13}NO_5$	88	+100 → +47.5
5	β-D-Glucose, 2-amino-2-deoxy-	$C_6H_{13}NO_5$	110–111	+28 → +47.5
6	D-Glucose, 3-amino-3-deoxy- (Kanosamine)	$C_6H_{13}NO_5$	128 d.	+19 [14°]
7	D-Glucose, 6-amino-6-deoxy-	$C_6H_{13}NO_5$	161–162 d.	+23 → +50.1 (hydrochloride)
8	D-Glucose, 2,6-diamino-2,6-dideoxy- (Neosamine C)	$C_6H_{14}N_2O_4$	>230	+61.5 (dihydrochloride)
9	D-Glucose, 3,6-dideoxy-3-dimethylamino- (Mycaminose)	$C_8H_{17}NO_4$	115–116	+31 (hydrochloride)
10	D-Glucose, 4,6-dideoxy-4-dimethylamino-	$C_8H_{17}NO_4$	192–193	+45.5 (hydrochloride)
11	L-Glucose, 2-deoxy-2-methylamino-	$C_7H_{15}NO_5$	130–132	−64
12	D-Gulose, 2-amino-1,6-anhydro-2-deoxy-	$C_6H_{11}NO_4$	250–260 d.	+41 ± 2 (hydrochloride)
13	D-Gulose, 2-amino-2-deoxy-	$C_6H_{13}NO_5$	152–162 d.	+5.6 → −18.7 (hydrochloride)

	Substance (Synonym)	Chemical Formula	Melting Point °C	Specific Rotation $[\alpha]_D$
	(A)	(B)	(C)	(D)
	Aldosamines (Con't)			
14	Hexose, 3,4,6-trideoxy-3-dimethyl-amino-D-*xylo*- (Desosamine; Pirocine)	$C_8H_{17}NO_3$	189–191 d.	+49.5 (*c* 10).(hydrochloride)
15	Hexose, a 4-acetamido-2-amino-2,4,6-trideoxy-	$C_8H_{16}N_2O_4$	216–219	+115 → +94 [26°] (*c* 0.05)
16	Hexose, an amino-deoxy-3-*O*-carboxyethyl-	$C_9H_{17}NO_7$	. . . .	. . . .
17	Hexose, a 2,6-diamino-2,6-dideoxy- (Neosamine B; Paramose)	$C_6H_{14}N_2O_4$	135–150 d.	+17.5 (*c* 0.9 (hydrochloride)
18	Hexose, a 3-dimethylamino-2,3,6-trideoxy- (Rhodosamine)	$C_8H_{17}NO_3$	. . . .	. . . .
19	D-Mannose, 2-amino-2-deoxy- (Mannosamine)	$C_6H_{13}NO_5$	142 d.	−4.3 (*c* 9) (hydrochloride)
20	D-Mannose, 3-amino-3,6-dideoxy- (Mycosamine)	$C_6H_{13}NO_4$	162	−11.5 (hydrochloride)
21	D-Talose, 2-amino-2-deoxy- (Talosamine)	$C_6H_{13}NO_5$	151–153	+3.4 → −5.7 (*c* 0.9) (hydrochloride)
22	L-Talose, 2-amino-2,6-dideoxy- (Pneumosamine)	$C_6H_{13}NO_4$	162–163	+6.9 → +10.4 (hydrochloride)
	Ketosamines			
23	Pentulose, 1-(*o*-carboxyanilino)-1-deoxy-D-*erythro*-	$C_{12}H_{14}NO_6$	. . . .	. . . .
24	Hexulose, 1-(*o*-carboxyanilino)-1-deoxy-D-*arabino*-	$C_{13}H_{16}NO_7$	. . . .	. . . .
25	Hexulose, 5-amino-5-deoxy-L-*xylo*-	$C_6H_{13}NO_5$	174–176	−62
26	Hexulose, 6-deoxy-6-(*N*-methyl-acetamido)-L-*xylo*-	$C_9H_{17}NO_6$	. . . .	. . . .

Part III. NATURAL ALDITOLS AND INOSITOLS (with Inososes and Inosamines)

	Substance (Synonym)	Chemical Formula	Melting Point °C	Specific Rotation $[\alpha]_D$
	(A)	(B)	(C)	(D)
	Alditols			
1	Glycerol	$C_3H_8O_3$	20	None
2	Glycerol, 1-deoxy- (1,2-Propane-diol)[1]	$C_3H_8O_2$	Oil, b.p. 188–189	None (racemic)
3	Erythritol	$C_4H_{10}O_4$	118–120	None (meso)
4	Erythritol, 1,4-dideoxy- (2,3-Butylene-glycol)	$C_4H_{10}O_2$	25, 34	None (meso)
5	D-Threitol, 1,4-dideoxy-	$C_4H_{10}O_2$	19	−13.0
6	L-Threitol, 1,4-dideoxy-	$C_4H_{10}O_2$	. . . .	+10.2
7	DL-Threitol, 1,4-dideoxy-	$C_4H_{10}O_2$	7.6	None (racemic)
8	D-Arabinitol	$C_5H_{12}O_5$	103	+7.82 (*c* 8, borax solution)
9	L-Arabinitol	$C_5H_{12}O_5$	101–102	−32 (*c* 0.4, 5% molybdate)
10	Ribitol (Adomitol)	$C_5H_{12}O_5$	102	None (meso)
11	Galactitol (Dulcitol)	$C_6H_{14}O_6$	186–188	None (meso)

	Substance (Synonym)	Chemical Formula	Melting Point °C	Specific Rotation $[\alpha]_D$
	(A)	(B)	(C)	(D)
	Alditols (Con't)			
12	D-Glucitol (Sorbitol)	$C_6H_{14}O_6$	112	−1.8 [15°]
13	D-Glucitol, 1,5-anhydro- (Polygalitol)	$C_6H_{12}O_5$	140–141	+42.4
14	L-Iditol	$C_6H_{14}O_6$	73.5	−3.5 (c 10)
15	D-Mannitol	$C_6H_{14}O_6$	166	−0.21
16	D-Mannitol, 1,5-anhydro- (Styracitol)	$C_6H_{12}O_5$	157	−49.9
17	Heptitol, D-glycero-D-galacto- (Heptitol, L-glycero-D-manno-; Perseitol)	$C_7H_{16}O_7$	183–185, 188	−1.1
18	Heptitol, D-glycero-D-gluco- (Heptitol, L-glycero-D-talo-; β-Sedoheptitol)	$C_7H_{16}O_7$	131–132	+46 (5% NH₄ molybdate)
19	Heptitol, D-glycero-D-manno- (Heptitol, D-glycero-D-talo-; Volemitol)	$C_7H_{16}O_7$	153	+2.65
20	Octitol, D-erythro-D-galacto-	$C_8H_{18}O_8 \cdot H_2O$	169–170	−11 (5% NH₄ molybdate)
	Inositols			
21	Betitol (a dideoxy inositol)	$C_6H_{12}O_4$	224	....
22	Bioinosose (scyllo-Inosose; myo-Inosose-2; a deoxy keto inositol)	$C_6H_{10}O_6$	198–200	None (meso)
23	h-Bornesitol (a myo-inositol monomethyl ether)	$C_7H_{14}O_6$	200	+31.6
24	l-Bornesitol (a myo-inositol monomethyl ether)	$C_7H_{14}O_6$	205–206	−32.1
25	Conduritol (a 2,3-dehydro-2,3-dideoxyinositol)	$C_6H_{10}O_4$	142–143	None (meso)
26	Cordycepic acid (a tetrahydroxycyclohexanecarboxylic acid)[2]	$C_7H_{12}O_6$	....	....
27	Dambonitol (a myo-inositol dimethyl ether)	$C_8H_{16}O_6$	206	None (meso)
28	DL-Inositol	$C_6H_{12}O_6$	253	None (racemic)
29	d-Inositol	$C_6H_{12}O_6$	....	+60
30	l-Inositol	$C_6H_{12}O_6$	240	−65
31	Laminitol (a C-methyl myo-inositol)	$C_7H_{14}O_6$	266–269	−3
32	Liriodendritol (a myo-inositol dimethyl ether)	$C_8H_{16}O_6$	224	−25
33	muco-Inositol monomethyl ether	$C_7H_{14}O_6$	322–325	....
34	myo-Inositol (meso-Inositol)	$C_6H_{12}O_6$	217–218	None (meso)
35	d-myo-Inosose-1 (a deoxy keto inositol)	$C_6H_{10}O_6$	138–139	+19.6
36	Mytilitol (a C-methyl scyllo-inositol)	$C_7H_{14}O_6$	259	None (meso)
37	neo-Inosamine-2 (a deoxy amino inositol)	$C_6H_{13}O_5N$	239–241 d.	None (meso)
38	d-Ononitol (a myo-inositol monomethyl ether)	$C_7H_{14}O_6$	172	+6.6
39	h-Pinitol (a dextro-inositol monomethyl ether)	$C_7H_{14}O_6$	186	+65.5
40	l-Pinitol (a levo-inositol monomethyl ether)	$C_7H_{14}O_6$	186	−65
41	l-Quebrachitol (a levo-inositol monomethyl ether)	$C_7H_{14}O_6$	190–191	−80.2 [28°]
42	d-Quercitol (a deoxy dextro-inositol)	$C_6H_{12}O_5$	235	+24.2
43	d-Quinic acid (a trideoxy carboxy dextro-inositol)	$C_7H_{12}O_6$	164	+44 (c 10)

Substance (Synonym)	Chemical Formula	Melting Point °C	Specific Rotation $[\alpha]_D$
(A)	(B)	(C)	(D)
		Inositols (Con't)	
44	*l*-Quinic acid (a trideoxy carboxy *levo*-inositol)	$C_7H_{12}O_6$	162	-42.1
45	Quinic acid, 5-dehydro-	$C_7H_{10}O_6$	140–142 (138 s.)	-82.4 [28°]
46	Scyllitol (*scyllo*-Inositol; Cocositol)	$C_6H_{12}O_6$	352–353	None (meso)
47	Sequoyitol (a *myo*-inositol monomethyl ether)	$C_7H_{14}O_6$	234–235	None (meso)
48	Shikimic acid (a 3,4-anhydro-quinic acid)	$C_7H_{10}O_5$	183–184	-200 [16°]
49	Shikimic acid, 5-dehydro-	$C_7H_8O_5$	150–152	-57.5 [28°] (EtOH)
50	Streptamine (2,4-diaminodideoxy-scyllitol)	$C_6H_{14}O_4N_2$	88, 210–250 d.	None (meso)
51	Streptamine, 2-deoxy-	$C_6H_{14}O_3N_2$	....	None (meso)
52	Streptadine (1,3-Dideoxy-1,3-diguanidino-scyllitol)	$C_8H_{18}N_6O_4$	....	None (meso)
53	Viburnitol (a deoxy *levo*-inositol)[3]	$C_6H_{12}O_5$	174	-73.9

[1] The 1-phosphate ester of this diol is said to occur in brain tissue and sea-urchin eggs. [2] Strong evidence that cordycepic acid is really D-mannitol. [3] Not an enantiomorph of *d*-quercitol; other isomeric relationship is involved.

Part IV. NATURAL ALDONIC, URONIC, AND ALDARIC ACIDS

Substance (Synonym)	Chemical Formula	Melting Point °C	Specific Rotation $[\alpha]_D$
(A)	(B)	(C)	(D)
		Aldonic Acids	
1	D-Glyceric acid	$C_3H_6O_4$	Gum	Dextro
2	L-Glyceric acid	$C_3H_6O_4$	Gum	Levo
3	D-Arabinonic acid	$C_5H_{10}O_6$	114–116	$+10.5$ (c 6)
4	L-Arabinonic acid	$C_5H_{10}O_6$	118–119	$-9.6 \rightarrow -41.7$[1]
5	L-Arabinonic-1,4-lactone	$C_5H_8O_5$	97–99	-72
6	D-Ribonic acid	$C_5H_{10}O_6$	112–113	-17.0
7	D-Xylonic acid	$C_5H_{10}O_6$	....	$-2.9 \rightarrow +20.1$[1]
8	L-Xylonic acid	$C_5H_{10}O_6$	....	-91.8[1]
9	D-Altronic acid	$C_6H_{12}O_7$	....	$+11.5 \rightarrow +24.8$[1] (Ca salt, N HCl)
10	D-Galactonic acid	$C_6H_{12}O_7$	122	$-11.2 \rightarrow +57.6$[1]
11	D-Gluconic acid	$C_6H_{12}O_7$	130–132 (110–112 s.)	$-6.7 \rightarrow +11.9$[1]
12	L-Gulonic acid	$C_6H_{12}O_7$	Exists only in soln.	[ca. 0°]
13	Hexsonic acid, 2-deoxy-D-*arabino*-	$C_6H_{12}O_6$	93–95	$+68$ (lactone)
14	2-Hexulosonic acid, D-*arabino*-	$C_6H_{10}O_7$	....	-81.7 (Na salt)
15	2-Hexulosonic acid, 3-deoxy-D-*erythro*-	$C_6H_{10}O_6$	....	-29.2 (c 6, Ca salt)
16	2-Hexulosonic acid, D-*lyxo*-	$C_6H_{10}O_7$	169	-5
17	5-Hexulosonic acid, D-*arabino*-	$C_6H_{10}O_7$	108–109	....
18	5-Hexulosonic acid, D-*xylo*-	$C_6H_{10}O_7$	....	-14.5
19	D-Mannonic acid	$C_6H_{12}O_7$	....	-15.6
20	D-Gluconic acid, O-β-D-galactopyranosyl- (1 → 4)- (Lactobionic acid)	$C_{12}H_{22}O_{12}$	....	$+25.1$ (Ca salt)

	Substance (Synonym)	Chemical Formula	Melting Point °C	Specific Rotation $[\alpha]_D$
	(A)	(B)	(C)	(D)
	Uronic Acids			
21	L-Lyxuronic acid	$C_5H_8O_6$	. . . .	. . . .
22	β-D-Galacturonic acid	$C_6H_{10}O_7$	160	$+27 \rightarrow +55.6$
23	α-D-Galacturonic acid·monohydrate	$C_6H_{12}O_8$	159–160 (110–115 s.)	$+97.9 \rightarrow +50.9$
24	D-Galacturonic acid, 2-amino-2-deoxy-	$C_6H_{11}O_6N$	160 d.	$+84.5$ (pH 2 HCl)
25	β-D-Glucuronic acid	$C_6H_{10}O_7$	156	$+11.7 \rightarrow +36.3$
26	D-Glucuronic acid, 2-amino-2-deoxy-	$C_6H_{11}O_6N$	120–172 d.	$+55$
27	D-Glucuronic acid, 3-O-methyl-	$C_7H_{12}O_7$	Syrup	$+6$
28	L-Guluronic acid	$C_6H_{10}O_7$	. . . .	. . . .
29	L-Iduronic acid	$C_6H_{10}O_7$	. . . .	$+30$
30	β-D-Mannuronic acid	$C_6H_{10}O_7$	165–167	$-47.9 \rightarrow -23.9$
31	α-D-Mannuronic acid·monohydrate	$C_6H_{12}O_8$	110 s., 120–130 d.	$+16 \rightarrow -6.1$ (c 6.8)
	Aldaric Acids			
32	D-Tartaric acid	$C_4H_6O_6$	170	-15
33	L-Tartaric acid	$C_4H_6O_6$	170	$+15$ [15°]
34	L-Malic acid	$C_4H_6O_5$	100	-2.3 (c 8.4)

[1] Equilibrates with the lactone.

These data for fats and oils were compiled originally for the Biology Data Book by H. J. Harwood, and R. P. Geyer. 1964. Data are reproduced here by permission of the copyright owners of the above publication, the Federation of American Societies for Experimental Biology, Washington, D.C. pp. 380–382.

Values are typical rather than average, and frequently were derived from specific analyses for particular samples (especially the constituent fatty acids). Extreme variations may occur, depending on a number

	Fat or Oil	Source	Constants				
			Melting (or Solidification) Point, °C	Specific Gravity (or Density)	Refractive Index $n_D^{40°}$	Iodine Value	Saponification Value
	(A)	(B)	(C)	(D)	(E)	(F)	(G)
	Land Animals						
1	Butterfat	*Bos taurus*	32.2	$0.911^{40°/15°}$	1.4548	36.1	227
2	Depot fat	*Homo sapiens*	(15)	$0.918^{15°}$	1.4602	67.6	196.2
3	Lard oil	*Sus scrofa*	(30.5)	$0.919^{15°}$	1.4615	58.6	194.6
4	Neat's-foot oil	*B. taurus*	....	$0.910^{25°}$	$1.464^{25°}$	69–76	190–199
5	Tallow, beef	*B. taurus*	....	....	....	49.5	197
6	Tallow, mutton	*Ovis aries*	(42.0)	$0.945^{15°}$	1.4565	40	194
	Marine Animals						
7	Cod-liver oil	*Gadus morhua*	....	0.925^{25}	$1.481^{25°}$	165	186
8	Herring oil	*Clupea harengus*	....	$0.900^{60°}$	$1.4610^{60°}$	140	192
9	Menhaden oil	*Brevoortia tyrannus*	....	$0.903^{60°}$	$1.4645^{60°}$	170	191
10	Sardine oil	*Sardinops caerulea*	....	$0.905^{60°}$	$1.4660^{60°}$	185	191
11	Sperm oil, body	*Physeter macrocephalus*	....	....	....	76–88	122–130
12	Sperm oil, head	*P. macrocephalus*	....	....	....	70	140–144
13	Whale oil	*Balaena mysticetus*	....	0.892^{60}	$1.460^{60°}$	120	195
	Plants						
14	Babassu oil	*Attalea funifera*	22–26	$(0.893^{60°})$	$1.443^{60°}$	15.5	247
15	Castor oil	*Ricinus communis*	(−18.0)	$0.961^{15°}$	1.4770	85.5	180.3
16	Cocoa butter	*Theobroma cacao*	34.1	$0.964^{15°}$	1.4568	36.5	193.8
17	Coconut oil	*Cocos nucifera*	25.1	$0.924^{15°}$	1.4493	10.4	268
18	Corn oil	*Zea mays*	(−20.0)	$0.922^{15°}$	1.4734	122.6	192.0
19	Cotton seed oil	*Gossypium hirsutum*	(−1.0)	$0.917^{25°}$	1.4735	105.7	194.3
20	Linseed oil	*Linum usitatissimum*	(−24.0)	$0.938^{15°}$	$1.4782^{25°}$	178.7	190.3
21	Mustard oil	*Brassica hirta*	....	$0.9145^{15°}$	1.475	102	174
22	Neem oil	*Melia azadirachta*	−3	$0.917^{15°}$	1.4615	71	194.5
23	Niger-seed oil	*Guizotia abyssinica*	....	$0.925^{15°}$	1.471	128.5	190
24	Oiticica oil	*Licania rigida*	....	$0.974^{25°}$	....	140–180	......
25	Olive oil	*Olea europaea sativa*	(−6.0)	$0.918^{15°}$	1.4679	81.1	189.7
26	Palm oil	*Elaeis guineensis*	35.0	$0.915^{15°}$	1.4578	54.2	199.1
27	Palm-kernel oil	*E. guineensis*	24.1	$0.923^{15°}$	1.4569	37.0	219.9
28	Peanut oil	*Arachis hypogaea*	(3.0)	$0.914^{15°}$	1.4691	93.4	192.1
29	Perilla oil	*Perilla frutescens*	....	$(0.935^{15°})$	$1.481^{25°}$	195	192
30	Poppy-seed oil	*Papaver somniferum*	(−15)	$0.925^{15°}$	1.4685	135	·194
31	Rapeseed oil	*Brassica campestris*	(−10)	$0.915^{15°}$	1.4706	98.6	174.7
32	Safflower oil	*Carthamus tinctorius*	....	$(0.900^{60°})$	$1.462^{60°}$	145	192
33	Sesame oil	*Sesamum indicum*	(−6.0)	$0.919^{25°}$	1.4646	106.6	187.9
34	Soybean oil	*Glycine soja*	(−16.0)	$0.927^{15°}$	1.4729	130.0	190.6
35	Sunflower-seed oil	*Helianthus annuus*	(−17.0)	$0.923^{15°}$	1.4694	125.5	188.7
36	Tung oil	*Aleurites fordi*	(−2.5)	$0.934^{15°}$	$1.5174^{25°}$	168.2	193.1
37	Wheat-germ oil	*Triticum aestivum*	....	....	....	125	......

[1] Caproic. [2] Capryli. [3] Capric. [4] Butyric. [5] Decenoic. [6] C_{12} monoethenoic. [7] C_{14} monoethenoic. [8] Gadoleic plus erucic. [9] C_{12} n-pentadecanoic. [10] C_{17} margaric. [11] 12-Methyl tetradecanoic. [12] C_{20} polyethenoic.

of variables such as source, treatment, and age of a fat or oil. **Specific Gravity** (column D) was calculated at the specified temperature (degrees centigrade) and referred to water at the same temperature, unless otherwise specified. **Density,** shown in parentheses (column D), was measured at the specified temperature (degrees centigrade). **Refractive Index** (column E) was measured at 50°C, unless otherwise specified.

Constituent Fatty Acids, g/100 g total fatty acids

| | Saturated | | | | | | Unsaturated | | | | |
| | Lauric | Myristic | Palmitic | Stearic | Arachidic | Other | Palmitoleic | Oleic | Linoleic | Linolenic | Other |
	(H)	(I)	(J)	(K)	(L)	(M)	(N)	(O)	(P)	(Q)	(R)
1	2.5	11.1	29.0	9.2	2.4	2.0[1]; 0.5[2]; 2.3[3]	4.6	26.7	3.6	....	3.6[4];0.1[5];0.1[6]; 0.9[7]1.4[8];1.0[9]; 1.0[10]; 0.4[11]
2	....	2.7	24.0	8.4	....	....	5	46.9	10.2	....	2.5[8]
3	....	1.3	28.3	11.9	....	....	2.7	47.5	6	....	0.2[7]; 2.1[8]
4	....	....	17–18	2–3	....	....	....	74–76	....	....	....
5	....	6.3	27.4	14.1	....	....	....	49.6	2.5	....	....
6	....	4.6	24.6	30.5	....	....	....	36.0	4.3	....	....
7	....	5.8	8.4	0.6	....	....	20.0	←—— 29.1 ——→		....	25.4[12]; 9.6[13]
8	....	7.3	13.0	Trace	....	....	4.9	....	....	20.7	30.1[12]; 23.2[13]
9	....	5.9	16.3	0.6	0.6	....	15.5	....	....	29.6	19.0[12]; 11.7[13]; 0.8[14]
10	....	5.1	14.6	3.2	....	....	11.8	←—— 17.8 ——→		....	18.1[12]; 14.0[13]; trace[7]; 15.4[15]
11	1	5	6.5	....	....	....	26.5	37	19	....	1[13]; 47; 19[16]
12	16	14	8	2	....	3.5[3]	15	17	6.5	....	4[6]; 14[7]; 6.5[16]
13	0.2	9.3	15.6	2.8	....	....	14.4	35.2	....	....	13.6[12]; 5.9[13]; 2.5[7]; 0.2[17]
14	44.1	15.4	8.5	2.7	0.2	0.2[1]; 4.8[2]; 6.6[3]	....	16.1	1.4	....	....
15	←——— 2.4 ———→						....	7.4	3.1	....	87[18]
16	....	....	24.4	35.4			....	38.1	2.1	....	....
17	45.4	18.0	10.5	2.3	0.4[19]	0.8[1]; 5.4[2]; 8.4[3]	0.4	7.5	Trace	....	....
18	....	1.4	10.2	3.0	....	....	1.5	49.6	34.3	....	....
19	....	1.4	23.4	1.1	1.3	....	2.0	22.9	47.8	....	....
20	....	....	6.3	2.5	0.5	....	....	19.0	24.1	47.4	0.2[11]
21	....	1.3[20]	....				....	27.2[20]	16.6[20]	1.8[20]	1.1[11]; 1.0[21]; 51.0[22]
22	....	2.6[20]	14.1[20]	24.0[20]	0.8[20]		....	58.5[20]	....	....	....
23	....	3.3[20]	8.2[20]	4.8[20]	0.5[20]		....	30.3[20]	57.3[20]	....	....
24	←——— 11.3[23] ———→						....	6.2	....	....	82.5[21]
25	....	Trace	6.9	2.3	0.1		....	84.4	4.6	....	....
26	....	1.4	40.1	5.5	....		....	42.7	10.3	....	....
27	46 9	14.1	8.8	1.3	....	2.7[2]; 7.0[3]	....	18.5	0.7	....	....
28	....	....	8.3	3.1	2.4	....	....	56.0	26.0	....	3.1[11]; 1.1[21]
29	←——— 9.6[23] ———→						....	17.8	....	17.5	....
30	....	....	4.8[20]	2.9[20]	....		....	30.1[20]	62.2[20]	....	....
31	....	....	1	....	....		....	32	15	1	50[22]
32	←——— 6.8[23] ———→						....	18.6	70.1	3.4	....
33	....	....	9.1	4.3	0.8	....	....	45.4	40.4	....	....
34	0.2	0.1	9.8	2.4	0.9	....	0.4	28.9	50.7	6.5	0.1[7]
35	....	....	5.6	2.2	0.9	....	....	25.1	66.2	....	....
36	←——— 4.6[23] ———→						....	4.1	0.6	....	90.7[25]
37	←——— 16.0[23] ———→						....	28.1	52.3	3.6	....

[13] C_{22} polyethenoic. [14] Behenic. [15] C_{14} polyethenoic. [16] Gadoleic. [17] C_{24} polyethenoic. [18] Ricinoleic. [19] Includes behenic and lignoceric. [20] Percent by weight. [21] Lignoceric. [22] Erucic. [23] Includes behenic. [24] Licanic. [25] Eleostearic.

WAXES

These data for waxes were compiled originally for the Biology Data Book by A. H. Warth. Data are reproduced here by permission of the copyright owners of the above publication, the American Societies for Experimental Biology, Washington, D.C. p. 382.

Specific Gravity (column C) was calculated at the specified temperature, degrees centigrade, and referred to water at the same temperature. **Density.** shown in parentheses (column C), and **Refractive Index** (column D) were measured at the specified temperature, degrees centigrade.

	Wax	Melting Point °C	Specific Gravity or (Density)	Refractive Index $n \frac{°C}{D}$	Iodine Value	Acid Value	Saponification Value
	(A)	(B)	(C)	(D)	(E)	(F)	(G)
1	Bamboo leaf	79–80	(0.961 25°)	. . . .	7.8[1]	14.5	43.4
2	Bayberry (myrtle)	46.7–48.8	(0.985 15°)	1.436 80°	2.9[2]–3.9[3]	3.5	20.5–21.7
3	Beeswax, crude	62–66	(0.927–0.970 15°)	1.439–1.483 40°	6.8–16.4[2]	16.8–35.8	89.3–149.0
4	Beeswax, white, U.S.P.	61–69	(0.959–0.975 15°)	1.447–1.465 65°	7–11[3]	17–24	90–96
5	Beeswax, yellow	62–65	(0.960–0.964 15°)	1.443–1.449 65°	6–11	18–24	90–97
6	Candelilla, refined	67–69	(0.982–0.986 15°)	1.454–1.463 85°	14.4–20.4	12.7–18.1	35–86
7	Cape berry[4]	40.5–45.0	(1.004–1.007 15°)	1.450 45°	0.6–2.4	2.5–3.7	211–215
8	Carandá	79.7–84.5	(0.990 25°)	. . . .	8.0–8.9	5.0–9.5	64.5–78.5
9	Carnauba	83–86	0.990–1.001 15°	1.467–1.472 40°	7.2–13.5	2.9–9.7	78–95
10	Castor oil, hydrogenated	83–88	(0.980–0.990 20°)	. . . .	2.5–8.5	1.0–5.0	177–181
11	Chinese insect	81.5–84.0	0.950–0.970 15°	1.457 40°	1.4	0.2–1.5	73–93
12	Cotton	68–71	0.959 15°	. . . .	24.5	32	70.6
13	Cranberry	207–218	(0.970–0.975 15°)	. . . .	44.2–53.2[2]	42.2–59.1	131–134
14	Douglas-fir bark	59.0–72.8	(1.030 25°)	1.468 80°	25.8–62.5	58.6–80.7	112–200
15	Esparto	67.5–78.1	0.988 15°	. . . .	22–23	22.7–23.9	69.8–79.3
16	Flax	61.5–69.8	0.908–0.985 15°	. . . .	21.6–28.8	17.5–48.3	77.5–101.5
17	Ghedda, E. Indian beeswax	60.5–66.4	0.956–0.973 15°	1.440 50°	5.6–12.6	5.8–7.9	84.5–118.3
18	Indian corn	80–81	. . . .	. . . .	4.2[2]	1.9	120.3
19	Japan wax	48–53	0.975–0.993 15°	. . . .	4.5–12.5	6–20	206.5–237.5
20	Jojoba	11.2–11.8	0.864–0.899 25°	1.465 25°	81.7–88.4[2]	0.2–0.6	92.2–95.0
21	Madagascar	88	. . . .	. . . .	3.2–5.3	17.7–28.0	140.0–159.6
22	Microcrystalline, amber	64–91	0.913–0.943 15°	1.424–1.452 80°	0	0	0
23	Microcrystalline, white	71–89	0.928–0.941 15°	1.441 80°	0	0	0
24	Montan, crude	76–86	(1.010–1.020 25°)	. . . .	13.9–17.6	22.7–31.0	59.4–92.0
25	Montan, refined	77–84	(1.010–1.030 25°)	. . . .	10–14	24–43	72–103
26	Orange peel	44.0–46.5	0.985 15°	1.502 20°	115.7[2]	48.3	120.9
27	Ouricury, refined	79.0–83.8	1.053 15°	. . . .	6.9–7.8[2]	3.4–21.1	61.8–85.8
28	Ozocerite, refined	74.4–75.0	0.907–0.920 15°	. . . .	0	0	0
29	Palm	74–86	(0.991–1.045 15°)	. . . .	8.9–16.9[2]	5.0–10.6	64.5–104.0
30	Paraffin, American	49–63	0.896–0.925 15°	1.442–1.448 80°	0	0	0
31	Peat wax, natural	73–76	0.980 15°	. . . .	16–40	60.0–73.3	73.9–136.0
32	Rice bran, refined	75.3–79.9	. . . .	1.469 30°	11.1–19.4	15–17	56.9–104.4
33	Shellac wax	79–82	0.971–0.980 15°	. . . .	6.0–8.8[3]	12.1–24.3	63.8–83.0
34	Sisal hemp	74–81	1.007–1.010 15°	. . . .	28–29[2]	16–19[2]	56–58
35	Sorghum grain	77–82	. . . .	. . . .	15.7–20.9	10.1–16.2	16–44
36	Spanish moss	79–80	. . . .	. . . .	33.0	25.0	120.4
37	Spermaceti	42–50	0.905–0.945 15°	1.440 70°	4.8–5.9	2.0–5.2	108–134
38	Sugarcane, crude	52–67	0.988–0.998 25°	. . . .	32–84	24–57	128–177
39	Sugarcane, double-refined	77–82	0.961–0.979 25°	1.510 25°	13–29	8–23	55–95
40	Wool wax, refined	36–43	0.932–0.945 15°	1.478–1.482 40°	15.0–46.9	5.6–22.0	80–127

[1] Wijs test. [2] Hanus test. [3] Hubl test. [4] *Myrica cordifolia*.

DIAMAGNETIC SUSCEPTIBILITIES OF ORGANIC COMPOUNDS

Compiled by George W. Smith

The following table contains values for the molar susceptibility of χ_M, specific susceptibility χ, and volumetric susceptibility K. The cgs Gaussian system of units is employed. In the Gaussian units the relation between magnetic induction B and magnetic field strength H is

$$B = H + 4\pi I \qquad (1)$$

where I is the magnetization or magnetic moment per unit volume. Actually, the quantities involved in equation (1) are all vectors, but one may assume that all three are collinear, a reasonable assumption for organic diamagnetic substances in the liquid state. For crystals I may vary with crystal orientation. Equation (1) may be rewritten

$$B = H + 4\pi KH = (I + 4\pi K)H \qquad (2)$$

Here, K is the magnetic susceptibility, often called the volumetric susceptibility and is a unitless quantity.

Other susceptibilities of use to chemists and physicists are the specific or mass susceptibility which is defined

$$\chi = K/\rho \qquad (3)$$

where ρ is the density of the sample in grams per cc., and the molar susceptibility which is defined as

$$\chi_M = M\chi = MK/\rho \qquad (4)$$

where M is the molecular weight of the substance in grams.

Temperatures, when listed, are enclosed in parentheses and are listed in degrees C.

Literature references for values contained in this table may be found in General Motors Research Laboratories publication GMR-317.

Compound	$-\chi_M \times 10^6$	$-\chi \times 10^6$	$-K \times 10^6$	Compound	$-\chi_M \times 10^6$	$-\chi \times 10^6$	$-K \times 10^6$
Acenaphthanthracene	184	.73		Amyl iodide	(118.7)	.5996 (18°)	(.910) (20°)
Acenaphthene	109.3	(.709)	(.726) (99°)	n-Amyl methyl ketone	80.50	.705₃	(.580) (15°)
Acetal	81.39	.688 (32°)	(.568) (32°)	Amyl nitrate	(76.4)	.574	
Acetaldehyde	22.70	.515₃	(.403) (18°)	iso-Amyl propionate	101.73	705₁ (25°)	(.609) (25°)
Acetamide	34.1	.577	(.618) (20°)	n-Amyl valerate	124.55	.723₉	(.638) (0°)
Acetic acid	31.54	.525 (32°)	(.551) (32°)	Anethole	(96.0)	.648	(.644) (15°)
Acetic anhydride	(52.8)	.517	(.562) (15°)	Aniline	62.95	(.676)	(.691) (20°)
Acetoaminofluorene	(141)	.63		Anisidine	(80.5)	.654	(.72) (20°)
Acetone	33.7₈	.581₁	(.460) (20°)	Anisole	72.79	(.673)	(.672) (15°)
Acetonitrile	28.0	(.682)	(.534) (20°)	Anthanthrene	204.2	.739	
Acetonylacetone	62.51	.547₆	(.531) (20°)	Anthanthrone	178.1	.581	
Acetophenone	72.05	.599₈	(.615) (20°)	Anthracene	(130)	.731	(.914) (27°)
Acetophenone oxime	79.9₀	.592₀		Anthracenedinitrile	154.6	(.678)	
Acetophenone oxime-O-methyl ether	92 3₁	.618₈		Anthracenonitrile	142.1	(.700)	
Acetoxime	44.4₂	607₆	(.480) (20°)	Anthraquinone	(119.6)	.575	(.825) (20°)
Acetoxime-O-benzyl ether	104.8₉	.642₇		Anthrazine	245.7	.646	
Acetoxime-O-methyl-ether	54.8₇	.629₈		Arabinose	85.70	.571	(.905) (20°)
Acetylacetone	54.88	.548₁	(.535) (20°)	Arbutoside	158.0	(.589)	
Acetyl chloride	38.9	.496	(.548) (20°)	Asarone	131.4	(.631)	(.735) (18°)
Acetylene	12.5	(.480)		Asparagine	69.5	(.526)	(.812) (15°)
Acetylphenylacetylene	86.9	.508		Aspartic acid	64.2 ± .4	(.482)	(.800) (12°)
Acetylthiophene	71.7	(.568)		Aurin	(161.4)	.556	
Acridine	(123.3)	.688	(.757) (20°)	p-Azoanisole	(147.7)	.610	
Adonitol	91.30	.600		Azobenzene	(106.8)	.586	.611 (70.5°)
Alanine	50.5	(.567)		p-Azophenetole	(171.7)	.635	
Allyl acetate	(56.7)	.566	(.525) (20°)	m-Azotoluene	(127.8)	.608	.643 (58°)
Allyl alcohol	36.70	.632	.540 (20°)	Azulene	98.5	.768	
1-Allylpyrrole	73.80	.685 (20°)		Barbituric acid (Anh.)	53.8	(.420)	
Aminoazobenzene	(118.3)	.600		Barbituric acid (.2H₂O)	78.6	(4.79)	
Aminoazotoluene	(142.2)	.631		Benzalazine	(123.7)	.594	
o-Aminoazotoluene	(138)	.61 ± .02		Benzaldehyde	60.78	(.573)	(.602) (15°)
α-Aminobutyric acid	62.1	(.602)		Benzaldoxime	(69.8)	.576	(.639) (20°)
Aminomethyldiethyldiazine	114.8	(.696)		Benzamide	(72.3)	.597	(.801) (4°)
4-Aminostilbene	122.5	(.628)		Benzanthrone	142.9	.620	
2-Aminothiazole	56.0	.564		Benzene	54.84	.702 (32°)	.611
n-Amyl acetate	89.06	684₅	.5979 (20.7°)	Benzidine	110.9	.603	(.754) (20°)
iso-Amyl acetate	89.40	.687	.599 (20°)	Benzil	(118.6)	.564	.616 (100°)
n-Amyl alcohol	(67.5)	.766	(.624) (20°)	Benzoic acid	70.28	(.575)	(.728) (15°)
γ-Amyl alcohol	(71.0)	.8060	(.655) (25°)	Benzoic anhydride	(124.9)	.552	(.662) (15°)
Inactive Amyl alcohol	69.06	783₅ (25°)		Benzonitrile	65.19	(.632)	(.638) (15°)
iso-Amyl alcohol	68.96	.782₃ (25°)	(.64) (15°)	Benzophenone	109.60	.601₃	(.66) (50°)
sec-Amyl alcohol	69.1	.785	(.635) (20°)	3,4-Benzopyrene	135.7	.538	
tert-Amyl alcohol	(70.9)	.804	(.654) (15°)	Benzopyrene	194.0		
n-Amylamine	69.4	(.796)	(.606) (20°)	Benzoyl acetone	(95.0)	.586	(.639) (60°)
iso-Amylamine	71.6	(.821)	(.616) (20°)	Benzoyl chloride	(75.8)	.539 (20°)	(.657) 15°)
n-Amylbenzene	112.55	(.759)	(.652) (20°)	Benzyl acetate	93.18	(.620)	(.655) (16°)
iso-Amyl bromide	(88.7)	.587	(.706) ₁20°)	Benzyl alcohol	71.83	(.664)	(.697) (15°)
iso-Amyl-n-butyrate	113.52	.717₄ (25°)	(.616) (25°)	Benzylamine	75.26	(.702)	(.690) (19°)
iso-Amyl chloride	(79.0)	.741	(.662) (20°)	Benzyl chloride	81.98	(.647)	(.713) (18°)
iso-Amyl cyanide	73.4	(.755)	(.609) (20°)	Benzyl formate	81.43	(.598)	(.646) (20°)
iso-Amylene	53.7	.766		Benzylideneaniline	(100.4)	.554	
Amylene bromide	(114.5)	.498		Benzylidene chloride	(97.9)	.608	(.763) (14°)
Amylene chloride	(95.2)	.675		Benzylidenemethylamine	(73.1)	.613	
iso-Amyl ether	(129)	.813	(.635) (15°)	Benzyl methyl ketone	83.44	.621₉	(.624) (20°)
iso-Amyl formate	78.38	.674₈	(.591) (25°)	Bibenzyl	(126.8)	.696	.671 (54.5°)
Amylidene chloride	(93.4)	.662					

Compound	$-\chi_M \times 10^6$	$-\chi \times 10^6$	$-K \times 10^6$	Compound	$-\chi_M \times 10^6$	$-\chi \times 10^6$	$-K \times 10^6$
3,4-Bis-(p-hydroxyphenyl)-2,4-hexadiene	(157)	.59		Chlorofumaric acid	67.02	(.445)	
m,m'-Bitolyl	(127.4)	.6993 (27.4°)	(.699) (16°)	p-Chloroiodo benzene	99.42	(.417)	(.786) (57°)
m,m'-Bitolyl sulfide	(140.0)	.6530 (27.4°)		Chloromaleic acid	67.36	(.448)	
Borneol	126.0	(.817)	(.826) (20°)	Chloromethylstilbene	144.8	(.633)	
Bromobenzene	78.92	.5030 (20°)	(.753) (20°)	α-Chloronaphthalene	107.60	.661	.789 (20°)
Bromobenzenediazocyanide	86.88	(.414)		m-Chloronitrobenzene	(74.8)	.475	.638 (48°)
Bromochloromethane	55.0 ± .6	(.425)	(.846) (19°)	o-Chlorophenol	77.4	(.602)	(.747) (18°)
Bromodichloromethane	66.3 ± .3	(.405)	(.812) (15°)	p-Chlorophenol	77.6	(.604)	(.789) (20°)
Bromoform	82.60	.327	.948 (20°)	1-(o-Chlorophenylazo)-2-napthol	161.0	(.570)	
Bromonaphthalene	(123.8)	.598		1-(p-Chlorophenylazo)-2-napthol	161.4	(.571)	
α-Bromonaphthalene	115.90	.560	.840 (20°)	Chlorotrifluoroethylene	49.1	.422	
m-Bromotoluene	(93.4)	.546	(.770) (20°)	Chlorotrifluoromethane	45.3 ± 1.5	(.434)	
Bromotrichloromethane	73.1 ± .7	(.369)	(.758) (0°)	Cholesterol	(284.2)	.735	(.784) (20°)
Butane	57.4	(.988)		Chrysene	166.67	.731	
iso-Butane	51.7	(.890)		Chrysoidine	(126.3)	.595	
1,4-Butanediol	61.5	(.682)	(.696) (20°)	Cinnamic acid	78.36	.529	(.660) (4°)
2-Butene (cis)	42.6	(.759)		Cinnamic acid (α-trans)	78.2	(.528)	
2-Butene (trans)	43.3	(.772)		Cinnamic acid (β-trans)	79.0	(.533)	
1-Butene-3,4-diacetate	95.5	(.555)		Cinnamic acid (cis-MP 68°)	77.6	(.524)	
2-Butene-1,4-diacetate (cis)	95.2	(.553)		Cinnamic acid (cis-MP 58°)	77.9	(.526)	
2-Butene-1,4-diacetate (trans)	95.1	(.552)		Cinnamic acid (cis-MP 42°)	83.2	(.562)	
2-Butene-1,4-diol (cis)	54.3	(.616)		Cinnamic aldehyde	(74.8)	.566	(.629) (15°)
2-Butene-1,4-diol (trans)	53.5	(.607)		Cinnamyl alcohol	(87.2)	.650	(.679) (20°)
n-Butyl acetate	77.47	.666₉ (25°)	(.583) (25°)	Cinnamylideneaniline	123.2	(.595)	
iso-Butyl acetate	78.52	.676₉	(.584) (25°)	Citral	(98.9)	.650	(.577) (20°)
n-Butyl alcohol	56.536 (20°)	.7627	(.6176) (20°)	Coronene	(243.3)	.810	
iso-Butyl alcohol	57.704 (20°)	(.7785)	(.624) (20°)	Coumarin	82.5	(.565)	(.528) (20°)
sec-Butyl alcohol	57.683 (20°)	(.7782)	(.629) (20°)	o-Cresol	72.90	.675	(.706) (20°)
tert-Butyl alcohol	57.42	.774₇ (25°)	(.611) (20°)	m-Cresol	72.02	.667 (26°)	(.690) (20°)
n-Butylamine	58.9	(.805)	(.596) (20°)	p-Cresol	72.1	.667 (26°)	(.690) (20°)
iso-Butylamine	59.8	(.818)	(.599) (20°)	o-Cresylmethyl ether	81.94	.671 (40°)	(.661) (15°)
9-Butyl anthracene	176.0	(.751)		m-Cresylmethyl ether	77.91	.638 (40°)	(.623) (15°)
n-Butylbenzene	100.79	(.751)	(.646) (20°)	p-Cresylmethyl ether	79.13	.648 (40°)	(.629) (19°)
iso-Butylbenzene	101.81	(.759)	(.648) (20°)	Cumene	89.53	.744₉	(.642)
tert-Butylbenzene	102.5	(.764)	(.662) (20°)	Cyamelide	(56.1)	.435	(.490) (15°)
n-Butyl benzoate	116.69	.654₈	(.656) (25°)	Cyameluric acid	101.1 (10°)	(.457)	
Butyl bromide	77.14	.563 (20°)	(.730) (20°)	9-Cyanoanthracene	142.1	(.699)	
iso-Butyl bromide	79.88	.583 (20°)	(.737) (20°)	Cyanogen	(21.6)	.415	(.359) (liq., 17°)
1-n-Butyl chloride	67.10	.725	.642 (20°)	Cyanuric acid	61.5	.476	(.842) (0°)
2-n-Butyl chloride	67.40	.728	.635 (20°)	Cyclobutanecarboxylic acid	58.16	.5816 (30°)	(.613) (30°)
n-Butyl cyanide	(62.8)	.7558 (27.4°)	(.606) (20°)	1,3-Cyclohexadiene	48.6	(.607)	(.510) (20°)
tert-Butyl cyclohexane	115.09	.8205	.6670 (20°)	1,4-Cyclohexadiene	48.7	(.608)	(.515) (20°)
1,4-Butyl diacetate	103.4	(.594)		Cyclohexane	68.13	.8100 (27.5°)	(.627) (20°)
n-Butyl ethyl ketone	80.73	.707₂	(.579) (20°)	Cyclohexanecarboxylic acid	83.24	.6499 (30°)	(.668) (30°)
n-Butyl formate	65.83	.644₆	(.571) (25°)	Cyclohexanol	73.40	.732	(.694) (20°)
iso-Butyl formate	66.79	.654₉	(.574) (25°)	Cyclohexanone	62.0₄	.632₃	(.599) (20°)
iso-Butylideneazine	(95.8)	.683		Cyclohexanone oxime	71.5₂	.632₁	
Butyl iodide	(93.6)	.5086 (18°)	(.822) (20°)	Cyclohexanoneoxime-O-methyl ether	82.9₆	.652₃	
iso-Butyl methyl ketone	70.05	.699₅	(.561) (20°)	Cyclohexene	57.5	(.700)	(.567) (20°)
tert-Butyl methyl ketone	69.86	.697₉	(.558) (16°)	Cyclohexenol	64.1	(.653)	
n-Butyl perfluor-n-butyrate	126.7	(.469)		Cyclooctane	91.4	(.815)	(.684) (20°)
p-tert-Butylphenol	108.0	(.719)	(.653) (114°)	Cyclooctene	84.6	(.769)	(.654) (20°)
Butyl sulfide	(113.7)	.7774 (27.4°)	(.652) (16°)	Cyclooctatetraene	(53.9)	.518	
Butyl thiocyanate	(79.38)	.6891 (27.4°)	(.659) (25°)	Cyclopentane	59.18	.8439	.6290 (20°)
2-Butyne-1,4-diacetate	95.9	(.564)		Cyclopentanecarboxylic acid	73.48	.6446 (30°)	(.677) (30°)
2-Butyne-1,4-dibenzoate	169.0	(.561)		Cyclopentanone	51.63	.6141 (30°)	(.582) (30°)
2-Butyne-1,4-diol	50.3	(.584)		Cyclopropane	39.9	(.948)	(.683) (−79°)
n-Butyraldehyde	46.08	.639₄	(.522) (20°)	Cyclopropanecarboxylic acid	45.33	.5271 (30°)	(.569) (30°)
iso-Butyraldehyde	46.38	.643₆	(.511) (20°)	p-Cymene	102.8	.766 (20°)	(.656) (20°)
iso-Butyraldoxime	56.1₂	.644₃	(.576) (20°)	Decalin	106.70	.7718	.6814 (20°)
n-Butyric acid	55.10	.625	.598 (20°)	cis-Decalin	(107.0)	.774	(.686) (35°)
iso-Butyric acid	56.06	.636₃ (25°)	(.601) (25°)	trans-Decalin	(107.7)	.779	(.670) (35°)
Butyronitrile	49.4	(.715)	(.569) (15°)	n-Decane	119.74	(.8416)	(.6143) (20°)
Butyrylphenylacetylene	(106.4)	.618		l-Deuterio pyrrole	48.75	.716 (20°)	
Cacodyl	(99.9)	.476	(.689) (15°)	Deuteroindene	80.88	.690	(.692) (13°)
Cacodylic acid	(79.9)	.579		Diacetal	(153.8)	.668	
Camphor	(103)	.68	(.67) (25°)	Di-iso-amylamine	(133.1)	.846	(.649) (21°)
Camphoric acid	129.0	(.644)	(.791) (20°)	Diazoacetic ester	57	(.50)	(.54) (24°)
Camphoric anhydride	(113)	.620	(.740) (20°)	Dibenzocoronene	289.4	.778	
n-Caproic acid	78.55	.676₂	(.624) (25°)	1,2,5,6-Dibenzofluorene	184	.69 ± .03	
Caproylphenylacetylene	(130 4)	.651		3,4,5,6-Dibenzophenanthrene	(203)	.73 ± .03	
n-Caprylic acid	101.60	.7053	(.642) (20°)	Dibenzphenanthrone	200.5	.716	
Carbanilide	134.05	(.6316)	(.783) (20°)	Dibenzpyrene	213.6	.706	
Carbazole	117.4	(.702)		Dibenzpyrenequinone	183.1	.551	
Carbon disulfide	42.2	554	(.699) (22°)	iso-Dibenzpyrenequinone	194.6	.586	
Carbon tetrabromide	93.73	.2826 (20°)	(.966)	Dibenzyl ketone	131.70	.626₂	
Carbon tetrachloride	66.60	.433	.691 (20°)	p-Dibromobenzene	(101.4)	.430	.786 (100°)
Carbon tetraiodide	(136)	.261	(1.13) (20°)	2,3-Dibromo-2-butene-1,4-diol	94.2	(.383)	
Carvacrol	(109.1)	.726	(.709) (20°)	Dibromodichloromethane	81.1 ± .4	(.334)	(.808) (25°)
Carvone	(92.2)	.614	(.590) (20°)	1,2-Dibromodiiodoethylene	(140.1)	.320	
Cetyl alcohol	(183.5)	.757 (17.5°)	(.619) (50°)	1,2-Dibromoethylene	(71.7)	.386	(.877) (17.5°)
Cetyl mercaptan	390.4	(1.510)		1,2-Dibromo-2-fluoroethane	(78.0)	.379	(.855) (17°)
Chloral	(67.7)	.459	(.694) (20°)	Dibromo-4-nitrophenol	(167.5)	.564	
Chloranil	(112.6)	.458		1,2-Dibromotetrachloroethane	(126.0)	.387	(1.049)
Chloracetic acid	48.1	(.509)	(.804) (20°)	Di-n-butylamine	103.7	(.802)	(.767) (20°)
Chloroacetone	(50.9)	.550	(.633) (20°)	Di-iso-butylamine	105.7	(.817)	(.609) (20°)
Chloroacetylchloride	53.7	(.475)	(.710) (0°)	Di-sec-butylamine	105.9	(.819)	(.641) (0°)
p-Chloranisole	89.1	(.625)		Di-iso-butyl ketone	104.30	.733₈	(.591) (20°)
Chlorobenzene	69.97	(.6216)	(.688) (20°)	Di-tert-butyl ketone	104.06	.732₁	
Chlorobenzene diazocyanide	65.02	(.393)		2,6-Di-tert-butyl-4-methyl phenol	165.3	(.750)	
Chlorodibromomethane	75.1 ± .4	(.361)	(.883) (15°)	2,4-Di-tert-butyl phenol	155.6	(.754)	
Chlorodifluoromethane	38.6	.446		Dibutyl phthalate	175.1	(.629)	(.657) (21°)
1-Chloro-2,3-dihydroxypropane	(77.9)	.604		Di-iso-butyralacetylene	(125.6)	.738	
Chlorodiphenylmethane	131.9	(.651)		Dicetyl sulfide	401.7	(.832)	
Chloroethylene	35.9	.574	(.528) (liq., 15°)	Dichloroacetic acid	58.2	(.451)	(.705) (20°)
Chloroform	59.30	.497	.740 (20°)	Dichloroacetyl chloride	69.0	(.468)	

Compound	$-\chi_M \times 10^6$	$-\chi \times 10^6$	$-K \times 10^6$	Compound	$-\chi_M \times 10^6$	$-\chi \times 10^6$	$-K \times 10^6$
o-Dichlorobenzene	84.26	.5734	(.748) (20°)	2,5-Dimethylpyrrole	71.92	.756 (20°)	(.707) (20°)
m-Dichlorobenzene	83.19	.5661	(.729) (20°)	α,ω-Dimethyl styrene	(90.7)	.686	
p-Dichlorobenzene	82.93	.5644	(.823) (20.5°)	Dimethyl succinate	81.50	.5581	(.625) (18°)
1,4-Dichloro-2-butyne	74.2	(.603)		Dimethyl sulfate	(62.2)	.493	(.657) (20°)
1,2-Dichloro-1,2-dibromoethane	(108.6)	.423		Dimethyl sulfide	(44.9)	.723	(.612) (21°)
1,1-Dichloro-difluoroethylene	60.0	.451		Dimethyltrichloromethylcarbinol	(105)	.59	
Dichlorodifluoromethane	52.2	.432	(.642) (−30°)	N,N-Dimethyl urea	55.1	(.625)	(.784)
1,1-Dichloroethylene	49.2	.508	(.635) (15°)	N,N'-Dimethyl urea	56.3	(.639)	(.730)
cis-1,2-Dichloroethylene	51.0	.526	(.679) (15°)	o-Dinitrobenzene	65.98	.3921	(.614) (17°)
trans-1,2-Dichloroethylene	48.9	.504	(.638) (15°)	m-Dinitrobenzene	70.53	.4197	(.659) (0°)
1,3-Dichloro-2-hydroxypropane	(80.1)	.621		p-Dinitrobenzene	68.30	.4064	(.660) (30°)
Dicyandiamide	44.55	(.530)	(.742) (14°)	2,4-Dinitrophenol	(73.1)	.397	(.668) (24°)
Dicyclohexanol acetylene	(151.6)	.682		Dinitroresorcinol	(62.4)	.312	
Dicyclohexyl	129.31	.7776	.6889 (20°)	1,4-Dioxane	52.16	.592 (32°)	(.606) (32°)
1,1-Dicyclohexylnonane	231.98	.7930	.7001 (20°)	Diphenyl	103.25	.6695	(.664) (73°)
Diethanolacetylene	(75.3)	.660		1,1-Diphenylallyl-3-chloride	146.1	(.639)	
Diethyl acetaldehyde	70.71	$.705_9$	(.576) (20°)	1,3-Diphenylallyl-3-chloride	140.7	(.615)	
Diethylallylacetophenone	146.2	(.676)	(.663) (16°)	Diphenylamine	(109.7)	.648	.686 (55.5°)
Diethyl allylmalonate	118.8	(.593)	(.602) (14°)	Diphenyl-bis-diazo cyanide	85.03	(.327)	
Diethylamine	56.8	(.777)	(.552) (18°)	Diphenylbutadiene	129.6	(.629)	
Diethylcyclohexylamine	(124.5)	.802	(.699) (0°)	Diphenylchloroarsine	(145.5)	.550	(.871) (40°)
Diethyl ethylmalonate	115.2	(.612)	(.614) (20°)	Diphenyldecapentaene	180.5	(.635)	
Diethyl ketone	58.1_4	$.675_1$	(.551) (19°)	Diphenyldiacetylene	(134.6)	.640	
Diethyl ketoxime	68.3_1	.6754		Diphenyldiazomethane	115	(.592)	
Diethyl malonate	(92.6)	.5782	(.611) (20°)	Diphenyldihydrotetrazine	129.9	(.545)	
Diethyl-3-(1-methyl butane) ethyl-malonate	175	(.677)		1,1-Diphenylethylene	(118.0)	.655	(.680) (14°)
Diethyl oxalate	81.71	.5595	(.603) (15°)	1,6-Diphenylhexane	171.81	.7208	.6877 (20°)
Diethyl phthalate	127.5	(.574)	(.645) (25°)	Diphenylhexatriene	146.9	(.632)	
Diethyl sebacate	(177.0)	.685	(.661) (20°)	Diphenylmethane	(115.7)	.688	.684 (35.5°)
Diethylstilbestrol	172.0	(.547)		Diphenylmethanol	119.1	.647	
Diethylstilbestrol dipropionate	265.2	.720		1,1-Diphenylnonane	206.32	.7357	.6935 (20°)
Diethyl succinate	105.07	.6035	(.628) (20°)	Diphenylpentatetraene	164.3	(.636)	
Diethyl sulfate	(86.8)	.563	(.667) (15°)	Diphenylphenoxyarsine	(225.2)	.567	
Diethyl sulfide	(67.9)	.753	(.630) (20°)	N,N-Diphenyl urea	126.3	(.595)	(.759)
Diethyl tartrate	(113.4)	.550	(.662) (20°)	N,N'-Diphenyl urea	127.5	(.600)	(.743) (20°)
Difluoroacetamide	(41.2)	.433		Di-n-propyl ketone	80.45	$.705_0$	(.576) (20°)
1-Difluoro-2-dibromoethane	(85.5)	.382	(.883) (20°)	Di-iso-propyl ketone	81.14	$.711_0$	(.573) (20°)
1,1-Difluoro-2,2-dichloroethyl amyl ether	129.84	(.587)	(.694) (20°)	Dipropyl oxalate	105.27	.6046	
1,1-Difluoro-2,2-dichloroethyl butyl ether	119.48	(.577)	(.703) (20°)	Di-iso-propyl oxalate	106.02	.6089	
1,1-Difluoro-2,2-dichloroethyl ethyl ether	96.13	(.537)	(.723) (20°)	Dodecyl alcohol	147.70	.7849 (20.7°)	(.652) (24°)
1,1-Difluoro-2,2-dichloroethyl methyl ether	80.68	(.489)	(.696) (20°)	Dulcitol	112.40	.617	(.905) (15°)
1,1-Difluoro-2,2-dichloroethyl propyl ether	107.19	(.555)	(.701) (20°)	Elaidic acid	204.8	(.725)	(.619) (79°)
Difluoroethanol	(41.3)	.503		Erythritol	73.80	.604	(.876) (20°)
Di-n-heptylamine	171.5	(.805)		Ethane	27.3_7	(.910)	(.511) (−100°)
Di-n-hexylamine	148.9	(.803)		4-Ethoxy-3-methoxybenzyl acetate	138.5	.619	
Dihydronaphthalene	(85.1)	.654	(.652) (12°)	4-Ethoxy-3-methoxybenzyl benzoate	177.3	.620	
o-Dimethoxybenzene	87.39	.6329	(.686) (25°)	1-Ethoxynaphthalene	119.9	(.696)	(.738) (20°)
m-Dimethoxybenzene	87.21	.6316	(.682) (0°)	2-Ethoxynaphthalene	119.2	(.692)	(.734) (25°)
p-Dimethoxybenzene	86.65	.6275	(.661) (55°)	Ethyl acetate	54.10	.614	.554 (20°)
o-(2,5-Dimethoxybenzoyl)-benzoic acid	161.0	(.562)		Ethyl acetoacetate	71.67	$.550_8$	(.565) (20°)
Dimethoxymethane	(47.3)	.621	(.532)	Ethylacetophenone	95.5	(.644)	(.639) (16°)
Dimethylacetophenone	96.8	(.653)	(.645) (16°)	Ethyl alcohol	33.60	.728	.575 (20°)
Dimethylallylacetophenone	122.4	(.650)	(.635) (16°)	Ethylally acetophenone	122.5	(.651)	(.634) (16°)
Dimethylaniline	89.66	(.740)		Ethyl amylpropiolate	(112.7)	.670	
2,2-Dimethylbutane	76.24	.8848	.5744 (20°)	Ethylaniline	89.30	(.737)	(.709)
2,3-Dimethylbutane	76.22	.8845	.5853 (20°)	9-Ethyl anthracene	153.0	(.741)	(.771) (99°)
2,3-Dimethyl-2-butene	65.9	(.783)	(.557)	Ethylbenzene	77.20	.7272	.6341 (29°)
Dimethylcyclohexanone	(84.8)	.672		Ethyl benzoate	93.32	$.621_1$	(.648) (25°)
1,2 and 1,3 Dimethylcyclopentanes	81.31	.8281	.6224 (20°)	Ethyl benzoylacetate	(115.3)	.600	(.673) (20°)
2,5-Dimethyl-2,5-dibromo-3-hexine	(135.6)	.506		Ethyl benzylidenecyanoacetate	(116.3)	.578	
Dimethyl diethylketo tetrahydro-furfurane	(116.2)	.753		Ethyl benzylmalonate	(154.5)	.6172	(.663) (20°)
2,5-Dimethyl-1-ethylpyrrole	94.61	.768 (20°)		Ethyl bromide	54.70	.502	.719 (20°)
2,5-Dimethyl-3-ethylpyrrole	93.87	.762 (20°)		Ethyl bromoacetate	(82.8)	.496	(.747) (20°)
2,5-Dimethylfuran	66.37	687 (20°)	(.620) (18°)	Ethyl-1-isobutylacetoacetate	(121.4)	.652	
Dimethyl furazan	57.27	.584		Ethyl butylmalonate	139.3	$.644_2$	(.629) (20°)
2,5-Dimethyl-4-heptene	100.6	(.797)		Ethyl-n-butyrate	(77.7)	.6693	(.585) (25°)
2,4-Dimethyl-2,4-hexadiene	(78.7)	.714		Ethyl-iso-butyrate	78.32	$.674_3$	(.583) (25°)
2,3-Dimethylhexane	98.77	.8648	.6164 (20°)	Ethyl chloroacetate	(72.3)	.590	(.684) (20°)
2,5-Dimethylhexane	98.15	.8593	.5969 (20°)	Ethyl cinnamate	(107.5)	.610	(.640) (20°)
3,4-Dimethylhexane	99.06	.8673	.6240 (20°)	Ethyl-iso-cyanate	(45.6)	.642	(.582) (16°)
2,6-Dimethyl-4 hexanol	116.9	.812		Ethyl cyanoacetate	(67.3)	.595	(.632) (20°)
2,5-Dimethyl-3-hexine-2,5-diol	(103.0)	.724		Ethylcyclohexane	91.09	.8118	.6324 (20°)
Dimethyl isoxazole	59.7	(.615)		Ethyldiallylacetophenone	147.4	(.646)	(.636) (16°)
Dimethylketo tetrahydrofurfurane	(68.5)	.600		Ethyl dibromocinnamate	174.5	.519	
Dimethyl malonate	69.69	.5277	(.609) (20°)	Ethyl dichloroacetate	85.2	(.543)	(.696) (20°)
1,6-Dimethylnaphthalene	113.3	(.725)		Ethyl diethylacetoacetate	(117.9)	.6328	(.615) (20°)
2,4-Dimethylnonane	134.68	(.862)	(.636) (20°)	Ethyl diethylmalonate	(140.4)	.6492	(.641)(20°)
3,4-Dimethylnonane	134.70	(.862)	(.647) (20°)	Ethyl dithiolacetate	(71.0)	.5904 (27.4°)	
4,5-Dimethylnonane	134.52	(.861)	(.647) (20°)	Ethylene	12.0	(.428)	(.242) (−102°)
2,6-Dimethyl-2,6,8-nonatriene	(108.8)	.724		Ethylene	15.30	.546 (32°)	(.309) (−102°)
Dimethyl-2,4-nonatriene	(148.8)	.990		Ethylene bromide	78.80	.419	.915 (20°)
2,6-Dimethyloctane	122.54	(.861)	(.627) (20°)	Ethylene chloride	59.62	.602 (32°)	(.757) (20°)
3,4-Dimethyloxadiazole	57.17	.583		Ethylenediamine	46.26	.771 (32°)	(.686) (20°)
Dimethyl oxalate	(55.7)	.472	(.542) (54°)	Ethylene iodide	104.7	.371 (32°)	(.791) (10°)
Dimethyl oxamide	(63.2)	.544		Ethylene oxide	30.7	(.697)	(.618) (7°)
2,2-Dimethylpentane	86.97	.8680	.5849 (20°)	Ethyl ether	55.10	.743	.534 (20°)
2,3-Dimethylpentane	87.51	.8733	.6070 (20°)	Ethyl ethylacetoacetate	93.9	.5937	(.582) (20°)
2,4-Dimethylpentane	87.48	.8732	.5876 (20°)	Ethyl ethylbutylmalonate	(163.3)	.6683	(.650) (20°)
2,2-Dimethylpropane	63.1	(.875)	(.536) (0°)	Ethyl ethylpropylmalonate	(152.4)	.6619	(.648) (20°)
2,5-Dimethyl-3-propyl-pyrrole	106.07	.773 (20°)		Ethyl formate	43.00	.580	.531 (20°)
2,4-Dimethylpyrrole	69.64	.732 (20°)	(.679) (14°)	Ethyl hexylpropiolate	129.9	.713	
				Ethyl hydroxylamine	(43.0)	.704	
				Ethylidene chloride	(57.4)	.580	(.681) (20°)
				Ethyl iodide	(69.7)	.4470 (17.5°)	(.864) (20°)
				Ethyl iodoacetate	(97.6)	.456	(.829) (13°)
				Ethyl lactate	(72.6)	.615	(.633) (25°)

Compound	$-\chi_M \times 10^6$	$-\chi \times 10^6$	$-K \times 10^6$	Compound	$-\chi_M \times 10^6$	$-\chi \times 10^6$	$-K \times 10^6$
Ethyl methylacetoacetate	(81.9)	.5684	(.569) (20°)	Indene (natural)	84.79	(.730)	(.723) 25°)
Ethyl methyl ketoxime	57.3₂	.658₀	(.530) (20°)	Indene (synthetic)	80.89	(.696)	(.690) (25°)
Ethyl-1-methyl-2-oxocyclohexane-carboxylate	112.1	(.608)		Indole	85.0	(.726)	
Ethyl methylphenylmalonate	(153.2)	.6121	(.658) (20°)	Iodobenzene	92.00	.451	.826 (20°)
Ethyl nitrophenylpropiolate	114.6	.523		Iodoform (in sol'n)	117.1	.2974 (20°)	(1.192) (17°)
Ethyl oxamate	62.0	(.529)	(.427) (19°)	1-Iodo-2-phenylacetylene	(110.1)	.483	
Ethyl perfluor-n-butyrate	103.5	(.427)		o-Iodotoluene	(112.2)	.5145 (30°)	(.874) (20°)
Ethyl phenylacetate	104.27	(.635)	(.656) (20°)	m-Iodotoluene	(112.3)	.5152 (30°)	(.875) (20°)
Ethyl phenylmalonate	(142.2)	.6017	(.659) (20°)	p-Iodotoluene	101.31	(.465)	(.780) (40°)
Ethyl phenylpropiolate	(104.2)	.598	(.636) (13°)	Leucine	84.9	(.647)	
Ethyl phosphate	(98.2)	.539	(.576) (20°)	iso-Leucine	84.9	(.647)	
Ethyl propionate	(66.5)	.6514	(.584) (15°)	Maleic acid	49.71	(.428)	(.681) (20°)
Ethyl propylacetoacetate	(105.7)	.6135	(.593) (20°)	Maleic anhydride	(35.8)	.365	(.341) (20°)
Ethyl-n-propyl ketone	69.03	.689₁	(.560) (22°)	Malonic acid	(46.3)	.4453	(.726) (15°)
Ethyl succinimide	(72.0)	.566		Mannitol	111.20	.610	(.908) (20°)
Ethyl sulfine	(67.0)	.631		Mannose	102.90	.571	(.879)
Ethyl sulfite	(75.4)	.546	(.604) (0°)	Mesitylene	92.32	.7682 (20°)	(.665) (20°)
Ethylsulfone ethyl ether	(81.8)	.592		Methane	12.2₇	(.765)	
Ethyl thiocyanate	(55.7)	.6392 (27.4°)	(.637) (25°)	Methione	91.0	(.610)	
Ethyl isothiocyanate	(59.0)	.6772 (27.4°)	(.680) (15°)	p-Methoxyazobenzene	(118.9)	.560	
Ethyl thiolacetate	(62.7)	.6019 (27.4°)	(.586) (25°)	o-Methoxybenzaldehyde	76.0	(.558)	(.632) (20°)
Ethyl thionacetate	(63.5)	.6098 (27.4°)		p-Methoxybenzaldehyde	78.0	(.572)	(.642) (20°)
Ethyl tribromoacetate	(119.5)	.368	(.821) (20°)	o-Methoxybenzyl alcohol	87.9	.637	(.664) (25°)
Ethyl trichloroacetate	(99.6)	.520	(.719) (20°)	1-Methoxynaphthalene	107.0	(.676)	(.741) (14°)
N-Ethyl urea	55.5	(.630)	(.764) (18°)	2-Methoxynaphthalene	107.6	(.680)	
Ethyl iso-valerate	(91.1)	.700	(.607) (20°)	1-(o-Methoxyphenylazo)-2-naphthol	163.6	(.588)	
Eucalyptol	(116.3)	.754	(.699) (20°)	Methoxysaligenin acetate	110.3	.613	
Eugenol and iso-eugenol	(102.1)	.622	(.663) (20°)	Methyl acetate	42.60	.575	.537 (20°)
Flavanthrone	241.0	.590		Methyl acetoacetate	59.60	.513₂	(.553) (20°)
Fluorene	110.5	.655		Methylacetylacetone	(65.0)	.569	
Fluorenone	99.4	.552	(.623) (100°)	Methyl alcohol	21.40	.668	.530 (20°)
Fluorobenzene	(58.4)	.608	(.623) (20°)	Methylallylaketone	111.9	(1.330)	
Fluorobromoacetic acid	(59.5)	.379		Methylamine	(27.0)	.870	(.608) (−11°)
Fluorodichloromethane	48.8	.474	(.676) (0°)	N-Methylaniline	82.74	(.773)	(.762) ‚20°)
p-Fluorophenetole	(88.0)	.628		9-Methylanthracene	146.5	.762	(.812) (99°)
Fluoro trichloroethylene	72.5	.485	(.742) (25°)	Methyl benzoate	81.59	.599₃	(.651) (25°)
Fluorotrichloromethane	58.7	.427	(.638) (17°)	Methyl-o-benzoylbenzoate	139.4	(.580)	(.690) (19°)
Formaldehyde	(18.6)	.62	(.51) (−20°)	Methylbenzylaniline	(132.2)	.670	
Formamide	(21.9)	.486	(.551) (20°)	Methyl bromide	42.8	.451	(1.044) (0°)
Formic acid	19.90	.432	.527 (20°)	2-Methylbutane	64.40	.8925	.5531 (20°)
β-Formylpropionic acid	55.3	(.542)		2-Methyl-2-butene	54.14	(.772)	(.516) (13°)
Fructose	102.60	.570		Methyl butyl ketone	(69.1)	.690	(.563) (15°)
Fulvene (Benzene χ_M measured to be 49)	42.9	(.549)	(.452) (20°)	Methyl iso-butyl ketone	(69.3)	.692	(.554) (20°)
Fulvene $\left(\chi \dfrac{54.8}{49}\right)$	48.0	(.614)	(.505) (20°)	Methyl tert-butyl ketone	(70.4)	.703	(.562) (16°)
				p-Methyl-o-tert-butylphenol	120.3	(.732)	
Fumaric acid	49.11	(.423)	(.692) (20°)	Methyl butyrate	(66.4)	.6498	(.588) (16°)
Furan	43.09	.633 (20°)	(.598) (15°)	o-Methylcarbanilide	154.0	(.681)	
Furfural	47.1	(.490)	(.568) (20°)	Methyl chloride	(32.0)	.633	
Galactose	103.00	.572		Methyl chloroacetate	58.1	(.535)	(.661) (20°)
Gallic acid	90.0	(.529)	(.896) (4°)	Methylcholanthrene	(182)	.68 ± .04	
Geraniol formate	(119.9)	.658	(.610) (20°)	3-Methylcholanthrene	194.0	(.723)	
Glucose	102.60	.570		Methylcyclohexane	78.91	.8038	.6181 (20°)
D-Glucose	101.5	(.563)	(.869) (25°)	2-Methylcyclohexanone	(74.0)	.660	(.610) (18°)
Glutamic acid	78.5	(.533)		3-Methylcyclohexanone	(74.8)	.667	(.610) (20°)
Glycerol	57.06	.619	.779 (20°)	4-Methylcyclohexanone	(63.5)	.566	(.516) (24°)
Glycine	40.3	(.537)	(.846) (50°)	Methylcyclopentane	70.17	.8338	.6245 (20°)
Glycol	38.80	.624	.698 (20°)	4-Methyl-2,6-di-tert-butylphenol	167.6	(.761)	
Guaiacol	(79.2)	.638	(.720) (21°)	Methyl dichloroacetate	73.1	(.511)	
Helianthrone	189.9	.497		Methyldiphenoxyphosphine oxide	(152.9)	.616	
1,2-Heptadiene	73.5	(.764)		Methyldiphenyltriazine	(155.1)	.627	
2,3-Heptadiene	72.1	(.749)		Methylene bromide	65.10	.375	.935 (20°)
Heptaldehyde	81.02	.709₆	(.603) (20°)	Methylene chloride	(46.6)	.549	(.733) (20°)
n-Heptane	85.24	.8507	.5817 (20°)	Methylene iodide	93.10	.348	1.156 (20°)
4-Heptanol	91.5	.789	(.647) (20°)	Methylene succinic acid	57.57	(.443)	(.723)
n-Heptanoic acid	88.60	.680	.626 (20°)	Methyl ether	26.3	.571	
n-Heptyl amine	93.1	(.808)	(.628) (20°)	Methylethylallylacetophenone	133.3	(.659)	(.643) (16°)
n-Heptyl benzene	134.41	.7625	.6528 (20°)	Methyl ethyl ketone	45.5₈	.632₂	(.509) (20°)
Heptyl cyclohexane	147.40	.8084	.6559 (20°)	Methyl formate	(32.0)	.5327	(.519) (20°)
n-Heptylic acid	89.74	.6900	(.630) (25°)	Methylfumaric acid	56.98	(.438)	(.642)
1-Heptyne	77.0	.801	(.584) (25°)	3-Methylheptane	97.99	.8580	.6056 (20°)
2-Heptyne	79.5	(.826)	(.615) (25°)	2-Methyl-4-heptene	88.0	(.784)	
Hexabromoethane	(148.0)	.294	(1.124) (20°)	5-Methyl-1,2-hexadiene	73.6	(.765)	(.553) (19°)
Hexachlorobenzene	(147.5)	.518	(1.059) (24°)	2-Methylhexane	86.24	.8607	.5841 (20°)
Hexachloroethane	(112.7)	.476	(.995) (20°)	Methyl hexyl ketone	(93.3)	.728	(.596) (20°)
Hexachlorohexatrione	(145.0)	.433		Methyl-m-hydroxybenzoate	88.4	(.581)	
n-Hexadecane	187.63	.8286	.6421 (20°)	Methyl-p-hydroxybenzoate	88.7	(.583)	
1,5-Hexadiene	(55.1)	.671	(.462) (20°)	Methyl iodide	(57.2)	.403	(.918) (20°)
2,3-Hexadiene	60.9	(.741)		Methylmaleic acid	57.84	(.446)	(.721)
n-Hexaldehyde	69.40	.693₀		9-Methyl-10-methoxyanthracene	158.1	(.711)	
2,2,4,7,9,9-Hexamethyldecane	191.52	.8458	.6596 (20°)	Methyl-o-methoxybenzoate	95.6	(.575)	(.665) (19°)
Hexamethyl disiloxane	118.9	.7324		Methyl-p-methoxybenzoate	98.6	(.593)	
Hexamethylene glycol	84.30	.713		Methyl-α-methoxy-isobutyrate	(81.9)	.620	
n-Hexane	(74.6)	.8654 (27.4°)	(.565)	1-Methylnaphthalene	102.8	(.723)	(.741) (14°)
Hexene	65.7	(.781)		2-Methylnaphthalene	102.6	(.722)	(.743) (20°)
Hexestrol	(165)	.61 ± .02		4-Methylnonane	121.39	(.853)	(.625) (20°)
n-Hexyl alcohol	79.20	.774	.637 (20°)	5-Methyl-5-nonene	111.6	(.796)	
n-Hexyl benzene	124.23 (20°)	(.767)	(.658) (20°)	4-Methyloctane	109.63	(.855)	(.618) (20°)
n-Hexyl methyl ketone	91.4₂	.713₁	(.583)	Methylol urea	48.3	(.493)	
n-Hexyl methyl ketoxime	102.5₈	.716₂	(.634) (20°)	2-Methylpentane	75.26	.8734	.5705 (20°)
Hexylpropiolamide	(103.7)	.677		3-Methylpentane	75.52	.8764	.5823 (20°)
Hydrindene	(78.5)	.664	(.639) (16°)	4-Methyl-2-pentanol	80.4	.788	(.641) (20°)
Hydroquinone	64.63	.587	(.797) (20°)	Methyl perfluor-n-butyrate	92.5	(.406)	
Hydroxyazobenzene	(99.7)	.503		Methyl phenylacetate	92.73	(.618)	(.645) (16°)
p-Hydroxybenzaldehyde	66.8	(.547)	(.618) (130°)	Methyl phenylpropiolate	95.6	.597	
4-Hydroxy-2-butanone	48.5	.55	(.573) (14°)	2-Methylpropene	44.4	(.791)	
				Methyl propionate	(55.0)	.6240	(.571) (20°)

Compound	$-\chi_M \times 10^6$	$-\chi \times 10^6$	$-K \times 10^6$	Compound	$-\chi_M \times 10^6$	$-\chi \times 10^6$	$-K \times 10^6$
Methyl-n-propyl ketone	57.41	.666₄	(.541) (15°)	Pentachloroethane	(99.1)	.490	(.819) (25°)
Methyl-iso-propyl ketone	58.45	.679₀	(.545) (20°)	Pentachlorohexadione	(129.5)	.452	
1-Methylpyrrole	58.56	.722 (20°)	(.664) (10°)	2,3-Pentadiene	49.1	(.721)	(.501) (20°)
2-Methylpyrrole	60.10	.741 (20°)	(.700)	n-Pentane	63.05	.8739	.5472 (20°)
Methyl salicylate	86.30	.567	.668 (20°)	2,4-Pentanediol	70.4	.677	
Methyl silicone	(172.7)	.730		Perfluoroacetic acid	43.3	(.380)	
α-Methyl styrene	(80.1)	.678	(.620) (20°)	Perfluoro-n-butyric acid	81.0	(.378)	
2-Methylthiazole	59.56	.601 (20°)		Perfluorobutyric anhydride	149.4	(.387)	
2-Methylthiophene	66.35	.676 (20°)	(.689) (20°)	Perfluorocyclooctane oxide	157.6	(.379)	
Methyl trichloroacetate	84.2	(.475)	(.707) (19°)	Perfluoropropionic acid	61.0	(.372)	
N-Methyl urea	44.6	(.602)	(.725)	Perhydroanthracene	146.01	.7592	.7178 (20°)
Morpholine	55.0	(.631)	(.631)	Perylene	166 8	.662	
Myleran	169.7	.69	(.834) (4°)	Phenanthrene	(127.9)	.718	(.763) (100°)
Myristic acid	176.0	(.771)	(.661) (60°)	Phenanthrenequinone	104.5	.502	(.698)
Naphthalaldehydic acid	117.6	(.588)		Phenanthrenonitrile	139.0	(.685)	
Naphthalene	(91.9)	.717	(.821) (20°)	o-Phenetidine	(101.7)	.741 (25°)	
Naphthalene picrate	185.9	(.523)		p-Phenetidine	(96.8)	.706 (25°)	(.749) (15°)
2-Naphthalenesulfonylamine	127.6	(.616)		Phenetole	(84.5)	.692	(.689) (20°)
2-Naphthalenesulfonyl chloride	121.91	(.538)		Phenol	60.21	(.640)	(.675) (45°)
meso-Naphthodianthrene	214.6	.612		Phenothiazine	114.8	(.576)	
meso-Naphthodianthrone	221.8	.583		Phenylacetaldehyde	72.01	.599₄	(.614) (20°)
1-Naphthol	98.2	.681	(.834) (4°)	Phenyl acetate	82.04	(.603)	(.647) (25°)
	97.0	.673	(.819) (4°)	Phenylacetic acid	82.72	(.608)	(.657) (80°)
2-Naphthol	98.25	(.682)	(.829) (4°)	Phenylacetylene	72.01	(.705)	(.655) (20°)
α-Naphthonitrile	103.3	(.674)	(.753) (5°)	1-Phenylazo-2-naphthol	137.6	(.554)	
β-Naphthonitrile	101.0	(.659)	(.721) (60°)	2-Phenylbensofuran	130.5	(.672)	
α-Naphthoquinone	73.5	(.465)	(.661)	1-Phenyl-4-benzoyl-1,3-butadiene	(140.3)	.599	
β-Naphthoquinone	67.9	(.429)		Phenylbutadiene	(85.7)	.658	
N-1-Naphthylacetamide	117.8	(.636)		4-Phenyl-1-butene	93.49	(.7077)	(.6239) (20°)
N-2-Naphthylacetamide	117.8	(.636)		Phenylbutyl acetate	134.5	.653	
1-Naphthylamine	98.8	.690	.757 (54°)	Phenyl n-butyrate	105.46	(.643)	
2-Naphthylamine	98.00	(.684)	(.726) (98°)	Phenyl iso-cyanate	(72.7)	.610	(.699) (20°)
1-Naphthylamine hydrochloride	(127.6)	.710		o-Phenylenediamine	71.98	.6662	
Nicotine	113.328	(.699)	(.705) (20°)	m-Phenylenediamine	70.53	.6529	(.723) (58°)
o-Nitroaniline	66.47	(.481)	(.694) (15°)	p-Phenylenediamine	70.28	.6503	
m-Nitroaniline	70.09	(.507)	(.725) (20°)	Phenyl ether	(108.1)	.635	(.681) (20°)
p-Nitroaniline	66.43	(.481)	(.691) (14°)	Phenylethyl sulfide	(94.4)	.6826 (27.4°)	
o-Nitrobenzaldehyde	68.23	.4517		Phenylfluoroform	(77.3)	.529	
m-Nitrobenzaldehyde	68.55	.4538		Phenylhydrazine	67.82	(.627)	(.688) (23°)
p-Nitrobenzaldehyde	66.57	.4407	(.507) (0°)	Phenylhydroxylamine	(68.2)	.625	
Nitrobenzene	61.80	.502	.604 (20°)	Phenyl mercaptan	(70.8)	.6425 (27.4°)	(.693) (20°)
Nitrobenzene diazo cyanide	59.22	(.336)		1-Phenyl-2-Methylbutane	113.53	(.766)	(.660) (20°)
o-Nitrobenzoic acid	76.11	.4556	(.718) (4°)	Phenylmethyl sulfide	(83.2)	.6695 (27.4°)	
m-Nitrobenzoic acid	80.22	.4802	(.717) (4°)	Phenylpropiolamide	(83.3)	.574	
p-Nitrobenzoic acid	78.81	.4718	(.731) (32°)	Phenyl propionate	93.79	(.625)	(.654) (25°)
o-Nitrobromobenzene	87.3	(.432)	(.700) (80°)	Phenylsulfone	(129.0)	.591	(.740) (20°)
m-Nitrobromobenzene	89.5	(.443)	(.755) (20°)	Phenyl thiocyanate	(81.5)	.6027 (27.4°)	(.677) (24°)
p-Nitrobromobenzene	89.6	(.444)	(.859) (22°)	Phenyl isothiocyanate	(86.0)	.6365 (27.4°)	(.719) (24°)
m-Nitro carbanilide	148.1	(.576)		1-Phenyl-4,6,6-trimethylheptane	173.90	(.796)	(.682) (20°)
Nitroethane	(35.4)	.472	(.497) (20°)	N-Phenyl urea	82.1	(.603)	(.785)
Nitromethane	21.1	.3457	(.391) (25°)	Phloroglucinol	(73.4)	.582	
1-Nitronaphthalene	98.47	(.569)	(.696) (62°)	Phthalamide	(91.3)	.556	
o-Nitrophenol	73.3	.527 (24°)	(.873) (20°)	Phthalic acid	83.61	.5035	(.802) (20°)
m-Nitrophenol	70.8	.509 (25°)	(.756)	iso-Phthalic acid	84.64	.5097	
p-Nitrophenol	69.5	.500 (22°)	(.740)	tere-Phthalic acid	83.51	.5029	(.759)
1-(m-Nitrophenylazo)-2-naphthol	142.0	(.484)		Phthalic anhydride	67.31	(.454)	(.694) (4°)
1-(p-Nitrophenylazo)-2-naphthol	141.7	(.483)		Phthalimide	(78.4)	.533	
Nitrophenylfluoroform	(84.1)	.440		Picric acid	84.38	(.368)	(.649)
2-Nitropropane	45.73	.5135	(.509) (20°)	Piperazine	56.8	(.659)	
Nitrosobenzene	59.1	(.552)		Piperidine	64.2	(.754)	(.650) (20°)
N-Nitrosodiethylamine	59.3	(.580)	(.546) (20°)	Propane	40.5	(.919)	(.538) (−45°)
p-Nitrosodiethylaniline	92.6	(.520)	(.644) (15°)	Propene	31.5	(.749)	(.456) (−47°)
p-Nitrosodimethylaniline	73.3	(.488)		Propionaldehyde	34.32	.591₀	(.477) (20°)
N-Nitrosodiphenylamine	110.7	(.558)		Propionic acid	43.50	.586	.582 (20°)
1-Nitroso-2-naphthol	83.9	(.485)		Propionitrile	38.5	(.699)	(.547) (21°)
2-Nitroso-1-naphthol	82.7	(.478)		Propionylphenylacetylene	(95.1)	.601	
4-Nitroso-1-naphthol	91.8	(.530)		Propiophenone	83.73	.624₀	(.631) (20°)
m-Nitrosonitrobenzene	66.0	(.433)		n-Propyl acetate	65.91	.645₈ (25°)	(.569) (25°)
p-Nitrosonitrobenzene	65.8	(.433)		iso-Propyl acetate	67.04	.656₄	(.566) (25°)
p-Nitrosophenol	50.7	(.412)		n-Propyl alcohol	45.176 (20°)	(.7518)	(.6047) (20°)
Nitrosopiperidine	(63.4)	.555	(.590) (20°)	iso-Propyl alcohol	45.794 (20°)	(.7621)	(.5985) (20°)
p-Nitrosotoluene	70.4	(.581)		9-Propylanthracene	164.0	(.744)	
o-Nitrotoluene	72.28	.5272	(.613) (20°)	n-Propylbenzene	89 24	(.742)	(.640) (20°)
m-Nitrotoluene	72.71	.5304	(.614) (20°)	n-Propyl benzoate	105.00	(.640)	(.646) (25°)
p-Nitrotoluene (in sol'n)	72.06	.5257	(.676) (20°)	n-Propyl bromide	(65.6)	.533	(.721) (20°)
n-Nonane	108.13	.8431	.6057 (20°)	iso-Propyl bromide	(65.1)	.529	(.6y3) (20°)
1,2-Octadiene	83.6	(.759)		Propyl butyrate	(89.4)	.6867	(.604) (15°)
n-Octane	96.63	.8460	.5949 (20°)	prim-Propyl chloride	56.10	.715	(.633) (20°)
Octanonoxime	(102.7)	.717		iso-Propylcyclohexane	102.65	8131	.6528 (20°)
Octyl alcohol	102.65	.7766 (20°)	(.640) (20°)	Propylenediamine	(58.1)	.784	(.688) (15°)
Octyl chloride	(114.9)	.773	(.676) (20°)	Propylene oxide	42.5	(.732)	(.629) (0°)
Octylcyclohexane	158.09	.8051	.6578 (20°)	Propyl formate	(55.0)	.6248	(.563) (20°)
Octylene	(89.5)	.798	(.576) (17°)	Propyl hexylpropiolate	(136.8)	.697	
Octylene bromide	(150.4)	.553		Propyl iodide	(84.3)	.4958 (30°)	(.864) (20°)
n-Octyl mercaptan	(115.1)	.7866 (27.4°)		Propyl propionate (extrap.)	(77.95)	.6711	(.593) (20°)
Oenanthylidene chloride	(116.5)	.689		Propyl sulfide	(92.1)	.7787 (27.4°)	(.634) (17°)
Oleic acid	208.5	(.738)	(.661) (18°)	N-Propyl urea	67.4	(.660)	
Opianic acid	111.5	(.530)		Pseudocumene	(101.6)	.845 (20°)	(.740) (20°)
Ovalene	353.8	.888		Pyramidone	149.0	(.645)	
Oxalic acid (anh.)	33.8	(.375)		Pyranthrene	266.9	.709	
Oxalic acid	60.05	(.4763)	(.787)	Pyranthrone	250.3	.616	
Oxamide	(39.0)	.443	(.738)	Pyrazine	37.6	(.469)	(.484) (61°)
Palmitic acid	198.6	(.775)	(.661) (62°)	Pyrene	147.9	.731	(.933) (0°)
Paraldehyde	(86.2)	.652	(.648) (20°)	Pyridine	49.21	(.622)	(.611) (20°)
Pentabromophenol	(194.0)	.397		Pyrocatechol	68.76	.6248	(.857) (15°)
Pentacene	(205.4)	.738		Pyrrole	47.6	(.709)	(.688) (20°)

DIAMAGNETIC SUSCEPTIBILITIES OF ORGANIC COMPOUNDS (Continued)

Compound	$-\chi_M \times 10^6$	$-\chi \times 10^6$	$-K \times 10^6$	Compound	$-\chi_M \times 10^6$	$-\chi \times 10^6$	$-K \times 10^6$
Pyrrolidine	54.8	(.771)	(.657) (23°)	Trianilinophosphine oxide	(201.7)	.624	
Quinoline	86.0	(.666)	(.729) (20°)	1,2,3-Tribromopropane	(117.9)	.420	(1.023) (23°)
Quinone	38.4	(.355)	(.468) (20°)	Tri-iso-butylamine	(156.8)	.846	(.646) (25°)
Quinonoxime	(50.4)	.409		Trichloroacetic acid (in sol'n)	73.0	(.44)	(.723) (46°)
Resorcinol	67.26	.6112	(.785) (15°)	Trichlorobenzene	(106.5)	.587	
Rhamnose	99.20	.605	(.890) (20°)	Trichloro-tert-butyl alcoho! (in sol'n)	98.01	.552	
Safrol and iso-Safro	(97.5)	.601	(.66) (20°)	Trichloroethylene	65.8	.501	(.734) (20°)
Salicylaldehyde	64.4	(.527)	(.615) (20°)	Trichloronitromethane	(75.3)	.458	(.756) (20°)
Salicylic acid	72.23	.523	(.755) (20°)	Triethvlamine	81.4	(.804)	(.586) (20°)
Saligenin	76.9	.620	(.720) (25°)	Triethyl citrate	(161.9)	.586	(.666) (20°)
Salol	(123.2)	.575	.678 (45°)	Triethyl phosphate	(125.3)	.688	(.735) (20°)
Salvarsan dihydrochloride	(246.1)	.518		Triethylphosphine	(90.0)	.762	(.610) (15°)
Selenophene	66.82	.510		Triethylphosphine oxide	(91.6)	.683	
iso-Selenophene	110–111	.84–.85		Triethyl phosphite	(104.8)	.631	(.611) (20°)
trans-Selenophene	70–77	.53–.59		Triethyl triazinetricarbonate	(164.1)	.552	
Sorbitol	107.80	.592		Trifluorocresol	(83.8)	.517	
Stearic acid	220.8	(.776)	(.657) (69°)	Tri-n-heptylamine	251.3	(.806)	
Stilbene	(120.0)	.666	(.646) (125°)	Tri-n-hexylamine	221.7	(.823)	
Stilbestrol	(130)	.62, .63		Trimethylacetophenone	108.2	(.667)	(.648) (16°)
Styrene	(68.2)	.655	(.594) (20°)	2,2,3-Trimethylbutane	88.36	.8818	.6086 (20°)
Succinic acid	(57.9)	.4902	(.767) (15°)	2,2,3-Trimethylpentane	99.86	.8743	.6261 (20°)
Succinic anhydride	(47.5)	.475	(.524)	2,2,4-Trimethylpentane	98.34	.8610	.5958 (20°)
Succinimide	(47.3)	.477	(.674) (16°)	2,3,5-Trimethylpyrrole	82.31	.754 (20°)	
Sulfamide	44.4	(.462)	(.832)	1,3,5-Trinitrobenzene	74.55	(.350)	(.591) (20°)
p-Sulfanilamide	80 15	(.465)		Triperfluorobuty!amine	253.0	(.377)	
Terpineol	111.9	(.725)	(.678) (room temp.)	Triphenoxyarsine	(195.2)	.551	
				Triphenylarsine	(177.0)	.578	
Tetrabenzylmonosilane	266.2	(.678)		Triphenylarsine dihydroxide	(270.5)	.795	
1,1,2,2-Tetrabromoethane	(123.4)	.357	(1.058) (20°)	Triphenylarsine oxide	(199.1)	.618	
Tetrabromoethylene	(114.8)	.334		Triphenylbismuthine	(196.8)	.447	(.708) (20°)
Tetracene	(168.0)	.736		Triphenylbismuthine dinitrate	(254.5)	.451	
1,1,2,2-Tetrachloroethane	(89.8)	.535	(.856) (20°)	Triphenylcarbinol	(175.7)	.675	(.802) (20°)
Tetrachloroethylene	81.6	.492	(.802) (15°)	Triphenylmethane	(165.6)	.678	.686 (100°)
Tetrahydroquinoline	(89.0)	.668	(.715) (4°)	Triphenylphosphine	(166.8)	.636	(.759)
Tetraiodoethylene	(164.3)	.309	(.922) (20°)	Triphenyl phosphite	(183.7)	.592	(.701) (18°)
Tetraiodopyrrole	(188.9)	.331		Triphenylstibine	(182.2)	.516	
Tetramethylketotetrahydrofurfurane	(104.7)	.736		Triphenylstibine dihydroxide	(238.5)	.616	
Tetranitromethane	43.02	.2195	(.360) (20°)	N,N′,N-Triphenyl urea	176.5	(.613)	
Tetraphenylbutadiene	228.0	(.636)		Triquinoyl	(133.0)	.426	
Tetraphenyldecapentaene	280.8	(.643)		Tropolone	61	.50	
Tetraphenylhexatriene	246.4	(.641)		Tryptophan	132.0	(.646)	
Tetraphenyloctatetraene	264.1	(.643)		Tyrosine	105.3	(.581)	
Tetraphenylrubene	344.0	(.646)		Undecane	131.84	(.8435)	(.6247) (20°)
Tetra-p-tolylmonosilane	276.4	(.704)		Urea	33.4	(.556)	(.742) (20°)
Tetrolic acetal	(97.8)	.688		Urethan	(57)	.64	(.63) (21°)
Tetronic acid	(52.5)	.525		iso-Valeraldehyde	(57.5)	.668	(.536) (17°)
Thiacoumerin	93.6	.577		n-Valeric acid	66.85	.6548	(.617) (20°)
Thiazole	50.55	.595 (20°)	(714) (17°)	iso-Valeric acid	(67.7)	.663	(.621) (15°)
Thiobarbituric acid	72.9	(.506)		Valerylphenylacetylene	(119.0)	.639	
Thiophene	57.38	.682 (20°)	(.726) (20°)	Valine	74.3	(.634)	
Tolane	(118.9)	.667	(.644) (100°)	Violanthrene	273.5	.641	
Toluene	66.11	.7176	.6179 (20°)	Violanthrone	204.8	.449	
o-Toluidine	76.0	.710 (24°)	(.709) (20°)	iso-Violanthrone	215.9	.473	
m-Toluidine	74.6	.697 (25°)	(.689) (20°)	Water	(13.00)	.7218 (20°)	(.7205) (20°)
p-Toluidine	72.1	.673 (25°)	(.704) (20°)	Water (value usually used as standard)	(12.97)	.720 (20°)	(.719) (20°)
α-Toluinitrile	76.87	(.656)	(.666) (18°)	Xanthone	(108.1)	.551	
1-(o-Tolylazo)-2-naphthol	148.7	(.567)		o-Xylene	77.78	.7327	.6440 (20°)
1-(p-Tolylazo)-2-naphthol	157.6	(.601)		m-Xylene	76.56	.7212	.6235 (20°)
Triallylacetophenone	152.5	(.634)		p-Xylene	76.78	.7232	.6226 (20°)
Tri-iso-amylamine	192	.845	(.647) (25°)	Xylose	84.80	.565	(.862) (20°)

FOUR-PLACE LOGARITHMS

N	0	1	2	3	4	5	6	7	8	9	Proportional Parts								
											1	2	3	4	5	6	7	8	9
10	0000	0043	0086	0128	0170	0212	0253	0294	0334	0374	*4	8	12	17	21	25	29	33	37
11	0414	0453	0492	0531	0569	0607	0645	0682	0719	0755	4	8	11	15	19	23	26	30	34
12	0792	0828	0864	0899	0934	0969	1004	1038	1072	1106	3	7	10	14	17	21	24	28	31
13	1139	1173	1206	1239	1271	1303	1335	1367	1399	1430	3	6	10	13	16	19	23	26	29
14	1461	1492	1523	1553	1584	1614	1644	1673	1703	1732	3	6	9	12	15	18	21	24	27
15	1761	1790	1818	1847	1875	1903	1931	1959	1987	2014	*3	6	8	11	14	17	20	22	25
16	2041	2068	2095	2122	2148	2175	2201	2227	2253	2279	3	5	8	11	13	16	18	21	24
17	2304	2330	2355	2380	2405	2430	2455	2480	2504	2529	2	5	7	10	12	15	17	20	22
18	2553	2577	2601	2625	2648	2672	2695	2718	2742	2765	2	5	7	9	12	14	16	19	21
19	2788	2810	2833	2856	2878	2900	2923	2945	2967	2989	2	4	7	9	11	13	16	18	20
20	3010	3032	3054	3075	3096	3118	3139	3160	3181	3201	2	4	6	8	11	13	15	17	19
21	3222	3243	3263	3284	3304	3324	3345	3365	3385	3404	2	4	6	8	10	12	14	16	18
22	3424	3444	3464	3483	3502	3522	3541	3560	3579	3598	2	4	6	8	10	12	14	15	17
23	3617	3636	3655	3674	3692	3711	3729	3747	3766	3784	2	4	6	7	9	11	13	15	17
24	3802	3820	3838	3856	3874	3892	3909	3927	3945	3962	2	4	5	7	9	11	12	14	16
25	3979	3997	4014	4031	4048	4065	4082	4099	4116	4133	2	3	5	7	9	10	12	14	15
26	4150	4166	4183	4200	4216	4232	4249	4265	4281	4298	2	3	5	7	8	10	11	13	15
27	4314	4330	4346	4362	4378	4393	4409	4425	4440	4456	2	3	5	6	8	9	11	13	14
28	4472	4487	4502	4518	4533	4548	4564	4579	4594	4609	2	3	5	6	8	9	11	12	14
29	4624	4639	4654	4669	4683	4698	4713	4728	4742	4757	1	3	4	6	7	9	10	12	13
30	4771	4786	4800	4814	4829	4843	4857	4871	4886	4900	1	3	4	6	7	9	10	11	13
31	4914	4928	4942	4955	4969	4983	4997	5011	5024	5038	1	3	4	6	7	8	10	11	12
32	5051	5065	5079	5092	5105	5119	5132	5145	5159	5172	1	3	4	5	7	8	9	11	12
33	5185	5198	5211	5224	5237	5250	5263	5276	5289	5302	1	3	4	5	6	8	9	10	12
34	5315	5328	5340	5353	5366	5378	5391	5403	5416	5428	1	3	4	5	6	8	9	10	11
35	5441	5453	5465	5478	5490	5502	5514	5527	5539	5551	1	2	4	5	6	7	9	10	11
36	5563	5575	5587	5599	5611	5623	5635	5647	5658	5670	1	2	4	5	6	7	8	10	11
37	5682	5694	5705	5717	5729	5740	5752	5763	5775	5786	1	2	3	5	6	7	8	9	10
38	5798	5809	5821	5832	5843	5855	5866	5877	5888	5899	1	2	3	5	6	7	8	9	10
39	5911	5922	5933	5944	5955	5966	5977	5988	5999	6010	1	2	3	4	5	7	8	9	10
40	6021	6031	6042	6053	6064	6075	6085	6096	6107	6117	1	2	3	4	5	6	8	9	10
41	6128	6138	6149	6160	6170	6180	6191	6201	6212	6222	1	2	3	4	5	6	7	8	9
42	6232	6243	6253	6263	6274	6284	6294	6304	6314	6325	1	2	3	4	5	6	7	8	9
43	6335	6345	6355	6365	6375	6385	6395	6405	6415	6425	1	2	3	4	5	6	7	8	9
44	6435	6444	6454	6464	6474	6484	6493	6503	6513	6522	1	2	3	4	5	6	7	8	9
45	6532	6542	6551	6561	6571	6580	6590	6599	6609	6618	1	2	3	4	5	6	7	8	9
46	6628	6637	6646	6656	6665	6675	6684	6693	6702	6712	1	2	3	4	5	6	7	7	8
47	6721	6730	6739	6749	6758	6767	6776	6785	6794	6803	1	2	3	4	5	5	6	7	8
48	6812	6821	6830	6839	6848	6857	6866	6875	6884	6893	1	2	3	4	4	5	6	7	8
49	6902	6911	6920	6928	6937	6946	6955	6964	6972	6981	1	2	3	4	4	5	6	7	8
50	6990	6998	7007	7016	7024	7033	7042	7050	7059	7067	1	2	3	3	4	5	6	7	8
51	7076	7084	7093	7101	7110	7118	7126	7135	7143	7152	1	2	3	3	4	5	6	7	8
52	7160	7168	7177	7185	7193	7202	7210	7218	7226	7235	1	2	2	3	4	5	6	7	7
53	7243	7251	7259	7267	7275	7284	7292	7300	7308	7316	1	2	2	3	4	5	6	6	7
54	7324	7332	7340	7348	7356	7364	7372	7380	7388	7396	1	2	2	3	4	5	6	6	7
N	0	1	2	3	4	5	6	7	8	9	1	2	3	4	5	6	7	8	9

* Interpolation in this section of the table is inaccurate.

N	0	1	2	3	4	5	6	7	8	9		Proportional Parts							
											1	2	3	4	5	6	7	8	9
55	7404	7412	7419	7427	7435	7443	7451	7459	7466	7474	1	2	2	3	4	5	5	6	7
56	7482	7490	7497	7505	7513	7520	7528	7536	7543	7551	1	2	2	3	4	5	5	6	7
57	7559	7566	7574	7582	7589	7597	7604	7612	7619	7627	1	2	2	3	4	5	5	6	7
58	7634	7642	7649	7657	7664	7672	7679	7686	7694	7701	1	1	2	3	4	4	5	6	7
59	7709	7716	7723	7731	7738	7745	7752	7760	7767	7774	1	1	2	3	4	4	5	6	7
60	7782	7789	7796	7803	7810	7818	7825	7832	7839	7846	1	1	2	3	4	4	5	6	6
61	7853	7860	7868	7875	7882	7889	7896	7903	7910	7917	1	1	2	3	4	4	5	6	6
62	7924	7931	7938	7945	7952	7959	7966	7973	7980	7987	1	1	2	3	3	4	5	6	6
63	7993	8000	8007	8014	8021	8028	8035	8041	8048	8055	1	1	2	3	3	4	5	5	6
64	8062	8069	8075	8082	8089	8096	8102	8109	8116	8122	1	1	2	3	3	4	5	5	6
65	8129	8136	8142	8149	8156	8162	8169	8176	8182	8189	1	1	2	3	3	4	5	5	6
66	8195	8202	8209	8215	8222	8228	8235	8241	8248	8254	1	1	2	3	3	4	5	5	6
67	8261	8267	8274	8280	8287	8293	8299	8306	8312	8319	1	1	2	3	3	4	5	5	6
68	8325	8331	8338	8344	8351	8357	8363	8370	8376	8382	1	1	2	3	3	4	4	5	6
69	8388	8395	8401	8407	8414	8420	8426	8432	8439	8445	1	1	2	2	3	4	4	5	6
70	8451	8457	8463	8470	8476	8482	8488	8494	8500	8506	1	1	2	2	3	4	4	5	6
71	8513	8519	8525	8531	8537	8543	8549	8555	8561	8567	1	1	2	2	3	4	4	5	5
72	8573	8579	8585	8591	8597	8603	8609	8615	8621	8627	1	1	2	2	3	4	4	5	5
73	8633	8639	8645	8651	8657	8663	8669	8675	8681	8686	1	1	2	2	3	4	4	5	5
74	8692	8698	8704	8710	8716	8722	8727	8733	8739	8745	1	1	2	2	3	4	4	5	5
75	8751	8756	8762	8768	8774	8779	8785	8791	8797	8802	1	1	2	2	3	3	4	5	5
76	8808	8814	8820	8825	8831	8837	8842	8848	8854	8859	1	1	2	2	3	3	4	5	5
77	8865	8871	8876	8882	8887	8893	8899	8904	8910	8915	1	1	2	2	3	3	4	4	5
78	8921	8927	8932	8938	8943	8949	8954	8960	8965	8971	1	1	2	2	3	3	4	4	5
79	8976	8982	8987	8993	8998	9004	9009	9015	9020	9025	1	1	2	2	3	3	4	4	5
80	9031	9036	9042	9047	9053	9058	9063	9069	9074	9079	1	1	2	2	3	3	4	4	5
81	9085	9090	9096	9101	9106	9112	9117	9122	9128	9133	1	1	2	2	3	3	4	4	5
82	9138	9143	9149	9154	9159	9165	9170	9175	9180	9186	1	1	2	2	3	3	4	4	5
83	9191	9196	9201	9206	9212	9217	9222	9227	9232	9238	1	1	2	2	3	3	4	4	5
84	9243	9248	9253	9258	9263	9269	9274	9279	9284	9289	1	1	2	2	3	3	4	4	5
85	9294	9299	9304	9309	9315	9320	9325	9330	9335	9340	1	1	2	2	3	3	4	4	5
86	9345	9350	9355	9360	9365	9370	9375	9380	9385	9390	1	1	2	2	3	3	4	4	5
87	9395	9400	9405	9410	9415	9420	9425	9430	9435	9440	0	1	1	2	2	3	3	4	4
88	9445	9450	9455	9460	9465	9469	9474	9479	9484	9489	0	1	1	2	2	3	3	4	4
89	9494	9499	9504	9509	9513	9518	9523	9528	9533	9538	0	1	1	2	2	3	3	4	4
90	9542	9547	9552	9557	9562	9566	9571	9576	9581	9586	0	1	1	2	2	3	3	4	4
91	9590	9595	9600	9605	9609	9614	9619	9624	9628	9633	0	1	1	2	2	3	3	4	4
92	9638	9643	9647	9652	9657	9661	9666	9671	9675	9680	0	1	1	2	2	3	3	4	4
93	9685	9689	9694	9699	9703	9708	9713	9717	9722	9727	0	1	1	2	2	3	3	4	4
94	9731	9736	9741	9745	9750	9754	9759	9763	9768	9773	0	1	1	2	2	3	3	4	4
95	9777	9782	9786	9791	9795	9800	9805	9809	9814	9818	0	1	1	2	2	3	3	4	4
96	9823	9827	9832	9836	9841	9845	9850	9854	9859	9863	0	1	1	2	2	3	3	4	4
97	9868	9872	9877	9881	9886	9890	9894	9899	9903	9908	0	1	1	2	2	3	3	4	4
98	9912	9917	9921	9926	9930	9934	9939	9943	9948	9952	0	1	1	2	2	3	3	4	4
99	9956	9961	9965	9969	9974	9978	9983	9987	9991	9996	0	1	1	2	2	3	3	3	4
N	0	1	2	3	4	5	6	7	8	9	1	2	3	4	5	6	7	8	9

PERIODIC TABLE OF THE ELEMENTS

KEY TO CHART

50 +2 +4	Sn	118.69	-18-18-4
Atomic Number →	← Oxidation States		
Symbol →			
Atomic Weight →	← Electron Configuration		

Transition Elements — Group 8

Main table (oxidation states · atomic weight · electron configuration):

1a	2a	3b	4b	5b	6b	7b	8	8	8	1b	2b	3a	4a	5a	6a	7a	0	Orbit
1 H +1 −1 1.00797 (1)																	**2 He** 0 4.0026 (2)	K
3 Li +1 6.939 2-1	**4 Be** +2 9.0122 2-2											**5 B** +3 10.811 2-3	**6 C** +2 +4 −4 12.01115 2-4	**7 N** +1+2+3+4+5 −1−2−3 14.0067 2-5	**8 O** −2 15.9994 2-6	**9 F** −1 18.9984 2-7	**10 Ne** 0 20.183 2-8	K-L
11 Na +1 22.9898 2-8-1	**12 Mg** +2 24.312 2-8-2											**13 Al** +3 26.9815 2-8-3	**14 Si** +2 +4 −4 28.086 2-8-4	**15 P** +3 +5 −3 30.9738 2-8-5	**16 S** +4 +6 −2 32.064 2-8-6	**17 Cl** +1+5+7 −1 35.453 2-8-7	**18 Ar** 0 39.948 2-8-8	K-L-M
19 K +1 39.102 -8-8-1	**20 Ca** +2 40.08 -8-8-2	**21 Sc** +3 44.956 -8-9-2	**22 Ti** +2+3+4 47.90 -8-10-2	**23 V** +2+3+4+5 50.942 -8-11-2	**24 Cr** +2+3+6 51.996 -8-13-1	**25 Mn** +2+3+4+7 54.9380 -8-13-2	**26 Fe** +2+3 55.847 -8-14-2	**27 Co** +2+3 58.9332 -8-15-2	**28 Ni** +2+3 58.71 -8-16-2	**29 Cu** +1+2 63.54 -8-18-1	**30 Zn** +1+2 65.37 -8-18-2	**31 Ga** +3 69.72 -8-18-3	**32 Ge** +2+4 72.59 -8-18-4	**33 As** +3+5 −3 74.9216 -8-18-5	**34 Se** +4+6 −2 78.96 -8-18-6	**35 Br** +1+5 −1 79.909 -8-18-7	**36 Kr** +1 83.80 -8-18-8	L-M-N
37 Rb +1 85.47 -18-8-1	**38 Sr** +2 87.62 -18-8-2	**39 Y** +3 88.905 -18-9-2	**40 Zr** +4 91.22 -18-10-2	**41 Nb** +3+5 92.906 -18-12-1	**42 Mo** +6 95.94 -18-13-1	**43 Tc** (99) -18-13-2	**44 Ru** +3 101.07 -18-15-1	**45 Rh** +3 102.905 -18-16-1	**46 Pd** +2+4 106.4 -18-18-0	**47 Ag** +1 107.870 -18-18-1	**48 Cd** +2 112.40 -18-18-2	**49 In** +3 114.82 -18-18-3	**50 Sn** +2+4 118.69 -18-18-4	**51 Sb** +3+5 −3 121.75 -18-18-5	**52 Te** +4+6 −2 127.60 -18-18-6	**53 I** +1+5+7 −1 126.9044 -18-18-7	**54 Xe** 0 131.30 -18-18-8	M-N-O
55 Cs +1 132.905 -18-8-1	**56 Ba** +2 137.34 -18-8-2	**57* La** +3 138.91 -18-9-2	**72 Hf** +4 178.49 -32-10-2	**73 Ta** +5 180.948 -32-11-2	**74 W** +6 183.85 -32-12-2	**75 Re** +4+6+7 186.2 -32-13-2	**76 Os** +3+4+6+8 190.2 -32-14-2	**77 Ir** +3+4 192.2 -32-15-2	**78 Pt** +2+4 195.09 -32-16-2	**79 Au** +1+3 196.967 -32-18-1	**80 Hg** +1+2 200.59 -32-18-2	**81 Tl** +1+3 204.37 -32-18-3	**82 Pb** +2+4 207.19 -32-18-4	**83 Bi** +3+5 208.980 -32-18-5	**84 Po** +2+4 (210) -32-18-6	**85 At** (210) -32-18-7	**86 Rn** (222) -32-18-8	N-O-P
87 Fr +1 (223) -18-8-1	**88 Ra** +2 (226) -18-8-2	**89** ** **Ac** +3 (227) -18-9-2																O-P-Q

*Lanthanides:

3b	4b	5b	6b	7b	8	8	8	1b	2b	3a	4a	5a	6a	Orbit
58 Ce +3+4 140.12 -19-9-2	**59 Pr** +3+4 140.907 -20-9-2	**60 Nd** +3 144.24 -22-8-2	**61 Pm** +3 (145) -23-8-2	**62 Sm** +2+3 150.35 -24-8-2	**63 Eu** +2+3 151.96 -25-8-2	**64 Gd** +3 157.25 -25-9-2	**65 Tb** +3 158.924 -26-9-2	**66 Dy** +3 162.50 -28-9-2	**67 Ho** +3 164.930 -29-8-2	**68 Er** +3 167.26 -30-8-2	**69 Tm** +3 168.934 -31-8-2	**70 Yb** +2+3 173.04 -32-8-2	**71 Lu** +3 174.97 -32-9-2	N-O-P

**Actinides:

3b	4b	5b	6b	7b	8	8	8	1b	2b	3a	4a	5a	6a	Orbit
90 Th +4 232.038 -19-9-2	**91 Pa** +5 +4 (231) -20-9-2	**92 U** +3+4+5+6 238.03 -21-9-2	**93 Np** +3+4+5+6 (237) -22-9-2	**94 Pu** +3+4+5+6 (242) -23-9-2	**95 Am** +3+4+5+6 (243) -24-9-2	**96 Cm** +3 (247) -25-9-2	**97 Bk** +3+4 (249) -26-9-2	**98 Cf** +3 (251) -28-8-2	**99 Es** (254) -29-8-2	**100 Fm** (252) -30-8-2	**101 Md** (256) -31-8-2	**102 No** (254) -32-8-2	**103 Lw** +3	O-P-Q

Numbers in parentheses are mass numbers of most stable isotope of that element.

ATOMIC WEIGHTS

For the sake of completeness all known elements are included in the list. Several of those more recently discovered are represented only by the unstable isotopes. The value in parenthesis in the atomic weight column is, in each case, the mass number of the most stable isotope.**

Name	Symbol	At. No.	International atomic weight		Valence	Name	Symbol	At. No.	International atomic weight		Valence
			1961	1959					1961	1959	
Actinium	Ac	89	....	(227)	....	Neodymium	Nd	60	144.24	144.27	3
Aluminum	Al	13	26.9815	26.98	3	Neon	Ne	10	20.183	20.183	0
Americium	Am	95	....	(243)	3, 4, 5, 6	Neptunium	Np	93	....	(237)	4, 5, 6
Antimony, stibium	Sb	51	121.75	121.76	3, 5	Nickel	Ni	28	58.71	58.71	2, 3
Argon	Ar	18	39.948	39.944	0	Niobium (columbium)	Nb	41	92.906	92.91	3, 5
Arsenic	As	33	74.9216	74.92	3, 5	Nitrogen	N	7	14.0067	14.008	3, 5
Astatine	At	85	....	(210)	1, 3, 5, 7	Nobelium	No	102	....	(254)	....
Barium	Ba	56	137.34	137.36	2	Osmium	Os	76	190.2	190.2	2, 3, 4, 8
Berkelium	Bk	97	....	(217)	3, 4	Oxygen	O	8	15.9994	16.000	2
Beryllium	Be	4	9.0122	9.013	2	Palladium	Pd	46	106.4	106.4	2, 4, 6
Bismuth	Bi	83	208.980	208.99	3, 5	Phosphorus	P	15	30.9738	30.975	3, 5
Boron	B	5	10.811	10.82	3	Platinum	Pt	78	195.09	195.09	2, 4
Bromine	Br	35	79.909	79.916	1, 3, 5, 7	Plutonium	Pu	94	....	(244)	3, 4, 5, 6
Cadmium	Cd	48	112.40	112.41	2	Polonium	Po	84	....	(209)	....
Calcium	Ca	20	40.08	40.08	2	Potassium, kalium	K	19	39.102	39.100	1
Californium	Cf	98	....	(251)	....	Praseodymium	Pr	59	140.907	140.92	3
Carbon	C	6	12.01115	12.011	2, 4	Promethium	Pm	61	....	(145)	3
Cerium	Ce	58	140.12	140.13	3, 4	Protactinium	Pa	91	....	(231)	....
Cesium	Cs	55	132.905	132.91	1	Radium	Ra	88	....	(226)	2
Chlorine	Cl	17	35.453	35.457	1, 3, 5, 7	Radon	Rn	86	....	(222)	0
Chromium	Cr	24	51.996	52.01	2, 3, 6	Rhenium	Re	75	186.2	186.22	....
Cobalt	Co	27	58.9332	58.94	2, 3	Rhodium	Rh	45	102.905	102.91	3
Columbium, see *Niobium*						Rubidium	Rb	37	85.47	85.48	1
Copper	Cu	29	63.54	63.54	1, 2	Ruthenium	Ru	44	101.07	101.1	3, 4, 6, 8
Curium	Cm	96	....	(247)	3	Samarium	Sm	62	150.35	150.35	2, 3
Dysprosium	Dy	66	162.50	162.51	3	Scandium	Sc	21	44.956	44.96	3
Einsteinium	Es	99	....	(254)	....	Selenium	Se	34	78.96	78.96	2, 4, 6
Erbium	Er	68	167.26	167.27	3	Silicon	Si	14	28.086	28.09	4
Europium	Eu	63	151.96	152.0	2, 3	Silver, argentum	Ag	47	107.870	107.873	1
Fermium	Fm	100	....	(257)	....	Sodium, natrium	Na	11	22.9898	22.991	1
Fluorine	F	9	18.9984	19.00	1	Strontium	Sr	38	87.62	87.63	2
Francium	Fr	87	....	(223)	1	Sulfur	S	16	32.064	32.066*	2, 4, 6
Gadolinium	Gd	64	157.25	157.26	3	Tantalum	Ta	73	180.948	180.95	5
Gallium	Ga	31	69.72	69.72	2, 3	Technetium	Tc	43	....	(97)	6, 7
Germanium	Ge	32	72.59	72.60	4	Tellurium	Te	52	127.60	127.61	2, 4, 6
Gold, aurum	Au	79	196.967	197.0	1, 3	Terbium	Tb	65	158.924	158.93	3
Hafnium	Hf	72	178.49	178.50	4	Thallium	Tl	81	204.37	204.39	1, 3
Helium	He	2	4.0026	4.003	0	Thorium	Th	90	232.038	(232)	4
Holmium	Ho	67	164.930	164.94	3	Thulium	Tm	69	168.934	168.94	3
Hydrogen	H	1	1.00797	1.0080	1	Tin, stannum	Sn	50	118.69	118.70	2, 4
Indium	In	49	114.82	114.82	3	Titanium	Ti	22	47.90	47.90	3, 4
Iodine	I	53	126.9044	126.91	1, 3, 5, 7	Tungsten (wolfram)	W	74	183.85	183.86	6
Iridium	Ir	77	192.2	192.2	3, 4	Uranium	U	92	238.03	238.07	4, 6
Iron, ferrum	Fe	26	55.847	55.85	2, 3	Vanadium	V	23	50.942	50.95	3, 5
Krypton	Kr	36	83.80	83.80	0	Xenon	Xe	54	131.30	131.30	0
Lanthanum	La	57	138.91	138.92	3	Ytterbium	Yb	70	173.04	173.04	2, 3
Lead, plumbum	Pb	82	207.19	207.21	2, 4	Yttrium	Y	39	88.905	88.91	3
Lithium	Li	3	6.939	6.940	1	Zinc	Zn	30	65.37	65.38	2
Lutetium	Lu	71	174.97	174.99	3	Zirconium	Zr	40	91.22	91.22	4
Magnesium	Mg	12	24.312	24.32	2						
Manganese	Mn	25	54.9380	54.94	2, 3, 4, 6, 7						
Mendelevium	Md	101	....	(256)	....						
Mercury, hydrargyrum	Hg	80	200.59	200.61	1, 2						
Molybdenum	Mo	42	95.94	95.95	3, 4, 6						

* Because of natural variations in the relative abundances of the isotopes of sulfur the atomic weight of this element has a range of ± 0.003.

** The 1959 atomic weights are based on O = 16.000 whereas those of 1961 are based on the isotope C¹².

478

ORGANIC COMPOUND INDEX

ORGANIC COMPOUND INDEX

ORGANIC COMPOUND INDEX

522

ORGANIC COMPOUND INDEX

Index

This Index lists the names of all tables and major subjects contained in this book in alphabetical order. The Index listing the individual compounds for which derivatives are cited begins on page 479.

SELECTED CRC HANDBOOK SERIES

CRC HANDBOOK OF BIOCHEMISTRY AND MOLECULAR BIOLOGY
Gerald D. Fasman
Brandeis University

CRC HANDBOOK SERIES IN CLINICAL LABORATORY SCIENCE
David Seligson
Yale University

CRC HANDBOOK OF ELECTROPHORESIS
Lena A. Lewis
Cleveland Clinic
J. J. Opplt
Metropolitan General Hospital

CRC HANDBOOK SERIES IN ENGINEERING IN MEDICINE AND BIOLOGY
David G. Fleming
Case Western Reserve University
Barry N. Feinberg
Purdue University

CRC HANDBOOK OF ENVIRONMENTAL CONTROL
Richard G. Bond
Univeristy of Minnesota
Conrad P. Straub
University of Minnesota

CRC FENAROLI'S HANDBOOK OF FLAVOR INGREDIENTS
Nicolo Bellanca
CIBA-GEIGY Corp.
Giovanni Fenaroli
University of Milano, Italy
Thomas E. Furia
Dynapol

CRC HANDBOOK OF MARINE SCIENCE
F. G. Walton Smith
International Oceanographic Foundation
Frederick A. Kalber
Hydrobiological Services
Joseph T. Baker
Vreni Murphy
Roche Institute of Marine Pharmacology, Australia

CRC HANDBOOK OF MATERIALS SCIENCE
C. T. Lynch
Wright-Patterson Air Force Base

CRC STANDARD MATH TABLES
William H. Beyer
University of Akron

CRC HANDBOOK OF MICROBIOLOGY
Allen I. Laskin
Esso Research and Engineering Co.
Hubert Lechevalier
Rutgers University

CRC HANDBOOK SERIES IN NUTRITION AND FOOD
Miloslav Rechcigl, Jr.
Agency for International Development

CRC ATLAS OF SCINTIMAGING FOR CLINICAL NUCLEAR MEDICINE
Henry N. Wellman
Indiana University School of Medicine

CRC ATLAS OF SPECTRAL DATA AND PHYSICAL CONSTANTS FOR ORGANIC COMPOUNDS
Jeanette Grasselli
Standard Oil Company (Ohio)
William M. Ritchey
Case Western Reserve University

CRC HANDBOOK SERIES IN ZOONOSES
James H. Steele
University of Texas